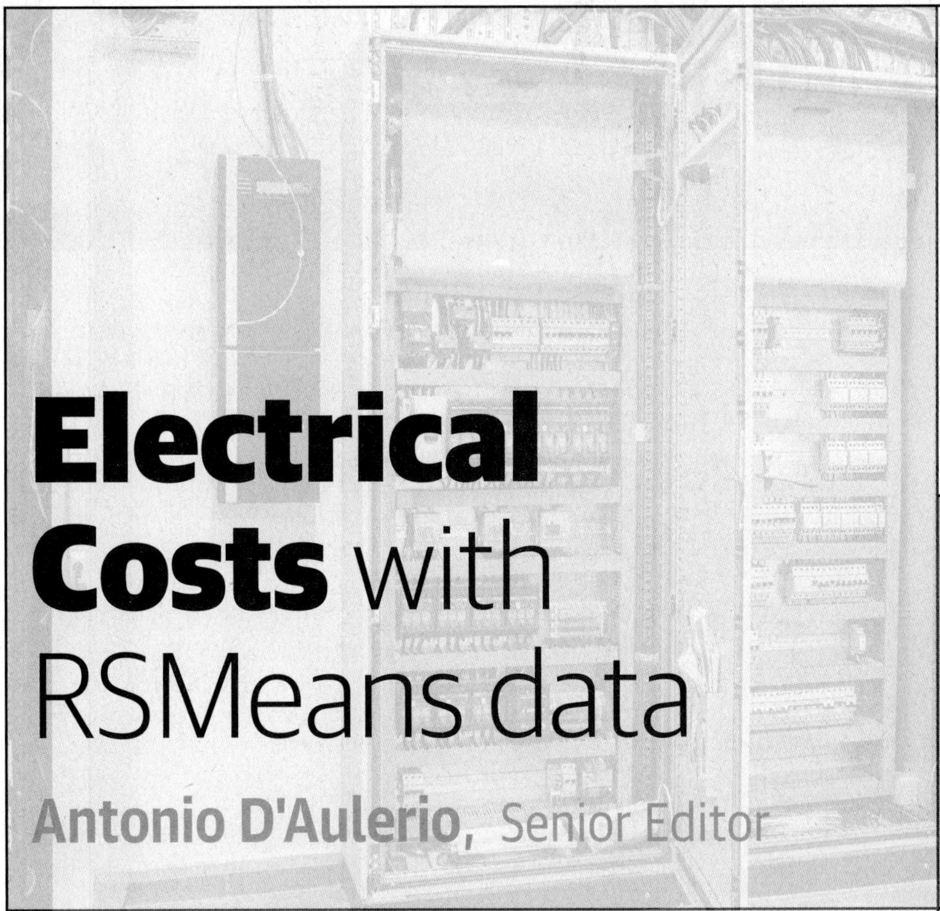

Electrical Costs with RSMeans data

Antonio D'Aulerio, Senior Editor

MW00657955

GORDIAN®

2023

46th annual edition

Chief Technology Officer
Chris Gaudreau

Chief Product Officer
Ted Kail

Director, Data Operations
Sam Giffin

Principal Engineer
Bob Mewis

Engineering and Research
Matthew Doheny, Sr. Manager

Engineers: Architectural Divisions
1, 3, 4, 5, 6, 7, 8, 9, 10, 11, 12, 13, 41
Sam Babbitt
Stephen Bell
Sergeleen Edouard
Richard Goldin
Scott Keller
Thomas Lane

Engineers: Civil Divisions and Wages
2, 31, 32, 33, 34, 35, 44, 46
Derrick Hale, PE
Christopher Babbitt
Michael Lynch
Elisa Mello
Giles Munyard
David Yazbek

Engineers: Mechanical, Electrical, Plumbing & Conveying Divisions
14, 21, 22, 23, 25, 26, 27, 28, 48
Joseph Kelble
Brian Adams
Michelle Curran
Antonio D'Aulerio
Thomas Lyons
Jake MacDonald

Contributing Engineers
John Melin, PE, Manager
Paul Cowan
Barry Hutchinson
Gerard Lafond, PE
Matthew Sorrentino

Production
Debra Panarelli, Manager
Jonathan Forgit
Sheryl Rose
Janice Thalin

Data Quality
Patrice Bruesch, QA Lead and Testing Strategist, Technology
David Byars
Ellen D'Amico

Cover Design
Blaire Collins

Data Management Ecosystem
Audrey Considine
Kedar Gaikwad
Todd Glowac
Srini Narla

RSMeans data from Gordian
Construction Publishers & Consultants
30 Patewood Dr., Suite 350
Greenville, SC 29615
United States of America
1.800.448.8182
rsmeans.com

Printed in the United States of America
ISSN 1540-6318
ISBN 978-1-955341-54-7

0033 $362.00 per copy (in United States)
Price is subject to change without prior notice.

Related Data and Services

Our engineers recommend the following products and services to complement *Electrical Costs with RSMeans data:*

Annual Cost Data Books

2023 Electrical Change Order Costs with RSMeans data
2023 Building Construction Costs with RSMeans data
2023 Mechanical Costs with RSMeans data

Reference Books

Electrical Estimating Methods
Estimating Building Costs
RSMeans Estimating Handbook
Green Building: Project Planning & Estimating
How to Estimate with RSMeans data
Plan Reading & Material Takeoff
Project Scheduling & Management for Construction

Virtual, Instructor-led & On-site Training Offerings

Unit Price Estimating
Training for Our Online Estimating Solution
Practical Project Management for Construction Professionals
Mechanical & Electrical Estimating

RSMeans data

For access to the latest cost data, an intuitive search, and an easy-to-use estimate builder, take advantage of the time savings available from our online application.

To learn more visit: **RSMeans.com/online**

Enterprise Solutions

Building owners, facility managers, building product manufacturers and attorneys across the public and private sectors engage with RSMeans data Enterprise to solve unique challenges where trusted construction cost data is critical.

To learn more visit: **RSMeans.com/Enterprise**

Custom Built Data Sets

Building and Space Models: Quickly plan construction costs across multiple locations based on geography, project size, building system component, product options and other variables for precise budgeting and cost control.

Predictive Analytics: Accurately plan future builds with custom graphical interactive dashboards, negotiate future costs of tenant build-outs and identify and compare national account pricing.

Consulting

Building Product Manufacturing Analytics: Validate your claims and assist with new product launches.

Third-Party Legal Resources: Used in cases of construction cost or estimate disputes, construction product failure vs. installation failure, eminent domain, class action construction product liability and more.

API

For resellers or internal application integration, RSMeans data is offered via API. Deliver Unit, Assembly and Square Foot Model data within your interface. To learn more about how you can provide your customers with the latest in localized construction cost data visit: **RSMeans.com/API**

GORDIAN®

Table of Contents

Foreword

The Value of RSMeans data from Gordian

Since 1942, RSMeans data has been the industry-standard materials, labor, and equipment cost information database for contractors, facility owners and managers, architects, engineers and anyone else that requires the latest localized construction cost information. More than 75 years later, the objective remains the same: to provide facility and construction professionals with the most current and comprehensive construction cost database possible.

With the constant influx of new construction methods and materials, in addition to ever-changing labor and material costs, last year's cost data is not reliable for today's designs, estimates or budgets. Gordian's cost engineers apply real-world construction experience to identify and quantify new building products and methodologies, adjust productivity rates and adjust costs to local market conditions across the nation. This adds up to more than 30,000 hours in cost research annually. This unparalleled construction cost expertise is why so many facility and construction professionals rely on RSMeans data year over year.

About Gordian

Gordian is the leading provider of facility and construction cost data, software, and services for all phases of the building lifecycle. From planning to design, procurement, construction, and operations, Gordian delivers groundbreaking solutions to contractors, architects, engineers, business and financial officers, and facility owners in local, state, and federal governments, education, healthcare, and other industries. A pioneer of Job Order Contracting (JOC), Gordian's offerings also include our proprietary RSMeans data and Facility Intelligence solutions. We develop and maintain the largest collection of labor, material, and equipment data and associated costs for all areas of construction. Gordian's solutions are accessed through our innovative software platforms and supported by a team of industry experts proven to help clients maximize efficiency, optimize cost savings, and increase building quality.

Our Commitment

At Gordian, we do more than talk about the quality of our data and the usefulness of its application. We stand behind all of our RSMeans data — from historical cost indexes to construction materials and techniques — to craft current costs and predict future trends. If you have any questions about our products or services, please call us toll-free at 800.448.8182 or visit our website at gordian.com.

How the Cost Data Is Built: An Overview

Unit Prices*
All cost data have been divided into 50 divisions according to the MasterFormat® system of classification and numbering.

Assemblies*
The cost data in this section have been organized in an "Assemblies" format. These assemblies are the functional elements of a building and are arranged according to the seven elements of the UNIFORMAT II classification system. For a complete explanation of a typical "Assembly", see "RSMeans data: Assemblies—How They Work."

*Residential Models**
Model buildings for four classes of construction – economy, average, custom, and luxury – are developed and shown with complete costs per square foot.

*Commercial/Industrial/ Institutional Models**
This section contains complete costs for 77 typical model buildings expressed as costs per square foot.

*Green Commercial/Industrial/ Institutional Models**
This section contains complete costs for 25 green model buildings expressed as costs per square foot.

*References**
This section includes information on Equipment Rental Costs, Crew Listings, Historical Cost Indexes, City Cost Indexes, Location Factors, Reference Tables and Change Orders, as well as a listing of abbreviations.

- **Equipment Rental Costs:** Included are the average costs to rent and operate hundreds of pieces of construction equipment.
- **Crew Listings**: This section lists all the crews referenced in the cost data. A crew is composed of more than one trade classification and/or the addition of power equipment to any trade classification. Power equipment is included in the cost of the crew. Costs are shown both with bare labor rates and with the installing contractor's overhead and profit added. For each, the total crew cost per eight-hour day and the composite cost per labor-hour are listed.

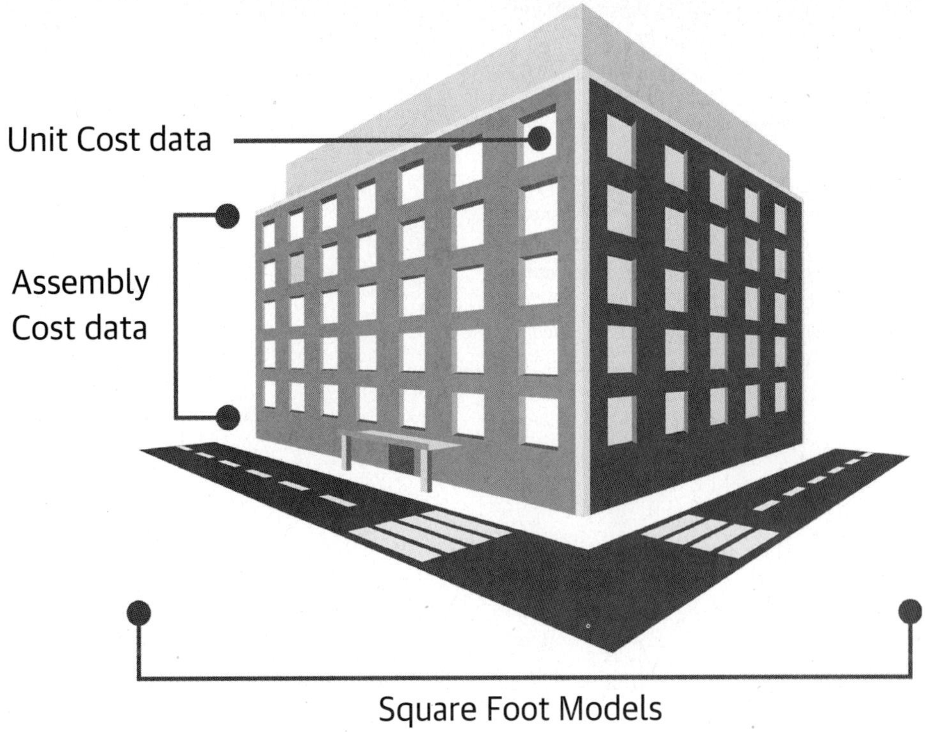

- **Historical Cost Indexes**: These indexes provide you with data to adjust construction costs over time.
- **City Cost Indexes**: All costs in this data set are U.S. national averages. Costs vary by region. You can adjust for this by CSI Division to over 730 cities in 900+ 3-digit zip codes throughout the U.S. and Canada by using this data.
- **Location Factors**: You can adjust total project costs to over 730 cities in 900+ 3-digit zip codes throughout the U.S. and Canada by using the weighted number, which applies across all divisions.
- **Reference Tables**: At the beginning of selected major classifications in the Unit Prices are reference numbers indicators. These numbers refer you to related information in the Reference Section. In this section, you'll find reference tables, explanations and estimating information that support how we develop the unit price data, technical data and estimating procedures.
- **Change Orders**: This section includes information on the factors that influence the pricing of change orders.
- **Abbreviations**: A listing of abbreviations used throughout this information, along with the terms they represent, is included.

Index (printed versions only)
A comprehensive listing of all terms and subjects will help you quickly find what you need when you are not sure where it occurs in MasterFormat®.

Conclusion
This information is designed to be as comprehensive and easy to use as possible.

The Construction Specifications Institute (CSI) and Construction Specifications Canada (CSC) have produced the 2018 edition of MasterFormat®, a system of titles and numbers used extensively to organize construction information.

All unit prices in the RSMeans cost data are now arranged in the 50-division MasterFormat® 2018 system.

* Not all information is available in all data sets

Note: The material prices in RSMeans cost data are "contractor's prices." They are the prices that contractors can expect to pay at the lumberyards, suppliers'/distributors' warehouses, etc. Small orders of specialty items would be higher than the costs shown, while very large orders, such as truckload lots, would be less. The variation would depend on the size, timing, and negotiating power of the contractor. The labor costs are primarily for new construction or major renovation rather than repairs or minor alterations. With reasonable exercise of judgment, the figures can be used for any building work.

Estimating with RSMeans data: Unit Prices

Following these steps will allow you to complete an accurate estimate using RSMeans data: Unit Prices.

1. Scope Out the Project

- Think through the project and identify the CSI divisions needed in your estimate.
- Identify the individual work tasks that will need to be covered in your estimate.
- The Unit Price data have been divided into 50 divisions according to CSI MasterFormat® 2018.
- In printed versions, the Unit Price Section Table of Contents on page 1 may also be helpful when scoping out your project.
- Experienced estimators find it helpful to begin with Division 2 and continue through completion. Division 1 can be estimated after the full project scope is known.

2. Quantify

- Determine the number of units required for each work task that you identified.
- Experienced estimators include an allowance for waste in their quantities. (Waste is not included in our Unit Price line items unless otherwise stated.)

3. Price the Quantities

- Use the search tools available to locate individual Unit Price line items for your estimate.
- Reference Numbers indicated within a Unit Price section refer to additional information that you may find useful.
- The crew indicates who is performing the work for that task. Crew codes are expanded in the Crew Listings in the Reference Section to include all trades and equipment that comprise the crew.
- The Daily Output is the amount of work the crew is expected to complete in one day.
- The Labor-Hours value is the amount of time it will take for the crew to install one unit of work.
- The abbreviated Unit designation indicates the unit of measure upon which the crew, productivity, and prices are based.
- Bare Costs are shown for materials, labor and equipment needed to complete the Unit Price line item. Bare costs do not include waste, project overhead, payroll insurance, payroll taxes, main office overhead or profit.
- The Total Incl O&P cost is the billing rate or invoice amount of the installing contractor or subcontractor who performs the work for the Unit Price line item.

4. Multiply

- Multiply the total number of units needed for your project by the Total Incl O&P cost for each Unit Price line item.
- Be careful that your take off unit of measure matches the unit of measure in the Unit column.
- The price you calculate is an estimate for a completed item of work.
- Keep scoping individual tasks, determining the number of units required for those tasks, matching each task with individual Unit Price line items and multiplying quantities by Total Incl O&P costs.
- An estimate completed in this manner is priced as if a subcontractor, or set of subcontractors, is performing the work. The estimate does not yet include Project Overhead or Estimate Summary components such as general contractor markups on subcontracted work, general contractor office overhead and profit, contingency and location factors.

5. Project Overhead

- Include project overhead items from Division 1-General Requirements.
- These items are needed to make the job run. They are typically, but not always, provided by the general contractor. Items include, but are not limited to, field personnel, insurance, performance bond, permits, testing, temporary utilities, field office and storage facilities, temporary scaffolding and platforms, equipment mobilization and demobilization, temporary roads and sidewalks, winter protection, temporary barricades and fencing, temporary security, temporary signs, field engineering and layout, final cleaning and commissioning.
- Each item should be quantified and matched to individual Unit Price line items in Division 1, then priced and added to your estimate.
- An alternate method of estimating project overhead costs is to apply a percentage of the total project cost – usually 5% to 15% with an average of 10% (see General Conditions).
- Include other project related expenses in your estimate such as:
  - Rented equipment not itemized in the Crew Listings
  - Rubbish handling throughout the project (see section 02 41 19.19)

6. Estimate Summary

- Include sales tax as required by laws of your state or county.
- Include the general contractor's markup on self-performed work, usually 5% to 15% with an average of 10%.
- Include the general contractor's markup on subcontracted work, usually 5% to 15% with an average of 10%.
- Include the general contractor's main office overhead and profit:
  - RSMeans data provides general guidelines on the general contractor's main office overhead (see section 01 31 13.60 and Reference Number R013113-50).
  - Markups will depend on the size of the general contractor's operations, projected annual revenue, the level of risk and the level of competition in the local area and for this project in particular.
- Include a contingency, usually 3% to 5%, if appropriate.
- Adjust your estimate to the project's location by using the City Cost Indexes or the Location Factors in the Reference Section:
  - Look at the rules in "How to Use the City Cost Indexes" to see how to apply the Indexes for your location.
  - When the proper Index or Factor has been identified for the project's location, convert it to a multiplier by dividing it by 100, then multiply that multiplier by your estimated total cost. The original estimated total cost will now be adjusted up or down from the national average to a total that is appropriate for your location.

Editors' Note:
We urge you to spend time reading and understanding the supporting material. An accurate estimate requires experience, knowledge, and careful calculation. The more you know about how we at RSMeans developed the data, the more accurate your estimate will be. In addition, it is important to take into consideration the reference material such as Equipment Listings, Crew Listings, City Cost Indexes, Location Factors, and Reference Tables.

How to Use the Cost Data: The Details

What's Behind the Numbers? The Development of Cost Data

RSMeans data engineers continually monitor developments in the construction industry to ensure reliable, thorough and up-to-date cost information. While overall construction costs may vary relative to general economic conditions, price fluctuations within the industry are dependent upon many factors. Individual price variations may, in fact, be opposite to overall economic trends. Therefore, costs are constantly tracked and complete updates are performed yearly. Also, new items are frequently added in response to changes in materials and methods.

Costs in U.S. Dollars

All costs represent U.S. national averages and are given in U.S. dollars. The City Cost Index (CCI) with RSMeans data can be used to adjust costs to a particular location. The CCI for Canada can be used to adjust U.S. national averages to local costs in Canadian dollars. No exchange rate conversion is necessary because it has already been factored in.

G The processes or products identified by the green symbol in our publications have been determined to be environmentally responsible and/or resource-efficient solely by RSMeans data engineering staff. The inclusion of the green symbol does not represent compliance with any specific industry association or standard.

Material Costs

RSMeans data engineers contact manufacturers, dealers, distributors and contractors all across the U.S. and Canada to determine national average material costs. If you have access to current material costs for your specific location, you may wish to make adjustments to reflect differences from the national average. Included within material costs are fasteners for a normal installation. RSMeans data engineers use manufacturers' recommendations, written specifications and/or standard construction practices for the sizing and spacing of fasteners. Adjustments to material costs may be required for your specific application or location. The manufacturer's warranty is assumed. Extended warranties are not included in the material costs. **Material costs do not include sales tax.**

Labor Costs

Labor costs are based upon a mathematical average of trade-specific wages in 30 major U.S. cities. The type of wage (union, open shop or residential) is identified on the inside back cover of printed publications or selected by the estimator when using the electronic products. Markups for the wages can also be found on the inside back cover of printed publications and/or under the labor references found in the electronic products.

- If wage rates in your area vary from those used, or if rate increases are expected within a given year, labor costs should be adjusted accordingly.

Labor costs reflect productivity based on actual working conditions. In addition to actual installation, these figures include time spent during a normal weekday on tasks, such as material receiving and handling, mobilization at the site, site movement, breaks and cleanup.

Productivity data is developed over an extended period so as not to be influenced by abnormal variations and reflects a typical average.

Equipment Costs

Equipment costs include not only rental but also operating costs for equipment under normal use. The operating costs include parts and labor for routine servicing, such as the repair and replacement of pumps, filters and worn lines. Normal operating expendables, such as fuel, lubricants, tires and electricity (where applicable) are also included. Extraordinary operating expendables with highly variable wear patterns, such as diamond bits and blades, are excluded. These costs are included under materials. Equipment rental rates are obtained from industry sources throughout North America – contractors, suppliers, dealers, manufacturers and distributors.

Rental rates can also be treated as reimbursement costs for contractor-owned equipment. Owned equipment costs include depreciation, loan payments, interest, taxes, insurance, storage and major repairs.

Equipment costs do not include operators' wages.

Equipment Cost/Day—The cost of equipment required for each crew is included in the Crew Listings in the Reference Section (small tools that are considered essential everyday tools are not listed out separately). The Crew Listings itemize specialized tools and heavy equipment along with labor trades. The daily cost of itemized equipment included in a crew is based on dividing the weekly bare rental rate by five (5) (number of working days per week), then adding the hourly operating cost times eight (8) (the number of hours per day). This Equipment Cost/Day is shown in the last column of the Equipment Rental Costs in the Reference Section.

Mobilization, Demobilization—The cost to move construction equipment from an equipment yard or rental company to the job site and back again is not included in equipment costs. Mobilization (to the site) and demobilization (from the site) costs can be found in the Unit Price Section. If a piece of equipment is already at the job site, it is not appropriate to utilize mobilization or demobilization costs again in an estimate.

Overhead and Profit

Total Cost including O&P for the installing contractor is shown in the last column of the Unit Price and/or Assemblies. This figure is the sum of the bare material cost plus 10% for profit, the bare labor cost plus total overhead and profit, and the bare equipment cost plus 10% for profit. Details for the calculation of overhead and profit on labor are shown on the inside back cover of the printed product and in the Reference Section of the electronic product.

General Conditions

Cost data in this dataset are presented in two ways: Bare Costs and Total Cost including O&P (Overhead and Profit). General Conditions, or General Requirements, of the contract should also be added to the Total Cost including O&P when applicable. Costs for General Conditions are listed in Division 1 of the Unit Price Section and in the Reference Section.

General Conditions for the installing contractor may range from 0% to 10% of the Total Cost including O&P. For the general or prime contractor, costs for General Conditions may range from 5% to 15% of the Total Cost including O&P, with a figure of 10% as the most typical allowance. If applicable, the Assemblies and Models sections use costs that include the installing contractor's overhead and profit (O&P).

Factors Affecting Costs

Costs can vary depending upon a number of variables. Here's a listing of some factors that affect costs and points to consider.

Quality: The prices for materials and the workmanship upon which productivity is based represent sound construction work. They are also in line with industry standard and manufacturer specifications and are frequently used by federal, state and local governments.

Overtime: We have made no allowance for overtime. If you anticipate premium time or work beyond normal working hours, be sure to make an appropriate adjustment to your labor costs.

Productivity: The productivity, daily output and labor-hour figures for each line item are based on an eight-hour work day in daylight hours in moderate temperatures and up to a 14' working height unless otherwise indicated. For work that extends beyond normal work hours or is performed under adverse conditions, productivity may decrease.

Size of Project: The size, scope of work and type of construction project will have a significant impact on cost. Economies of scale can reduce costs for large projects. Unit costs can often run higher for small projects.

Location: Material prices are for metropolitan areas. However, in dense urban areas, traffic and site storage limitations may increase costs. Beyond a 20-mile radius of metropolitan areas, extra trucking or transportation charges may also increase the material costs slightly. On the other hand, lower wage rates may be in effect. Be sure to consider both of these factors when preparing an estimate, particularly if the job site is located in a central city or remote rural location. In addition, highly specialized subcontract items may require travel and per-diem expenses for mechanics.

Other Factors

- Season of year
- Contractor management
- Weather conditions
- Local union restrictions
- Building code requirements
- Availability of:
  - adequate energy
  - skilled labor
  - building materials
- Owner's special requirements/restrictions
- Safety requirements
- Environmental considerations
- Access

Unpredictable Factors: General business conditions influence "in-place" costs of all items. Substitute materials and construction methods may have to be employed. These may affect the installed cost and/or life cycle costs. Such factors may be difficult to evaluate and cannot necessarily be predicted on the basis of the job's location in a particular section of the country. Thus, where these factors apply, you may find significant but unavoidable cost variations for which you will have to apply a measure of judgment to your estimate.

Rounding of Costs

In printed publications only, all unit prices in excess of $5.00 have been rounded to make them easier to use and still maintain adequate precision of the results.

How Subcontracted Items Affect Costs

A considerable portion of all large construction jobs is usually subcontracted. In fact, the percentage done by subcontractors is constantly increasing and may run over 90%. Since the workers employed by these companies do nothing else but install their particular products, they soon become experts in that line. As a result, installation by these firms is accomplished so efficiently that the total in-place cost, even with the general contractor's overhead and profit, is no more, and often less, than if the principal contractor had handled the installation. Companies that deal with construction specialties are anxious to have their products perform well and, consequently, the installation will be the best possible.

Contingencies

The allowance for contingencies generally provides for unforeseen construction difficulties. On alterations or repair jobs, 20% is not too much. If drawings are final and only field contingencies are being considered, 2% or 3% is probably sufficient and often nothing needs to be added. Contractually, changes in plans will be covered by extras. The contractor should consider inflationary price trends and possible material shortages during the course of the job. These escalation factors are dependent upon both economic conditions and the anticipated time between the estimate and actual construction. If drawings are not complete or approved, or a budget cost is wanted, it is wise to add 5% to 10%. Contingencies, then, are a matter of judgment.

Important Estimating Considerations

The productivity, or daily output, of each craftsman or crew assumes a well-managed job where tradesmen with the proper tools and equipment, along with the appropriate construction materials, are present. Included are daily set-up and cleanup time, break time and plan layout time. Unless otherwise indicated, time for material movement on site (for items that can be transported by hand) of up to 200' into the building and to the first or second floor is also included. If material has to be transported by other means, over greater distances or to higher floors, an additional allowance should be considered by the estimator.

While horizontal movement is typically a sole function of distances, vertical transport introduces other variables that can significantly impact productivity. In an occupied building, the use of elevators (assuming access, size and required protective measures are acceptable) must be understood at the time of the estimate. For new construction, hoist wait and cycle times can easily be 15 minutes and may result in scheduled access extending beyond the normal work day. Finally, all vertical transport will impose strict weight limits likely to preclude the use of any motorized material handling.

The productivity, or daily output, also assumes installation that meets manufacturer/designer/standard specifications. A time allowance for quality control checks, minor adjustments and any task required to ensure proper function or operation is also included. For items that require connections to services, time is included for positioning, leveling, securing the unit and making all the necessary connections (and start up where applicable) to ensure a complete installation. Estimating of the services themselves (electrical, plumbing, water, steam, hydraulics, dust collection, etc.) is separate.

In some cases, the estimator must consider the use of a crane and an appropriate crew for the installation of large or heavy items. For those situations where a crane is not included in the assigned crew and as part of the line item cost, then equipment rental costs, mobilization and demobilization costs, and operator and support personnel costs must be considered.

Labor-Hours

The labor-hours expressed in this publication are derived by dividing the total daily labor-hours for the crew by the daily output. Based on average installation time and the assumptions listed above, the labor-hours include: direct labor, indirect labor and nonproductive time. A typical day for a craftsman might include but is not limited to:

- Direct Work
  - □ Measuring and layout
  - □ Preparing materials
  - □ Actual installation
  - □ Quality assurance/quality control
- Indirect Work
  - □ Reading plans or specifications
  - □ Preparing space
  - □ Receiving materials
  - □ Material movement
  - □ Giving or receiving instruction
  - □ Miscellaneous
- Non-Work
  - □ Chatting
  - □ Personal issues
  - □ Breaks
  - □ Interruptions (i.e., sickness, weather, material or equipment shortages, etc.)

If any of the items for a typical day do not apply to the particular work or project situation, the estimator should make any necessary adjustments.

Final Checklist

Estimating can be a straightforward process provided you remember the basics. Here's a checklist of some of the steps you should remember to complete before finalizing your estimate.

Did you remember to:

- Factor in the City Cost Index for your locale?
- Take into consideration which items have been marked up and by how much?
- Mark up the entire estimate sufficiently for your purposes?
- Read the background information on techniques and technical matters that could impact your project time span and cost?
- Include all components of your project in the final estimate?
- Double check your figures for accuracy?
- Call RSMeans data engineers if you have any questions about your estimate or the data you've used? Remember, Gordian stands behind all of our products, including our extensive RSMeans data solutions. If you have any questions about your estimate, about the costs you've used from our data or even about the technical aspects of the job that may affect your estimate, feel free to call the Gordian RSMeans editors at 800.448.8182.

Unit Price Section

Table of Contents

RSMeans data: Unit Prices—How They Work

All RSMeans data: Unit Prices are organized in the same way.

03 30 Cast-In-Place Concrete

03 30 53 – Miscellaneous Cast-In-Place Concrete

03 30 53.40 Concrete In Place		Crew	Daily Output	Labor-Hours	Unit	2023 Bare Costs Material	Labor	Equipment	Total	Total Incl O&P
0010	CONCRETE IN PLACE									
0020	Including forms (4 uses), Grade 60 rebar, concrete (Portland cement									
0050	Type I), placement and finishing unless otherwise indicated									
3540	Equipment pad (3000 psi), 3′ x 3′ x 6″ thick	C-14H	45	1.067	Ea.	83	61.50	.66	145.16	183
3550	4′ x 4′ x 6″ thick		30	1.600		120	92	.99	212.99	270
3560	5′ x 5′ x 8″ thick		18	2.667		216	153	1.65	370.65	470
3570	6′ x 6′ x 8″ thick		14	3.429		284	197	2.13	483.13	610
3580	8′ x 8′ x 10″ thick		8	6		590	345	3.72	938.72	1,175
3590	10′ x 10′ x 12″ thick		5	9.600		980	550	5.95	1,535.95	1,900
3800	Footings (3000 psi), spread under 1 C.Y.	C-14C	28	4	C.Y.	257	224	1.08	482.08	620
3813	Install new concrete (3000 psi) light pole base, 24″ diam. x 8′	C-1	2.66	12.030		430	670		1,100	1,475
3825	1 C.Y. to 5 C.Y.	C-14C	43	2.605		330	146	.70	476.70	580
3850	Over 5 C.Y.	″	75	1.493		315	84	.40	399.40	470
3900	Footings, strip (3000 psi), 18″ x 9″, unreinforced	C-14L	40	2.400		211	131	.74	342.74	430

It is important to understand the structure of RSMeans data: Unit Prices so that you can find information easily and use it correctly.

1 Line Numbers

Line Numbers consist of 12 characters, which identify a unique location in the database for each task. The first six (6) or eight (8) digits conform to the Construction Specifications Institute MasterFormat® 2018. The remainder of the digits are a further breakdown in order to arrange items in understandable groups of similar tasks. Line numbers are consistent across all of our publications, so a line number in any of our products will always refer to the same item of work.

2 Descriptions

Descriptions are shown in a hierarchical structure to make them readable. In order to read a complete description, read up through the indents to the top of the section. Include everything that is above and to the left that is not contradicted by information below. For instance, the complete description for line 03 30 53.40 3550 is "Concrete in place, including forms (4 uses), Grade 60 rebar, concrete (Portland cement Type 1), placement and finishing unless otherwise indicated; Equipment pad (3,000 psi), 4' × 4' × 6" thick."

3 RSMeans data

When using **RSMeans data**, it is important to read through an entire section to ensure that you use the data that most closely matches your work. Note that sometimes there is additional information shown in the section that may improve your price. There are frequently lines that further describe, add to or adjust data for specific situations.

4 Reference Information

Gordian's engineers have created **reference** information to assist you in your estimate. **If** there is information that applies to a section, it will be indicated at the start of the section. The Reference Section is located in the back of the data set.

5 Crews

Crews include labor and/or equipment necessary to accomplish each task. In this case, Crew C-14H is used. Gordian's staff selects a crew to represent the workers and equipment that are typically used for that task. In this case, Crew C-14H consists of one carpenter foreperson (outside), two carpenters, one rodman, one laborer, one cement finisher and one gas engine vibrator. Details of all crews can be found in the Reference Section.

Crews - Standard

Crew No.	Bare Costs		Incl. Subs O&P		Cost Per Labor-Hour	
Crew C-14H	**Hr.**	**Daily**	**Hr.**	**Daily**	**Bare Costs**	**Incl. O&P**
1 Carpenter Foreman (outside)	$60.60	$484.80	$90.20	$721.60	$57.43	$85.32
2 Carpenters	58.60	937.60	87.25	1396.00		
1 Rodman (reinf.)	64.55	516.40	96.40	771.20		
1 Laborer	47.25	378.00	70.35	562.80		
1 Cement Finisher	55.00	440.00	80.45	643.60		
1 Gas Engine Vibrator		29.68		32.65	.62	.68
48 L.H., Daily Totals		$2786.48		$4127.85	$58.05	$86.00

6 Daily Output

The **Daily Output** is the amount of work that the crew can do in a normal 8-hour workday, including mobilization, layout, movement of materials and cleanup. In this case, crew C-14H can install thirty 4' × 4' × 6" thick concrete pads in a day. Daily output is variable and based on many factors, including the size of the job, location and environmental conditions. RSMeans data represents work done in daylight (or adequate lighting) and temperate conditions.

7 Labor-Hours

The figure in the **Labor-Hours** column is the amount of labor required to perform one unit of work—in this case the amount of labor required to construct one 4' × 4' equipment pad. This figure is calculated by dividing the number of hours of labor in the crew by the daily output (48 labor-hours divided by 30 pads = 1.6 hours of labor per pad). Multiply 1.6 times 60 to see the value in minutes: 60 × 1.6 = 96 minutes. Note: The labor-hour figure is not dependent on the crew size. A change in crew size will result in a corresponding change in daily output, but the labor-hours per unit of work will not change.

8 Unit of Measure

Unit Prices include the typical **Unit of Measure** used for estimating that item. For concrete-in-place the typical unit is cubic yards (C.Y.) or each (Ea.). For installing broadloom carpet it is square yard and for gypsum board it is square foot. The estimator needs to take special care that the unit in the data matches the unit in the take-off. Unit conversions may be found in the Reference Section.

9 Bare Costs

Bare Costs are the costs of materials, labor, and equipment that the installing contractor pays. They represent the cost, in U.S. dollars, for one unit of work. They do not include any markups for profit or labor burden.

10 Bare Total

The **Total column** represents the total bare cost for the installing contractor in U.S. dollars. In this case, the sum of $120 for material + $92 for labor + $.99 for equipment is $212.99.

11 Total Incl O&P

The **Total Incl O&P column** is the total cost, including overhead and profit, that the installing contractor will charge the customer. This represents the cost of materials plus 10% profit, the cost of labor plus labor burden and 10% profit, and the cost of equipment plus 10% profit. It does not include the general contractor's overhead and profit. Note: See the inside back cover of the printed product or the Reference Section of the electronic product for details on how the labor burden is calculated.

National Average

*The RSMeans data in our print publications represent a "national average" cost. This data should be modified to the project location using the **City Cost Indexes** or **Location Factors** tables found in the Reference Section. Use the Location Factors to adjust estimate totals if the project covers multiple trades. Use the City Cost Indexes (CCI) for single trade projects or projects where a more detailed analysis is required. All figures in the two tables are derived from the same research. The last row of data in the CCI – the weighted average – is the same as the numbers reported for each location in the location factor table.*

RSMeans data: Unit Prices— How They Work (Continued)

Project Name: Pre-Engineered Steel Building		Architect: As Shown						
Location:	Anywhere, USA						01/01/23	STD
1 Line Number	Description	Qty	Unit	Material	Labor	Equipment	SubContract	Estimate Total
03 30 53.40 3940	Strip footing, 12" x 24", reinforced	15	C.Y.	$3,345.00	$1,965.00	$9.45	$0.00	
03 30 53.40 3950	Strip footing, 12" x 36", reinforced	34	C.Y.	$7,140.00	$3,570.00	$17.00	$0.00	
03 11 13.65 3000	Concrete slab edge forms	500	L.F.	$415.00	$1,485.00	$0.00	$0.00	
03 22 11.10 0200	Welded wire fabric reinforcing	150	C.S.F.	$9,225.00	$5,025.00	$0.00	$0.00	
03 31 13.35 0300	Ready mix concrete, 4000 psi for slab on grade	278	C.Y.	$45,036.00	$0.00	$0.00	$0.00	
03 31 13.70 4300	Place, strike off & consolidate concrete slab	278	C.Y.	$0.00	$5,977.00	$150.12	$0.00	
03 35 13.30 0250	Machine float & trowel concrete slab	15,000	S.F.	$0.00	$10,950.00	$750.00	$0.00	
03 15 16.20 0140	Cut control joints in concrete slab	950	L.F.	$38.00	$465.50	$95.00	$0.00	
03 39 23.13 0300	Sprayed concrete curing membrane	150	C.S.F.	$2,400.00	$1,192.50	$0.00	$0.00	
Division 03	**Subtotal**			**$67,599.00**	**$30,630.00**	**$1,021.57**	**$0.00**	**$99,250.57**
08 36 13.10 2650	Manual 10' x 10' steel sectional overhead door	8	Ea.	$14,200.00	$4,160.00	$0.00	$0.00	
08 36 13.10 2860	Insulation and steel back panel for OH door	800	S.F.	$5,360.00	$0.00	$0.00	$0.00	
Division 08	**Subtotal**			**$19,560.00**	**$4,160.00**	**$0.00**	**$0.00**	**$23,720.00**
13 34 19.50 1100	Pre-Engineered Steel Building, 100' x 150' x 24'	15,000	SF Flr.	$0.00	$0.00	$0.00	$420,000.00	
13 34 19.50 6050	Framing for PESB door opening, 3' x 7'	4	Opng.	$0.00	$0.00	$0.00	$2,600.00	
13 34 19.50 6100	Framing for PESB door opening, 10' x 10'	8	Opng.	$0.00	$0.00	$0.00	$10,800.00	
13 34 19.50 6200	Framing for PESB window opening, 4' x 3'	6	Opng.	$0.00	$0.00	$0.00	$3,870.00	
13 34 19.50 5750	PESB door, 3' x 7', single leaf	4	Opng.	$3,320.00	$828.00	$0.00	$0.00	
13 34 19.50 7750	PESB sliding window, 4' x 3' with screen	6	Opng.	$3,120.00	$702.00	$67.80	$0.00	
13 34 19.50 6550	PESB gutter, eave type, 26 ga., painted	300	L.F.	$2,670.00	$969.00	$0.00	$0.00	
13 34 19.50 8650	PESB roof vent, 12" wide x 10' long	15	Ea.	$750.00	$3,870.00	$0.00	$0.00	
13 34 19.50 6900	PESB insulation, vinyl faced, 4" thick	27,400	S.F.	$42,470.00	$11,234.00	$0.00	$0.00	
Division 13	**Subtotal**			**$52,330.00**	**$17,603.00**	**$67.80**	**$437,270.00**	**$507,270.80**
		Subtotal		**$139,489.00**	**$52,393.00**	**$1,089.37**	**$437,270.00**	**$630,241.37**
Division 01	2 **General Requirements @ 7%**			**9,764.23**	**3,667.51**	**76.26**	**30,608.90**	
		Estimate Subtotal		**$149,253.23**	**$56,060.51**	**$1,165.63**	**$467,878.90**	**$630,241.37**
	3	**Sales Tax @ 5%**		**7,462.66**		**58.28**	**11,696.97**	
		Subtotal A		**156,715.89**	**56,060.51**	**1,223.91**	**479,575.87**	
	4	**GC O & P**		**15,671.59**	**28,142.38**	**122.39**	**47,957.59**	
		Subtotal B		**172,387.48**	**84,202.89**	**1,346.30**	**527,533.46**	**$785,470.12**
	5	**Contingency @ 5%**						**39,273.51**
		Subtotal C						**$824,743.63**
	6	**Bond @ $12/1000 +10% O&P**						**10,886.62**
		Subtotal D						**$835,630.25**
	7	**Location Adjustment Factor**			**112.50**			**104,453.78**
		Grand Total						**$940,084.03**

This estimate is based on an interactive spreadsheet. You are free to download it and adjust it to your methodology.
A copy of this spreadsheet is available at **RSMeans.com/2023books.**

Sample Estimate

This sample demonstrates the elements of an estimate, including a tally of the RSMeans data lines and a summary of the markups on a contractor's work to arrive at a total cost to the owner. The Location Factor with RSMeans data is added at the bottom of the estimate to adjust the cost of the work to a specific location.

1 Work Performed

The body of the estimate shows the RSMeans data selected, including the line number, a brief description of each item, its take-off unit and quantity, and the bare costs of materials, labor and equipment. This estimate also includes a column titled "SubContract." This data is taken from the column "Total Incl O&P" and represents the total that a subcontractor would charge a general contractor for the work, including the sub's markup for overhead and profit.

2 Division 1, General Requirements

This is the first division numerically but the last division estimated. Division 1 includes project-wide needs provided by the general contractor. These requirements vary by project but may include temporary facilities and utilities, security, testing, project cleanup, etc. For small projects a percentage can be used — typically between 5% and 15% of project cost. For large projects the costs may be itemized and priced individually.

3 Sales Tax

If the work is subject to state or local sales taxes, the amount must be added to the estimate. Sales tax may be added to material costs, equipment costs and subcontracted work. In this case, sales tax was added in all three categories. It was assumed that approximately half the subcontracted work would be material cost, so the tax was applied to 50% of the subcontract total.

4 GC O&P

This entry represents the general contractor's markup on material, labor, equipment and subcontractor costs. Our standard markup on materials, equipment and subcontracted work is 10%. In this estimate, the markup on the labor performed by the GC's workers uses "Skilled Workers Average" shown in Column F on the table "Installing Contractor's Overhead & Profit," which can be found on the inside back cover of the printed product or in the Reference Section of the electronic product.

5 Contingency

A factor for contingency may be added to any estimate to represent the cost of unknowns that may occur between the time that the estimate is performed and the time the project is constructed. The amount of the allowance will depend on the stage of design at which the estimate is done and the contractor's assessment of the risk involved. Refer to section 01 21 16.50 for contingency allowances.

6 Bonds

Bond costs should be added to the estimate. The figures here represent a typical performance bond, ensuring the owner that if the general contractor does not complete the obligations in the construction contract the bonding company will pay the cost for completion of the work.

7 Location Adjustment

Published prices are based on national average costs. If necessary, adjust the total cost of the project using a location factor from the "Location Factor" table or the "City Cost Index" table. Use location factors if the work is general, covering multiple trades. If the work is by a single trade (e.g., masonry) use the more specific data found in the "City Cost Indexes."

Estimating Tips

01 20 00 Price and Payment Procedures

- Allowances that should be added to estimates to cover contingencies and job conditions that are not included in the national average material and labor costs are shown in Section 01 21.
- When estimating historic preservation projects (depending on the condition of the existing structure and the owner's requirements), a 15–20% contingency or allowance is recommended, regardless of the stage of the drawings.

01 30 00 Administrative Requirements

- Before determining a final cost estimate, it is good practice to review all the items listed in Subdivisions 01 31 and 01 32 to make final adjustments for items that may need customizing to specific job conditions.
- Requirements for initial and periodic submittals can represent a significant cost to the General Requirements of a job. Thoroughly check the submittal specifications when estimating a project to determine any costs that should be included.

01 40 00 Quality Requirements

- All projects will require some degree of quality control. This cost is not included in the unit cost of construction listed in each division. Depending upon the terms of the contract, the various costs of inspection and testing can be the responsibility of either the owner or the contractor. Be sure to include the required costs in your estimate.

01 50 00 Temporary Facilities and Controls

- Barricades, access roads, safety nets, scaffolding, security, and many more requirements for the execution of a safe project are elements of direct cost. These costs can easily be overlooked when preparing an estimate. When looking through the major classifications of this subdivision, determine which items apply to each division in your estimate.
- Construction equipment rental costs can be found in the Reference Section in Section 01 54 33. Operators' wages are not included in equipment rental costs.
- Equipment mobilization and demobilization costs are not included in equipment rental costs and must be considered separately.
- The cost of small tools provided by the installing contractor for his workers is covered in the "Overhead" column on the "Installing Contractor's Overhead and Profit" table that lists labor trades, base rates, and markups. Therefore, it is included in the "Total Incl. O&P" cost of any unit price line item.

01 70 00 Execution and Closeout Requirements

- When preparing an estimate, thoroughly read the specifications to determine the requirements for Contract Closeout. Final cleaning, record documentation, operation and maintenance data, warranties and bonds, and spare parts and maintenance materials can all be elements of cost for the completion of a contract. Do not overlook these in your estimate.

Reference Numbers

Reference numbers are shown at the beginning of some major classifications. These numbers refer to related items in the Reference Section. The reference information may be an estimating procedure, an alternate pricing method, or technical information.

Note: Not all subdivisions listed here necessarily appear. ■

01 11 Summary of Work

01 11 31 – Professional Consultants

01 11 31.20 Construction Management Fees		Crew	Daily Output	Labor-Hours	Unit	2023 Bare Costs Material	Labor	Equipment	Total	Total Incl O&P
0010	**CONSTRUCTION MANAGEMENT FEES**									
0020	$1,000,000 job, minimum				Project				4.50%	4.50%
0050	Maximum								7.50%	7.50%
0060	For work to $100,000								10%	10%
0300	$50,000,000 job, minimum								2.50%	2.50%
0350	Maximum								4%	4%

01 11 31.30 Engineering Fees		Crew	Daily Output	Labor-Hours	Unit	Material	Labor	Equipment	Total	Total Incl O&P
0010	**ENGINEERING FEES** R011110-30									
0020	Educational planning consultant, minimum				Project				.50%	.50%
0100	Maximum				"				2.50%	2.50%
0200	Electrical, minimum				Contrct				4.10%	4.10%
0300	Maximum								10.10%	10.10%
0400	Elevator & conveying systems, minimum								2.50%	2.50%
0500	Maximum								5%	5%
0600	Food service & kitchen equipment, minimum								8%	8%
0700	Maximum								12%	12%
1000	Mechanical (plumbing & HVAC), minimum								4.10%	4.10%
1100	Maximum								10.10%	10.10%

01 21 Allowances

01 21 16 – Contingency Allowances

01 21 16.50 Contingencies		Crew	Daily Output	Labor-Hours	Unit	Material	Labor	Equipment	Total	Total Incl O&P
0010	**CONTINGENCIES**, Add to estimate									
0020	Conceptual stage				Project				20%	20%
0050	Schematic stage								15%	15%
0100	Preliminary working drawing stage (Design Dev.)								10%	10%
0150	Final working drawing stage								3%	3%

01 21 53 – Factors Allowance

01 21 53.50 Factors		Crew	Daily Output	Labor-Hours	Unit	Material	Labor	Equipment	Total	Total Incl O&P
0010	**FACTORS** Cost adjustments									
0100	Add to construction costs for particular job requirements									
0500	Cut & patch to match existing construction, add, minimum				Costs	2%	3%			
0550	Maximum					5%	9%			
0800	Dust protection, add, minimum					1%	2%			
0850	Maximum					4%	11%			
1100	Equipment usage curtailment, add, minimum					1%	1%			
1150	Maximum					3%	10%			
1400	Material handling & storage limitation, add, minimum					1%	1%			
1450	Maximum					6%	7%			
1700	Protection of existing work, add, minimum					2%	2%			
1750	Maximum					5%	7%			
2000	Shift work requirements, add, minimum						5%			
2050	Maximum						30%			
2300	Temporary shoring and bracing, add, minimum					2%	5%			
2350	Maximum					5%	12%			

01 21 53 – Factors Allowance

01 21 53.60 Security Factors

		Crew	Daily Output	Labor-Hours	Unit	2023 Bare Costs Material	Labor	Equipment	Total	Total Incl O&P
0010	**SECURITY FACTORS** R012153-60									
0100	Additional costs due to security requirements									
0110	Daily search of personnel, supplies, equipment and vehicles									
0120	Physical search, inventory and doc of assets, at entry				Costs		30%			
0130	At entry and exit						50%			
0140	Physical search, at entry						6.25%			
0150	At entry and exit						12.50%			
0160	Electronic scan search, at entry						2%			
0170	At entry and exit						4%			
0180	Visual inspection only, at entry						.25%			
0190	At entry and exit						.50%			
0200	ID card or display sticker only, at entry						.12%			
0210	At entry and exit						.25%			
0220	Day 1 as described below, then visual only for up to 5 day job duration									
0230	Physical search, inventory and doc of assets, at entry				Costs		5%			
0240	At entry and exit						10%			
0250	Physical search, at entry						1.25%			
0260	At entry and exit						2.50%			
0270	Electronic scan search, at entry						.42%			
0280	At entry and exit						.83%			
0290	Day 1 as described below, then visual only for 6-10 day job duration									
0300	Physical search, inventory and doc of assets, at entry				Costs		2.50%			
0310	At entry and exit						5%			
0320	Physical search, at entry						.63%			
0330	At entry and exit						1.25%			
0340	Electronic scan search, at entry						.21%			
0350	At entry and exit						.42%			
0360	Day 1 as described below, then visual only for 11-20 day job duration									
0370	Physical search, inventory and doc of assets, at entry				Costs		1.25%			
0380	At entry and exit						2.50%			
0390	Physical search, at entry						.31%			
0400	At entry and exit						.63%			
0410	Electronic scan search, at entry						.10%			
0420	At entry and exit						.21%			
0430	Beyond 20 days, costs are negligible									
0440	Escort required to be with tradesperson during work effort				Costs		6.25%			

01 21 53.65 Infectious Disease Precautions

		Crew	Daily Output	Labor-Hours	Unit	Material	Labor	Equipment	Total	Total Incl O&P
0010	**INFECTIOUS DISEASE PRECAUTIONS** R012153-65									
0100	Additional costs due to infectious disease precautions									
0120	Daily temperature checks				Costs		1%			
0130	Donning & doffing masks and gloves						1%			
0140	Washing hands						1%			
0150	Informational meetings						2%			
0160	Maintaining social distance						1%			
0170	Disinfecting tools or equipment						3%			
0200	N95 rated masks				Ea.	2.33			2.33	2.56
0210	Surgical masks				"	.74			.74	.82
0220	Black nitrile disposable gloves				Pair	.70			.70	.77
0250	Hand washing station & 2 x weekly service				Week				158	174

01 21 Allowances

01 21 55 – Job Conditions Allowance

01 21 55.50 Job Conditions		Crew	Daily Output	Labor-Hours	Unit	Material	2023 Bare Costs Labor	Equipment	Total	Total Incl O&P
0010	**JOB CONDITIONS** Modifications to applicable									
0020	cost summaries									
0100	Economic conditions, favorable, deduct				Project				2%	2%
0200	Unfavorable, add								5%	5%
0300	Hoisting conditions, favorable, deduct								2%	2%
0400	Unfavorable, add								5%	5%
0700	Labor availability, surplus, deduct								1%	1%
0800	Shortage, add								10%	10%
0900	Material storage area, available, deduct								1%	1%
1000	Not available, add								2%	2%
1100	Subcontractor availability, surplus, deduct								5%	5%
1200	Shortage, add								12%	12%
1300	Work space, available, deduct								2%	2%
1400	Not available, add								5%	5%

01 21 57 – Overtime Allowance

01 21 57.50 Overtime		Crew	Daily Output	Labor-Hours	Unit	Material	Labor	Equipment	Total	Total Incl O&P
0010	**OVERTIME** for early completion of projects or where R012909-90									
0020	labor shortages exist, add to usual labor, up to				Costs		100%			

01 21 63 – Taxes

01 21 63.10 Taxes		Crew	Daily Output	Labor-Hours	Unit	Material	Labor	Equipment	Total	Total Incl O&P
0010	**TAXES** R012909-80									
0020	Sales tax, State, average				%	5.08%				
0050	Maximum R012909-85					7.50%				
0200	Social Security, on first $118,500 of wages						7.65%			
0300	Unemployment, combined Federal and State, minimum R012909-86						.60%			
0350	Average						9.60%			
0400	Maximum						12%			

01 31 Project Management and Coordination

01 31 13 – Project Coordination

01 31 13.20 Field Personnel		Crew	Daily Output	Labor-Hours	Unit	Material	Labor	Equipment	Total	Total Incl O&P
0010	**FIELD PERSONNEL**									
0020	Clerk, average				Week		500		500	750
0100	Field engineer, junior engineer						1,700		1,700	2,549
0120	Engineer						2,180		2,180	3,269
0140	Senior engineer						2,660		2,660	3,989
0160	General purpose laborer, average	1 Clab	.20	40			1,900		1,900	2,825
0180	Project manager, minimum						2,175		2,175	3,262
0200	Average						2,500		2,500	3,749
0220	Maximum						2,850		2,850	4,274
0240	Superintendent, minimum						2,150		2,150	3,224
0260	Average						2,325		2,325	3,525
0280	Maximum						2,650		2,650	4,025
0290	Timekeeper, average						1,350		1,350	2,050

01 31 13.30 Insurance		Crew	Daily Output	Labor-Hours	Unit	Material	Labor	Equipment	Total	Total Incl O&P
0010	**INSURANCE** R013113-40									
0020	Builders risk, standard, minimum				Job				.24%	.24%
0050	Maximum R013113-50								.80%	.80%
0200	All-risk type, minimum								.25%	.25%

01 31 Project Management and Coordination

01 31 13 – Project Coordination

01 31 13.30 Insurance		Crew	Daily Output	Labor-Hours	Unit	Material	Labor (2023 Bare Costs)	Equipment	Total	Total Incl O&P
0250	Maximum R013113-60				Job				.62%	.62%
0400	Contractor's equipment floater, minimum				Value				.50%	.50%
0450	Maximum				"				1.50%	1.50%
0600	Public liability, average				Job				2.02%	2.02%
0800	Workers' compensation & employer's liability, average									
0850	by trade, carpentry, general				Payroll		8.92%			
1000	Electrical						3.92%			
1150	Insulation						8.13%			
1450	Plumbing						4.42%			
1550	Sheet metal work (HVAC)						5.86%			

01 31 13.50 General Contractor's Mark-Up		Crew	Daily Output	Labor-Hours	Unit	Material	Labor	Equipment	Total	Total Incl O&P
0010	**GENERAL CONTRACTOR'S MARK-UP** on Change Orders									
0200	Extra work, by subcontractors, add				%				10%	10%
0250	By General Contractor, add								15%	15%
0400	Omitted work, by subcontractors, deduct all but								5%	5%
0450	By General Contractor, deduct all but								7.50%	7.50%
0600	Overtime work, by subcontractors, add								15%	15%
0650	By General Contractor, add								10%	10%

01 31 13.80 Overhead and Profit		Crew	Daily Output	Labor-Hours	Unit	Material	Labor	Equipment	Total	Total Incl O&P
0010	**OVERHEAD & PROFIT** Allowance to add to items in this R013113-50									
0020	book that do not include Subs O&P, average				%				25%	
0100	Allowance to add to items in this book that R013113-55									
0110	do include Subs O&P, minimum				%				5%	5%
0150	Average								10%	10%
0200	Maximum								15%	15%
0300	Typical, by size of project, under $100,000								30%	
0350	$500,000 project								25%	
0400	$2,000,000 project								20%	
0450	Over $10,000,000 project								15%	

01 31 13.90 Performance Bond		Crew	Daily Output	Labor-Hours	Unit	Material	Labor	Equipment	Total	Total Incl O&P
0010	**PERFORMANCE BOND** R013113-80									
0020	For buildings, minimum				Job				.60%	.60%
0100	Maximum				"				2.50%	2.50%

01 31 14 – Facilities Services Coordination

01 31 14.20 Lock Out/Tag Out		Crew	Daily Output	Labor-Hours	Unit	Material	Labor	Equipment	Total	Total Incl O&P
0010	**LOCK OUT/TAG OUT**									
0020	Miniature circuit breaker lock out device	1 Elec	220	.036	Ea.	38	2.45		40.45	45
0030	Miniature pin circuit breaker lock out device		220	.036		33	2.45		35.45	40
0040	Single circuit breaker lock out device		220	.036		36	2.45		38.45	43
0050	Multi-pole circuit breaker lock out device (15 to 225 Amp)		210	.038		32.50	2.57		35.07	39.50
0060	Large 3 pole circuit breaker lock out device (over 225 Amp)		210	.038		37	2.57		39.57	44.50
0080	Square D I-Line circuit breaker lock out device		210	.038		112	2.57		114.57	127
0090	Lock out disconnect switch, 30 to 100 Amp		330	.024		23	1.63		24.63	28
0100	100 to 400 Amp		330	.024		23	1.63		24.63	28
0110	Over 400 Amp		330	.024		23	1.63		24.63	28
0120	Lock out hasp for multiple lockout tags		200	.040		7.40	2.69		10.09	12.10
0130	Electrical cord plug lock out device		220	.036		11.90	2.45		14.35	16.75
0140	Electrical plug prong lock out device (3-wire grounding plug)		220	.036		7.90	2.45		10.35	12.30
0150	Wall switch lock out		200	.040		34.50	2.69		37.19	41.50
0160	Fire alarm pull station lock out	1 Stpi	200	.040		32	2.90		34.90	39.50
0170	Sprinkler valve tamper and flow switch lock out device	1 Skwk	220	.036		30.50	2.23		32.73	37

01 31 Project Management and Coordination

01 31 14 – Facilities Services Coordination

01 31 14.20 Lock Out/Tag Out		Crew	Daily Output	Labor-Hours	Unit	Material	Labor	Equipment	Total	Total Incl O&P
0180	Lock out sign	1 Skwk	330	.024	Ea.	18.80	1.48		20.28	22.50
0190	Lock out tag	↓	440	.018	↓	5.70	1.11		6.81	7.90

(Material, Labor, Equipment and Total are 2023 Bare Costs.)

01 32 Construction Progress Documentation

01 32 33 – Photographic Documentation

01 32 33.50 Photographs

		Crew	Daily Output	Labor-Hours	Unit	Material	Labor	Equipment	Total	Total Incl O&P
0010	**PHOTOGRAPHS**									
0020	8" x 10", 4 shots, 2 prints ea., std. mounting				Set	570			570	625
0100	Hinged linen mounts					580			580	635
0200	8" x 10", 4 shots, 2 prints each, in color					600			600	660
0300	For I.D. slugs, add to all above				↓	5.35			5.35	5.85
1500	Time lapse equipment, camera and projector, buy				Ea.	2,725			2,725	2,975
1550	Rent per month				"	1,375			1,375	1,525
1700	Cameraman and processing, black & white				Day	1,350			1,350	1,500
1720	Color				"	1,600			1,600	1,750

01 41 Regulatory Requirements

01 41 26 – Permit Requirements

01 41 26.50 Permits

		Crew	Daily Output	Labor-Hours	Unit	Material	Labor	Equipment	Total	Total Incl O&P
0010	**PERMITS**									
0020	Rule of thumb, most cities, minimum				Job				.50%	.50%
0100	Maximum				"				2%	2%

01 51 Temporary Utilities

01 51 13 – Temporary Electricity

01 51 13.50 Temporary Power Equip (Pro-Rated Per Job)

		Crew	Daily Output	Labor-Hours	Unit	Material	Labor	Equipment	Total	Total Incl O&P
0010	**TEMPORARY POWER EQUIP (PRO-RATED PER JOB)** R015113-65									
0020	Service, overhead feed, 3 use									
0030	100 Amp	1 Elec	1.25	6.400	Ea.	955	430		1,385	1,700
0040	200 Amp		1	8		1,175	540		1,715	2,100
0050	400 Amp		.75	10.667		2,225	720		2,945	3,525
0060	600 Amp	↓	.50	16	↓	3,300	1,075		4,375	5,225
0100	Underground feed, 3 use									
0110	100 Amp	1 Elec	2	4	Ea.	995	269		1,264	1,500
0120	200 Amp		1.15	6.957		1,350	470		1,820	2,175
0130	400 Amp		1	8		2,325	540		2,865	3,350
0140	600 Amp		.75	10.667		2,875	720		3,595	4,250
0150	800 Amp		.50	16		4,375	1,075		5,450	6,400
0160	1000 Amp		.35	22.857		4,825	1,550		6,375	7,600
0170	1200 Amp		.25	32		5,425	2,150		7,575	9,175
0180	2000 Amp	↓	.20	40	↓	6,525	2,700		9,225	11,200
0200	Transformers, 3 use									
0210	30 kVA	1 Elec	1	8	Ea.	1,350	540		1,890	2,300
0220	45 kVA		.75	10.667		1,450	720		2,170	2,675
0230	75 kVA		.50	16		2,475	1,075		3,550	4,300
0240	112.5 kVA	↓	.40	20	↓	2,775	1,350		4,125	5,050
0250	Feeder, PVC, CU wire in trench									

01 51 13.50 Temporary Power Equip (Pro-Rated Per Job)		Crew	Daily Output	Labor-Hours	Unit	2023 Bare Costs Material	Labor	Equipment	Total	Total Incl O&P
0260	60 Amp	1 Elec	96	.083	L.F.	6.75	5.60		12.35	15.75
0270	100 Amp		85	.094		11.90	6.35		18.25	22.50
0280	200 Amp		59	.136		27.50	9.15		36.65	44
0290	400 Amp		42	.190		66.50	12.85		79.35	92
0300	Feeder, PVC, aluminum wire in trench									
0310	60 Amp	1 Elec	96	.083	L.F.	6.30	5.60		11.90	15.30
0320	100 Amp		85	.094		6.80	6.35		13.15	16.90
0330	200 Amp		59	.136		15	9.15		24.15	30
0340	400 Amp		42	.190		30	12.85		42.85	52
0350	Feeder, EMT, CU wire									
0360	60 Amp	1 Elec	90	.089	L.F.	6.20	6		12.20	15.70
0370	100 Amp		80	.100		12.65	6.75		19.40	24
0380	200 Amp		60	.133		25	9		34	41
0390	400 Amp		35	.229		65	15.40		80.40	94.50
0400	Feeder, EMT, aluminum wire									
0410	60 Amp	1 Elec	90	.089	L.F.	8.25	6		14.25	18
0420	100 Amp		80	.100		10.05	6.75		16.80	21
0430	200 Amp		60	.133		18.55	9		27.55	34
0440	400 Amp		35	.229		35	15.40		50.40	61.50
0500	Equipment, 3 use									
0510	Spider box, 50 Amp	1 Elec	8	1	Ea.	345	67.50		412.50	475
0520	Lighting cord, 100′		8	1		150	67.50		217.50	265
0530	Light stanchion		8	1		39.50	67.50		107	144
0540	Temporary cords, 100′, 3 use									
0550	Feeder cord, 50 Amp	1 Elec	16	.500	Ea.	209	33.50		242.50	280
0560	Feeder cord, 100 Amp		12	.667		1,075	45		1,120	1,250
0570	Tap cord, 50 Amp		12	.667		600	45		645	725
0580	Tap cord, 100 Amp		6	1.333		1,025	90		1,115	1,250
0590	Temporary cords, 50′, 3 use									
0600	Feeder cord, 50 Amp	1 Elec	16	.500	Ea.	251	33.50		284.50	325
0610	Feeder cord, 100 Amp		12	.667		900	45		945	1,050
0620	Tap cord, 50 Amp		12	.667		257	45		302	350
0630	Tap cord, 100 Amp		6	1.333		555	90		645	745
0700	Connections									
0710	Compressor or pump									
0720	30 Amp	1 Elec	7	1.143	Ea.	26	77		103	143
0730	60 Amp		5.30	1.509		39	102		141	194
0740	100 Amp		4	2		93	135		228	305
0750	Tower crane									
0760	60 Amp	1 Elec	4.50	1.778	Ea.	39	120		159	221
0770	100 Amp	″	3	2.667	″	93	180		273	370
0780	Manlift									
0790	Single	1 Elec	3	2.667	Ea.	58	180		238	330
0800	Double	″	2	4	″	107	269		376	515
0810	Welder with disconnect									
0820	50 Amp	1 Elec	5	1.600	Ea.	320	108		428	515
0830	100 Amp		3.80	2.105		515	142		657	775
0840	200 Amp		2.50	3.200		955	216		1,171	1,375
0850	400 Amp		1	8		2,225	540		2,765	3,250
0860	Office trailer									
0870	60 Amp	1 Elec	4.50	1.778	Ea.	211	120		331	410
0880	100 Amp		3	2.667		268	180		448	560
0890	200 Amp		2	4		975	269		1,244	1,475

01 51 Temporary Utilities

01 51 13 – Temporary Electricity

01 51 13.80 Temporary Utilities		Crew	Daily Output	Labor-Hours	Unit	2023 Bare Costs Material	Labor	Equipment	Total	Total Incl O&P
0010	**TEMPORARY UTILITIES**									
0350	Lighting, lamps, wiring, outlets, 40,000 S.F. building, 8 strings	1 Elec	34	.235	CSF Flr	3.58	15.85		19.43	27.50
0360	16 strings	"	17	.471		7.15	31.50		38.65	55
0400	Power for temp lighting only, 6.6 KWH, per month								.92	1.01
0430	11.8 KWH, per month								1.65	1.82
0450	23.6 KWH, per month								3.30	3.63
0600	Power for job duration incl. elevator, etc., minimum								53	58
0650	Maximum								110	121
0675	Temporary cooling				Ea.	1,100			1,100	1,225

01 52 Construction Facilities

01 52 13 – Field Offices and Sheds

01 52 13.20 Office and Storage Space

		Crew	Daily Output	Labor-Hours	Unit	Material	Labor	Equipment	Total	Total Incl O&P
0010	**OFFICE AND STORAGE SPACE**									
0020	Office trailer, furnished, no hookups, 20′ x 8′, buy	2 Skwk	1	16	Ea.	10,500	980		11,480	13,000
0250	Rent per month					201			201	221
0300	32′ x 8′, buy	2 Skwk	.70	22.857		15,800	1,400		17,200	19,400
0350	Rent per month					255			255	280
0400	50′ x 10′, buy	2 Skwk	.60	26.667		31,900	1,625		33,525	37,600
0450	Rent per month					370			370	405
0500	50′ x 12′, buy	2 Skwk	.50	32		27,100	1,950		29,050	32,800
0550	Rent per month					475			475	520
0700	For air conditioning, rent per month, add					55.50			55.50	61
0800	For delivery, add per mile				Mile	12.55			12.55	13.80
0900	Bunk house trailer, 8′ x 40′ duplex dorm with kitchen, no hookups, buy	2 Carp	1	16	Ea.	93,500	940		94,440	104,500
0910	9 man with kitchen and bath, no hookups, buy		1	16		95,500	940		96,440	106,500
0920	18 man sleeper with bath, no hookups, buy		1	16		103,000	940		103,940	115,000
1000	Portable buildings, prefab, on skids, economy, 8′ x 8′		265	.060	S.F.	105	3.54		108.54	121
1100	Deluxe, 8′ x 12′		150	.107	"	90.50	6.25		96.75	109
1200	Storage boxes, 20′ x 8′, buy	2 Skwk	1.80	8.889	Ea.	5,025	545		5,570	6,350
1250	Rent per month					126			126	138
1300	40′ x 8′, buy	2 Skwk	1.40	11.429		7,925	700		8,625	9,775
1350	Rent per month					155			155	170

01 52 13.40 Field Office Expense

		Crew	Daily Output	Labor-Hours	Unit	Material	Labor	Equipment	Total	Total Incl O&P
0010	**FIELD OFFICE EXPENSE**									
0100	Office equipment rental average				Month	239			239	263
0120	Office supplies, average				"	94.50			94.50	104
0125	Office trailer rental, see Section 01 52 13.20									
0140	Telephone bill; avg. bill/month incl. long dist.				Month	91.50			91.50	100
0160	Lights & HVAC				"	171			171	188

01 54 Construction Aids

01 54 16 – Temporary Hoists

01 54 16.50 Weekly Forklift Crew		Crew	Daily Output	Labor-Hours	Unit	Material	2023 Bare Costs Labor	Equipment	Total	Total Incl O&P
0010	**WEEKLY FORKLIFT CREW**									
0100	All-terrain forklift, 45′ lift, 35′ reach, 9000 lb. capacity	A-3P	.20	40	Week		2,400	3,375	5,775	7,250

01 54 19 – Temporary Cranes

01 54 19.50 Daily Crane Crews		Crew	Daily Output	Labor-Hours	Unit	Material	Labor	Equipment	Total	Total Incl O&P
0010	**DAILY CRANE CREWS** for small jobs, portal to portal R015433-15									
0100	12-ton truck-mounted hydraulic crane	A-3H	1	8	Day		530	2,150	2,680	3,175
0200	25-ton	A-3I	1	8			530	2,275	2,805	3,300
0300	40-ton	A-3J	1	8			530	2,450	2,980	3,500
0400	55-ton	A-3K	1	16			980	2,625	3,605	4,325
0500	80-ton	A-3L	1	16			980	2,800	3,780	4,525
0900	If crane is needed on a Saturday, Sunday or Holiday									
0910	At time-and-a-half, add				Day		50%			
0920	At double time, add				"		100%			

01 54 19.60 Monthly Tower Crane Crew		Crew	Daily Output	Labor-Hours	Unit	Material	Labor	Equipment	Total	Total Incl O&P
0010	**MONTHLY TOWER CRANE CREW**, excludes concrete footing									
0100	Static tower crane, 130′ high, 106′ jib, 6200 lb. capacity	A-3N	.05	176	Month		11,700	41,600	53,300	63,000

01 54 23 – Temporary Scaffolding and Platforms

01 54 23.70 Scaffolding		Crew	Daily Output	Labor-Hours	Unit	Material	Labor	Equipment	Total	Total Incl O&P
0010	**SCAFFOLDING** R015423-10									
0015	Steel tube, regular, no plank, labor only to erect & dismantle									
0090	Building exterior, wall face, 1 to 5 stories, 6′-4″ x 5′ frames	3 Carp	8	3	C.S.F.		176		176	262
0200	6 to 12 stories	4 Carp	8	4			234		234	350
0301	13 to 20 stories	5 Clab	8	5			236		236	350
0460	Building interior, wall face area, up to 16′ high	3 Carp	12	2			117		117	175
0560	16′ to 40′ high		10	2.400			141		141	209
0800	Building interior floor area, up to 30′ high		150	.160	C.C.F.		9.40		9.40	13.95
0900	Over 30′ high	4 Carp	160	.200	"		11.70		11.70	17.45
0906	Complete system for face of walls, no plank, material only rent/mo				C.S.F.	95.50			95.50	105
0908	Interior spaces, no plank, material only rent/mo				C.C.F.	6.30			6.30	6.95
0910	Steel tubular, heavy duty shoring, buy									
0920	Frames 5′ high 2′ wide				Ea.	83			83	91.50
0925	5′ high 4′ wide					99.50			99.50	110
0930	6′ high 2′ wide					100			100	110
0935	6′ high 4′ wide					124			124	136
0940	Accessories									
0945	Cross braces				Ea.	21			21	23
0950	U-head, 8″ x 8″					18.40			18.40	20.50
0955	J-head, 4″ x 8″					17.05			17.05	18.75
0960	Base plate, 7″ x 7″					15.45			15.45	17
0965	Leveling jack					19.25			19.25	21
1000	Steel tubular, regular, buy									
1100	Frames 3′ high 5′ wide				Ea.	92			92	101
1150	5′ high 5′ wide					111			111	122
1200	6′-4″ high 5′ wide					119			119	131
1350	7′-6″ high 6′ wide					98.50			98.50	108
1500	Accessories, cross braces					17.20			17.20	18.95
1550	Guardrail post					17.05			17.05	18.75
1600	Guardrail 7′ section					10.75			10.75	11.80
1650	Screw jacks & plates					20.50			20.50	22.50
1700	Sidearm brackets					14.50			14.50	15.95
1750	8″ casters					34			34	37.50

01 54 Construction Aids

01 54 23 – Temporary Scaffolding and Platforms

01 54 23.70 Scaffolding		Crew	Daily Output	Labor-Hours	Unit	2023 Bare Costs Material	Labor	Equipment	Total	Total Incl O&P
1800	Plank 2" x 10" x 16'-0"				Ea.	77.50			77.50	85.50
1900	Stairway section					360			360	395
1910	Stairway starter bar					18.15			18.15	20
1920	Stairway inside handrail					102			102	112
1930	Stairway outside handrail					112			112	123
1940	Walk-thru frame guardrail				↓	51.50			51.50	56.50
2000	Steel tubular, regular, rent/mo.									
2100	Frames 3' high 5' wide				Ea.	10.70			10.70	11.75
2150	5' high 5' wide					10.70			10.70	11.75
2200	6'-4" high 5' wide					7			7	7.70
2250	7'-6" high 6' wide					12.10			12.10	13.30
2500	Accessories, cross braces					3			3	3.30
2550	Guardrail post					3.60			3.60	3.96
2600	Guardrail 7' section					13.55			13.55	14.90
2650	Screw jacks & plates					4.50			4.50	4.95
2700	Sidearm brackets					12			12	13.20
2750	8" casters					10			10	11
2800	Outrigger for rolling tower					12.75			12.75	14.05
2850	Plank 2" x 10" x 16'-0"					12.10			12.10	13.30
2900	Stairway section					39			39	43
2940	Walk-thru frame guardrail				↓	10.80			10.80	11.90
3000	Steel tubular, heavy duty shoring, rent/mo.									
3250	5' high 2' & 4' wide				Ea.	10.30			10.30	11.30
3300	6' high 2' & 4' wide					10.30			10.30	11.30
3500	Accessories, cross braces					1.11			1.11	1.22
3600	U-head, 8" x 8"					3.03			3.03	3.33
3650	J-head, 4" x 8"					3.03			3.03	3.33
3700	Base plate, 8" x 8"					1.11			1.11	1.22
3750	Leveling jack					3.01			3.01	3.31
5700	Planks, 2" x 10" x 16'-0", labor only to erect & remove to 50' H	3 Carp	72	.333			19.55		19.55	29
5800	Over 50' high	4 Carp	80	.400	↓		23.50		23.50	35

01 54 23.75 Scaffolding Specialties		Crew	Daily Output	Labor-Hours	Unit	Material	Labor	Equipment	Total	Total Incl O&P
0010	**SCAFFOLDING SPECIALTIES**									
1500	Sidewalk bridge using tubular steel scaffold frames including									
1510	planking (material cost is rent/month)	3 Carp	45	.533	L.F.	11.40	31.50		42.90	59
1600	For 2 uses per month, deduct from all above					50%				
1700	For 1 use every 2 months, add to all above					100%				
1900	Catwalks, 20" wide, no guardrails, 7' span, buy				Ea.	229			229	252
2000	10' span, buy					291			291	320
3720	Putlog, standard, 8' span, with hangers, buy					49			49	54
3750	12' span, buy					106			106	116
3760	Trussed type, 16' span, buy					545			545	600
3790	22' span, buy					550			550	605
3795	Rent per month					34			34	37.50
3800	Rolling ladders with handrails, 30" wide, buy, 2 step					296			296	325
4000	7 step					900			900	990
4050	10 step					1,275			1,275	1,400
4100	Rolling towers, buy, 5' wide, 7' long, 10' high					1,425			1,425	1,550
4200	For additional 5' high sections, to buy				↓	257			257	283
4300	Complete incl. wheels, railings, outriggers,									
4350	21' high, to buy				Ea.	2,175			2,175	2,400
4400	Rent/month = 5% of purchase cost				"	109			109	119

01 54 Construction Aids

01 54 26 – Temporary Swing Staging

01 54 26.50 Swing Staging		Crew	Daily Output	Labor-Hours	Unit	Material	2023 Bare Costs Labor	Equipment	Total	Total Incl O&P
0010	**SWING STAGING**, 500 lb. cap., 2' wide to 24' long, hand operated									
0020	Steel cable type, with 60' cables, buy				Ea.	8,100			8,100	8,925
0030	Rent per month				"	810			810	890
2200	Move swing staging (setup and remove)	E-4	2	16	Move		1,050	73.50	1,123.50	1,675

01 54 36 – Equipment Mobilization

01 54 36.50 Mobilization

		Crew	Daily Output	Labor-Hours	Unit	Material	Labor	Equipment	Total	Total Incl O&P
0010	**MOBILIZATION** (Use line item again for demobilization) R015436-50									
0015	Up to 25 mi. haul dist. (50 mi. RT for mob/demob crew)									
1200	Small equipment, placed in rear of, or towed by pickup truck	A-3A	4	2	Ea.		119	48	167	231
1300	Equipment hauled on 3-ton capacity towed trailer	A-3Q	2.67	3			179	101	280	380
1400	20-ton capacity	B-34U	2	8			460	245	705	955
1500	40-ton capacity	B-34N	2	8			475	375	850	1,125
1600	50-ton capacity	B-34V	1	24			1,450	1,200	2,650	3,500
1700	Crane, truck-mounted, up to 75 ton (driver only)	1 Eqhv	4	2			133		133	197
1800	Over 75 ton (with chase vehicle)	A-3E	2.50	6.400			390	76.50	466.50	665
2400	Crane, large lattice boom, requiring assembly	B-34W	.50	144	↓		8,375	8,450	16,825	21,800
2500	For each additional 5 miles haul distance, add						10%	10%		
3000	For large pieces of equipment, allow for assembly/knockdown									
3100	For mob/demob of micro-tunneling equip, see Section 33 05 07.36									

01 55 Vehicular Access and Parking

01 55 23 – Temporary Roads

01 55 23.50 Roads and Sidewalks

		Crew	Daily Output	Labor-Hours	Unit	Material	Labor	Equipment	Total	Total Incl O&P
0010	**ROADS AND SIDEWALKS** Temporary									
0050	Roads, gravel fill, no surfacing, 4" gravel depth	B-14	715	.067	S.Y.	8.25	3.33	.39	11.97	14.45
0100	8" gravel depth	"	615	.078	"	16.45	3.88	.45	20.78	24.50
1000	Ramp, 3/4" plywood on 2" x 6" joists, 16" OC	2 Carp	300	.053	S.F.	3.56	3.13		6.69	8.55
1100	On 2" x 10" joists, 16" OC	"	275	.058	"	5.25	3.41		8.66	10.85

01 56 Temporary Barriers and Enclosures

01 56 13 – Temporary Air Barriers

01 56 13.90 Winter Protection

		Crew	Daily Output	Labor-Hours	Unit	Material	Labor	Equipment	Total	Total Incl O&P
0010	**WINTER PROTECTION**									
0100	Framing to close openings	2 Clab	500	.032	S.F.	1.19	1.51		2.70	3.56
0200	Tarpaulins hung over scaffolding, 8 uses, not incl. scaffolding		1500	.011		.24	.50		.74	1.01
0300	Prefab fiberglass panels, steel frame, 8 uses	↓	1200	.013	↓	3.19	.63		3.82	4.45

01 56 16 – Temporary Dust Barriers

01 56 16.10 Dust Barriers, Temporary

		Crew	Daily Output	Labor-Hours	Unit	Material	Labor	Equipment	Total	Total Incl O&P
0010	**DUST BARRIERS, TEMPORARY**, erect and dismantle									
0020	Spring loaded telescoping pole & head, to 12', erect and dismantle	1 Clab	240	.033	Ea.		1.58		1.58	2.35
0025	Cost per day (based upon 250 days)				Day	.61			.61	.67
0030	To 21', erect and dismantle	1 Clab	240	.033	Ea.		1.58		1.58	2.35
0035	Cost per day (based upon 250 days)				Day	1.21			1.21	1.33
0040	Accessories, caution tape reel, erect and dismantle	1 Clab	480	.017	Ea.		.79		.79	1.17
0045	Cost per day (based upon 250 days)				Day	.31			.31	.34
0060	Foam rail and connector, erect and dismantle	1 Clab	240	.033	Ea.		1.58		1.58	2.35
0065	Cost per day (based upon 250 days)				Day	.26			.26	.29
0070	Caution tape	1 Clab	384	.021	C.L.F.	1.99	.98		2.97	3.66

01 56 Temporary Barriers and Enclosures

01 56 16 – Temporary Dust Barriers

01 56 16.10 Dust Barriers, Temporary		Crew	Daily Output	Labor-Hours	Unit	2023 Bare Costs Material	Labor	Equipment	Total	Total Incl O&P
0080	Zipper, standard duty	1 Clab	60	.133	Ea.	16.15	6.30		22.45	27
0090	Heavy duty		48	.167	″	23.50	7.90		31.40	38
0100	Polyethylene sheet, 4 mil		37	.216	Sq.	5.35	10.20		15.55	21
0110	6 mil		37	.216	″	6.85	10.20		17.05	22.50
1000	Dust partition, 6 mil polyethylene, 1″ x 3″ frame	2 Carp	2000	.008	S.F.	.39	.47		.86	1.13
1080	2″ x 4″ frame	″	2000	.008	″	.91	.47		1.38	1.70
1085	Negative air machine, 1800 CFM				Ea.	990			990	1,100
1090	Adhesive strip application, 2″ width	1 Clab	192	.042	C.L.F.	13.50	1.97		15.47	17.80
4000	Dust & infectious control partition, adj. to 10′ high, obscured, 4′ panel	2 Carp	90	.178	Ea.	595	10.40		605.40	670
4010	3′ panel		90	.178		560	10.40		570.40	635
4020	2′ panel		90	.178		440	10.40		450.40	500
4030	1′ panel	1 Carp	90	.089		292	5.20		297.20	330
4040	6″ panel	″	90	.089		270	5.20		275.20	305
4050	2′ panel with HEPA filtered discharge port	2 Carp	90	.178		510	10.40		520.40	575
4060	3′ panel with 32″ door		90	.178		920	10.40		930.40	1,025
4070	4′ panel with 36″ door		90	.178		1,025	10.40		1,035.40	1,150
4080	4′-6″ panel with 44″ door		90	.178		1,225	10.40		1,235.40	1,375
4090	Hinged corner		80	.200		188	11.70		199.70	223
4100	Outside corner		80	.200		156	11.70		167.70	188
4110	T post		80	.200		166	11.70		177.70	199
4120	Accessories, ceiling grid clip		360	.044		7.25	2.60		9.85	11.90
4130	Panel locking clip		360	.044		5	2.60		7.60	9.40
4140	Panel joint closure strip		360	.044		8.30	2.60		10.90	13
4150	Screw jack		360	.044		7.15	2.60		9.75	11.80
4160	Digital pressure difference gauge					290			290	320
4180	Combination lockset	1 Carp	13	.615		205	36		241	279
4185	Sealant tape, 2″ wide	1 Clab	192	.042	C.L.F.	13.50	1.97		15.47	17.80
4190	System in place, including door and accessories									
4200	Based upon 25 uses	2 Carp	51	.314	L.F.	10.05	18.40		28.45	38.50
4210	Based upon 50 uses		51	.314		5.05	18.40		23.45	33
4230	Based upon 100 uses		51	.314		2.51	18.40		20.91	30.50

01 56 23 – Temporary Barricades

01 56 23.10 Barricades		Crew	Daily Output	Labor-Hours	Unit	Material	Labor	Equipment	Total	Total Incl O&P
0010	**BARRICADES**									
0020	5′ high, 3 rail @ 2″ x 8″, fixed	2 Carp	20	.800	L.F.	13.45	47		60.45	85
0150	Movable		30	.533		12.15	31.50		43.65	60
1000	Guardrail, wooden, 3′ high, 1″ x 6″ on 2″ x 4″ posts		200	.080		2.48	4.69		7.17	9.75
1100	2″ x 6″ on 4″ x 4″ posts		165	.097		4.26	5.70		9.96	13.15
1200	Portable metal with base pads, buy					17.25			17.25	18.95
1250	Typical installation, assume 10 reuses	2 Carp	600	.027		2.87	1.56		4.43	5.50
1300	Barricade tape, polyethylene, 7 mil, 3″ wide x 300′ long roll	1 Clab	128	.063	Ea.	5.95	2.95		8.90	10.95
3000	Detour signs, set up and remove									
3010	Reflective aluminum, MUTCD, 24″ x 24″, post mounted	1 Clab	20	.400	Ea.	4.26	18.90		23.16	32.50
4000	Roof edge portable barrier stands and warning flags, 50 uses	1 Rohe	9100	.001	L.F.	.10	.03		.13	.17
4010	100 uses	″	9100	.001	″	.05	.03		.08	.12

01 56 26 – Temporary Fencing

01 56 26.50 Temporary Fencing		Crew	Daily Output	Labor-Hours	Unit	Material	Labor	Equipment	Total	Total Incl O&P
0010	**TEMPORARY FENCING**									
0020	Chain link, 11 ga., 4′ high	2 Clab	400	.040	L.F.	2.20	1.89		4.09	5.25
0100	6′ high		300	.053		5.35	2.52		7.87	9.65
0200	Rented chain link, 6′ high, to 1000′ (up to 12 mo.)		400	.040		3.16	1.89		5.05	6.30
0250	Over 1000′ (up to 12 mo.)		300	.053		3.73	2.52		6.25	7.85

01 56 Temporary Barriers and Enclosures

01 56 26 – Temporary Fencing

01 56 26.50 Temporary Fencing		Crew	Daily Output	Labor-Hours	Unit	2023 Bare Costs Material	Labor	Equipment	Total	Total Incl O&P
0350	Plywood, painted, 2″ x 4″ frame, 4′ high	A-4	135	.178	L.F.	9.60	9.90		19.50	25.50
0400	4″ x 4″ frame, 8′ high	″	110	.218		18.30	12.15		30.45	38
0500	Wire mesh on 4″ x 4″ posts, 4′ high	2 Carp	100	.160		13.05	9.40		22.45	28.50
0550	8′ high	″	80	.200	↓	19.65	11.70		31.35	39

01 56 29 – Temporary Protective Walkways

01 56 29.50 Protection		Crew	Daily Output	Labor-Hours	Unit	Material	Labor	Equipment	Total	Total Incl O&P
0010	**PROTECTION**									
0020	Stair tread, 2″ x 12″ planks, 1 use	1 Carp	75	.107	Tread	12.75	6.25		19	23.50
0100	Exterior plywood, 1/2″ thick, 1 use		65	.123		3.47	7.20		10.67	14.55
0200	3/4″ thick, 1 use		60	.133	↓	5.15	7.80		12.95	17.30
2200	Sidewalks, 2″ x 12″ planks, 2 uses		350	.023	S.F.	2.12	1.34		3.46	4.33
2300	Exterior plywood, 2 uses, 1/2″ thick		750	.011		.58	.63		1.21	1.57
2400	5/8″ thick		650	.012		.69	.72		1.41	1.82
2500	3/4″ thick	↓	600	.013	↓	.86	.78		1.64	2.10

01 58 Project Identification

01 58 13 – Temporary Project Signage

01 58 13.50 Signs		Crew	Daily Output	Labor-Hours	Unit	Material	Labor	Equipment	Total	Total Incl O&P
0010	**SIGNS**									
0020	High intensity reflectorized, no posts, buy				Ea.	16.35			16.35	17.95

01 66 Product Storage and Handling Requirements

01 66 19 – Material Handling

01 66 19.10 Material Handling		Crew	Daily Output	Labor-Hours	Unit	Material	Labor	Equipment	Total	Total Incl O&P
0010	**MATERIAL HANDLING**									
0020	Above 2nd story, via stairs, per C.Y. of material per floor	2 Clab	145	.110	C.Y.		5.20		5.20	7.75
0030	Via elevator, per C.Y. of material		240	.067			3.15		3.15	4.69
0050	Distances greater than 200′, per C.Y. of material per each addl 200′	↓	300	.053	↓		2.52		2.52	3.75

01 74 Cleaning and Waste Management

01 74 13 – Progress Cleaning

01 74 13.20 Cleaning Up		Crew	Daily Output	Labor-Hours	Unit	Material	Labor	Equipment	Total	Total Incl O&P
0010	**CLEANING UP**									
0020	After job completion, allow, minimum				Job				.30%	.30%
0040	Maximum				″				1%	1%
0050	Cleanup of floor area, continuous, per day, during const.	A-5	24	.750	M.S.F.	4.56	36	3.77	44.33	62.50
0100	Final by GC at end of job	″	11.50	1.565	″	4.82	75	7.85	87.67	126

01 91 Commissioning

01 91 13 – General Commissioning Requirements

01 91 13.50 Building Commissioning		Crew	Daily Output	Labor-Hours	Unit	Material	2023 Bare Costs Labor	Equipment	Total	Total Incl O&P
0010	**BUILDING COMMISSIONING**									
0100	Systems operation and verification during turnover				%				.25%	.25%
0150	Including all systems subcontractors								.50%	.50%
0200	Systems design assistance, operation, verification and training								.50%	.50%
0250	Including all systems subcontractors				↓				1%	1%

01 93 Facility Maintenance

01 93 13 – Facility Maintenance Procedures

01 93 13.16 Electrical Facilities Maintenance		Crew	Daily Output	Labor-Hours	Unit	Material	Labor	Equipment	Total	Total Incl O&P
0010	**ELECTRICAL FACILITIES MAINTENANCE**									
0700	Cathodic protection systems									
0720	Check and adjust reading on rectifier	1 Elec	20	.400	Ea.		27		27	40
0730	Check pipe to soil potential		20	.400			27		27	40
0740	Replace lead connection		4	2			135		135	200
0800	Control device, install		5.70	1.404			94.50		94.50	140
0810	Disassemble, clean and reinstall		7	1.143			77		77	114
0820	Replace		10.70	.748			50.50		50.50	75
0830	Trouble shoot	↓	10	.800	↓		54		54	80
0900	Demolition, for electrical demolition see Section 26 05 05.10									
1000	Distribution systems and equipment install or repair a breaker									
1010	In power panels up to 200 amps	1 Elec	7	1.143	Ea.		77		77	114
1020	Over 200 amps		2	4			269		269	400
1030	Reset breaker or replace fuse		20	.400			27		27	40
1100	Megger test MCC (each stack)		4	2			135		135	200
1110	MCC vacuum and clean (each stack)		5.30	1.509			102		102	151
2500	Remove and replace or maint., road fixture & lamp		3	2.667		1,550	180		1,730	1,975
2510	Fluorescent fixture	↓	7	1.143		233	77		310	370
2515	Relamp (fluor.) facility area each tube, spot	1 Clab	24	.333		8.15	15.75		23.90	32.50
2516	Group		100	.080		8.15	3.78		11.93	14.60
2518	Fluorescent fixture, clean (area)	↓	44	.182		.08	8.60		8.68	12.90
2520	Incandescent fixture	1 Elec	11	.727		53.50	49		102.50	132
2530	Lamp (incandescent or fluorescent)	1 Clab	60	.133		8.15	6.30		14.45	18.35
2535	Replace cord in socket lamp	1 Elec	13	.615		3.95	41.50		45.45	66
2540	Ballast electronic type for two tubes		8	1		17.95	67.50		85.45	120
2541	Starter		30	.267		3.89	17.95		21.84	31
2545	Replace other lighting parts		11	.727		14.10	49		63.10	88.50
2550	Switch		11	.727		4.23	49		53.23	77.50
2555	Receptacle		11	.727		12.90	49		61.90	87
2560	Floodlight	↓	4	2		221	135		356	445
2570	Christmas lighting, indoor, per string	1 Clab	16	.500			23.50		23.50	35
2580	Outdoor		13	.615			29		29	43.50
2590	Test battery operated emergency lights	↓	40	.200			9.45		9.45	14.05
2600	Repair and replace component in communication system	1 Elec	6	1.333		73.50	90		163.50	214
2700	Repair misc. appliances (incl. clocks, vent fan, blower, etc.)	"	6	1.333			90		90	133
2710	Reset clocks & timers	1 Clab	50	.160			7.55		7.55	11.25
2720	Adjust time delay relays	1 Elec	16	.500			33.50		33.50	50
2730	Test specific gravity of lead-acid batteries	1 Clab	80	.100	↓		4.73		4.73	7.05
3000	Motors and generators									
3020	Disassemble, clean and reinstall motor, up to 1/4 HP	1 Elec	4	2	Ea.		135		135	200
3030	Up to 3/4 HP		3	2.667			180		180	267
3040	Up to 10 HP	↓	2	4	↓		269		269	400

01 93 13 – Facility Maintenance Procedures

01 93 13.16 Electrical Facilities Maintenance		Crew	Daily Output	Labor-Hours	Unit	Material	2023 Bare Costs Labor	Equipment	Total	Total Incl O&P
3050	Replace part, up to 1/4 HP	1 Elec	6	1.333	Ea.		90		90	133
3060	Up to 3/4 HP		4	2			135		135	200
3070	Up to 10 HP		3	2.667			180		180	267
3080	Megger test motor windings		5.33	1.501			101		101	150
3082	Motor vibration check		16	.500			33.50		33.50	50
3084	Oil motor bearings		25	.320			21.50		21.50	32
3086	Run test emergency generator for 30 minutes		11	.727			49		49	73
3090	Rewind motor, up to 1/4 HP		3	2.667			180		180	267
3100	Up to 3/4 HP		2	4			269		269	400
3110	Up to 10 HP		1.50	5.333			360		360	535
3150	Generator, repair or replace part		4	2			135		135	200
3160	Repair DC generator		2	4			269		269	400
4000	Stub pole, install or remove		3	2.667			180		180	267
4500	Transformer maintenance up to 15 kVA	▼	2.70	2.963	▼		200		200	297

Division Notes

	CREW	DAILY OUTPUT	LABOR-HOURS	UNIT	BARE COSTS MAT.	LABOR	EQUIP.	TOTAL	TOTAL INCL O&P

Estimating Tips

02 30 00 Subsurface Investigation

In preparing estimates on structures involving earthwork or foundations, all information concerning soil characteristics should be obtained. Look particularly for hazardous waste, evidence of prior dumping of debris, and previous stream beds.

02 40 00 Demolition and Structure Moving

The costs shown for selective demolition do not include rubbish handling or disposal. These items should be estimated separately using RSMeans data or other sources.

- Historic preservation often requires that the contractor remove materials from the existing structure, rehab them, and replace them. The estimator must be aware of any related measures and precautions that must be taken when doing selective demolition and cutting and patching. Requirements may include special handling and storage, as well as security.
- In addition to Subdivision 02 41 00, you can find selective demolition items in each division. Example: Roofing demolition is in Division 7.
- Absent of any other specific reference, an approximate demolish-in-place cost can be obtained by halving the new-install labor cost. To remove for reuse, allow the entire new-install labor figure.

02 40 00 Building Deconstruction

This section provides costs for the careful dismantling and recycling of most low-rise building materials.

02 50 00 Containment of Hazardous Waste

This section addresses on-site hazardous waste disposal costs.

02 80 00 Hazardous Material Disposal/Remediation

This subdivision includes information on hazardous waste handling, asbestos remediation, lead remediation, and mold remediation. See reference numbers R028213-20 and R028319-60 for further guidance in using these unit price lines.

02 90 00 Monitoring Chemical Sampling, Testing Analysis

This section provides costs for on-site sampling and testing hazardous waste.

Reference Numbers

Reference numbers are shown at the beginning of some major classifications. These numbers refer to related items in the Reference Section. The reference information may be an estimating procedure, an alternate pricing method, or technical information.

Note: Not all subdivisions listed here necessarily appear. ■

02 41 Demolition

02 41 13 – Selective Site Demolition

02 41 13.17 Demolish, Remove Pavement and Curb

	02 41 13.17 Demolish, Remove Pavement and Curb	Crew	Daily Output	Labor-Hours	Unit	Material	2023 Bare Costs Labor	Equipment	Total	Total Incl O&P
0010	DEMOLISH, REMOVE PAVEMENT AND CURB R024119-10									
5010	Pavement removal, bituminous roads, up to 3" thick	B-38	690	.058	S.Y.		3.09	1.93	5.02	6.70
5050	4"-6" thick		420	.095			5.10	3.17	8.27	11.05
5100	Bituminous driveways		640	.063			3.33	2.08	5.41	7.25
5200	Concrete to 6" thick, hydraulic hammer, mesh reinforced		255	.157			8.35	5.20	13.55	18.20
5300	Rod reinforced		200	.200			10.65	6.65	17.30	23
5400	Concrete, 7"-24" thick, plain		33	1.212	C.Y.		64.50	40.50	105	141
5500	Reinforced		24	1.667	"		89	55.50	144.50	193
5600	With hand held air equipment, bituminous, to 6" thick	B-39	1900	.025	S.F.		1.25	.16	1.41	2.05
5700	Concrete to 6" thick, no reinforcing		1600	.030			1.49	.20	1.69	2.43
5800	Mesh reinforced		1400	.034			1.70	.22	1.92	2.78
5900	Rod reinforced		765	.063			3.12	.41	3.53	5.10

02 41 13.23 Utility Line Removal

	02 41 13.23 Utility Line Removal	Crew	Daily Output	Labor-Hours	Unit	Material	Labor	Equipment	Total	Total Incl O&P
0010	UTILITY LINE REMOVAL									
0015	No hauling, abandon catch basin or manhole	B-6	7	3.429	Ea.		176	39.50	215.50	305
0020	Remove existing catch basin or manhole, masonry		4	6			310	69.50	379.50	535
0030	Catch basin or manhole frames and covers, stored		13	1.846			95	21.50	116.50	165
0040	Remove and reset		7	3.429			176	39.50	215.50	305

02 41 13.30 Minor Site Demolition

	02 41 13.30 Minor Site Demolition	Crew	Daily Output	Labor-Hours	Unit	Material	Labor	Equipment	Total	Total Incl O&P
0010	MINOR SITE DEMOLITION R024119-10									
4000	Sidewalk removal, bituminous, 2" thick	B-6	350	.069	S.Y.		3.52	.79	4.31	6.10
4010	2-1/2" thick		325	.074			3.80	.85	4.65	6.60
4050	Brick, set in mortar		185	.130			6.65	1.50	8.15	11.60
4100	Concrete, plain, 4"		160	.150			7.70	1.73	9.43	13.40
4110	Plain, 5"		140	.171			8.80	1.98	10.78	15.30
4120	Plain, 6"		120	.200			10.30	2.31	12.61	17.85
4200	Mesh reinforced, concrete, 4"		150	.160			8.20	1.85	10.05	14.30
4210	5" thick		131	.183			9.40	2.12	11.52	16.35
4220	6" thick		112	.214			11	2.48	13.48	19.10

02 41 19 – Selective Demolition

02 41 19.13 Selective Building Demolition

	02 41 19.13 Selective Building Demolition	Crew	Daily Output	Labor-Hours	Unit	Material	Labor	Equipment	Total	Total Incl O&P
0010	SELECTIVE BUILDING DEMOLITION									
0020	Costs related to selective demolition of specific building components									
0025	are included under Common Work Results (XX 05)									
0030	in the component's appropriate division.									

02 41 19.16 Selective Demolition, Cutout

	02 41 19.16 Selective Demolition, Cutout	Crew	Daily Output	Labor-Hours	Unit	Material	Labor	Equipment	Total	Total Incl O&P
0010	SELECTIVE DEMOLITION, CUTOUT R024119-10									
0020	Concrete, elev. slab, light reinforcement, under 6 C.F.	B-9	65	.615	C.F.		29.50	4.81	34.31	49
0050	Light reinforcing, over 6 C.F.	"	75	.533	"		25.50	4.17	29.67	42.50
6000	Walls, interior, not including re-framing,									
6010	openings to 5 S.F.									
6100	Drywall to 5/8" thick	1 Clab	24	.333	Ea.		15.75		15.75	23.50
6200	Paneling to 3/4" thick		20	.400			18.90		18.90	28
6300	Plaster, on gypsum lath		20	.400			18.90		18.90	28
6340	On wire lath		14	.571			27		27	40

02 41 19.19 Selective Demolition

	02 41 19.19 Selective Demolition	Crew	Daily Output	Labor-Hours	Unit	Material	Labor	Equipment	Total	Total Incl O&P
0010	SELECTIVE DEMOLITION, Rubbish Handling R024119-10									
0020	The following are to be added to the demolition prices									
0600	Dumpster, weekly rental, 1 dump/week, 6 C.Y. capacity (2 tons)				Week	415			415	455
0700	10 C.Y. capacity (3 tons)					480			480	530
0725	20 C.Y. capacity (5 tons) R024119-20					565			565	625

02 41 19.19 Selective Demolition		Crew	Daily Output	Labor-Hours	Unit	2023 Bare Costs Material	Labor	Equipment	Total	Total Incl O&P
0800	30 C.Y. capacity (7 tons)				Week	730			730	800
0840	40 C.Y. capacity (10 tons)					775			775	850
2000	Load, haul, dump and return, 0′-50′ haul, hand carried	2 Clab	24	.667	C.Y.		31.50		31.50	47
2005	Wheeled		37	.432			20.50		20.50	30.50
2040	0′-100′ haul, hand carried		16.50	.970			46		46	68
2045	Wheeled		25	.640			30		30	45
2050	Forklift	A-3R	25	.320			19.10	12.45	31.55	42
2080	Haul and return, add per each extra 100′ haul, hand carried	2 Clab	35.50	.451			21.50		21.50	31.50
2085	Wheeled		54	.296			14		14	21
2120	For travel in elevators, up to 10 floors, add		140	.114			5.40		5.40	8.05
2130	0′-50′ haul, incl. up to 5 riser stairs, hand carried		23	.696			33		33	49
2135	Wheeled		35	.457			21.50		21.50	32
2140	6-10 riser stairs, hand carried		22	.727			34.50		34.50	51
2145	Wheeled		34	.471			22		22	33
2150	11-20 riser stairs, hand carried		20	.800			38		38	56.50
2155	Wheeled		31	.516			24.50		24.50	36.50
2160	21-40 riser stairs, hand carried		16	1			47.50		47.50	70.50
2165	Wheeled		24	.667			31.50		31.50	47
2170	0′-100′ haul, incl. 5 riser stairs, hand carried		15	1.067			50.50		50.50	75
2175	Wheeled		23	.696			33		33	49
2180	6-10 riser stairs, hand carried		14	1.143			54		54	80.50
2185	Wheeled		21	.762			36		36	53.50
2190	11-20 riser stairs, hand carried		12	1.333			63		63	94
2195	Wheeled		18	.889			42		42	62.50
2200	21-40 riser stairs, hand carried		8	2			94.50		94.50	141
2205	Wheeled		12	1.333			63		63	94
2210	Haul and return, add per each extra 100′ haul, hand carried		35.50	.451			21.50		21.50	31.50
2215	Wheeled		54	.296			14		14	21
2220	For each additional flight of stairs, up to 5 risers, add		550	.029	Flight		1.37		1.37	2.05
2225	6-10 risers, add		275	.058			2.75		2.75	4.09
2230	11-20 risers, add		138	.116			5.50		5.50	8.15
2235	21-40 risers, add		69	.232			10.95		10.95	16.30
3000	Loading & trucking, including 2 mile haul, chute loaded	B-16	45	.711	C.Y.		35.50	17.60	53.10	72.50
3040	Hand loading truck, 50′ haul	"	48	.667			33	16.50	49.50	67.50
3080	Machine loading truck	B-17	120	.267			14	5.80	19.80	27.50
5000	Haul, per mile, up to 8 C.Y. truck	B-34B	1165	.007			.38	.68	1.06	1.32
5100	Over 8 C.Y. truck	"	1550	.005			.29	.51	.80	.99

02 41 19.20 Selective Demolition, Dump Charges

		Crew	Daily Output	Labor-Hours	Unit	Material	Labor	Equipment	Total	Total Incl O&P
0010	**SELECTIVE DEMOLITION, DUMP CHARGES** R024119-10									
0020	Dump charges, typical urban city, tipping fees only									
0100	Building construction materials				Ton	74			74	81
0200	Trees, brush, lumber					63			63	69.50
0300	Rubbish only					63			63	69.50
0500	Reclamation station, usual charge					74			74	81

02 41 19.27 Selective Demolition, Torch Cutting

		Crew	Daily Output	Labor-Hours	Unit	Material	Labor	Equipment	Total	Total Incl O&P
0010	**SELECTIVE DEMOLITION, TORCH CUTTING** R024119-10									
0020	Steel, 1″ thick plate	E-25	333	.024	L.F.	2.91	1.60	.04	4.55	5.70
0040	1″ diameter bar	"	600	.013	Ea.	.48	.89	.02	1.39	1.93
1000	Oxygen lance cutting, reinforced concrete walls									
1040	12″-16″ thick walls	1 Clab	10	.800	L.F.		38		38	56.50
1080	24″ thick walls		6	1.333	"		63		63	94
0401	For cleaning/transporting tanks (1.5 lb./100 gal. cap)		500	.016	Lb.	1.35	.76		2.11	2.62

02 82 Asbestos Remediation

02 82 13 – Asbestos Abatement

02 82 13.47 Asbestos Waste Pkg., Handling, and Disp.

		Crew	Daily Output	Labor-Hours	Unit	2023 Bare Costs Material	Labor	Equipment	Total	Total Incl O&P
0010	**ASBESTOS WASTE PACKAGING, HANDLING, AND DISPOSAL**									
0100	Collect and bag bulk material, 3 C.F. bags, by hand	A-9	400	.160	Ea.	1.20	10.45		11.65	17.30
0200	Large production vacuum loader	A-12	880	.073		1.75	4.75	.93	7.43	10.20
1000	Double bag and decontaminate	A-9	960	.067		1.20	4.35		5.55	7.95
2000	Containerize bagged material in drums, per 55gal drum	″	800	.080		29	5.20		34.20	39.50
3000	Cart bags 50′ to dumpster	2 Asbe	400	.040			2.61		2.61	3.99
5000	Disposal charges, not including haul, minimum				C.Y.				61	67
5020	Maximum				″				355	395
9000	For type B (supplied air) respirator equipment, add				%				10%	10%

02 87 19 – Bio-Hazard and Infectious Disease Control Remediation

02 87 19.10 Temporary Barriers, Including Ppe

		Crew	Daily Output	Labor-Hours	Unit	2023 Bare Costs Material	Labor	Equipment	Total	Total Incl O&P
0010	**TEMPORARY BARRIERS, including PPE**									
0100	Infectious control partition, adjustable to 10′ high, obscured, 4′ panel	2 Carp	75	.213	Ea.	595	12.50		607.50	675
0110	3′ panel		75	.213		565	12.50		577.50	640
0120	2′ panel		75	.213		440	12.50		452.50	505
0130	1′ panel	1 Carp	75	.107		293	6.25		299.25	330
0140	6″ panel	″	75	.107		271	6.25		277.25	305
0150	2′ panel with HEPA filtered discharge port	2 Carp	75	.213		515	12.50		527.50	585
0160	3′ panel with 32″ door		75	.213		920	12.50		932.50	1,050
0170	4′ panel with 36″ door		75	.213		1,025	12.50		1,037.50	1,150
0180	4′-6″ panel with 44″ door		75	.213		1,225	12.50		1,237.50	1,375
0190	Hinged corner		68	.235		189	13.80		202.80	229
0200	Outside corner		68	.235		157	13.80		170.80	194
0210	T post		68	.235		167	13.80		180.80	205
0220	Accessories, ceiling grid clip		300	.053		7.60	3.13		10.73	13
0230	Panel locking clip		300	.053		5.35	3.13		8.48	10.55
0240	Panel joint closure strip		300	.053		8.60	3.13		11.73	14.15
0250	Screw jack		300	.053		7.50	3.13		10.63	12.90
0260	Digital pressure difference gauge					290			290	320
0280	Combination lockset	1 Carp	11	.727		209	42.50		251.50	294
0285	Sealant tape, 2″ wide	1 Clab	165	.048	C.L.F.	13.80	2.29		16.09	18.55
0290	System in place, including door and accessories									
0300	Based upon 25 uses	2 Carp	43	.372	L.F.	12.40	22		34.40	46
0310	Based upon 50 uses		43	.372		7.35	22		29.35	40.50
0330	Based upon 100 uses		43	.372		4.85	22		26.85	38
0400	Separation barrier, 2″ x 4″ @ 16″ O.C., 1/2″ plywood each side, 8′ high		340	.047	S.F.	5.30	2.76		8.06	9.90
0410	12′ high		275	.058		5.20	3.41		8.61	10.85
0420	16′ high		170	.094		5.35	5.50		10.85	14.10
0430	5/8″ FR GWB each side, 8′ high		290	.055		3.51	3.23		6.74	8.65
0440	12′ high		235	.068		3.37	3.99		7.36	9.65
0450	16′ high		144	.111		3.30	6.50		9.80	13.35

02 87 19.20 Temporary Protection, Including Ppe

		Crew	Daily Output	Labor-Hours	Unit	2023 Bare Costs Material	Labor	Equipment	Total	Total Incl O&P
0010	**TEMPORARY PROTECTION, including PPE**									
0100	Infectious control protection, 6 mil plastic sheeting, applied to floors	1 Skwk	1900	.004	S.F.	.07	.26		.33	.47
0110	Applied to walls		1400	.006		.07	.35		.42	.61
0120	Applied to ceilings		1000	.008		.07	.49		.56	.82
0130	Sealant tape, 2″ wide	1 Clab	165	.048	C.L.F.	13.80	2.29		16.09	18.55
0140	Floor covering, 1/8″ tempered hardboard	2 Carp	878	.018	S.F.	.73	1.07		1.80	2.39
0150	1/2″ CDX		878	.018		1.42	1.07		2.49	3.15
0160	3/4″ CDX		755	.021		1.98	1.24		3.22	4.02

02 87 19 – Bio-Hazard and Infectious Disease Control Remediation

02 87 19.30 Infectious Control Equipment and Supplies

	02 87 19.30 Infectious Control Equipment and Supplies	Crew	Daily Output	Labor-Hours	Unit	2023 Bare Costs Material	Labor	Equipment	Total	Total Incl O&P
0010	**INFECTIOUS CONTROL EQUIPMENT AND SUPPLIES**									
0100	Entry/exit decontamination chamber, portable, 10 uses	A-10C	12	2	Ea.	259	131	30	420	520
0105	Negative air machine, 1800 CFM					990			990	1,100
0110	Disposable polyethylene bags, 6 mil, 3 C.F.					1.20			1.20	1.32
0120	Negative air machine, 1800 CFM					990			990	1,100
0130	Paper towels, carton of 12, 350′ rolls					77			77	85
0140	Heavy duty wipes, 160 per box					38.50			38.50	42
0200	Tent, including frame, weights, roof, walls, 5′ x 5′	2 Skwk	32	.500		2,150	30.50		2,180.50	2,425
0205	5′ x 10′		24	.667		2,500	41		2,541	2,800
0210	10′ x 10′		24	.667		3,125	41		3,166	3,475
0220	13′ x 26′		12	1.333		7,475	81.50		7,556.50	8,350
0230	13′ x 26′, flat roof infirmary		12	1.333		7,600	81.50		7,681.50	8,475
0240	13′ x 26′, drive through screening		12	1.333		8,800	81.50		8,881.50	9,800
0242	LED light kit for tents, 15 watt	1 Elec	48	.167		199	11.25		210.25	236
0244	Halogen heating kit, 1500 watt	″	48	.167		500	11.25		511.25	565
0250	Medical partition system, including frame, drapes, 5′ x 5′	2 Skwk	48	.333		1,300	20.50		1,320.50	1,450

02 87 19.40 Infectious Control Cleaning, Includes Ppe

	02 87 19.40 Infectious Control Cleaning, Includes Ppe	Crew	Daily Output	Labor-Hours	Unit	Material	Labor	Equipment	Total	Total Incl O&P
0010	**INFECTIOUS CONTROL CLEANING, Includes PPE**									
0100	Infectious control cleaning, including PPE and antimicrobial spray, floors	1 Skwk	3600	.002	S.F.	.06	.14		.20	.27
0110	Walls		3000	.003		.06	.16		.22	.32
0120	Ceilings		2700	.003		.07	.18		.25	.34
0130	Countertops		3300	.002		.06	.15		.21	.29
0140	Other surfaces		2600	.003		.07	.19		.26	.35
0150	Plumbing fixtures		14	.571	Ea.	4.07	35		39.07	57
0160	Bathroom accessories		30	.267		1.87	16.35		18.22	26.50
0170	Kitchen appliance		9	.889		7	54.50		61.50	89.50
0180	Electrical switches and receptacles		140	.057		.41	3.50		3.91	5.70
0190	Work station		9	.889		7.50	54.50		62	90.50
0200	Door and window hardware		88	.091		.62	5.55		6.17	9.05
0250	Supply / return ductwork, up to 2 S.F. cross section		240	.033	L.F.	.50	2.04		2.54	3.62
0260	2 to 4 S.F. cross section		192	.042		.74	2.55		3.29	4.65
0270	4 to 8 S.F. cross section		144	.056		.92	3.40		4.32	6.10
0280	8 SF cross section		102	.078		1.40	4.80		6.20	8.75
0300	Duct coil		5	1.600	Ea.	11.95	98		109.95	160
0310	Duct damper and vane set		77	.104		1.61	6.35		7.96	11.30
0320	Fan coil unit or VAV box		8	1		7.25	61.50		68.75	100
0330	Air handling unit and coil		2	4		29	245		274	400
0340	Grill / diffuser or register		32	.250		2.14	15.30		17.44	25.50

Division Notes

		CREW	DAILY OUTPUT	LABOR-HOURS	UNIT	BARE COSTS MAT.	LABOR	EQUIP.	TOTAL	TOTAL INCL O&P

Estimating Tips

General

- Carefully check all the plans and specifications. Concrete often appears on drawings other than structural drawings, including mechanical and electrical drawings for equipment pads. The cost of cutting and patching is often difficult to estimate. See Subdivision 03 81 for Concrete Cutting, Subdivision 02 41 19.16 for Cutout Demolition, Subdivision 03 05 05.10 for Concrete Demolition, and Subdivision 02 41 19.19 for Rubbish Handling (handling, loading, and hauling of debris).
- Always obtain concrete prices from suppliers near the job site. A volume discount can often be negotiated, depending upon competition in the area. Remember to add for waste, particularly for slabs and footings on grade.

03 10 00 Concrete Forming and Accessories

- A primary cost for concrete construction is forming. Most jobs today are constructed with prefabricated forms. The selection of the forms best suited for the job and the total square feet of forms required for efficient concrete forming and placing are key elements in estimating concrete construction. Enough forms must be available for erection to make efficient use of the concrete placing equipment and crew.
- Concrete accessories for forming and placing depend upon the systems used. Study the plans and specifications to ensure that all special accessory requirements have been included in the cost estimate, such as anchor bolts, inserts, and hangers.
- Included within costs for forms-in-place are all necessary bracing and shoring.

03 20 00 Concrete Reinforcing

- Ascertain that the reinforcing steel supplier has included all accessories, cutting, bending, and an allowance for lapping, splicing, and waste. A good rule of thumb is 10% for lapping, splicing, and waste. Also, 10% waste should be allowed for welded wire fabric.
- The unit price items in the subdivisions for Reinforcing In Place, Glass Fiber Reinforcing, and Welded Wire Fabric include the labor to install accessories such as beam and slab bolsters, high chairs, and bar ties and tie wire. The material cost for these accessories is not included; they may be obtained from the Accessories Subdivisions.

03 30 00 Cast-In-Place Concrete

- When estimating structural concrete, pay particular attention to requirements for concrete additives, curing methods, and surface treatments. Special consideration for climate, hot or cold, must be included in your estimate. Be sure to include requirements for concrete placing equipment and concrete finishing.
- For accurate concrete estimating, the estimator must consider each of the following major components individually: forms, reinforcing steel, ready-mix concrete, placement of the concrete, and finishing of the top surface. For faster estimating, Subdivision 03 30 53.40 for Concrete-In-Place can be used; here, various items of concrete work are presented that include the costs of all five major components (unless specifically stated otherwise).

03 40 00 Precast Concrete
03 50 00 Cast Decks and Underlayment

- The cost of hauling precast concrete structural members is often an important factor. For this reason, it is important to get a quote from the nearest supplier. It may become economically feasible to set up precasting beds on the site if the hauling costs are prohibitive.

Reference Numbers

Reference numbers are shown at the beginning of some major classifications. These numbers refer to related items in the Reference Section. The reference information may be an estimating procedure, an alternate pricing method, or technical information.

Note: Not all subdivisions listed here necessarily appear. ■

03 01 Maintenance of Concrete

03 01 30 – Maintenance of Cast-In-Place Concrete

03 01 30.62 Concrete Patching		Crew	Daily Output	Labor-Hours	Unit	Material	Labor	Equipment	Total	Total Incl O&P
						2023 Bare Costs				
0010	CONCRETE PATCHING									
0100	Floors, 1/4" thick, small areas, regular grout	1 Cefi	170	.047	S.F.	1.24	2.59		3.83	5.15
0150	Epoxy grout	"	100	.080	"	16.80	4.40		21.20	25
2000	Walls, including chipping, cleaning and epoxy grout									
2100	1/4" deep	1 Cefi	65	.123	S.F.	6	6.75		12.75	16.50
2150	1/2" deep		50	.160		12	8.80		20.80	26
2200	3/4" deep	↓	40	.200	↓	18	11		29	36

03 11 Concrete Forming

03 11 13 – Structural Cast-In-Place Concrete Forming

03 11 13.40 Forms In Place, Equipment Foundations		Crew	Daily Output	Labor-Hours	Unit	Material	Labor	Equipment	Total	Total Incl O&P
0010	FORMS IN PLACE, EQUIPMENT FOUNDATIONS									
0020	1 use	C-2	160	.300	SFCA	8.05	17.10		25.15	34.50
0050	2 use		190	.253		4.43	14.40		18.83	26.50
0100	3 use		200	.240		3.22	13.70		16.92	24
0150	4 use	↓	205	.234	↓	2.63	13.35		15.98	23

03 11 13.45 Forms In Place, Footings		Crew	Daily Output	Labor-Hours	Unit	Material	Labor	Equipment	Total	Total Incl O&P
0010	FORMS IN PLACE, FOOTINGS									
0020	Continuous wall, plywood, 1 use	C-1	375	.085	SFCA	14.35	4.76		19.11	23
0050	2 use		440	.073		7.90	4.06		11.96	14.75
0100	3 use		470	.068		5.75	3.80		9.55	11.95
0150	4 use		485	.066		4.67	3.68		8.35	10.65
5000	Spread footings, job-built lumber, 1 use		305	.105		5.85	5.85		11.70	15.15
5050	2 use		371	.086		3.24	4.81		8.05	10.70
5100	3 use		401	.080		2.34	4.45		6.79	9.20
5150	4 use	↓	414	.077	↓	1.90	4.31		6.21	8.50

03 11 13.65 Forms In Place, Slab On Grade		Crew	Daily Output	Labor-Hours	Unit	Material	Labor	Equipment	Total	Total Incl O&P
0010	FORMS IN PLACE, SLAB ON GRADE									
3000	Edge forms, wood, 4 use, on grade, to 6" high	C-1	600	.053	L.F.	.83	2.97		3.80	5.35
6000	Trench forms in floor, wood, 1 use		160	.200	SFCA	5.40	11.15		16.55	22.50
6050	2 use		175	.183		2.96	10.20		13.16	18.45
6100	3 use		180	.178		2.15	9.90		12.05	17.10
6150	4 use	↓	185	.173	↓	1.75	9.65		11.40	16.25

03 15 Concrete Accessories

03 15 05 – Concrete Forming Accessories

03 15 05.75 Sleeves and Chases		Crew	Daily Output	Labor-Hours	Unit	Material	Labor	Equipment	Total	Total Incl O&P
0010	SLEEVES AND CHASES									
0100	Plastic, 1 use, 12" long, 2" diameter	1 Carp	100	.080	Ea.	3.41	4.69		8.10	10.75
0150	4" diameter		90	.089		.91	5.20		6.11	8.75
0200	6" diameter		75	.107		17.45	6.25		23.70	28.50
0250	12" diameter		60	.133		50.50	7.80		58.30	67.50
5000	Sheet metal, 2" diameter G		100	.080		3.30	4.69		7.99	10.65
5100	4" diameter G		90	.089		4.12	5.20		9.32	12.30
5150	6" diameter G		75	.107		5.20	6.25		11.45	15
5200	12" diameter G		60	.133		9.80	7.80		17.60	22.50
6000	Steel pipe, 2" diameter G		100	.080		17.45	4.69		22.14	26
6100	4" diameter G		90	.089		49	5.20		54.20	62
6150	6" diameter G	↓	75	.107	↓	90	6.25		96.25	108

03 15 Concrete Accessories

03 15 05 – Concrete Forming Accessories

03 15 05.75 Sleeves and Chases			Crew	Daily Output	Labor-Hours	Unit	Material	Labor	Equipment	Total	Total Incl O&P
							2023 Bare Costs				
6200	12″ diameter	G	1 Carp	60	.133	Ea.	136	7.80		143.80	162

03 15 16 – Concrete Construction Joints

03 15 16.20 Control Joints, Saw Cut

			Crew	Daily Output	Labor-Hours	Unit	Material	Labor	Equipment	Total	Total Incl O&P
0010	**CONTROL JOINTS, SAW CUT**										
0100	Sawcut control joints in green concrete										
0120	1″ depth		C-27	2000	.008	L.F.	.03	.44	.09	.56	.77
0140	1-1/2″ depth			1800	.009		.04	.49	.10	.63	.88
0160	2″ depth			1600	.010		.06	.55	.11	.72	.98
0180	Sawcut joint reservoir in cured concrete										
0182	3/8″ wide x 3/4″ deep, with single saw blade		C-27	1000	.016	L.F.	.04	.88	.18	1.10	1.53
0184	1/2″ wide x 1″ deep, with double saw blades			900	.018		.08	.98	.20	1.26	1.74
0186	3/4″ wide x 1-1/2″ deep, with double saw blades			800	.020		.17	1.10	.22	1.49	2.04
0190	Water blast joint to wash away laitance, 2 passes		C-29	2500	.003			.15	.04	.19	.28
0200	Air blast joint to blow out debris and air dry, 2 passes		C-28	2000	.004			.22	.02	.24	.34
0300	For backer rod, see Section 07 91 23.10										
0342	For joint sealant, see Section 07 92 13.20										

03 15 19 – Cast-In Concrete Anchors

03 15 19.10 Anchor Bolts

			Crew	Daily Output	Labor-Hours	Unit	Material	Labor	Equipment	Total	Total Incl O&P
0010	**ANCHOR BOLTS**										
0015	Made from recycled materials										
0025	Single bolts installed in fresh concrete, no templates										
0030	Hooked w/nut and washer, 1/2″ diameter, 8″ long	G	1 Carp	132	.061	Ea.	2.23	3.55		5.78	7.75
0040	12″ long	G		131	.061		2.48	3.58		6.06	8.10
0050	5/8″ diameter, 8″ long	G		129	.062		4.02	3.63		7.65	9.85
0060	12″ long	G		127	.063		4.95	3.69		8.64	10.95
0070	3/4″ diameter, 8″ long	G		127	.063		4.95	3.69		8.64	10.95
0080	12″ long	G		125	.064		6.20	3.75		9.95	12.40

03 15 19.45 Machinery Anchors

			Crew	Daily Output	Labor-Hours	Unit	Material	Labor	Equipment	Total	Total Incl O&P
0010	**MACHINERY ANCHORS**, heavy duty, incl. sleeve, floating base nut,										
0020	lower stud & coupling nut, fiber plug, connecting stud, washer & nut.										
0030	For flush mounted embedment in poured concrete heavy equip. pads.										
0200	Stud & bolt, 1/2″ diameter	G	E-16	40	.400	Ea.	89	26	3.68	118.68	142
0300	5/8″ diameter	G		35	.457		104	30	4.20	138.20	165
0500	3/4″ diameter	G		30	.533		126	35	4.90	165.90	197
0600	7/8″ diameter	G		25	.640		141	42	5.90	188.90	226
0800	1″ diameter	G		20	.800		154	52.50	7.35	213.85	258
0900	1-1/4″ diameter	G		15	1.067		204	70	9.80	283.80	345

03 21 Reinforcement Bars

03 21 11 – Plain Steel Reinforcement Bars

03 21 11.60 Reinforcing In Place

			Crew	Daily Output	Labor-Hours	Unit	Material	Labor	Equipment	Total	Total Incl O&P
0010	**REINFORCING IN PLACE**, 50-60 ton lots, A615 Grade 60										
0020	Includes labor, but not material cost, to install accessories										
0030	Made from recycled materials										
0502	Footings, #4 to #7	G	4 Rodm	4200	.008	Lb.	.71	.49		1.20	1.51
0552	#8 to #18	G		7200	.004		.71	.29		1	1.21
0602	Slab on grade, #3 to #7	G		4200	.008		.71	.49		1.20	1.51
0900	For other than 50-60 ton lots										
1000	Under 10 ton job, #3 to #7, add						25%	10%			
1010	#8 to #18, add						20%	10%			

03 21 Reinforcement Bars

03 21 11 – Plain Steel Reinforcement Bars

03 21 11.60 Reinforcing In Place		Crew	Daily Output	Labor-Hours	Unit	2023 Bare Costs Material	Labor	Equipment	Total	Total Incl O&P
1050	10-50 ton job, #3 to #7, add					10%				
1060	#8 to #18, add					5%				
1100	60-100 ton job, #3 to #7, deduct					5%				
1110	#8 to #18, deduct					10%				
1150	Over 100 ton job, #3 to #7, deduct					10%				
1160	#8 to #18, deduct					15%				

03 22 Fabric and Grid Reinforcing

03 22 11 – Plain Welded Wire Fabric Reinforcing

03 22 11.10 Plain Welded Wire Fabric

		Crew	Daily Output	Labor-Hours	Unit	Material	Labor	Equipment	Total	Total Incl O&P
0010	**PLAIN WELDED WIRE FABRIC** ASTM A185									
0020	Includes labor, but not material cost, to install accessories									
0050	Sheets									
0100	6 x 6 - W1.4 x W1.4 (10 x 10) 21 lb./C.S.F. G	2 Rodm	35	.457	C.S.F.	37.50	29.50		67	85.50

03 22 13 – Galvanized Welded Wire Fabric Reinforcing

03 22 13.10 Galvanized Welded Wire Fabric

		Crew	Daily Output	Labor-Hours	Unit	Material	Labor	Equipment	Total	Total Incl O&P
0010	**GALVANIZED WELDED WIRE FABRIC**									
0100	Add to plain welded wire pricing for galvanized welded wire				Lb.	.28			.28	.31

03 22 16 – Epoxy-Coated Welded Wire Fabric Reinforcing

03 22 16.10 Epoxy-Coated Welded Wire Fabric

		Crew	Daily Output	Labor-Hours	Unit	Material	Labor	Equipment	Total	Total Incl O&P
0010	**EPOXY-COATED WELDED WIRE FABRIC**									
0100	Add to plain welded wire pricing for epoxy-coated welded wire				Lb.	.56			.56	.61

03 30 Cast-In-Place Concrete

03 30 53 – Miscellaneous Cast-In-Place Concrete

03 30 53.40 Concrete In Place

		Crew	Daily Output	Labor-Hours	Unit	Material	Labor	Equipment	Total	Total Incl O&P
0010	**CONCRETE IN PLACE**									
0020	Including forms (4 uses), Grade 60 rebar, concrete (Portland cement									
0050	Type I), placement and finishing unless otherwise indicated									
3540	Equipment pad (3000 psi), 3′ x 3′ x 6″ thick	C-14H	45	1.067	Ea.	83	61.50	.66	145.16	183
3550	4′ x 4′ x 6″ thick		30	1.600		120	92	.99	212.99	270
3560	5′ x 5′ x 8″ thick		18	2.667		216	153	1.65	370.65	470
3570	6′ x 6′ x 8″ thick		14	3.429		284	197	2.13	483.13	610
3580	8′ x 8′ x 10″ thick		8	6		590	345	3.72	938.72	1,175
3590	10′ x 10′ x 12″ thick		5	9.600		980	550	5.95	1,535.95	1,900
3800	Footings (3000 psi), spread under 1 C.Y.	C-14C	28	4	C.Y.	257	224	1.08	482.08	620
3813	Install new concrete (3000 psi) light pole base, 24″ diam. x 8′	C-1	2.66	12.030		430	670		1,100	1,475
3825	1 C.Y. to 5 C.Y.	C-14C	43	2.605		330	146	.70	476.70	580
3850	Over 5 C.Y.	″	75	1.493		315	84	.40	399.40	470
3900	Footings, strip (3000 psi), 18″ x 9″, unreinforced	C-14L	40	2.400		211	131	.74	342.74	430
3920	18″ x 9″, reinforced	C-14C	35	3.200		245	179	.86	424.86	540
3925	20″ x 10″, unreinforced	C-14L	45	2.133		202	117	.66	319.66	395
3930	20″ x 10″, reinforced	C-14C	40	2.800		229	157	.76	386.76	485
3935	24″ x 12″, unreinforced	C-14L	55	1.745		194	95.50	.54	290.04	355
3940	24″ x 12″, reinforced	C-14C	48	2.333		223	131	.63	354.63	440
3945	36″ x 12″, unreinforced	C-14L	70	1.371		184	75	.43	259.43	315
3950	36″ x 12″, reinforced	C-14C	60	1.867		210	105	.50	315.50	390
4000	Foundation mat (3000 psi), under 10 C.Y.	″	38.67	2.896		310	162	.78	472.78	585

03 30 Cast-In-Place Concrete

03 30 53 – Miscellaneous Cast-In-Place Concrete

03 30 53.40 Concrete In Place		Crew	Daily Output	Labor-Hours	Unit	Material	2023 Bare Costs Labor	Equipment	Total	Total Incl O&P
4650	Slab on grade (3500 psi), not including finish, 4" thick	C-14E	60.75	1.449	C.Y.	204	83.50	.49	287.99	350
4700	6" thick	"	92	.957	↓	191	55	.33	246.33	292
4701	Thickened slab edge (3500 psi), for slab on grade poured									
4702	monolithically with slab; depth is in addition to slab thickness;									
4703	formed vertical outside edge, earthen bottom and inside slope									
4705	8" deep x 8" wide bottom, unreinforced	C-14L	2190	.044	L.F.	6.10	2.40	.01	8.51	10.25
4710	8" x 8", reinforced	C-14C	1670	.067		9.45	3.76	.02	13.23	16
4715	12" deep x 12" wide bottom, unreinforced	C-14L	1800	.053		11.80	2.92	.02	14.74	17.35
4720	12" x 12", reinforced	C-14C	1310	.086		17.95	4.80	.02	22.77	27
4725	16" deep x 16" wide bottom, unreinforced	C-14L	1440	.067		19.30	3.65	.02	22.97	26.50
4730	16" x 16", reinforced	C-14C	1120	.100		26.50	5.60	.03	32.13	38
4735	20" deep x 20" wide bottom, unreinforced	C-14L	1150	.083		28.50	4.56	.03	33.09	38.50
4740	20" x 20", reinforced	C-14C	920	.122		38	6.85	.03	44.88	52
4745	24" deep x 24" wide bottom, unreinforced	C-14L	930	.103		40	5.65	.03	45.68	52.50
4750	24" x 24", reinforced	C-14C	740	.151	↓	52	8.50	.04	60.54	70

03 31 Structural Concrete

03 31 13 – Heavyweight Structural Concrete

03 31 13.35 Heavyweight Concrete, Ready Mix

		Crew	Daily Output	Labor-Hours	Unit	Material	Labor	Equipment	Total	Total Incl O&P
0010	**HEAVYWEIGHT CONCRETE, READY MIX**, delivered									
0012	Includes local aggregate, sand, Portland cement (Type I) and water									
0015	Excludes all additives and treatments									
0020	2000 psi				C.Y.	148			148	163
0100	2500 psi					151			151	166
0150	3000 psi					154			154	170
0200	3500 psi					158			158	174
0300	4000 psi					162			162	178
1000	For high early strength (Portland cement Type III), add					10%				
1300	For winter concrete (hot water), add					8.50			8.50	9.35
1410	For mid-range water reducer, add					6.40			6.40	7.05
1420	For high-range water reducer/superplasticizer, add					8.50			8.50	9.35
1430	For retarder, add					6.05			6.05	6.65
1440	For non-Chloride accelerator, add					9.50			9.50	10.45
1450	For Chloride accelerator, per 1%, add					5			5	5.50
1460	For fiber reinforcing, synthetic (1 lb./C.Y.), add					10.40			10.40	11.45
1500	For Saturday delivery, add				↓	15			15	16.50
1510	For truck holding/waiting time past 1st hour per load, add				Hr.	143			143	157
1520	For short load (less than 4 C.Y.), add per load				Ea.	125			125	138
2000	For all lightweight aggregate, add				C.Y.	45%				

03 31 13.70 Placing Concrete

		Crew	Daily Output	Labor-Hours	Unit	Material	Labor	Equipment	Total	Total Incl O&P
0010	**PLACING CONCRETE**									
0020	Includes labor and equipment to place, level (strike off) and consolidate									
1200	Duct bank, direct chute	C-6	155	.310	C.Y.		15.15	.38	15.53	23
1900	Footings, continuous, shallow, direct chute	"	120	.400			19.55	.50	20.05	29.50
1950	Pumped	C-20	150	.427			21.50	5.90	27.40	38.50
2000	With crane and bucket	C-7	90	.800			41	28.50	69.50	92
2100	Footings, continuous, deep, direct chute	C-6	140	.343			16.75	.43	17.18	25.50
2150	Pumped	C-20	160	.400			20	5.55	25.55	36
2200	With crane and bucket	C-7	110	.655			33.50	23.50	57	75
2400	Footings, spread, under 1 C.Y., direct chute	C-6	55	.873			42.50	1.08	43.58	64.50
2450	Pumped	C-20	65	.985	↓		49.50	13.65	63.15	89

03 31 Structural Concrete

03 31 13 – Heavyweight Structural Concrete

03 31 13.70 Placing Concrete		Crew	Daily Output	Labor-Hours	Unit	Material	2023 Bare Costs Labor	Equipment	Total	Total Incl O&P
2500	With crane and bucket	C-7	45	1.600	C.Y.		82	57	139	184
2600	Over 5 C.Y., direct chute	C-6	120	.400			19.55	.50	20.05	29.50
2650	Pumped	C-20	150	.427			21.50	5.90	27.40	38.50
2700	With crane and bucket	C-7	100	.720			37	25.50	62.50	83
2900	Foundation mats, over 20 C.Y., direct chute	C-6	350	.137			6.70	.17	6.87	10.15
2950	Pumped	C-20	400	.160			8.05	2.22	10.27	14.45
3000	With crane and bucket	C-7	300	.240	↓		12.25	8.55	20.80	27.50

03 35 Concrete Finishing

03 35 13 – High-Tolerance Concrete Floor Finishing

03 35 13.30 Finishing Floors, High Tolerance

		Crew	Daily Output	Labor-Hours	Unit	Material	Labor	Equipment	Total	Total Incl O&P
0010	**FINISHING FLOORS, HIGH TOLERANCE**									
0012	Finishing of fresh concrete flatwork requires that concrete									
0013	first be placed, struck off & consolidated									
0015	Basic finishing for various unspecified flatwork									
0100	Bull float only	C-10	4000	.006	S.F.		.31		.31	.46
0125	Bull float & manual float		2000	.012			.63		.63	.92
0150	Bull float, manual float & broom finish, w/edging & joints		1850	.013			.68		.68	1
0200	Bull float, manual float & manual steel trowel	↓	1265	.019	↓		.99		.99	1.46
0210	For specified Random Access Floors in ACI Classes 1, 2, 3 and 4 to achieve									
0215	Composite Overall Floor Flatness and Levelness values up to FF35/FL25									
0250	Bull float, machine float & machine trowel (walk-behind)	C-10C	1715	.014	S.F.		.73	.05	.78	1.13
0300	Power screed, bull float, machine float & trowel (walk-behind)	C-10D	2400	.010			.52	.07	.59	.85
0350	Power screed, bull float, machine float & trowel (ride-on)	C-10E	4000	.006	↓		.31	.08	.39	.55
0352	For specified Random Access Floors in ACI Classes 5, 6, 7 and 8 to achieve									
0354	Composite Overall Floor Flatness and Levelness values up to FF50/FL50									
0356	Add for two-dimensional restraightening after power float	C-10	6000	.004	S.F.		.21		.21	.31
0358	For specified Random or Defined Access Floors in ACI Class 9 to achieve									
0360	Composite Overall Floor Flatness and Levelness values up to FF100/FL100									
0362	Add for two-dimensional restraightening after bull float & power float	C-10	3000	.008	S.F.		.42		.42	.62
0364	For specified Superflat Defined Access Floors in ACI Class 9 to achieve									
0366	Minimum Floor Flatness and Levelness values of FF100/FL100									
0368	Add for 2-dim'l restraightening after bull float, power float, power trowel	C-10	2000	.012	S.F.		.63		.63	.92

03 54 Cast Underlayment

03 54 16 – Hydraulic Cement Underlayment

03 54 16.50 Cement Underlayment

		Crew	Daily Output	Labor-Hours	Unit	Material	Labor	Equipment	Total	Total Incl O&P
0010	**CEMENT UNDERLAYMENT**									
2510	Underlayment, P.C. based, self-leveling, 4100 psi, pumped, 1/4" thick	C-8	20000	.003	S.F.	2.37	.15	.04	2.56	2.88
2520	1/2" thick		19000	.003		4.74	.15	.04	4.93	5.50
2530	3/4" thick		18000	.003		7.10	.16	.05	7.31	8.10
2540	1" thick		17000	.003		9.50	.17	.05	9.72	10.75
2550	1-1/2" thick	↓	15000	.004		14.20	.19	.06	14.45	16
2560	Hand placed, 1/2" thick	C-18	450	.020		4.74	.95	.33	6.02	7
2610	Topping, P.C. based, self-leveling, 6100 psi, pumped, 1/4" thick	C-8	20000	.003		2.45	.15	.04	2.64	2.96
2620	1/2" thick		19000	.003		4.89	.15	.04	5.08	5.70
2630	3/4" thick		18000	.003		7.35	.16	.05	7.56	8.35
2660	1" thick		17000	.003		9.80	.17	.05	10.02	11.05
2670	1-1/2" thick	↓	15000	.004	↓	14.70	.19	.06	14.95	16.50

03 54 Cast Underlayment

03 54 16 – Hydraulic Cement Underlayment

03 54 16.50 Cement Underlayment		Crew	Daily Output	Labor-Hours	Unit	2023 Bare Costs Material	Labor	Equipment	Total	Total Incl O&P
2680	Hand placed, 1/2" thick	C-18	450	.020	S.F.	4.89	.95	.33	6.17	7.20

03 63 Epoxy Grouting

03 63 05 – Grouting of Dowels and Fasteners

03 63 05.10 Epoxy Only		Crew	Daily Output	Labor-Hours	Unit	Material	Labor	Equipment	Total	Total Incl O&P
0010	**EPOXY ONLY**									
1500	Chemical anchoring, epoxy cartridge, excludes layout, drilling, fastener									
1530	For fastener 3/4" diam. x 6" embedment	2 Skwk	72	.222	Ea.	4.69	13.60		18.29	25.50
1535	1" diam. x 8" embedment		66	.242		7.05	14.85		21.90	30.50
1540	1-1/4" diam. x 10" embedment		60	.267		14.05	16.35		30.40	40
1545	1-3/4" diam. x 12" embedment		54	.296		23.50	18.15		41.65	53.50
1550	14" embedment		48	.333		28	20.50		48.50	61.50
1555	2" diam. x 12" embedment		42	.381		37.50	23.50		61	76.50
1560	18" embedment	↓	32	.500	↓	47	30.50		77.50	97.50

03 81 Concrete Cutting

03 81 13 – Flat Concrete Sawing

03 81 13.50 Concrete Floor/Slab Cutting		Crew	Daily Output	Labor-Hours	Unit	Material	Labor	Equipment	Total	Total Incl O&P
0010	**CONCRETE FLOOR/SLAB CUTTING**									
0050	Includes blade cost, layout and set-up time									
0300	Saw cut concrete slabs, plain, up to 3" deep	B-89	1060	.015	L.F.	.10	.85	.63	1.58	2.07
0320	Each additional inch of depth		3180	.005		.03	.28	.21	.52	.69
0400	Mesh reinforced, up to 3" deep		980	.016		.11	.92	.68	1.71	2.25
0420	Each additional inch of depth		2940	.005		.04	.31	.23	.58	.75
0500	Rod reinforced, up to 3" deep		800	.020		.14	1.13	.83	2.10	2.75
0520	Each additional inch of depth	↓	2400	.007	↓	.05	.38	.28	.71	.91

03 81 13.75 Concrete Saw Blades		Crew	Daily Output	Labor-Hours	Unit	Material	Labor	Equipment	Total	Total Incl O&P
0010	**CONCRETE SAW BLADES**									
3000	Blades for saw cutting, included in cutting line items									
3020	Diamond, 12" diameter				Ea.	216			216	238
3040	18" diameter					340			340	375
3080	24" diameter					480			480	530
3120	30" diameter					855			855	940
3160	36" diameter					1,200			1,200	1,325
3200	42" diameter				↓	1,850			1,850	2,025

03 82 Concrete Boring

03 82 13 – Concrete Core Drilling

03 82 13.10 Core Drilling		Crew	Daily Output	Labor-Hours	Unit	Material	Labor	Equipment	Total	Total Incl O&P
0010	**CORE DRILLING**									
0015	Includes bit cost, layout and set-up time									
0020	Reinforced concrete slab, up to 6" thick									
0100	1" diameter core	B-89A	17	.941	Ea.	.22	51	6.95	58.17	84.50
0150	For each additional inch of slab thickness in same hole, add		1440	.011		.04	.60	.08	.72	1.03
0200	2" diameter core		16.50	.970		.30	52.50	7.15	59.95	86.50
0250	For each additional inch of slab thickness in same hole, add		1080	.015		.05	.80	.11	.96	1.38
0300	3" diameter core	↓	16	1	↓	.43	54.50	7.40	62.33	89.50

03 82 Concrete Boring

03 82 13 – Concrete Core Drilling

03 82 13.10 Core Drilling		Crew	Daily Output	Labor-Hours	Unit	Material	Labor	Equipment	Total	Total Incl O&P
						2023 Bare Costs				
0350	For each additional inch of slab thickness in same hole, add	B-89A	720	.022	Ea.	.07	1.21	.16	1.44	2.06
0500	4″ diameter core		15	1.067		.57	58	7.85	66.42	96
0550	For each additional inch of slab thickness in same hole, add		480	.033		.10	1.81	.25	2.16	3.08
0700	6″ diameter core		14	1.143		.91	62	8.45	71.36	103
0750	For each additional inch of slab thickness in same hole, add		360	.044		.15	2.41	.33	2.89	4.14
0900	8″ diameter core		13	1.231		1.32	67	9.10	77.42	111
0950	For each additional inch of slab thickness in same hole, add		288	.056		.22	3.01	.41	3.64	5.20
1100	10″ diameter core		12	1.333		1.62	72.50	9.85	83.97	121
1150	For each additional inch of slab thickness in same hole, add		240	.067		.27	3.62	.49	4.38	6.25
1300	12″ diameter core		11	1.455		1.85	79	10.75	91.60	132
1350	For each additional inch of slab thickness in same hole, add		206	.078		.31	4.21	.57	5.09	7.25
1500	14″ diameter core		10	1.600		2.29	87	11.80	101.09	146
1550	For each additional inch of slab thickness in same hole, add		180	.089		.38	4.82	.66	5.86	8.35
1700	18″ diameter core		9	1.778		2.98	96.50	13.10	112.58	162
1750	For each additional inch of slab thickness in same hole, add		144	.111		.50	6.05	.82	7.37	10.45
1754	24″ diameter core		8	2		4.73	109	14.75	128.48	183
1756	For each additional inch of slab thickness in same hole, add		120	.133		.79	7.25	.98	9.02	12.75
1760	For horizontal holes, add to above						20%	20%		
1770	Prestressed hollow core plank, 8″ thick									
1780	1″ diameter core	B-89A	17.50	.914	Ea.	.30	49.50	6.75	56.55	81.50
1790	For each additional inch of plank thickness in same hole, add		3840	.004		.04	.23	.03	.30	.41
1794	2″ diameter core		17.25	.928		.40	50.50	6.85	57.75	83.50
1796	For each additional inch of plank thickness in same hole, add		2880	.006		.05	.30	.04	.39	.56
1800	3″ diameter core		17	.941		.57	51	6.95	58.52	85
1810	For each additional inch of plank thickness in same hole, add		1920	.008		.07	.45	.06	.58	.83
1820	4″ diameter core		16.50	.970		.76	52.50	7.15	60.41	87
1830	For each additional inch of plank thickness in same hole, add		1280	.013		.10	.68	.09	.87	1.21
1840	6″ diameter core		15.50	1.032		1.21	56	7.60	64.81	93.50
1850	For each additional inch of plank thickness in same hole, add		960	.017		.15	.90	.12	1.17	1.66
1860	8″ diameter core		15	1.067		1.76	58	7.85	67.61	97
1870	For each additional inch of plank thickness in same hole, add		768	.021		.22	1.13	.15	1.50	2.10
1880	10″ diameter core		14	1.143		2.16	62	8.45	72.61	105
1890	For each additional inch of plank thickness in same hole, add		640	.025		.27	1.36	.18	1.81	2.53
1900	12″ diameter core		13.50	1.185		2.47	64.50	8.75	75.72	108
1910	For each additional inch of plank thickness in same hole, add		548	.029		.31	1.58	.22	2.11	2.95

03 82 16 – Concrete Drilling

03 82 16.10 Concrete Impact Drilling		Crew	Daily Output	Labor-Hours	Unit	Material	Labor	Equipment	Total	Total Incl O&P
0010	**CONCRETE IMPACT DRILLING**									
0020	Includes bit cost, layout and set-up time, no anchors									
0050	Up to 4″ deep in concrete/brick floors/walls									
0100	Holes, 1/4″ diameter	1 Carp	75	.107	Ea.	.04	6.25		6.29	9.35
0150	For each additional inch of depth in same hole, add		430	.019		.01	1.09		1.10	1.63
0200	3/8″ diameter		63	.127		.03	7.45		7.48	11.15
0250	For each additional inch of depth in same hole, add		340	.024		.01	1.38		1.39	2.06
0300	1/2″ diameter		50	.160		.04	9.40		9.44	14
0350	For each additional inch of depth in same hole, add		250	.032		.01	1.88		1.89	2.80
0400	5/8″ diameter		48	.167		.05	9.75		9.80	14.60
0450	For each additional inch of depth in same hole, add		240	.033		.01	1.95		1.96	2.92
0500	3/4″ diameter		45	.178		.08	10.40		10.48	15.60
0550	For each additional inch of depth in same hole, add		220	.036		.02	2.13		2.15	3.19
0600	7/8″ diameter		43	.186		.07	10.90		10.97	16.35
0650	For each additional inch of depth in same hole, add		210	.038		.02	2.23		2.25	3.34

03 82 Concrete Boring

03 82 16 – Concrete Drilling

03 82 16.10 Concrete Impact Drilling		Crew	Daily Output	Labor-Hours	Unit	Material	Labor	Equipment	Total	Total Incl O&P
						2023 Bare Costs				
0700	1" diameter	1 Carp	40	.200	Ea.	.16	11.70		11.86	17.65
0750	For each additional inch of depth in same hole, add		190	.042		.04	2.47		2.51	3.72
0800	1-1/4" diameter		38	.211		.23	12.35		12.58	18.60
0850	For each additional inch of depth in same hole, add		180	.044		.06	2.60		2.66	3.94
0900	1-1/2" diameter		35	.229		.35	13.40		13.75	20.50
0950	For each additional inch of depth in same hole, add	↓	165	.048	↓	.09	2.84		2.93	4.33
1000	For ceiling installations, add						40%			

Division Notes

		CREW	DAILY OUTPUT	LABOR-HOURS	UNIT	BARE COSTS MAT.	LABOR	EQUIP.	TOTAL	TOTAL INCL O&P

Estimating Tips

05 05 00 Common Work Results for Metals

- Nuts, bolts, washers, connection angles, and plates can add a significant amount to both the tonnage of a structural steel job and the estimated cost. As a rule of thumb, add 10% to the total weight to account for these accessories.
- Type 2 steel construction, commonly referred to as "simple construction," consists generally of field-bolted connections with lateral bracing supplied by other elements of the building, such as masonry walls or x-bracing. The estimator should be aware, however, that shop connections may be accomplished by welding or bolting. The method may be particular to the fabrication shop and may have an impact on the estimated cost.

05 10 00 Structural Steel

- Steel items can be obtained from two sources: a fabrication shop or a metals service center. Fabrication shops can fabricate items under more controlled conditions than crews in the field can. They are also more efficient and can produce items more economically. Metal service centers serve as a source of long mill shapes to both fabrication shops and contractors.
- Most line items in this structural steel subdivision, and most items in 05 50 00 Metal Fabrications, are indicated as being shop fabricated. The bare material cost for these shop fabricated items is the "Invoice Cost" from the shop and includes the mill base price of steel plus mill extras, transportation to the shop, shop drawings and detailing where warranted, shop fabrication and handling, sandblasting and a shop coat of primer paint, all necessary structural bolts, and delivery to the job site. The bare labor cost and bare equipment cost for these shop fabricated items are for field installation or erection.
- Line items in Subdivision 05 12 23.40 Lightweight Framing, and other items scattered in Division 5, are indicated as being field fabricated. The bare material cost for these field fabricated items is the "Invoice Cost" from the metals service center and includes the mill base price of steel plus mill extras, transportation to the metals service center, material handling, and delivery of long lengths of mill shapes to the job site. Material costs for structural bolts and welding rods should be added to the estimate. The bare labor cost and bare equipment cost for these items are for both field fabrication and field installation or erection, and include time for cutting, welding, and drilling in the fabricated metal items. Drilling into concrete and fasteners to fasten field fabricated items to other work is not included and should be added to the estimate.

05 20 00 Steel Joist Framing

- In any given project the total weight of open web steel joists is determined by the loads to be supported and the design. However, economies can be realized in minimizing the amount of labor used to place the joists. This is done by maximizing the joist spacing and therefore minimizing the number of joists required to be installed on the job. Certain spacings and locations may be required by the design, but in other cases maximizing the spacing and keeping it as uniform as possible will keep the costs down.

05 30 00 Steel Decking

- The takeoff and estimating of a metal deck involve more than the area of the floor or roof and the type of deck specified or shown on the drawings. Many different sizes and types of openings may exist. Small openings for individual pipes or conduits may be drilled after the floor/roof is installed, but larger openings may require special deck lengths as well as reinforcing or structural support. The estimator should determine who will be supplying this reinforcing. Additionally, some deck terminations are part of the deck package, such as screed angles and pour stops, and others will be part of the steel contract, such as angles attached to structural members and cast-in-place angles and plates. The estimator must ensure that all pieces are accounted for in the complete estimate.

05 50 00 Metal Fabrications

- The most economical steel stairs are those that use common materials, standard details, and most importantly, a uniform and relatively simple method of field assembly. Commonly available A36/A992 channels and plates are very good choices for the main stringers of the stairs, as are angles and tees for the carrier members. Risers and treads are usually made by specialty shops, and it is most economical to use a typical detail in as many places as possible. The stairs should be pre-assembled and shipped directly to the site. The field connections should be simple and straightforward enough to be accomplished efficiently, and with minimum equipment and labor.

Reference Numbers

Reference numbers are shown at the beginning of some major classifications. These numbers refer to related items in the Reference Section. The reference information may be an estimating procedure, an alternate pricing method, or technical information.

Note: Not all subdivisions listed here necessarily appear. ■

05 05 19 – Post-Installed Concrete Anchors

05 05 19.10 Chemical Anchors			Crew	Daily Output	Labor-Hours	Unit	Material	Labor	Equipment	Total	Total Incl O&P
							2023 Bare Costs				
0010	**CHEMICAL ANCHORS**										
0020	Includes layout & drilling										
1430	Chemical anchor, w/rod & epoxy cartridge, 3/4" diameter x 9-1/2" long		B-89A	27	.593	Ea.	9.55	32	4.37	45.92	63.50
1435	1" diameter x 11-3/4" long			24	.667		17.10	36	4.92	58.02	78
1440	1-1/4" diameter x 14" long			21	.762		33.50	41.50	5.60	80.60	105
1445	1-3/4" diameter x 15" long			20	.800		67.50	43.50	5.90	116.90	146
1450	18" long			17	.941		81	51	6.95	138.95	174
1455	2" diameter x 18" long			16	1		123	54.50	7.40	184.90	224
1460	24" long			15	1.067		160	58	7.85	225.85	271

05 05 19.20 Expansion Anchors			Crew	Daily Output	Labor-Hours	Unit	Material	Labor	Equipment	Total	Total Incl O&P
0010	**EXPANSION ANCHORS**										
0100	Anchors for concrete, brick or stone, no layout and drilling										
0200	Expansion shields, zinc, 1/4" diameter, 1-5/16" long, single	G	1 Carp	90	.089	Ea.	.57	5.20		5.77	8.40
0300	1-3/8" long, double	G		85	.094		.75	5.50		6.25	9.05
0400	3/8" diameter, 1-1/2" long, single	G		85	.094		.92	5.50		6.42	9.20
0500	2" long, double	G		80	.100		1.60	5.85		7.45	10.50
0600	1/2" diameter, 2-1/16" long, single	G		80	.100		1.60	5.85		7.45	10.50
0700	2-1/2" long, double	G		75	.107		1.98	6.25		8.23	11.50
0800	5/8" diameter, 2-5/8" long, single	G		75	.107		2.56	6.25		8.81	12.10
0900	2-3/4" long, double	G		70	.114		3.57	6.70		10.27	13.90
1000	3/4" diameter, 2-3/4" long, single	G		70	.114		4.07	6.70		10.77	14.45
1100	3-15/16" long, double	G		65	.123		6.20	7.20		13.40	17.60
2100	Hollow wall anchors for gypsum wall board, plaster or tile										
2300	1/8" diameter, short	G	1 Carp	160	.050	Ea.	.43	2.93		3.36	4.83
2400	Long	G		150	.053		.37	3.13		3.50	5.05
2500	3/16" diameter, short	G		150	.053		.85	3.13		3.98	5.60
2600	Long	G		140	.057		.97	3.35		4.32	6.05
2700	1/4" diameter, short	G		140	.057		1.18	3.35		4.53	6.30
2800	Long	G		130	.062		.97	3.61		4.58	6.40
3000	Toggle bolts, bright steel, 1/8" diameter, 2" long	G		85	.094		.30	5.50		5.80	8.55
3100	4" long	G		80	.100		.29	5.85		6.14	9.05
3400	1/4" diameter, 3" long	G		75	.107		.46	6.25		6.71	9.80
3500	6" long	G		70	.114		.69	6.70		7.39	10.70
3600	3/8" diameter, 3" long	G		70	.114		1.18	6.70		7.88	11.25
3700	6" long	G		60	.133		1.91	7.80		9.71	13.75
3800	1/2" diameter, 4" long	G		60	.133		2.70	7.80		10.50	14.60
3900	6" long	G		50	.160		3.29	9.40		12.69	17.55
4000	Nailing anchors										
4100	Nylon nailing anchor, 1/4" diameter, 1" long		1 Carp	3.20	2.500	C	16.65	147		163.65	236
4200	1-1/2" long			2.80	2.857		19.10	167		186.10	270
4300	2" long			2.40	3.333		23	195		218	315
4400	Metal nailing anchor, 1/4" diameter, 1" long	G		3.20	2.500		14.85	147		161.85	234
4500	1-1/2" long	G		2.80	2.857		19	167		186	270
4600	2" long	G		2.40	3.333		22.50	195		217.50	315
5000	Screw anchors for concrete, masonry,										
5100	stone & tile, no layout or drilling included										
5700	Lag screw shields, 1/4" diameter, short	G	1 Carp	90	.089	Ea.	.31	5.20		5.51	8.10
5900	3/8" diameter, short	G		85	.094		.68	5.50		6.18	8.95
6100	1/2" diameter, short	G		80	.100		.84	5.85		6.69	9.65
6300	5/8" diameter, short	G		70	.114		1.25	6.70		7.95	11.35
6600	Lead, #6 & #8, 3/4" long	G		260	.031		.32	1.80		2.12	3.03
6700	#10 - #14, 1-1/2" long	G		200	.040		.69	2.34		3.03	4.25

05 05 Common Work Results for Metals

05 05 19 – Post-Installed Concrete Anchors

05 05 19.20 Expansion Anchors			Crew	Daily Output	Labor-Hours	Unit	2023 Bare Costs Material	Labor	Equipment	Total	Total Incl O&P
6800	#16 & #18, 1-1/2" long	G	1 Carp	160	.050	Ea.	.99	2.93		3.92	5.45
6900	Plastic, #6 & #8, 3/4" long			260	.031		.03	1.80		1.83	2.71
7100	#10 & #12, 1" long			220	.036		.05	2.13		2.18	3.23
8000	Wedge anchors, not including layout or drilling										
8050	Carbon steel, 1/4" diameter, 1-3/4" long	G	1 Carp	150	.053	Ea.	.86	3.13		3.99	5.60
8100	3-1/4" long	G		140	.057		1.14	3.35		4.49	6.25
8150	3/8" diameter, 2-1/4" long	G		145	.055		.46	3.23		3.69	5.30
8200	5" long	G		140	.057		.81	3.35		4.16	5.90
8250	1/2" diameter, 2-3/4" long	G		140	.057		1	3.35		4.35	6.10
8300	7" long	G		125	.064		1.71	3.75		5.46	7.50
8350	5/8" diameter, 3-1/2" long	G		130	.062		2.45	3.61		6.06	8.05
8400	8-1/2" long	G		115	.070		5.20	4.08		9.28	11.80
8450	3/4" diameter, 4-1/4" long	G		115	.070		3.97	4.08		8.05	10.40
8500	10" long	G		95	.084		9	4.93		13.93	17.30
8550	1" diameter, 6" long	G		100	.080		9.05	4.69		13.74	16.95
8575	9" long	G		85	.094		11.75	5.50		17.25	21
8600	12" long	G		75	.107		12.70	6.25		18.95	23.50
8650	1-1/4" diameter, 9" long	G		70	.114		55	6.70		61.70	70.50
8700	12" long	G		60	.133		70.50	7.80		78.30	89
8750	For type 303 stainless steel, add						350%				
8800	For type 316 stainless steel, add						450%				
8950	Self-drilling concrete screw, hex washer head, 3/16" diam. x 1-3/4" long	G	1 Carp	300	.027	Ea.	.25	1.56		1.81	2.61
8960	2-1/4" long	G		250	.032		.26	1.88		2.14	3.08
8970	Phillips flat head, 3/16" diam. x 1-3/4" long	G		300	.027		.20	1.56		1.76	2.55
8980	2-1/4" long	G		250	.032		.21	1.88		2.09	3.02

05 05 21 – Fastening Methods for Metal

05 05 21.15 Drilling Steel		Crew	Daily Output	Labor-Hours	Unit	Material	Labor	Equipment	Total	Total Incl O&P
0010	**DRILLING STEEL**									
1910	Drilling & layout for steel, up to 1/4" deep, no anchor									
1920	Holes, 1/4" diameter	1 Sswk	112	.071	Ea.	.06	4.61		4.67	7.15
1925	For each additional 1/4" depth, add		336	.024		.06	1.54		1.60	2.43
1930	3/8" diameter		104	.077		.04	4.97		5.01	7.70
1935	For each additional 1/4" depth, add		312	.026		.04	1.66		1.70	2.60
1940	1/2" diameter		96	.083		.07	5.40		5.47	8.40
1945	For each additional 1/4" depth, add		288	.028		.07	1.79		1.86	2.84
1950	5/8" diameter		88	.091		.07	5.85		5.92	9.15
1955	For each additional 1/4" depth, add		264	.030		.07	1.96		2.03	3.09
1960	3/4" diameter		80	.100		.13	6.45		6.58	10.10
1965	For each additional 1/4" depth, add		240	.033		.13	2.15		2.28	3.45
1970	7/8" diameter		72	.111		.11	7.15		7.26	11.15
1975	For each additional 1/4" depth, add		216	.037		.11	2.39		2.50	3.80
1980	1" diameter		64	.125		.24	8.05		8.29	12.70
1985	For each additional 1/4" depth, add		192	.042		.24	2.69		2.93	4.40
1990	For drilling up, add						40%			

05 05 23 – Metal Fastenings

05 05 23.10 Bolts and Hex Nuts			Crew	Daily Output	Labor-Hours	Unit	Material	Labor	Equipment	Total	Total Incl O&P
0010	**BOLTS & HEX NUTS**, Steel, A307										
0100	1/4" diameter, 1/2" long	G	1 Sswk	140	.057	Ea.	.09	3.69		3.78	5.80
0200	1" long	G		140	.057		.11	3.69		3.80	5.80
0300	2" long	G		130	.062		.14	3.97		4.11	6.25
0400	3" long	G		130	.062		.21	3.97		4.18	6.35
0500	4" long	G		120	.067		.23	4.30		4.53	6.90

05 05 23 – Metal Fastenings

05 05 23.10 Bolts and Hex Nuts

Line	05 05 23.10 Bolts and Hex Nuts		Crew	Daily Output	Labor-Hours	Unit	2023 Bare Costs Material	Labor	Equipment	Total	Total Incl O&P
0600	3/8" diameter, 1" long	G	1 Sswk	130	.062	Ea.	.23	3.97		4.20	6.35
0700	2" long	G		130	.062		.29	3.97		4.26	6.40
0800	3" long	G		120	.067		.38	4.30		4.68	7.05
0900	4" long	G		120	.067		.48	4.30		4.78	7.20
1000	5" long	G		115	.070		.59	4.49		5.08	7.55
1100	1/2" diameter, 1-1/2" long	G		120	.067		.59	4.30		4.89	7.30
1200	2" long	G		120	.067		.67	4.30		4.97	7.40
1300	4" long	G		115	.070		1.03	4.49		5.52	8.05
1400	6" long	G		110	.073		1.41	4.69		6.10	8.80
1500	8" long	G		105	.076		1.84	4.92		6.76	9.55
1600	5/8" diameter, 1-1/2" long	G		120	.067		1.41	4.30		5.71	8.20
1700	2" long	G		120	.067		1.55	4.30		5.85	8.35
1800	4" long	G		115	.070		2.20	4.49		6.69	9.30
1900	6" long	G		110	.073		2.80	4.69		7.49	10.35
2000	8" long	G		105	.076		4.12	4.92		9.04	12.10
2100	10" long	G		100	.080		5.15	5.15		10.30	13.60
2200	3/4" diameter, 2" long	G		120	.067		1.90	4.30		6.20	8.75
2300	4" long	G		110	.073		2.69	4.69		7.38	10.20
2400	6" long	G		105	.076		3.44	4.92		8.36	11.35
2500	8" long	G		95	.084		5.15	5.45		10.60	14
2600	10" long	G		85	.094		6.75	6.10		12.85	16.75
2700	12" long	G		80	.100		7.85	6.45		14.30	18.60
2800	1" diameter, 3" long	G		105	.076		4.70	4.92		9.62	12.70
2900	6" long	G		90	.089		6.95	5.75		12.70	16.50
3000	12" long	G		75	.107		12.65	6.90		19.55	24.50
3100	For galvanized, add						75%				
3200	For stainless, add						350%				

05 05 23.30 Lag Screws

Line	Description		Crew	Daily Output	Labor-Hours	Unit	Material	Labor	Equipment	Total	Total Incl O&P
0010	**LAG SCREWS**										
0020	Steel, 1/4" diameter, 2" long	G	1 Carp	200	.040	Ea.	.15	2.34		2.49	3.66
0100	3/8" diameter, 3" long	G		150	.053		.51	3.13		3.64	5.20
0200	1/2" diameter, 3" long	G		130	.062		1.15	3.61		4.76	6.60
0300	5/8" diameter, 3" long	G		120	.067		1.83	3.91		5.74	7.80

05 05 23.35 Machine Screws

Line	Description		Crew	Daily Output	Labor-Hours	Unit	Material	Labor	Equipment	Total	Total Incl O&P
0010	**MACHINE SCREWS**										
0020	Steel, round head, #8 x 1" long	G	1 Carp	4.80	1.667	C	5.05	97.50		102.55	151
0110	#8 x 2" long	G		2.40	3.333		8.40	195		203.40	300
0200	#10 x 1" long	G		4	2		7.10	117		124.10	183
0300	#10 x 2" long	G		2	4		12	234		246	365

05 05 23.50 Powder Actuated Tools and Fasteners

Line	Description		Crew	Daily Output	Labor-Hours	Unit	Material	Labor	Equipment	Total	Total Incl O&P
0010	**POWDER ACTUATED TOOLS & FASTENERS**										
0020	Stud driver, .22 caliber, single shot					Ea.	95.50			95.50	105
0100	.27 caliber, semi automatic, strip					"	575			575	635
0300	Powder load, single shot, .22 cal, power level 2, brown					C	7.25			7.25	8
0400	Strip, .27 cal, power level 4, red						15.05			15.05	16.60
0600	Drive pin, .300 x 3/4" long	G	1 Carp	4.80	1.667		5.40	97.50		102.90	151
0700	.300 x 3" long with washer	G	"	4	2		13.85	117		130.85	190

05 05 23.70 Structural Blind Bolts

Line	Description		Crew	Daily Output	Labor-Hours	Unit	Material	Labor	Equipment	Total	Total Incl O&P
0010	**STRUCTURAL BLIND BOLTS**										
0100	1/4" diameter x 1/4" grip	G	1 Sswk	240	.033	Ea.	.98	2.15		3.13	4.39
0150	1/2" grip	G		216	.037		.93	2.39		3.32	4.70
0200	3/8" diameter x 1/2" grip	G		232	.034		1.91	2.23		4.14	5.55

05 05 Common Work Results for Metals

05 05 23 – Metal Fastenings

05 05 23.70 Structural Blind Bolts			Crew	Daily Output	Labor-Hours	Unit	Material	Labor (2023 Bare Costs)	Equipment	Total	Total Incl O&P
0250	3/4" grip	G	1 Sswk	208	.038	Ea.	2	2.48		4.48	6
0300	1/2" diameter x 1/2" grip	G		224	.036		4.14	2.31		6.45	8.10
0350	3/4" grip	G		200	.040		4.14	2.58		6.72	8.55
0400	5/8" diameter x 3/4" grip	G		216	.037		6.50	2.39		8.89	10.85
0450	1" grip	G	↓	192	.042	↓	6.50	2.69		9.19	11.30

05 12 Structural Steel Framing

05 12 23 – Structural Steel for Buildings

05 12 23.60 Pipe Support Framing			Crew	Daily Output	Labor-Hours	Unit	Material	Labor	Equipment	Total	Total Incl O&P
0010	**PIPE SUPPORT FRAMING**										
0020	Under 10#/L.F., shop fabricated	G	E-4	3900	.008	Lb.	2.21	.53	.04	2.78	3.29
0200	10.1 to 15#/L.F.	G		4300	.007		2.17	.48	.03	2.68	3.18
0400	15.1 to 20#/L.F.	G		4800	.007		2.14	.43	.03	2.60	3.05
0600	Over 20#/L.F.	G	↓	5400	.006	↓	2.11	.39	.03	2.53	2.94

05 35 Raceway Decking Assemblies

05 35 13 – Steel Cellular Decking

05 35 13.50 Cellular Decking			Crew	Daily Output	Labor-Hours	Unit	Material	Labor	Equipment	Total	Total Incl O&P
0010	**CELLULAR DECKING**										
0015	Made from recycled materials										
0200	Cellular units, galv, 1-1/2" deep, Type BC, 20-20 ga., over 15 squares	G	E-4	1460	.022	S.F.	13.15	1.43	.10	14.68	16.75
0250	18-20 ga.	G		1420	.023		10.30	1.47	.10	11.87	13.65
0300	18-18 ga.	G		1390	.023		10.55	1.50	.11	12.16	14.10
0320	16-18 ga.	G		1360	.024		18.25	1.53	.11	19.89	22.50
0340	16-16 ga.	G		1330	.024		20.50	1.57	.11	22.18	25
0400	3" deep, Type NC, galvanized, 20-20 ga.	G		1375	.023		14.45	1.51	.11	16.07	18.35
0500	18-20 ga.	G		1350	.024		12.05	1.54	.11	13.70	15.75
0600	18-18 ga.	G		1290	.025		12	1.61	.11	13.72	15.80
0700	16-18 ga.	G		1230	.026		19.60	1.69	.12	21.41	24
0800	16-16 ga.	G		1150	.028		21.50	1.81	.13	23.44	26.50
1000	4-1/2" deep, Type JC, galvanized, 18-20 ga.	G		1100	.029		13.90	1.89	.13	15.92	18.35
1100	18-18 ga.	G		1040	.031		13.80	2	.14	15.94	18.45
1200	16-18 ga.	G		980	.033		22.50	2.12	.15	24.77	28.50
1300	16-16 ga.	G	↓	935	.034	↓	24.50	2.23	.16	26.89	30.50
1900	For multi-story or congested site, add							50%			

Division Notes

		CREW	DAILY OUTPUT	LABOR-HOURS	UNIT	BARE COSTS MAT.	LABOR	EQUIP.	TOTAL	TOTAL INCL O&P

Estimating Tips

06 05 00 Common Work Results for Wood, Plastics, and Composites

- Common to any wood-framed structure are the accessory connector items such as screws, nails, adhesives, hangers, connector plates, straps, angles, and hold-downs. For typical wood-framed buildings, such as residential projects, the aggregate total for these items can be significant, especially in areas where seismic loading is a concern. For floor and wall framing, the material cost is based on 10 to 25 lbs. of accessory connectors per MBF. Hold-downs, hangers, and other connectors should be taken off by the piece.

  Included with material costs are fasteners for a normal installation. Gordian's RSMeans engineers use manufacturers' recommendations, written specifications, and/or standard construction practice for the sizing and spacing of fasteners. Prices for various fasteners are shown for informational purposes only. Adjustments should be made if unusual fastening conditions exist.

06 10 00 Carpentry

- Lumber is a traded commodity and therefore sensitive to supply and demand in the marketplace. Even with "budgetary" estimating of wood-framed projects, it is advisable to call local suppliers for the latest market pricing.
- The common quantity unit for wood-framed projects is "thousand board feet" (MBF). A board foot is a volume of wood—1" x 1' x 1' or 144 cubic inches. Board-foot quantities are generally calculated using nominal material dimensions—dressed sizes are ignored. Board foot per lineal foot of any stick of lumber can be calculated by dividing the nominal cross-sectional area by 12. As an example, 2,000 lineal feet of 2 x 12 equates to 4 MBF by dividing the nominal area, 2 x 12, by 12, which equals 2, and multiplying that by 2,000 to give 4,000 board feet. This simple rule applies to all nominal dimensioned lumber.
- Waste is an issue of concern at the quantity takeoff for any area of construction. Framing lumber is sold in even foot lengths, i.e., 8', 10', 12', 14', 16', and depending on spans, wall heights, and the grade of lumber, waste is inevitable. A rule of thumb for lumber waste is 5–10% depending on material quality and the complexity of the framing.
- Wood in various forms and shapes is used in many projects, even where the main structural framing is steel, concrete, or masonry. Plywood as a back-up partition material and 2x boards used as blocking and cant strips around roof edges are two common examples. The estimator should ensure that the costs of all wood materials are included in the final estimate.

06 20 00 Finish Carpentry

- It is necessary to consider the grade of workmanship when estimating labor costs for erecting millwork and an interior finish. In practice, there are three grades: premium, custom, and economy. The RSMeans daily output for base and case moldings is in the range of 200 to 250 L.F. per carpenter per day. This is appropriate for most average custom-grade projects. For premium projects, an adjustment to productivity of 25–50% should be made, depending on the complexity of the job.

Reference Numbers

Reference numbers are shown at the beginning of some major classifications. These numbers refer to related items in the Reference Section. The reference information may be an estimating procedure, an alternate pricing method, or technical information.

Note: Not all subdivisions listed here necessarily appear. ■

06 16 Sheathing

06 16 36 – Wood Panel Product Sheathing

06 16 36.10 Sheathing		Crew	Daily Output	Labor-Hours	Unit	2023 Bare Costs Material	Labor	Equipment	Total	Total Incl O&P
0010	**SHEATHING**									
0012	Plywood on roofs, CDX									
0030	5/16" thick	2 Carp	1600	.010	S.F.	.99	.59		1.58	1.96
0035	Pneumatic nailed		1952	.008		.99	.48		1.47	1.81
0050	3/8" thick		1525	.010		1.08	.61		1.69	2.11
0055	Pneumatic nailed		1860	.009		1.08	.50		1.58	1.94
0100	1/2" thick		1400	.011		1.16	.67		1.83	2.27
0105	Pneumatic nailed		1708	.009		1.16	.55		1.71	2.09
0200	5/8" thick		1300	.012		1.37	.72		2.09	2.58
0205	Pneumatic nailed		1586	.010		1.37	.59		1.96	2.39
0300	3/4" thick		1200	.013		1.71	.78		2.49	3.04
0305	Pneumatic nailed		1464	.011		1.71	.64		2.35	2.83
0500	Plywood on walls, with exterior CDX, 3/8" thick		1200	.013		1.08	.78		1.86	2.35
0505	Pneumatic nailed		1488	.011		1.08	.63		1.71	2.13
0600	1/2" thick		1125	.014		1.16	.83		1.99	2.51
0605	Pneumatic nailed		1395	.011		1.16	.67		1.83	2.27
0700	5/8" thick		1050	.015		1.37	.89		2.26	2.84
0705	Pneumatic nailed		1302	.012		1.37	.72		2.09	2.58
0800	3/4" thick		975	.016		1.71	.96		2.67	3.31
0805	Pneumatic nailed	▼	1209	.013	▼	1.71	.78		2.49	3.03

Estimating Tips

07 10 00 Dampproofing and Waterproofing

- Be sure of the job specifications before pricing this subdivision. The difference in cost between waterproofing and dampproofing can be great. Waterproofing will hold back standing water. Dampproofing prevents the transmission of water vapor. Also included in this section are vapor retarding membranes.

07 20 00 Thermal Protection

- Insulation and fireproofing products are measured by area, thickness, volume, or R-value. Specifications may give only what the specific R-value should be in a certain situation. The estimator may need to choose the type of insulation to meet that R-value.

07 30 00 Steep Slope Roofing 07 40 00 Roofing and Siding Panels

- Many roofing and siding products are bought and sold by the square. One square is equal to an area that measures 100 square feet.

  This simple change in unit of measure could create a large error if the estimator is not observant. Accessories necessary for a complete installation must be figured into any calculations for both material and labor.

07 50 00 Membrane Roofing 07 60 00 Flashing and Sheet Metal 07 70 00 Roofing and Wall Specialties and Accessories

- The items in these subdivisions compose a roofing system. No one component completes the installation, and all must be estimated. Built-up or single-ply membrane roofing systems are made up of many products and installation trades. Wood blocking at roof perimeters or penetrations, parapet coverings, reglets, roof drains, gutters, downspouts, sheet metal flashing, skylights, smoke vents, and roof hatches all need to be considered along with the roofing material. Several different installation trades will need to work together on the roofing system. Inherent difficulties in the scheduling and coordination of various trades must be accounted for when estimating labor costs.

07 90 00 Joint Protection

- To complete the weather-tight shell, the sealants and caulkings must be estimated. Where different materials meet—at expansion joints, at flashing penetrations, and at hundreds of other locations throughout a construction project—caulking and sealants provide another line of defense against water penetration. Often, an entire system is based on the proper location and placement of caulking or sealants. The detailed drawings that are included as part of a set of architectural plans show typical locations for these materials. When caulking or sealants are shown at typical locations, this means the estimator must include them for all the locations where this detail is applicable. Be careful to keep different types of sealants separate, and remember to consider backer rods and primers if necessary.

Reference Numbers

Reference numbers are shown at the beginning of some major classifications. These numbers refer to related items in the Reference Section. The reference information may be an estimating procedure, an alternate pricing method, or technical information.

Note: Not all subdivisions listed here necessarily appear. ■

07 84 13.10 Firestopping		Crew	Daily Output	Labor-Hours	Unit	2023 Bare Costs Material	Labor	Equipment	Total	Total Incl O&P
0010	**FIRESTOPPING** R078413-30									
0100	Metallic piping, non insulated									
0110	Through walls, 2″ diameter	1 Carp	16	.500	Ea.	11.75	29.50		41.25	56.50
0120	4″ diameter		14	.571		20.50	33.50		54	72.50
0130	6″ diameter		12	.667		30	39		69	91
0140	12″ diameter		10	.800		25.50	47		72.50	98.50
0150	Through floors, 2″ diameter		32	.250		5.90	14.65		20.55	28.50
0160	4″ diameter		28	.286		10.30	16.75		27.05	36.50
0170	6″ diameter		24	.333		15.05	19.55		34.60	45.50
0180	12″ diameter		20	.400		13.25	23.50		36.75	49.50
0190	Metallic piping, insulated									
0200	Through walls, 2″ diameter	1 Carp	16	.500	Ea.	20.50	29.50		50	66
0210	4″ diameter		14	.571		30	33.50		63.50	83
0220	6″ diameter		12	.667		40.50	39		79.50	103
0230	12″ diameter		10	.800		69	47		116	146
0240	Through floors, 2″ diameter		32	.250		10.30	14.65		24.95	33.50
0250	4″ diameter		28	.286		15.05	16.75		31.80	41.50
0260	6″ diameter		24	.333		20	19.55		39.55	51
0270	12″ diameter		20	.400		34.50	23.50		58	73
0280	Non metallic piping, non insulated									
0290	Through walls, 2″ diameter	1 Carp	12	.667	Ea.	71.50	39		110.50	137
0300	4″ diameter		10	.800		132	47		179	215
0310	6″ diameter		8	1		252	58.50		310.50	365
0330	Through floors, 2″ diameter		16	.500		45	29.50		74.50	93
0340	4″ diameter		6	1.333		82.50	78		160.50	207
0350	6″ diameter		6	1.333		150	78		228	280
0370	Ductwork, insulated & non insulated, round									
0380	Through walls, 6″ diameter	1 Carp	12	.667	Ea.	40.50	39		79.50	103
0390	12″ diameter		10	.800		69	47		116	146
0400	18″ diameter		8	1		84	58.50		142.50	180
0410	Through floors, 6″ diameter		16	.500		20	29.50		49.50	65.50
0420	12″ diameter		14	.571		15.05	33.50		48.55	66.50
0430	18″ diameter		12	.667		18.20	39		57.20	78
0440	Ductwork, insulated & non insulated, rectangular									
0450	With stiffener/closure angle, through walls, 6″ x 12″	1 Carp	8	1	Ea.	53	58.50		111.50	146
0460	12″ x 24″		6	1.333		106	78		184	232
0470	24″ x 48″		4	2		212	117		329	410
0480	With stiffener/closure angle, through floors, 6″ x 12″		10	.800		10.75	47		57.75	82
0490	12″ x 24″		8	1		53	58.50		111.50	146
0500	24″ x 48″		6	1.333		106	78		184	232
0510	Multi trade openings									
0520	Through walls, 6″ x 12″	1 Carp	2	4	Ea.	80.50	234		314.50	440
0530	12″ x 24″	″	1	8		217	470		687	940
0540	24″ x 48″	2 Carp	1	16		655	940		1,595	2,125
0550	48″ x 96″	″	.75	21.333		2,625	1,250		3,875	4,725
0560	Through floors, 6″ x 12″	1 Carp	2	4		49.50	234		283.50	405
0570	12″ x 24″	″	1	8		65.50	470		535.50	770
0580	24″ x 48″	2 Carp	.75	21.333		142	1,250		1,392	2,000
0590	48″ x 96″	″	.50	32		335	1,875		2,210	3,175
0600	Structural penetrations, through walls									
0610	Steel beams, W8 x 10	1 Carp	8	1	Ea.	76	58.50		134.50	171
0620	W12 x 14		6	1.333		110	78		188	237
0630	W21 x 44		5	1.600		169	94		263	325

07 84 Firestopping

07 84 13 – Penetration Firestopping

07 84 13.10 Firestopping		Crew	Daily Output	Labor-Hours	Unit	Material	2023 Bare Costs Labor	Equipment	Total	Total Incl O&P
0640	W36 x 135	1 Carp	3	2.667	Ea.	240	156		396	495
0650	Bar joists, 18" deep		6	1.333		44	78		122	165
0660	24" deep		6	1.333		62.50	78		140.50	185
0670	36" deep		5	1.600		93.50	94		187.50	243
0680	48" deep	↓	4	2	↓	135	117		252	325
0690	Construction joints, floor slab at exterior wall									
0700	Precast, brick, block or drywall exterior									
0710	2" wide joint	1 Carp	125	.064	L.F.	11.30	3.75		15.05	18.05
0720	4" wide joint	"	75	.107	"	17.45	6.25		23.70	28.50
0730	Metal panel, glass or curtain wall exterior									
0740	2" wide joint	1 Carp	40	.200	L.F.	12.85	11.70		24.55	31.50
0750	4" wide joint	"	25	.320	"	14.60	18.75		33.35	44
0760	Floor slab to drywall partition									
0770	Flat joint	1 Carp	100	.080	L.F.	14.80	4.69		19.49	23.50
0780	Fluted joint		50	.160		17.20	9.40		26.60	33
0790	Etched fluted joint	↓	75	.107	↓	20.50	6.25		26.75	32
0800	Floor slab to concrete/masonry partition									
0810	Flat joint	1 Carp	75	.107	L.F.	17.25	6.25		23.50	28.50
0820	Fluted joint	"	50	.160	"	18.80	9.40		28.20	34.50
0830	Concrete/CMU wall joints									
0840	1" wide	1 Carp	100	.080	L.F.	21	4.69		25.69	30
0850	2" wide		75	.107		32.50	6.25		38.75	45.50
0860	4" wide	↓	50	.160	↓	37	9.40		46.40	54.50
0870	Concrete/CMU floor joints									
0880	1" wide	1 Carp	200	.040	L.F.	22	2.34		24.34	27.50
0890	2" wide		150	.053		25.50	3.13		28.63	32.50
0900	4" wide	↓	100	.080	↓	37	4.69		41.69	47.50

07 91 Preformed Joint Seals

07 91 13 – Compression Seals

07 91 13.10 Compression Seals		Crew	Daily Output	Labor-Hours	Unit	Material	Labor	Equipment	Total	Total Incl O&P
0010	**COMPRESSION SEALS**									
4900	O-ring type cord, 1/4"	1 Bric	472	.017	L.F.	.54	.97		1.51	2.05
4910	1/2"		440	.018		1.44	1.05		2.49	3.15
4920	3/4"		424	.019		2.88	1.08		3.96	4.80
4930	1"		408	.020		5.80	1.13		6.93	8.05
4940	1-1/4"		384	.021		13.90	1.20		15.10	17.10
4950	1-1/2"		368	.022		17.10	1.25		18.35	20.50
4960	1-3/4"		352	.023		19.95	1.31		21.26	24
4970	2"	↓	344	.023	↓	35	1.34		36.34	40

07 91 23 – Backer Rods

07 91 23.10 Backer Rods		Crew	Daily Output	Labor-Hours	Unit	Material	Labor	Equipment	Total	Total Incl O&P
0010	**BACKER RODS**									
0030	Backer rod, polyethylene, 1/4" diameter	1 Bric	4.60	1.739	C.L.F.	7	100		107	158
0050	1/2" diameter		4.60	1.739		16	100		116	168
0070	3/4" diameter		4.60	1.739		17	100		117	169
0090	1" diameter	↓	4.60	1.739	↓	30	100		130	183

07 91 Preformed Joint Seals

07 91 26 – Joint Fillers

07 91 26.10 Joint Fillers		Crew	Daily Output	Labor-Hours	Unit	2023 Bare Costs Material	Labor	Equipment	Total	Total Incl O&P
0010	**JOINT FILLERS**									
4360	Butyl rubber filler, 1/4" x 1/4"	1 Bric	290	.028	L.F.	.36	1.59		1.95	2.78
4365	1/2" x 1/2"		250	.032		1.44	1.84		3.28	4.34
4370	1/2" x 3/4"		210	.038		2.16	2.19		4.35	5.65
4375	3/4" x 3/4"		230	.035		3.24	2		5.24	6.55
4380	1" x 1"		180	.044		4.31	2.56		6.87	8.60
4390	For coloring, add					12%				
4980	Polyethylene joint backing, 1/4" x 2"	1 Bric	2.08	3.846	C.L.F.	14	221		235	345
4990	1/4" x 6"		1.28	6.250	"	150	360		510	705
5600	Silicone, room temp vulcanizing foam seal, 1/4" x 1/2"		1312	.006	L.F.	.37	.35		.72	.94
5610	1/2" x 1/2"		656	.012		.74	.70		1.44	1.86
5620	1/2" x 3/4"		442	.018		1.11	1.04		2.15	2.78
5630	3/4" x 3/4"		328	.024		1.67	1.40		3.07	3.94
5640	1/8" x 1"		1312	.006		.37	.35		.72	.94
5650	1/8" x 3"		442	.018		1.11	1.04		2.15	2.78
5670	1/4" x 3"		295	.027		2.22	1.56		3.78	4.78
5680	1/4" x 6"		148	.054		4.44	3.11		7.55	9.55
5690	1/2" x 6"		82	.098		8.90	5.60		14.50	18.15
5700	1/2" x 9"		52.50	.152		13.30	8.75		22.05	28
5710	1/2" x 12"		33	.242		17.75	13.95		31.70	40.50

07 92 Joint Sealants

07 92 13 – Elastomeric Joint Sealants

07 92 13.20 Caulking and Sealant Options

07 92 13.20 Caulking and Sealant Options		Crew	Daily Output	Labor-Hours	Unit	Material	Labor	Equipment	Total	Total Incl O&P
0010	**CAULKING AND SEALANT OPTIONS**									
0050	Latex acrylic based, bulk				Gal.	39			39	43
0055	Bulk in place 1/4" x 1/4" bead	1 Bric	300	.027	L.F.	.12	1.53		1.65	2.44
0060	1/4" x 3/8"		294	.027		.21	1.56		1.77	2.58
0065	1/4" x 1/2"		288	.028		.27	1.60		1.87	2.70
0075	3/8" x 3/8"		284	.028		.31	1.62		1.93	2.77
0080	3/8" x 1/2"		280	.029		.41	1.64		2.05	2.92
0085	3/8" x 5/8"		276	.029		.51	1.67		2.18	3.07
0095	3/8" x 3/4"		272	.029		.61	1.69		2.30	3.22
0100	1/2" x 1/2"		275	.029		.55	1.67		2.22	3.11
0105	1/2" x 5/8"		269	.030		.69	1.71		2.40	3.32
0110	1/2" x 3/4"		263	.030		.82	1.75		2.57	3.54
0115	1/2" x 7/8"		256	.031		.96	1.80		2.76	3.76
0120	1/2" x 1"		250	.032		1.10	1.84		2.94	3.97
0125	3/4" x 3/4"		244	.033		1.24	1.89		3.13	4.19
0130	3/4" x 1"		225	.036		1.65	2.04		3.69	4.88
0135	1" x 1"		200	.040		2.19	2.30		4.49	5.85
0190	Cartridges				Gal.	47			47	52
0200	11 fl. oz. cartridge				Ea.	4.06			4.06	4.47
0600	1/2" x 1/2"	1 Bric	275	.029	L.F.	.66	1.67		2.33	3.24
3200	Polyurethane, 1 or 2 component				Gal.	70.50			70.50	77.50
3300	Cartridges				"	84			84	92.50
3500	Bulk, in place, 1/4" x 1/4"	1 Bric	300	.027	L.F.	.23	1.53		1.76	2.55
3655	1/2" x 1/4"		288	.028		.46	1.60		2.06	2.90
3800	3/4" x 3/8"		272	.029		1.04	1.69		2.73	3.68
3900	1" x 1/2"		250	.032		1.83	1.84		3.67	4.77

07 92 19 – Acoustical Joint Sealants

07 92 19.10 Acoustical Sealant		Crew	Daily Output	Labor-Hours	Unit	2023 Bare Costs Material	Labor	Equipment	Total	Total Incl O&P
0010	**ACOUSTICAL SEALANT**									
0020	Acoustical sealant, elastomeric, cartridges				Ea.	5.45			5.45	5.95
0025	In place, 1/4" x 1/4"	1 Bric	300	.027	L.F.	.22	1.53		1.75	2.54
0030	1/4" x 1/2"		288	.028		.44	1.60		2.04	2.89
0035	1/2" x 1/2"		275	.029		.89	1.67		2.56	3.49
0040	1/2" x 3/4"		263	.030		1.33	1.75		3.08	4.09
0045	3/4" x 3/4"		244	.033		2	1.89		3.89	5.05
0050	1" x 1"	↓	200	.040	↓	3.55	2.30		5.85	7.35

Division Notes

I		CREW	DAILY OUTPUT	LABOR-HOURS	UNIT	BARE COSTS MAT.	LABOR	EQUIP.	TOTAL	TOTAL INCL O&P

Estimating Tips

08 10 00 Doors and Frames

All exterior doors should be addressed for their energy conservation (insulation and seals).

- Most metal doors and frames look alike, but there may be significant differences among them. When estimating these items, be sure to choose the line item that most closely compares to the specification or door schedule requirements regarding:
  - ☐ type of metal
  - ☐ metal gauge
  - ☐ door core material
  - ☐ fire rating
  - ☐ finish
- Wood and plastic doors vary considerably in price. The primary determinant is the veneer material. Lauan, birch, and oak are the most common veneers. Other variables include the following:
  - ☐ hollow or solid core
  - ☐ fire rating
  - ☐ flush or raised panel
  - ☐ finish
- Door pricing includes bore for cylindrical locksets and mortise for hinges.

08 30 00 Specialty Doors and Frames

- There are many varieties of special doors, and they are usually priced per each. Add frames, hardware, or operators required for a complete installation.

08 40 00 Entrances, Storefronts, and Curtain Walls

- Glazed curtain walls consist of the metal tube framing and the glazing material. The cost data in this subdivision is presented for the metal tube framing alone or the composite wall. If your estimate requires a detailed takeoff of the framing, be sure to add the glazing cost and any tints.

08 50 00 Windows

- Steel windows are unglazed and aluminum can be glazed or unglazed. Some metal windows are priced without glass. Refer to 08 80 00 Glazing for glass pricing. The grade C indicates commercial grade windows, usually ASTM C-35.
- All wood windows and vinyl are priced preglazed. The glazing is insulating glass. Add the cost of screens and grills if required and not already included.

08 70 00 Hardware

- Hardware costs add considerably to the cost of a door. The most efficient method to determine the hardware requirements for a project is to review the door and hardware schedule together. One type of door may have different hardware, depending on the door usage.
- Door hinges are priced by the pair, with most doors requiring 1-1/2 pairs per door. The hinge prices do not include installation labor because it is included in door installation. Hinges are classified according to the frequency of use, base material, and finish.

08 80 00 Glazing

- Different openings require different types of glass. The most common types are:
  - ☐ float
  - ☐ tempered
  - ☐ insulating
  - ☐ impact-resistant
  - ☐ ballistic-resistant
- Most exterior windows are glazed with insulating glass. Entrance doors and window walls, where the glass is less than 18" from the floor, are generally glazed with tempered glass. Interior windows and some residential windows are glazed with float glass.
- Coastal communities require the use of impact-resistant glass, dependent on wind speed.
- The insulation or 'u' value is a strong consideration, along with solar heat gain, to determine total energy efficiency.

Reference Numbers

Reference numbers are shown at the beginning of some major classifications. These numbers refer to related items in the Reference Section. The reference information may be an estimating procedure, an alternate pricing method, or technical information.

Note: Not all subdivisions listed here necessarily appear. ■

08 31 13 – Access Doors and Frames

08 31 13.10 Types of Framed Access Doors		Crew	Daily Output	Labor-Hours	Unit	2023 Bare Costs Material	Labor	Equipment	Total	Total Incl O&P
0010	**TYPES OF FRAMED ACCESS DOORS**									
4000	Recessed door for drywall									
4100	Metal 12" x 12"	1 Carp	6	1.333	Ea.	45.50	78		123.50	166
4150	12" x 24"		5.50	1.455		68.50	85		153.50	202
4200	24" x 36"	↓	5	1.600	↓	130	94		224	283

Estimating Tips

General

- Room Finish Schedule: A complete set of plans should contain a room finish schedule. If one is not available, it would be well worth the time and effort to obtain one.

09 20 00 Plaster and Gypsum Board

- Lath is estimated by the square yard plus a 5% allowance for waste. Furring, channels, and accessories are measured by the linear foot. An extra foot should be allowed for each accessory miter or stop.
- Plaster is also estimated by the square yard. Deductions for openings vary by preference, from zero deduction to 50% of all openings over 2 feet in width. The estimator should allow one extra square foot for each linear foot of horizontal interior or exterior angle located below the ceiling level. Also, double the areas of small radius work.
- Drywall accessories, studs, track, and acoustical caulking are all measured by the linear foot. Drywall taping is figured by the square foot. Gypsum wallboard is estimated by the square foot. No material deductions should be made for door or window openings under 32 S.F.

09 60 00 Flooring

- Tile and terrazzo areas are taken off on a square foot basis. Trim and base materials are measured by the linear foot. Accent tiles are listed per each. Two basic methods of installation are used. Mud set is approximately 30% more expensive than thin set. The cost of grout is included with tile unit price lines unless otherwise noted. In terrazzo work, be sure to include the linear footage of embedded decorative strips, grounds, machine rubbing, and power cleanup.
- Wood flooring is available in strip, parquet, or block configuration. The latter two types are set in adhesives with quantities estimated by the square foot. The laying pattern will influence labor costs and material waste. In addition to the material and labor for laying wood floors, the estimator must make allowances for sanding and finishing these areas, unless the flooring is prefinished.
- Sheet flooring is measured by the square yard. Roll widths vary, so consideration should be given to use the most economical width, as waste must be figured into the total quantity. Consider also the installation methods available—direct glue down or stretched. Direct glue-down installation is assumed with sheet carpet unit price lines unless otherwise noted.

09 70 00 Wall Finishes

- Wall coverings are estimated by the square foot. The area to be covered is measured—length by height of the wall above the baseboards—to calculate the square footage of each wall. This figure is divided by the number of square feet in the single roll which is being used. Deduct, in full, the areas of openings such as doors and windows. Where a pattern match is required allow 25–30% waste.

09 80 00 Acoustic Treatment

- Acoustical systems fall into several categories. The takeoff of these materials should be by the square foot of area with a 5% allowance for waste. Do not forget about scaffolding, if applicable, when estimating these systems.

09 90 00 Painting and Coating

- New line items created for cut-ins with reference diagram.
- A major portion of the work in painting involves surface preparation. Be sure to include cleaning, sanding, filling, and masking costs in the estimate.
- Protection of adjacent surfaces is not included in painting costs. When considering the method of paint application, an important factor is the amount of protection and masking required. These must be estimated separately and may be the determining factor in choosing the method of application.

Reference Numbers

Reference numbers are shown at the beginning of some major classifications. These numbers refer to related items in the Reference Section. The reference information may be an estimating procedure, an alternate pricing method, or technical information.

Note: Not all subdivisions listed here necessarily appear. ■

09 22 Supports for Plaster and Gypsum Board

09 22 03 – Fastening Methods for Finishes

09 22 03.20 Drilling Plaster/Drywall		Crew	Daily Output	Labor-Hours	Unit	Material	Labor	Equipment	Total	Total Incl O&P
						2023 Bare Costs				
0010	DRILLING PLASTER/DRYWALL									
1100	Drilling & layout for drywall/plaster walls, up to 1" deep, no anchor									
1200	Holes, 1/4" diameter	1 Carp	150	.053	Ea.	.01	3.13		3.14	4.66
1300	3/8" diameter		140	.057			3.35		3.35	4.99
1400	1/2" diameter		130	.062			3.61		3.61	5.35
1500	3/4" diameter		120	.067		.01	3.91		3.92	5.80
1600	1" diameter		110	.073		.02	4.26		4.28	6.35
1700	1-1/4" diameter		100	.080		.03	4.69		4.72	7.05
1800	1-1/2" diameter		90	.089		.04	5.20		5.24	7.80
1900	For ceiling installations, add						40%			

09 57 Special Function Ceilings

09 57 53 – Security Ceiling Assemblies

09 57 53.10 Ceiling Assem., Security, Radio Freq. Shielding

		Crew	Daily Output	Labor-Hours	Unit	Material	Labor	Equipment	Total	Total Incl O&P
0010	CEILING ASSEMBLY, SECURITY, RADIO FREQUENCY SHIELDING									
0020	Prefabricated, galvanized steel	2 Carp	375	.043	SF Surf	7.50	2.50		10	11.95
0050	5 oz., copper ceiling panel		155	.103		6.10	6.05		12.15	15.70
0110	12 oz., copper ceiling panel		140	.114		12.70	6.70		19.40	24
0250	Ceiling hangers	E-1	45	.533	Ea.	49.50	34	3.27	86.77	110
0300	Shielding transition, 11 ga. preformed angles	"	1365	.018	L.F.	49.50	1.12	.11	50.73	56.50

09 69 Access Flooring

09 69 13 – Rigid-Grid Access Flooring

09 69 13.10 Access Floors

		Crew	Daily Output	Labor-Hours	Unit	Material	Labor	Equipment	Total	Total Incl O&P
0010	ACCESS FLOORS									
0015	Access floor pkg. including panel, pedestal, & stringers 1500 lbs. load									
0100	Package pricing, conc. fill panels, no fin., 6" ht.	4 Carp	750	.043	S.F.	4.48	2.50		6.98	8.65
0105	12" ht.		750	.043		4.56	2.50		7.06	8.70
0110	18" ht.		750	.043		4.63	2.50		7.13	8.80
0115	24" ht.		750	.043		4.71	2.50		7.21	8.90
0120	Package pricing, steel panels, no fin., 6" ht.		750	.043		7.50	2.50		10	11.95
0125	12" ht.		750	.043		7.50	2.50		10	11.95
0130	18" ht.		750	.043		7.50	2.50		10	11.95
0135	24" ht.		750	.043		7.55	2.50		10.05	12
0140	Package pricing, wood core panels, no fin., 6" ht.		750	.043		5.45	2.50		7.95	9.70
0145	12" ht.		750	.043		5.50	2.50		8	9.75
0150	18" ht.		750	.043		5.50	2.50		8	9.75
0155	24" ht.		750	.043		5.55	2.50		8.05	9.80
0160	Pkg. pricing, conc. fill pnls, no stringers, no fin., 6" ht, 1250 lbs. load		700	.046		17.35	2.68		20.03	23
0165	12" ht.		700	.046		17.60	2.68		20.28	23.50
0170	18" ht.		700	.046		17.75	2.68		20.43	23.50
0175	24" ht.		700	.046		18	2.68		20.68	24
0250	Panels, 2' x 2' conc. fill, no fin.	2 Carp	500	.032		22	1.88		23.88	27.50
0255	With 1/8" high pressure laminate		500	.032		54.50	1.88		56.38	63
0260	Metal panels with 1/8" high pressure laminate		500	.032		65	1.88		66.88	74.50
0265	Wood core panels with 1/8" high pressure laminate		500	.032		42.50	1.88		44.38	50
0400	Aluminum panels, no fin.		500	.032		34	1.88		35.88	40.50
0600	For carpet covering, add					8.95			8.95	9.85
0700	For vinyl floor covering, add					9.50			9.50	10.45

09 69 13 – Rigid-Grid Access Flooring

09 69 13.10 Access Floors		Crew	Daily Output	Labor-Hours	Unit	2023 Bare Costs Material	Labor	Equipment	Total	Total Incl O&P
0900	For high pressure laminate covering, add				S.F.	7.90			7.90	8.65
0910	For snap on stringer system, add	2 Carp	1000	.016	↓	1.41	.94		2.35	2.95
1000	Machine cutouts after initial installation	1 Carp	50	.160	Ea.	19.15	9.40		28.55	35
1050	Pedestals, 6" to 12"	2 Carp	85	.188		8.95	11.05		20	26.50
1100	Air conditioning grilles, 4" x 12"	1 Carp	17	.471		70.50	27.50		98	119
1150	4" x 18"	"	14	.571	↓	96.50	33.50		130	156
1200	Approach ramps, steel	2 Carp	60	.267	S.F.	29	15.65		44.65	55
1300	Aluminum	"	40	.400	"	34	23.50		57.50	72.50
1500	Handrail, 2 rail, aluminum	1 Carp	15	.533	L.F.	122	31.50		153.50	182

Division Notes

		CREW	DAILY OUTPUT	LABOR-HOURS	UNIT	BARE COSTS MAT.	BARE COSTS LABOR	BARE COSTS EQUIP.	BARE COSTS TOTAL	TOTAL INCL O&P

Estimating Tips

General

- The items in this division are usually priced per square foot or each.
- Many items in Division 10 require some type of support system or special anchors that are not usually furnished with the item. The required anchors must be added to the estimate in the appropriate division.
- Some items in Division 10, such as lockers, may require assembly before installation. Verify the amount of assembly required. Assembly can often exceed installation time.

10 20 00 Interior Specialties

- Support angles and blocking are not included in the installation of toilet compartments, shower/dressing compartments, or cubicles. Appropriate line items from Division 5 or 6 may need to be added to support the installations.
- Toilet partitions are priced by the stall. A stall consists of a side wall, pilaster, and door with hardware. Toilet tissue holders and grab bars are extra.
- The required acoustical rating of a folding partition can have a significant impact on costs. Verify the sound transmission coefficient rating of the panel priced against the specification requirements.
- Grab bar installation does not include supplemental blocking or backing to support the required load. When grab bars are installed at an existing facility, provisions must be made to attach the grab bars to a solid structure.

Reference Numbers

Reference numbers are shown at the beginning of some major classifications. These numbers refer to related items in the Reference Section. The reference information may be an estimating procedure, an alternate pricing method, or technical information.

Note: Not all subdivisions listed here necessarily appear. ■

10 28 16.20 Medicine Cabinets		Crew	Daily Output	Labor-Hours	Unit	2023 Bare Costs Material	Labor	Equipment	Total	Total Incl O&P
0010	**MEDICINE CABINETS**									
0020	With mirror, sst frame, 16" x 22", unlighted	1 Carp	14	.571	Ea.	279	33.50		312.50	355
0100	Wood frame		14	.571		106	33.50		139.50	166
0300	Sliding mirror doors, 20" x 16" x 4-3/4", unlighted		7	1.143		165	67		232	281
0400	24" x 19" x 8-1/2", lighted		5	1.600		178	94		272	335
0600	Triple door, 30" x 32", unlighted, plywood body		7	1.143		293	67		360	420
0700	Steel body		7	1.143		225	67		292	350
0900	Oak door, wood body, beveled mirror, single door		7	1.143		189	67		256	310
1000	Double door		6	1.333		480	78		558	640
1200	Hotel cabinets, stainless, with lower shelf, unlighted		10	.800		400	47		447	510
1300	Lighted		5	1.600		350	94		444	525

Estimating Tips

General

- The items in this division are usually priced per square foot or each. Many of these items are purchased by the owner for installation by the contractor. Check the specifications for responsibilities and include time for receiving, storage, installation, and mechanical and electrical hookups in the appropriate divisions.
- Many items in Division 11 require some type of support system that is not usually furnished with the item. Examples of these systems include blocking for the attachment of casework and support angles/blocking for ceiling-hung projection screens. The required blocking or supports must be added to the estimate in the appropriate division.
- Some items in Division 11 may require assembly or electrical hookups. Verify the amount of assembly required or the need for a hard electrical connection and add the appropriate costs.

Reference Numbers

Reference numbers are shown at the beginning of some major classifications. These numbers refer to related items in the Reference Section. The reference information may be an estimating procedure, an alternate pricing method, or technical information.

11 12 Parking Control Equipment

11 12 13 – Parking Key and Card Control Units

11 12 13.10 Parking Control Units		Crew	Daily Output	Labor-Hours	Unit	2023 Bare Costs Material	Labor	Equipment	Total	Total Incl O&P
0010	**PARKING CONTROL UNITS**									
5100	Card reader	1 Elec	2	4	Ea.	820	269		1,089	1,300
5120	Proximity with customer display	2 Elec	1	16		3,175	1,075		4,250	5,100
6000	Parking control software, basic functionality	1 Elec	.50	16		1,150	1,075		2,225	2,850
6020	Multi-function	″	.20	40		3,425	2,700		6,125	7,775

11 12 16 – Parking Ticket Dispensers

11 12 16.10 Ticket Dispensers		Crew	Daily Output	Labor-Hours	Unit	Material	Labor	Equipment	Total	Total Incl O&P
0010	**TICKET DISPENSERS**									
5900	Ticket spitter with time/date stamp, standard	2 Elec	2	8	Ea.	10,300	540		10,840	12,100
5920	Mag stripe encoding	″	2	8	″	16,400	540		16,940	18,900

11 12 26 – Parking Fee Collection Equipment

11 12 26.13 Parking Fee Coin Collection Equipment		Crew	Daily Output	Labor-Hours	Unit	Material	Labor	Equipment	Total	Total Incl O&P
0010	**PARKING FEE COIN COLLECTION EQUIPMENT**									
5200	Cashier booth, average	B-22	1	30	Ea.	8,275	1,650	290	10,215	11,900
5300	Collector station, pay on foot	2 Elec	.20	80		97,000	5,400		102,400	114,500
5320	Credit card only	″	.50	32		17,900	2,150		20,050	22,900

11 12 26.23 Fee Equipment		Crew	Daily Output	Labor-Hours	Unit	Material	Labor	Equipment	Total	Total Incl O&P
0010	**FEE EQUIPMENT**									
5600	Fee computer	1 Elec	1.50	5.333	Ea.	3,375	360		3,735	4,250

11 12 33 – Parking Gates

11 12 33.13 Lift Arm Parking Gates		Crew	Daily Output	Labor-Hours	Unit	Material	Labor	Equipment	Total	Total Incl O&P
0010	**LIFT ARM PARKING GATES**									
5000	Barrier gate with programmable controller	2 Elec	3	5.333	Ea.	2,975	360		3,335	3,800
5020	Industrial		3	5.333		945	360		1,305	1,575
5050	Non-programmable, with reader and 12′ arm		3	5.333		1,500	360		1,860	2,175
5500	Exit verifier		1	16		2,625	1,075		3,700	4,475
5700	Full sign, 4″ letters	1 Elec	2	4		1,075	269		1,344	1,575
5800	Inductive loop	2 Elec	4	4		188	269		457	605
5950	Vehicle detector, microprocessor based	1 Elec	3	2.667		158	180		338	440

11 21 Retail and Service Equipment

11 21 73 – Commercial Laundry and Dry Cleaning Equipment

11 21 73.13 Dry Cleaning Equipment		Crew	Daily Output	Labor-Hours	Unit	Material	Labor	Equipment	Total	Total Incl O&P
0010	**DRY CLEANING EQUIPMENT**									
2000	Dry cleaners, electric, 20 lb. capacity, not incl. rough-in	L-1	.20	80	Ea.	40,500	5,575		46,075	53,000
2050	25 lb. capacity		.17	94.118		61,000	6,550		67,550	77,000
2100	30 lb. capacity		.15	107		64,000	7,425		71,425	81,500
2150	60 lb. capacity		.09	178		91,000	12,400		103,400	119,000

11 21 73.19 Finishing Equipment		Crew	Daily Output	Labor-Hours	Unit	Material	Labor	Equipment	Total	Total Incl O&P
0010	**FINISHING EQUIPMENT**									
3500	Folders, blankets & sheets, minimum	1 Elec	.17	47.059	Ea.	41,600	3,175		44,775	50,500
3700	King size with automatic stacker		.10	80		75,000	5,400		80,400	90,500
3800	For conveyor delivery, add		.45	17.778		19,100	1,200		20,300	22,800

11 21 73.23 Commercial Ironing Equipment		Crew	Daily Output	Labor-Hours	Unit	Material	Labor	Equipment	Total	Total Incl O&P
0010	**COMMERCIAL IRONING EQUIPMENT**									
4500	Ironers, institutional, 110″, single roll	1 Elec	.20	40	Ea.	40,300	2,700		43,000	48,300

11 21 Retail and Service Equipment

11 21 73 – Commercial Laundry and Dry Cleaning Equipment

11 21 73.26 Commercial Washers and Extractors		Crew	Daily Output	Labor-Hours	Unit	2023 Bare Costs Material	Labor	Equipment	Total	Total Incl O&P
0010	**COMMERCIAL WASHERS AND EXTRACTORS**, not including rough-in									
6000	Combination washer/extractor, 20 lb. capacity	L-6	1.50	8	Ea.	5,950	565		6,515	7,400
6100	30 lb. capacity		.80	15		12,700	1,050		13,750	15,500
6200	50 lb. capacity		.68	17.647		16,000	1,250		17,250	19,500
6300	75 lb. capacity		.30	40		15,800	2,825		18,625	21,600
6350	125 lb. capacity	↓	.16	75	↓	34,800	5,275		40,075	46,200
11 21 73.33 Coin-Operated Laundry Equipment										
0010	**COIN-OPERATED LAUNDRY EQUIPMENT**									
5290	Clothes washer									
5300	Commercial, coin operated, average	1 Plum	3	2.667	Ea.	1,575	192		1,767	2,000

11 30 Residential Equipment

11 30 13 – Residential Appliances

11 30 13.15 Cooking Equipment		Crew	Daily Output	Labor-Hours	Unit	Material	Labor	Equipment	Total	Total Incl O&P
0010	**COOKING EQUIPMENT**									
0020	Cooking range, 30" free standing, 1 oven, minimum	2 Clab	10	1.600	Ea.	700	75.50		775.50	885
0050	Maximum		4	4		935	189		1,124	1,300
0700	Free standing, 1 oven, 21" wide range, minimum		10	1.600		795	75.50		870.50	990
0750	21" wide, maximum	↓	4	4		560	189		749	895
0900	Countertop cooktops, 4 burner, standard, minimum	1 Elec	6	1.333		315	90		405	480
0950	Maximum		3	2.667		540	180		720	860
1050	As above, but with grill and griddle attachment, minimum		6	1.333		5,425	90		5,515	6,075
1100	Maximum		3	2.667		5,025	180		5,205	5,800
1200	Induction cooktop, 30" wide		3	2.667		1,925	180		2,105	2,400
1250	Microwave oven, minimum		4	2		160	135		295	375
1300	Maximum	↓	2	4	↓	450	269		719	895
11 30 13.17 Kitchen Cleaning Equipment										
0010	**KITCHEN CLEANING EQUIPMENT**									
2750	Dishwasher, built-in, 2 cycles, minimum	L-1	4	4	Ea.	500	279		779	965
2800	Maximum		2	8		980	560		1,540	1,900
2950	4 or more cycles, minimum		4	4		680	279		959	1,150
2960	Average		4	4		905	279		1,184	1,400
3000	Maximum	↓	2	8	↓	790	560		1,350	1,700
11 30 13.18 Waste Disposal Equipment										
0010	**WASTE DISPOSAL EQUIPMENT**									
3300	Garbage disposal, sink type, minimum	L-1	10	1.600	Ea.	124	112		236	300
3350	Maximum	"	10	1.600	"	256	112		368	445
11 30 13.19 Kitchen Ventilation Equipment										
0010	**KITCHEN VENTILATION EQUIPMENT**									
4150	Hood for range, 2 speed, vented, 30" wide, minimum	L-3	5	3.200	Ea.	110	204		314	425
4200	Maximum		3	5.333		1,150	340		1,490	1,750
4300	42" wide, minimum		5	3.200		175	204		379	495
4330	Custom		5	3.200		167	204		371	490
4350	Maximum	↓	3	5.333		204	340		544	730
4500	For ventless hood, 2 speed, add					70			70	77
4650	For vented 1 speed, deduct from maximum				↓	130			130	143
11 30 13.24 Washers										
0010	**WASHERS**									
5000	Residential, 4 cycle, average	1 Plum	3	2.667	Ea.	1,150	192		1,342	1,550

11 30 Residential Equipment

11 30 15 – Miscellaneous Residential Appliances

11 30 15.23 Water Heaters		Crew	Daily Output	Labor-Hours	Unit	Material	2023 Bare Costs Labor	Equipment	Total	Total Incl O&P
0010	WATER HEATERS									
6900	Electric, glass lined, 30 gallon, minimum	L-1	5	3.200	Ea.	750	223		973	1,150
6950	Maximum		3	5.333		1,050	370		1,420	1,700
7100	80 gallon, minimum		2	8		2,100	560		2,660	3,125
7150	Maximum	↓	1	16	↓	2,900	1,125		4,025	4,850

11 30 15.43 Air Quality		Crew	Daily Output	Labor-Hours	Unit	Material	Labor	Equipment	Total	Total Incl O&P
0010	AIR QUALITY									
2450	Dehumidifier, portable, automatic, 15 pint	1 Elec	4	2	Ea.	184	135		319	400
2550	40 pint		3.75	2.133		330	144		474	580
3550	Heater, electric, built-in, 1250 watt, ceiling type, minimum		4	2		136	135		271	350
3600	Maximum		3	2.667		258	180		438	550
3700	Wall type, minimum		4	2		117	135		252	330
3750	Maximum		3	2.667		135	180		315	415
3900	1500 watt wall type, with blower		4	2		227	135		362	450
3950	3000 watt	↓	3	2.667		224	180		404	515
4850	Humidifier, portable, 8 gallons/day					170			170	187
5000	15 gallons/day				↓	276			276	305

11 32 Unit Kitchens

11 32 13 – Metal Unit Kitchens

11 32 13.10 Commercial Unit Kitchens		Crew	Daily Output	Labor-Hours	Unit	Material	Labor	Equipment	Total	Total Incl O&P
0010	COMMERCIAL UNIT KITCHENS									
1500	Combination range, refrigerator and sink, 30" wide, minimum	L-1	2	8	Ea.	1,300	560		1,860	2,250
1550	Maximum		1	16		1,525	1,125		2,650	3,325
1570	60" wide, average		1.40	11.429		2,075	795		2,870	3,450
1590	72" wide, average		1.20	13.333		2,075	930		3,005	3,650
1600	Office model, 48" wide		2	8		3,300	560		3,860	4,450
1620	Refrigerator and sink only	↓	2.40	6.667	↓	3,425	465		3,890	4,475
1640	Combination range, refrigerator, sink, microwave									
1660	Oven and ice maker	L-1	.80	20	Ea.	5,925	1,400		7,325	8,600

11 41 Foodservice Storage Equipment

11 41 13 – Refrigerated Food Storage Cases

11 41 13.20 Refrigerated Food Storage Equipment		Crew	Daily Output	Labor-Hours	Unit	Material	Labor	Equipment	Total	Total Incl O&P
0010	REFRIGERATED FOOD STORAGE EQUIPMENT									
2350	Cooler, reach-in, beverage, 6' long	Q-1	6	2.667	Ea.	3,875	173		4,048	4,525

11 42 Food Preparation Equipment

11 42 10 – Commercial Food Preparation Equipment

11 42 10.10 Choppers, Mixers and Misc. Equipment		Crew	Daily Output	Labor-Hours	Unit	Material	Labor	Equipment	Total	Total Incl O&P
						2023 Bare Costs				
0010	**CHOPPERS, MIXERS AND MISC. EQUIPMENT**									
1850	Coffee urn, twin 6 gallon urns	1 Plum	2	4	Ea.	3,325	288		3,613	4,075
3800	Food mixers, bench type, 20 quarts	L-7	7	4		3,175	226		3,401	3,800
3900	60 quarts	"	5	5.600		13,500	315		13,815	15,300

11 44 Food Cooking Equipment

11 44 13 – Commercial Ranges

11 44 13.10 Cooking Equipment		Crew	Daily Output	Labor-Hours	Unit	Material	Labor	Equipment	Total	Total Incl O&P
0010	**COOKING EQUIPMENT**									
0020	Bake oven, gas, one section	Q-1	8	2	Ea.	4,400	130		4,530	5,050
1300	Broiler, without oven, standard	"	8	2		3,825	130		3,955	4,425
1550	Infrared	L-7	4	7		8,175	395		8,570	9,575
6350	Kettle, w/steam jacket, tilting, w/positive lock, SS, 20 gallons		7	4		16,500	226		16,726	18,400
6600	60 gallons		6	4.667		23,000	264		23,264	25,700
8850	Steamer, electric 27 KW		7	4		42,200	226		42,426	46,800
9100	Electric, 10 KW or gas 100,000 BTU		5	5.600		30,000	315		30,315	33,500
9150	Toaster, conveyor type, 16-22 slices/minute					1,050			1,050	1,150
9200	For deluxe models of above equipment, add					75%				
9400	Rule of thumb: Equipment cost based									
9410	on kitchen work area									
9420	Office buildings, minimum	L-7	77	.364	S.F.	152	20.50		172.50	198
9450	Maximum		58	.483		246	27.50		273.50	310
9550	Public eating facilities, minimum		77	.364		201	20.50		221.50	252
9600	Maximum		46	.609		325	34.50		359.50	405
9750	Hospitals, minimum		58	.483		196	27.50		223.50	257
9800	Maximum		39	.718		360	40.50		400.50	455

11 46 Food Dispensing Equipment

11 46 16 – Service Line Equipment

11 46 16.10 Commercial Food Dispensing Equipment		Crew	Daily Output	Labor-Hours	Unit	Material	Labor	Equipment	Total	Total Incl O&P
0010	**COMMERCIAL FOOD DISPENSING EQUIPMENT**									
3300	Food warmer, counter, 1.2 KW				Ea.	655			655	720
3550	1.6 KW					800			800	880
5750	Ice dispenser 567 pound	Q-1	6	2.667		6,250	173		6,423	7,125

11 48 Foodservice Cleaning and Disposal Equipment

11 48 13 – Commercial Dishwashers

11 48 13.10 Dishwashers		Crew	Daily Output	Labor-Hours	Unit	Material	Labor	Equipment	Total	Total Incl O&P
0010	**DISHWASHERS**									
2700	Dishwasher, commercial, rack type									
2720	10 to 12 racks/hour	Q-1	3.20	5	Ea.	38,500	325		38,825	42,900
2730	Energy star rated, 35 to 40 racks/hour G		1.30	12.308		6,350	800		7,150	8,175
2740	50 to 60 racks/hour G		1.30	12.308		9,050	800		9,850	11,200

11 52 Audio-Visual Equipment

11 52 16 – Projectors

	11 52 16.10 Movie Equipment	Crew	Daily Output	Labor-Hours	Unit	Material	Labor	Equipment	Total	Total Incl O&P
						2023 Bare Costs				
0010	**MOVIE EQUIPMENT**									
0020	Changeover, minimum				Ea.	575			575	630
0100	Maximum					1,275			1,275	1,400
0800	Lamphouses, incl. rectifiers, xenon, 1,000 watt	1 Elec	2	4		9,425	269		9,694	10,800
0900	1,600 watt		2	4		10,100	269		10,369	11,500
1000	2,000 watt		1.50	5.333		860	360		1,220	1,475
1100	4,000 watt		1.50	5.333		13,000	360		13,360	14,700
3700	Sound systems, incl. amplifier, mono, minimum		.90	8.889		9,675	600		10,275	11,600
3800	Dolby/Super Sound, maximum		.40	20		23,000	1,350		24,350	27,300
4100	Dual system, 2 channel, front surround, minimum		.70	11.429		5,900	770		6,670	7,650
4200	Dolby/Super Sound, 4 channel, maximum		.40	20		22,100	1,350		23,450	26,300
5300	Speakers, recessed behind screen, minimum		2	4		2,150	269		2,419	2,750
5400	Maximum		1	8		4,625	540		5,165	5,875
7000	For automation, varying sophistication, minimum		1	8	System	3,050	540		3,590	4,150
7100	Maximum	2 Elec	.30	53.333	"	7,100	3,600		10,700	13,200

	11 52 16.20 Movie Equipment- Digital	Crew	Daily Output	Labor-Hours	Unit	Material	Labor	Equipment	Total	Total Incl O&P
0010	**MOVIE EQUIPMENT- DIGITAL**									
1000	Digital 2K projection system, 98" DMD	1 Elec	2	4	Ea.	59,500	269		59,769	66,000
1100	OEM lens		2	4		6,975	269		7,244	8,075
2000	Pedestal with power distribution		2	4		2,600	269		2,869	3,250
3000	Software		2	4		2,200	269		2,469	2,825

11 53 Laboratory Equipment

11 53 19 – Laboratory Sterilizers

	11 53 19.13 Sterilizers	Crew	Daily Output	Labor-Hours	Unit	Material	Labor	Equipment	Total	Total Incl O&P
0010	**STERILIZERS**									
0700	Glassware washer, undercounter, minimum	L-1	1.80	8.889	Ea.	8,325	620		8,945	10,100
0710	Maximum	"	1	16	"	18,300	1,125		19,425	21,800

11 53 33 – Emergency Safety Appliances

	11 53 33.13 Emergency Equipment	Crew	Daily Output	Labor-Hours	Unit	Material	Labor	Equipment	Total	Total Incl O&P
0010	**EMERGENCY EQUIPMENT**									
1400	Safety equipment, eye wash, hand held				Ea.	420			420	460
1450	Deluge shower				"	294			294	325

11 53 43 – Service Fittings and Accessories

	11 53 43.13 Fittings	Crew	Daily Output	Labor-Hours	Unit	Material	Labor	Equipment	Total	Total Incl O&P
0010	**FITTINGS**									
8000	Alternate pricing method: as percent of lab furniture									
8050	Installation, not incl. plumbing & duct work				% Furn.				22%	22%
8100	Plumbing, final connections, simple system								10%	10%
8110	Moderately complex system								15%	15%
8120	Complex system								20%	20%
8150	Electrical, simple system								10%	10%
8160	Moderately complex system								20%	20%
8170	Complex system								35%	35%

11 61 Broadcast, Theater, and Stage Equipment

11 61 33 – Rigging Systems and Controls

11 61 33.10 Controls		Crew	Daily Output	Labor-Hours	Unit	Material	Labor	Equipment	Total	Total Incl O&P
						2023 Bare Costs				
0010	**CONTROLS**									
0050	Control boards with dimmers and breakers, minimum	1 Elec	1	8	Ea.	3,875	540		4,415	5,075
0100	Average		.50	16		800	1,075		1,875	2,475
0150	Maximum	↓	.20	40	↓	121,500	2,700		124,200	137,500

11 66 Athletic Equipment

11 66 43 – Interior Scoreboards

11 66 43.10 Scoreboards		Crew	Daily Output	Labor-Hours	Unit	Material	Labor	Equipment	Total	Total Incl O&P
0010	**SCOREBOARDS**									
7000	Baseball, minimum	R-3	1.30	15.385	Ea.	5,625	1,025	148	6,798	7,925
7200	Maximum		.05	400		11,500	26,900	3,850	42,250	57,000
7300	Football, minimum		.86	23.256		5,650	1,575	224	7,449	8,800
7400	Maximum		.20	100		15,200	6,725	965	22,890	27,800
7500	Basketball (one side), minimum		2.07	9.662		530	650	93	1,273	1,650
7600	Maximum		.30	66.667		7,675	4,500	645	12,820	15,800
7700	Hockey-basketball (four sides), minimum		.25	80		11,200	5,375	770	17,345	21,300
7800	Maximum	↓	.15	133	↓	19,100	8,975	1,275	29,350	35,700

11 71 Medical Sterilizing Equipment

11 71 10 – Medical Sterilizers & Distillers

11 71 10.10 Sterilizers and Distillers		Crew	Daily Output	Labor-Hours	Unit	Material	Labor	Equipment	Total	Total Incl O&P
0010	**STERILIZERS AND DISTILLERS**									
6200	Steam generators, electric 10 kW to 180 kW, freestanding									
6250	Minimum	1 Elec	3	2.667	Ea.	6,450	180		6,630	7,375
6300	Maximum	"	.70	11.429	"	3,400	770		4,170	4,900

11 72 Examination and Treatment Equipment

11 72 53 – Treatment Equipment

11 72 53.13 Medical Treatment Equipment		Crew	Daily Output	Labor-Hours	Unit	Material	Labor	Equipment	Total	Total Incl O&P
0010	**MEDICAL TREATMENT EQUIPMENT**									
6700	Surgical lights, doctor's office, single arm	2 Elec	2	8	Ea.	3,575	540		4,115	4,725
6750	Dual arm	"	1	16	"	6,125	1,075		7,200	8,350

11 76 Operating Room Equipment

11 76 10 – Equipment for Operating Rooms

11 76 10.10 Surgical Equipment		Crew	Daily Output	Labor-Hours	Unit	Material	Labor	Equipment	Total	Total Incl O&P
0010	**SURGICAL EQUIPMENT**									
6800	Surgical lights, major operating room, dual head, minimum	2 Elec	1	16	Ea.	5,525	1,075		6,600	7,675
6850	Maximum	"	1	16	"	7,000	1,075		8,075	9,300

11 78 Mortuary Equipment

11 78 13 – Mortuary Refrigerators

11 78 13.10 Mortuary and Autopsy Equipment		Crew	Daily Output	Labor-Hours	Unit	2023 Bare Costs Material	Labor	Equipment	Total	Total Incl O&P
0010	**MORTUARY AND AUTOPSY EQUIPMENT**									
0015	Autopsy table, standard	1 Plum	1	8	Ea.	8,550	575		9,125	10,300

11 78 16 – Crematorium Equipment

11 78 16.10 Crematory		Crew	Daily Output	Labor-Hours	Unit	Material	Labor	Equipment	Total	Total Incl O&P
0010	**CREMATORY**									
1500	Crematory, not including building, 1 place	Q-3	.20	160	Ea.	77,500	11,000		88,500	102,000
1750	2 place	"	.10	320	"	111,000	21,900		132,900	154,500

11 82 Facility Solid Waste Handling Equipment

11 82 26 – Facility Waste Compactors

11 82 26.10 Compactors		Crew	Daily Output	Labor-Hours	Unit	Material	Labor	Equipment	Total	Total Incl O&P
0010	**COMPACTORS**									
0020	Compactors, 115 volt, 250 lbs./hr., chute fed	L-4	1	24	Ea.	11,900	1,350		13,250	15,100
1000	Heavy duty industrial compactor, 0.5 C.Y. capacity		1	24		10,600	1,350		11,950	13,700
1050	1.0 C.Y. capacity		1	24		16,200	1,350		17,550	19,800
1100	3.0 C.Y. capacity		.50	48		27,700	2,675		30,375	34,500
1150	5.0 C.Y. capacity		.50	48		35,000	2,675		37,675	42,500
1200	Combination shredder/compactor (5,000 lbs./hr.)	↓	.50	48		68,000	2,675		70,675	78,500
1400	For handling hazardous waste materials, 55 gallon drum packer, std.					20,800			20,800	22,900
1410	55 gallon drum packer w/HEPA filter					25,000			25,000	27,600
1420	55 gallon drum packer w/charcoal & HEPA filter					33,400			33,400	36,700
1430	All of the above made explosion proof, add					1,950			1,950	2,150
5800	Shredder, industrial, minimum					28,000			28,000	30,800
5850	Maximum					141,000			141,000	155,000
5900	Baler, industrial, minimum					10,600			10,600	11,600
5950	Maximum				↓	615,500			615,500	677,000

Estimating Tips

General

- The items in this division are usually priced per square foot or each. Most of these items are purchased by the owner and installed by the contractor. Do not assume the items in Division 12 will be purchased and installed by the contractor. Check the specifications for responsibilities and include receiving, storage, installation, and mechanical and electrical hookups in the appropriate divisions.
- Some items in this division require some type of support system that is not usually furnished with the item. Examples of these systems include blocking for the attachment of casework and heavy drapery rods. The required blocking must be added to the estimate in the appropriate division.

Reference Numbers

Reference numbers are shown at the beginning of some major classifications. These numbers refer to related items in the Reference Section. The reference information may be an estimating procedure, an alternate pricing method, or technical information.

12 46 Furnishing Accessories

12 46 19 – Clocks

12 46 19.50 Wall Clocks		Crew	Daily Output	Labor-Hours	Unit	Material	2023 Bare Costs Labor	Equipment	Total	Total Incl O&P
0010	**WALL CLOCKS**									
0080	12" diameter, single face	1 Elec	8	1	Ea.	147	67.50		214.50	262
0100	Double face	"	6.20	1.290	"	147	87		234	291

Estimating Tips

General

- The items and systems in this division are usually estimated, purchased, supplied, and installed as a unit by one or more subcontractors. The estimator must ensure that all parties are operating from the same set of specifications and assumptions, and that all necessary items are estimated and will be provided. Many times the complex items and systems are covered, but the more common ones, such as excavation or a crane, are overlooked for the very reason that everyone assumes nobody could miss them. The estimator should be the central focus and be able to ensure that all systems are complete.
- It is important to consider factors such as site conditions, weather, shape and size of building, as well as labor availability as they may impact the overall cost of erecting special structures and systems included in this division.
- Another area where problems can develop in this division is at the interface between systems. The estimator must ensure, for instance, that anchor bolts, nuts, and washers are estimated and included for the air-supported structures and pre-engineered buildings to be bolted to their foundations. Utility supply is a common area where essential items or pieces of equipment can be missed or overlooked because each subcontractor may feel it is another's responsibility. The estimator should also be aware of certain items which may be supplied as part of a package but installed by others, and ensure that the installing contractor's estimate includes the cost of installation. Conversely, the estimator must also ensure that items are not costed by two different subcontractors, resulting in an inflated overall estimate.

13 30 00 Special Structures

- The foundations and floor slab, as well as rough mechanical and electrical, should be estimated, as this work is required for the assembly and erection of the structure. Generally, as noted in the data set, the pre-engineered building comes as a shell. Pricing is based on the size and structural design parameters stated in the reference section. Additional features, such as windows and doors with their related structural framing, must also be included by the estimator. Here again, the estimator must have a clear understanding of the scope of each portion of the work and all the necessary interfaces.

Reference Numbers

Reference numbers are shown at the beginning of some major classifications. These numbers refer to related items in the Reference Section. The reference information may be an estimating procedure, an alternate pricing method, or technical information.

Note: Not all subdivisions listed here necessarily appear. ■

13 11 Swimming Pools

13 11 13 – Below-Grade Swimming Pools

13 11 13.50 Swimming Pools		Crew	Daily Output	Labor-Hours	Unit	Material	Labor (2023 Bare Costs)	Equipment	Total	Total Incl O&P
0010	**SWIMMING POOLS** Residential in-ground, vinyl lined									
0020	Concrete sides, w/equip, sand bottom	B-52	300	.187	SF Surf	43	10.15	2.10	55.25	65
0100	Metal or polystyrene sides	B-14	410	.117		81	5.80	.68	87.48	98.50
0200	Add for vermiculite bottom					4.09			4.09	4.50
0500	Gunite bottom and sides, white plaster finish									
0600	12′ x 30′ pool	B-52	145	.386	SF Surf	60.50	21	4.34	85.84	102
0720	16′ x 32′ pool		155	.361		54.50	19.60	4.06	78.16	93.50
0750	20′ x 40′ pool		250	.224		48.50	12.15	2.52	63.17	74.50
0810	Concrete bottom and sides, tile finish									
0820	12′ x 30′ pool	B-52	80	.700	SF Surf	61	38	7.85	106.85	132
0830	16′ x 32′ pool		95	.589		50.50	32	6.60	89.10	110
0840	20′ x 40′ pool		130	.431		40	23.50	4.84	68.34	84
1100	Motel, gunite with plaster finish, incl. medium									
1150	capacity filtration & chlorination	B-52	115	.487	SF Surf	74.50	26.50	5.45	106.45	127
1200	Municipal, gunite with plaster finish, incl. high									
1250	capacity filtration & chlorination	B-52	100	.560	SF Surf	96.50	30.50	6.30	133.30	158
1350	Add for formed gutters				L.F.	142			142	156
1360	Add for stainless steel gutters				"	420			420	460
1700	Filtration and deck equipment only, as % of total				Total				20%	20%
1800	Automatic vacuum, hand tools, etc., 20′ x 40′ pool				SF Pool				.56	.62
1900	5,000 S.F. pool				"				.11	.12

13 11 23 – On-Grade Swimming Pools

13 11 23.50 Swimming Pools		Crew	Daily Output	Labor-Hours	Unit	Material	Labor	Equipment	Total	Total Incl O&P
0010	**SWIMMING POOLS** Residential above ground, steel construction									
0100	Round, 15′ diam.	B-80A	3	8	Ea.	975	380	130	1,485	1,775
0120	18′ diam.		2.50	9.600		1,025	455	156	1,636	2,000
0140	21′ diam.		2	12		1,150	565	195	1,910	2,325
0160	24′ diam.		1.80	13.333		1,325	630	217	2,172	2,625
0180	27′ diam.		1.50	16		1,650	755	261	2,666	3,225
0200	30′ diam.		1	24		1,925	1,125	390	3,440	4,225
0220	Oval, 12′ x 24′		2.30	10.435		1,675	495	170	2,340	2,775
0240	15′ x 30′		1.80	13.333		4,875	630	217	5,722	6,525
0260	18′ x 33′		1	24		2,650	1,125	390	4,165	5,050

13 11 46 – Swimming Pool Accessories

13 11 46.50 Swimming Pool Equipment		Crew	Daily Output	Labor-Hours	Unit	Material	Labor	Equipment	Total	Total Incl O&P
0010	**SWIMMING POOL EQUIPMENT**									
0020	Diving stand, stainless steel, 3 meter	2 Carp	.40	40	Ea.	20,300	2,350		22,650	25,800
2100	Lights, underwater, 12 volt, with transformer, 300 watt	1 Elec	1	8		291	540		831	1,125
2200	110 volt, 500 watt, standard		1	8		320	540		860	1,150
2400	Low water cutoff type		1	8		345	540		885	1,175
2800	Heaters, see Section 23 52 28.10									

13 12 Fountains

13 12 13 – Exterior Fountains

13 12 13.10 Outdoor Fountains		Crew	Daily Output	Labor-Hours	Unit	Material	2023 Bare Costs Labor	Equipment	Total	Total Incl O&P
0010	**OUTDOOR FOUNTAINS**									
0100	Outdoor fountain, 48" high with bowl and figures	2 Clab	2	8	Ea.	430	380		810	1,050
0200	Commercial, concrete or cast stone, 40-60" H, simple		2	8		1,100	380		1,480	1,775
0220	Average		2	8		2,100	380		2,480	2,900
0240	Ornate		2	8		4,800	380		5,180	5,850
0260	Metal, 72" high		2	8		1,700	380		2,080	2,450
0280	90" high		2	8		2,450	380		2,830	3,275
0300	120" high		2	8		5,875	380		6,255	7,025
0320	Resin or fiberglass, 40-60" H, wall type		2	8		770	380		1,150	1,400
0340	Waterfall type		2	8		1,300	380		1,680	2,000

13 12 23 – Interior Fountains

13 12 23.10 Indoor Fountains		Crew	Daily Output	Labor-Hours	Unit	Material	Labor	Equipment	Total	Total Incl O&P
0010	**INDOOR FOUNTAINS**									
0100	Commercial, floor type, resin or fiberglass, lighted, cascade type	2 Clab	2	8	Ea.	480	380		860	1,100
0120	Tiered type		2	8		720	380		1,100	1,350
0140	Waterfall type		2	8		2,475	380		2,855	3,275

13 21 Controlled Environment Rooms

13 21 13 – Clean Rooms

13 21 13.50 Clean Room Components		Crew	Daily Output	Labor-Hours	Unit	Material	Labor	Equipment	Total	Total Incl O&P
0010	**CLEAN ROOM COMPONENTS**									
1100	Clean room, soft wall, 12' x 12', Class 100	1 Carp	.18	44.444	Ea.	16,500	2,600		19,100	22,100
1110	Class 1,000		.18	44.444		17,400	2,600		20,000	23,000
1120	Class 10,000		.21	38.095		15,500	2,225		17,725	20,300
1130	Class 100,000		.21	38.095		12,700	2,225		14,925	17,200
2800	Ceiling grid support, slotted channel struts 4'-0" OC, ea. way				S.F.				5.90	6.50
3000	Ceiling panel, vinyl coated foil on mineral substrate									
3020	Sealed, non-perforated				S.F.				3.72	4.13
4000	Ceiling panel seal, silicone sealant, 150 L.F./gal.	1 Carp	150	.053	L.F.	.28	3.13		3.41	4.96
4100	Two sided adhesive tape	"	240	.033	"	.13	1.95		2.08	3.05
4200	Clips, one per panel				Ea.	1			1	1.10
6000	HEPA filter, 2' x 4', 99.97% eff., 3" dp beveled frame (silicone seal)					380			380	415
6040	6" deep skirted frame (channel seal)					515			515	570
6100	99.99% efficient, 3" deep beveled frame (silicone seal)					480			480	530
6140	6" deep skirted frame (channel seal)					560			560	615
6200	99.999% efficient, 3" deep beveled frame (silicone seal)					635			635	695
6240	6" deep skirted frame (channel seal)					670			670	735
7000	Wall panel systems, including channel strut framing									
7020	Polyester coated aluminum, particle board				S.F.				18.20	18.20
7100	Porcelain coated aluminum, particle board								32	32
7400	Wall panel support, slotted channel struts, to 12' high								16.35	16.35

13 24 Special Activity Rooms

13 24 16 – Saunas

13 24 16.50 Saunas and Heaters		Crew	Daily Output	Labor-Hours	Unit	Material	Labor (2023 Bare Costs)	Equipment	Total	Total Incl O&P
0010	SAUNAS AND HEATERS									
0020	Prefabricated, incl. heater & controls, 7′ high, 6′ x 4′, C/C	L-7	2.20	12.727	Ea.	5,825	720		6,545	7,500
0050	6′ x 4′, C/P		2	14		4,750	795		5,545	6,400
0400	6′ x 5′, C/C		2	14		5,900	795		6,695	7,650
0450	6′ x 5′, C/P		2	14		5,675	795		6,470	7,425
0600	6′ x 6′, C/C		1.80	15.556		15,600	880		16,480	18,400
0650	6′ x 6′, C/P		1.80	15.556		6,325	880		7,205	8,275
0800	6′ x 9′, C/C		1.60	17.500		8,175	990		9,165	10,500
0850	6′ x 9′, C/P		1.60	17.500		6,425	990		7,415	8,550
1000	8′ x 12′, C/C		1.10	25.455		19,800	1,450		21,250	24,000
1050	8′ x 12′, C/P		1.10	25.455		23,300	1,450		24,750	27,800
1200	8′ x 8′, C/C		1.40	20		10,800	1,125		11,925	13,500
1250	8′ x 8′, C/P		1.40	20		7,850	1,125		8,975	10,300
1400	8′ x 10′, C/C		1.20	23.333		9,975	1,325		11,300	13,000
1450	8′ x 10′, C/P		1.20	23.333		9,100	1,325		10,425	12,000
1600	10′ x 12′, C/C		1	28		15,700	1,575		17,275	19,700
1650	10′ x 12′, C/P	↓	1	28		15,700	1,575		17,275	19,700
2500	Heaters only (incl. above), wall mounted, to 200 C.F.					1,125			1,125	1,250
2750	To 300 C.F.					1,275			1,275	1,400
3000	Floor standing, to 720 C.F., 10,000 watts, w/controls	1 Elec	3	2.667		3,250	180		3,430	3,850
3250	To 1,000 C.F., 16,000 watts	"	3	2.667	↓	4,475	180		4,655	5,175

13 24 26 – Steam Baths

13 24 26.50 Steam Baths and Components		Crew	Daily Output	Labor-Hours	Unit	Material	Labor	Equipment	Total	Total Incl O&P
0010	STEAM BATHS AND COMPONENTS									
0020	Heater, timer & head, single, to 140 C.F.	1 Plum	1.20	6.667	Ea.	2,375	480		2,855	3,325
0500	To 300 C.F.		1.10	7.273		6,500	525		7,025	7,900
1000	Commercial size, with blow-down assembly, to 800 C.F.		.90	8.889		6,750	640		7,390	8,375
1500	To 2,500 C.F.	↓	.80	10		7,975	720		8,695	9,850
2000	Multiple, motels, apts., 2 baths, w/blow-down assm., 500 C.F.	Q-1	1.30	12.308		7,450	800		8,250	9,400
2500	4 baths	"	.70	22.857	↓	11,200	1,475		12,675	14,600

13 47 Facility Protection

13 47 13 – Cathodic Protection

13 47 13.16 Cathodic Prot. for Underground Storage Tanks		Crew	Daily Output	Labor-Hours	Unit	Material	Labor	Equipment	Total	Total Incl O&P
0010	CATHODIC PROTECTION FOR UNDERGROUND STORAGE TANKS									
1000	Anodes, magnesium type, 9 #	R-15	18.50	2.595	Ea.	45	172	18.70	235.70	325
1010	17 #		13	3.692		92.50	244	26.50	363	495
1020	32 #		10	4.800		136	320	34.50	490.50	655
1030	48 #	↓	7.20	6.667		174	440	48	662	900
1100	Graphite type w/epoxy cap, 3″ x 60″ (32 #)	R-22	8.40	4.438		160	274		434	580
1110	4″ x 80″ (68 #)		6	6.213		278	385		663	875
1120	6″ x 72″ (80 #)		5.20	7.169		1,675	440		2,115	2,500
1130	6″ x 36″ (45 #)	↓	9.60	3.883		850	239		1,089	1,300
2000	Rectifiers, silicon type, air cooled, 28 V/10 A	R-19	3.50	5.714		2,675	385		3,060	3,500
2010	20 V/20 A		3.50	5.714		2,675	385		3,060	3,525
2100	Oil immersed, 28 V/10 A		3	6.667		2,725	450		3,175	3,675
2110	20 V/20 A	↓	3	6.667	↓	3,600	450		4,050	4,625
3000	Anode backfill, coke breeze	R-22	3850	.010	Lb.	.31	.60		.91	1.23
4000	Cable, HMWPE, No. 8		2.40	15.533	M.L.F.	975	960		1,935	2,500
4010	No. 6	↓	2.40	15.533	↓	1,275	960		2,235	2,850

13 47 Facility Protection

13 47 13 – Cathodic Protection

13 47 13.16 Cathodic Prot. for Underground Storage Tanks		Crew	Daily Output	Labor-Hours	Unit	Material	2023 Bare Costs Labor	Equipment	Total	Total Incl O&P
4020	No. 4	R-22	2.40	15.533	M.L.F.	2,075	960		3,035	3,700
4030	No. 2		2.40	15.533		3,000	960		3,960	4,725
4040	No. 1		2.20	16.945		2,250	1,050		3,300	4,050
4050	No. 1/0		2.20	16.945		4,700	1,050		5,750	6,725
4060	No. 2/0		2.20	16.945		6,000	1,050		7,050	8,150
4070	No. 4/0		2	18.640		9,600	1,150		10,750	12,300
5000	Test station, 7 terminal box, flush curb type w/lockable cover	R-19	12	1.667	Ea.	90	112		202	266
5010	Reference cell, 2" diam. PVC conduit, cplg., plug, set flush	"	4.80	4.167	"	179	281		460	615

13 49 Radiation Protection

13 49 13 – Integrated X-Ray Shielding Assemblies

13 49 13.50 Lead Sheets

13 49 13.50 Lead Sheets		Crew	Daily Output	Labor-Hours	Unit	Material	2023 Bare Costs Labor	Equipment	Total	Total Incl O&P
0010	**LEAD SHEETS**									
0300	Lead sheets, 1/16" thick	2 Lath	135	.119	S.F.	11.90	6.95		18.85	23
0400	1/8" thick		120	.133		26.50	7.80		34.30	40.50
0500	Lead shielding, 1/4" thick		135	.119		50	6.95		56.95	65
0550	1/2" thick		120	.133		93.50	7.80		101.30	114
0950	Lead headed nails (average 1 lb. per sheet)				Lb.	25			25	27.50
1000	Butt joints in 1/8" lead or thicker, 2" batten strip x 7' long	2 Lath	240	.067	Ea.	55.50	3.90		59.40	66.50
1200	X-ray protection, average radiography or fluoroscopy									
1210	room, up to 300 S.F. floor, 1/16" lead, economy	2 Lath	.25	64	Total	21,200	3,750		24,950	28,900
1500	7'-0" walls, deluxe	"	.15	107	"	25,500	6,225		31,725	37,200
1600	Deep therapy X-ray room, 250 kV capacity,									
1800	up to 300 S.F. floor, 1/4" lead, economy	2 Lath	.08	200	Total	59,500	11,700		71,200	82,500
1900	7'-0" walls, deluxe	"	.06	267	"	73,000	15,600		88,600	103,000

13 49 19 – Lead-Lined Materials

13 49 19.50 Shielding Lead

13 49 19.50 Shielding Lead		Crew	Daily Output	Labor-Hours	Unit	Material	2023 Bare Costs Labor	Equipment	Total	Total Incl O&P
0010	**SHIELDING LEAD**									
0100	Laminated lead in wood doors, 1/16" thick, no hardware				S.F.	84			84	92.50
0200	Lead lined door frame, not incl. hardware,									
0210	1/16" thick lead, butt prepared for hardware	1 Lath	2.40	3.333	Ea.	450	195		645	780
0850	Window frame with 1/16" lead and voice passage, 36" x 60"	2 Glaz	2	8		5,250	450		5,700	6,450
0870	24" x 36" frame		4	4		2,350	224		2,574	2,900
0900	Lead gypsum board, 5/8" thick with 1/16" lead		160	.100	S.F.	14.05	5.60		19.65	24
0910	1/8" lead		140	.114		28	6.40		34.40	40
0930	1/32" lead	2 Lath	200	.080		7.55	4.68		12.23	15.15

13 49 21 – Lead Glazing

13 49 21.50 Lead Glazing

13 49 21.50 Lead Glazing		Crew	Daily Output	Labor-Hours	Unit	Material	2023 Bare Costs Labor	Equipment	Total	Total Incl O&P
0010	**LEAD GLAZING**									
0600	Lead glass, 1/4" thick, 2.0 mm LE, 12" x 16"	2 Glaz	13	1.231	Ea.	595	69		664	760
0700	24" x 36"		8	2		2,100	112		2,212	2,500
0800	36" x 60"		2	8		5,050	450		5,500	6,250
2000	X-ray viewing panels, clear lead plastic									
2010	7 mm thick, 0.3 mm LE, 2.3 lb./S.F.	H-3	139	.115	S.F.	410	5.80		415.80	460
2020	12 mm thick, 0.5 mm LE, 3.9 lb./S.F.		82	.195		550	9.85		559.85	620
2030	18 mm thick, 0.8 mm LE, 5.9 lb./S.F.		54	.296		670	14.95		684.95	760
2040	22 mm thick, 1.0 mm LE, 7.2 lb./S.F.		44	.364		1,100	18.35		1,118.35	1,250
2050	35 mm thick, 1.5 mm LE, 11.5 lb./S.F.		28	.571		1,450	29		1,479	1,650
2060	46 mm thick, 2.0 mm LE, 15.0 lb./S.F.		21	.762		1,900	38.50		1,938.50	2,150

13 49 Radiation Protection

13 49 23 – Integrated RFI/EMI Shielding Assemblies

13 49 23.50 Modular Shielding Partitions		Crew	Daily Output	Labor-Hours	Unit	2023 Bare Costs Material	Labor	Equipment	Total	Total Incl O&P
0010	**MODULAR SHIELDING PARTITIONS**									
4000	X-ray barriers, modular, panels mounted within framework for									
4002	attaching to floor, wall or ceiling, upper portion is clear lead									
4005	plastic window panels 48"H, lower portion is opaque leaded									
4008	steel panels 36"H, structural supports not incl.									
4010	1-section barrier, 36"W x 84"H overall									
4020	0.5 mm LE panels	H-3	6.40	2.500	Ea.	3,650	126		3,776	4,200
4030	0.8 mm LE panels		6.40	2.500		16,000	126		16,126	17,800
4040	1.0 mm LE panels		5.33	3.002		13,500	152		13,652	15,000
4050	1.5 mm LE panels		5.33	3.002		26,100	152		26,252	28,900
4060	2-section barrier, 72"W x 84"H overall									
4070	0.5 mm LE panels	H-3	4	4	Ea.	10,300	202		10,502	11,700
4080	0.8 mm LE panels		4	4		8,700	202		8,902	9,875
4090	1.0 mm LE panels		3.56	4.494		25,200	227		25,427	28,000
5000	1.5 mm LE panels		3.20	5		4,750	253		5,003	5,600
5010	3-section barrier, 108"W x 84"H overall									
5020	0.5 mm LE panels	H-3	3.20	5	Ea.	33,700	253		33,953	37,400
5030	0.8 mm LE panels		3.20	5		34,700	253		34,953	38,600
5040	1.0 mm LE panels		2.67	5.993		13,500	305		13,805	15,300
5050	1.5 mm LE panels		2.46	6.504		26,200	330		26,530	29,300
7000	X-ray barriers, mobile, mounted within framework w/casters on									
7005	bottom, clear lead plastic window panels on upper portion,									
7010	opaque on lower, 30"W x 75"H overall, incl. framework									
7020	24"H upper w/0.5 mm LE, 48"H lower w/0.8 mm LE	1 Carp	16	.500	Ea.	5,800	29.50		5,829.50	6,425
7030	48"W x 75"H overall, incl. framework									
7040	36"H upper w/0.5 mm LE, 36"H lower w/0.8 mm LE	1 Carp	16	.500	Ea.	8,700	29.50		8,729.50	9,625
7050	36"H upper w/1.0 mm LE, 36"H lower w/1.5 mm LE	"	16	.500	"	4,750	29.50		4,779.50	5,275
7060	72"W x 75"H overall, incl. framework									
7070	36"H upper w/0.5 mm LE, 36"H lower w/0.8 mm LE	1 Carp	16	.500	Ea.	13,500	29.50		13,529.50	14,800
7080	36"H upper w/1.0 mm LE, 36"H lower w/1.5 mm LE	"	16	.500	"	10,400	29.50		10,429.50	11,400

13 49 33 – Radio Frequency Shielding

13 49 33.50 Shielding, Radio Frequency		Crew	Daily Output	Labor-Hours	Unit	Material	Labor	Equipment	Total	Total Incl O&P
0010	**SHIELDING, RADIO FREQUENCY**									
0020	Prefabricated, galvanized steel	2 Carp	375	.043	SF Surf	7.50	2.50		10	11.95
0040	5 oz., copper floor panel		480	.033		6.10	1.95		8.05	9.60
0050	5 oz., copper wall/ceiling panel		155	.103		6.10	6.05		12.15	15.70
0100	12 oz., copper floor panel		470	.034		12.70	1.99		14.69	16.90
0110	12 oz., copper wall/ceiling panel		140	.114		12.70	6.70		19.40	24
0150	Door, copper/wood laminate, 4' x 7'		1.50	10.667	Ea.	11,400	625		12,025	13,400

Estimating Tips

Pipe for fire protection and all uses is located in Subdivisions 21 11 13 and 22 11 13.

The labor adjustment factors listed in Subdivision 22 01 02.20 also apply to Division 21.

Many, but not all, areas in the U.S. require backflow protection in the fire system. Insurance underwriters may have specific requirements for the type of materials to be installed or design requirements based on the hazard to be protected. Local jurisdictions may have requirements not covered by code. It is advisable to be aware of any special conditions.

For your reference, the following is a list of the most applicable Fire Codes and Standards, which may be purchased from the NFPA, 1 Batterymarch Park, Quincy, MA 02169-7471.

- NFPA 1: Uniform Fire Code
- NFPA 10: Portable Fire Extinguishers
- NFPA 11: Low-, Medium-, and High-Expansion Foam
- NFPA 12: Carbon Dioxide Extinguishing Systems (Also companion 12A)
- NFPA 13: Installation of Sprinkler Systems (Also companion 13D, 13E, and 13R)
- NFPA 14: Installation of Standpipe and Hose Systems
- NFPA 15: Water Spray Fixed Systems for Fire Protection
- NFPA 16: Installation of Foam-Water Sprinkler and Foam-Water Spray Systems
- NFPA 17: Dry Chemical Extinguishing Systems (Also companion 17A)
- NFPA 18: Wetting Agents
- NFPA 20: Installation of Stationary Pumps for Fire Protection
- NFPA 22: Water Tanks for Private Fire Protection
- NFPA 24: Installation of Private Fire Service Mains and their Appurtenances
- NFPA 25: Inspection, Testing and Maintenance of Water-Based Fire Protection

Reference Numbers

Reference numbers are shown at the beginning of some major classifications. These numbers refer to related items in the Reference Section. The reference information may be an estimating procedure, an alternate pricing method, or technical information.

Note: "Powered in part by CINX™, based on licensed proprietary information of Harrison Publishing House, Inc."

Note: Trade Service, in part, has been used as a reference source for some of the material prices used in Division 21.

21 21 Carbon-Dioxide Fire-Extinguishing Systems

21 21 16 – Carbon-Dioxide Fire-Extinguishing Equipment

21 21 16.50 CO2 Fire Extinguishing System		Crew	Daily Output	Labor-Hours	Unit	2023 Bare Costs Material	Labor	Equipment	Total	Total Incl O&P
0010	**CO_2 FIRE EXTINGUISHING SYSTEM**									
0100	Control panel, single zone with batteries (2 zones det., 1 suppr.)	1 Elec	1	8	Ea.	1,400	540		1,940	2,350
0150	Multizone (4) with batteries (8 zones det., 4 suppr.)	"	.50	16		3,400	1,075		4,475	5,350
1000	Dispersion nozzle, CO_2, 3" x 5"	1 Plum	18	.444		176	32		208	241
2000	Extinguisher, CO_2 system, high pressure, 75 lb. cylinder	Q-1	6	2.667		1,575	173		1,748	1,975
2100	100 lb. cylinder	"	5	3.200		2,200	208		2,408	2,725
3000	Electro/mechanical release	L-1	4	4		1,175	279		1,454	1,700
3400	Manual pull station	1 Plum	6	1.333		102	96		198	255
4000	Pneumatic damper release	"	8	1		365	72		437	505

21 22 Clean-Agent Fire-Extinguishing Systems

21 22 16 – Clean-Agent Fire-Extinguishing Equipment

21 22 16.50 Clean-Agent Extinguishing Systems		Crew	Daily Output	Labor-Hours	Unit	Material	Labor	Equipment	Total	Total Incl O&P
0010	**CLEAN-AGENT EXTINGUISHING SYSTEMS**									
0020	FM200 fire extinguishing system									
1100	Dispersion nozzle FM200, 1-1/2"	1 Plum	14	.571	Ea.	280	41		321	370
2400	Extinguisher, FM200 system, filled, with mounting bracket									
2460	26 lb. container	Q-1	8	2	Ea.	2,425	130		2,555	2,875
2480	44 lb. container		7	2.286		3,150	148		3,298	3,675
2500	63 lb. container		6	2.667		4,450	173		4,623	5,150
2520	101 lb. container		5	3.200		6,450	208		6,658	7,375
2540	196 lb. container		4	4		7,775	259		8,034	8,925
6000	FM200 system, simple nozzle layout, with broad dispersion				C.F.	2.11			2.11	2.32
6010	Extinguisher, FM200 system, filled, with mounting bracket									
6020	Complex nozzle layout and/or including underfloor dispersion				C.F.	4.20			4.20	4.62
6100	20,000 C.F. 2 exits, 8' clng					2.35			2.35	2.59
6200	100,000 C.F. 4 exits, 8' clng					2.13			2.13	2.34
6300	250,000 C.F. 6 exits, 8' clng					1.79			1.79	1.97
7010	HFC-227ea fire extinguishing system									
7100	Cylinders with clean-agent									
7110	Does not include pallet jack/fork lift rental fees									
7120	70 lb. cyl, w/35 lb. agent, no solenoid	Q-12	14	1.143	Ea.	3,950	73		4,023	4,450
7130	70 lb. cyl w/70 lb. agent, no solenoid		10	1.600		5,200	102		5,302	5,875
7140	70 lb. cyl w/35 lb. agent, w/solenoid		14	1.143		4,650	73		4,723	5,200
7150	70 lb. cyl w/70 lb. agent, w/solenoid		10	1.600		5,875	102		5,977	6,600
7220	250 lb. cyl, w/125 lb. agent, no solenoid		8	2		9,175	127		9,302	10,300
7230	250 lb. cyl, w/250 lb. agent, no solenoid		5	3.200		9,175	204		9,379	10,400
7240	250 lb. cyl, w/125 lb. agent, w/solenoid		8	2		10,000	127		10,127	11,300
7250	250 lb. cyl, w/250 lb. agent, w/solenoid		5	3.200		14,400	204		14,604	16,200
7320	560 lb. cyl, w/300 lb. agent, no solenoid		4	4		17,500	255		17,755	19,700
7330	560 lb. cyl, w/560 lb. agent, no solenoid		2.50	6.400		26,800	410		27,210	30,000
7340	560 lb. cyl, w/300 lb. agent, w/solenoid		4	4		18,600	255		18,855	20,900
7350	560 lb. cyl, w/560 lb. agent, w/solenoid		2.50	6.400		27,700	410		28,110	31,100
7420	1,200 lb. cyl, w/600 lb. agent, no solenoid	Q-13	4	8		33,400	540		33,940	37,500
7430	1,200 lb. cyl, w/1,200 lb. agent, no solenoid		3	10.667		54,500	720		55,220	61,000
7440	1,200 lb. cyl, w/600 lb. agent, w/solenoid		4	8		64,500	540		65,040	72,000
7450	1,200 lb. cyl, w/1,200 lb. agent, w/solenoid		3	10.667		101,500	720		102,220	112,500
7500	Accessories									
7510	Dispersion nozzle	1 Spri	16	.500	Ea.	151	35.50		186.50	219
7520	Agent release panel	1 Elec	4	2		102	135		237	310
7530	Maintenance switch	"	6	1.333		320	90		410	490

21 22 16 – Clean-Agent Fire-Extinguishing Equipment

21 22 16.50 Clean-Agent Extinguishing Systems		Crew	Daily Output	Labor-Hours	Unit	2023 Bare Costs Material	Labor	Equipment	Total	Total Incl O&P
7540	Solenoid valve, 12v dc	1 Spri	8	1	Ea.	273	71		344	405
7550	12v ac		8	1		670	71		741	840
7560	12v dc, explosion proof	↓	8	1	↓	705	71		776	880

Division Notes

	CREW	DAILY OUTPUT	LABOR-HOURS	UNIT	BARE COSTS MAT.	LABOR	EQUIP.	TOTAL	TOTAL INCL O&P

Estimating Tips

22 10 00 Plumbing Piping and Pumps

This subdivision is primarily basic pipe and related materials. The pipe may be used by any of the mechanical disciplines, i.e., plumbing, fire protection, heating, and air conditioning.

Note: CPVC plastic piping approved for fire protection is located in 21 11 13.

- The labor adjustment factors listed in Subdivision 22 01 02.20 apply throughout Divisions 21, 22, and 23. CAUTION: the correct percentage may vary for the same items. For example, the percentage add for the basic pipe installation should be based on the maximum height that the installer must install for that particular section. If the pipe is to be located 14' above the floor but it is suspended on threaded rod from beams, the bottom flange of which is 18' high (4' rods), then the height is actually 18' and the add is 20%. The pipe cover, however, does not have to go above the 14' and so the add should be 10%.
- Most pipe is priced first as straight pipe with a joint (coupling, weld, etc.) every 10' and a hanger usually every 10'. There are exceptions with hanger spacing such as for cast iron pipe (5') and plastic pipe (3 per 10'). Following each type of pipe there are several lines listing sizes and the amount to be subtracted to delete couplings and hangers. This is for pipe that is to be buried or supported together on trapeze hangers. The reason that the couplings are deleted is that these runs are usually long, and frequently longer lengths of pipe are used. By deleting the couplings, the estimator is expected to look up and add back the correct reduced number of couplings.
- When preparing an estimate, it may be necessary to approximate the fittings. Fittings usually run between 25% and 50% of the cost of the pipe. The lower percentage is for simpler runs, and the higher number is for complex areas, such as mechanical rooms.
- For historic restoration projects, the systems must be as invisible as possible, and pathways must be sought for pipes, conduit, and ductwork. While installations in accessible spaces (such as basements and attics) are relatively straightforward to estimate, labor costs may be more difficult to determine when delivery systems must be concealed.

22 40 00 Plumbing Fixtures

- Plumbing fixture costs usually require two lines: the fixture itself and its "rough-in, supply, and waste."
- In the Assemblies Section (Plumbing D2010) for the desired fixture, the System Components Group at the center of the page shows the fixture on the first line. The rest of the list (fittings, pipe, tubing, etc.) will total up to what we refer to in the Unit Price section as "Rough-in, supply, waste, and vent." Note that for most fixtures we allow a nominal 5' of tubing to reach from the fixture to a main or riser.
- Remember that gas- and oil-fired units need venting.

Reference Numbers

Reference numbers are shown at the beginning of some major classifications. These numbers refer to related items in the Reference Section. The reference information may be an estimating procedure, an alternate pricing method, or technical information.

Note: Not all subdivisions listed here necessarily appear. ■

Note: "Powered in part by CINX™, based on licensed proprietary information of Harrison Publishing House, Inc."

Note: Trade Service, in part, has been used as a reference source for some of the material prices used in Division 22.

22 01 Operation and Maintenance of Plumbing

22 01 02 – Labor Adjustments

22 01 02.10 Boilers, General		Crew	Daily Output	Labor-Hours	Unit	Material	2023 Bare Costs Labor	Equipment	Total	Total Incl O&P
0010	**BOILERS, GENERAL**, Prices do not include flue piping, elec. wiring,									
0020	gas or oil piping, boiler base, pad, or tankless unless noted									
0100	Boiler H.P.: 10 KW = 34 lb./steam/hr. = 33,475 BTU/hr.									
0150	To convert SFR to BTU rating: Hot water, 150 x SFR;									
0160	Forced hot water, 180 x SFR; steam, 240 x SFR									

22 01 02.20 Labor Adjustment Factors		Crew	Daily Output	Labor-Hours	Unit	Material	Labor	Equipment	Total	Total Incl O&P
0010	**LABOR ADJUSTMENT FACTORS** (For Div. 21, 22 and 23) R220102-20									
0100	Labor factors: The below are reasonable suggestions, but									
0110	each project must be evaluated for its own peculiarities, and									
0120	the adjustments be increased or decreased depending on the									
0130	severity of the special conditions.									
1000	Add to labor for elevated installation (Above floor level)									
1080	10′ to 14.5′ high						10%			
1100	15′ to 19.5′ high						20%			
1120	20′ to 24.5′ high						25%			
1140	25′ to 29.5′ high						35%			
1160	30′ to 34.5′ high						40%			
1180	35′ to 39.5′ high						50%			
1200	40′ and higher						55%			
2000	Add to labor for crawl space									
2100	3′ high						40%			
2140	4′ high						30%			
3000	Add to labor for multi-story building									
3010	For new construction (No elevator available)									
3100	Add for floors 3 thru 10						5%			
3110	Add for floors 11 thru 15						10%			
3120	Add for floors 16 thru 20						15%			
3130	Add for floors 21 thru 30						20%			
3140	Add for floors 31 and up						30%			
3170	For existing structure (Elevator available)									
3180	Add for work on floor 3 and above						2%			
4000	Add to labor for working in existing occupied buildings									
4100	Hospital						35%			
4140	Office building						25%			
4180	School						20%			
4220	Factory or warehouse						15%			
4260	Multi dwelling						15%			
5000	Add to labor, miscellaneous									
5100	Cramped shaft						35%			
5140	Congested area						15%			
5180	Excessive heat or cold						30%			
9000	Labor factors: The above are reasonable suggestions, but									
9010	each project should be evaluated for its own peculiarities.									
9100	Other factors to be considered are:									
9140	Movement of material and equipment through finished areas									
9180	Equipment room									
9220	Attic space									
9260	No service road									
9300	Poor unloading/storage area									
9340	Congested site area/heavy traffic									

22 05 Common Work Results for Plumbing

22 05 23 – General-Duty Valves for Plumbing Piping

22 05 23.20 Valves, Bronze		Crew	Daily Output	Labor-Hours	Unit	2023 Bare Costs Material	Labor	Equipment	Total	Total Incl O&P
0010	**VALVES, BRONZE**									
8800	Water heater water & gas safety shut off									
8810	Protection against a leaking water heater									
8814	Shut off valve	1 Plum	16	.500	Ea.	196	36		232	269
8818	Water heater dam		32	.250		52.50	18		70.50	85
8822	Gas control wiring harness		32	.250		25.50	18		43.50	55
8830	Whole house flood safety shut off									
8834	Connections									
8838	3/4" NPT	1 Plum	12	.667	Ea.	1,100	48		1,148	1,275
8842	1" NPT		11	.727		1,125	52.50		1,177.50	1,300
8846	1-1/4" NPT		10	.800		1,150	57.50		1,207.50	1,350

22 05 29 – Hangers and Supports for Plumbing Piping and Equipment

22 05 29.10 Hangers & Supp. for Plumb'g/HVAC Pipe/Equip.		Crew	Daily Output	Labor-Hours	Unit	Material	Labor	Equipment	Total	Total Incl O&P
0010	**HANGERS AND SUPPORTS FOR PLUMB'G/HVAC PIPE/EQUIP.**									
0011	TYPE numbers per MSS-SP58									
0050	Brackets									
0060	Beam side or wall, malleable iron, TYPE 34									
0070	3/8" threaded rod size	1 Plum	48	.167	Ea.	8.40	12		20.40	27
0080	1/2" threaded rod size		48	.167		15	12		27	34.50
0090	5/8" threaded rod size		48	.167		25.50	12		37.50	46
0100	3/4" threaded rod size		48	.167		23	12		35	43
0110	7/8" threaded rod size		48	.167		25	12		37	45.50
0120	For concrete installation, add						30%			
0150	Wall, welded steel, medium, TYPE 32									
0160	0 size, 12" wide, 18" deep	1 Plum	34	.235	Ea.	695	16.95		711.95	790
0170	1 size, 18" wide, 24" deep		34	.235		825	16.95		841.95	930
0180	2 size, 24" wide, 30" deep		34	.235		1,100	16.95		1,116.95	1,225
0300	Clamps									
0310	C-clamp, for mounting on steel beam flange, w/locknut, TYPE 23									
0320	3/8" threaded rod size	1 Plum	160	.050	Ea.	6.15	3.60		9.75	12.15
0330	1/2" threaded rod size		160	.050		7.65	3.60		11.25	13.80
0340	5/8" threaded rod size		160	.050		10.30	3.60		13.90	16.65
0350	3/4" threaded rod size		160	.050		6.85	3.60		10.45	12.85
0750	Riser or extension pipe, carbon steel, TYPE 8									
0760	3/4" pipe size	1 Plum	48	.167	Ea.	4.40	12		16.40	22.50
0770	1" pipe size		47	.170		4.54	12.25		16.79	23.50
0780	1-1/4" pipe size		46	.174		8.10	12.55		20.65	27.50
0790	1-1/2" pipe size		45	.178		6	12.80		18.80	25.50
0800	2" pipe size		43	.186		6.15	13.40		19.55	27
0810	2-1/2" pipe size		41	.195		6.40	14.05		20.45	28
0820	3" pipe size		40	.200		7.20	14.40		21.60	29.50
0830	3-1/2" pipe size		39	.205		21	14.80		35.80	45
0840	4" pipe size		38	.211		8.85	15.15		24	32.50
0850	5" pipe size		37	.216		29	15.60		44.60	54.50
0860	6" pipe size		36	.222		35.50	16		51.50	63
1150	Insert, concrete									
1160	Wedge type, carbon steel body, malleable iron nut, galvanized									
1170	1/4" threaded rod size	1 Plum	96	.083	Ea.	24	6		30	35
1180	3/8" threaded rod size		96	.083		2.17	6		8.17	11.35
1190	1/2" threaded rod size		96	.083		2.37	6		8.37	11.55
1200	5/8" threaded rod size		96	.083		3.24	6		9.24	12.50
1210	3/4" threaded rod size		96	.083		3.56	6		9.56	12.85

22 05 29 – Hangers and Supports for Plumbing Piping and Equipment

22 05 29.10 Hangers & Supp. for Plumb'g/HVAC Pipe/Equip.		Crew	Daily Output	Labor-Hours	Unit	2023 Bare Costs Material	Labor	Equipment	Total	Total Incl O&P
1220	7/8" threaded rod size	1 Plum	96	.083	Ea.	52.50	6		58.50	67
2650	Rods, carbon steel									
2660	Continuous thread									
2670	1/4" thread size	1 Plum	144	.056	L.F.	.43	4		4.43	6.40
2680	3/8" thread size		144	.056		.46	4		4.46	6.45
2690	1/2" thread size		144	.056		.72	4		4.72	6.75
2700	5/8" thread size		144	.056		1.03	4		5.03	7.10
2710	3/4" thread size		144	.056		1.81	4		5.81	7.95
2720	7/8" thread size		144	.056		2.27	4		6.27	8.45
2725	1/4" thread size, bright finish		144	.056		1.94	4		5.94	8.10
2726	1/2" thread size, bright finish		144	.056		9.95	4		13.95	16.90
2730	For galvanized, add					40%				
4400	U-bolt, carbon steel									
4410	Standard, with nuts, TYPE 42									
4420	1/2" pipe size	1 Plum	160	.050	Ea.	2.56	3.60		6.16	8.15
4430	3/4" pipe size		158	.051		3.32	3.65		6.97	9.10
4450	1" pipe size		152	.053		3.52	3.79		7.31	9.50
4460	1-1/4" pipe size		148	.054		4.01	3.89		7.90	10.20
4470	1-1/2" pipe size		143	.056		4.33	4.03		8.36	10.75
4480	2" pipe size		139	.058		4.66	4.15		8.81	11.35
4490	2-1/2" pipe size		134	.060		7.80	4.30		12.10	14.95
4500	3" pipe size		128	.063		8.20	4.50		12.70	15.70
4510	3-1/2" pipe size		122	.066		8.55	4.72		13.27	16.50
4520	4" pipe size		117	.068		8.80	4.93		13.73	17.05
4530	5" pipe size		114	.070		7.20	5.05		12.25	15.50
4540	6" pipe size		111	.072		14.95	5.20		20.15	24
4580	For plastic coating on 1/2" thru 6" size, add					150%				
8800	Wire cable support system									
8810	Cable with hook terminal and locking device									
8830	2 mm (.079") diam. cable (100 lb. cap.)									
8840	1 m (3.3') length, with hook	1 Shee	96	.083	Ea.	5.90	5.85		11.75	15.30
8850	2 m (6.6') length, with hook		84	.095		7	6.70		13.70	17.75
8860	3 m (9.9') length, with hook		72	.111		7.80	7.80		15.60	20.50
8870	5 m (16.4') length, with hook	Q-9	60	.267		9.55	16.85		26.40	36
8880	10 m (32.8') length, with hook	"	30	.533		13.70	33.50		47.20	65.50
8900	3 mm (.118") diam. cable (200 lb. cap.)									
8910	1 m (3.3') length, with hook	1 Shee	96	.083	Ea.	17.15	5.85		23	27.50
8920	2 m (6.6') length, with hook		84	.095		.85	6.70		7.55	11
8930	3 m (9.9') length, with hook		72	.111		21	7.80		28.80	35
8940	5 m (16.4') length, with hook	Q-9	60	.267		18.20	16.85		35.05	45.50
8950	10 m (32.8') length, with hook	"	30	.533		16.30	33.50		49.80	68.50
9000	Cable system accessories									
9010	Anchor bolt, 3/8", with nut	1 Shee	140	.057	Ea.	3.85	4.01		7.86	10.30
9020	Air duct corner protector		160	.050		1.70	3.51		5.21	7.15
9030	Air duct support attachment		140	.057		3.56	4.01		7.57	9.95
9040	Flange clip, hammer-on style									
9044	For flange thickness 3/32"-9/64", 160 lb. cap.	1 Shee	180	.044	Ea.	.88	3.12		4	5.65
9048	For flange thickness 1/8"-1/4", 200 lb. cap.		160	.050		.98	3.51		4.49	6.40
9052	For flange thickness 5/16"-1/2", 200 lb. cap.		150	.053		2.10	3.74		5.84	7.95
9056	For flange thickness 9/16"-3/4", 200 lb. cap.		140	.057		2.62	4.01		6.63	8.95
9060	Wire insulation protection tube		180	.044	L.F.	.89	3.12		4.01	5.70
9070	Wire cutter				Ea.	140			140	154

22 33 Electric Domestic Water Heaters

22 33 13 – Instantaneous Electric Domestic Water Heaters

22 33 13.10 Hot Water Dispensers		Crew	Daily Output	Labor-Hours	Unit	Material	2023 Bare Costs Labor	Equipment	Total	Total Incl O&P
0010	**HOT WATER DISPENSERS**									
0160	Commercial, 100 cup, 11.3 amp	1 Plum	14	.571	Ea.	455	41		496	560
3180	Household, 60 cup	"	14	.571	"	239	41		280	325

22 33 30 – Residential, Electric Domestic Water Heaters

22 33 30.13 Residential, Small-Capacity Elec. Water Heaters		Crew	Daily Output	Labor-Hours	Unit	Material	Labor	Equipment	Total	Total Incl O&P
0010	**RESIDENTIAL, SMALL-CAPACITY ELECTRIC DOMESTIC WATER HEATERS**									
1000	Residential, electric, glass lined tank, 5 yr., 10 gal., single element R224000-10	1 Plum	2.30	3.478	Ea.	440	251		691	860
1040	20 gallon, single element R224000-20		2.20	3.636		480	262		742	920
1060	30 gallon, double element		2.20	3.636		835	262		1,097	1,300
1080	40 gallon, double element		2	4		865	288		1,153	1,375
1100	52 gallon, double element		2	4		1,500	288		1,788	2,075
1120	66 gallon, double element		1.80	4.444		2,050	320		2,370	2,725
1140	80 gallon, double element		1.60	5		2,325	360		2,685	3,075
1180	120 gallon, double element		1.40	5.714		3,200	410		3,610	4,150

22 33 33 – Light-Commercial Electric Domestic Water Heaters

22 33 33.10 Commercial Electric Water Heaters		Crew	Daily Output	Labor-Hours	Unit	Material	Labor	Equipment	Total	Total Incl O&P
0010	**COMMERCIAL ELECTRIC WATER HEATERS**									
4000	Commercial, 100° rise. NOTE: for each size tank, a range of									
4010	heaters between the ones shown is available									
4020	Electric									
4100	5 gal., 3 kW, 12 GPH, 208 volt	1 Plum	2	4	Ea.	4,750	288		5,038	5,650
4120	10 gal., 6 kW, 25 GPH, 208 volt		2	4		5,200	288		5,488	6,125
4130	30 gal., 24 kW, 98 GPH, 208 volt		1.92	4.167		8,325	300		8,625	9,600
4136	40 gal., 36 kW, 148 GPH, 208 volt		1.88	4.255		10,600	305		10,905	12,200
4140	50 gal., 9 kW, 37 GPH, 208 volt		1.80	4.444		6,500	320		6,820	7,625
4160	50 gal., 36 kW, 148 GPH, 208 volt		1.80	4.444		11,000	320		11,320	12,600
4180	80 gal., 12 kW, 49 GPH, 208 volt		1.50	5.333		8,050	385		8,435	9,425
4200	80 gal., 36 kW, 148 GPH, 208 volt		1.50	5.333		12,500	385		12,885	14,300
4220	100 gal., 36 kW, 148 GPH, 208 volt		1.20	6.667		13,400	480		13,880	15,400
4240	120 gal., 36 kW, 148 GPH, 208 volt		1.20	6.667		13,900	480		14,380	16,000
4260	150 gal., 15 kW, 61 GPH, 480 volt		1	8		36,000	575		36,575	40,500
4280	150 gal., 120 kW, 490 GPH, 480 volt		1	8		48,900	575		49,475	55,000
4300	200 gal., 15 kW, 61 GPH, 480 volt	Q-1	1.70	9.412		38,100	610		38,710	42,900
4320	200 gal., 120 kW, 490 GPH, 480 volt		1.70	9.412		51,500	610		52,110	57,500
4340	250 gal., 15 kW, 61 GPH, 480 volt		1.50	10.667		39,500	690		40,190	44,400
4360	250 gal., 150 kW, 615 GPH, 480 volt		1.50	10.667		48,300	690		48,990	54,000
4380	300 gal., 30 kW, 123 GPH, 480 volt		1.30	12.308		43,400	800		44,200	49,000
4400	300 gal., 180 kW, 738 GPH, 480 volt		1.30	12.308		75,000	800		75,800	83,500
4420	350 gal., 30 kW, 123 GPH, 480 volt		1.10	14.545		38,600	945		39,545	43,800
4440	350 gal., 180 kW, 738 GPH, 480 volt		1.10	14.545		54,500	945		55,445	61,500
4460	400 gal., 30 kW, 123 GPH, 480 volt		1	16		53,000	1,050		54,050	59,500
4480	400 gal., 210 kW, 860 GPH, 480 volt		1	16		88,000	1,050		89,050	98,500
4500	500 gal., 30 kW, 123 GPH, 480 volt		.80	20		61,500	1,300		62,800	70,000
4520	500 gal., 240 kW, 984 GPH, 480 volt		.80	20		103,000	1,300		104,300	115,000
4540	600 gal., 30 kW, 123 GPH, 480 volt	Q-2	1.20	20		69,500	1,350		70,850	78,000
4560	600 gal., 300 kW, 1,230 GPH, 480 volt		1.20	20		121,500	1,350		122,850	135,500
4580	700 gal., 30 kW, 123 GPH, 480 volt		1	24		61,500	1,625		63,125	70,000
4600	700 gal., 300 kW, 1,230 GPH, 480 volt		1	24		92,500	1,625		94,125	104,000
4620	800 gal., 60 kW, 245 GPH, 480 volt		.90	26.667		83,000	1,800		84,800	94,000
4640	800 gal., 300 kW, 1,230 GPH, 480 volt		.90	26.667		94,500	1,800		96,300	106,000
4660	1,000 gal., 60 kW, 245 GPH, 480 volt		.70	34.286		72,500	2,300		74,800	83,500
4680	1,000 gal., 480 kW, 1,970 GPH, 480 volt		.70	34.286		120,500	2,300		122,800	136,000

22 33 Electric Domestic Water Heaters

22 33 33 – Light-Commercial Electric Domestic Water Heaters

22 33 33.10 Commercial Electric Water Heaters		Crew	Daily Output	Labor-Hours	Unit	2023 Bare Costs Material	Labor	Equipment	Total	Total Incl O&P
4700	1,200 gal., 60 kW, 245 GPH, 480 volt	Q-2	.60	40	Ea.	82,000	2,700		84,700	94,500
4720	1,200 gal., 480 kW, 1,970 GPH, 480 volt		.60	40		125,000	2,700		127,700	141,000
4740	1,500 gal., 60 kW, 245 GPH, 480 volt		.50	48		108,000	3,225		111,225	124,000
4760	1,500 gal., 480 kW, 1,970 GPH, 480 volt		.50	48		150,000	3,225		153,225	170,000
5400	Modulating step control for under 90 kW, 2-5 steps	1 Elec	5.30	1.509		955	102		1,057	1,200
5440	For above 90 kW, 1 through 5 steps beyond standard, add		3.20	2.500		256	168		424	530
5460	For above 90 kW, 6 through 10 steps beyond standard, add		2.70	2.963		570	200		770	920
5480	For above 90 kW, 11 through 18 steps beyond standard, add		1.60	5		845	335		1,180	1,425

22 34 Fuel-Fired Domestic Water Heaters

22 34 30 – Residential Gas Domestic Water Heaters

22 34 30.13 Residential, Atmos, Gas Domestic Wtr Heaters		Crew	Daily Output	Labor-Hours	Unit	Material	Labor	Equipment	Total	Total Incl O&P
0010	RESIDENTIAL, ATMOSPHERIC, GAS DOMESTIC WATER HEATERS									
2000	Gas fired, foam lined tank, 10 yr., vent not incl.									
2040	30 gallon	1 Plum	2	4	Ea.	2,100	288		2,388	2,750
2060	40 gallon		1.90	4.211		725	305		1,030	1,250
2080	50 gallon		1.80	4.444		825	320		1,145	1,375
2090	60 gallon		1.70	4.706		1,800	340		2,140	2,475
2100	75 gallon		1.50	5.333		1,325	385		1,710	2,050
2120	100 gallon		1.30	6.154		2,525	445		2,970	3,425
2900	Water heater, safety-drain pan, 26" round		20	.400		20	29		49	65
3000	Tank leak safety, water & gas shut off see 22 05 23.20 8800									

22 34 46 – Oil-Fired Domestic Water Heaters

22 34 46.10 Residential Oil-Fired Water Heaters		Crew	Daily Output	Labor-Hours	Unit	Material	Labor	Equipment	Total	Total Incl O&P
0010	RESIDENTIAL OIL-FIRED WATER HEATERS									
3000	Oil fired, glass lined tank, 5 yr., vent not included, 30 gallon	1 Plum	2	4	Ea.	1,600	288		1,888	2,175
3040	50 gallon		1.80	4.444		1,450	320		1,770	2,075
3060	70 gallon		1.50	5.333		2,225	385		2,610	3,025

Estimating Tips

The labor adjustment factors listed in Subdivision 22 01 02.20 also apply to Division 23.

23 10 00 Facility Fuel Systems

- The prices in this subdivision for above- and below-ground storage tanks do not include foundations or hold-down slabs, unless noted. The estimator should refer to Divisions 3 and 31 for foundation system pricing. In addition to the foundations, required tank accessories, such as tank gauges, leak detection devices, and additional manholes and piping, must be added to the tank prices.

23 50 00 Central Heating Equipment

- When estimating the cost of an HVAC system, check to see who is responsible for providing and installing the temperature control system. It is possible to overlook controls, assuming that they would be included in the electrical estimate.
- When looking up a boiler, be careful on specified capacity. Some manufacturers rate their products on output while others use input.
- Include HVAC insulation for pipe, boiler, and duct (wrap and liner).
- Be careful when looking up mechanical items to get the correct pressure rating and connection type (thread, weld, flange).

23 70 00 Central HVAC Equipment

- Combination heating and cooling units are sized by the air conditioning requirements. (See Reference No. R236000-20 for the preliminary sizing guide.)
- A ton of air conditioning is nominally 400 CFM.
- Rectangular duct is taken off by the linear foot for each size, but its cost is usually estimated by the pound. Remember that SMACNA standards now base duct on internal pressure.
- Prefabricated duct is estimated and purchased like pipe: straight sections and fittings.
- Note that cranes or other lifting equipment are not included on any lines in Division 23. For example, if a crane is required to lift a heavy piece of pipe into place high above a gym floor, or to put a rooftop unit on the roof of a four-story building, etc., it must be added. Due to the potential for extreme variation—from nothing additional required to a major crane or helicopter—we feel that including a nominal amount for "lifting contingency" would be useless and detract from the accuracy of the estimate. When using equipment rental cost data from RSMeans, do not forget to include the cost of the operator(s).

Reference Numbers

Reference numbers are shown at the beginning of some major classifications. These numbers refer to related items in the Reference Section. The reference information may be an estimating procedure, an alternate pricing method, or technical information.

Note: Not all subdivisions listed here necessarily appear. ■

Note: "Powered in part by CINX™, based on licensed proprietary information of Harrison Publishing House, Inc."

Note: Trade Service, in part, has been used as a reference source for some of the material prices used in Division 23.

23 05 Common Work Results for HVAC

23 05 02 – HVAC General

23 05 02.10 Air Conditioning, General	Crew	Daily Output	Labor-Hours	Unit	Material	Labor	Equipment	Total	Total Incl O&P
					2023 Bare Costs				
0010 **AIR CONDITIONING, GENERAL** Prices are for standard efficiencies (SEER 13)									
0020 for upgrade to SEER 14 add					10%				

23 05 93 – Testing, Adjusting, and Balancing for HVAC

23 05 93.10 Balancing, Air

23 05 93.10 Balancing, Air	Crew	Daily Output	Labor-Hours	Unit	Material	Labor	Equipment	Total	Total Incl O&P
0010 **BALANCING, AIR** (Subcontractor's quote incl. material and labor)									
0900 Heating and ventilating equipment									
1000 Centrifugal fans, utility sets				Ea.				420	420
1100 Heating and ventilating unit								630	630
1200 In-line fan								630	630
1300 Propeller and wall fan								119	119
1400 Roof exhaust fan								280	280
2000 Air conditioning equipment, central station								910	910
2100 Built-up low pressure unit								840	840
2200 Built-up high pressure unit								980	980
2300 Built-up high pressure dual duct								1,550	1,550
2400 Built-up variable volume								1,825	1,825
2500 Multi-zone A.C. and heating unit								630	630
2600 For each zone over one, add								140	140
2700 Package A.C. unit								350	350
2800 Rooftop heating and cooling unit								490	490
3000 Supply, return, exhaust, registers & diffusers, avg. height ceiling								84	84
3100 High ceiling								126	126
3200 Floor height								70	70
3300 Off mixing box								56	56
3500 Induction unit								91	91
3600 Lab fume hood								420	420
3700 Linear supply								210	210
3800 Linear supply high								245	245
4000 Linear return								70	70
4100 Light troffers								84	84
4200 Moduline - master								84	84
4300 Moduline - slaves								42	42
4400 Regenerators								560	560
4500 Taps into ceiling plenums								105	105
4600 Variable volume boxes				↓				84	84

23 05 93.20 Balancing, Water

23 05 93.20 Balancing, Water	Crew	Daily Output	Labor-Hours	Unit	Material	Labor	Equipment	Total	Total Incl O&P
0010 **BALANCING, WATER** (Subcontractor's quote incl. material and labor)									
0050 Air cooled condenser				Ea.				256	256
0080 Boiler								515	515
0100 Cabinet unit heater								88	88
0200 Chiller								620	620
0300 Convector								73	73
0400 Converter								365	365
0500 Cooling tower								475	475
0600 Fan coil unit, unit ventilator								132	132
0700 Fin tube and radiant panels								146	146
0800 Main and duct re-heat coils								135	135
0810 Heat exchanger								135	135
0900 Main balancing cocks								110	110
1000 Pumps								320	320
1100 Unit heater				↓				102	102

23 09 23 – Direct-Digital Control System for HVAC

23 09 23.10 Control Components/DDC Systems		Crew	Daily Output	Labor-Hours	Unit	2023 Bare Costs Material	Labor	Equipment	Total	Total Incl O&P
0010	**CONTROL COMPONENTS/DDC SYSTEMS** (Sub's quote incl. M & L)									
0100	Analog inputs									
0110	Sensors (avg. 50′ run in 1/2″ EMT)									
0120	Duct temperature				Ea.				465	465
0130	Space temperature								665	665
0140	Duct humidity, +/- 3%								595	595
0150	Space humidity, +/- 2%								1,150	1,150
0160	Duct static pressure								680	680
0170	CFM/transducer								920	920
0172	Water temperature								940	940
0174	Water flow								3,450	3,450
0176	Water pressure differential								975	975
0177	Steam flow								2,400	2,400
0178	Steam pressure								1,025	1,025
0180	KW/transducer								1,350	1,350
0182	KWH totalization (not incl. elec. meter pulse xmtr.)								625	625
0190	Space static pressure								1,075	1,075
1000	Analog outputs (avg. 50′ run in 1/2″ EMT)									
1010	P/I transducer				Ea.				635	635
1020	Analog output, matl. in MUX								305	305
1030	Pneumatic (not incl. control device)								645	645
1040	Electric (not incl. control device)								380	380
2000	Status (alarms)									
2100	Digital inputs (avg. 50′ run in 1/2″ EMT)									
2110	Freeze				Ea.				435	435
2120	Fire								395	395
2130	Differential pressure (air)	2 Elec	3	5.333		385	360		745	960
2140	Differential pressure (water)								975	975
2150	Current sensor								435	435
2160	Duct high temperature thermostat								570	570
2170	Duct smoke detector								705	705
2200	Digital output (avg. 50′ run in 1/2″ EMT)									
2210	Start/stop				Ea.				340	340
2220	On/off (maintained contact)				″				585	585
3000	Controller MUX panel, incl. function boards									
3100	48 point				Ea.				5,275	5,275
3110	128 point				″				7,225	7,225
3200	DDC controller (avg. 50′ run in conduit)									
3210	Mechanical room									
3214	16 point controller (incl. 120 volt/1 phase power supply)				Ea.				3,275	3,275
3229	32 point controller (incl. 120 volt/1 phase power supply)				″				5,425	5,425
3230	Includes software programming and checkout									
3260	Space									
3266	VAV terminal box (incl. space temp. sensor)				Ea.				840	840
3280	Host computer (avg. 50′ run in conduit)									
3281	Package complete with PC, keyboard,									
3282	printer, monitor, basic software				Ea.				3,150	3,150
4000	Front end costs									
4100	Computer (P.C.) with software program				Ea.				6,350	6,350
4200	Color graphics software								3,925	3,925
4300	Color graphics slides								490	490
4350	Additional printer								980	980
4400	Communications trunk cable				L.F.				3.80	3.80

23 09 23 – Direct-Digital Control System for HVAC

23 09 23.10 Control Components/DDC Systems		Crew	Daily Output	Labor-Hours	Unit	Material	Labor	Equipment	Total	Total Incl O&P
						2023 Bare Costs				
4500	Engineering labor (not incl. dftg.)				Point				94	94
4600	Calibration labor								120	120
4700	Start-up, checkout labor				↓				120	120
4800	Programming labor, as req'd									
5000	Communications bus (data transmission cable)									
5010	#18 twisted shielded pair in 1/2" EMT conduit				C.L.F.				380	380
8000	Applications software									
8050	Basic maintenance manager software (not incl. data base entry)				Ea.				1,950	1,950
8100	Time program				Point				6.85	6.85
8120	Duty cycle								13.65	13.65
8140	Optimum start/stop								41.50	41.50
8160	Demand limiting								20.50	20.50
8180	Enthalpy program				↓				41.50	41.50
8200	Boiler optimization				Ea.				1,225	1,225
8220	Chiller optimization				"				1,625	1,625
8240	Custom applications									
8260	Cost varies with complexity									

23 09 43 – Pneumatic Control System for HVAC

23 09 43.10 Pneumatic Control Systems		Crew	Daily Output	Labor-Hours	Unit	Material	Labor	Equipment	Total	Total Incl O&P
0010	**PNEUMATIC CONTROL SYSTEMS**									
0011	Including a nominal 50' of tubing. Add control panelboard if req'd.									
0100	Heating and ventilating, split system									
0200	Mixed air control, economizer cycle, panel readout, tubing									
0220	Up to 10 tons G	Q-19	.68	35.294	Ea.	6,600	2,325		8,925	10,700
0240	For 10 to 20 tons G		.63	37.915		7,425	2,500		9,925	11,900
0260	For over 20 tons G		.58	41.096		8,050	2,700		10,750	12,900
0270	Enthalpy cycle, up to 10 tons		.50	48.387		7,625	3,200		10,825	13,200
0280	For 10 to 20 tons		.46	52.174		8,250	3,450		11,700	14,200
0290	For over 20 tons	↓	.42	56.604	↓	8,225	3,725		11,950	14,600
0300	Heating coil, hot water, 3 way valve,									
0320	Freezestat, limit control on discharge, readout	Q-5	.69	23.088	Ea.	4,900	1,500		6,400	7,625
0500	Cooling coil, chilled water, room									
0520	Thermostat, 3 way valve	Q-5	2	8	Ea.	2,100	520		2,620	3,100
0600	Cooling tower, fan cycle, damper control,									
0620	Control system including water readout in/out at panel	Q-19	.67	35.821	Ea.	8,675	2,375		11,050	13,100
1000	Unit ventilator, day/night operation,									
1100	freezestat, ASHRAE, cycle 2	Q-19	.91	26.374	Ea.	4,650	1,750		6,400	7,700
2000	Compensated hot water from boiler, valve control,									
2100	readout and reset at panel, up to 60 GPM	Q-19	.55	43.956	Ea.	9,425	2,900		12,325	14,700
2120	For 120 GPM		.51	47.059		9,275	3,100		12,375	14,800
2140	For 240 GPM		.49	49.180		10,500	3,250		13,750	16,400
3000	Boiler room combustion air, damper to 5 S.F., controls		1.37	17.582		4,325	1,150		5,475	6,500
3500	Fan coil, heating and cooling valves, 4 pipe control system		3	8		2,050	530		2,580	3,025
3600	Heat exchanger system controls	↓	.86	27.907	↓	4,075	1,850		5,925	7,225
3900	Multizone control (one per zone), includes thermostat, damper									
3910	motor and reset of discharge temperature	Q-5	.51	31.373	Ea.	4,175	2,050		6,225	7,650
4000	Pneumatic thermostat, including controlling room radiator valve	"	2.43	6.593		1,250	430		1,680	2,025
4040	Program energy saving optimizer G	Q-19	1.21	19.786		10,800	1,300		12,100	13,900
4060	Pump control system	"	3	8		1,925	530		2,455	2,900
4080	Reheat coil control system, not incl. coil	Q-5	2.43	6.593	↓	1,625	430		2,055	2,450
4500	Air supply for pneumatic control system									
4600	Tank mounted duplex compressor, starter, alternator,									

23 09 Instrumentation and Control for HVAC

23 09 43 – Pneumatic Control System for HVAC

23 09 43.10 Pneumatic Control Systems		Crew	Daily Output	Labor-Hours	Unit	2023 Bare Costs Material	Labor	Equipment	Total	Total Incl O&P
4620	piping, dryer, PRV station and filter									
4630	1/2 HP	Q-19	.68	35.139	Ea.	16,900	2,325		19,225	22,100
4640	3/4 HP		.64	37.383		16,300	2,475		18,775	21,600
4650	1 HP		.61	39.539		18,500	2,600		21,100	24,200
4660	1-1/2 HP		.58	41.739		19,000	2,750		21,750	25,000
4680	3 HP		.55	43.956		25,900	2,900		28,800	32,800
4690	5 HP		.42	57.143		49,200	3,775		52,975	59,500
4800	Main air supply, includes 3/8" copper main and labor	Q-5	1.82	8.791	C.L.F.	570	575		1,145	1,475
7000	Static pressure control for air handling unit, includes pressure									
7010	sensor, receiver controller, readout and damper motors	Q-19	.64	37.383	Ea.	13,500	2,475		15,975	18,500
8600	VAV boxes, incl. thermostat, damper motor, reheat coil & tubing	Q-5	1.46	10.989	"	1,950	720		2,670	3,200

23 09 53 – Pneumatic and Electric Control System for HVAC

23 09 53.10 Control Components		Crew	Daily Output	Labor-Hours	Unit	Material	Labor	Equipment	Total	Total Incl O&P
0010	**CONTROL COMPONENTS**									
0700	Controller, receiver									
0850	Electric, single snap switch	1 Elec	4	2	Ea.	720	135		855	995
0860	Dual snap switches	"	3	2.667	"	970	180		1,150	1,350
3590	Sensor, electric operated									
3620	Humidity	1 Elec	8	1	Ea.	215	67.50		282.50	335
3650	Pressure		8	1		375	67.50		442.50	510
3680	Temperature		10	.800		167	54		221	264
5000	Thermostats									
5200	24 hour, automatic, clock G	1 Shee	8	1	Ea.	226	70		296	355
5220	Electric, low voltage, 2 wire	1 Elec	13	.615		39	41.50		80.50	105
5230	3 wire	"	10	.800		44.50	54		98.50	129
7090	Valves, motor controlled, including actuator									
7100	Electric motor actuated									
7200	Brass, two way, screwed									
7210	1/2" pipe size	L-6	36	.333	Ea.	395	23.50		418.50	470
7220	3/4" pipe size		30	.400		670	28		698	775
7230	1" pipe size		28	.429		775	30		805	900
7240	1-1/2" pipe size		19	.632		870	44.50		914.50	1,025
7250	2" pipe size		16	.750		1,225	53		1,278	1,425
7350	Brass, three way, screwed									
7360	1/2" pipe size	L-6	33	.364	Ea.	400	25.50		425.50	480
7370	3/4" pipe size		27	.444		485	31.50		516.50	575
7380	1" pipe size		25.50	.471		605	33		638	720
7384	1-1/4" pipe size		21	.571		820	40.50		860.50	960
7390	1-1/2" pipe size		17	.706		460	50		510	580
7400	2" pipe size		14	.857		615	60.50		675.50	765
7550	Iron body, two way, flanged									
7560	2-1/2" pipe size	L-6	4	3	Ea.	545	211		756	915
7570	3" pipe size		3	4		1,025	282		1,307	1,550
7580	4" pipe size		2	6		1,475	425		1,900	2,225
7850	Iron body, three way, flanged									
7860	2-1/2" pipe size	L-6	3	4	Ea.	1,000	282		1,282	1,525
7870	3" pipe size		2.50	4.800		1,175	340		1,515	1,800
7880	4" pipe size		2	6		1,850	425		2,275	2,650

23 34 HVAC Fans

23 34 13 – Axial HVAC Fans

23 34 13.10 Axial Flow HVAC Fans		Crew	Daily Output	Labor-Hours	Unit	2023 Bare Costs Material	Labor	Equipment	Total	Total Incl O&P
0010	**AXIAL FLOW HVAC FANS**									
0020	Air conditioning and process air handling									
1500	Vaneaxial, low pressure, 2,000 CFM, 1/2 HP	Q-20	3.60	5.556	Ea.	2,625	355		2,980	3,400
1520	4,000 CFM, 1 HP		3.20	6.250		2,725	400		3,125	3,600
1540	8,000 CFM, 2 HP		2.80	7.143		3,675	455		4,130	4,725
1560	16,000 CFM, 5 HP		2.40	8.333		5,650	535		6,185	7,025

23 34 14 – Blower HVAC Fans

23 34 14.10 Blower Type HVAC Fans		Crew	Daily Output	Labor-Hours	Unit	Material	Labor	Equipment	Total	Total Incl O&P
0010	**BLOWER TYPE HVAC FANS**									
2000	Blowers, direct drive with motor, complete									
2020	1,045 CFM @ 0.5" S.P., 1/5 HP	Q-20	18	1.111	Ea.	360	71		431	505
2040	1,385 CFM @ 0.5" S.P., 1/4 HP		18	1.111		335	71		406	475
2060	1,640 CFM @ 0.5" S.P., 1/3 HP		18	1.111		340	71		411	480
2080	1,760 CFM @ 0.5" S.P., 1/2 HP		18	1.111		325	71		396	460
2090	4 speed									
2100	1,164 to 1,739 CFM @ 0.5" S.P., 1/3 HP	Q-20	16	1.250	Ea.	360	80		440	515
2120	1,467 to 2,218 CFM @ 1.0" S.P., 3/4 HP	"	14	1.429	"	355	91.50		446.50	525
2500	Ceiling fan, right angle, extra quiet, 0.10" S.P.									
2520	95 CFM	Q-20	20	1	Ea.	300	64		364	425
2540	210 CFM		19	1.053		355	67.50		422.50	490
2560	385 CFM		18	1.111		455	71		526	605
2580	885 CFM		16	1.250		890	80		970	1,100
2600	1,650 CFM		13	1.538		1,225	98.50		1,323.50	1,500
2620	2,960 CFM		11	1.818		1,650	116		1,766	1,975
2680	For speed control switch, add	1 Elec	16	.500		165	33.50		198.50	231
7500	Utility set, steel construction, pedestal, 1/4" S.P.									
7520	Direct drive, 150 CFM, 1/8 HP	Q-20	6.40	3.125	Ea.	1,000	200		1,200	1,400
7540	485 CFM, 1/6 HP		5.80	3.448		1,225	221		1,446	1,675
7560	1,950 CFM, 1/2 HP		4.80	4.167		1,475	267		1,742	2,025
7580	2,410 CFM, 3/4 HP		4.40	4.545		2,975	291		3,266	3,700
7600	3,328 CFM, 1-1/2 HP		3	6.667		2,950	425		3,375	3,875
7680	V-belt drive, drive cover, 3 phase									
7700	800 CFM, 1/4 HP	Q-20	6	3.333	Ea.	1,275	213		1,488	1,725
7720	1,300 CFM, 1/3 HP		5	4		1,325	256		1,581	1,825
7740	2,000 CFM, 1 HP		4.60	4.348		1,575	278		1,853	2,150
7760	2,900 CFM, 3/4 HP		4.20	4.762		2,125	305		2,430	2,775
7780	3,600 CFM, 3/4 HP		4	5		2,600	320		2,920	3,350
7800	4,800 CFM, 1 HP		3.50	5.714		3,075	365		3,440	3,925
7820	6,700 CFM, 1-1/2 HP		3	6.667		3,800	425		4,225	4,825
7830	7,500 CFM, 2 HP		2.50	8		5,150	510		5,660	6,450
7840	11,000 CFM, 3 HP		2	10		6,875	640		7,515	8,525
7860	13,000 CFM, 3 HP		1.60	12.500		7,000	800		7,800	8,900
7880	15,000 CFM, 5 HP		1	20		7,250	1,275		8,525	9,900
7900	17,000 CFM, 7-1/2 HP		.80	25		7,750	1,600		9,350	10,900
7920	20,000 CFM, 7-1/2 HP		.80	25		9,225	1,600		10,825	12,600

23 34 16 – Centrifugal HVAC Fans

23 34 16.10 Centrifugal Type HVAC Fans		Crew	Daily Output	Labor-Hours	Unit	Material	Labor	Equipment	Total	Total Incl O&P
0010	**CENTRIFUGAL TYPE HVAC FANS**									
0200	In-line centrifugal, supply/exhaust booster									
0220	aluminum wheel/hub, disconnect switch, 1/4" S.P.									
0240	500 CFM, 10" diameter connection	Q-20	3	6.667	Ea.	1,725	425		2,150	2,550
0260	1,380 CFM, 12" diameter connection		2	10		2,025	640		2,665	3,175

23 34 16 – Centrifugal HVAC Fans

23 34 16.10 Centrifugal Type HVAC Fans		Crew	Daily Output	Labor-Hours	Unit	Material	Labor	Equipment	Total	Total Incl O&P
						2023 Bare Costs				
0280	1,520 CFM, 16" diameter connection	Q-20	2	10	Ea.	1,875	640		2,515	3,025
0300	2,560 CFM, 18" diameter connection		1	20		2,075	1,275		3,350	4,225
0320	3,480 CFM, 20" diameter connection		.80	25		2,400	1,600		4,000	5,025
0326	5,080 CFM, 20" diameter connection		.75	26.667		2,575	1,700		4,275	5,425
3500	Centrifugal, airfoil, motor and drive, complete									
3520	1,000 CFM, 1/2 HP	Q-20	2.50	8	Ea.	2,275	510		2,785	3,275
3540	2,000 CFM, 1 HP		2	10		2,475	640		3,115	3,675
3560	4,000 CFM, 3 HP		1.80	11.111		3,250	710		3,960	4,625
3580	8,000 CFM, 7-1/2 HP		1.40	14.286		4,900	915		5,815	6,775
3600	12,000 CFM, 10 HP		1	20		6,675	1,275		7,950	9,275
5000	Utility set, centrifugal, V belt drive, motor									
5020	1/4" S.P., 1,200 CFM, 1/4 HP	Q-20	6	3.333	Ea.	2,500	213		2,713	3,075
5040	1,520 CFM, 1/3 HP		5	4		3,025	256		3,281	3,700
5060	1,850 CFM, 1/2 HP		4	5		3,025	320		3,345	3,800
5080	2,180 CFM, 3/4 HP		3	6.667		3,425	425		3,850	4,425
5100	1/2" S.P., 3,600 CFM, 1 HP		2	10		3,500	640		4,140	4,800
5120	4,250 CFM, 1-1/2 HP		1.60	12.500		5,050	800		5,850	6,750
5140	4,800 CFM, 2 HP		1.40	14.286		6,325	915		7,240	8,325
5160	6,920 CFM, 5 HP		1.30	15.385		6,900	985		7,885	9,050
5180	7,700 CFM, 7-1/2 HP		1.20	16.667		7,500	1,075		8,575	9,850
5200	For explosion proof motor, add					15%				
5500	Fans, industrial exhauster, for air which may contain granular matl.									
5520	1,000 CFM, 1-1/2 HP	Q-20	2.50	8	Ea.	3,825	510		4,335	5,000
5540	2,000 CFM, 3 HP		2	10		4,500	640		5,140	5,900
5560	4,000 CFM, 7-1/2 HP		1.80	11.111		6,200	710		6,910	7,900
5580	8,000 CFM, 15 HP		1.40	14.286		8,025	915		8,940	10,200
5600	12,000 CFM, 30 HP		1	20		12,500	1,275		13,775	15,600
7000	Roof exhauster, centrifugal, aluminum housing, 12" galvanized									
7020	curb, bird screen, back draft damper, 1/4" S.P.									
7100	Direct drive, 320 CFM, 11" sq. damper	Q-20	7	2.857	Ea.	815	183		998	1,175
7120	600 CFM, 11" sq. damper		6	3.333		1,050	213		1,263	1,475
7140	815 CFM, 13" sq. damper		5	4		1,050	256		1,306	1,525
7160	1,450 CFM, 13" sq. damper		4.20	4.762		1,450	305		1,755	2,050
7180	2,050 CFM, 16" sq. damper		4	5		2,175	320		2,495	2,875
7200	V-belt drive, 1,650 CFM, 12" sq. damper		6	3.333		1,350	213		1,563	1,825
7220	2,750 CFM, 21" sq. damper		5	4		162	256		418	565
7230	3,500 CFM, 21" sq. damper		4.50	4.444		1,950	284		2,234	2,575
7240	4,910 CFM, 23" sq. damper		4	5		2,200	320		2,520	2,900
7260	8,525 CFM, 28" sq. damper		3	6.667		3,050	425		3,475	4,000
7280	13,760 CFM, 35" sq. damper		2	10		4,050	640		4,690	5,400
7300	20,558 CFM, 43" sq. damper		1	20		8,625	1,275		9,900	11,400
7320	For 2 speed winding, add					15%				
7340	For explosion proof motor, add					825			825	905
7360	For belt driven, top discharge, add					15%				
8500	Wall exhausters, centrifugal, auto damper, 1/8" S.P.									
8520	Direct drive, 610 CFM, 1/20 HP	Q-20	14	1.429	Ea.	1,350	91.50		1,441.50	1,600
8540	796 CFM, 1/12 HP		13	1.538		1,650	98.50		1,748.50	1,950
8560	822 CFM, 1/6 HP		12	1.667		1,275	107		1,382	1,550
8580	1,320 CFM, 1/4 HP		12	1.667		1,225	107		1,332	1,500
8600	1,756 CFM, 1/4 HP		11	1.818		1,500	116		1,616	1,825
8620	1,983 CFM, 1/4 HP		10	2		1,525	128		1,653	1,900
8640	2,900 CFM, 1/2 HP		9	2.222		4,125	142		4,267	4,750
8660	3,307 CFM, 3/4 HP		8	2.500		1,775	160		1,935	2,200

23 34 16 – Centrifugal HVAC Fans

23 34 16.10 Centrifugal Type HVAC Fans		Crew	Daily Output	Labor-Hours	Unit	Material	Labor	Equipment	Total	Total Incl O&P
						2023 Bare Costs				
9500	V-belt drive, 3 phase									
9520	2,800 CFM, 1/4 HP	Q-20	9	2.222	Ea.	2,275	142		2,417	2,750
9540	3,740 CFM, 1/2 HP		8	2.500		2,375	160		2,535	2,850
9560	4,400 CFM, 3/4 HP		7	2.857		2,400	183		2,583	2,925
9580	5,700 CFM, 1-1/2 HP		6	3.333		2,500	213		2,713	3,075

23 34 23 – HVAC Power Ventilators

23 34 23.10 HVAC Power Circulators and Ventilators

		Crew	Daily Output	Labor-Hours	Unit	Material	Labor	Equipment	Total	Total Incl O&P
0010	**HVAC POWER CIRCULATORS AND VENTILATORS**									
3000	Paddle blade air circulator, 3 speed switch									
3020	42", 5,000 CFM high, 3,000 CFM low G	1 Elec	2.40	3.333	Ea.	179	225		404	530
3040	52", 6,500 CFM high, 4,000 CFM low G	"	2.20	3.636	"	154	245		399	535
3100	For antique white motor, same cost									
3200	For brass plated motor, same cost									
3300	For light adaptor kit, add G				Ea.	43.50			43.50	48
6000	Propeller exhaust, wall shutter									
6020	Direct drive, one speed, 0.075" S.P.									
6100	653 CFM, 1/30 HP	Q-20	10	2	Ea.	320	128		448	545
6120	1,033 CFM, 1/20 HP		9	2.222		277	142		419	520
6140	1,323 CFM, 1/15 HP		8	2.500		525	160		685	820
6160	2,444 CFM, 1/4 HP		7	2.857		365	183		548	675
6300	V-belt drive, 3 phase									
6320	6,175 CFM, 3/4 HP	Q-20	5	4	Ea.	1,300	256		1,556	1,800
6340	7,500 CFM, 3/4 HP		5	4		1,350	256		1,606	1,850
6360	10,100 CFM, 1 HP		4.50	4.444		1,550	284		1,834	2,150
6380	14,300 CFM, 1-1/2 HP		4	5		1,875	320		2,195	2,550
6400	19,800 CFM, 2 HP		3	6.667		2,150	425		2,575	3,025
6420	26,250 CFM, 3 HP		2.60	7.692		2,650	490		3,140	3,650
6440	38,500 CFM, 5 HP		2.20	9.091		3,325	580		3,905	4,550
6460	46,000 CFM, 7-1/2 HP		2	10		3,425	640		4,065	4,725
6480	51,500 CFM, 10 HP		1.80	11.111		3,475	710		4,185	4,900
6650	Residential, bath exhaust, grille, back draft damper									
6660	50 CFM	Q-20	24	.833	Ea.	50	53.50		103.50	135
6670	110 CFM		22	.909		111	58		169	210
6680	Light combination, squirrel cage, 100 watt, 70 CFM		24	.833		153	53.50		206.50	248
6700	Light/heater combination, ceiling mounted									
6710	70 CFM, 1,450 watt	Q-20	24	.833	Ea.	189	53.50		242.50	288
6800	Heater combination, recessed, 70 CFM		24	.833		85.50	53.50		139	174
6820	With 2 infrared bulbs		23	.870		101	55.50		156.50	195
6900	Kitchen exhaust, grille, complete, 160 CFM		22	.909		146	58		204	248
6910	180 CFM		20	1		110	64		174	217
6920	270 CFM		18	1.111		215	71		286	345
6930	350 CFM		16	1.250		173	80		253	310
6940	Residential roof jacks and wall caps									
6944	Wall cap with back draft damper									
6946	3" & 4" diam. round duct	1 Shee	11	.727	Ea.	25	51		76	105
6948	6" diam. round duct	"	11	.727	"	60	51		111	143
6958	Roof jack with bird screen and back draft damper									
6960	3" & 4" diam. round duct	1 Shee	11	.727	Ea.	31	51		82	112
6962	3-1/4" x 10" rectangular duct	"	10	.800	"	39.50	56		95.50	128
6980	Transition									
6982	3-1/4" x 10" to 6" diam. round	1 Shee	20	.400	Ea.	26.50	28		54.50	72
8020	Attic, roof type									

23 34 23 – HVAC Power Ventilators

23 34 23.10 HVAC Power Circulators and Ventilators		Crew	Daily Output	Labor-Hours	Unit	2023 Bare Costs Material	Labor	Equipment	Total	Total Incl O&P
8030	Aluminum dome, damper & curb									
8080	12" diameter, 1,000 CFM (gravity)	1 Elec	10	.800	Ea.	700	54		754	855
8090	16" diameter, 1,500 CFM (gravity)		9	.889		850	60		910	1,025
8100	20" diameter, 2,500 CFM (gravity)		8	1		1,050	67.50		1,117.50	1,250
8110	26" diameter, 4,000 CFM (gravity)		7	1.143		1,250	77		1,327	1,500
8120	32" diameter, 6,500 CFM (gravity)		6	1.333		1,725	90		1,815	2,025
8130	38" diameter, 8,000 CFM (gravity)		5	1.600		2,550	108		2,658	2,975
8140	50" diameter, 13,000 CFM (gravity)		4	2		3,725	135		3,860	4,275
8160	Plastic, ABS dome									
8180	1,050 CFM	1 Elec	14	.571	Ea.	207	38.50		245.50	284
8200	1,600 CFM	"	12	.667	"	310	45		355	405
8240	Attic, wall type, with shutter, one speed									
8250	12" diameter, 1,000 CFM	1 Elec	14	.571	Ea.	515	38.50		553.50	620
8260	14" diameter, 1,500 CFM		12	.667		555	45		600	675
8270	16" diameter, 2,000 CFM		9	.889		630	60		690	780
8290	Whole house, wall type, with shutter, one speed									
8300	30" diameter, 4,800 CFM	1 Elec	7	1.143	Ea.	1,350	77		1,427	1,600
8310	36" diameter, 7,000 CFM		6	1.333		1,475	90		1,565	1,725
8320	42" diameter, 10,000 CFM		5	1.600		1,650	108		1,758	1,950
8330	48" diameter, 16,000 CFM		4	2		2,050	135		2,185	2,450
8340	For two speed, add					123			123	135
8350	Whole house, lay-down type, with shutter, one speed									
8360	30" diameter, 4,500 CFM	1 Elec	8	1	Ea.	1,425	67.50		1,492.50	1,675
8370	36" diameter, 6,500 CFM		7	1.143		1,550	77		1,627	1,825
8380	42" diameter, 9,000 CFM		6	1.333		1,700	90		1,790	1,975
8390	48" diameter, 12,000 CFM		5	1.600		1,925	108		2,033	2,275
8440	For two speed, add					92			92	101
8450	For 12 hour timer switch, add	1 Elec	32	.250		92	16.85		108.85	126

23 34 39.10 Powerfoil		Crew	Daily Output	Labor-Hours	Unit	Material	Labor	Equipment	Total	Total Incl O&P
0010	**POWERFOIL**									
2301	Powerfoil, 8' diameter	R-1A	2.40	6.667	Ea.	9,475	405		9,880	11,000
2302	10'		2.40	6.667		9,575	405		9,980	11,100
2303	12'		2.40	6.667		9,700	405		10,105	11,300
2304	14'		2.40	6.667		9,800	405		10,205	11,400
2305	16'		2	8		9,900	485		10,385	11,600
2306	18'		2	8		10,000	485		10,485	11,700
2307	20'		2	8		10,100	485		10,585	11,800
2308	24'		2	8		10,400	485		10,885	12,100
2400	Powerfoil with Hybrid Airfoil									
2401	12'	R-1A	2	8	Ea.	10,200	485		10,685	12,000
2402	14'		2	8		10,400	485		10,885	12,100
2403	16'		1.75	9.143		10,500	555		11,055	12,300
2404	18'		1.75	9.143		10,600	555		11,155	12,400
2405	20'		1.75	9.143		10,700	555		11,255	12,500
2406	24'		1.75	9.143		10,900	555		11,455	12,800

23 52 Heating Boilers

23 52 13 – Electric Boilers

23 52 13.10 Electric Boilers, ASME		Crew	Daily Output	Labor-Hours	Unit	2023 Bare Costs Material	Labor	Equipment	Total	Total Incl O&P
0010	**ELECTRIC BOILERS, ASME**, Standard controls and trim									
1000	Steam, 6 KW, 20.5 MBH	Q-19	1.20	20	Ea.	4,525	1,325		5,850	6,950
1040	9 KW, 30.7 MBH		1.20	20		4,350	1,325		5,675	6,750
1060	18 KW, 61.4 MBH		1.20	20		4,475	1,325		5,800	6,900
1080	24 KW, 81.8 MBH		1.10	21.818		5,175	1,450		6,625	7,850
1120	36 KW, 123 MBH		1.10	21.818		5,725	1,450		7,175	8,450
1160	60 KW, 205 MBH		1	24		7,175	1,575		8,750	10,200
1220	112 KW, 382 MBH		.75	32		9,950	2,100		12,050	14,100
1240	148 KW, 505 MBH		.65	36.923		10,300	2,425		12,725	15,000
1260	168 KW, 573 MBH		.60	40		21,400	2,650		24,050	27,500
1280	222 KW, 758 MBH		.55	43.636		25,000	2,875		27,875	31,800
1300	296 KW, 1,010 MBH		.45	53.333		26,500	3,525		30,025	34,400
1320	300 KW, 1,023 MBH		.40	60		26,400	3,950		30,350	34,900
1340	370 KW, 1,263 MBH		.35	68.571		29,200	4,525		33,725	38,900
1360	444 KW, 1,515 MBH		.30	80		31,300	5,275		36,575	42,300
1380	518 KW, 1,768 MBH	Q-21	.36	88.889		32,700	6,000		38,700	44,900
1400	592 KW, 2,020 MBH		.34	94.118		35,900	6,375		42,275	48,900
1420	666 KW, 2,273 MBH		.32	100		37,300	6,775		44,075	51,000
1460	740 KW, 2,526 MBH		.28	114		38,800	7,725		46,525	54,000
1480	814 KW, 2,778 MBH		.25	128		45,900	8,650		54,550	63,500
1500	962 KW, 3,283 MBH		.22	145		45,500	9,825		55,325	64,500
1520	1,036 KW, 3,536 MBH		.20	160		47,600	10,800		58,400	68,500
1540	1,110 KW, 3,788 MBH		.19	168		50,500	11,400		61,900	72,500
1560	2,070 KW, 7,063 MBH		.18	178		69,000	12,000		81,000	94,000
1580	2,250 KW, 7,677 MBH		.17	188		81,000	12,700		93,700	108,000
1600	2,340 KW, 7,984 MBH		.16	200		103,500	13,500		117,000	133,500
2000	Hot water, 7.5 KW, 25.6 MBH	Q-19	1.30	18.462		5,150	1,225		6,375	7,500
2020	15 KW, 51.2 MBH		1.30	18.462		5,450	1,225		6,675	7,825
2040	30 KW, 102 MBH		1.20	20		5,550	1,325		6,875	8,075
2060	45 KW, 164 MBH		1.20	20		5,425	1,325		6,750	7,925
2070	60 KW, 205 MBH		1.20	20		5,800	1,325		7,125	8,350
2080	75 KW, 256 MBH		1.10	21.818		6,125	1,450		7,575	8,900
2100	90 KW, 307 MBH		1.10	21.818		6,175	1,450		7,625	8,925
2120	105 KW, 358 MBH		1	24		7,150	1,575		8,725	10,200
2140	120 KW, 410 MBH		.90	26.667		6,825	1,750		8,575	10,100
2160	135 KW, 461 MBH		.75	32		7,575	2,100		9,675	11,500
2180	150 KW, 512 MBH		.65	36.923		7,975	2,425		10,400	12,400
2200	165 KW, 563 MBH		.60	40		8,200	2,650		10,850	13,000
2220	296 KW, 1,010 MBH		.55	43.636		16,300	2,875		19,175	22,200
2280	370 KW, 1,263 MBH		.40	60		18,000	3,950		21,950	25,800
2300	444 KW, 1,515 MBH		.35	68.571		21,700	4,525		26,225	30,700
2340	518 KW, 1,768 MBH	Q-21	.44	72.727		24,000	4,925		28,925	33,700
2360	592 KW, 2,020 MBH		.43	74.419		26,300	5,025		31,325	36,500
2400	666 KW, 2,273 MBH		.40	80		28,500	5,400		33,900	39,500
2420	740 KW, 2,526 MBH		.39	82.051		28,700	5,550		34,250	39,900
2440	814 KW, 2,778 MBH		.38	84.211		30,900	5,700		36,600	42,500
2460	888 KW, 3,031 MBH		.37	86.486		33,400	5,850		39,250	45,500
2480	962 KW, 3,283 MBH		.36	88.889		35,400	6,000		41,400	47,900
2500	1,036 KW, 3,536 MBH		.34	94.118		36,600	6,375		42,975	49,700
2520	1,110 KW, 3,788 MBH		.33	96.970		39,900	6,550		46,450	53,500
2540	1,440 KW, 4,915 MBH		.32	100		44,300	6,775		51,075	59,000
2560	1,560 KW, 5,323 MBH		.31	103		50,500	6,975		57,475	66,000
2580	1,680 KW, 5,733 MBH		.30	107		54,000	7,225		61,225	70,000

23 52 Heating Boilers

23 52 13 – Electric Boilers

23 52 13.10 Electric Boilers, ASME		Crew	Daily Output	Labor-Hours	Unit	2023 Bare Costs Material	Labor	Equipment	Total	Total Incl O&P
2600	1,800 KW, 6,143 MBH	Q-21	.29	110	Ea.	57,500	7,475		64,975	74,500
2620	1,980 KW, 6,757 MBH		.28	114		60,500	7,725		68,225	78,000
2640	2,100 KW, 7,167 MBH		.27	119		69,000	8,025		77,025	88,000
2660	2,220 KW, 7,576 MBH		.26	123		70,000	8,325		78,325	89,500
2680	2,400 KW, 8,191 MBH		.25	128		73,000	8,650		81,650	93,000
2700	2,610 KW, 8,905 MBH		.24	133		77,000	9,025		86,025	98,000
2720	2,790 KW, 9,519 MBH		.23	139		81,000	9,400		90,400	103,000
2740	2,970 KW, 10,133 MBH		.21	152		83,000	10,300		93,300	106,500
2760	3,150 KW, 10,748 MBH		.19	168		80,000	11,400		91,400	105,000
2780	3,240 KW, 11,055 MBH		.18	178		82,000	12,000		94,000	108,000
2800	3,420 KW, 11,669 MBH		.17	188		95,500	12,700		108,200	124,000
2820	3,600 KW, 12,283 MBH	↓	.16	200	↓	100,500	13,500		114,000	130,500

23 52 28 – Swimming Pool Boilers

23 52 28.10 Swimming Pool Heaters		Crew	Daily Output	Labor-Hours	Unit	Material	Labor	Equipment	Total	Total Incl O&P
0010	**SWIMMING POOL HEATERS**, Not including wiring, external									
0020	piping, base or pad									
2000	Electric, 12 KW, 4,800 gallon pool	Q-19	3	8	Ea.	2,450	530		2,980	3,475
2020	15 KW, 7,200 gallon pool		2.80	8.571		2,575	565		3,140	3,700
2040	24 KW, 9,600 gallon pool		2.40	10		3,300	660		3,960	4,625
2060	30 KW, 12,000 gallon pool		2	12		3,375	790		4,165	4,875
2080	36 KW, 14,400 gallon pool		1.60	15		3,925	990		4,915	5,800
2100	57 KW, 24,000 gallon pool	↓	1.20	20	↓	4,375	1,325		5,700	6,800
9000	To select pool heater: 12 BTUH x S.F. pool area									
9010	X temperature differential = required output									
9050	For electric, KW = gallons x 2.5 divided by 1,000									
9100	For family home type pool, double the									
9110	Rated gallon capacity = 1/2°F rise per hour									

23 54 Furnaces

23 54 13 – Electric-Resistance Furnaces

23 54 13.10 Electric Furnaces		Crew	Daily Output	Labor-Hours	Unit	Material	Labor	Equipment	Total	Total Incl O&P
0010	**ELECTRIC FURNACES**, Hot air, blowers, std. controls									
1000	Electric, UL listed									
1070	10.2 MBH	Q-20	4.40	4.545	Ea.	365	291		656	835
1080	17.1 MBH		4.60	4.348		450	278		728	915
1100	34.1 MBH		4.40	4.545		560	291		851	1,050
1120	51.6 MBH		4.20	4.762		620	305		925	1,150
1140	68.3 MBH		4	5		615	320		935	1,150
1160	85.3 MBH	↓	3.80	5.263	↓	650	335		985	1,225

23 82 16 – Air Coils

23 82 16.20 Duct Heaters		Crew	Daily Output	Labor-Hours	Unit	Material	Labor	Equipment	Total	Total Incl O&P
						2023 Bare Costs				
0010	**DUCT HEATERS**, Electric, 480 V, 3 Ph.									
0020	Finned tubular insert, 500°F									
0100	8" wide x 6" high, 4.0 kW	Q-20	16	1.250	Ea.	940	80		1,020	1,150
0120	12" high, 8.0 kW		15	1.333		1,550	85.50		1,635.50	1,825
0140	18" high, 12.0 kW		14	1.429		2,175	91.50		2,266.50	2,525
0160	24" high, 16.0 kW		13	1.538		2,800	98.50		2,898.50	3,225
0180	30" high, 20.0 kW		12	1.667		3,425	107		3,532	3,925
0300	12" wide x 6" high, 6.7 kW		15	1.333		995	85.50		1,080.50	1,225
0320	12" high, 13.3 kW		14	1.429		1,600	91.50		1,691.50	1,900
0340	18" high, 20.0 kW		13	1.538		2,250	98.50		2,348.50	2,625
0360	24" high, 26.7 kW		12	1.667		2,900	107		3,007	3,350
0380	30" high, 33.3 kW		11	1.818		3,550	116		3,666	4,075
0500	18" wide x 6" high, 13.3 kW		14	1.429		1,075	91.50		1,166.50	1,325
0520	12" high, 26.7 kW		13	1.538		1,850	98.50		1,948.50	2,175
0540	18" high, 40.0 kW		12	1.667		2,450	107		2,557	2,850
0560	24" high, 53.3 kW		11	1.818		3,250	116		3,366	3,750
0580	30" high, 66.7 kW		10	2		4,075	128		4,203	4,675
0700	24" wide x 6" high, 17.8 kW		13	1.538		1,200	98.50		1,298.50	1,475
0720	12" high, 35.6 kW		12	1.667		2,000	107		2,107	2,350
0740	18" high, 53.3 kW		11	1.818		2,825	116		2,941	3,300
0760	24" high, 71.1 kW		10	2		3,625	128		3,753	4,175
0780	30" high, 88.9 kW		9	2.222		4,425	142		4,567	5,100
0900	30" wide x 6" high, 22.2 kW		12	1.667		1,275	107		1,382	1,550
0920	12" high, 44.4 kW		11	1.818		2,100	116		2,216	2,500
0940	18" high, 66.7 kW		10	2		3,000	128		3,128	3,500
0960	24" high, 88.9 kW		9	2.222		4,300	142		4,442	4,975
0980	30" high, 111.0 kW		8	2.500		4,700	160		4,860	5,400
1400	Note decreased kW available for									
1410	each duct size at same cost									
1420	See line 5000 for modifications and accessories									
2000	Finned tubular flange with insulated									
2020	terminal box, 500°F									
2100	12" wide x 36" high, 54 kW	Q-20	10	2	Ea.	4,625	128		4,753	5,275
2120	40" high, 60 kW		9	2.222		5,325	142		5,467	6,075
2200	24" wide x 36" high, 118.8 kW		9	2.222		5,625	142		5,767	6,400
2220	40" high, 132 kW		8	2.500		5,850	160		6,010	6,675
2400	36" wide x 8" high, 40 kW		11	1.818		2,375	116		2,491	2,775
2420	16" high, 80 kW		10	2		3,125	128		3,253	3,650
2440	24" high, 120 kW		9	2.222		4,100	142		4,242	4,750
2460	32" high, 160 kW		8	2.500		5,250	160		5,410	6,025
2480	36" high, 180 kW		7	2.857		6,475	183		6,658	7,400
2500	40" high, 200 kW		6	3.333		7,175	213		7,388	8,225
2600	40" wide x 8" high, 45 kW		11	1.818		2,450	116		2,566	2,875
2620	16" high, 90 kW		10	2		3,375	128		3,503	3,925
2640	24" high, 135 kW		9	2.222		4,300	142		4,442	4,950
2660	32" high, 180 kW		8	2.500		5,725	160		5,885	6,525
2680	36" high, 202.5 kW		7	2.857		6,575	183		6,758	7,525
2700	40" high, 225 kW		6	3.333		7,500	213		7,713	8,575
2800	48" wide x 8" high, 54.8 kW		10	2		2,575	128		2,703	3,025
2820	16" high, 109.8 kW		9	2.222		3,575	142		3,717	4,150
2840	24" high, 164.4 kW		8	2.500		4,550	160		4,710	5,250
2860	32" high, 219.2 kW		7	2.857		6,050	183		6,233	6,925
2880	36" high, 246.6 kW		6	3.333		6,975	213		7,188	8,000

23 82 Convection Heating and Cooling Units

23 82 16 – Air Coils

23 82 16.20 Duct Heaters		Crew	Daily Output	Labor-Hours	Unit	2023 Bare Costs Material	Labor	Equipment	Total	Total Incl O&P
2900	40″ high, 274 kW	Q-20	5	4	Ea.	7,875	256		8,131	9,050
3000	56″ wide x 8″ high, 64 kW		9	2.222		2,925	142		3,067	3,450
3020	16″ high, 128 kW		8	2.500		4,050	160		4,210	4,725
3040	24″ high, 192 kW		7	2.857		4,925	183		5,108	5,700
3060	32″ high, 256 kW		6	3.333		6,875	213		7,088	7,900
3080	36″ high, 288 kW		5	4		7,900	256		8,156	9,050
3100	40″ high, 320 kW		4	5		8,725	320		9,045	10,100
3200	64″ wide x 8″ high, 74 kW		8	2.500		3,025	160		3,185	3,575
3220	16″ high, 148 kW		7	2.857		4,175	183		4,358	4,875
3240	24″ high, 222 kW		6	3.333		5,325	213		5,538	6,175
3260	32″ high, 296 kW		5	4		7,125	256		7,381	8,225
3280	36″ high, 333 kW		4	5		8,500	320		8,820	9,825
3300	40″ high, 370 kW		3	6.667		9,375	425		9,800	10,900
3800	Note decreased kW available for									
3820	each duct size at same cost									
5000	Duct heater modifications and accessories									
5120	T.C.O. limit auto or manual reset	Q-20	42	.476	Ea.	154	30.50		184.50	215
5140	Thermostat		28	.714		655	45.50		700.50	790
5160	Overheat thermocouple (removable)		7	2.857		930	183		1,113	1,300
5180	Fan interlock relay		18	1.111		224	71		295	355
5200	Air flow switch		20	1		194	64		258	310
5220	Split terminal box cover		100	.200		64	12.80		76.80	89.50
8000	To obtain BTU multiply kW by 3413									

23 83 Radiant Heating Units

23 83 33 – Electric Radiant Heaters

23 83 33.10 Electric Heating		Crew	Daily Output	Labor-Hours	Unit	Material	Labor	Equipment	Total	Total Incl O&P
0010	**ELECTRIC HEATING**, not incl. conduit or feed wiring									
1100	Rule of thumb: Baseboard units, including control	1 Elec	4.40	1.818	KW	138	122		260	335
1300	Baseboard heaters, 2′ long, 350 watt		8	1	Ea.	41.50	67.50		109	146
1400	3′ long, 750 watt		8	1		44.50	67.50		112	149
1600	4′ long, 1,000 watt		6.70	1.194		54	80.50		134.50	179
1800	5′ long, 935 watt		5.70	1.404		64.50	94.50		159	211
2000	6′ long, 1,500 watt		5	1.600		72.50	108		180.50	240
2200	7′ long, 1,310 watt		4.40	1.818		74	122		196	264
2400	8′ long, 2,000 watt		4	2		89.50	135		224.50	299
2600	9′ long, 1,680 watt		3.60	2.222		99.50	150		249.50	330
2800	10′ long, 1,875 watt		3.30	2.424		97.50	163		260.50	350
2950	Wall heaters with fan, 120 to 277 volt									
3160	Recessed, residential, 750 watt	1 Elec	6	1.333	Ea.	96.50	90		186.50	239
3170	1,000 watt		6	1.333		385	90		475	560
3180	1,250 watt		5	1.600		132	108		240	305
3190	1,500 watt		4	2		415	135		550	660
3210	2,000 watt		4	2		122	135		257	335
3230	2,500 watt		3.50	2.286		425	154		579	695
3240	3,000 watt		3	2.667		380	180		560	680
3250	4,000 watt		2.70	2.963		380	200		580	715
3260	Commercial, 750 watt		6	1.333		264	90		354	425
3270	1,000 watt		6	1.333		252	90		342	410
3280	1,250 watt		5	1.600		252	108		360	435
3290	1,500 watt		4	2		251	135		386	475

23 83 33.10 Electric Heating		Crew	Daily Output	Labor-Hours	Unit	Material	2023 Bare Costs Labor	Equipment	Total	Total Incl O&P
3300	2,000 watt	1 Elec	4	2	Ea.	252	135		387	475
3310	2,500 watt		3.50	2.286		252	154		406	505
3320	3,000 watt		3	2.667		425	180		605	730
3330	4,000 watt		2.70	2.963		580	200		780	930
3600	Thermostats, integral		16	.500		34	33.50		67.50	87.50
3800	Line voltage, 1 pole		8	1		34.50	67.50		102	138
3810	2 pole		8	1		27	67.50		94.50	130
4000	Heat trace system, 400 degree R238313-10									
4020	115 V, 2.5 watts/L.F.	1 Elec	530	.015	L.F.	11.70	1.02		12.72	14.35
4030	5 watts/L.F. R238313-20		530	.015		11.70	1.02		12.72	14.35
4050	10 watts/L.F.		530	.015		8.60	1.02		9.62	11
4060	208 V, 5 watts/L.F.		530	.015		11.70	1.02		12.72	14.35
4080	480 V, 8 watts/L.F.		530	.015		11.70	1.02		12.72	14.35
4200	Heater raceway									
4260	Heat transfer cement									
4280	1 gallon				Ea.	96.50			96.50	106
4300	5 gallon				"	283			283	310
4320	Cable tie									
4340	3/4" pipe size	1 Elec	470	.017	Ea.	.03	1.15		1.18	1.73
4360	1" pipe size		444	.018		.03	1.21		1.24	1.83
4380	1-1/4" pipe size		400	.020		.03	1.35		1.38	2.03
4400	1-1/2" pipe size		355	.023		.03	1.52		1.55	2.29
4420	2" pipe size		320	.025		.02	1.68		1.70	2.52
4440	3" pipe size		160	.050		.02	3.37		3.39	5
4460	4" pipe size		100	.080		.07	5.40		5.47	8.10
4480	Thermostat NEMA 3R, 22 amp, 0-150 degree, 10' cap.		8	1		210	67.50		277.50	330
4500	Thermostat NEMA 4X, 25 amp, 40 degree, 5-1/2' cap.		7	1.143		210	77		287	345
4520	Thermostat NEMA 4X, 22 amp, 25-325 degree, 10' cap.		7	1.143		575	77		652	750
4540	Thermostat NEMA 4X, 22 amp, 15-140 degree		6	1.333		470	90		560	655
4580	Thermostat NEMA 4, 7, 9, 22 amp, 25-325 degree, 10' cap.		3.60	2.222		690	150		840	980
4600	Thermostat NEMA 4, 7, 9, 22 amp, 15-140 degree		3	2.667		645	180		825	975
4720	Fiberglass application tape, 36 yard roll		11	.727		58	49		107	137
5000	Radiant heating ceiling panels, 2' x 4', 500 watt		16	.500		325	33.50		358.50	405
5050	750 watt		16	.500		320	33.50		353.50	400
5200	For recessed plaster frame, add		32	.250		138	16.85		154.85	176
5300	Infrared quartz heaters, 120 volts, 1,000 watt		6.70	1.194		300	80.50		380.50	450
5350	1,500 watt		5	1.600		315	108		423	510
5400	240 volts, 1,500 watt		5	1.600		282	108		390	470
5450	2,000 watt		4	2		320	135		455	555
5500	3,000 watt		3	2.667		345	180		525	645
5550	4,000 watt		2.60	3.077		370	207		577	715
5570	Modulating control		.80	10		156	675		831	1,175
5600	Unit heaters, heavy duty, with fan & mounting bracket									
5650	Single phase, 208-240-277 volt, 3 kW	1 Elec	6	1.333	Ea.	610	90		700	805
5750	5 kW		5.50	1.455		640	98		738	845
5800	7 kW		5	1.600		855	108		963	1,100
5850	10 kW		4	2		1,200	135		1,335	1,525
5950	15 kW		3.80	2.105		2,025	142		2,167	2,425
6000	480 volt, 3 kW		6	1.333		525	90		615	715
6020	4 kW		5.80	1.379		365	93		458	545
6040	5 kW		5.50	1.455		375	98		473	560
6060	7 kW		5	1.600		580	108		688	800
6080	10 kW		4	2		1,200	135		1,335	1,525

23 83 33.10 Electric Heating		Crew	Daily Output	Labor-Hours	Unit	Material	2023 Bare Costs Labor	Equipment	Total	Total Incl O&P
6100	13 kW	1 Elec	3.80	2.105	Ea.	2,150	142		2,292	2,575
6120	15 kW		3.70	2.162		1,075	146		1,221	1,400
6140	20 kW		3.50	2.286		2,925	154		3,079	3,450
6300	3 phase, 208-240 volt, 5 kW		5.50	1.455		535	98		633	735
6320	7 kW		5	1.600		860	108		968	1,100
6340	10 kW		4	2		885	135		1,020	1,175
6360	15 kW		3.70	2.162		1,675	146		1,821	2,075
6380	20 kW		3.50	2.286		2,975	154		3,129	3,500
6400	25 kW		3.30	2.424		3,150	163		3,313	3,700
6500	480 volt, 5 kW		5.50	1.455		760	98		858	980
6520	7 kW		5	1.600		1,075	108		1,183	1,325
6540	10 kW		4	2		1,025	135		1,160	1,350
6560	13 kW		3.80	2.105		1,775	142		1,917	2,150
6580	15 kW		3.70	2.162		1,675	146		1,821	2,050
6600	20 kW		3.50	2.286		2,475	154		2,629	2,950
6620	25 kW		3.30	2.424		3,775	163		3,938	4,400
6630	30 kW		3	2.667		4,275	180		4,455	4,975
6640	40 kW		2	4		5,175	269		5,444	6,100
6650	50 kW		1.60	5		5,975	335		6,310	7,075
6800	Vertical discharge heaters, with fan									
6820	Single phase, 208-240-277 volt, 10 kW	1 Elec	4	2	Ea.	1,050	135		1,185	1,350
6840	15 kW		3.70	2.162		1,750	146		1,896	2,175
6900	3 phase, 208-240 volt, 10 kW		4	2		1,125	135		1,260	1,450
6920	15 kW		3.70	2.162		1,750	146		1,896	2,150
6940	20 kW		3.50	2.286		3,225	154		3,379	3,775
6960	25 kW		3.30	2.424		3,550	163		3,713	4,150
6980	30 kW		3	2.667		3,350	180		3,530	3,950
7000	40 kW		2	4		4,800	269		5,069	5,675
7020	50 kW		1.60	5		5,500	335		5,835	6,550
7100	480 volt, 10 kW		4	2		1,325	135		1,460	1,650
7120	15 kW		3.70	2.162		2,150	146		2,296	2,600
7140	20 kW		3.50	2.286		2,950	154		3,104	3,475
7160	25 kW		3.30	2.424		3,875	163		4,038	4,500
7180	30 kW		3	2.667		4,225	180		4,405	4,925
7200	40 kW		2	4		4,375	269		4,644	5,225
7410	Sill height convector heaters, 5" high x 2' long, 500 watt		6.70	1.194		415	80.50		495.50	580
7420	3' long, 750 watt		6.50	1.231		490	83		573	665
7430	4' long, 1,000 watt		6.20	1.290		570	87		657	755
7440	5' long, 1,250 watt		5.50	1.455		645	98		743	855
7450	6' long, 1,500 watt		4.80	1.667		730	112		842	970
7460	8' long, 2,000 watt		3.60	2.222		995	150		1,145	1,325
7470	10' long, 2,500 watt		3	2.667		1,225	180		1,405	1,625
7900	Cabinet convector heaters, 240 volt, three phase,									
7920	3' long, 2,000 watt	1 Elec	5.30	1.509	Ea.		102		102	151
7940	3,000 watt		5.30	1.509		1,925	102		2,027	2,250
7960	4,000 watt		5.30	1.509		1,975	102		2,077	2,325
7980	6,000 watt		4.60	1.739		2,050	117		2,167	2,425
8000	8,000 watt		4.60	1.739		2,125	117		2,242	2,500
8020	4' long, 4,000 watt		4.60	1.739		1,850	117		1,967	2,200
8040	6,000 watt		4	2		1,925	135		2,060	2,300
8060	8,000 watt		4	2		2,025	135		2,160	2,425
8080	10,000 watt		4	2		2,050	135		2,185	2,450
8100	Available also in 208 or 277 volt									

23 83 Radiant Heating Units

23 83 33 – Electric Radiant Heaters

23 83 33.10 Electric Heating		Crew	Daily Output	Labor-Hours	Unit	Material	Labor	Equipment	Total	Total Incl O&P
						2023 Bare Costs				
8200	Cabinet unit heaters, 120 to 277 volt, 1 pole,									
8220	wall mounted, 2 kW	1 Elec	4.60	1.739	Ea.	1,850	117		1,967	2,200
8230	3 kW		4.60	1.739		1,925	117		2,042	2,275
8240	4 kW		4.40	1.818		1,975	122		2,097	2,350
8250	5 kW		4.40	1.818		2,025	122		2,147	2,400
8260	6 kW		4.20	1.905		2,050	128		2,178	2,450
8270	8 kW		4	2		2,125	135		2,260	2,525
8280	10 kW		3.80	2.105		2,050	142		2,192	2,450
8290	12 kW		3.50	2.286		1,950	154		2,104	2,375
8300	13.5 kW		2.90	2.759		2,125	186		2,311	2,600
8310	16 kW		2.70	2.963		2,175	200		2,375	2,675
8320	20 kW		2.30	3.478		3,300	234		3,534	3,975
8330	24 kW		1.90	4.211		3,350	284		3,634	4,100
8350	Recessed, 2 kW		4.40	1.818		2,050	122		2,172	2,425
8370	3 kW		4.40	1.818		2,125	122		2,247	2,500
8380	4 kW		4.20	1.905		2,175	128		2,303	2,575
8390	5 kW		4.20	1.905		2,225	128		2,353	2,650
8400	6 kW		4	2		2,025	135		2,160	2,425
8410	8 kW		3.80	2.105		2,125	142		2,267	2,550
8420	10 kW		3.50	2.286		2,650	154		2,804	3,150
8430	12 kW		2.90	2.759		2,675	186		2,861	3,225
8440	13.5 kW		2.70	2.963		2,700	200		2,900	3,250
8450	16 kW		2.30	3.478		2,700	234		2,934	3,325
8460	20 kW		1.90	4.211		3,225	284		3,509	3,975
8470	24 kW		1.60	5		3,275	335		3,610	4,100
8490	Ceiling mounted, 2 kW		3.20	2.500		2,050	168		2,218	2,500
8510	3 kW		3.20	2.500		2,125	168		2,293	2,575
8520	4 kW		3	2.667		2,175	180		2,355	2,650
8530	5 kW		3	2.667		2,225	180		2,405	2,725
8540	6 kW		2.80	2.857		2,250	192		2,442	2,750
8550	8 kW		2.40	3.333		2,325	225		2,550	2,875
8560	10 kW		2.20	3.636		2,150	245		2,395	2,725
8570	12 kW		2	4		2,175	269		2,444	2,800
8580	13.5 kW		1.50	5.333		2,225	360		2,585	2,975
8590	16 kW		1.30	6.154		2,275	415		2,690	3,125
8600	20 kW		.90	8.889		3,225	600		3,825	4,450
8610	24 kW		.60	13.333		3,275	900		4,175	4,925
8630	208 to 480 V, 3 pole									
8650	Wall mounted, 2 kW	1 Elec	4.60	1.739	Ea.	2,050	117		2,167	2,425
8670	3 kW		4.60	1.739		1,925	117		2,042	2,275
8680	4 kW		4.40	1.818		1,975	122		2,097	2,350
8690	5 kW		4.40	1.818		2,025	122		2,147	2,400
8700	6 kW		4.20	1.905		2,050	128		2,178	2,450
8710	8 kW		4	2		2,125	135		2,260	2,525
8720	10 kW		3.80	2.105		2,050	142		2,192	2,450
8730	12 kW		3.50	2.286		2,075	154		2,229	2,525
8740	13.5 kW		2.90	2.759		2,125	186		2,311	2,600
8750	16 kW		2.70	2.963		2,175	200		2,375	2,675
8760	20 kW		2.30	3.478		3,100	234		3,334	3,750
8770	24 kW		1.90	4.211		3,350	284		3,634	4,100
8790	Recessed, 2 kW		4.40	1.818		2,050	122		2,172	2,425
8810	3 kW		4.40	1.818		2,125	122		2,247	2,500
8820	4 kW		4.20	1.905		2,175	128		2,303	2,575

23 83 33 – Electric Radiant Heaters

23 83 33.10 Electric Heating		Crew	Daily Output	Labor-Hours	Unit	2023 Bare Costs Material	Labor	Equipment	Total	Total Incl O&P
8830	5 kW	1 Elec	4.20	1.905	Ea.	2,225	128		2,353	2,650
8840	6 kW		4	2		2,250	135		2,385	2,675
8850	8 kW		3.80	2.105		2,325	142		2,467	2,750
8860	10 kW		3.50	2.286		2,150	154		2,304	2,575
8870	12 kW		2.90	2.759		2,175	186		2,361	2,675
8880	13.5 kW		2.70	2.963		2,225	200		2,425	2,750
8890	16 kW		2.30	3.478		3,400	234		3,634	4,075
8900	20 kW		1.90	4.211		3,450	284		3,734	4,225
8920	24 kW		1.60	5		3,500	335		3,835	4,350
8940	Ceiling mount, 2 kW		3.20	2.500		2,050	168		2,218	2,500
8950	3 kW		3.20	2.500		2,125	168		2,293	2,575
8960	4 kW		3	2.667		2,175	180		2,355	2,650
8970	5 kW		3	2.667		2,225	180		2,405	2,725
8980	6 kW		2.80	2.857		2,250	192		2,442	2,750
8990	8 kW		2.40	3.333		2,125	225		2,350	2,675
9000	10 kW		2.20	3.636		2,650	245		2,895	3,300
9020	13.5 kW		1.50	5.333		2,700	360		3,060	3,475
9030	16 kW		1.30	6.154		3,400	415		3,815	4,350
9040	20 kW		.90	8.889		3,450	600		4,050	4,700
9060	24 kW		.60	13.333		3,275	900		4,175	4,925
9230	13.5 kW, 40,956 BTU		2.20	3.636		2,150	245		2,395	2,725
9250	24 kW, 81,912 BTU	▼	2	4	▼	2,375	269		2,644	3,000

Division Notes

			DAILY	LABOR-		BARE COSTS				TOTAL
I		CREW	OUTPUT	HOURS	UNIT	MAT.	LABOR	EQUIP.	TOTAL	INCL O&P

Estimating Tips

- When estimating material costs for special systems, it is always prudent to obtain manufacturers' quotations for equipment prices and special installation requirements that may affect the total cost.
- For cost modifications for elevated tray installation, add the percentages to labor according to the height of the installation and only to the quantities exceeding the different height levels, not to the total tray quantities. Refer to subdivision 26 01 02.20 for labor adjustment factors.
- Do not overlook the costs for equipment used in the installation.

Reference Numbers

Reference numbers are shown at the beginning of some major classifications. These numbers refer to related items in the Reference Section. The reference information may be an estimating procedure, an alternate pricing method, or technical information.

Note: Trade Service, in part, has been used as a reference source for some of the material prices used in Division 25.

25 05 Common Work Results for Integrated Automation

25 05 28 – Pathways for Integrated Automation

25 05 28.39 Surface Raceways for Integrated Automation		Crew	Daily Output	Labor-Hours	Unit	Material	2023 Bare Costs Labor	Equipment	Total	Total Incl O&P
0010	**SURFACE RACEWAYS FOR INTEGRATED AUTOMATION**									
1000	Din rail, G type, 15 mm, steel, galvanized, 3′, for termination blocks	1 Elec	48	.167	Ea.	16.05	11.25		27.30	34.50
1010	32 mm, steel, galvanized, 3′, for termination blocks		48	.167		17.10	11.25		28.35	35.50
1020	35 mm, steel, galvanized, 3′, for termination blocks		48	.167		22	11.25		33.25	40.50
1030	Din rail, rail mounted, 35 mm, aluminum, 3′, for termination blocks		48	.167		27	11.25		38.25	46
1040	35 mm, aluminum,6′, for termination blocks		48	.167		23	11.25		34.25	41.50
2000	Terminal block, Din mounted, 35 mm, medium screw, connector end bracket		48	.167		3.13	11.25		14.38	20
2010	35 mm, large screw, connector end bracket		48	.167		5.65	11.25		16.90	23
2020	Large screw, connector end bracket		48	.167		6.35	11.25		17.60	23.50
3000	Terminal block, feed through, 35 mm, Din mounted, 600V, 20A		48	.167		1.04	11.25		12.29	17.85
3010	35 mm, Din mounted, 600V, 30A		48	.167		1.34	11.25		12.59	18.15
3020	Terminal block, fuse holder, LED indicator, Din mounted, 110V, 6A		48	.167		7.95	11.25		19.20	25.50
3030	Din mounted, 220V, 6A		48	.167		8.10	11.25		19.35	25.50
3040	Din mounted, 300V, 6A	▼	48	.167	▼	8.50	11.25		19.75	26

25 36 Integrated Automation Instrumentation & Terminal Devices

25 36 19 – Integrated Automation Current Sensors

25 36 19.10 Integrated Automation Current Sensors		Crew	Daily Output	Labor-Hours	Unit	Material	Labor	Equipment	Total	Total Incl O&P
0010	**INTEGRATED AUTOMATION CURRENT SENSORS**									
1000	Current limiter inrush, 100 to 480 VAC, 10A, power supply	1 Elec	48	.167	Ea.	95.50	11.25		106.75	122

Estimating Tips

26 05 00 Common Work Results for Electrical

- Conduit should be taken off in three main categories—power distribution, branch power, and branch lighting—so the estimator can concentrate on systems and components, therefore making it easier to ensure all items have been accounted for.
- For cost modifications for elevated conduit installation, add the percentages to labor according to the height of installation and only to the quantities exceeding the different height levels, not to the total conduit quantities. Refer to subdivision 26 01 02.20 for labor adjustment factors.
- Remember that aluminum wiring of equal ampacity is larger in diameter than copper and may require larger conduit.
- If more than three wires at a time are being pulled, deduct percentages from the labor hours of that grouping of wires.
- When taking off grounding systems, identify separately the type and size of wire, and list each unique type of ground connection.
- The estimator should take the weights of materials into consideration when completing a takeoff. Topics to consider include: How will the materials be supported? What methods of support are available? How high will the support structure have to reach? Will the final support structure be able to withstand the total burden? Is the support material included or separate from the fixture, equipment, and material specified?
- Do not overlook the costs for equipment used in the installation. If scaffolding or highlifts are available in the field, contractors may use them in lieu of the proposed ladders and rolling staging.

26 20 00 Low-Voltage Electrical Transmission

- Supports and concrete pads may be shown on drawings for the larger equipment, or the support system may be only a piece of plywood for the back of a panelboard. In either case, they must be included in the costs.

26 40 00 Electrical and Cathodic Protection

- When taking off cathodic protection systems, identify the type and size of cable, and list each unique type of anode connection.

26 50 00 Lighting

- Fixtures should be taken off room by room using the fixture schedule, specifications, and the ceiling plan. For large concentrations of lighting fixtures in the same area, deduct the percentages from labor hours.

Reference Numbers

Reference numbers are shown at the beginning of some major classifications. These numbers refer to related items in the Reference Section. The reference information may be an estimating procedure, an alternate pricing method, or technical information.

Note: Not all subdivisions listed here necessarily appear. ■

Note: "Powered in part by CINX™, based on licensed proprietary information of Harrison Publishing House, Inc."

Note: The following companies, in part, have been used as a reference source for some of the material prices used in Division 26:

Electriflex

Trade Service

26 01 Operation and Maintenance of Electrical Systems

26 01 02 – Labor Adjustment

26 01 02.20 Labor Adjustment Factors		Crew	Daily Output	Labor-Hours	Unit	Material	2023 Bare Costs Labor	Equipment	Total	Total Incl O&P
0010	**LABOR ADJUSTMENT FACTORS** (For Div. 26, 27 and 28) R260519-90									
0100	Subtract from labor for Economy of Scale for Wire									
0110	4-5 wires						25%			
0120	6-10 wires						30%			
0130	11-15 wires						35%			
0140	over 15 wires						40%			
0150	Labor adjustment factors (For Div. 26, 27, 28 and 48)									
0200	Labor factors: The below are reasonable suggestions, but									
0210	each project must be evaluated for its own peculiarities, and									
0220	the adjustments be increased or decreased depending on the									
0230	severity of the special conditions.									
1000	Add to labor for elevated installation (above floor level)									
1010	10′ to 14.5′ high						10%			
1020	15′ to 19.5′ high						20%			
1030	20′ to 24.5′ high						25%			
1040	25′ to 29.5′ high						35%			
1050	30′ to 34.5′ high						40%			
1060	35′ to 39.5′ high						50%			
1070	40′ and higher						55%			
2000	Add to labor for crawl space									
2010	3′ high						40%			
2020	4′ high						30%			
3000	Add to labor for multi-story building									
3100	For new construction (No elevator available)									
3110	Add for floors 3 thru 10						5%			
3120	Add for floors 11 thru 15						10%			
3130	Add for floors 16 thru 20						15%			
3140	Add for floors 21 thru 30						20%			
3150	Add for floors 31 and up						30%			
3200	For existing structure (Elevator available)									
3210	Add for work on floor 3 and above						2%			
4000	Add to labor for working in existing occupied buildings									
4010	Hospital						35%			
4020	Office building						25%			
4030	School						20%			
4040	Factory or warehouse						15%			
4050	Multi-dwelling						15%			
5000	Add to labor, miscellaneous									
5010	Cramped shaft						35%			
5020	Congested area						15%			
5030	Excessive heat or cold						30%			
6000	Labor factors: the above are reasonable suggestions, but									
6100	each project should be evaluated for its own peculiarities									
6200	Other factors to be considered are:									
6210	Movement of material and equipment through finished areas						10%			
6220	Equipment room min security direct access w/authorization						15%			
6230	Attic space						25%			
6240	No service road						25%			
6250	Poor unloading/storage area, no hydraulic lifts or jacks						20%			
6260	Congested site area/heavy traffic						20%			
7000	Correctional facilities (no compounding division 1 adjustment factors)									
7010	Minimum security w/facilities escort						30%			
7020	Medium security w/facilities and correctional officer escort						40%			

26 01 Operation and Maintenance of Electrical Systems

26 01 02 – Labor Adjustment

26 01 02.20 Labor Adjustment Factors		Crew	Daily Output	Labor-Hours	Unit	Material	2023 Bare Costs Labor	Equipment	Total	Total Incl O&P
7030	Max security w/facilities & correctional officer escort (no inmate contact)						50%			

26 01 40 – Operation and Maintenance of Electrical Protection Systems

26 01 40.51 Electrical Systems Repair and Replacement		Crew	Daily Output	Labor-Hours	Unit	Material	Labor	Equipment	Total	Total Incl O&P
0010	ELECTRICAL SYSTEMS REPAIR AND REPLACEMENT									
3000	Remove and replace (reinstall), switch cover	1 Elec	60	.133	Ea.		9		9	13.35
3020	Outlet cover	"	60	.133	"		9		9	13.35

26 01 50 – Operation and Maintenance of Lighting

26 01 50.81 Luminaire Replacement		Crew	Daily Output	Labor-Hours	Unit	Material	Labor	Equipment	Total	Total Incl O&P
0010	LUMINAIRE REPLACEMENT									
0100	Fluorescent fixtures, elevate from work area	1 Elec	96	.083	Ea.	24.50	5.60		30.10	35.50
0962	Remove and install new replacement lens, 2′ x 2′ troffer		16	.500		18.90	33.50		52.40	71
0964	2′ x 4′ troffer		16	.500		15.45	33.50		48.95	67
3200	Remove and replace (reinstall), lighting fixture	↓	4	2	↓		135		135	200

26 05 Common Work Results for Electrical

26 05 05 – Selective Demolition for Electrical

26 05 05.10 Electrical Demolition		Crew	Daily Output	Labor-Hours	Unit	Material	Labor	Equipment	Total	Total Incl O&P
0010	ELECTRICAL DEMOLITION R260105-30									
0020	Electrical demolition, conduit to 10′ high, incl. fittings & hangers									
0100	Rigid galvanized steel, 1/2″ to 1″ diameter	1 Elec	242	.033	L.F.		2.23		2.23	3.31
0120	1-1/4″ to 2″	"	200	.040			2.69		2.69	4
0140	2-1/2″ to 3-1/2″	2 Elec	302	.053			3.57		3.57	5.30
0160	4″ to 6″	"	160	.100			6.75		6.75	10
0170	PVC #40, 1/2″ to 1″	1 Elec	410	.020			1.31		1.31	1.95
0172	1-1/4″ to 2″		350	.023			1.54		1.54	2.29
0174	2-1/2″	↓	250	.032			2.16		2.16	3.20
0176	3″ to 3-1/2″	2 Elec	340	.047			3.17		3.17	4.71
0178	4″ to 6″	"	230	.070			4.69		4.69	6.95
0200	Electric metallic tubing (EMT), 1/2″ to 1″	1 Elec	394	.020			1.37		1.37	2.03
0220	1-1/4″ to 1-1/2″		326	.025			1.65		1.65	2.46
0240	2″ to 3″	↓	236	.034			2.28		2.28	3.39
0260	3-1/2″ to 4″	2 Elec	310	.052	↓		3.48		3.48	5.15
0270	Armored cable (BX) avg. 50′ runs									
0280	#14, 2 wire	1 Elec	690	.012	L.F.		.78		.78	1.16
0290	#14, 3 wire		571	.014			.94		.94	1.40
0300	#12, 2 wire		605	.013			.89		.89	1.32
0310	#12, 3 wire		514	.016			1.05		1.05	1.56
0320	#10, 2 wire		514	.016			1.05		1.05	1.56
0330	#10, 3 wire		425	.019			1.27		1.27	1.88
0340	#8, 3 wire	↓	342	.023	↓		1.58		1.58	2.34
0350	Non metallic sheathed cable (Romex)									
0360	#14, 2 wire	1 Elec	720	.011	L.F.		.75		.75	1.11
0370	#14, 3 wire		657	.012			.82		.82	1.22
0380	#12, 2 wire		629	.013			.86		.86	1.27
0390	#10, 3 wire	↓	450	.018	↓		1.20		1.20	1.78
0400	Wiremold raceway, including fittings & hangers									
0420	No. 3000	1 Elec	250	.032	L.F.		2.16		2.16	3.20
0440	No. 4000		217	.037			2.48		2.48	3.69
0460	No. 6000		166	.048			3.25		3.25	4.82
0462	Plugmold with receptacle	↓	114	.070	↓		4.73		4.73	7

26 05 05 – Selective Demolition for Electrical

26 05 05.10 Electrical Demolition		Crew	Daily Output	Labor-Hours	Unit	Material	2023 Bare Costs Labor	Equipment	Total	Total Incl O&P
0465	Telephone/power pole	1 Elec	12	.667	Ea.		45		45	66.50
0470	Non-metallic, straight section	↓	480	.017	L.F.		1.12		1.12	1.67
0500	Channels, steel, including fittings & hangers									
0520	3/4" x 1-1/2"	1 Elec	308	.026	L.F.		1.75		1.75	2.60
0540	1-1/2" x 1-1/2"		269	.030			2		2	2.98
0560	1-1/2" x 1-7/8"	↓	229	.035	↓		2.35		2.35	3.50
0600	Copper bus duct, indoor, 3 phase									
0610	Including hangers & supports									
0620	225 amp	2 Elec	135	.119	L.F.		8		8	11.85
0640	400 amp		106	.151			10.15		10.15	15.10
0660	600 amp		86	.186			12.55		12.55	18.60
0680	1,000 amp		60	.267			17.95		17.95	26.50
0700	1,600 amp		40	.400			27		27	40
0720	3,000 amp	↓	10	1.600	↓		108		108	160
0800	Plug-in switches, 600 V 3 ph., incl. disconnecting									
0820	wire, conduit terminations, 30 amp	1 Elec	15.50	.516	Ea.		35		35	51.50
0840	60 amp		13.90	.576			39		39	57.50
0850	100 amp		10.40	.769			52		52	77
0860	200 amp	↓	6.20	1.290			87		87	129
0880	400 amp	2 Elec	5.40	2.963			200		200	297
0900	600 amp		3.40	4.706			315		315	470
0920	800 amp		2.60	6.154			415		415	615
0940	1,200 amp		2	8			540		540	800
0960	1,600 amp		1.70	9.412			635		635	940
0961	Remove and Replace, Voltage monitoring, 120/240 V	↓	1.70	9.412	↓		635		635	940
1010	Safety switches, 250 or 600 V, incl. disconnection									
1050	of wire & conduit terminations									
1100	30 amp	1 Elec	12.30	.650	Ea.		44		44	65
1120	60 amp		8.80	.909			61		61	91
1140	100 amp		7.30	1.096			74		74	110
1160	200 amp	↓	5	1.600			108		108	160
1180	400 amp	2 Elec	6.80	2.353			158		158	236
1200	600 amp	"	4.60	3.478			234		234	350
1202	Explosion proof, 60 amp	1 Elec	8.80	.909			61		61	91
1204	100 amp		5	1.600			108		108	160
1206	200 amp	↓	3.33	2.402	↓		162		162	240
1210	Panel boards, incl. removal of all breakers,									
1220	conduit terminations & wire connections									
1230	3 wire, 120/240 V, 100A, to 20 circuits	1 Elec	2.60	3.077	Ea.		207		207	310
1240	200 amps, to 42 circuits	2 Elec	2.60	6.154			415		415	615
1241	225 amps, to 42 circuits		2.40	6.667			450		450	665
1250	400 amps, to 42 circuits	↓	2.20	7.273			490		490	730
1260	4 wire, 120/208 V, 125A, to 20 circuits	1 Elec	2.40	3.333			225		225	335
1270	200 amps, to 42 circuits	2 Elec	2.40	6.667			450		450	665
1280	400 amps, to 42 circuits		1.92	8.333			560		560	835
1285	600 amps, to 42 circuits	↓	1.60	10	↓		675		675	1,000
1300	Transformer, dry type, 1 phase, incl. removal of									
1320	supports, wire & conduit terminations									
1340	1 kVA	1 Elec	7.70	1.039	Ea.		70		70	104
1360	5 kVA		4.70	1.702			115		115	170
1380	10 kVA	↓	3.60	2.222			150		150	222
1400	37.5 kVA	2 Elec	3	5.333			360		360	535
1420	75 kVA	"	2.50	6.400	↓		430		430	640

26 05 05.10 Electrical Demolition		Crew	Daily Output	Labor-Hours	Unit	Material	2023 Bare Costs Labor	Equipment	Total	Total Incl O&P
1440	3 phase to 600 V, primary									
1460	3 kVA	1 Elec	3.87	2.067	Ea.		139		139	207
1480	15 kVA	2 Elec	3.67	4.360	"		294		294	435
1481	15 kVA		40	.400	kVA		27		27	40
1490	25 kVA		3.51	4.558	Ea.		305		305	455
1500	30 kVA		3.42	4.678			315		315	470
1510	45 kVA		3.18	5.031			340		340	505
1511	45 kVA		150	.107	kVA		7.20		7.20	10.70
1520	75 kVA		2.69	5.948	Ea.		400		400	595
1530	112.5 kVA	R-3	2.90	6.897			465	66.50	531.50	765
1540	150 kVA		2.70	7.407			500	71.50	571.50	820
1550	300 kVA		1.80	11.111			750	107	857	1,225
1560	500 kVA		1.40	14.286			960	138	1,098	1,575
1570	750 kVA		1.10	18.182			1,225	175	1,400	2,025
1571	750 kVA		700	.029	kVA		1.92	.28	2.20	3.16
1600	Pull boxes & cabinets, sheet metal, incl. removal									
1620	of supports and conduit terminations									
1640	6″ x 6″ x 4″	1 Elec	31.10	.257	Ea.		17.30		17.30	26
1660	12″ x 12″ x 4″		23.30	.343			23		23	34.50
1680	24″ x 24″ x 6″		12.30	.650			44		44	65
1700	36″ x 36″ x 8″		7.70	1.039			70		70	104
1720	Junction boxes, 4″ sq. & oct.		80	.100			6.75		6.75	10
1740	Handy box		107	.075			5.05		5.05	7.50
1760	Switch box		107	.075			5.05		5.05	7.50
1780	Receptacle & switch plates		257	.031			2.10		2.10	3.12
1790	Receptacles & switches, 15 to 30 amp		135	.059			3.99		3.99	5.95
1800	Wire, THW-THWN-THHN, removed from									
1810	in place conduit, to 10′ high									
1830	#14	1 Elec	65	.123	C.L.F.		8.30		8.30	12.30
1840	#12		55	.145			9.80		9.80	14.55
1850	#10		45.50	.176			11.85		11.85	17.60
1860	#8		40.40	.198			13.35		13.35	19.80
1870	#6		32.60	.245			16.55		16.55	24.50
1880	#4	2 Elec	53	.302			20.50		20.50	30
1890	#3		50	.320			21.50		21.50	32
1900	#2		44.60	.359			24		24	36
1910	1/0		33.20	.482			32.50		32.50	48
1920	2/0		29.20	.548			37		37	55
1930	3/0		25	.640			43		43	64
1940	4/0		22	.727			49		49	73
1950	250 kcmil		20	.800			54		54	80
1960	300 kcmil		19	.842			56.50		56.50	84.50
1970	350 kcmil		18	.889			60		60	89
1980	400 kcmil		17	.941			63.50		63.50	94
1990	500 kcmil		16.20	.988			66.50		66.50	99
2000	Interior fluorescent fixtures, incl. supports									
2010	& whips, to 10′ high									
2100	Recessed drop-in 2′ x 2′, 2 lamp	2 Elec	35	.457	Ea.		31		31	46
2110	2′ x 2′, 4 lamp		30	.533			36		36	53.50
2120	2′ x 4′, 2 lamp		33	.485			32.50		32.50	48.50
2140	2′ x 4′, 4 lamp		30	.533			36		36	53.50
2160	4′ x 4′, 4 lamp		20	.800			54		54	80
2180	Surface mount, acrylic lens & hinged frame									

26 05 05 – Selective Demolition for Electrical

26 05 05.10 Electrical Demolition		Crew	Daily Output	Labor-Hours	Unit	Material	2023 Bare Costs Labor	Equipment	Total	Total Incl O&P
2200	1′ x 4′, 2 lamp	2 Elec	44	.364	Ea.		24.50		24.50	36.50
2210	6″ x 4′, 2 lamp		44	.364			24.50		24.50	36.50
2220	2′ x 2′, 2 lamp		44	.364			24.50		24.50	36.50
2260	2′ x 4′, 4 lamp		33	.485			32.50		32.50	48.50
2280	4′ x 4′, 4 lamp		23	.696			47		47	69.50
2281	4′ x 4′, 6 lamp	↓	23	.696	↓		47		47	69.50
2300	Strip fixtures, surface mount									
2320	4′ long, 1 lamp	2 Elec	53	.302	Ea.		20.50		20.50	30
2340	4′ long, 2 lamp		50	.320			21.50		21.50	32
2360	8′ long, 1 lamp		42	.381			25.50		25.50	38
2380	8′ long, 2 lamp	↓	40	.400	↓		27		27	40
2400	Pendant mount, industrial, incl. removal									
2410	of chain or rod hangers, to 10′ high									
2420	4′ long, 2 lamp	2 Elec	35	.457	Ea.		31		31	46
2421	4′ long, 4 lamp		35	.457			31		31	46
2440	8′ long, 2 lamp	↓	27	.593	↓		40		40	59.50
2460	Interior incandescent, surface, ceiling									
2470	or wall mount, to 10′ high									
2480	Metal cylinder type, 75 Watt	2 Elec	62	.258	Ea.		17.40		17.40	26
2500	150 Watt		62	.258			17.40		17.40	26
2502	300 Watt	↓	53	.302	↓		20.50		20.50	30
2520	Metal halide, high bay									
2540	400 Watt	2 Elec	15	1.067	Ea.		72		72	107
2560	1,000 Watt		12	1.333			90		90	133
2580	150 Watt, low bay		20	.800			54		54	80
2585	Globe type, ceiling mount		62	.258			17.40		17.40	26
2586	Can type, recessed mount	↓	62	.258	↓		17.40		17.40	26
2600	Exterior fixtures, incandescent, wall mount									
2620	100 Watt	2 Elec	50	.320	Ea.		21.50		21.50	32
2640	Quartz, 500 Watt		33	.485			32.50		32.50	48.50
2660	1,500 Watt	↓	27	.593	↓		40		40	59.50
2680	Wall pack, mercury vapor									
2700	175 Watt	2 Elec	25	.640	Ea.		43		43	64
2720	250 Watt	″	25	.640			43		43	64
7000	Weatherhead/mast, 2″	1 Elec	16	.500			33.50		33.50	50
7002	3″		10	.800			54		54	80
7004	3-1/2″		8.50	.941			63.50		63.50	94
7006	4″		8	1	↓		67.50		67.50	100
7100	Service entry cable, #6, +#6 neutral		420	.019	L.F.		1.28		1.28	1.91
7102	#4, +#4 neutral		360	.022			1.50		1.50	2.22
7104	#2, +#4 neutral		345	.023			1.56		1.56	2.32
7106	#2, +#2 neutral	↓	330	.024	↓		1.63		1.63	2.43
9900	Add to labor for higher elevated installation									
9905	10′ to 14.5′ high, add						10%			
9910	15′ to 20′ high, add						20%			
9920	20′ to 25′ high, add						25%			
9930	25′ to 30′ high, add						35%			
9940	30′ to 35′ high, add						40%			
9950	35′ to 40′ high, add						50%			
9960	Over 40′ high, add						55%			

26 05 05 – Selective Demolition for Electrical

26 05 05.15 Electrical Demolition, Grounding

	26 05 05.15 Electrical Demolition, Grounding	Crew	Daily Output	Labor-Hours	Unit	Material	2023 Bare Costs Labor	Equipment	Total	Total Incl O&P
0010	**ELECTRICAL DEMOLITION, GROUNDING** Addition									
0100	Ground clamp, bronze	1 Elec	64	.125	Ea.		8.40		8.40	12.50
0140	Water pipe ground clamp, bronze, heavy duty		24	.333			22.50		22.50	33.50
0150	Ground rod, 8′ to 10′		13	.615			41.50		41.50	61.50
0200	Ground wire, bare armored	2 Elec	900	.018	L.F.		1.20		1.20	1.78
0240	Bare copper or aluminum	"	2800	.006	"		.38		.38	.57

26 05 05.20 Electrical Demolition, Wiring Methods

	26 05 05.20 Electrical Demolition, Wiring Methods	Crew	Daily Output	Labor-Hours	Unit	Material	2023 Bare Costs Labor	Equipment	Total	Total Incl O&P
0010	**ELECTRICAL DEMOLITION, WIRING METHODS** Addition									
0100	Armored cable, w/PVC jacket, in cable tray									
0110	#6 R024119-10	1 Elec	9.30	.860	C.L.F.		58		58	86
0120	#4	2 Elec	16.20	.988			66.50		66.50	99
0130	#2		13.80	1.159			78		78	116
0140	#1		12	1.333			90		90	133
0150	1/0		10.80	1.481			100		100	148
0160	2/0		10.20	1.569			106		106	157
0170	3/0		9.60	1.667			112		112	167
0180	4/0		9	1.778			120		120	178
0190	250 kcmil	3 Elec	10.80	2.222			150		150	222
0210	350 kcmil		9.90	2.424			163		163	243
0230	500 kcmil		9	2.667			180		180	267
0240	750 kcmil		8.10	2.963			200		200	297
1100	Control cable, 600 V or less									
1110	3 wires	1 Elec	24	.333	C.L.F.		22.50		22.50	33.50
1120	5 wires		20	.400			27		27	40
1130	7 wires		16.50	.485			32.50		32.50	48.50
1140	9 wires		15	.533			36		36	53.50
1150	12 wires	2 Elec	26	.615			41.50		41.50	61.50
1160	15 wires		22	.727			49		49	73
1170	19 wires		19	.842			56.50		56.50	84.50
1180	25 wires		16	1			67.50		67.50	100
1500	Mineral insulated (MI) cable, 600 V									
1510	#10	1 Elec	4.80	1.667	C.L.F.		112		112	167
1520	#8		4.50	1.778			120		120	178
1530	#6		4.20	1.905			128		128	191
1540	#4	2 Elec	7.20	2.222			150		150	222
1550	#2		6.60	2.424			163		163	243
1560	#1		6.30	2.540			171		171	254
1570	1/0		6	2.667			180		180	267
1580	2/0		5.70	2.807			189		189	281
1590	3/0		5.40	2.963			200		200	297
1600	4/0		4.80	3.333			225		225	335
1610	250 kcmil	3 Elec	7.20	3.333			225		225	335
1620	500 kcmil	"	5.90	4.068			274		274	405
2000	Shielded cable, XLP shielding, to 35 kV									
2010	#4	2 Elec	13.20	1.212	C.L.F.		81.50		81.50	121
2020	#1		12	1.333			90		90	133
2030	1/0		11.40	1.404			94.50		94.50	140
2040	2/0		10.80	1.481			100		100	148
2050	4/0		9.60	1.667			112		112	167
2060	250 kcmil	3 Elec	13.50	1.778			120		120	178
2070	350 kcmil		11.70	2.051			138		138	205
2080	500 kcmil		11.20	2.143			144		144	215

26 05 05 – Selective Demolition for Electrical

26 05 05.20 Electrical Demolition, Wiring Methods		Crew	Daily Output	Labor-Hours	Unit	Material	2023 Bare Costs Labor	Equipment	Total	Total Incl O&P
2090	750 kcmil	3 Elec	10.80	2.222	C.L.F.		150		150	222
3000	Modular flexible wiring									
3010	Cable set	1 Elec	120	.067	Ea.		4.49		4.49	6.65
3020	Conversion module		48	.167			11.25		11.25	16.70
3030	Switching assembly	↓	96	.083	↓		5.60		5.60	8.35
3200	Undercarpet									
3210	Power or telephone, flat cable	1 Elec	1320	.006	L.F.		.41		.41	.61
3220	Transition block assemblies w/fitting		75	.107	Ea.		7.20		7.20	10.70
3230	Floor box with fitting		60	.133			9		9	13.35
3300	Data system, cable with connection	↓	50	.160	↓		10.80		10.80	16
4000	Cable tray, including fitting & support									
4010	Galvanized steel, 6″ wide	2 Elec	310	.052	L.F.		3.48		3.48	5.15
4020	9″ wide		295	.054			3.65		3.65	5.45
4030	12″ wide		285	.056			3.78		3.78	5.60
4040	18″ wide		270	.059			3.99		3.99	5.95
4050	24″ wide		260	.062			4.14		4.14	6.15
4060	30″ wide		240	.067			4.49		4.49	6.65
4070	36″ wide		220	.073			4.90		4.90	7.30
4110	Aluminum, 6″ wide		420	.038			2.57		2.57	3.81
4120	9″ wide		415	.039			2.60		2.60	3.86
4130	12″ wide		390	.041			2.76		2.76	4.11
4140	18″ wide		370	.043			2.91		2.91	4.33
4150	24″ wide		350	.046			3.08		3.08	4.58
4160	30″ wide		325	.049			3.32		3.32	4.93
4170	36″ wide	↓	300	.053			3.59		3.59	5.35
4310	Cable channel, aluminum, 4″ wide straight	1 Elec	240	.033	↓		2.25		2.25	3.34
4320	Cable tray fittings, 6″ to 9″ wide	2 Elec	27	.593	Ea.		40		40	59.50
4330	12″ to 18″ wide	″	19	.842	″		56.50		56.50	84.50
5000	Conduit nipples, with locknuts and bushings									
5020	1/2″	1 Elec	108	.074	Ea.		4.99		4.99	7.40
5040	3/4″		96	.083			5.60		5.60	8.35
5060	1″		81	.099			6.65		6.65	9.90
5080	1-1/4″		69	.116			7.80		7.80	11.60
5100	1-1/2″		60	.133			9		9	13.35
5120	2″		54	.148			10		10	14.85
5140	2-1/2″		45	.178			11.95		11.95	17.80
5160	3″		36	.222			14.95		14.95	22
5180	3-1/2″		33	.242			16.35		16.35	24.50
5200	4″		27	.296			19.95		19.95	29.50
5220	5″		21	.381			25.50		25.50	38
5240	6″		18	.444	↓		30		30	44.50
5500	Electric nonmetallic tubing (ENT), flexible, 1/2″ to 1″ diameter		690	.012	L.F.		.78		.78	1.16
5510	1-1/4″ to 2″ diameter		300	.027			1.80		1.80	2.67
5600	Flexible metallic tubing, steel, 3/8″ to 3/4″ diameter		600	.013			.90		.90	1.33
5610	1″ to 1-1/4″ diameter		260	.031			2.07		2.07	3.08
5620	1-1/2″ to 2″ diameter		140	.057			3.85		3.85	5.70
5630	2-1/2″ diameter	↓	100	.080			5.40		5.40	8
5640	3″ to 3-1/2″ diameter	2 Elec	150	.107			7.20		7.20	10.70
5650	4″ diameter	″	100	.160			10.80		10.80	16
5700	Sealtite flexible conduit, 3/8″ to 3/4″ diameter	1 Elec	420	.019			1.28		1.28	1.91
5710	1″ to 1-1/4″ diameter		180	.044			2.99		2.99	4.45
5720	1-1/2″ to 2″ diameter		120	.067			4.49		4.49	6.65
5730	2-1/2″ diameter	↓	80	.100	↓		6.75		6.75	10

26 05 05.20 Electrical Demolition, Wiring Methods

	26 05 05.20 Electrical Demolition, Wiring Methods	Crew	Daily Output	Labor-Hours	Unit	Material	2023 Bare Costs Labor	Equipment	Total	Total Incl O&P
5740	3″ diameter	2 Elec	150	.107	L.F.		7.20		7.20	10.70
5750	4″ diameter	″	100	.160			10.80		10.80	16
5800	Wiring duct, plastic, 1-1/2″ to 2-1/2″ wide	1 Elec	360	.022			1.50		1.50	2.22
5810	3″ wide		330	.024			1.63		1.63	2.43
5820	4″ wide		300	.027			1.80		1.80	2.67
6000	Floor box and carpet flange		9	.889	Ea.		60		60	89
6300	Wireway, with fittings and supports, to 10′ high									
6310	2-1/2″ x 2-1/2″	1 Elec	180	.044	L.F.		2.99		2.99	4.45
6320	4″ x 4″	″	160	.050			3.37		3.37	5
6330	6″ x 6″	2 Elec	240	.067			4.49		4.49	6.65
6340	8″ x 8″		160	.100			6.75		6.75	10
6350	10″ x 10″		120	.133			9		9	13.35
6360	12″ x 12″		80	.200			13.45		13.45	20
6400	Cable reel with receptacle, 120 V/208 V		13	1.231	Ea.		83		83	123
6500	Equipment connection, to 10 HP	1 Elec	23	.348			23.50		23.50	35
6510	To 15 to 30 HP		18	.444			30		30	44.50
6520	To 40 to 60 HP		15	.533			36		36	53.50
6530	To 75 to 100 HP		10	.800			54		54	80
7008	Receptacle, explosion proof, 120 V, to 30 A		16	.500			33.50		33.50	50
7020	Dimmer switch, 2,000 W or less		62	.129			8.70		8.70	12.90

26 05 05.25 Electrical Demolition, Electrical Power

	26 05 05.25 Electrical Demolition, Electrical Power	Crew	Daily Output	Labor-Hours	Unit	Material	Labor	Equipment	Total	Total Incl O&P
0010	**ELECTRICAL DEMOLITION, ELECTRICAL POWER** R024119-10									
0100	Meter centers and sockets									
0120	Meter socket, 4 terminal R260105-30	1 Elec	8.40	.952	Ea.		64		64	95.50
0140	Trans-socket, 13 terminal, 400 A	″	3.60	2.222			150		150	222
0160	800 A	2 Elec	4.40	3.636			245		245	365
0200	Meter center, 400 A		5.80	2.759			186		186	276
0210	600 A		4	4			269		269	400
0220	800 A		3.30	4.848			325		325	485
0230	1,200 A		2.80	5.714			385		385	570
0240	1,600 A		2.50	6.400			430		430	640
0300	Base meter devices, 3 meter		3.60	4.444			299		299	445
0310	4 meter		3.30	4.848			325		325	485
0320	5 meter		2.90	5.517			370		370	550
0330	6 meter		2.20	7.273			490		490	730
0340	7 meter		2	8			540		540	800
0350	8 meter		1.90	8.421			565		565	845
0400	Branch meter devices									
0410	Socket w/circuit breaker 200 A, 2 meter	2 Elec	3.30	4.848	Ea.		325		325	485
0420	3 meter		2.90	5.517			370		370	550
0430	4 meter		2.60	6.154			415		415	615
0450	Main circuit breaker, 400 A		5.80	2.759			186		186	276
0460	600 A		4	4			269		269	400
0470	800 A		3.30	4.848			325		325	485
0480	1,200 A		2.80	5.714			385		385	570
0490	1,600 A		2.50	6.400			430		430	640
0500	Main lug terminal box, 800 A		3.40	4.706			315		315	470
0510	1,200 A		2.60	6.154			415		415	615
1000	Motors, 230/460 V, 60 Hz, 3/4 HP	1 Elec	10.70	.748			50.50		50.50	75
1010	5 HP		9	.889			60		60	89
1020	10 HP		8	1			67.50		67.50	100
1030	15 HP		6.40	1.250			84		84	125

26 05 05.25 Electrical Demolition, Electrical Power		Crew	Daily Output	Labor-Hours	Unit	Material	2023 Bare Costs Labor	Equipment	Total	Total Incl O&P
1040	20 HP	2 Elec	10.40	1.538	Ea.		104		104	154
1050	50 HP		9.60	1.667			112		112	167
1060	75 HP		5.60	2.857			192		192	286
1070	100 HP	3 Elec	5.40	4.444			299		299	445
1080	150 HP		3.60	6.667			450		450	665
1090	200 HP		3	8			540		540	800
1200	Variable frequency drive, 460 V, for 5 HP motor size	1 Elec	3.20	2.500			168		168	250
1210	10 HP motor size	"	2.70	2.963			200		200	297
1220	20 HP motor size	2 Elec	3.60	4.444			299		299	445
1230	50 HP motor size	"	2.10	7.619			515		515	765
1240	75 HP motor size	R-3	2.20	9.091			610	87.50	697.50	1,000
1250	100 HP motor size		2	10			675	96.50	771.50	1,100
1260	150 HP motor size		2	10			675	96.50	771.50	1,100
1270	200 HP motor size		1.70	11.765			790	114	904	1,300
2000	Generator set w/accessories, 3 phase 4 wire, 277/480 V									
2010	7.5 kW	3 Elec	2	12	Ea.		810		810	1,200
2020	20 kW		1.70	14.118			950		950	1,425
2040	30 kW		1.33	18.045			1,225		1,225	1,800
2041	30 kW		40	.600	KW		40.50		40.50	60
2060	50 kW		1	24	Ea.		1,625		1,625	2,400
2080	100 kW		.75	32			2,150		2,150	3,200
2100	150 kW		.63	38.095			2,575		2,575	3,825
2120	250 kW		.59	40.678			2,750		2,750	4,075
2140	400 kW		.50	48			3,225		3,225	4,800
2160	500 kW		.44	54.545			3,675		3,675	5,450
2180	750 kW	4 Elec	.56	57.143			3,850		3,850	5,725
2200	1,000 kW		.46	69.565			4,675		4,675	6,975
2201	1,000 kW		400	.080	KW		5.40		5.40	8
2910	Single phase, 120 V, 1 kVA	1 Elec	10	.800	Ea.		54		54	80
3000	Uninterruptible power supply system (UPS)									
3010	Single phase, 120 V, 1 kVA	1 Elec	3.20	2.500	Ea.		168		168	250
3020	2 kVA	2 Elec	3.60	4.444			299		299	445
3030	5 kVA	3 Elec	2.50	9.600			645		645	960
3040	10 kVA		2.30	10.435			705		705	1,050
3050	15 kVA		1.80	13.333			900		900	1,325
4000	Transformer, incl. support, wire & conduit termination									
4010	Buck-boost, single phase, 120/240 V, 0.1 kVA	1 Elec	25	.320	Ea.		21.50		21.50	32
4020	0.5 kVA		12.50	.640			43		43	64
4030	1 kVA		6.30	1.270			85.50		85.50	127
4040	5 kVA		3.80	2.105			142		142	211
4800	5 kV or 15 kV primary, 277/480 V second, 112.5 kVA	R-3	3.50	5.714			385	55	440	630
4801	5 kV or 15 kV primary, 277/480 V second, 112.5 kVA		400	.050	kVA		3.37	.48	3.85	5.55
4810	150 kVA		2.70	7.407	Ea.		500	71.50	571.50	820
4811	150 kVA		412	.049	kVA		3.27	.47	3.74	5.40
4820	225 kVA		2.30	8.696	Ea.		585	84	669	965
4821	225 kVA		512	.039	kVA		2.63	.38	3.01	4.32
4830	500 kVA		1.45	13.793	Ea.		930	133	1,063	1,525
4831	500 kVA		700	.029	kVA		1.92	.28	2.20	3.16
4840	750 kVA		1.33	15.038	Ea.		1,025	145	1,170	1,650
4841	750 kVA		1065	.019	kVA		1.26	.18	1.44	2.08
4850	1,000 kVA		1.25	16	Ea.		1,075	154	1,229	1,775
4851	1,000 kVA		1250	.016	kVA		1.08	.15	1.23	1.77
4860	2,000 kVA		1.05	19.048	Ea.		1,275	184	1,459	2,100

26 05 05 – Selective Demolition for Electrical

26 05 05.25 Electrical Demolition, Electrical Power		Crew	Daily Output	Labor-Hours	Unit	Material	2023 Bare Costs Labor	Equipment	Total	Total Incl O&P
4861	2,000 kVA	R-3	20000	.001	kVA		.07	.01	.08	.11
4870	3,000 kVA		.75	26.667	Ea.		1,800	257	2,057	2,950
4871	3,000 kVA		2200	.009	kVA		.61	.09	.70	1.01
6010	Isolation panel, 3 kVA	1 Elec	2.30	3.478	Ea.		234		234	350
6020	5 kVA		2.20	3.636			245		245	365
6030	7.5 kVA		2.10	3.810			257		257	380
6040	10 kVA		1.80	4.444			299		299	445
6050	15 kVA		1.40	5.714			385		385	570
7000	Power filters & conditioners									
7100	Automatic voltage regulator	2 Elec	6	2.667	Ea.		180		180	267
7200	Capacitor, 1 kVAR	1 Elec	8.60	.930			62.50		62.50	93
7210	5 kVAR		5.80	1.379			93		93	138
7220	10 kVAR		4.80	1.667			112		112	167
7230	15 kVAR		4.20	1.905			128		128	191
7240	20 kVAR		3.50	2.286			154		154	229
7250	30 kVAR		3.40	2.353			158		158	236
7260	50 kVAR		3.20	2.500			168		168	250
7400	Computer isolator transformer									
7410	Single phase, 120/240 V, 0.5 kVAR	1 Elec	12.80	.625	Ea.		42		42	62.50
7420	1 kVAR		8.50	.941			63.50		63.50	94
7430	2.5 kVAR		6.40	1.250			84		84	125
7440	5 kVAR		3.70	2.162			146		146	216
7500	Computer regulator transformer									
7510	Single phase, 240 V, 0.5 kVAR	1 Elec	8.50	.941	Ea.		63.50		63.50	94
7520	1 kVAR		6.40	1.250			84		84	125
7530	2 kVAR		3.20	2.500			168		168	250
7540	Single phase, plug-in unit 120 V, 0.5 kVAR		26	.308			20.50		20.50	31
7550	1 kVAR		17	.471			31.50		31.50	47
7600	Power conditioner transformer									
7610	Single phase 115 V - 240 V, 3 kVA	2 Elec	5.10	3.137	Ea.		211		211	315
7620	5 kVA	"	3.70	4.324			291		291	435
7630	7.5 kVA	3 Elec	4.80	5			335		335	500
7640	10 kVA	"	4.30	5.581			375		375	560
7700	Transient suppressor/voltage regulator									
7710	Single phase 115 or 220 V, 1 kVA	1 Elec	8.50	.941	Ea.		63.50		63.50	94
7720	2 kVA		7.30	1.096			74		74	110
7730	4 kVA		6.80	1.176			79		79	118
7800	Transient voltage suppressor transformer									
7810	Single phase, 115 or 220 V, 3.6 kVA	1 Elec	12.80	.625	Ea.		42		42	62.50
7820	7.2 kVA		11.50	.696			47		47	69.50
7830	14.4 kVA		10.20	.784			53		53	78.50
7840	Single phase, plug-in, 120 V, 1.8 kVA		26	.308			20.50		20.50	31
8000	Power measurement & control									
8010	Switchboard instruments, 3 phase 4 wire, indicating unit	1 Elec	25	.320	Ea.		21.50		21.50	32
8020	Recording unit		12	.667			45		45	66.50
8100	3 current transformers, 3 phase 4 wire, 5 to 800 A		6.40	1.250			84		84	125
8110	1,000 to 1,500 A		4.20	1.905			128		128	191
8120	2,000 to 4,000 A		3.20	2.500			168		168	250

26 05 05.30 Electrical Demolition, Transmission and Distribution		Crew	Daily Output	Labor-Hours	Unit	Material	Labor	Equipment	Total	Total Incl O&P
0010	ELECTRICAL DEMOLITION, TRANSMISSION & DISTRIBUTION									
0100	Load interrupter switch, 600 A, NEMA 1, 4.8 kV	R-3	1.33	15.038	Ea.		1,025	145	1,170	1,650
0120	13.8 kV R024119-10	"	1.27	15.748			1,050	152	1,202	1,750

26 05 05 – Selective Demolition for Electrical

26 05 05.30 Electrical Demolition, Transmission and Distribution		Crew	Daily Output	Labor-Hours	Unit	Material	2023 Bare Costs Labor	Equipment	Total	Total Incl O&P
0200	Lightning arrester, 4.8 kV	1 Elec	9	.889	Ea.		60		60	89
0220	13.8 kV R260105-30		6.67	1.199			81		81	120
0300	Alarm or option items		3.33	2.402			162		162	240

26 05 05.35 Electrical Demolition, L.V. Distribution		Crew	Daily Output	Labor-Hours	Unit	Material	2023 Bare Costs Labor	Equipment	Total	Total Incl O&P
0010	**ELECTRICAL DEMOLITION, L.V. DISTRIBUTION** Addition R024119-10									
0100	Circuit breakers in enclosure									
0120	Enclosed (NEMA 1), 600 V, 3 pole, 30 A R260105-30	1 Elec	12.30	.650	Ea.		44		44	65
0140	60 A		8.80	.909			61		61	91
0160	100 A		7.30	1.096			74		74	110
0180	225 A		5	1.600			108		108	160
0200	400 A	2 Elec	6.80	2.353			158		158	236
0220	600 A		4.60	3.478			234		234	350
0240	800 A		3.60	4.444			299		299	445
0260	1,200 A		3.10	5.161			350		350	515
0280	1,600 A		2.80	5.714			385		385	570
0300	2,000 A		2.50	6.400			430		430	640
0400	Enclosed (NEMA 7), 600 V, 3 pole, 50 A	1 Elec	8.80	.909			61		61	91
0410	100 A		5.80	1.379			93		93	138
0420	150 A		3.80	2.105			142		142	211
0430	250 A	2 Elec	6.20	2.581			174		174	258
0440	400 A	"	4.60	3.478			234		234	350
0460	Manual motor starter, NEMA 1	1 Elec	24	.333			22.50		22.50	33.50
0480	NEMA 4 or NEMA 7		15	.533			36		36	53.50
0500	Time switches, single pole single throw		15.40	.519			35		35	52
0520	Photo cell		30	.267			17.95		17.95	26.50
0540	Load management device, 4 loads		7.70	1.039			70		70	104
0550	8 loads		3.80	2.105			142		142	211
0560	Master light control panel	2 Elec	2	8			540		540	800
0600	Transfer switches, enclosed, 30 A	1 Elec	12	.667			45		45	66.50
0610	60 A		9.50	.842			56.50		56.50	84.50
0620	100 A		6.50	1.231			83		83	123
0630	150 A	2 Elec	12	1.333			90		90	133
0640	260 A		10	1.600			108		108	160
0660	400 A		8	2			135		135	200
0670	600 A		5	3.200			216		216	320
0680	800 A		4	4			269		269	400
0690	1,200 A		3.50	4.571			310		310	460
0700	1,600 A		3	5.333			360		360	535
0710	2,000 A		2.50	6.400			430		430	640
0800	Air terminal with base and connector	1 Elec	24	.333			22.50		22.50	33.50
1000	Enclosed controller, NEMA 1, 30 A		13.80	.580			39		39	58
1020	60 A		11.50	.696			47		47	69.50
1040	100 A		9.60	.833			56		56	83.50
1060	150 A		7.70	1.039			70		70	104
1080	200 A		5.40	1.481			100		100	148
1100	400 A	2 Elec	6.90	2.319			156		156	232
1120	600 A		4.60	3.478			234		234	350
1140	800 A		3.80	4.211			284		284	420
1160	1,200 A		3.10	5.161			350		350	515
1200	Control station, NEMA 1	1 Elec	30	.267			17.95		17.95	26.50
1220	NEMA 7		23	.348			23.50		23.50	35
1230	Control switches, push button		69	.116			7.80		7.80	11.60

26 05 05 – Selective Demolition for Electrical

26 05 05.35 Electrical Demolition, L.V. Distribution		Crew	Daily Output	Labor-Hours	Unit	Material	2023 Bare Costs Labor	Equipment	Total	Total Incl O&P
1240	Indicating light unit	1 Elec	120	.067	Ea.		4.49		4.49	6.65
1250	Relay	↓	15	.533	↓		36		36	53.50
2000	Motor control center components									
2020	Starter, NEMA 1, size 1	1 Elec	9	.889	Ea.		60		60	89
2040	Size 2	2 Elec	13.30	1.203			81		81	120
2060	Size 3		6.70	2.388			161		161	239
2080	Size 4		5.30	3.019			203		203	300
2100	Size 5	↓	3.30	4.848			325		325	485
2120	NEMA 7, size 1	1 Elec	8.70	.920			62		62	92
2140	Size 2	2 Elec	12.70	1.260			85		85	126
2160	Size 3		6.30	2.540			171		171	254
2180	Size 4		5	3.200			216		216	320
2200	Size 5	↓	3.20	5			335		335	500
2300	Fuse, light contactor, NEMA 1, 30 A	1 Elec	9	.889			60		60	89
2310	60 A		6.70	1.194			80.50		80.50	120
2320	100 A		3.30	2.424			163		163	243
2330	200 A	↓	2.70	2.963			200		200	297
2350	Motor control center, incoming section	2 Elec	4	4			269		269	400
2352	Structure per section	"	4.20	3.810			257		257	380
2400	Starter & structure, 10 HP	1 Elec	9	.889			60		60	89
2410	25 HP	2 Elec	13.30	1.203			81		81	120
2420	50 HP		6.70	2.388			161		161	239
2430	75 HP		5.30	3.019			203		203	300
2440	100 HP		4.70	3.404			229		229	340
2450	200 HP		3.30	4.848			325		325	485
2460	400 HP	↓	2.70	5.926	↓		400		400	595
2500	Motor starter & control									
2510	Motor starter, NEMA 1, 5 HP	1 Elec	8.90	.899	Ea.		60.50		60.50	90
2520	10 HP	"	6.20	1.290			87		87	129
2530	25 HP	2 Elec	8.40	1.905			128		128	191
2540	50 HP		6.90	2.319			156		156	232
2550	100 HP		4.60	3.478			234		234	350
2560	200 HP		3.50	4.571			310		310	460
2570	400 HP	↓	3.10	5.161			350		350	515
2610	Motor starter, NEMA 7, 5 HP	1 Elec	6.20	1.290			87		87	129
2620	10 HP	"	4.20	1.905			128		128	191
2630	25 HP	2 Elec	6.90	2.319			156		156	232
2640	50 HP		4.60	3.478			234		234	350
2650	100 HP		3.50	4.571			310		310	460
2660	200 HP	↓	1.90	8.421			565		565	845
2710	Combination control unit, NEMA 1, 5 HP	1 Elec	6.90	1.159			78		78	116
2720	10 HP	"	5	1.600			108		108	160
2730	25 HP	2 Elec	7.70	2.078			140		140	208
2740	50 HP		5.10	3.137			211		211	315
2750	100 HP	↓	3.10	5.161			350		350	515
2810	NEMA 7, 5 HP	1 Elec	5	1.600			108		108	160
2820	10 HP	"	3.90	2.051			138		138	205
2830	25 HP	2 Elec	5.10	3.137			211		211	315
2840	50 HP		3.10	5.161			350		350	515
2850	100 HP		2.30	6.957			470		470	695
2860	200 HP	↓	1.50	10.667	↓		720		720	1,075
3000	Panelboard or load center circuit breaker									
3010	Bolt-on or plug in, 15 A to 50 A	1 Elec	20	.400	Ea.		27		27	40

26 05 05 – Selective Demolition for Electrical

26 05 05.35 Electrical Demolition, L.V. Distribution		Crew	Daily Output	Labor-Hours	Unit	Material	2023 Bare Costs Labor	Equipment	Total	Total Incl O&P
3020	60 A to 70 A	1 Elec	16	.500	Ea.		33.50		33.50	50
3030	Bolt-on, 80 A to 100 A		14	.571			38.50		38.50	57
3040	Up to 250 A		7.30	1.096			74		74	110
3050	Motor operated, 30 A		13	.615			41.50		41.50	61.50
3060	60 A		10	.800			54		54	80
3070	100 A		8	1			67.50		67.50	100
3200	Switchboard circuit breaker									
3210	15 A to 60 A	1 Elec	19	.421	Ea.		28.50		28.50	42
3220	70 A to 100 A		14	.571			38.50		38.50	57
3230	125 A to 400 A		10	.800			54		54	80
3240	450 A to 600 A		5.30	1.509			102		102	151
3250	700 A to 800 A		4.30	1.860			125		125	186
3260	1,000 A		3.30	2.424			163		163	243
3270	1,200 A		2.70	2.963			200		200	297
3500	Switchboard, incoming section, 400 A	2 Elec	3.70	4.324			291		291	435
3510	600 A		3.30	4.848			325		325	485
3520	800 A		2.90	5.517			370		370	550
3530	1,200 A		2.40	6.667			450		450	665
3540	1,600 A		2.20	7.273			490		490	730
3550	2,000 A		2.10	7.619			515		515	765
3560	3,000 A		1.90	8.421			565		565	845
3570	4,000 A		1.70	9.412			635		635	940
3610	Distribution section, 600 A		4	4			269		269	400
3620	800 A		3.60	4.444			299		299	445
3630	1,200 A		3.10	5.161			350		350	515
3640	1,600 A		2.90	5.517			370		370	550
3650	2,000 A		2.70	5.926			400		400	595
3710	Transition section, 600 A		3.80	4.211			284		284	420
3720	800 A		3.30	4.848			325		325	485
3730	1,200 A		2.70	5.926			400		400	595
3740	1,600 A		2.40	6.667			450		450	665
3750	2,000 A		2.20	7.273			490		490	730
3760	2,500 A		2.10	7.619			515		515	765
3770	3,000 A		1.90	8.421			565		565	845
4000	Bus duct, aluminum or copper, 30 A	1 Elec	200	.040	L.F.		2.69		2.69	4
4020	60 A		160	.050			3.37		3.37	5
4040	100 A		140	.057			3.85		3.85	5.70
5000	Feedrail, trolley busway, up to 60 A		160	.050			3.37		3.37	5
5020	100 A		120	.067			4.49		4.49	6.65
5040	Busway, 50 A		200	.040			2.69		2.69	4
6000	Fuse, 30 A		133	.060	Ea.		4.05		4.05	6
6010	60 A		133	.060			4.05		4.05	6
6020	100 A		105	.076			5.15		5.15	7.65
6030	200 A		95	.084			5.65		5.65	8.45
6040	400 A		80	.100			6.75		6.75	10
6050	600 A		53	.151			10.15		10.15	15.10
6060	601 A to 1,200 A		42	.190			12.85		12.85	19.05
6070	1,500 A to 1,600 A		34	.235			15.85		15.85	23.50
6080	1,800 A to 2,500 A		26	.308			20.50		20.50	31
6090	4,000 A		21	.381			25.50		25.50	38
6100	4,500 A to 5,000 A		18	.444			30		30	44.50
6120	6,000 A		15	.533			36		36	53.50
6200	Fuse plug or fustat		100	.080			5.40		5.40	8

26 05 05.50 Electrical Demolition, Lighting		Crew	Daily Output	Labor-Hours	Unit	Material	2023 Bare Costs Labor	Equipment	Total	Total Incl O&P
0010	**ELECTRICAL DEMOLITION, LIGHTING** Addition R024119-10									
0100	Fixture hanger, flexible, 1/2" diameter	1 Elec	36	.222	Ea.		14.95		14.95	22
0120	3/4" diameter R260105-30	"	30	.267	"		17.95		17.95	26.50
3000	Light pole, anchor base, excl. concrete bases									
3010	Metal light pole, 10'	2 Elec	24	.667	Ea.		45		45	66.50
3020	16'	"	18	.889			60		60	89
3030	20'	R-3	8.70	2.299			155	22	177	255
3035	25'		8.60	2.326			157	22.50	179.50	258
3038	30'		6	3.333			224	32	256	370
3039	35'		6	3.333			224	32	256	370
3040	40'		6	3.333			224	32	256	370
3100	Wood light pole, 10'	2 Elec	36	.444			30		30	44.50
3120	20'	"	24	.667			45		45	66.50
3140	Bollard light, 42"	1 Elec	9	.889			60		60	89
3160	Walkway luminaire	"	8.10	.988			66.50		66.50	99
4000	Explosion proof									
4010	Metal halide, 175 W	1 Elec	8.70	.920	Ea.		62		62	92
4020	250 W	"	8.10	.988			66.50		66.50	99
4030	400 W	2 Elec	14.40	1.111			75		75	111
4050	High pressure sodium, 70 W	1 Elec	9	.889			60		60	89
4060	100 W		9	.889			60		60	89
4070	150 W		8.10	.988			66.50		66.50	99
4100	Incandescent		8.70	.920			62		62	92
4200	Fluorescent		8.10	.988			66.50		66.50	99
5000	Ballast, fluorescent fixture		24	.333			22.50		22.50	33.50
5040	High intensity discharge fixture		24	.333			22.50		22.50	33.50
5300	Exit and emergency lighting									
5310	Exit light	1 Elec	24	.333	Ea.		22.50		22.50	33.50
5320	Emergency battery pack lighting unit		12	.667			45		45	66.50
5330	Remote lamp only		80	.100			6.75		6.75	10
5340	Self-contained fluorescent lamp pack		30	.267			17.95		17.95	26.50
5500	Track lighting, 8' section	2 Elec	40	.400			27		27	40
5510	Track lighting fixture	1 Elec	64	.125			8.40		8.40	12.50
5800	Energy saving devices									
5810	Occupancy sensor	1 Elec	21	.381	Ea.		25.50		25.50	38
5820	Automatic wall switch		72	.111			7.50		7.50	11.10
5830	Remote power pack		30	.267			17.95		17.95	26.50
5840	Photoelectric control		24	.333			22.50		22.50	33.50
5850	Fixture whip		100	.080			5.40		5.40	8
6000	Lamps									
6010	Fluorescent	1 Elec	200	.040	Ea.		2.69		2.69	4
6030	High intensity discharge lamp, up to 400 W		68	.118			7.90		7.90	11.80
6040	Up to 1,000 W		45	.178			11.95		11.95	17.80
6050	Quartz		90	.089			6		6	8.90
6070	Incandescent		360	.022			1.50		1.50	2.22
6080	Exterior, PAR		290	.028			1.86		1.86	2.76
6090	Guards for fluorescent lamp		24	.333			22.50		22.50	33.50

26 05 13.10 Cable Terminations

26 05 13.10 Cable Terminations		Crew	Daily Output	Labor-Hours	Unit	2023 Bare Costs Material	Labor	Equipment	Total	Total Incl O&P
0010	**CABLE TERMINATIONS**, 5 kV to 35 kV									
0100	Indoor, insulation diameter range 0.64" to 1.08"									
0300	Padmount, 5 kV	1 Elec	8	1	Ea.	119	67.50		186.50	231
0400	10 kV		6.40	1.250		159	84		243	300
0500	15 kV		6	1.333		189	90		279	340
0600	25 kV	↓	5.60	1.429	↓	287	96		383	460
0700	Insulation diameter range 1.05" to 1.8"									
0800	Padmount, 5 kV	1 Elec	8	1	Ea.	210	67.50		277.50	330
0900	10 kV		6	1.333		229	90		319	385
1000	15 kV		5.60	1.429		228	96		324	395
1100	25 kV	↓	5.30	1.509	↓	325	102		427	505
1200	Insulation diameter range 1.53" to 2.32"									
1300	Padmount, 5 kV	1 Elec	7.40	1.081	Ea.	250	73		323	385
1400	10 kV		5.60	1.429		249	96		345	415
1500	15 kV		5.30	1.509		291	102		393	470
1600	25 kV	↓	5	1.600	↓	485	108		593	690
1700	Outdoor systems, #4 stranded to 1/0 stranded									
1800	5 kV	1 Elec	7.40	1.081	Ea.	164	73		237	289
1900	15 kV		5.30	1.509		222	102		324	395
2000	25 kV		5	1.600		253	108		361	440
2100	35 kV		4.80	1.667		370	112		482	575
2200	#1 solid to 4/0 stranded, 5 kV		6.90	1.159		177	78		255	310
2300	15 kV		5	1.600		253	108		361	440
2400	25 kV		4.80	1.667		281	112		393	475
2500	35 kV		4.60	1.739		555	117		672	785
2600	2/0 solid to 350 kcmil stranded, 5 kV		6.40	1.250		225	84		309	375
2700	15 kV		4.80	1.667		305	112		417	500
2800	25 kV		4.60	1.739		375	117		492	590
2900	35 kV		4.40	1.818		440	122		562	665
3000	400 kcmil compact to 750 kcmil stranded, 5 kV		6	1.333		305	90		395	470
3100	15 kV		4.60	1.739		410	117		527	625
3200	25 kV		4.40	1.818		620	122		742	865
3300	35 kV		4.20	1.905		710	128		838	975
3400	1,000 kcmil, 5 kV		5.60	1.429		289	96		385	465
3500	15 kV		4.40	1.818		410	122		532	630
3600	25 kV		4.20	1.905		535	128		663	775
3700	35 kV	↓	4	2	↓	710	135		845	985

26 05 13.16 Medium-Voltage, Single Cable

26 05 13.16 Medium-Voltage, Single Cable		Crew	Daily Output	Labor-Hours	Unit	Material	Labor	Equipment	Total	Total Incl O&P
0010	**MEDIUM-VOLTAGE, SINGLE CABLE** Splicing & terminations not included									
0040	Copper, XLP shielding, 5 kV, #6	2 Elec	4.40	3.636	C.L.F.	182	245		427	565
0050	#4		4.40	3.636		236	245		481	625
0100	#2		4	4		251	269		520	675
0200	#1		4	4		355	269		624	795
0400	1/0		3.80	4.211		400	284		684	860
0600	2/0		3.60	4.444		430	299		729	920
0800	4/0	↓	3.20	5		660	335		995	1,225
1000	250 kcmil	3 Elec	4.50	5.333		785	360		1,145	1,400
1200	350 kcmil		3.90	6.154		1,025	415		1,440	1,750
1400	500 kcmil	↓	3.60	6.667		1,075	450		1,525	1,875
1600	15 kV, ungrounded neutral, #1	2 Elec	4	4		390	269		659	830
1800	1/0		3.80	4.211		465	284		749	930
2000	2/0	↓	3.60	4.444	↓	530	299		829	1,025

26 05 13 – Medium-Voltage Cables

26 05 13.16 Medium-Voltage, Single Cable

	26 05 13.16 Medium-Voltage, Single Cable	Crew	Daily Output	Labor-Hours	Unit	Material	2023 Bare Costs Labor	Equipment	Total	Total Incl O&P
2200	4/0	2 Elec	3.20	5	C.L.F.	705	335		1,040	1,275
2400	250 kcmil	3 Elec	4.50	5.333		780	360		1,140	1,400
2600	350 kcmil		3.90	6.154		985	415		1,400	1,700
2800	500 kcmil		3.60	6.667		1,100	450		1,550	1,900
3000	25 kV, grounded neutral, 1/0	2 Elec	3.60	4.444		645	299		944	1,150
3200	2/0		3.40	4.706		710	315		1,025	1,250
3400	4/0		3	5.333		890	360		1,250	1,525
3600	250 kcmil	3 Elec	4.20	5.714		1,100	385		1,485	1,800
3800	350 kcmil		3.60	6.667		1,300	450		1,750	2,100
3900	500 kcmil		3.30	7.273		1,525	490		2,015	2,400
4000	35 kV, grounded neutral, 1/0	2 Elec	3.40	4.706		655	315		970	1,200
4200	2/0		3.20	5		805	335		1,140	1,375
4400	4/0		2.80	5.714		1,000	385		1,385	1,675
4600	250 kcmil	3 Elec	3.90	6.154		1,175	415		1,590	1,925
4800	350 kcmil		3.30	7.273		1,425	490		1,915	2,300
5000	500 kcmil		3	8		1,675	540		2,215	2,650
5050	Aluminum, XLP shielding, 5 kV, #2	2 Elec	5	3.200		284	216		500	630
5070	#1		4.40	3.636		294	245		539	690
5090	1/0		4	4		340	269		609	775
5100	2/0		3.80	4.211		380	284		664	840
5150	4/0		3.60	4.444		450	299		749	940
5200	250 kcmil	3 Elec	4.80	5		545	335		880	1,100
5220	350 kcmil		4.50	5.333		645	360		1,005	1,250
5240	500 kcmil		3.90	6.154		825	415		1,240	1,525
5260	750 kcmil		3.60	6.667		1,100	450		1,550	1,875
5300	15 kV aluminum, XLP, #1	2 Elec	4.40	3.636		365	245		610	765
5320	1/0		4	4		375	269		644	815
5340	2/0		3.80	4.211		405	284		689	865
5360	4/0		3.60	4.444		495	299		794	990
5380	250 kcmil	3 Elec	4.80	5		595	335		930	1,150
5400	350 kcmil		4.50	5.333		665	360		1,025	1,275
5420	500 kcmil		3.90	6.154		920	415		1,335	1,650
5440	750 kcmil		3.60	6.667		1,225	450		1,675	2,025

26 05 19 – Low-Voltage Electrical Power Conductors and Cables

26 05 19.13 Undercarpet Electrical Power Cables

	26 05 19.13 Undercarpet Electrical Power Cables	Crew	Daily Output	Labor-Hours	Unit	Material	Labor	Equipment	Total	Total Incl O&P
0010	**UNDERCARPET ELECTRICAL POWER CABLES** R260519-80									
0020	Power System									
0100	Cable flat, 3 conductor, #12, w/attached bottom shield	1 Elec	982	.008	L.F.	6.05	.55		6.60	7.45
0200	Shield, top, steel		1768	.005	"	5.50	.30		5.80	6.50
0250	Splice, 3 conductor		48	.167	Ea.	16.60	11.25		27.85	35
0300	Top shield		96	.083		1.56	5.60		7.16	10.05
0350	Tap		40	.200		21.50	13.45		34.95	43.50
0400	Insulating patch, splice, tap & end		48	.167		53.50	11.25		64.75	75
0450	Fold		230	.035			2.34		2.34	3.48
0500	Top shield, tap & fold		96	.083		1.56	5.60		7.16	10.05
0700	Transition, block assembly		77	.104		77.50	7		84.50	96
0750	Receptacle frame & base		32	.250		42.50	16.85		59.35	72
0800	Cover receptacle		120	.067		3.59	4.49		8.08	10.60
0850	Cover blank		160	.050		4.24	3.37		7.61	9.65
0860	Receptacle, direct connected, single		25	.320		91	21.50		112.50	132
0870	Dual		16	.500		150	33.50		183.50	215
0880	Combination high & low, tension		21	.381		110	25.50		135.50	159

26 05 19.13 Undercarpet Electrical Power Cables		Crew	Daily Output	Labor-Hours	Unit	2023 Bare Costs Material	Labor	Equipment	Total	Total Incl O&P
0900	Box, floor with cover	1 Elec	20	.400	Ea.	92.50	27		119.50	142
0920	Floor service w/barrier		4	2		261	135		396	485
1000	Wall, surface, with cover		20	.400		61	27		88	107
1100	Wall, flush, with cover		20	.400		42.50	27		69.50	87
1450	Cable flat, 5 conductor #12, w/attached bottom shield		800	.010	L.F.	9.95	.67		10.62	11.95
1550	Shield, top, steel		1768	.005	"	9.85	.30		10.15	11.30
1600	Splice, 5 conductor		48	.167	Ea.	27	11.25		38.25	46
1650	Top shield		96	.083		1.56	5.60		7.16	10.05
1700	Tap		48	.167		35.50	11.25		46.75	55.50
1750	Insulating patch, splice tap & end		83	.096		62.50	6.50		69	78
1800	Transition, block assembly		77	.104		56	7		63	72
1850	Box, wall, flush with cover		20	.400		56.50	27		83.50	103
1900	Cable flat, 4 conductor #12		933	.009	L.F.	7.10	.58		7.68	8.65
1950	3 conductor #10		982	.008		7	.55		7.55	8.50
1960	4 conductor #10		933	.009		9.15	.58		9.73	10.90
1970	5 conductor #10		884	.009		11.15	.61		11.76	13.20
2500	Telephone System									
2510	Transition fitting wall box, surface	1 Elec	24	.333	Ea.	75.50	22.50		98	117
2520	Flush		24	.333		75.50	22.50		98	117
2530	Flush, for PC board		24	.333		75.50	22.50		98	117
2540	Floor service box		4	2		279	135		414	505
2550	Cover, surface					25			25	27.50
2560	Flush					25			25	27.50
2570	Flush for PC board					25			25	27.50
2700	Floor fitting w/duplex jack & cover	1 Elec	21	.381		70	25.50		95.50	115
2720	Low profile		53	.151		21	10.15		31.15	38.50
2740	Miniature w/duplex jack		53	.151		39	10.15		49.15	58
2760	25 pair kit		21	.381		53.50	25.50		79	97
2780	Low profile		53	.151		21.50	10.15		31.65	39
2800	Call director kit for 5 cable		19	.421		99.50	28.50		128	152
2820	4 pair kit		19	.421		102	28.50		130.50	154
2840	3 pair kit		19	.421		126	28.50		154.50	180
2860	Comb. 25 pair & 3 conductor power		21	.381		99.50	25.50		125	148
2880	5 conductor power		21	.381		97.50	25.50		123	145
2900	PC board, 8 per 3 pair		161	.050		74	3.35		77.35	86.50
2920	6 per 4 pair		161	.050		74	3.35		77.35	86.50
2940	3 pair adapter		161	.050		67	3.35		70.35	79
2950	Plug		77	.104		3.75	7		10.75	14.55
2960	Couplers		321	.025		10.55	1.68		12.23	14.15
3000	Bottom shield for 25 pair cable		4420	.002	L.F.	1	.12		1.12	1.28
3020	4 pair		4420	.002		.47	.12		.59	.70
3040	Top shield for 25 pair cable		4420	.002		1	.12		1.12	1.28
3100	Cable assembly, double-end, 50', 25 pair		11.80	.678	Ea.	260	45.50		305.50	355
3110	3 pair		23.60	.339		92	23		115	135
3120	4 pair		23.60	.339		99.50	23		122.50	144
3140	Bulk 3 pair		1473	.005	L.F.	1.57	.37		1.94	2.27
3160	4 pair		1473	.005	"	1.94	.37		2.31	2.67
3500	Data System									
3520	Cable 25 conductor w/connection 40', 75 ohm	1 Elec	14.50	.552	Ea.	90	37		127	154
3530	Single lead		22	.364		245	24.50		269.50	305
3540	Dual lead		22	.364		261	24.50		285.50	325
3560	Shields same for 25 conductor as 25 pair telephone									
3570	Single & dual, none required									

26 05 19.13 Undercarpet Electrical Power Cables

26 05 19.13 Undercarpet Electrical Power Cables		Crew	Daily Output	Labor-Hours	Unit	2023 Bare Costs Material	Labor	Equipment	Total	Total Incl O&P
3590	BNC coax connectors, plug	1 Elec	40	.200	Ea.	17.40	13.45		30.85	39
3600	TNC coax connectors, plug	"	40	.200	"	18.65	13.45		32.10	40.50
3700	Cable-bulk									
3710	Single lead	1 Elec	1473	.005	L.F.	4.22	.37		4.59	5.20
3720	Dual lead	"	1473	.005	"	6.10	.37		6.47	7.25
3730	Hand tool crimp				Ea.	690			690	760
3740	Hand tool notch				"	24			24	26.50
3750	Boxes & floor fitting same as telephone									
3790	Data cable notching, 90°	1 Elec	97	.082	Ea.		5.55		5.55	8.25
3800	180°		60	.133			9		9	13.35
8100	Drill floor		160	.050		5.35	3.37		8.72	10.85
8200	Marking floor		1600	.005	L.F.		.34		.34	.50
8300	Tape, hold down		6400	.001	"	.21	.08		.29	.36
8350	Tape primer, 500′ per can		96	.083	Ea.	79.50	5.60		85.10	96
8400	Tool, splicing				"	56			56	61.50

26 05 19.20 Armored Cable

26 05 19.20 Armored Cable		Crew	Daily Output	Labor-Hours	Unit	2023 Bare Costs Material	Labor	Equipment	Total	Total Incl O&P
0010	**ARMORED CABLE** R260519-20									
0050	600 volt, copper (BX), #14, 2 conductor, solid	1 Elec	2.40	3.333	C.L.F.	40	225		265	380
0100	3 conductor, solid		2.20	3.636		74.50	245		319.50	445
0120	4 conductor, solid		2	4		104	269		373	515
0150	#12, 2 conductor, solid		2.30	3.478		45.50	234		279.50	400
0200	3 conductor, solid		2	4		76.50	269		345.50	485
0220	4 conductor, solid		1.80	4.444		93.50	299		392.50	550
0250	#10, 2 conductor, solid		2	4		78	269		347	485
0300	3 conductor, solid		1.60	5		125	335		460	635
0320	4 conductor, solid		1.40	5.714		168	385		553	755
0340	#8, 2 conductor, stranded		1.50	5.333		174	360		534	725
0350	3 conductor, stranded		1.30	6.154		174	415		589	805
0370	4 conductor, stranded		1.10	7.273		450	490		940	1,225
0380	#6, 2 conductor, stranded		1.30	6.154		257	415		672	900
0390	#4, 3 conductor, stranded		1.40	5.714		550	385		935	1,175
0400	3 conductor with PVC jacket, in cable tray, #6		3.10	2.581		345	174		519	640
0450	#4	2 Elec	5.40	2.963		645	200		845	1,000
0500	#2		4.60	3.478		745	234		979	1,175
0550	#1		4	4		980	269		1,249	1,475
0600	1/0		3.60	4.444		1,100	299		1,399	1,675
0650	2/0		3.40	4.706		1,050	315		1,365	1,625
0700	3/0		3.20	5		1,775	335		2,110	2,450
0750	4/0		3	5.333		2,125	360		2,485	2,850
0800	250 kcmil	3 Elec	3.60	6.667		2,625	450		3,075	3,575
0850	350 kcmil		3.30	7.273		3,300	490		3,790	4,375
0900	500 kcmil		3	8		4,575	540		5,115	5,825
0910	4 conductor with PVC jacket, in cable tray, #6	1 Elec	2.70	2.963		1,375	200		1,575	1,825
0920	#4	2 Elec	4.60	3.478		815	234		1,049	1,250
0930	#2		4	4		1,475	269		1,744	2,025
0940	#1		3.60	4.444		1,800	299		2,099	2,425
0950	1/0		3.40	4.706		1,425	315		1,740	2,025
0960	2/0		3.20	5		1,750	335		2,085	2,425
0970	3/0		3	5.333		2,300	360		2,660	3,075
0980	4/0		2.40	6.667		2,100	450		2,550	3,000
0990	250 kcmil	3 Elec	3.30	7.273		3,225	490		3,715	4,275
1000	350 kcmil		3	8		4,325	540		4,865	5,575

26 05 19.20 Armored Cable		Crew	Daily Output	Labor-Hours	Unit	Material	Labor	Equipment	Total	Total Incl O&P
						2023 Bare Costs				
1010	500 kcmil	3 Elec	2.70	8.889	C.L.F.	6,000	600		6,600	7,500
1050	5 kV, copper, 3 conductor with PVC jacket,									
1060	non-shielded, in cable tray, #4	2 Elec	380	.042	L.F.	14.85	2.84		17.69	20.50
1100	#2		360	.044		14.35	2.99		17.34	20.50
1200	#1		300	.053		15.45	3.59		19.04	22.50
1400	1/0		290	.055		21	3.72		24.72	28.50
1600	2/0		260	.062		25	4.14		29.14	33.50
2000	4/0		240	.067		26	4.49		30.49	35
2100	250 kcmil	3 Elec	330	.073		31.50	4.90		36.40	42.50
2150	350 kcmil		315	.076		41.50	5.15		46.65	53.50
2200	500 kcmil		270	.089		59.50	6		65.50	74.50
2400	15 kV, copper, 3 conductor with PVC jacket galv., steel armored									
2500	grounded neutral, in cable tray, #2	2 Elec	300	.053	L.F.	23	3.59		26.59	31
2600	#1		280	.057		24.50	3.85		28.35	32.50
2800	1/0		260	.062		28	4.14		32.14	37
2900	2/0		220	.073		37.50	4.90		42.40	49
3000	4/0		190	.084		42.50	5.65		48.15	55.50
3100	250 kcmil	3 Elec	270	.089		47.50	6		53.50	61
3150	350 kcmil		240	.100		56	6.75		62.75	71.50
3200	500 kcmil		210	.114		75	7.70		82.70	94
3400	15 kV, copper, 3 conductor with PVC jacket,									
3450	ungrounded neutral, in cable tray, #2	2 Elec	260	.062	L.F.	25	4.14		29.14	33.50
3500	#1		230	.070		27.50	4.69		32.19	37.50
3600	1/0		200	.080		31.50	5.40		36.90	43
3700	2/0		190	.084		39	5.65		44.65	51.50
3800	4/0		160	.100		47	6.75		53.75	61.50
4000	250 kcmil	3 Elec	210	.114		55	7.70		62.70	72
4050	350 kcmil		195	.123		72	8.30		80.30	92
4100	500 kcmil		180	.133		87.50	9		96.50	110
4200	600 volt, aluminum, 3 conductor in cable tray with PVC jacket									
4300	#2	2 Elec	540	.030	L.F.	5.95	2		7.95	9.45
4400	#1		460	.035		5.50	2.34		7.84	9.55
4500	1/0		400	.040		6.55	2.69		9.24	11.20
4600	2/0		360	.044		6.90	2.99		9.89	12.05
4700	3/0		340	.047		7.80	3.17		10.97	13.25
4800	4/0		320	.050		9.40	3.37		12.77	15.35
4900	250 kcmil	3 Elec	450	.053		11.30	3.59		14.89	17.80
5000	350 kcmil		360	.067		14.05	4.49		18.54	22
5200	500 kcmil		330	.073		17.50	4.90		22.40	26.50
5300	750 kcmil		285	.084		21.50	5.65		27.15	32.50
5400	600 volt, aluminum, 4 conductor in cable tray with PVC jacket									
5410	#2	2 Elec	520	.031	L.F.	5.50	2.07		7.57	9.15
5430	#1		440	.036		6.70	2.45		9.15	11
5450	1/0		380	.042		7.85	2.84		10.69	12.80
5470	2/0		340	.047		8	3.17		11.17	13.50
5480	3/0		320	.050		9.40	3.37		12.77	15.35
5500	4/0		300	.053		11.05	3.59		14.64	17.50
5520	250 kcmil	3 Elec	420	.057		11.85	3.85		15.70	18.75
5540	350 kcmil		330	.073		15.30	4.90		20.20	24
5560	500 kcmil		300	.080		19.20	5.40		24.60	29
5580	750 kcmil		270	.089		26.50	6		32.50	38
5600	5 kV, aluminum, unshielded in cable tray, #2 with PVC jacket	2 Elec	380	.042		6.90	2.84		9.74	11.80
5700	#1 with PVC jacket		360	.044		7.40	2.99		10.39	12.60

26 05 19.20 Armored Cable		Crew	Daily Output	Labor-Hours	Unit	2023 Bare Costs Material	Labor	Equipment	Total	Total Incl O&P
5800	1/0 with PVC jacket	2 Elec	300	.053	L.F.	7.95	3.59		11.54	14.10
6000	2/0 with PVC jacket		290	.055		7.80	3.72		11.52	14.05
6200	3/0 with PVC jacket		260	.062		9.75	4.14		13.89	16.85
6300	4/0 with PVC jacket		240	.067		10.95	4.49		15.44	18.70
6400	250 kcmil with PVC jacket	3 Elec	330	.073		12	4.90		16.90	20.50
6500	350 kcmil with PVC jacket		315	.076		14.10	5.15		19.25	23
6600	500 kcmil with PVC jacket		300	.080		16.70	5.40		22.10	26.50
6800	750 kcmil with PVC jacket		270	.089		20.50	6		26.50	31.50
6900	15 kV, aluminum, shielded-grounded, #2 with PVC jacket	2 Elec	320	.050		15.75	3.37		19.12	22.50
7000	#1 with PVC jacket		300	.053		15.55	3.59		19.14	22.50
7200	1/0 with PVC jacket		280	.057		17.50	3.85		21.35	25
7300	2/0 with PVC jacket		260	.062		17	4.14		21.14	25
7400	3/0 with PVC jacket		240	.067		19.10	4.49		23.59	27.50
7500	4/0 with PVC jacket		220	.073		19.60	4.90		24.50	29
7600	250 kcmil with PVC jacket	3 Elec	300	.080		22.50	5.40		27.90	32.50
7700	350 kcmil with PVC jacket		270	.089		25	6		31	36.50
7800	500 kcmil with PVC jacket		240	.100		30.50	6.75		37.25	43.50
8000	750 kcmil with PVC jacket		204	.118		36	7.90		43.90	51.50
8200	15 kV, aluminum, shielded-ungrounded, #1 with PVC jacket	2 Elec	250	.064		18.95	4.31		23.26	27.50
8300	1/0 with PVC jacket		230	.070		19.60	4.69		24.29	28.50
8400	2/0 with PVC jacket		210	.076		22.50	5.15		27.65	32
8500	3/0 with PVC jacket		200	.080		22	5.40		27.40	32
8600	4/0 with PVC jacket		190	.084		24	5.65		29.65	34.50
8700	250 kcmil with PVC jacket	3 Elec	270	.089		25.50	6		31.50	37
8800	350 kcmil with PVC jacket		240	.100		29	6.75		35.75	42
8900	500 kcmil with PVC jacket		210	.114		35	7.70		42.70	50
8950	750 kcmil with PVC jacket		174	.138		43.50	9.30		52.80	62
9010	600 volt, copper (MC) steel clad, #14, 2 wire	R-1A	8.16	1.961	C.L.F.	64.50	119		183.50	248
9020	3 wire		7.21	2.219		83.50	135		218.50	292
9030	4 wire		6.69	2.392		215	145		360	450
9040	#12, 2 wire		7.21	2.219		93.50	135		228.50	305
9050	3 wire		6.69	2.392		110	145		255	335
9060	4 wire		6.04	2.649		148	161		309	400
9070	#10, 2 wire		6.04	2.649		110	161		271	360
9080	3 wire		5.65	2.832		190	172		362	465
9090	4 wire		5.23	3.059		223	185		408	520
9100	#8, 2 wire, stranded		3.94	4.061		226	246		472	615
9110	3 wire, stranded		3.40	4.706		325	285		610	785
9120	4 wire, stranded		2.80	5.714		430	345		775	985
9130	#6, 2 wire, stranded		3.45	4.638		340	281		621	790
9200	600 volt, copper (MC) aluminum clad, #14, 2 wire		8.16	1.961		79	119		198	264
9210	3 wire		7.21	2.219		90	135		225	299
9220	4 wire		6.69	2.392		184	145		329	415
9230	#12, 2 wire		7.21	2.219		69.50	135		204.50	276
9240	3 wire		6.69	2.392		138	145		283	365
9250	4 wire		6.04	2.649		178	161		339	435
9260	#10, 2 wire		6.04	2.649		164	161		325	420
9270	3 wire		5.65	2.832		242	172		414	520
9280	4 wire		5.23	3.059		320	185		505	630
9600	Alum (MC) aluminum clad, #6, 3 conductor w/#6 grnd		2.75	5.818		265	355		620	815
9610	4 conductor w/#6 grnd		2.29	6.987		300	425		725	960
9620	#4, 3 conductor w/#6 grnd	R-1B	3.13	7.668		380	450		830	1,075
9630	4 conductor w/#6 grnd		2.67	8.989		390	525		915	1,200

26 05 19.20 Armored Cable

26 05 19.20 Armored Cable		Crew	Daily Output	Labor-Hours	Unit	2023 Bare Costs Material	Labor	Equipment	Total	Total Incl O&P
9640	#2, 3 conductor w/#4 grnd	R-1B	2.59	9.266	C.L.F.	460	540		1,000	1,300
9650	4 conductor w/#4 grnd		2.21	10.860		570	635		1,205	1,575
9660	#1, 3 conductor w/#4 grnd		2.15	11.163		630	650		1,280	1,675
9670	4 conductor w/#4 grnd		1.85	12.973		860	755		1,615	2,075
9680	1/0, 3 conductor w/#4 grnd		2.16	11.111		650	650		1,300	1,675
9690	4 conductor w/#4 grnd		1.73	13.873		855	810		1,665	2,150
9700	2/0, 3 conductor w/#4 grnd		1.91	12.565		625	735		1,360	1,775
9710	4 conductor w/#4 grnd		1.53	15.686		870	915		1,785	2,300
9720	3/0, 3 conductor w/#4 grnd		1.75	13.714		750	800		1,550	2,025
9730	4 conductor w/#4 grnd		1.40	17.143		1,200	1,000		2,200	2,800
9740	4/0, 3 conductor w/#2 grnd		1.54	15.584		875	910		1,785	2,300
9750	4 conductor w/#2 grnd		1.23	19.512		1,600	1,150		2,750	3,450
9760	250 kcmil, 3 conductor w/#1 grnd	R-1C	1.90	16.842		1,175	1,025	62.50	2,262.50	2,900
9770	4 conductor w/#1 grnd		1.52	21.053		2,000	1,275	78	3,353	4,175
9780	350 kcmil, 3 conductor w/1/0 grnd		1.76	18.182		1,375	1,100	67.50	2,542.50	3,225
9790	4 conductor w/1/0 grnd		1.41	22.695		2,400	1,375	84	3,859	4,800
9800	500 kcmil, 3 conductor w/#1 grnd		1.64	19.512		2,900	1,175	72	4,147	5,025
9810	4 conductor w/2/0 grnd		1.31	24.427		3,100	1,475	90.50	4,665.50	5,700
9840	750 kcmil, 3 conductor w/1/0 grnd		1.31	24.427		3,500	1,475	90.50	5,065.50	6,150
9850	4 conductor w/3/0 grnd		1.04	30.769		4,600	1,875	114	6,589	7,950

26 05 19.25 Cable Connectors

26 05 19.25 Cable Connectors		Crew	Daily Output	Labor-Hours	Unit	Material	Labor	Equipment	Total	Total Incl O&P
0010	**CABLE CONNECTORS**									
0100	600 volt, nonmetallic, #14-2 wire	1 Elec	160	.050	Ea.	3.03	3.37		6.40	8.35
0200	#14-3 wire to #12-2 wire		133	.060		3.03	4.05		7.08	9.35
0300	#12-3 wire to #10-2 wire		114	.070		3.03	4.73		7.76	10.35
0400	#10-3 wire to #14-4 and #12-4 wire		100	.080		3.03	5.40		8.43	11.35
0500	#8-3 wire to #10-4 wire		80	.100		5.05	6.75		11.80	15.55
0600	#6-3 wire		40	.200		6.80	13.45		20.25	27.50
0800	SER, 3 #8 insulated + 1 #8 ground		32	.250		7.50	16.85		24.35	33.50
0900	3 #6 + 1 #6 ground		24	.333		9.35	22.50		31.85	44
1000	3 #4 + 1 #6 ground		22	.364		8.20	24.50		32.70	45.50
1100	3 #2 + 1 #4 ground		20	.400		18.50	27		45.50	60.50
1200	3 1/0 + 1 #2 ground		18	.444		54	30		84	104
1400	3 2/0 + 1 #1 ground		16	.500		43	33.50		76.50	97.50
1600	3 4/0 + 1 #2/0 ground		14	.571		44.50	38.50		83	106
1800	600 volt, armored, #14-2 wire		80	.100		2.05	6.75		8.80	12.25
2200	#14-4, #12-3 and #10-2 wire		40	.200		.97	13.45		14.42	21
2400	#12-4, #10-3 and #8-2 wire		32	.250		4.13	16.85		20.98	29.50
2600	#8-3 and #10-4 wire		26	.308		6.70	20.50		27.20	38.50
2650	#8-4 wire		22	.364		7.15	24.50		31.65	44.50
2652	Non-PVC jacket connector, #6-3 wire, #6-4 wire		22	.364		103	24.50		127.50	151
2660	1/0-3 wire		11	.727		98	49		147	181
2670	300 kcmil-3 wire		6	1.333		178	90		268	330
2680	700 kcmil-3 wire		4	2		227	135		362	450
2700	PVC jacket connector, #6-3 wire, #6-4 wire		16	.500		8.20	33.50		41.70	59
2800	#4-3 wire, #4-4 wire		16	.500		8.20	33.50		41.70	59
2900	#2-3 wire		12	.667		8.20	45		53.20	75.50
3000	#1-3 wire, #2-4 wire		12	.667		21	45		66	89.50
3200	1/0-3 wire		11	.727		21	49		70	96
3400	2/0-3 wire, 1/0-4 wire		10	.800		21	54		75	103
3500	3/0-3 wire, 2/0-4 wire		9	.889		30	60		90	122
3600	4/0-3 wire, 3/0-4 wire		7	1.143		30	77		107	147

26 05 19 – Low-Voltage Electrical Power Conductors and Cables

26 05 19.25 Cable Connectors		Crew	Daily Output	Labor-Hours	Unit	Material	Labor	Equipment	Total	Total Incl O&P
						2023 Bare Costs				
3800	250 kcmil-3 wire, 4/0-4 wire	1 Elec	6	1.333	Ea.	52	90		142	191
4000	350 kcmil-3 wire, 250 kcmil-4 wire		5	1.600		52	108		160	218
4100	350 kcmil-4 wire		4	2		265	135		400	490
4200	500 kcmil-3 wire		4	2		265	135		400	490
4250	500 kcmil-4 wire, 750 kcmil-3 wire		3.50	2.286		325	154		479	585
4300	750 kcmil-4 wire		3	2.667		325	180		505	620
4400	5 kV, armored, #4		8	1		38	67.50		105.50	142
4600	#2		8	1		44.50	67.50		112	149
4800	#1		8	1		67.50	67.50		135	174
5000	1/0		6.40	1.250		124	84		208	261
5200	2/0		5.30	1.509		124	102		226	287
5500	4/0		4	2		124	135		259	335
5600	250 kcmil		3.60	2.222		124	150		274	360
5650	350 kcmil		3.20	2.500		138	168		306	400
5700	500 kcmil		2.50	3.200		269	216		485	615
5720	750 kcmil		2.20	3.636		350	245		595	755
5750	1,000 kcmil		2	4		535	269		804	985
5800	15 kV, armored, #1		4	2		192	135		327	410
5900	1/0		4	2		240	135		375	465
6000	3/0		3.60	2.222		425	150		575	690
6100	4/0		3.40	2.353		475	158		633	760
6200	250 kcmil		3.20	2.500		460	168		628	755
6300	350 kcmil		2.70	2.963		485	200		685	825
6400	500 kcmil	↓	2	4	↓	735	269		1,004	1,200

26 05 19.30 Cable Splicing		Crew	Daily Output	Labor-Hours	Unit	Material	Labor	Equipment	Total	Total Incl O&P
0010	**CABLE SPLICING** URD or similar, ideal conditions									
0100	#6 stranded to #1 stranded, 5 kV	1 Elec	4	2	Ea.	180	135		315	400
0120	15 kV		3.60	2.222		247	150		397	495
0140	25 kV		3.20	2.500		425	168		593	715
0200	#1 stranded to 4/0 stranded, 5 kV		3.60	2.222		187	150		337	430
0210	15 kV		3.20	2.500		254	168		422	530
0220	25 kV		2.80	2.857		425	192		617	750
0300	4/0 stranded to 500 kcmil stranded, 5 kV		3.30	2.424		187	163		350	450
0310	15 kV		2.90	2.759		445	186		631	765
0320	25 kV		2.50	3.200		490	216		706	855
0400	500 kcmil, 5 kV		3.20	2.500		232	168		400	505
0410	15 kV		2.80	2.857		485	192		677	820
0420	25 kV		2.30	3.478		490	234		724	885
0500	600 kcmil, 5 kV		2.90	2.759		232	186		418	530
0510	15 kV		2.40	3.333		420	225		645	795
0520	25 kV		2	4		455	269		724	900
0600	750 kcmil, 5 kV		2.60	3.077		232	207		439	565
0610	15 kV		2.20	3.636		420	245		665	825
0620	25 kV		1.90	4.211		455	284		739	920
0700	1,000 kcmil, 5 kV		2.30	3.478		232	234		466	605
0710	15 kV		1.90	4.211		455	284		739	920
0720	25 kV	↓	1.60	5	↓	495	335		830	1,050

26 05 19.35 Cable Terminations		Crew	Daily Output	Labor-Hours	Unit	Material	Labor	Equipment	Total	Total Incl O&P
0010	**CABLE TERMINATIONS**									
0015	Wire connectors, screw type, #22 to #14	1 Elec	260	.031	Ea.	.04	2.07		2.11	3.12
0020	#18 to #12		240	.033		.16	2.25		2.41	3.52
0035	#16 to #10	↓	230	.035	↓	.22	2.34		2.56	3.72

26 05 19.35 Cable Terminations		Crew	Daily Output	Labor-Hours	Unit	Material	2023 Bare Costs Labor	Equipment	Total	Total Incl O&P
0040	#14 to #8	1 Elec	210	.038	Ea.	.54	2.57		3.11	4.40
0045	#12 to #6		180	.044		.60	2.99		3.59	5.10
0050	Terminal lugs, solderless, #16 to #10		50	.160		.35	10.80		11.15	16.40
0100	#8 to #4		30	.267		.70	17.95		18.65	27.50
0150	#2 to #1		22	.364		.86	24.50		25.36	37.50
0200	1/0 to 2/0		16	.500		1.60	33.50		35.10	52
0250	3/0		12	.667		9.45	45		54.45	77
0300	4/0		11	.727		42	49		91	120
0350	250 kcmil		9	.889		3.50	60		63.50	93
0400	350 kcmil		7	1.143		3.61	77		80.61	118
0450	500 kcmil		6	1.333		8.70	90		98.70	143
0500	600 kcmil		5.80	1.379		8.55	93		101.55	147
0550	750 kcmil		5.20	1.538		12.30	104		116.30	168
0600	Split bolt connectors, tapped, #6		16	.500		3.04	33.50		36.54	53.50
0650	#4		14	.571		3.06	38.50		41.56	60.50
0700	#2		12	.667		3.56	45		48.56	70.50
0750	#1		11	.727		7.05	49		56.05	81
0800	1/0		10	.800		7.05	54		61.05	88
0850	2/0		9	.889		10.15	60		70.15	100
0900	3/0		7.20	1.111		13.70	75		88.70	126
1000	4/0		6.40	1.250		15.70	84		99.70	142
1100	250 kcmil		5.70	1.404		15.70	94.50		110.20	157
1200	300 kcmil		5.30	1.509		33	102		135	187
1400	350 kcmil		4.60	1.739		33	117		150	210
1500	500 kcmil	▼	4	2	▼	48	135		183	253
1600	Crimp 1 hole lugs, copper or aluminum, 600 volt									
1620	#14	1 Elec	60	.133	Ea.	.75	9		9.75	14.20
1630	#12		50	.160		1.58	10.80		12.38	17.75
1640	#10		45	.178		1.58	11.95		13.53	19.55
1780	#8		36	.222		2.19	14.95		17.14	24.50
1800	#6		30	.267		2.50	17.95		20.45	29.50
2000	#4		27	.296		3.16	19.95		23.11	33
2200	#2		24	.333		4.48	22.50		26.98	38.50
2400	#1		20	.400		6.55	27		33.55	47
2500	1/0		17.50	.457		7.55	31		38.55	54.50
2600	2/0		15	.533		7.30	36		43.30	61.50
2800	3/0		12	.667		8.80	45		53.80	76
3000	4/0		11	.727		9.35	49		58.35	83.50
3200	250 kcmil		9	.889		11.15	60		71.15	101
3400	300 kcmil		8	1		12.85	67.50		80.35	114
3500	350 kcmil		7	1.143		15.90	77		92.90	132
3600	400 kcmil		6.50	1.231		17.80	83		100.80	143
3800	500 kcmil		6	1.333		21.50	90		111.50	157
4000	600 kcmil		5.80	1.379		45	93		138	188
4200	700 kcmil		5.50	1.455		49	98		147	200
4400	750 kcmil	▼	5.20	1.538	▼	49	104		153	208
4500	Crimp 2-way connectors, copper or alum., 600 volt									
4510	#14	1 Elec	60	.133	Ea.	2.92	9		11.92	16.55
4520	#12		50	.160		3.11	10.80		13.91	19.40
4530	#10		45	.178		3.27	11.95		15.22	21.50
4540	#8		27	.296		3.31	19.95		23.26	33
4600	#6		25	.320		4.68	21.50		26.18	37
4800	#4	▼	23	.348	▼	6.15	23.50		29.65	42

26 05 19 – Low-Voltage Electrical Power Conductors and Cables

26 05 19.35 Cable Terminations		Crew	Daily Output	Labor-Hours	Unit	Material	Labor	Equipment	Total	Total Incl O&P
						2023 Bare Costs				
5000	#2	1 Elec	20	.400	Ea.	6.90	27		33.90	47.50
5200	#1		16	.500		8.35	33.50		41.85	59
5400	1/0		13	.615		8.80	41.50		50.30	71
5420	2/0		12	.667		9.45	45		54.45	77
5440	3/0		11	.727		10.50	49		59.50	84.50
5460	4/0		10	.800		12.45	54		66.45	93.50
5480	250 kcmil		9	.889		21.50	60		81.50	113
5500	300 kcmil		8.50	.941		21.50	63.50		85	118
5520	350 kcmil		8	1		24.50	67.50		92	127
5540	400 kcmil		7.30	1.096		28	74		102	141
5560	500 kcmil		6.20	1.290		37.50	87		124.50	171
5580	600 kcmil		5.50	1.455		75.50	98		173.50	229
5600	700 kcmil		4.50	1.778		98.50	120		218.50	286
5620	750 kcmil		4	2		86	135		221	295
7000	Compression equipment adapter, aluminum wire, #6		30	.267		7.15	17.95		25.10	34.50
7020	#4		27	.296		7.30	19.95		27.25	37.50
7040	#2		24	.333		12.75	22.50		35.25	47.50
7060	#1		20	.400		19.65	27		46.65	61.50
7080	1/0		18	.444		20.50	30		50.50	67
7100	2/0		15	.533		13.80	36		49.80	68.50
7140	4/0		11	.727		16.80	49		65.80	91.50
7160	250 kcmil		9	.889		17.60	60		77.60	108
7180	300 kcmil		8	1		19.20	67.50		86.70	121
7200	350 kcmil		7	1.143		22	77		99	138
7220	400 kcmil		6.50	1.231		24	83		107	150
7240	500 kcmil		6	1.333		27.50	90		117.50	163
7260	600 kcmil		5.80	1.379		33.50	93		126.50	175
7280	750 kcmil		5.20	1.538		35.50	104		139.50	194
8000	Compression tool, hand					2,000			2,000	2,175
8100	Hydraulic					3,125			3,125	3,425
8500	Hydraulic dies					455			455	500

26 05 19.50 Mineral Insulated Cable		Crew	Daily Output	Labor-Hours	Unit	Material	Labor	Equipment	Total	Total Incl O&P
0010	**MINERAL INSULATED CABLE** 600 volt									
0100	1 conductor, #12	1 Elec	1.60	5	C.L.F.	475	335		810	1,025
0200	#10		1.60	5		715	335		1,050	1,300
0400	#8		1.50	5.333		805	360		1,165	1,425
0500	#6		1.40	5.714		960	385		1,345	1,625
0600	#4	2 Elec	2.40	6.667		1,300	450		1,750	2,100
0800	#2		2.20	7.273		1,825	490		2,315	2,725
0900	#1		2.10	7.619		2,100	515		2,615	3,100
1000	1/0		2	8		2,450	540		2,990	3,500
1100	2/0		1.90	8.421		2,950	565		3,515	4,100
1200	3/0		1.80	8.889		3,525	600		4,125	4,775
1400	4/0		1.60	10		4,075	675		4,750	5,475
1410	250 kcmil	3 Elec	2.40	10		4,600	675		5,275	6,050
1420	350 kcmil		1.95	12.308		5,400	830		6,230	7,150
1430	500 kcmil		1.95	12.308		6,750	830		7,580	8,650
1500	2 conductor, #12	1 Elec	1.40	5.714		1,175	385		1,560	1,875
1600	#10		1.20	6.667		1,450	450		1,900	2,275
1800	#8		1.10	7.273		1,550	490		2,040	2,425
2000	#6		1.05	7.619		2,275	515		2,790	3,275
2100	#4	2 Elec	2	8		3,075	540		3,615	4,200

26 05 19.50 Mineral Insulated Cable

	26 05 19.50 Mineral Insulated Cable	Crew	Daily Output	Labor-Hours	Unit	Material	2023 Bare Costs Labor	Equipment	Total	Total Incl O&P
2200	3 conductor, #12	1 Elec	1.20	6.667	C.L.F.	1,450	450		1,900	2,275
2400	#10		1.10	7.273		1,675	490		2,165	2,550
2600	#8		1.05	7.619		2,075	515		2,590	3,075
2800	#6		1	8		2,750	540		3,290	3,825
3000	#4	2 Elec	1.80	8.889		3,450	600		4,050	4,675
3100	4 conductor, #12	1 Elec	1.20	6.667		1,550	450		2,000	2,375
3200	#10		1.10	7.273		1,850	490		2,340	2,750
3400	#8		1	8		2,425	540		2,965	3,475
3600	#6		.90	8.889		3,150	600		3,750	4,375
3620	7 conductor, #12		1.10	7.273		1,975	490		2,465	2,900
3640	#10		1	8		2,600	540		3,140	3,675
3800	Terminations, 600 volt, 1 conductor, #12		8	1	Ea.	24.50	67.50		92	127
4000	#10		7.60	1.053		24.50	71		95.50	132
4100	#8		7.30	1.096		24.50	74		98.50	137
4200	#6		6.70	1.194		24.50	80.50		105	147
4400	#4		6.20	1.290		24.50	87		111.50	156
4600	#2		5.70	1.404		37	94.50		131.50	181
4800	#1		5.30	1.509		37	102		139	192
5000	1/0		5	1.600		37	108		145	201
5100	2/0		4.70	1.702		37	115		152	211
5200	3/0		4.30	1.860		37	125		162	227
5400	4/0		4	2		82.50	135		217.50	291
5410	250 kcmil		4	2		82.50	135		217.50	291
5420	350 kcmil		4	2		116	135		251	325
5430	500 kcmil		4	2		116	135		251	325
5500	2 conductor, #12		6.70	1.194		24.50	80.50		105	147
5600	#10		6.40	1.250		37	84		121	166
5800	#8		6.20	1.290		37	87		124	170
6000	#6		5.70	1.404		37	94.50		131.50	181
6200	#4		5.30	1.509		82.50	102		184.50	242
6400	3 conductor, #12		5.70	1.404		37	94.50		131.50	181
6500	#10		5.50	1.455		37	98		135	187
6600	#8		5.20	1.538		37	104		141	195
6800	#6		4.80	1.667		37	112		149	208
7200	#4		4.60	1.739		82.50	117		199.50	265
7400	4 conductor, #12		4.60	1.739		41	117		158	220
7500	#10		4.40	1.818		41	122		163	228
7600	#8		4.20	1.905		41	128		169	237
8400	#6		4	2		86.50	135		221.50	296
8500	7 conductor, #12		3.50	2.286		41.50	154		195.50	275
8600	#10		3	2.667		89.50	180		269.50	365
8800	Crimping tool, plier type					91			91	100
9000	Stripping tool					345			345	380
9200	Hand vise					102			102	113

26 05 19.55 Non-Metallic Sheathed Cable

	26 05 19.55 Non-Metallic Sheathed Cable	Crew	Daily Output	Labor-Hours	Unit	Material	Labor	Equipment	Total	Total Incl O&P
0010	**NON-METALLIC SHEATHED CABLE** 600 volt									
0100	Copper with ground wire (Romex)									
0150	#14, 2 conductor	1 Elec	2.70	2.963	C.L.F.	47	200		247	350
0200	3 conductor		2.40	3.333		59	225		284	400
0220	4 conductor		2.20	3.636		98	245		343	475
0250	#12, 2 conductor		2.50	3.200		62.50	216		278.50	390
0300	3 conductor		2.20	3.636		88	245		333	460

26 05 19.55	Non-Metallic Sheathed Cable	Crew	Daily Output	Labor-Hours	Unit	Material	2023 Bare Costs Labor	Equipment	Total	Total Incl O&P
0320	4 conductor	1 Elec	2	4	C.L.F.	151	269		420	565
0350	#10, 2 conductor		2.20	3.636		111	245		356	490
0400	3 conductor		1.80	4.444		139	299		438	600
0420	4 conductor		1.60	5		238	335		573	760
0430	#8, 2 conductor		1.60	5		212	335		547	735
0450	3 conductor		1.50	5.333		290	360		650	855
0500	#6, 3 conductor		1.40	5.714		830	385		1,215	1,475
0520	#4, 3 conductor	2 Elec	2.40	6.667		1,100	450		1,550	1,900
0540	#2, 3 conductor	"	2.20	7.273		1,700	490		2,190	2,600
0550	SE type SER aluminum cable, 3 RHW and									
0600	1 bare neutral, 3 #8 & 1 #8	1 Elec	1.60	5	C.L.F.	230	335		565	755
0650	3 #6 & 1 #6	"	1.40	5.714		239	385		624	835
0700	3 #4 & 1 #6	2 Elec	2.40	6.667		300	450		750	995
0750	3 #2 & 1 #4		2.20	7.273		425	490		915	1,200
0800	3 #1/0 & 1 #2		2	8		535	540		1,075	1,400
0850	3 #2/0 & 1 #1		1.80	8.889		710	600		1,310	1,675
0900	3 #4/0 & 1 #2/0		1.60	10		975	675		1,650	2,075
1000	URD - triplex underground distribution cable, alum. 2 #4 + #4 neutral		2.80	5.714		206	385		591	795
1010	2 #2 + #4 neutral		2.65	6.038		255	405		660	885
1020	2 #2 + #2 neutral		2.55	6.275		261	425		686	920
1030	2 1/0 + #2 neutral		2.40	6.667		310	450		760	1,000
1040	2 1/0 + 1/0 neutral		2.30	6.957		365	470		835	1,100
1050	2 2/0 + #1 neutral		2.20	7.273		345	490		835	1,100
1060	2 2/0 + 2/0 neutral		2.10	7.619		410	515		925	1,225
1070	2 3/0 + 1/0 neutral		1.95	8.205		485	555		1,040	1,350
1080	2 3/0 + 3/0 neutral		1.95	8.205		580	555		1,135	1,450
1090	2 4/0 + 2/0 neutral		1.85	8.649		485	580		1,065	1,400
1100	2 4/0 + 4/0 neutral		1.85	8.649		655	580		1,235	1,575
1450	UF underground feeder cable, copper with ground, #14, 2 conductor	1 Elec	4	2		48.50	135		183.50	254
1500	#12, 2 conductor		3.50	2.286		84	154		238	320
1550	#10, 2 conductor		3	2.667		137	180		317	420
1600	#14, 3 conductor		3.50	2.286		87.50	154		241.50	325
1650	#12, 3 conductor		3	2.667		127	180		307	405
1700	#10, 3 conductor		2.50	3.200		180	216		396	520
1710	#8, 3 conductor		2	4		375	269		644	815
1720	#6, 3 conductor		1.80	4.444		575	299		874	1,075
2400	SEU service entrance cable, copper 2 conductors, #8 + #8 neutral		1.50	5.333		219	360		579	775
2600	#6 + #8 neutral		1.30	6.154		315	415		730	960
2800	#6 + #6 neutral		1.30	6.154		340	415		755	990
3000	#4 + #6 neutral	2 Elec	2.20	7.273		480	490		970	1,250
3200	#4 + #4 neutral		2.20	7.273		535	490		1,025	1,325
3400	#3 + #5 neutral		2.10	7.619		530	515		1,045	1,350
3600	#3 + #3 neutral		2.10	7.619		710	515		1,225	1,550
3800	#2 + #4 neutral		2	8		800	540		1,340	1,675
4000	#1 + #1 neutral		1.90	8.421		845	565		1,410	1,775
4200	1/0 + 1/0 neutral		1.80	8.889		1,825	600		2,425	2,900
4400	2/0 + 2/0 neutral		1.70	9.412		1,850	635		2,485	3,000
4600	3/0 + 3/0 neutral		1.60	10		2,525	675		3,200	3,775
4620	4/0 + 4/0 neutral		1.45	11.034		2,825	745		3,570	4,200
4800	Aluminum 2 conductors, #8 + #8 neutral	1 Elec	1.60	5		191	335		526	710
5000	#6 + #6 neutral	"	1.40	5.714		202	385		587	795
5100	#4 + #6 neutral	2 Elec	2.50	6.400		242	430		672	905
5200	#4 + #4 neutral		2.40	6.667		255	450		705	945

26 05 19.55 Non-Metallic Sheathed Cable		Crew	Daily Output	Labor-Hours	Unit	2023 Bare Costs Material	Labor	Equipment	Total	Total Incl O&P
5300	#2 + #4 neutral	2 Elec	2.30	6.957	C.L.F.	325	470		795	1,050
5400	#2 + #2 neutral		2.20	7.273		350	490		840	1,125
5450	1/0 + #2 neutral		2.10	7.619		500	515		1,015	1,325
5500	1/0 + 1/0 neutral		2	8		510	540		1,050	1,375
5550	2/0 + #1 neutral		1.90	8.421		550	565		1,115	1,450
5600	2/0 + 2/0 neutral		1.80	8.889		545	600		1,145	1,500
5800	3/0 + 1/0 neutral		1.70	9.412		380	635		1,015	1,350
6000	3/0 + 3/0 neutral		1.70	9.412		785	635		1,420	1,800
6200	4/0 + 2/0 neutral		1.60	10		725	675		1,400	1,800
6400	4/0 + 4/0 neutral		1.60	10		760	675		1,435	1,850
6500	Service entrance cap for copper SEU									
6600	100 amp	1 Elec	12	.667	Ea.	7.75	45		52.75	75
6700	150 amp		10	.800		17.05	54		71.05	99
6800	200 amp		8	1		25	67.50		92.50	128

26 05 19.70 Portable Cord

Line	Description	Crew	Daily Output	Labor-Hours	Unit	Material	Labor	Equipment	Total	Total Incl O&P
0010	**PORTABLE CORD** 600 volt									
0100	Type SO, #18, 2 conductor	1 Elec	980	.008	L.F.	.29	.55		.84	1.14
0110	3 conductor		980	.008		.35	.55		.90	1.21
0120	#16, 2 conductor		840	.010		.34	.64		.98	1.32
0130	3 conductor		840	.010		.46	.64		1.10	1.46
0140	4 conductor		840	.010		.58	.64		1.22	1.59
0240	#14, 2 conductor		840	.010		.54	.64		1.18	1.54
0250	3 conductor		840	.010		.62	.64		1.26	1.63
0260	4 conductor		840	.010		.80	.64		1.44	1.83
0280	#12, 2 conductor		840	.010		.73	.64		1.37	1.75
0290	3 conductor		840	.010		.90	.64		1.54	1.94
0300	4 conductor		840	.010		1.07	.64		1.71	2.13
0320	#10, 2 conductor		765	.010		1.02	.70		1.72	2.17
0330	3 conductor		765	.010		1.22	.70		1.92	2.39
0340	4 conductor		765	.010		1.35	.70		2.05	2.54
0360	#8, 2 conductor		555	.014		1.68	.97		2.65	3.29
0370	3 conductor		540	.015		1.82	1		2.82	3.48
0380	4 conductor		525	.015		2.17	1.03		3.20	3.92
0400	#6, 2 conductor		525	.015		2.69	1.03		3.72	4.49
0410	3 conductor		490	.016		2.58	1.10		3.68	4.47
0420	4 conductor		415	.019		3.01	1.30		4.31	5.25
0440	#4, 2 conductor	2 Elec	830	.019		3.58	1.30		4.88	5.85
0450	3 conductor		700	.023		4.19	1.54		5.73	6.90
0460	4 conductor		660	.024		5.30	1.63		6.93	8.30
0480	#2, 2 conductor		450	.036		5.30	2.39		7.69	9.40
0490	3 conductor		350	.046		6.80	3.08		9.88	12.10
0500	4 conductor		280	.057		8.20	3.85		12.05	14.70
2000	See 26 27 26.20 for Wiring Devices Elements									

26 05 19.75 Modular Flexible Wiring System

Line	Description	Crew	Daily Output	Labor-Hours	Unit	Material	Labor	Equipment	Total	Total Incl O&P
0010	**MODULAR FLEXIBLE WIRING SYSTEM**									
0020	Commercial system grid ceiling									
0100	Conversion Module	1 Elec	32	.250	Ea.	7.75	16.85		24.60	33.50
0120	Fixture cable, for fixture to fixture, 3 conductor, 15′ long		40	.200		39	13.45		52.45	63
0150	Extender cable, 3 conductor, 15′ long		48	.167		30.50	11.25		41.75	50
0200	Switch drop, 1 level, 9′ long		32	.250		26	16.85		42.85	53.50
0220	2 level, 9′ long		32	.250		43.50	16.85		60.35	73
0250	Power tee, 9′ long		32	.250		54.50	16.85		71.35	85

26 05 19 – Low-Voltage Electrical Power Conductors and Cables

26 05 19.75 Modular Flexible Wiring System		Crew	Daily Output	Labor-Hours	Unit	2023 Bare Costs Material	Labor	Equipment	Total	Total Incl O&P
1020	Industrial system open ceiling									
1100	Converter, interface between hardwiring and modular wiring	1 Elec	32	.250	Ea.	23.50	16.85		40.35	51
1120	Fixture cable, for fixture to fixture, 3 conductor, 21′ long		32	.250		136	16.85		152.85	174
1125	3 conductor, 25′ long		24	.333		175	22.50		197.50	226
1130	3 conductor, 31′ long		19	.421		155	28.50		183.50	212
1150	Fixture cord drop, 10′ long		40	.200		42	13.45		55.45	66

26 05 19.90 Wire		Crew	Daily Output	Labor-Hours	Unit	Material	Labor	Equipment	Total	Total Incl O&P
0010	**WIRE**, normal installation conditions in wireway, conduit, cable tray									
0020	600 volt, copper type THW, solid, #14 R260519-90	1 Elec	13	.615	C.L.F.	22	41.50		63.50	86
0030	#12		11	.727		17.05	49		66.05	92
0040	#10		10	.800		34.50	54		88.50	118
0050	Stranded, #14		13	.615		16.65	41.50		58.15	80
0100	#12		11	.727		23	49		72	98.50
0120	#10 R260519-92		10	.800		34.50	54		88.50	118
0140	#8		8	1		53	67.50		120.50	158
0160	#6 R260519-93		6.50	1.231		75.50	83		158.50	206
0180	#4	2 Elec	10.60	1.509		142	102		244	305
0200	#3 R260519-94		10	1.600		171	108		279	350
0220	#2		9	1.778		226	120		346	425
0240	#1 R260533-22		8	2		249	135		384	475
0260	1/0		6.60	2.424		300	163		463	575
0280	2/0		5.80	2.759		415	186		601	730
0300	3/0		5	3.200		495	216		711	865
0350	4/0		4.40	3.636		560	245		805	985
0400	250 kcmil	3 Elec	6	4		720	269		989	1,200
0420	300 kcmil		5.70	4.211		945	284		1,229	1,475
0450	350 kcmil		5.40	4.444		1,100	299		1,399	1,650
0480	400 kcmil		5.10	4.706		1,225	315		1,540	1,825
0490	500 kcmil		4.80	5		1,550	335		1,885	2,225
0500	600 kcmil		3.90	6.154		1,950	415		2,365	2,775
0510	750 kcmil		3.30	7.273		3,650	490		4,140	4,750
0520	1,000 kcmil		2.70	8.889		4,075	600		4,675	5,375
0540	600 volt, aluminum type THHN, stranded, #6	1 Elec	8	1		49	67.50		116.50	154
0560	#4	2 Elec	13	1.231		64	83		147	194
0580	#2		10.60	1.509		80.50	102		182.50	240
0600	#1		9	1.778		111	120		231	300
0620	1/0		8	2		122	135		257	335
0640	2/0		7.20	2.222		145	150		295	380
0680	3/0		6.60	2.424		181	163		344	440
0700	4/0		6.20	2.581		200	174		374	480
0720	250 kcmil	3 Elec	8.70	2.759		242	186		428	540
0740	300 kcmil		8.10	2.963		330	200		530	660
0760	350 kcmil		7.50	3.200		355	216		571	710
0780	400 kcmil		6.90	3.478		395	234		629	785
0800	500 kcmil		6	4		430	269		699	875
0850	600 kcmil		5.70	4.211		565	284		849	1,050
0880	700 kcmil		5.10	4.706		670	315		985	1,200
0900	750 kcmil		4.80	5		665	335		1,000	1,225
0910	1,000 kcmil		3.78	6.349		965	430		1,395	1,675
0920	600 volt, copper type THWN-THHN, solid, #14	1 Elec	13	.615		14.15	41.50		55.65	77
0940	#12		11	.727		21	49		70	96
0960	#10		10	.800		33.50	54		87.50	117

26 05 19 – Low-Voltage Electrical Power Conductors and Cables

26 05 19.90 Wire		Crew	Daily Output	Labor-Hours	Unit	Material	Labor	Equipment	Total	Total Incl O&P
						2023 Bare Costs				
1000	Stranded, #14	1 Elec	13	.615	C.L.F.	13.50	41.50		55	76.50
1200	#12		11	.727		54.50	49		103.50	133
1250	#10		10	.800		31	54		85	114
1300	#8		8	1		63	67.50		130.50	170
1350	#6		6.50	1.231		98	83		181	231
1400	#4	2 Elec	10.60	1.509		154	102		256	320
1450	#3		10	1.600		189	108		297	370
1500	#2		9	1.778		236	120		356	440
1550	#1		8	2		265	135		400	490
1600	1/0		6.60	2.424		315	163		478	595
1650	2/0		5.80	2.759		405	186		591	720
1700	3/0		5	3.200		500	216		716	870
2000	4/0		4.40	3.636		635	245		880	1,075
2200	250 kcmil	3 Elec	6	4		715	269		984	1,200
2400	300 kcmil		5.70	4.211		860	284		1,144	1,375
2600	350 kcmil		5.40	4.444		1,025	299		1,324	1,575
2700	400 kcmil		5.10	4.706		1,150	315		1,465	1,725
2800	500 kcmil		4.80	5		1,475	335		1,810	2,125
2802	600 kcmil		3.90	6.154		1,500	415		1,915	2,275
2804	750 kcmil		3.30	7.273		3,100	490		3,590	4,150
2805	1,000 kcmil		1.94	12.371		4,900	835		5,735	6,650
2900	600 volt, copper type XHHW, solid, #14	1 Elec	13	.615		25	41.50		66.50	88.50
2920	#12		11	.727		101	49		150	184
2940	#10		10	.800		156	54		210	251
3000	Stranded, #14		13	.615		22.50	41.50		64	86
3020	#12		11	.727		30.50	49		79.50	107
3040	#10		10	.800		45	54		99	130
3060	#8		8	1		79	67.50		146.50	187
3080	#6		6.50	1.231		123	83		206	259
3100	#4	2 Elec	10.60	1.509		178	102		280	345
3110	#3		10	1.600		223	108		331	405
3120	#2		9	1.778		274	120		394	480
3140	#1		8	2		320	135		455	550
3160	1/0		6.60	2.424		375	163		538	660
3180	2/0		5.80	2.759		475	186		661	795
3200	3/0		5	3.200		605	216		821	985
3220	4/0		4.40	3.636		740	245		985	1,175
3240	250 kcmil	3 Elec	6	4		870	269		1,139	1,350
3260	300 kcmil		5.70	4.211		1,025	284		1,309	1,550
3280	350 kcmil		5.40	4.444		1,175	299		1,474	1,750
3300	400 kcmil		5.10	4.706		1,425	315		1,740	2,025
3320	500 kcmil		4.80	5		1,700	335		2,035	2,350
3340	600 kcmil		3.90	6.154		2,125	415		2,540	2,975
3360	750 kcmil		3.30	7.273		3,375	490		3,865	4,450
3380	1,000 kcmil		2.40	10		5,025	675		5,700	6,525
5020	600 volt, aluminum type XHHW, stranded, #6	1 Elec	8	1		54.50	67.50		122	160
5040	#4	2 Elec	13	1.231		66.50	83		149.50	196
5060	#2		10.60	1.509		82.50	102		184.50	242
5080	#1		9	1.778		113	120		233	305
5100	1/0		8	2		128	135		263	340
5120	2/0		7.20	2.222		148	150		298	385
5140	3/0		6.60	2.424		182	163		345	445
5160	4/0		6.20	2.581		204	174		378	480

26 05 19.90 Wire		Crew	Daily Output	Labor-Hours	Unit	2023 Bare Costs Material	Labor	Equipment	Total	Total Incl O&P
5180	250 kcmil	3 Elec	8.70	2.759	C.L.F.	248	186		434	550
5200	300 kcmil		8.10	2.963		345	200		545	675
5220	350 kcmil		7.50	3.200		355	216		571	710
5240	400 kcmil		6.90	3.478		410	234		644	805
5260	500 kcmil		6	4		445	269		714	890
5280	600 kcmil		5.70	4.211		585	284		869	1,075
5300	700 kcmil		5.40	4.444		715	299		1,014	1,225
5320	750 kcmil		5.10	4.706		680	315		995	1,225
5340	1,000 kcmil		3.60	6.667		1,100	450		1,550	1,900
5390	600 volt, copper type XLPE-USE (RHW), solid, #14	1 Elec	12	.667		22.50	45		67.50	91
5400	#12		11	.727		45	49		94	123
5420	#10		10	.800		59.50	54		113.50	146
5440	Stranded, #14		13	.615		25.50	41.50		67	89.50
5460	#12		11	.727		47.50	49		96.50	126
5480	#10		10	.800		55	54		109	140
5500	#8		8	1		95.50	67.50		163	205
5520	#6		6.50	1.231		137	83		220	274
5540	#4	2 Elec	10.60	1.509		209	102		311	380
5560	#2		9	1.778		315	120		435	530
5580	#1		8	2		350	135		485	585
5600	1/0		6.60	2.424		445	163		608	735
5620	2/0		5.80	2.759		550	186		736	880
5640	3/0		5	3.200		690	216		906	1,075
5660	4/0		4.40	3.636		880	245		1,125	1,325
5680	250 kcmil	3 Elec	6	4		905	269		1,174	1,400
5700	300 kcmil		5.70	4.211		1,375	284		1,659	1,925
5720	350 kcmil		5.40	4.444		1,375	299		1,674	1,975
5740	400 kcmil		5.10	4.706		1,400	315		1,715	2,025
5760	500 kcmil		4.80	5		1,750	335		2,085	2,425
5780	600 kcmil		3.90	6.154		2,075	415		2,490	2,900
5800	750 kcmil		3.30	7.273		3,700	490		4,190	4,775
5820	1,000 kcmil		2.70	8.889		3,800	600		4,400	5,075
5840	600 volt, aluminum type XLPE-USE (RHW), stranded, #6	1 Elec	8	1		66	67.50		133.50	173
5860	#4	2 Elec	13	1.231		76	83		159	207
5880	#2		10.60	1.509		102	102		204	263
5900	#1		9	1.778		138	120		258	330
5920	1/0		8	2		158	135		293	375
5940	2/0		7.20	2.222		185	150		335	425
5960	3/0		6.60	2.424		193	163		356	455
5980	4/0		6.20	2.581		252	174		426	535
6000	250 kcmil	3 Elec	8.70	2.759		345	186		531	655
6020	300 kcmil		8.10	2.963		355	200		555	685
6040	350 kcmil		7.50	3.200		390	216		606	745
6060	400 kcmil		6.90	3.478		450	234		684	845
6080	500 kcmil		6	4		515	269		784	965
6100	600 kcmil		5.70	4.211		795	284		1,079	1,300
6110	700 kcmil		5.40	4.444		830	299		1,129	1,350
6120	750 kcmil		5.10	4.706		840	315		1,155	1,400

26 05 23.10 Control Cable		Crew	Daily Output	Labor-Hours	Unit	Material	Labor	Equipment	Total	Total Incl O&P
						2023 Bare Costs				
0010	CONTROL CABLE									
0020	600 volt, copper, #14 THWN wire with PVC jacket, 2 wires	1 Elec	9	.889	C.L.F.	48	60		108	142
0030	3 wires		8	1		81	67.50		148.50	190
0100	4 wires		7	1.143		137	77		214	265
0150	5 wires		6.50	1.231		186	83		269	325
0200	6 wires		6	1.333		138	90		228	285
0300	8 wires		5.30	1.509		245	102		347	420
0400	10 wires		4.80	1.667		243	112		355	435
0500	12 wires		4.30	1.860		261	125		386	475
0600	14 wires		3.80	2.105		330	142		472	575
0700	16 wires		3.50	2.286		415	154		569	690
0800	18 wires		3.30	2.424		465	163		628	755
0810	19 wires		3.10	2.581		365	174		539	665
0900	20 wires		3	2.667		355	180		535	660
1000	22 wires		2.80	2.857		525	192		717	860

26 05 23.20 Special Wires and Fittings		Crew	Daily Output	Labor-Hours	Unit	Material	Labor	Equipment	Total	Total Incl O&P
0010	SPECIAL WIRES & FITTINGS									
0100	Fixture TFFN 600 volt 90°C stranded, #18	1 Elec	13	.615	C.L.F.	24	41.50		65.50	88
0150	#16		13	.615		37.50	41.50		79	103
0500	Thermostat, jacket non-plenum, twisted, #18-2 conductor		8	1		29.50	67.50		97	133
0550	#18-3 conductor		7	1.143		38	77		115	156
0600	#18-4 conductor		6.50	1.231		42	83		125	170
0650	#18-5 conductor		6	1.333		49	90		139	187
0700	#18-6 conductor		5.50	1.455		63	98		161	215
0750	#18-7 conductor		5	1.600		67.50	108		175.50	234
0800	#18-8 conductor		4.80	1.667		54	112		166	226
2460	Tray cable, type TC, copper, #16-2 conductor		9.40	.851		43.50	57.50		101	133
2464	#16-3 conductor		8.40	.952		76	64		140	179
2468	#16-4 conductor		7.30	1.096		75	74		149	193
2472	#16-5 conductor		6.70	1.194		62	80.50		142.50	188
2476	#16-7 conductor		5.50	1.455		85	98		183	240
2480	#16-9 conductor		5	1.600		106	108		214	277
2484	#16-12 conductor	2 Elec	8.80	1.818		176	122		298	375
2488	#16-15 conductor		7.20	2.222		185	150		335	425
2492	#16-19 conductor		6.60	2.424		228	163		391	495
2496	#16-25 conductor		6.40	2.500		320	168		488	605
2500	#14-2 conductor	1 Elec	9	.889		26.50	60		86.50	118
2520	#14-3 conductor		8	1		39.50	67.50		107	144
2540	#14-4 conductor		7	1.143		60	77		137	180
2560	#14-5 conductor		6.50	1.231		63	83		146	193
2564	#14-7 conductor		5.30	1.509		123	102		225	287
2568	#14-9 conductor	2 Elec	9.60	1.667		137	112		249	320
2572	#14-12 conductor		8.60	1.860		192	125		317	395
2576	#14-15 conductor		7.20	2.222		300	150		450	550
2578	#14-19 conductor		6.20	2.581		330	174		504	625
2582	#14-25 conductor		5.30	3.019		490	203		693	840
2590	#12-2 conductor	1 Elec	8.40	.952		72.50	64		136.50	175
2592	#12-3 conductor		7.60	1.053		56.50	71		127.50	167
2594	#12-4 conductor		6.60	1.212		128	81.50		209.50	262
2596	#12-5 conductor		6.20	1.290		160	87		247	305
2598	#12-7 conductor	2 Elec	10.40	1.538		159	104		263	330
2602	#12-9 conductor		8.80	1.818		295	122		417	505

26 05 23 – Control-Voltage Electrical Power Cables

26 05 23.20 Special Wires and Fittings		Crew	Daily Output	Labor-Hours	Unit	Material	Labor	Equipment	Total	Total Incl O&P
						2023 Bare Costs				
2604	#12-12 conductor	2 Elec	7.80	2.051	C.L.F.	282	138		420	515
2606	#12-15 conductor		6.80	2.353		340	158		498	605
2608	#12-19 conductor		6	2.667		415	180		595	725
2610	#12-25 conductor	3 Elec	7.70	3.117		565	210		775	935
2618	#10-2 conductor	1 Elec	8	1		91	67.50		158.50	200
2622	#10-3 conductor	"	7.30	1.096		138	74		212	261
2624	#10-4 conductor	2 Elec	12.80	1.250		207	84		291	355
2626	#10-5 conductor		11.80	1.356		218	91.50		309.50	375
2628	#10-7 conductor		9.40	1.702		305	115		420	505
2630	#10-9 conductor		8.40	1.905		277	128		405	495
2632	#10-12 conductor		7.20	2.222		510	150		660	780
2640	300 V, copper braided shield, PVC jacket									
2650	2 conductor #18 stranded	1 Elec	7	1.143	C.L.F.	16.90	77		93.90	133
2660	3 conductor #18 stranded		6	1.333		20.50	90		110.50	156
2670	4 conductor #18 stranded		6	1.333		160	90		250	310
3000	Strain relief grip for cable									
3050	Cord, top, #12-3	1 Elec	40	.200	Ea.	16.75	13.45		30.20	38.50
3060	#12-4		40	.200		16.75	13.45		30.20	38.50
3070	#12-5		39	.205		19.70	13.80		33.50	42
3100	#10-3		39	.205		19.70	13.80		33.50	42
3110	#10-4		38	.211		19.70	14.20		33.90	42.50
3120	#10-5		38	.211		23	14.20		37.20	46.50
3200	Bottom, #12-3		40	.200		22.50	13.45		35.95	45
3210	#12-4		40	.200		22.50	13.45		35.95	45
3220	#12-5		39	.205		21.50	13.80		35.30	44.50
3230	#10-3		39	.205		21.50	13.80		35.30	44.50
3300	#10-4		38	.211		21.50	14.20		35.70	45
3310	#10-5		38	.211		24	14.20		38.20	47
3400	Cable ties, standard, 4″ length		190	.042		.20	2.84		3.04	4.43
3410	7″ length		160	.050		.23	3.37		3.60	5.25
3420	14.5″ length		90	.089		.56	6		6.56	9.50
3430	Heavy, 14.5″ length		80	.100		.77	6.75		7.52	10.85
3500	Cable gland, nylon, 1/4″ NPT thread		60	.133		3.52	9		12.52	17.20
3510	Cable gland, nylon, 3/8″ NPT thread		60	.133		4.05	9		13.05	17.80
3520	Cable gland, nylon, 1/2″ NPT thread		60	.133		5.05	9		14.05	18.95
3530	Cable gland, nylon, 3/4″ NPT thread		60	.133		7.55	9		16.55	21.50
3540	Cable gland, nylon, 1″ NPT thread		60	.133		10.85	9		19.85	25.50
3550	Cable gland, nylon, 1-1/4″ NPT thread		60	.133		14.15	9		23.15	29
3970	U-cable guards									
3980	.75″ x 5′ U-cable guard,14 gauge	1 Elec	24	.333	Ea.	33.50	22.50		56	70.50
3990	.75″ x 8′ U-cable guard,14 gauge		24	.333		34	22.50		56.50	71
4000	1-1/8″ x 5′ U-cable guard		24	.333		26	22.50		48.50	62
4010	1-1/8″ x 8′ U-cable guard		24	.333		43.50	22.50		66	81.50
4020	2-3/16″ x 5′ U-cable guard		24	.333		50.50	22.50		73	89
4030	2-3/16″ x 8′ U-cable guard		24	.333		66.50	22.50		89	107
4040	3-3/16″ x 5′ U-cable guard		24	.333		62.50	22.50		85	103
4050	3-3/16″ x 8′ U-cable guard		24	.333		87.50	22.50		110	130
4060	4″ x 8′ U-cable guard		24	.333		62.50	22.50		85	102
4070	2″ x 9′ flanged-cable guard		20	.400		147	27		174	202
4080	3″ x 9′ flanged-cable guard		20	.400		187	27		214	246
4090	3.5″ x 9′ flanged-cable guard		20	.400		220	27		247	282
5000	2″ x 5′ flanged-cable guard, extension		20	.400		127	27		154	180
5010	3″ x 5′ flanged-cable guard, extension		20	.400		174	27		201	231

26 05 23 – Control-Voltage Electrical Power Cables

26 05 23.20 Special Wires and Fittings		Crew	Daily Output	Labor-Hours	Unit	Material	Labor	Equipment	Total	Total Incl O&P
5020	.5" x 8' U-cable guard, black plastic	1 Elec	26	.308	Ea.	8.30	20.50		28.80	40
5030	.75" x 8' U-cable guard, black plastic		26	.308		11.10	20.50		31.60	43
5040	1" x 8' U-cable guard, black plastic		26	.308		16.05	20.50		36.55	48.50

26 05 26 – Grounding and Bonding for Electrical Systems

26 05 26.80 Grounding

		Crew	Daily Output	Labor-Hours	Unit	Material	Labor	Equipment	Total	Total Incl O&P
0010	**GROUNDING** R260526-80									
0030	Rod, copper clad, 8' long, 1/2" diameter	1 Elec	5.50	1.455	Ea.	29.50	98		127.50	178
0040	5/8" diameter		5.50	1.455		22	98		120	171
0050	3/4" diameter		5.30	1.509		50	102		152	206
0080	10' long, 1/2" diameter		4.80	1.667		37	112		149	208
0090	5/8" diameter		4.60	1.739		32.50	117		149.50	210
0100	3/4" diameter		4.40	1.818		61	122		183	249
0130	15' long, 3/4" diameter		4	2		102	135		237	310
0150	Coupling, bronze, 1/2" diameter					8.50			8.50	9.35
0160	5/8" diameter					7.85			7.85	8.60
0170	3/4" diameter					20			20	22
0190	Drive studs, 1/2" diameter					23.50			23.50	25.50
0210	5/8" diameter					24			24	26.50
0220	3/4" diameter					35			35	38.50
0230	Clamp, bronze, 1/2" diameter	1 Elec	32	.250		4.76	16.85		21.61	30.50
0240	5/8" diameter		32	.250		2.57	16.85		19.42	28
0250	3/4" diameter		32	.250		4.27	16.85		21.12	29.50
0260	Wire ground bare armored, #8-1 conductor		2	4	C.L.F.	78	269		347	485
0270	#6-1 conductor		1.80	4.444		151	299		450	610
0280	#4-1 conductor		1.60	5		149	335		484	665
0320	Bare copper wire, #14 solid		14	.571		13.10	38.50		51.60	71.50
0330	#12		13	.615		13.75	41.50		55.25	76.50
0340	#10		12	.667		34	45		79	104
0350	#8		11	.727		59.50	49		108.50	139
0360	#6		10	.800		89.50	54		143.50	179
0370	#4		8	1		146	67.50		213.50	261
0380	#2		5	1.600		240	108		348	425
0390	Bare copper wire, stranded, #8		11	.727		36	49		85	113
0400	#6		10	.800		99.50	54		153.50	189
0450	#4	2 Elec	16	1		159	67.50		226.50	275
0600	#2		10	1.600		247	108		355	430
0650	#1		9	1.778		240	120		360	440
0700	1/0		8	2		330	135		465	565
0750	2/0		7.20	2.222		415	150		565	675
0800	3/0		6.60	2.424		480	163		643	775
1000	4/0		5.70	2.807		655	189		844	1,000
1200	250 kcmil	3 Elec	7.20	3.333		815	225		1,040	1,225
1210	300 kcmil		6.60	3.636		1,200	245		1,445	1,700
1220	350 kcmil		6	4		1,175	269		1,444	1,675
1230	400 kcmil		5.70	4.211		1,625	284		1,909	2,225
1240	500 kcmil		5.10	4.706		1,575	315		1,890	2,200
1260	750 kcmil		3.60	6.667		2,400	450		2,850	3,300
1270	1,000 kcmil		3	8		2,275	540		2,815	3,300
1360	Bare aluminum, stranded, #6	1 Elec	9	.889		16.05	60		76.05	107
1370	#4	2 Elec	16	1		33.50	67.50		101	137
1380	#2		13	1.231		141	83		224	279
1390	#1		10.60	1.509		46.50	102		148.50	203

(Material, Labor, Equipment and Total columns: 2023 Bare Costs)

26 05 26.80 Grounding		Crew	Daily Output	Labor-Hours	Unit	Material	Labor (2023 Bare Costs)	Equipment (2023 Bare Costs)	Total (2023 Bare Costs)	Total Incl O&P
1400	1/0	2 Elec	9	1.778	C.L.F.	86	120		206	273
1410	2/0		8	2		102	135		237	315
1420	3/0		7.20	2.222		137	150		287	375
1430	4/0		6.60	2.424		143	163		306	400
1440	250 kcmil	3 Elec	9.30	2.581		75	174		249	340
1450	300 kcmil		8.70	2.759		124	186		310	415
1460	400 kcmil		7.50	3.200		108	216		324	440
1470	500 kcmil		6.90	3.478		170	234		404	535
1480	600 kcmil		6	4		213	269		482	635
1490	700 kcmil		5.70	4.211		236	284		520	680
1500	750 kcmil		5.10	4.706		261	315		576	755
1510	1,000 kcmil		4.80	5		266	335		601	790
1800	Water pipe ground clamps, heavy duty									
2000	Bronze, 1/2" to 1" diameter	1 Elec	8	1	Ea.	39	67.50		106.50	143
2100	1-1/4" to 2" diameter		8	1		40	67.50		107.50	144
2200	2-1/2" to 3" diameter		6	1.333		87	90		177	229
2400	Grounding, exothermic welding									
2500	Exothermic welding reusable mold, cable to cable, parallel, vertical	1 Elec	8	1	Ea.	560	67.50		627.50	720
2505	Splice single		8	1		475	67.50		542.50	625
2510	Splice single to double		8	1		590	67.50		657.50	745
2520	Cable to cable, termination, Tee		8	1		550	67.50		617.50	705
2530	Cable to rod, termination, Tee		8	1		435	67.50		502.50	575
2535	Cable to rebar over, termination, Tee		8	1		134	67.50		201.50	247
2540	Cable to rod, termination, 90 Deg		8	1		355	67.50		422.50	495
2550	Cable to vertical flat steel		8	1		555	67.50		622.50	710
2555	Cable to 45 Deg		8	1		595	67.50		662.50	750
2730	Exothermic weld, 4/0 wire to 1" ground rod		7	1.143		4.61	77		81.61	119
2740	4/0 wire to building steel		7	1.143		4.61	77		81.61	119
2750	4/0 wire to motor frame		7	1.143		4.61	77		81.61	119
2760	4/0 wire to 4/0 wire		7	1.143		4.61	77		81.61	119
2770	4/0 wire to #4 wire		7	1.143		4.61	77		81.61	119
2780	4/0 wire to #8 wire		7	1.143		4.61	77		81.61	119
2790	Mold, reusable, for above					166			166	183
2800	Brazed connections, #6 wire	1 Elec	12	.667		18.70	45		63.70	87
3000	#2 wire		10	.800		25	54		79	108
3100	3/0 wire		8	1		37.50	67.50		105	141
3200	4/0 wire		7	1.143		43	77		120	161
3400	250 kcmil wire		5	1.600		50	108		158	215
3600	500 kcmil wire		4	2		61.50	135		196.50	268
3700	Insulated ground wire, copper #14		13	.615	C.L.F.	13.50	41.50		55	76.50
3710	#12		11	.727		54.50	49		103.50	133
3720	#10		10	.800		31	54		85	114
3730	#8		8	1		63	67.50		130.50	170
3740	#6		6.50	1.231		98	83		181	231
3750	#4	2 Elec	10.60	1.509		154	102		256	320
3770	#2		9	1.778		236	120		356	440
3780	#1		8	2		265	135		400	490
3790	1/0		6.60	2.424		315	163		478	595
3800	2/0		5.80	2.759		405	186		591	720
3810	3/0		5	3.200		500	216		716	870
3820	4/0		4.40	3.636		635	245		880	1,075
3830	250 kcmil	3 Elec	6	4		715	269		984	1,200
3840	300 kcmil		5.70	4.211		860	284		1,144	1,375

26 05 26 – Grounding and Bonding for Electrical Systems

26 05 26.80 Grounding		Crew	Daily Output	Labor-Hours	Unit	Material	2023 Bare Costs Labor	Equipment	Total	Total Incl O&P
3850	350 kcmil	3 Elec	5.40	4.444	C.L.F.	1,025	299		1,324	1,575
3860	400 kcmil		5.10	4.706		1,150	315		1,465	1,725
3870	500 kcmil		4.80	5		1,475	335		1,810	2,125
3880	600 kcmil		3.90	6.154		1,950	415		2,365	2,775
3890	750 kcmil		3.30	7.273		3,650	490		4,140	4,750
3900	1,000 kcmil		2.70	8.889		4,075	600		4,675	5,375
3960	Insulated ground wire, aluminum, #6	1 Elec	8	1		49	67.50		116.50	154
3970	#4	2 Elec	13	1.231		64	83		147	194
3980	#2		10.60	1.509		80.50	102		182.50	240
3990	#1		9	1.778		111	120		231	300
4000	1/0		8	2		122	135		257	335
4010	2/0		7.20	2.222		145	150		295	380
4020	3/0		6.60	2.424		181	163		344	440
4030	4/0		6.20	2.581		200	174		374	480
4040	250 kcmil	3 Elec	8.70	2.759		242	186		428	540
4050	300 kcmil		8.10	2.963		330	200		530	660
4060	350 kcmil		7.50	3.200		355	216		571	710
4070	400 kcmil		6.90	3.478		395	234		629	785
4080	500 kcmil		6	4		430	269		699	875
4090	600 kcmil		5.70	4.211		565	284		849	1,050
4100	700 kcmil		5.10	4.706		670	315		985	1,200
4110	750 kcmil		4.80	5		665	335		1,000	1,225
5000	Copper electrolytic ground rod system									
5010	Includes augering hole, mixing bentonite clay,									
5020	Installing rod, and terminating ground wire									
5100	Straight vertical type, 2″ diam.									
5120	8.5′ long, clamp connection	1 Elec	2.67	2.996	Ea.	880	202		1,082	1,275
5130	With exothermic weld connection		1.95	4.103		850	276		1,126	1,350
5140	10′ long		2.35	3.404		870	229		1,099	1,300
5150	With exothermic weld connection		1.78	4.494		1,075	305		1,380	1,650
5160	12′ long		2.16	3.704		1,175	249		1,424	1,650
5170	With exothermic weld connection		1.67	4.790		1,275	325		1,600	1,875
5180	20′ long		1.74	4.598		1,700	310		2,010	2,325
5190	With exothermic weld connection		1.40	5.714		1,600	385		1,985	2,325
5195	40′ long with exothermic weld connection	2 Elec	2	8		3,550	540		4,090	4,700
5200	L-shaped, 2″ diam.									
5220	4′ vert. x 10′ horiz., clamp connection	1 Elec	5.33	1.501	Ea.	1,525	101		1,626	1,825
5230	With exothermic weld connection	″	3.08	2.597	″	1,525	175		1,700	1,950
5300	Protective box at grade level, with breather slots									
5320	Round 12″ long, fiberlyte	1 Elec	32	.250	Ea.	150	16.85		166.85	190
5330	Concrete	″	16	.500		132	33.50		165.50	195
5400	Bentonite clay, 50# bag, 1 per 10′ of rod					61			61	67
5500	Equipotential earthing bar	1 Elec	2	4		160	269		429	575
7000	Exothermic welding kit, multi vertical	″	8	1		1,075	67.50		1,142.50	1,300

26 05 29 – Hangers and Supports for Electrical Systems

26 05 29.20 Hangers		Crew	Daily Output	Labor-Hours	Unit	Material	Labor	Equipment	Total	Total Incl O&P
0010	**HANGERS** R260533-21									
0015	See section 22 05 29.10 for additional items									
0030	Conduit supports									
0050	Strap w/2 holes, rigid steel conduit									
0100	1/2″ diameter	1 Elec	470	.017	Ea.	.22	1.15		1.37	1.94
0150	3/4″ diameter		440	.018		.26	1.22		1.48	2.11

26 05 29.20 Hangers		Crew	Daily Output	Labor-Hours	Unit	Material	2023 Bare Costs Labor	Equipment	Total	Total Incl O&P
0200	1" diameter	1 Elec	400	.020	Ea.	.19	1.35		1.54	2.21
0300	1-1/4" diameter		355	.023		.28	1.52		1.80	2.57
0350	1-1/2" diameter		320	.025		.43	1.68		2.11	2.97
0400	2" diameter		266	.030		.52	2.03		2.55	3.58
0500	2-1/2" diameter		160	.050		.78	3.37		4.15	5.85
0550	3" diameter		133	.060		.92	4.05		4.97	7
0600	3-1/2" diameter		100	.080		5.85	5.40		11.25	14.40
0650	4" diameter		80	.100		1.56	6.75		8.31	11.70
0700	EMT, 1/2" diameter		470	.017		.13	1.15		1.28	1.84
0800	3/4" diameter		440	.018		.25	1.22		1.47	2.10
0850	1" diameter		400	.020		.31	1.35		1.66	2.34
0900	1-1/4" diameter		355	.023		.46	1.52		1.98	2.77
0950	1-1/2" diameter		320	.025		.45	1.68		2.13	3
1000	2" diameter		266	.030		.63	2.03		2.66	3.70
1100	2-1/2" diameter		160	.050		1	3.37		4.37	6.10
1150	3" diameter		133	.060		1.44	4.05		5.49	7.60
1200	3-1/2" diameter		100	.080		2.03	5.40		7.43	10.25
1250	4" diameter		80	.100		2.26	6.75		9.01	12.50
1400	Hanger, with bolt, 1/2" diameter		200	.040		1.07	2.69		3.76	5.20
1450	3/4" diameter		190	.042		.33	2.84		3.17	4.57
1500	1" diameter		176	.045		1.37	3.06		4.43	6.05
1550	1-1/4" diameter		160	.050		1.57	3.37		4.94	6.75
1600	1-1/2" diameter		140	.057		2.66	3.85		6.51	8.65
1650	2" diameter		130	.062		3.24	4.14		7.38	9.70
1700	2-1/2" diameter		100	.080		3.86	5.40		9.26	12.25
1750	3" diameter		64	.125		4.97	8.40		13.37	17.95
1800	3-1/2" diameter		50	.160		5.70	10.80		16.50	22.50
1850	4" diameter		40	.200		10.35	13.45		23.80	31.50
1900	Riser clamps, conduit, 1/2" diameter		40	.200		9.15	13.45		22.60	30
1950	3/4" diameter		36	.222		9.80	14.95		24.75	33
2000	1" diameter		30	.267		10	17.95		27.95	37.50
2100	1-1/4" diameter		27	.296		12.05	19.95		32	43
2150	1-1/2" diameter		27	.296		13.20	19.95		33.15	44
2200	2" diameter		20	.400		11.65	27		38.65	53
2250	2-1/2" diameter		20	.400		13.85	27		40.85	55
2300	3" diameter		18	.444		15.05	30		45.05	61
2350	3-1/2" diameter		18	.444		11.75	30		41.75	57.50
2400	4" diameter		14	.571		17.95	38.50		56.45	76.50
2500	Threaded rod, painted, 1/4" diameter		260	.031	L.F.	1.68	2.07		3.75	4.93
2600	3/8" diameter		200	.040		11.20	2.69		13.89	16.35
2700	1/2" diameter		140	.057		16	3.85		19.85	23.50
2800	5/8" diameter		100	.080		10.10	5.40		15.50	19.10
2900	3/4" diameter		60	.133		10.25	9		19.25	24.50
2940	Couplings painted, 1/4" diameter				C	156			156	171
2960	3/8" diameter					186			186	205
2970	1/2" diameter					233			233	257
2980	5/8" diameter					525			525	580
2990	3/4" diameter					1,050			1,050	1,150
3000	Nuts, galvanized, 1/4" diameter					24.50			24.50	27
3050	3/8" diameter					32			32	35
3100	1/2" diameter					76			76	84
3150	5/8" diameter					112			112	123
3200	3/4" diameter					172			172	189

26 05 29 – Hangers and Supports for Electrical Systems

26 05 29.20 Hangers		Crew	Daily Output	Labor-Hours	Unit	2023 Bare Costs Material	Labor	Equipment	Total	Total Incl O&P
3250	Washers, galvanized, 1/4" diameter				C	24.50			24.50	27
3300	3/8" diameter					32			32	35.50
3350	1/2" diameter					53			53	58.50
3400	5/8" diameter					141			141	155
3450	3/4" diameter					168			168	185
3500	Lock washers, galvanized, 1/4" diameter					18.75			18.75	20.50
3550	3/8" diameter					29			29	32
3600	1/2" diameter					33			33	36.50
3650	5/8" diameter					38.50			38.50	42.50
3700	3/4" diameter					73			73	80.50
3705	Metal channel slotted, 304 stainless steel or aluminum									
3707	304 stainless steel, 12GA, 1-5/8" x 1-5/8"	1 Elec	50	.160	L.F.	27	10.80		37.80	45.50
3710	304 stainless steel, 1' long, 12GA, 1-5/8" x 1-5/8"		50	.160	Ea.	27	10.80		37.80	45.50
3712	Per L.F.		50	.160	L.F.	27	10.80		37.80	45.50
3715	304 stainless steel, 1'6" long, 12GA, 1-5/8" x 1-5/8"		33.33	.240	Ea.	38	16.15		54.15	65.50
3717	Per L.F.		50	.160		25.50	10.80		36.30	44
3720	304 stainless steel, 2' long, 12GA, 1-5/8" x 1-5/8"		25	.320		50.50	21.50		72	87.50
3722	Per L.F.		50	.160	L.F.	25	10.80		35.80	43.50
3725	304 stainless steel, 3' long, 12GA, 1-5/8" x 1-5/8"		16.67	.480	Ea.	75.50	32.50		108	132
3730	304 stainless steel, 4' long, 12GA, 1-5/8" x 1-5/8"		12.50	.640		92	43		135	165
3735	304 stainless steel, 5' long, 12GA, 1-5/8" x 1-5/8"		10	.800		122	54		176	214
3740	304 stainless steel, 10' long, 12GA, 1-5/8" x 1-5/8"		5	1.600		214	108		322	395
3742	Aluminum, 12GA, 1-5/8" x 1-5/8"		50	.160	L.F.	8.05	10.80		18.85	25
3745	Aluminum, 1' length, 12GA, 1-5/8" x 1-5/8"		50	.160	Ea.	8.05	10.80		18.85	25
3750	Aluminum, 1'6" length, 12GA, 1-5/8" x 1-5/8"		33.33	.240		11.75	16.15		27.90	37
3755	Aluminum, 2' length, 12GA, 1-5/8" x 1-5/8"		25	.320		15.75	21.50		37.25	49.50
3760	Aluminum, 3' length, 12GA, 1-5/8" x 1-5/8"		16.67	.480		23.50	32.50		56	74
3765	Aluminum, 4' length, 12GA, 1-5/8" x 1-5/8"		12.50	.640		31	43		74	98
3770	Aluminum, 5' length, 12GA, 1-5/8" x 1-5/8"		10	.800		37.50	54		91.50	121
3775	Aluminum, 10' length, 12GA, 1-5/8" x 1-5/8"		5	1.600		67	108		175	234
3800	Channels, steel, 3/4" x 1-1/2", 14 ga.		80	.100	L.F.	7.20	6.75		13.95	17.90
3900	1-1/2" x 1-1/2", 12 ga.		70	.114		8.15	7.70		15.85	20.50
4000	1-7/8" x 1-1/2"		60	.133		51	9		60	69.50
4100	3" x 1-1/2"		50	.160		43	10.80		53.80	63.50
4110	1-5/8" x 13/16", 16 ga.		80	.100		5.25	6.75		12	15.75
4114	Trapeze channel support, 12" wide, steel, 12 ga.		8.80	.909	Ea.	57.50	61		118.50	155
4116	18" wide, steel		8.30	.964	"	61.50	65		126.50	165
4120	1-5/8" x 1-5/8", 14 ga.		70	.114	L.F.	6.95	7.70		14.65	19.10
4130	1-5/8" x 7/8", 12 ga.		70	.114		6.35	7.70		14.05	18.40
4140	1-5/8" x 1-3/8", 12 ga.		60	.133		7.65	9		16.65	22
4150	1-5/8" x 1-5/8", 12 ga.		50	.160		13.15	10.80		23.95	30.50
4160	Flat plate fitting, 2 hole, 3-1/2", material only				Ea.	3.46			3.46	3.81
4170	3 hole, 1-7/16" x 4-1/8"					5.35			5.35	5.90
4200	Spring nuts, long, 1/4"	1 Elec	120	.067		.73	4.49		5.22	7.45
4250	3/8"		100	.080		1.16	5.40		6.56	9.30
4300	1/2"		80	.100		1.04	6.75		7.79	11.15
4350	Spring nuts, short, 1/4"		120	.067		1.99	4.49		6.48	8.85
4400	3/8"		100	.080		2.08	5.40		7.48	10.30
4450	1/2"		80	.100		3.04	6.75		9.79	13.35
4500	Closure strip		200	.040	L.F.	10.25	2.69		12.94	15.30
4550	End cap		60	.133	Ea.	2.20	9		11.20	15.75
4600	End connector 3/4" conduit		40	.200		9	13.45		22.45	30
4650	Junction box, 1 channel		16	.500		139	33.50		172.50	203

26 05 29.20 Hangers		Crew	Daily Output	Labor-Hours	Unit	Material	2023 Bare Costs Labor	Equipment	Total	Total Incl O&P
4700	2 channel	1 Elec	14	.571	Ea.	187	38.50		225.50	263
4750	3 channel		12	.667		263	45		308	355
4800	4 channel		10	.800		305	54		359	415
4850	Splice plate		40	.200		13.40	13.45		26.85	35
4900	Continuous concrete insert, 1-1/2″ deep, 1′ long		16	.500		32	33.50		65.50	85
4950	2′ long		14	.571		38	38.50		76.50	99
5000	3′ long		12	.667		41	45		86	112
5050	4′ long		10	.800		59.50	54		113.50	145
5100	6′ long		8	1		89	67.50		156.50	198
5150	3/4″ deep, 1′ long		16	.500		35	33.50		68.50	88.50
5200	2′ long		14	.571		35	38.50		73.50	95.50
5250	3′ long		12	.667		36.50	45		81.50	107
5300	4′ long		10	.800		60	54		114	146
5350	6′ long		8	1		90	67.50		157.50	199
5400	90° angle fitting 2-1/8″ x 2-1/8″		60	.133		5.75	9		14.75	19.70
5450	Supports, suspension rod type, small		60	.133		132	9		141	158
5500	Large		40	.200		111	13.45		124.45	142
5550	Beam clamp, small		60	.133		40	9		49	57.50
5600	Large		40	.200		56.50	13.45		69.95	82.50
5650	U-support, small		60	.133		9.90	9		18.90	24.50
5700	Large		40	.200		14.45	13.45		27.90	36
5750	Concrete insert, cast, for up to 1/2″ threaded rod		16	.500		27.50	33.50		61	80
5800	Beam clamp, 1/4″ clamp, for 1/4″ threaded drop rod		32	.250		5.55	16.85		22.40	31
5900	3/8″ clamp, for 3/8″ threaded drop rod		32	.250		9.70	16.85		26.55	35.50
6000	Strap, rigid conduit, 1/2″ diameter		540	.015		1.82	1		2.82	3.48
6050	3/4″ diameter		440	.018		1.85	1.22		3.07	3.86
6100	1″ diameter		420	.019		2.09	1.28		3.37	4.21
6150	1-1/4″ diameter		400	.020		2.99	1.35		4.34	5.30
6200	1-1/2″ diameter		400	.020		3.08	1.35		4.43	5.40
6250	2″ diameter		267	.030		3.18	2.02		5.20	6.50
6300	2-1/2″ diameter		267	.030		3.65	2.02		5.67	7
6350	3″ diameter		160	.050		4.01	3.37		7.38	9.40
6400	3-1/2″ diameter		133	.060		4.47	4.05		8.52	10.90
6450	4″ diameter		100	.080		5.10	5.40		10.50	13.60
6500	5″ diameter		80	.100		16.15	6.75		22.90	28
6550	6″ diameter		60	.133		23.50	9		32.50	39.50
6600	EMT, 1/2″ diameter		540	.015		1.20	1		2.20	2.80
6650	3/4″ diameter		440	.018		1.46	1.22		2.68	3.43
6700	1″ diameter		420	.019		1.49	1.28		2.77	3.55
6750	1-1/4″ diameter		400	.020		1.79	1.35		3.14	3.97
6800	1-1/2″ diameter		400	.020		2.09	1.35		3.44	4.30
6850	2″ diameter		267	.030		2.45	2.02		4.47	5.70
6900	2-1/2″ diameter		267	.030		2.41	2.02		4.43	5.65
6950	3″ diameter		160	.050		2.50	3.37		5.87	7.75
6970	3-1/2″ diameter		133	.060		2.87	4.05		6.92	9.15
6990	4″ diameter		100	.080		3.49	5.40		8.89	11.85
7000	Clip, 1 hole for rigid conduit, 1/2″ diameter		500	.016		.25	1.08		1.33	1.88
7050	3/4″ diameter		470	.017		.30	1.15		1.45	2.03
7100	1″ diameter		440	.018		1.95	1.22		3.17	3.97
7150	1-1/4″ diameter		400	.020		.81	1.35		2.16	2.89
7200	1-1/2″ diameter		355	.023		1.23	1.52		2.75	3.61
7250	2″ diameter		320	.025		1.30	1.68		2.98	3.93
7300	2-1/2″ diameter	↓	266	.030	↓	3.68	2.03		5.71	7.05

26 05 29 – Hangers and Supports for Electrical Systems

26 05 29.20 Hangers		Crew	Daily Output	Labor-Hours	Unit	Material	2023 Bare Costs Labor	Equipment	Total	Total Incl O&P
7350	3" diameter	1 Elec	160	.050	Ea.	4.04	3.37		7.41	9.45
7400	3-1/2" diameter		133	.060		6.15	4.05		10.20	12.75
7450	4" diameter		100	.080		5.95	5.40		11.35	14.55
7500	5" diameter		80	.100		196	6.75		202.75	226
7550	6" diameter		60	.133		370	9		379	420
7600	Hammer on purlin clip, 1/4" hole, 1/16" flange		60	.133		.98	9		9.98	14.45
7610	1/4" hole threaded,1/4" flange, rod hanger		60	.133		2.22	9		11.22	15.80
7620	3/8" hole threaded,1/4" flange, rod hanger		60	.133		2.49	9		11.49	16.10
7630	Z purlin clip, 1/4" & 3/8" flange threaded rod hanger		60	.133		2.20	9		11.20	15.75
7640	1/2" rigid, 3/4" conduit, 1" flange		60	.133		2.19	9		11.19	15.75
7650	1" conduit, 1" flange		60	.133		2.43	9		11.43	16
7660	1-1/4" conduit, 1" flange		60	.133		2.98	9		11.98	16.65
7670	Push-in type conduit clip 3/4" EMT, with 9/32" hole		60	.133		.75	9		9.75	14.20
7680	3/4" EMT, 1/2" rigid		60	.133		2.09	9		11.09	15.65
7690	Push-in type tandem conduit clip 3/4" - 1" EMT, 1/2" - 3/4" rigid		60	.133		2.16	9		11.16	15.75
7820	Conduit hangers, with bolt & 12" rod, 1/2" diameter		150	.053		12.30	3.59		15.89	18.85
7830	3/4" diameter		145	.055		11.55	3.72		15.27	18.20
7840	1" diameter		135	.059		12.60	3.99		16.59	19.80
7850	1-1/4" diameter		120	.067		12.80	4.49		17.29	20.50
7860	1-1/2" diameter		110	.073		13.90	4.90		18.80	22.50
7870	2" diameter		100	.080		19.25	5.40		24.65	29
7880	2-1/2" diameter		80	.100		19.90	6.75		26.65	32
7890	3" diameter		60	.133		21	9		30	36.50
7900	3-1/2" diameter		45	.178		21.50	11.95		33.45	42
7910	4" diameter		35	.229		26.50	15.40		41.90	52
7920	5" diameter		30	.267		20.50	17.95		38.45	49
7930	6" diameter		25	.320		33	21.50		54.50	68.50
7950	Jay clamp, 1/2" diameter		32	.250		4.37	16.85		21.22	30
7960	3/4" diameter		32	.250		6.40	16.85		23.25	32
7970	1" diameter		32	.250		7.65	16.85		24.50	33.50
7980	1-1/4" diameter		30	.267		10.10	17.95		28.05	37.50
7990	1-1/2" diameter		30	.267		13.25	17.95		31.20	41
8000	2" diameter		30	.267		19	17.95		36.95	47.50
8010	2-1/2" diameter		28	.286		27	19.25		46.25	58
8020	3" diameter		28	.286		27	19.25		46.25	58
8030	3-1/2" diameter		25	.320		115	21.50		136.50	159
8040	4" diameter		25	.320		115	21.50		136.50	159
8050	5" diameter		20	.400		236	27		263	300
8060	6" diameter		16	.500		450	33.50		483.50	545
8070	Channels, 3/4" x 1-1/2" w/12" rods for 1/2" to 1" conduit		30	.267		22	17.95		39.95	50.50
8080	1-1/2" x 1-1/2" w/12" rods for 1-1/4" to 2" conduit		28	.286		21.50	19.25		40.75	52
8090	1-1/2" x 1-1/2" w/12" rods for 2-1/2" to 4" conduit		26	.308		20.50	20.50		41	53.50
8100	1-1/2" x 1-7/8" w/12" rods for 5" to 6" conduit		24	.333		112	22.50		134.50	157
8110	Beam clamp, conduit, plastic coated steel, 1/2" diam.		30	.267		48	17.95		65.95	79
8120	3/4" diameter		30	.267		50.50	17.95		68.45	82
8130	1" diameter		30	.267		53.50	17.95		71.45	85.50
8140	1-1/4" diameter		28	.286		63	19.25		82.25	97.50
8150	1-1/2" diameter		28	.286		91.50	19.25		110.75	129
8160	2" diameter		28	.286		107	19.25		126.25	147
8170	2-1/2" diameter		26	.308		146	20.50		166.50	191
8180	3" diameter		26	.308		157	20.50		177.50	204
8190	3-1/2" diameter		23	.348		126	23.50		149.50	173
8200	4" diameter		23	.348		137	23.50		160.50	185

26 05 29 – Hangers and Supports for Electrical Systems

26 05 29.20 Hangers		Crew	Daily Output	Labor-Hours	Unit	Material	Labor	Equipment	Total	Total Incl O&P
						2023 Bare Costs				
8210	5" diameter	1 Elec	18	.444	Ea.	395	30		425	480
8220	Channels, plastic coated									
8250	3/4" x 1-1/2", w/12" rods for 1/2" to 1" conduit	1 Elec	28	.286	Ea.	71	19.25		90.25	107
8260	1-1/2" x 1-1/2", w/12" rods for 1-1/4" to 2" conduit		26	.308		88.50	20.50		109	129
8270	1-1/2" x 1-1/2", w/12" rods for 2-1/2" to 3-1/2" conduit		24	.333		96.50	22.50		119	140
8280	1-1/2" x 1-7/8", w/12" rods for 4" to 5" conduit		22	.364		160	24.50		184.50	213
8290	1-1/2" x 1-7/8", w/12" rods for 6" conduit		20	.400		176	27		203	233
8320	Conduit hangers, plastic coated steel, with bolt & 12" rod, 1/2" diam.		140	.057		45.50	3.85		49.35	55.50
8330	3/4" diameter		135	.059		47	3.99		50.99	57.50
8340	1" diameter		125	.064		47.50	4.31		51.81	58.50
8350	1-1/4" diameter		110	.073		50.50	4.90		55.40	63
8360	1-1/2" diameter		100	.080		56.50	5.40		61.90	70.50
8370	2" diameter		90	.089		62.50	6		68.50	78
8380	2-1/2" diameter		70	.114		74.50	7.70		82.20	93
8390	3" diameter		50	.160		90	10.80		100.80	115
8400	3-1/2" diameter		35	.229		66	15.40		81.40	95.50
8410	4" diameter		25	.320		133	21.50		154.50	178
8420	5" diameter		20	.400		146	27		173	200
9000	Parallel type, conduit beam clamp, 1/2"		32	.250		15.20	16.85		32.05	41.50
9010	3/4"		32	.250		7.45	16.85		24.30	33
9020	1"		32	.250		8.20	16.85		25.05	34
9030	1-1/4"		30	.267		21	17.95		38.95	49.50
9040	1-1/2"		30	.267		24	17.95		41.95	52.50
9050	2"		30	.267		14.80	17.95		32.75	43
9060	2-1/2"		28	.286		29.50	19.25		48.75	61
9070	3"		28	.286		34.50	19.25		53.75	66.50
9090	4"		25	.320		39	21.50		60.50	75
9110	Right angle, conduit beam clamp, 1/2"		32	.250		13.85	16.85		30.70	40
9120	3/4"		32	.250		14.60	16.85		31.45	41
9130	1"		32	.250		13.85	16.85		30.70	40.50
9140	1-1/4"		30	.267		13.75	17.95		31.70	41.50
9150	1-1/2"		30	.267		14.45	17.95		32.40	42.50
9160	2"		30	.267		9.75	17.95		27.70	37
9170	2-1/2"		28	.286		10.90	19.25		30.15	40.50
9180	3"		28	.286		12.75	19.25		32	42.50
9190	3-1/2"		25	.320		16.35	21.50		37.85	50
9200	4"		25	.320		17.10	21.50		38.60	51
9230	Adjustable, conduit hanger, 1/2"		32	.250		13.55	16.85		30.40	40
9240	3/4"		32	.250		11.35	16.85		28.20	37.50
9250	1"		32	.250		10.55	16.85		27.40	36.50
9260	1-1/4"		30	.267		13.55	17.95		31.50	41.50
9270	1-1/2"		30	.267		16.75	17.95		34.70	45
9280	2"		30	.267		20	17.95		37.95	48.50
9290	2-1/2"		28	.286		21	19.25		40.25	51.50
9300	3"		28	.286		24	19.25		43.25	55
9310	3-1/2"		25	.320		49.50	21.50		71	86.50
9320	4"		25	.320		39	21.50		60.50	74.50
9330	5"		20	.400		41	27		68	85
9340	6"		16	.500		60.50	33.50		94	117
9350	Combination conduit hanger, 3/8"		32	.250		25.50	16.85		42.35	53
9360	Adjustable flange, 3/8"		32	.250		29.50	16.85		46.35	57.50

26 05 Common Work Results for Electrical

26 05 29 – Hangers and Supports for Electrical Systems

26 05 29.30 Fittings and Channel Support		Crew	Daily Output	Labor-Hours	Unit	2023 Bare Costs Material	Labor	Equipment	Total	Total Incl O&P
0010	**FITTINGS & CHANNEL SUPPORT**									
0020	Rooftop channel support									
0200	2-7/8" L x 1-5/8" W, 12 ga. pre galv., dbl. base	1 Elec	46	.174	Ea.	4.07	11.70		15.77	22
0210	2-7/8" L x 1-5/8" W, 12 ga. hot dip galv., dbl. base		46	.174		2.37	11.70		14.07	20
0220	2-7/16" L x 1-5/8" W, 12 ga. pre galv., sngl base		48	.167		1.95	11.25		13.20	18.85
0230	2-7/16" L x 1-5/8" W, 12 ga. hot dip galv., sngl base		48	.167		6.95	11.25		18.20	24.50
0240	13/16" L x 1-5/8" W, 14 ga. pre galv., sngl base		56	.143		19	9.60		28.60	35.50
0250	13/16" L x 1-5/8" W, 14 ga. hot dip galv., sngl base		56	.143		6.80	9.60		16.40	22
0260	1-5/8" L x 1-5/8" W, 12 ga. pre galv., sngl base		54	.148		22	10		32	39
0270	1-5/8" L x 1-5/8" W, 12 ga. hot dip galv., sngl base		54	.148		1.90	10		11.90	16.95
0280	1-5/8" x 28", 12 ga. pre galv., dbl. H block base		42	.190		4.12	12.85		16.97	23.50
0290	1-5/8" x 36", 12 ga. pre galv., dbl. H block base		40	.200		4.36	13.45		17.81	25
0300	1-5/8" x 42", 12 ga. pre galv., dbl. H block base		34	.235		4.90	15.85		20.75	29
0310	1-5/8" x 50", 12 ga. pre galv., dbl. H block base		38	.211		5.20	14.20		19.40	27
0320	1-5/8" x 60", 12 ga. pre galv., dbl. H block base		36	.222		5.75	14.95		20.70	28.50
0330	13/16" x 8" H, threaded rod pre galv., H block base		35	.229		2.77	15.40		18.17	26
0340	13/16" x 12" H, threaded rod pre galv., H block base		34.60	.231		3.46	15.55		19.01	27
0350	1-5/8" x 16" H, threaded rod dbl. H block base		34	.235		5.15	15.85		21	29
0360	1-5/8" x 12" H, pre galv., dbl. H block base		34.60	.231		9.90	15.55		25.45	34
0370	1-5/8" x 24"H, pre galv., dbl. H block base		34	.235		10.45	15.85		26.30	35
0380	3-1/4" x 24" H, pre galv., dbl. H block base		32	.250		23.50	16.85		40.35	51
0390	3-1/4" x 36" H, pre galv., dbl. H block base		30	.267		26	17.95		43.95	55

26 05 33 – Raceway and Boxes for Electrical Systems

26 05 33.13 Conduit		Crew	Daily Output	Labor-Hours	Unit	Material	Labor	Equipment	Total	Total Incl O&P
0010	**CONDUIT** To 10' high, includes 2 terminations, 2 elbows, R260533-20									
0020	11 beam clamps, and 11 couplings per 100 L.F.									
0300	Aluminum, 1/2" diameter	1 Elec	100	.080	L.F.	1.96	5.40		7.36	10.15
0500	3/4" diameter R260533-25		90	.089		2.77	6		8.77	11.95
0700	1" diameter		80	.100		3.79	6.75		10.54	14.15
1000	1-1/4" diameter		70	.114		4.97	7.70		12.67	16.90
1030	1-1/2" diameter		65	.123		6.30	8.30		14.60	19.20
1050	2" diameter		60	.133		8.80	9		17.80	23
1070	2-1/2" diameter		50	.160		12.80	10.80		23.60	30
1100	3" diameter	2 Elec	90	.178		17.75	11.95		29.70	37.50
1130	3-1/2" diameter		80	.200		24	13.45		37.45	46.50
1140	4" diameter		70	.229		27.50	15.40		42.90	53
1150	5" diameter		50	.320		45.50	21.50		67	82.50
1160	6" diameter		40	.400		70.50	27		97.50	118
1161	Field bends, 45° to 90°, 1/2" diameter	1 Elec	53	.151	Ea.		10.15		10.15	15.10
1162	3/4" diameter		47	.170			11.45		11.45	17.05
1163	1" diameter		44	.182			12.25		12.25	18.20
1164	1-1/4" diameter		23	.348			23.50		23.50	35
1165	1-1/2" diameter		21	.381			25.50		25.50	38
1166	2" diameter		16	.500			33.50		33.50	50
1170	Elbows, 1/2" diameter		40	.200		11.30	13.45		24.75	32.50
1200	3/4" diameter		32	.250		13.35	16.85		30.20	39.50
1230	1" diameter		28	.286		21	19.25		40.25	51.50
1250	1-1/4" diameter		24	.333		32	22.50		54.50	69
1270	1-1/2" diameter		20	.400		39.50	27		66.50	83.50
1300	2" diameter		16	.500		61.50	33.50		95	118
1330	2-1/2" diameter		12	.667		101	45		146	178
1350	3" diameter		8	1		169	67.50		236.50	286

26 05 33.13 Conduit		Crew	Daily Output	Labor-Hours	Unit	Material	Labor	Equipment	Total	Total Incl O&P
						2023 Bare Costs				
1370	3-1/2" diameter	1 Elec	6	1.333	Ea.	285	90		375	450
1400	4" diameter		5	1.600		282	108		390	470
1410	5" diameter		4	2		570	135		705	830
1420	6" diameter		2.50	3.200		910	216		1,126	1,325
1430	Couplings, 1/2" diameter		320	.025		3.44	1.68		5.12	6.30
1450	3/4" diameter		192	.042		5.15	2.81		7.96	9.85
1470	1" diameter		160	.050		6.70	3.37		10.07	12.40
1500	1-1/4" diameter		120	.067		7.90	4.49		12.39	15.35
1530	1-1/2" diameter		96	.083		9.85	5.60		15.45	19.15
1550	2" diameter		80	.100		13.80	6.75		20.55	25
1570	2-1/2" diameter		69	.116		31	7.80		38.80	45.50
1600	3" diameter		64	.125		40	8.40		48.40	57
1630	3-1/2" diameter		56	.143		58	9.60		67.60	78.50
1650	4" diameter		53	.151		66.50	10.15		76.65	88.50
1670	5" diameter		48	.167		139	11.25		150.25	170
1690	6" diameter		46	.174		212	11.70		223.70	251
1691	See note on line 26 05 33.13 9995 R260533-30									
1750	Rigid galvanized steel, 1/2" diameter	1 Elec	90	.089	L.F.	4.47	6		10.47	13.80
1770	3/4" diameter		80	.100		4.84	6.75		11.59	15.30
1800	1" diameter		65	.123		7.35	8.30		15.65	20.50
1830	1-1/4" diameter		60	.133		10.75	9		19.75	25
1850	1-1/2" diameter		55	.145		12.25	9.80		22.05	28
1870	2" diameter		45	.178		15.45	11.95		27.40	35
1900	2-1/2" diameter		35	.229		30.50	15.40		45.90	56.50
1930	3" diameter	2 Elec	50	.320		34	21.50		55.50	69
1950	3-1/2" diameter		44	.364		43	24.50		67.50	84
1970	4" diameter		40	.400		46	27		73	90.50
1980	5" diameter		30	.533		88	36		124	151
1990	6" diameter		20	.800		123	54		177	215
1991	Field bends, 45° to 90°, 1/2" diameter	1 Elec	44	.182	Ea.		12.25		12.25	18.20
1992	3/4" diameter		40	.200			13.45		13.45	20
1993	1" diameter		36	.222			14.95		14.95	22
1994	1-1/4" diameter		19	.421			28.50		28.50	42
1995	1-1/2" diameter		18	.444			30		30	44.50
1996	2" diameter		13	.615			41.50		41.50	61.50
2000	Elbows, 1/2" diameter		32	.250		8	16.85		24.85	34
2030	3/4" diameter		28	.286		8.10	19.25		27.35	37.50
2050	1" diameter		24	.333		10.70	22.50		33.20	45.50
2070	1-1/4" diameter		18	.444		17.85	30		47.85	64
2100	1-1/2" diameter		16	.500		19.50	33.50		53	71.50
2130	2" diameter		12	.667		30	45		75	99.50
2150	2-1/2" diameter		8	1		64.50	67.50		132	171
2170	3" diameter		6	1.333		87	90		177	229
2200	3-1/2" diameter		4.20	1.905		122	128		250	325
2220	4" diameter		4	2		141	135		276	355
2230	5" diameter		3.50	2.286		375	154		529	645
2240	6" diameter		2	4		565	269		834	1,025
2250	Couplings, 1/2" diameter		267	.030		2.31	2.02		4.33	5.55
2270	3/4" diameter		160	.050		2.69	3.37		6.06	7.95
2300	1" diameter		133	.060		3.79	4.05		7.84	10.15
2330	1-1/4" diameter		100	.080		5.55	5.40		10.95	14.10
2350	1-1/2" diameter		80	.100		6.10	6.75		12.85	16.75
2370	2" diameter		67	.119		7.65	8.05		15.70	20.50

26 05 33.13 Conduit		Crew	Daily Output	Labor-Hours	Unit	Material	Labor	Equipment	Total	Total Incl O&P
						2023 Bare Costs				
2400	2-1/2" diameter	1 Elec	57	.140	Ea.	23.50	9.45		32.95	40
2430	3" diameter		53	.151		28	10.15		38.15	46
2450	3-1/2" diameter		47	.170		39.50	11.45		50.95	60.50
2470	4" diameter		44	.182		33	12.25		45.25	54.50
2480	5" diameter		40	.200		79	13.45		92.45	107
2490	6" diameter		38	.211		116	14.20		130.20	149
2491	See note on line 26 05 33.13 9995 R260533-30									
2500	Steel, intermediate conduit (IMC), 1/2" diameter	1 Elec	100	.080	L.F.	3.13	5.40		8.53	11.45
2530	3/4" diameter		90	.089		3.89	6		9.89	13.20
2550	1" diameter		70	.114		5.80	7.70		13.50	17.85
2570	1-1/4" diameter		65	.123		8	8.30		16.30	21
2600	1-1/2" diameter		60	.133		10	9		19	24.50
2630	2" diameter		50	.160		12.40	10.80		23.20	29.50
2650	2-1/2" diameter		40	.200		24	13.45		37.45	46.50
2670	3" diameter	2 Elec	60	.267		31	17.95		48.95	61
2700	3-1/2" diameter		54	.296		38.50	19.95		58.45	71.50
2730	4" diameter		50	.320		42.50	21.50		64	78.50
2731	Field bends, 45° to 90°, 1/2" diameter	1 Elec	44	.182	Ea.		12.25		12.25	18.20
2732	3/4" diameter		40	.200			13.45		13.45	20
2733	1" diameter		36	.222			14.95		14.95	22
2734	1-1/4" diameter		19	.421			28.50		28.50	42
2735	1-1/2" diameter		18	.444			30		30	44.50
2736	2" diameter		13	.615			41.50		41.50	61.50
2750	Elbows, 1/2" diameter		32	.250		5.55	16.85		22.40	31
2770	3/4" diameter		28	.286		11.30	19.25		30.55	41
2800	1" diameter		24	.333		21	22.50		43.50	56.50
2830	1-1/4" diameter		18	.444		24	30		54	71
2850	1-1/2" diameter		16	.500		28	33.50		61.50	81
2870	2" diameter		12	.667		42.50	45		87.50	114
2900	2-1/2" diameter		8	1		95	67.50		162.50	205
2930	3" diameter		6	1.333		129	90		219	275
2950	3-1/2" diameter		4.20	1.905		206	128		334	415
2970	4" diameter		4	2		240	135		375	465
3000	Couplings, 1/2" diameter		293	.027		2.31	1.84		4.15	5.25
3030	3/4" diameter		176	.045		2.69	3.06		5.75	7.50
3050	1" diameter		147	.054		3.79	3.67		7.46	9.60
3070	1-1/4" diameter		110	.073		5.55	4.90		10.45	13.40
3100	1-1/2" diameter		88	.091		6.10	6.10		12.20	15.85
3130	2" diameter		73	.110		7.65	7.40		15.05	19.35
3150	2-1/2" diameter		63	.127		23.50	8.55		32.05	38.50
3170	3" diameter		59	.136		28	9.15		37.15	44.50
3200	3-1/2" diameter		52	.154		39.50	10.35		49.85	59
3230	4" diameter		49	.163		33	11		44	53
3231	See note on line 26 05 33.13 9995 R260533-30									
4100	Rigid steel, plastic coated, 40 mil thick									
4130	1/2" diameter	1 Elec	80	.100	L.F.	14.85	6.75		21.60	26.50
4150	3/4" diameter		70	.114		15.85	7.70		23.55	29
4170	1" diameter		55	.145		19.15	9.80		28.95	35.50
4200	1-1/4" diameter		50	.160		24.50	10.80		35.30	43
4230	1-1/2" diameter		45	.178		31	11.95		42.95	52
4250	2" diameter		35	.229		39	15.40		54.40	66
4270	2-1/2" diameter		25	.320		60.50	21.50		82	99
4300	3" diameter	2 Elec	44	.364		68.50	24.50		93	112

26 05 33 – Raceway and Boxes for Electrical Systems

26 05 33.13 Conduit		Crew	Daily Output	Labor-Hours	Unit	Material	2023 Bare Costs Labor	Equipment	Total	Total Incl O&P
4330	3-1/2" diameter	2 Elec	40	.400	L.F.	81.50	27		108.50	130
4350	4" diameter		36	.444		93	30		123	147
4370	5" diameter		30	.533		226	36		262	305
4400	Elbows, 1/2" diameter	1 Elec	28	.286	Ea.	32	19.25		51.25	64
4430	3/4" diameter		24	.333		21	22.50		43.50	56.50
4450	1" diameter		18	.444		23.50	30		53.50	70
4470	1-1/4" diameter		16	.500		49	33.50		82.50	104
4500	1-1/2" diameter		12	.667		58	45		103	131
4530	2" diameter		8	1		62.50	67.50		130	169
4550	2-1/2" diameter		6	1.333		156	90		246	305
4570	3" diameter		4.20	1.905		146	128		274	350
4600	3-1/2" diameter		4	2		335	135		470	570
4630	4" diameter		3.80	2.105		300	142		442	540
4650	5" diameter		3.50	2.286		880	154		1,034	1,200
4680	Couplings, 1/2" diameter		213	.038		9.35	2.53		11.88	14
4700	3/4" diameter		128	.063		10.35	4.21		14.56	17.65
4730	1" diameter		107	.075		7.90	5.05		12.95	16.20
4750	1-1/4" diameter		80	.100		14.50	6.75		21.25	26
4770	1-1/2" diameter		64	.125		10.80	8.40		19.20	24.50
4800	2" diameter		53	.151		18.50	10.15		28.65	35.50
4830	2-1/2" diameter		46	.174		62	11.70		73.70	86
4850	3" diameter		43	.186		53.50	12.55		66.05	77.50
4870	3-1/2" diameter		38	.211		67.50	14.20		81.70	95.50
4900	4" diameter		36	.222		80	14.95		94.95	110
4950	5" diameter		32	.250		350	16.85		366.85	410
4951	See note on line 26 05 33.13 9995 R260533-30									
5000	Electric metallic tubing (EMT), 1/2" diameter	1 Elec	170	.047	L.F.	1.25	3.17		4.42	6.10
5020	3/4" diameter		130	.062		1.94	4.14		6.08	8.30
5040	1" diameter		115	.070		3.28	4.69		7.97	10.55
5060	1-1/4" diameter		100	.080		5.40	5.40		10.80	13.95
5080	1-1/2" diameter		90	.089		6.75	6		12.75	16.30
5100	2" diameter		80	.100		8.25	6.75		15	19.10
5120	2-1/2" diameter		60	.133		10.90	9		19.90	25.50
5140	3" diameter	2 Elec	100	.160		13.70	10.80		24.50	31
5160	3-1/2" diameter		90	.178		17.65	11.95		29.60	37.50
5180	4" diameter		80	.200		18.60	13.45		32.05	40.50
5200	Field bends, 45° to 90°, 1/2" diameter	1 Elec	89	.090	Ea.		6.05		6.05	9
5220	3/4" diameter		80	.100			6.75		6.75	10
5240	1" diameter		73	.110			7.40		7.40	10.95
5260	1-1/4" diameter		38	.211			14.20		14.20	21
5280	1-1/2" diameter		36	.222			14.95		14.95	22
5300	2" diameter		26	.308			20.50		20.50	31
5320	Offsets, 1/2" diameter		65	.123			8.30		8.30	12.30
5340	3/4" diameter		62	.129			8.70		8.70	12.90
5360	1" diameter		53	.151			10.15		10.15	15.10
5380	1-1/4" diameter		30	.267			17.95		17.95	26.50
5400	1-1/2" diameter		28	.286			19.25		19.25	28.50
5420	2" diameter		20	.400			27		27	40
5700	Elbows, 1" diameter		40	.200		7.25	13.45		20.70	28
5720	1-1/4" diameter		32	.250		9.60	16.85		26.45	35.50
5740	1-1/2" diameter		24	.333		11.05	22.50		33.55	45.50
5760	2" diameter		20	.400		15.75	27		42.75	57.50
5780	2-1/2" diameter		12	.667		33	45		78	103

26 05 33.13 Conduit		Crew	Daily Output	Labor-Hours	Unit	2023 Bare Costs Material	Labor	Equipment	Total	Total Incl O&P
5800	3" diameter	1 Elec	9	.889	Ea.	51	60		111	145
5820	3-1/2" diameter		7	1.143		66.50	77		143.50	187
5840	4" diameter		6	1.333		79	90		169	220
6200	Couplings, set screw, steel, 1/2" diameter		235	.034		1.71	2.29		4	5.30
6220	3/4" diameter		188	.043		2.59	2.87		5.46	7.10
6240	1" diameter		157	.051		4.32	3.43		7.75	9.85
6260	1-1/4" diameter		118	.068		9.05	4.57		13.62	16.75
6280	1-1/2" diameter		94	.085		12.55	5.75		18.30	22.50
6300	2" diameter		78	.103		16.85	6.90		23.75	29
6320	2-1/2" diameter		67	.119		9.35	8.05		17.40	22.50
6340	3" diameter		59	.136		10.60	9.15		19.75	25.50
6360	3-1/2" diameter		47	.170		12.65	11.45		24.10	31
6380	4" diameter	↓	43	.186	↓	13.75	12.55		26.30	34
6381	See note on line 26 05 33.13 9995 R260533-30									
6500	Box connectors, set screw, steel, 1/2" diameter	1 Elec	120	.067	Ea.	1.26	4.49		5.75	8.05
6520	3/4" diameter		110	.073		2.05	4.90		6.95	9.55
6540	1" diameter		90	.089		3.89	6		9.89	13.20
6560	1-1/4" diameter		70	.114		7.55	7.70		15.25	19.80
6580	1-1/2" diameter		60	.133		10.95	9		19.95	25.50
6600	2" diameter		50	.160		15.10	10.80		25.90	32.50
6620	2-1/2" diameter		36	.222		10.65	14.95		25.60	34
6640	3" diameter		27	.296		10	19.95		29.95	40.50
6680	3-1/2" diameter		21	.381		12.25	25.50		37.75	51.50
6700	4" diameter		16	.500		13.45	33.50		46.95	65
6740	Insulated box connectors, set screw, steel, 1/2" diameter		120	.067		1.73	4.49		6.22	8.55
6760	3/4" diameter		110	.073		2.75	4.90		7.65	10.35
6780	1" diameter		90	.089		5.05	6		11.05	14.45
6800	1-1/4" diameter		70	.114		9.15	7.70		16.85	21.50
6820	1-1/2" diameter		60	.133		12.95	9		21.95	27.50
6840	2" diameter		50	.160		18.80	10.80		29.60	36.50
6860	2-1/2" diameter		36	.222		96	14.95		110.95	128
6880	3" diameter		27	.296		113	19.95		132.95	155
6900	3-1/2" diameter		21	.381		158	25.50		183.50	212
6920	4" diameter		16	.500		173	33.50		206.50	240
7000	EMT to conduit adapters, 1/2" diameter (compression)		70	.114		5.75	7.70		13.45	17.75
7020	3/4" diameter		60	.133		8.20	9		17.20	22.50
7040	1" diameter		50	.160		12.65	10.80		23.45	30
7060	1-1/4" diameter		40	.200		19.60	13.45		33.05	41.50
7080	1-1/2" diameter		30	.267		25	17.95		42.95	54
7100	2" diameter		25	.320		36	21.50		57.50	71.50
7200	EMT to Greenfield adapters, 1/2" to 3/8" diameter (compression)		90	.089		3.43	6		9.43	12.65
7220	1/2" diameter		90	.089		7.55	6		13.55	17.20
7240	3/4" diameter		80	.100		9.95	6.75		16.70	21
7260	1" diameter		70	.114		27	7.70		34.70	41
7270	1-1/4" diameter		60	.133		31.50	9		40.50	48.50
7280	1-1/2" diameter		50	.160		35.50	10.80		46.30	55
7290	2" diameter		40	.200		53.50	13.45		66.95	79
7400	EMT, LB, LR or LL fittings with covers, 1/2" diameter, set screw		24	.333		9.20	22.50		31.70	43.50
7420	3/4" diameter		20	.400		11.65	27		38.65	53
7440	1" diameter		16	.500		18.25	33.50		51.75	70
7450	1-1/4" diameter		13	.615		26.50	41.50		68	90.50
7460	1-1/2" diameter		11	.727		34	49		83	111
7470	2" diameter	↓	9	.889	↓	56	60		116	151

26 05 33.13 Conduit		Crew	Daily Output	Labor-Hours	Unit	2023 Bare Costs Material	Labor	Equipment	Total	Total Incl O&P
7600	EMT, "T" fittings with covers, 1/2" diameter, set screw	1 Elec	16	.500	Ea.	6.10	33.50		39.60	57
7620	3/4" diameter		15	.533		8.40	36		44.40	62.50
7640	1" diameter		12	.667		10.95	45		55.95	78.50
7650	1-1/4" diameter		11	.727		19.20	49		68.20	94
7660	1-1/2" diameter		10	.800		26	54		80	109
7670	2" diameter		8	1		29.50	67.50		97	133
8000	EMT, expansion fittings, no jumper, 1/2" diameter		24	.333		97	22.50		119.50	140
8020	3/4" diameter		20	.400		128	27		155	181
8040	1" diameter		16	.500		175	33.50		208.50	242
8060	1-1/4" diameter		13	.615		200	41.50		241.50	282
8080	1-1/2" diameter		11	.727		271	49		320	370
8100	2" diameter		9	.889		385	60		445	515
8110	2-1/2" diameter		7	1.143		535	77		612	705
8120	3" diameter		6	1.333		655	90		745	855
8140	4" diameter		5	1.600		1,200	108		1,308	1,450
8200	Split adapter, 1/2" diameter		110	.073		6.65	4.90		11.55	14.60
8210	3/4" diameter		90	.089		4.76	6		10.76	14.15
8220	1" diameter		70	.114		8.25	7.70		15.95	20.50
8230	1-1/4" diameter		60	.133		11.20	9		20.20	25.50
8240	1-1/2" diameter		50	.160		16.05	10.80		26.85	33.50
8250	2" diameter		36	.222		44.50	14.95		59.45	70.50
8300	1 hole clips, 1/2" diameter		500	.016		.35	1.08		1.43	1.99
8320	3/4" diameter		470	.017		.46	1.15		1.61	2.21
8340	1" diameter		444	.018		.84	1.21		2.05	2.72
8360	1-1/4" diameter		400	.020		1.12	1.35		2.47	3.23
8380	1-1/2" diameter		355	.023		1.71	1.52		3.23	4.14
8400	2" diameter		320	.025		2.69	1.68		4.37	5.45
8420	2-1/2" diameter		266	.030		2.92	2.03		4.95	6.20
8440	3" diameter		160	.050		3.92	3.37		7.29	9.30
8460	3-1/2" diameter		133	.060		5.10	4.05		9.15	11.60
8480	4" diameter		100	.080		6.60	5.40		12	15.25
8500	Clamp back spacers, 1/2" diameter		500	.016		1.79	1.08		2.87	3.57
8510	3/4" diameter		470	.017		1.89	1.15		3.04	3.78
8520	1" diameter		444	.018		3.51	1.21		4.72	5.65
8530	1-1/4" diameter		400	.020		5.55	1.35		6.90	8.10
8540	1-1/2" diameter		355	.023		6.25	1.52		7.77	9.10
8550	2" diameter		320	.025		10.60	1.68		12.28	14.20
8560	2-1/2" diameter		266	.030		18.85	2.03		20.88	23.50
8570	3" diameter		160	.050		76	3.37		79.37	88.50
8580	3-1/2" diameter		133	.060		89	4.05		93.05	104
8590	4" diameter		100	.080		128	5.40		133.40	149
8600	Offset connectors, 1/2" diameter		40	.200		3.11	13.45		16.56	23.50
8610	3/4" diameter		32	.250		5.10	16.85		21.95	30.50
8620	1" diameter		24	.333		5.10	22.50		27.60	39
8650	90° pulling elbows, female, 1/2" diameter, with gasket		24	.333		16.05	22.50		38.55	51
8660	3/4" diameter		20	.400		25.50	27		52.50	68
8700	Couplings, compression, 1/2" diameter, steel		78	.103		2.77	6.90		9.67	13.30
8710	3/4" diameter		67	.119		3.86	8.05		11.91	16.20
8720	1" diameter		59	.136		6.65	9.15		15.80	21
8730	1-1/4" diameter		47	.170		12.60	11.45		24.05	31
8740	1-1/2" diameter		38	.211		18.35	14.20		32.55	41
8750	2" diameter		31	.258		25	17.40		42.40	53.50
8760	2-1/2" diameter	↓	24	.333	↓	112	22.50		134.50	157

26 05 33.13 Conduit		Crew	Daily Output	Labor-Hours	Unit	2023 Bare Costs Material	Labor	Equipment	Total	Total Incl O&P
8770	3″ diameter	1 Elec	21	.381	Ea.	140	25.50		165.50	192
8780	3-1/2″ diameter		19	.421		227	28.50		255.50	292
8790	4″ diameter		16	.500		232	33.50		265.50	305
8791	See note on line 26 05 33.13 9995 R260533-30									
8800	Box connectors, compression, 1/2″ diam., steel	1 Elec	120	.067	Ea.	.73	4.49		5.22	7.45
8810	3/4″ diameter		110	.073		.89	4.90		5.79	8.30
8820	1″ diameter		90	.089		1.63	6		7.63	10.70
8830	1-1/4″ diameter		70	.114		2.72	7.70		10.42	14.45
8840	1-1/2″ diameter		60	.133		4.56	9		13.56	18.35
8850	2″ diameter		50	.160		6.10	10.80		16.90	22.50
8860	2-1/2″ diameter		36	.222		16.10	14.95		31.05	39.50
8870	3″ diameter		27	.296		25.50	19.95		45.45	57.50
8880	3-1/2″ diameter		21	.381		36.50	25.50		62	78
8890	4″ diameter		16	.500		32	33.50		65.50	85
8900	Box connectors, insulated compression, 1/2″ diam., steel		120	.067		.83	4.49		5.32	7.55
8910	3/4″ diameter		110	.073		1.11	4.90		6.01	8.50
8920	1″ diameter		90	.089		1.69	6		7.69	10.75
8930	1-1/4″ diameter		70	.114		3.71	7.70		11.41	15.55
8940	1-1/2″ diameter		60	.133		5.05	9		14.05	18.90
8950	2″ diameter		50	.160		7.85	10.80		18.65	24.50
8960	2-1/2″ diameter		36	.222		24.50	14.95		39.45	49
8970	3″ diameter		27	.296		35.50	19.95		55.45	68.50
8980	3-1/2″ diameter		21	.381		45.50	25.50		71	88
8990	4″ diameter		16	.500		53.50	33.50		87	109
9100	PVC, schedule 40, 1/2″ diameter		190	.042	L.F.	1.90	2.84		4.74	6.30
9110	3/4″ diameter		145	.055		2.08	3.72		5.80	7.80
9120	1″ diameter		125	.064		3.45	4.31		7.76	10.20
9130	1-1/4″ diameter		110	.073		4.01	4.90		8.91	11.70
9140	1-1/2″ diameter		100	.080		6	5.40		11.40	14.60
9150	2″ diameter		90	.089		8.55	6		14.55	18.30
9160	2-1/2″ diameter		65	.123		10.90	8.30		19.20	24.50
9170	3″ diameter	2 Elec	110	.145		11.70	9.80		21.50	27.50
9180	3-1/2″ diameter		100	.160		15.65	10.80		26.45	33
9190	4″ diameter		90	.178		16.30	11.95		28.25	35.50
9200	5″ diameter		70	.229		22	15.40		37.40	47.50
9210	6″ diameter		60	.267		30.50	17.95		48.45	60
9220	Elbows, 1/2″ diameter	1 Elec	50	.160	Ea.	1.06	10.80		11.86	17.15
9225	3/4″ diameter		42	.190		1.14	12.85		13.99	20.50
9230	1″ diameter		35	.229		1.75	15.40		17.15	25
9235	1-1/4″ diameter		28	.286		2.67	19.25		21.92	31.50
9240	1-1/2″ diameter		20	.400		3.51	27		30.51	44
9245	2″ diameter	R-1A	36.40	.440		5.80	26.50		32.30	46
9250	2-1/2″ diameter		26.70	.599		8.10	36.50		44.60	63
9255	3″ diameter		22.90	.699		13.55	42.50		56.05	78
9260	3-1/2″ diameter		22.20	.721		21	43.50		64.50	88
9265	4″ diameter		18.20	.879		32.50	53.50		86	115
9270	5″ diameter		12.10	1.322		42	80		122	165
9275	6″ diameter		11.10	1.441		76	87.50		163.50	214
9312	Couplings, 1/2″ diameter	1 Elec	50	.160		.65	10.80		11.45	16.70
9314	3/4″ diameter		42	.190		.33	12.85		13.18	19.40
9316	1″ diameter		35	.229		.51	15.40		15.91	23.50
9318	1-1/4″ diameter		28	.286		.69	19.25		19.94	29.50
9320	1-1/2″ diameter		20	.400		1.06	27		28.06	41

26 05 33.13 Conduit		Crew	Daily Output	Labor-Hours	Unit	Material	2023 Bare Costs Labor	Equipment	Total	Total Incl O&P
9322	2″ diameter	R-1A	36.40	.440	Ea.	1.35	26.50		27.85	41
9324	2-1/2″ diameter		26.70	.599		3.53	36.50		40.03	58
9326	3″ diameter		22.90	.699		3.42	42.50		45.92	67
9328	3-1/2″ diameter		22.20	.721		3.95	43.50		47.45	69.50
9330	4″ diameter		18.20	.879		5.15	53.50		58.65	84.50
9332	5″ diameter		12.10	1.322		14.75	80		94.75	135
9334	6″ diameter		11.10	1.441		21	87.50		108.50	153
9335	See note on line 26 05 33.13 9995 R260533-30									
9340	Field bends, 45° & 90°, 1/2″ diameter	1 Elec	45	.178	Ea.		11.95		11.95	17.80
9350	3/4″ diameter		40	.200			13.45		13.45	20
9360	1″ diameter		35	.229			15.40		15.40	23
9370	1-1/4″ diameter		32	.250			16.85		16.85	25
9380	1-1/2″ diameter		27	.296			19.95		19.95	29.50
9390	2″ diameter		20	.400			27		27	40
9400	2-1/2″ diameter		16	.500			33.50		33.50	50
9410	3″ diameter		13	.615			41.50		41.50	61.50
9420	3-1/2″ diameter		12	.667			45		45	66.50
9430	4″ diameter		10	.800			54		54	80
9440	5″ diameter		9	.889			60		60	89
9450	6″ diameter		8	1			67.50		67.50	100
9460	PVC adapters, 1/2″ diameter		50	.160		.32	10.80		11.12	16.35
9470	3/4″ diameter		42	.190		.54	12.85		13.39	19.65
9480	1″ diameter		38	.211		.69	14.20		14.89	22
9490	1-1/4″ diameter		35	.229		.86	15.40		16.26	24
9500	1-1/2″ diameter		32	.250		1.18	16.85		18.03	26.50
9510	2″ diameter		27	.296		1.55	19.95		21.50	31
9520	2-1/2″ diameter		23	.348		2.63	23.50		26.13	38
9530	3″ diameter		18	.444		3.82	30		33.82	48.50
9540	3-1/2″ diameter		13	.615		5.15	41.50		46.65	67
9550	4″ diameter		11	.727		6.80	49		55.80	80.50
9560	5″ diameter		8	1		13.20	67.50		80.70	115
9570	6″ diameter		6	1.333		17.95	90		107.95	153
9580	PVC-LB, LR or LL fittings & covers									
9590	1/2″ diameter	1 Elec	20	.400	Ea.	4.41	27		31.41	45
9600	3/4″ diameter		16	.500		6.30	33.50		39.80	57
9610	1″ diameter		12	.667		7	45		52	74
9620	1-1/4″ diameter		9	.889		11.45	60		71.45	102
9630	1-1/2″ diameter		7	1.143		12.45	77		89.45	128
9640	2″ diameter		6	1.333		22.50	90		112.50	158
9650	2-1/2″ diameter		6	1.333		83.50	90		173.50	225
9660	3″ diameter		5	1.600		84.50	108		192.50	253
9670	3-1/2″ diameter		4	2		95	135		230	305
9680	4″ diameter		3	2.667		90.50	180		270.50	365
9690	PVC-tee fitting & cover									
9700	1/2″	1 Elec	14	.571	Ea.	7	38.50		45.50	64.50
9710	3/4″		13	.615		8.10	41.50		49.60	70.50
9720	1″		10	.800		8.55	54		62.55	89.50
9730	1-1/4″		9	.889		15.20	60		75.20	106
9740	1-1/2″		8	1		21.50	67.50		89	124
9750	2″		7	1.143		29	77		106	146
9760	PVC-reducers, 3/4″ x 1/2″ diameter					2.01			2.01	2.21
9770	1″ x 1/2″ diameter					4.78			4.78	5.25
9780	1″ x 3/4″ diameter					4.72			4.72	5.20

26 05 33.13 Conduit		Crew	Daily Output	Labor-Hours	Unit	Material	Labor	Equipment	Total	Total Incl O&P
						2023 Bare Costs				
9790	1-1/4" x 3/4" diameter				Ea.	3.16			3.16	3.48
9800	1-1/4" x 1" diameter					6.45			6.45	7.10
9810	1-1/2" x 1-1/4" diameter					7.75			7.75	8.50
9820	2" x 1-1/4" diameter					8.10			8.10	8.90
9830	2-1/2" x 2" diameter					27.50			27.50	30.50
9840	3" x 2" diameter					24.50			24.50	26.50
9850	4" x 3" diameter					29			29	31.50
9860	Cement, quart					27.50			27.50	30.50
9870	Gallon					134			134	147
9880	Heat bender, to 6" diameter				↓	1,700			1,700	1,875
9900	Add to labor for higher elevated installation									
9905	10' to 14.5' high, add						10%			
9910	15' to 20' high, add						20%			
9920	20' to 25' high, add						25%			
9930	25' to 30' high, add						35%			
9940	30' to 35' high, add						40%			
9950	35' to 40' high, add						50%			
9960	Over 40' high, add						55%			
9995	Do not include labor when adding couplings to a fitting installation R260533-30									

26 05 33.14 Conduit		Crew	Daily Output	Labor-Hours	Unit	Material	Labor	Equipment	Total	Total Incl O&P
0010	**CONDUIT** To 10' high, includes 11 couplings per 100'									
0200	Electric metallic tubing, 1/2" diameter	1 Elec	435	.018	L.F.	.96	1.24		2.20	2.89
0220	3/4" diameter		253	.032		1.63	2.13		3.76	4.97
0240	1" diameter		207	.039		2.78	2.60		5.38	6.90
0260	1-1/4" diameter		173	.046		4.76	3.11		7.87	9.90
0280	1-1/2" diameter		153	.052		6	3.52		9.52	11.85
0300	2" diameter		130	.062		7.30	4.14		11.44	14.15
0320	2-1/2" diameter	↓	92	.087		9.20	5.85		15.05	18.80
0340	3" diameter	2 Elec	148	.108		11.60	7.30		18.90	23.50
0360	3-1/2" diameter		134	.119		15.20	8.05		23.25	28.50
0380	4" diameter	↓	114	.140		15.55	9.45		25	31
0500	Steel rigid galvanized, 1/2" diameter	1 Elec	146	.055		3.81	3.69		7.50	9.70
0520	3/4" diameter		125	.064		3.95	4.31		8.26	10.75
0540	1" diameter		93	.086		6.25	5.80		12.05	15.45
0560	1-1/4" diameter		88	.091		9.20	6.10		15.30	19.25
0580	1-1/2" diameter		80	.100		10.30	6.75		17.05	21.50
0600	2" diameter		65	.123		12.65	8.30		20.95	26
0620	2-1/2" diameter	↓	48	.167		25.50	11.25		36.75	44.50
0640	3" diameter	2 Elec	64	.250		28.50	16.85		45.35	56
0660	3-1/2" diameter		60	.267		37.50	17.95		55.45	68
0680	4" diameter		52	.308		38.50	20.50		59	73
0700	5" diameter		50	.320		75	21.50		96.50	115
0720	6" diameter	↓	48	.333		100	22.50		122.50	145
1000	Steel intermediate conduit (IMC), 1/2" diameter R260533-25	1 Elec	155	.052		2.58	3.48		6.06	8
1010	3/4" diameter		130	.062		2.98	4.14		7.12	9.40
1020	1" diameter		100	.080		4.57	5.40		9.97	13
1030	1-1/4" diameter		93	.086		6.40	5.80		12.20	15.65
1040	1-1/2" diameter		85	.094		8	6.35		14.35	18.20
1050	2" diameter		70	.114		10	7.70		17.70	22.50
1060	2-1/2" diameter	↓	53	.151		20.50	10.15		30.65	37.50
1070	3" diameter	2 Elec	80	.200		26.50	13.45		39.95	49
1080	3-1/2" diameter	↓	70	.229	↓	32	15.40		47.40	58

26 05 33.14 Conduit		Crew	Daily Output	Labor-Hours	Unit	2023 Bare Costs Material	Labor	Equipment	Total	Total Incl O&P
1090	4" diameter	2 Elec	60	.267	L.F.	34.50	17.95		52.45	64.50

26 05 33.15 Conduit Nipples

		Crew	Daily Output	Labor-Hours	Unit	Material	Labor	Equipment	Total	Total Incl O&P
0010	**CONDUIT NIPPLES** With locknuts and bushings									
0100	Aluminum, 1/2" diameter, close	1 Elec	36	.222	Ea.	11.65	14.95		26.60	35
0120	1-1/2" long		36	.222		12	14.95		26.95	35
0140	2" long		36	.222		14.15	14.95		29.10	37.50
0160	2-1/2" long		36	.222		15.70	14.95		30.65	39.50
0180	3" long		36	.222		12.45	14.95		27.40	35.50
0200	3-1/2" long		36	.222		16.95	14.95		31.90	40.50
0220	4" long		36	.222		14.30	14.95		29.25	37.50
0240	5" long		36	.222		18.90	14.95		33.85	43
0260	6" long		36	.222		14.95	14.95		29.90	38.50
0280	8" long		36	.222		24.50	14.95		39.45	49
0300	10" long		36	.222		21	14.95		35.95	45
0320	12" long		36	.222		19.55	14.95		34.50	43.50
0340	3/4" diameter, close		32	.250		17.30	16.85		34.15	44
0360	1-1/2" long		32	.250		17.20	16.85		34.05	44
0380	2" long		32	.250		17.05	16.85		33.90	44
0400	2-1/2" long		32	.250		19.75	16.85		36.60	47
0420	3" long		32	.250		17.70	16.85		34.55	44.50
0440	3-1/2" long		32	.250		22	16.85		38.85	49
0460	4" long		32	.250		18.55	16.85		35.40	45.50
0480	5" long		32	.250		19.25	16.85		36.10	46
0500	6" long		32	.250		23	16.85		39.85	50
0520	8" long		32	.250		32.50	16.85		49.35	60.50
0540	10" long		32	.250		40	16.85		56.85	69.50
0560	12" long		32	.250		37	16.85		53.85	65.50
0580	1" diameter, close		27	.296		26.50	19.95		46.45	59
0600	2" long		27	.296		31	19.95		50.95	63.50
0620	2-1/2" long		27	.296		32	19.95		51.95	65
0640	3" long		27	.296		29	19.95		48.95	61
0660	3-1/2" long		27	.296		33.50	19.95		53.45	66.50
0680	4" long		27	.296		29.50	19.95		49.45	61.50
0700	5" long		27	.296		39.50	19.95		59.45	73
0720	6" long		27	.296		34	19.95		53.95	66.50
0740	8" long		27	.296		43	19.95		62.95	76.50
0760	10" long		27	.296		36.50	19.95		56.45	69.50
0780	12" long		27	.296		55	19.95		74.95	89.50
0800	1-1/4" diameter, close		23	.348		39	23.50		62.50	78
0820	2" long		23	.348		44	23.50		67.50	83.50
0840	2-1/2" long		23	.348		37	23.50		60.50	76
0860	3" long		23	.348		47.50	23.50		71	87.50
0880	3-1/2" long		23	.348		73	23.50		96.50	116
0900	4" long		23	.348		52	23.50		75.50	92.50
0920	5" long		23	.348		57	23.50		80.50	98
0940	6" long		23	.348		50.50	23.50		74	90.50
0960	8" long		23	.348		60.50	23.50		84	102
0980	10" long		23	.348		66.50	23.50		90	108
1000	12" long		23	.348		78.50	23.50		102	122
1020	1-1/2" diameter, close		20	.400		52	27		79	97.50
1040	2" long		20	.400		54.50	27		81.50	99.50
1060	2-1/2" long		20	.400		54.50	27		81.50	100

26 05 33.15 Conduit Nipples		Crew	Daily Output	Labor-Hours	Unit	Material	Labor	Equipment	Total	Total Incl O&P
						2023 Bare Costs				
1080	3″ long	1 Elec	20	.400	Ea.	60.50	27		87.50	107
1100	3-1/2″ long		20	.400		62	27		89	108
1120	4″ long		20	.400		54	27		81	99.50
1140	5″ long		20	.400		72.50	27		99.50	120
1160	6″ long		20	.400		59	27		86	105
1180	8″ long		20	.400		71	27		98	119
1200	10″ long		20	.400		85	27		112	134
1220	12″ long		20	.400		94.50	27		121.50	144
1240	2″ diameter, close		18	.444		68	30		98	120
1260	2-1/2″ long		18	.444		73	30		103	125
1280	3″ long		18	.444		68.50	30		98.50	120
1300	3-1/2″ long		18	.444		78.50	30		108.50	131
1320	4″ long		18	.444		75	30		105	127
1340	5″ long		18	.444		95	30		125	149
1360	6″ long		18	.444		82.50	30		112.50	136
1380	8″ long		18	.444		112	30		142	168
1400	10″ long		18	.444		110	30		140	166
1420	12″ long		18	.444		129	30		159	187
1440	2-1/2″ diameter, close		15	.533		169	36		205	239
1460	3″ long		15	.533		187	36		223	259
1480	3-1/2″ long		15	.533		185	36		221	258
1500	4″ long		15	.533		190	36		226	263
1520	5″ long		15	.533		193	36		229	267
1540	6″ long		15	.533		204	36		240	279
1560	8″ long		15	.533		238	36		274	315
1580	10″ long		15	.533		228	36		264	305
1600	12″ long		15	.533		256	36		292	335
1620	3″ diameter, close		12	.667		217	45		262	305
1640	3″ long		12	.667		212	45		257	300
1660	3-1/2″ long		12	.667		238	45		283	330
1680	4″ long		12	.667		216	45		261	305
1700	5″ long		12	.667		235	45		280	325
1720	6″ long		12	.667		269	45		314	365
1740	8″ long		12	.667		274	45		319	365
1760	10″ long		12	.667		293	45		338	390
1780	12″ long		12	.667		330	45		375	430
1800	3-1/2″ diameter, close		11	.727		440	49		489	560
1820	4″ long		11	.727		445	49		494	565
1840	5″ long		11	.727		455	49		504	575
1860	6″ long		11	.727		465	49		514	585
1880	8″ long		11	.727		485	49		534	610
1900	10″ long		11	.727		510	49		559	635
1920	12″ long		11	.727		535	49		584	660
1940	4″ diameter, close		9	.889		420	60		480	555
1960	4″ long		9	.889		405	60		465	535
1980	5″ long		9	.889		505	60		565	645
2000	6″ long		9	.889		485	60		545	625
2020	8″ long		9	.889		440	60		500	570
2040	10″ long		9	.889		450	60		510	585
2060	12″ long		9	.889		570	60		630	715
2080	5″ diameter, close		7	1.143		705	77		782	890
2100	5″ long		7	1.143		740	77		817	925
2120	6″ long	↓	7	1.143	↓	1,050	77		1,127	1,275

26 05 33.15 Conduit Nipples		Crew	Daily Output	Labor-Hours	Unit	2023 Bare Costs Material	Labor	Equipment	Total	Total Incl O&P
2140	8" long	1 Elec	7	1.143	Ea.	790	77		867	985
2160	10" long		7	1.143		850	77		927	1,050
2180	12" long		7	1.143		970	77		1,047	1,200
2200	6" diameter, close		6	1.333		1,450	90		1,540	1,725
2220	5" long		6	1.333		1,475	90		1,565	1,750
2240	6" long		6	1.333		1,375	90		1,465	1,650
2260	8" long		6	1.333		1,550	90		1,640	1,825
2280	10" long		6	1.333		1,650	90		1,740	1,925
2300	12" long		6	1.333		1,625	90		1,715	1,925
2320	Rigid galvanized steel, 1/2" diameter, close		32	.250		4.34	16.85		21.19	30
2340	1-1/2" long		32	.250		4.58	16.85		21.43	30
2360	2" long		32	.250		4.78	16.85		21.63	30.50
2380	2-1/2" long		32	.250		4.92	16.85		21.77	30.50
2400	3" long		32	.250		5.05	16.85		21.90	30.50
2420	3-1/2" long		32	.250		5.15	16.85		22	30.50
2440	4" long		32	.250		5.45	16.85		22.30	31
2460	5" long		32	.250		5.65	16.85		22.50	31
2480	6" long		32	.250		6.20	16.85		23.05	32
2500	8" long		32	.250		8.60	16.85		25.45	34.50
2520	10" long		32	.250		10.30	16.85		27.15	36.50
2540	12" long		32	.250		10.20	16.85		27.05	36
2560	3/4" diameter, close		27	.296		6.35	19.95		26.30	36.50
2580	2" long		27	.296		6.65	19.95		26.60	37
2600	2-1/2" long		27	.296		6.85	19.95		26.80	37
2620	3" long		27	.296		7.05	19.95		27	37.50
2640	3-1/2" long		27	.296		7.15	19.95		27.10	37.50
2660	4" long		27	.296		7.50	19.95		27.45	38
2680	5" long		27	.296		7.90	19.95		27.85	38
2700	6" long		27	.296		8.45	19.95		28.40	39
2720	8" long		27	.296		10.80	19.95		30.75	41.50
2740	10" long		27	.296		12.85	19.95		32.80	43.50
2760	12" long		27	.296		12.90	19.95		32.85	43.50
2780	1" diameter, close		23	.348		9.95	23.50		33.45	46
2800	2" long		23	.348		10.15	23.50		33.65	46
2820	2-1/2" long		23	.348		10.50	23.50		34	46.50
2840	3" long		23	.348		10.75	23.50		34.25	47
2860	3-1/2" long		23	.348		11.25	23.50		34.75	47.50
2880	4" long		23	.348		11.40	23.50		34.90	47.50
2900	5" long		23	.348		12	23.50		35.50	48
2920	6" long		23	.348		12.40	23.50		35.90	48.50
2940	8" long		23	.348		15.15	23.50		38.65	51.50
2960	10" long		23	.348		17.50	23.50		41	54.50
2980	12" long		23	.348		18.55	23.50		42.05	55.50
3000	1-1/4" diameter, close		20	.400		11.80	27		38.80	53
3020	2" long		20	.400		12	27		39	53
3040	3" long		20	.400		12.65	27		39.65	54
3060	3-1/2" long		20	.400		13.15	27		40.15	54.50
3080	4" long		20	.400		13.40	27		40.40	55
3100	5" long		20	.400		14.20	27		41.20	55.50
3120	6" long		20	.400		14.90	27		41.90	56.50
3140	8" long		20	.400		18.50	27		45.50	60.50
3160	10" long		20	.400		22	27		49	64
3180	12" long		20	.400		23	27		50	65.50

26 05 33.15 Conduit Nipples		Crew	Daily Output	Labor-Hours	Unit	2023 Bare Costs Material	Labor	Equipment	Total	Total Incl O&P
3200	1-1/2" diameter, close	1 Elec	18	.444	Ea.	19.80	30		49.80	66.50
3220	2" long		18	.444		20	30		50	66.50
3240	2-1/2" long		18	.444		20.50	30		50.50	67
3260	3" long		18	.444		21	30		51	67.50
3280	3-1/2" long		18	.444		21.50	30		51.50	68
3300	4" long		18	.444		22	30		52	69
3320	5" long		18	.444		23	30		53	70
3340	6" long		18	.444		24.50	30		54.50	71.50
3360	8" long		18	.444		29	30		59	76
3380	10" long		18	.444		32	30		62	79.50
3400	12" long		18	.444		32.50	30		62.50	80.50
3420	2" diameter, close		16	.500		25	33.50		58.50	78
3440	2-1/2" long		16	.500		26	33.50		59.50	79
3460	3" long		16	.500		27	33.50		60.50	79.50
3480	3-1/2" long		16	.500		28	33.50		61.50	81
3500	4" long		16	.500		28.50	33.50		62	81.50
3520	5" long		16	.500		30	33.50		63.50	83
3540	6" long		16	.500		31.50	33.50		65	84.50
3560	8" long		16	.500		36	33.50		69.50	89.50
3580	10" long		16	.500		39.50	33.50		73	93.50
3600	12" long		16	.500		41.50	33.50		75	95.50
3620	2-1/2" diameter, close		13	.615		86.50	41.50		128	157
3640	3" long		13	.615		87	41.50		128.50	157
3660	3-1/2" long		13	.615		89.50	41.50		131	160
3680	4" long		13	.615		90	41.50		131.50	161
3700	5" long		13	.615		93.50	41.50		135	165
3720	6" long		13	.615		95.50	41.50		137	167
3740	8" long		13	.615		102	41.50		143.50	174
3760	10" long		13	.615		107	41.50		148.50	180
3780	12" long		13	.615		111	41.50		152.50	184
3800	3" diameter, close		12	.667		85	45		130	160
3820	3" long		12	.667		86	45		131	161
3900	3-1/2" long		12	.667		90.50	45		135.50	166
3920	4" long		12	.667		89.50	45		134.50	165
3940	5" long		12	.667		93	45		138	169
3960	6" long		12	.667		96.50	45		141.50	173
3980	8" long		12	.667		104	45		149	182
4000	10" long		12	.667		110	45		155	188
4020	12" long		12	.667		119	45		164	197
4040	3-1/2" diameter, close		10	.800		139	54		193	233
4060	4" long		10	.800		146	54		200	240
4080	5" long		10	.800		145	54		199	239
4100	6" long		10	.800		151	54		205	246
4120	8" long		10	.800		161	54		215	257
4140	10" long		10	.800		170	54		224	267
4160	12" long		10	.800		176	54		230	274
4180	4" diameter, close		8	1		271	67.50		338.50	400
4200	4" long		8	1		276	67.50		343.50	405
4220	5" long		8	1		281	67.50		348.50	410
4240	6" long		8	1		284	67.50		351.50	415
4260	8" long		8	1		293	67.50		360.50	420
4280	10" long		8	1		305	67.50		372.50	435
4300	12" long		8	1		315	67.50		382.50	445

26 05 33.15 Conduit Nipples		Crew	Daily Output	Labor-Hours	Unit	2023 Bare Costs Material	Labor	Equipment	Total	Total Incl O&P
4320	5" diameter, close	1 Elec	6	1.333	Ea.	330	90		420	500
4340	5" long		6	1.333		360	90		450	530
4360	6" long		6	1.333		350	90		440	520
4380	8" long		6	1.333		385	90		475	555
4400	10" long		6	1.333		380	90		470	555
4420	12" long		6	1.333		390	90		480	565
4440	6" diameter, close		5	1.600		635	108		743	855
4460	5" long		5	1.600		625	108		733	850
4480	6" long		5	1.600		675	108		783	905
4500	8" long		5	1.600		695	108		803	920
4520	10" long		5	1.600		705	108		813	935
4540	12" long		5	1.600		720	108		828	950
4560	Plastic coated, 40 mil thick, 1/2" diameter, 2" long		32	.250		38.50	16.85		55.35	67.50
4580	2-1/2" long		32	.250		38	16.85		54.85	66.50
4600	3" long		32	.250		33	16.85		49.85	61
4680	3-1/2" long		32	.250		44	16.85		60.85	73.50
4700	4" long		32	.250		50.50	16.85		67.35	80.50
4720	5" long		32	.250		43	16.85		59.85	72.50
4740	6" long		32	.250		41.50	16.85		58.35	70.50
4760	8" long		32	.250		44	16.85		60.85	73.50
4780	10" long		32	.250		44.50	16.85		61.35	74
4800	12" long		32	.250		44.50	16.85		61.35	74
4820	3/4" diameter, 2" long		26	.308		40.50	20.50		61	75.50
4840	2-1/2" long		26	.308		41	20.50		61.50	76
4860	3" long		26	.308		41	20.50		61.50	76
4880	3-1/2" long		26	.308		44	20.50		64.50	79
4900	4" long		26	.308		39.50	20.50		60	74.50
4920	5" long		26	.308		39.50	20.50		60	74.50
4940	6" long		26	.308		48	20.50		68.50	84
4960	8" long		26	.308		48	20.50		68.50	83.50
4980	10" long		26	.308		47.50	20.50		68	83.50
5000	12" long		26	.308		55.50	20.50		76	92
5020	1" diameter, 2" long		22	.364		39	24.50		63.50	79
5040	2-1/2" long		22	.364		40.50	24.50		65	81
5060	3" long		22	.364		42.50	24.50		67	83
5080	3-1/2" long		22	.364		47	24.50		71.50	88.50
5100	4" long		22	.364		48	24.50		72.50	89.50
5120	5" long		22	.364		47.50	24.50		72	88.50
5140	6" long		22	.364		52	24.50		76.50	93.50
5160	8" long		22	.364		54.50	24.50		79	96.50
5180	10" long		22	.364		54	24.50		78.50	96
5200	12" long		22	.364		56.50	24.50		81	99
5220	1-1/4" diameter, 2" long		18	.444		47	30		77	96
5240	2-1/2" long		18	.444		51	30		81	101
5260	3" long		18	.444		54	30		84	104
5280	3-1/2" long		18	.444		54	30		84	104
5300	4" long		18	.444		58.50	30		88.50	109
5320	5" long		18	.444		59	30		89	109
5340	6" long		18	.444		61	30		91	112
5360	8" long		18	.444		60	30		90	111
5380	10" long		18	.444		67	30		97	118
5400	12" long		18	.444		80	30		110	133
5420	1-1/2" diameter, 2" long		16	.500		52.50	33.50		86	108

26 05 33 – Raceway and Boxes for Electrical Systems

26 05 33.15 Conduit Nipples		Crew	Daily Output	Labor-Hours	Unit	2023 Bare Costs Material	Labor	Equipment	Total	Total Incl O&P
5440	2-1/2" long	1 Elec	16	.500	Ea.	68	33.50		101.50	125
5460	3" long		16	.500		61	33.50		94.50	117
5480	3-1/2" long		16	.500		63	33.50		96.50	120
5500	4" long		16	.500		63.50	33.50		97	120
5520	5" long		16	.500		69.50	33.50		103	127
5540	6" long		16	.500		79	33.50		112.50	137
5560	8" long		16	.500		78	33.50		111.50	136
5580	10" long		16	.500		91.50	33.50		125	151
5600	12" long		16	.500		106	33.50		139.50	167
5620	2" diameter, 2-1/2" long		14	.571		71	38.50		109.50	135
5640	3" long		14	.571		67.50	38.50		106	132
5660	3-1/2" long		14	.571		83	38.50		121.50	149
5680	4" long		14	.571		83.50	38.50		122	149
5700	5" long		14	.571		85	38.50		123.50	151
5720	6" long		14	.571		84.50	38.50		123	150
5740	8" long		14	.571		103	38.50		141.50	170
5760	10" long		14	.571		130	38.50		168.50	200
5780	12" long		14	.571		138	38.50		176.50	209
5800	2-1/2" diameter, 3-1/2" long		12	.667		172	45		217	257
5820	4" long		12	.667		168	45		213	252
5840	5" long		12	.667		208	45		253	296
5860	6" long		12	.667		197	45		242	284
5880	8" long		12	.667		223	45		268	315
5900	10" long		12	.667		232	45		277	320
5920	12" long		12	.667		280	45		325	375
5940	3" diameter, 3-1/2" long		11	.727		162	49		211	251
5960	4" long		11	.727		179	49		228	270
5980	5" long		11	.727		192	49		241	284
6000	6" long		11	.727		207	49		256	300
6020	8" long		11	.727		250	49		299	350
6040	10" long		11	.727		265	49		314	365
6060	12" long		11	.727		276	49		325	380
6080	3-1/2" diameter, 4" long		9	.889		257	60		317	370
6100	5" long		9	.889		267	60		327	380
6120	6" long		9	.889		291	60		351	410
6140	8" long		9	.889		310	60		370	435
6160	10" long		9	.889		385	60		445	515
6180	12" long		9	.889		460	60		520	595
6200	4" diameter, 4" long		7.50	1.067		395	72		467	540
6220	5" long		7.50	1.067		400	72		472	545
6240	6" long		7.50	1.067		405	72		477	550
6260	8" long		7.50	1.067		440	72		512	590
6280	10" long		7.50	1.067		540	72		612	700
6300	12" long		7.50	1.067		520	72		592	675
6320	5" diameter, 5" long		5.50	1.455		335	98		433	510
6340	6" long		5.50	1.455		365	98		463	545
6360	8" long		5.50	1.455		370	98		468	555
6380	10" long		5.50	1.455		380	98		478	565
6400	12" long		5.50	1.455		405	98		503	590
6420	6" diameter, 5" long		4.50	1.778		665	120		785	910
6440	6" long		4.50	1.778		670	120		790	920
6460	8" long		4.50	1.778		690	120		810	935
6480	10" long		4.50	1.778		700	120		820	950

26 05 33.15 Conduit Nipples		Crew	Daily Output	Labor-Hours	Unit	Material (2023 Bare Costs)	Labor (2023 Bare Costs)	Equipment (2023 Bare Costs)	Total (2023 Bare Costs)	Total Incl O&P
6500	12″ long	1 Elec	4.50	1.778	Ea.	720	120		840	975

26 05 33.16 Boxes for Electrical Systems

		Crew	Daily Output	Labor-Hours	Unit	Material	Labor	Equipment	Total	Total Incl O&P
0010	**BOXES FOR ELECTRICAL SYSTEMS** R260533-65									
0020	Pressed steel, octagon, 4″	1 Elec	20	.400	Ea.	3.11	27		30.11	43.50
0040	For Romex or BX		20	.400		4.17	27		31.17	44.50
0050	For Romex or BX, with bracket		20	.400		5.70	27		32.70	46.50
0060	Covers, blank		64	.125		1.01	8.40		9.41	13.60
0100	Extension rings		40	.200		3.47	13.45		16.92	24
0150	Square, 4″		20	.400		3.26	27		30.26	43.50
0160	For Romex or BX		20	.400		8.30	27		35.30	49
0170	For Romex or BX, with bracket		20	.400		9.35	27		36.35	50.50
0200	Extension rings		40	.200		3.85	13.45		17.30	24
0220	2-1/8″ deep, 1″ KO		20	.400		6.95	27		33.95	47.50
0250	Covers, blank		64	.125		1.42	8.40		9.82	14.05
0260	Raised device		64	.125		2.66	8.40		11.06	15.45
0300	Plaster rings		64	.125		2.87	8.40		11.27	15.65
0350	Square, 4-11/16″		20	.400		7.35	27		34.35	48
0370	2-1/8″ deep, 3/4″ to 1-1/4″ KO		20	.400		8.80	27		35.80	49.50
0400	Extension rings		40	.200		7.95	13.45		21.40	29
0450	Covers, blank		53	.151		2.64	10.15		12.79	18
0460	Raised device		53	.151		7.90	10.15		18.05	24
0500	Plaster rings		53	.151		5.30	10.15		15.45	21
0550	Handy box		27	.296		3.97	19.95		23.92	34
0560	Covers, device		64	.125		.97	8.40		9.37	13.55
0600	Extension rings		54	.148		4.51	10		14.51	19.80
0650	Switchbox		27	.296		6.30	19.95		26.25	36.50
0660	Romex or BX		27	.296		5.40	19.95		25.35	35.50
0670	with bracket		27	.296		9.50	19.95		29.45	40
0680	Partition, metal		27	.296		5.15	19.95		25.10	35
0700	Masonry, 1 gang, 2-1/2″ deep		27	.296		9.55	19.95		29.50	40
0710	3-1/2″ deep		27	.296		9.55	19.95		29.50	40
0750	2 gang, 2-1/2″ deep		20	.400		17.85	27		44.85	59.50
0760	3-1/2″ deep		20	.400		14.45	27		41.45	56
0800	3 gang, 2-1/2″ deep		13	.615		21.50	41.50		63	85
0850	4 gang, 2-1/2″ deep		10	.800		19	54		73	101
0860	5 gang, 2-1/2″ deep		9	.889		25.50	60		85.50	118
0870	6 gang, 2-1/2″ deep		8	1		80.50	67.50		148	189
0880	Masonry thru-the-wall, 1 gang, 4″ block		16	.500		68.50	33.50		102	126
0890	6″ block		16	.500		119	33.50		152.50	181
0900	8″ block		16	.500		122	33.50		155.50	185
0920	2 gang, 6″ block		16	.500		178	33.50		211.50	246
0940	Bar hanger with 3/8″ stud, for wood and masonry boxes		53	.151		6.75	10.15		16.90	22.50
0950	Concrete, set flush, 4″ deep		20	.400		25	27		52	67.50
1000	Plate with 3/8″ stud		80	.100		11.95	6.75		18.70	23
1100	Concrete, floor, 1 gang		5.30	1.509		216	102		318	390
1150	2 gang		4	2		335	135		470	565
1200	3 gang		2.70	2.963		450	200		650	790
1250	For duplex receptacle, pedestal mounted, add		24	.333		126	22.50		148.50	173
1270	Flush mounted, add		27	.296		30.50	19.95		50.45	63
1300	For telephone, pedestal mounted, add		30	.267		107	17.95		124.95	144
1350	Carpet flange, 1 gang		53	.151		112	10.15		122.15	138
1400	Cast, 1 gang, FS (2″ deep), 1/2″ hub		12	.667		35	45		80	105

26 05 33.16 Boxes for Electrical Systems		Crew	Daily Output	Labor-Hours	Unit	Material	Labor	Equipment	Total	Total Incl O&P
						2023 Bare Costs				
1410	3/4" hub	1 Elec	12	.667	Ea.	36.50	45		81.50	107
1420	FD (2-11/16" deep), 1/2" hub		12	.667		24.50	45		69.50	93.50
1430	3/4" hub		12	.667		27.50	45		72.50	97
1450	2 gang, FS, 1/2" hub		10	.800		64	54		118	151
1460	3/4" hub		10	.800		67.50	54		121.50	154
1470	FD, 1/2" hub		10	.800		79.50	54		133.50	168
1480	3/4" hub		10	.800		76	54		130	164
1500	3 gang, FS, 3/4" hub		9	.889		118	60		178	219
1510	Switch cover, 1 gang, FS		64	.125		9.50	8.40		17.90	23
1520	2 gang		53	.151		15.15	10.15		25.30	32
1530	Duplex receptacle cover, 1 gang, FS		64	.125		8.90	8.40		17.30	22.50
1540	2 gang, FS		53	.151		14.35	10.15		24.50	31
1542	Weatherproof blank cover, 1 gang		64	.125		.77	8.40		9.17	13.35
1544	2 gang		53	.151		1.41	10.15		11.56	16.65
1550	Weatherproof switch cover, 1 gang		64	.125		6.75	8.40		15.15	19.90
1554	2 gang		53	.151		11.60	10.15		21.75	28
1600	Weatherproof receptacle cover, 1 gang		64	.125		3.21	8.40		11.61	16.05
1604	2 gang		53	.151		16.10	10.15		26.25	33
1620	Weatherproof receptacle cover, tamper resistant, 1 gang		58	.138		15.90	9.30		25.20	31.50
1624	2 gang		48	.167		27.50	11.25		38.75	47
1750	FSC, 1 gang, 1/2" hub		11	.727		38	49		87	115
1760	3/4" hub		11	.727		41.50	49		90.50	119
1770	2 gang, 1/2" hub		9	.889		71	60		131	168
1780	3/4" hub		9	.889		77.50	60		137.50	174
1790	FDC, 1 gang, 1/2" hub		11	.727		44.50	49		93.50	122
1800	3/4" hub		11	.727		45.50	49		94.50	123
1810	2 gang, 1/2" hub		9	.889		90.50	60		150.50	189
1820	3/4" hub		9	.889		81	60		141	178
1850	Weatherproof in-use cover, 1 gang		64	.125		34.50	8.40		42.90	50
1870	2 gang		53	.151		32	10.15		42.15	50
2000	Poke-thru fitting, fire rated, for 3-3/4" floor		6.80	1.176		240	79		319	380
2040	For 7" floor		6.80	1.176		345	79		424	500
2100	Pedestal, 15 amp, duplex receptacle & blank plate		5.25	1.524		185	103		288	355
2120	Duplex receptacle and telephone plate		5.25	1.524		185	103		288	355
2140	Pedestal, 20 amp, duplex recept. & phone plate		5	1.600		186	108		294	365
2160	Telephone plate, both sides		5.25	1.524		172	103		275	340
2200	Abandonment plate		32	.250		70	16.85		86.85	102

26 05 33.17 Outlet Boxes, Plastic		Crew	Daily Output	Labor-Hours	Unit	Material	Labor	Equipment	Total	Total Incl O&P
0010	**OUTLET BOXES, PLASTIC**									
0050	4" diameter, round with 2 mounting nails	1 Elec	25	.320	Ea.	3.25	21.50		24.75	35.50
0100	Bar hanger mounted		25	.320		5.05	21.50		26.55	37.50
0200	4", square with 2 mounting nails		25	.320		5.40	21.50		26.90	38
0300	Plaster ring		64	.125		2.13	8.40		10.53	14.85
0400	Switch box with 2 mounting nails, 1 gang		30	.267		2.12	17.95		20.07	29
0500	2 gang		25	.320		3.52	21.50		25.02	36
0600	3 gang		20	.400		5.95	27		32.95	46.50
0700	Old work box		30	.267		4.15	17.95		22.10	31
1400	PVC, FSS, 1 gang, 1/2" hub		14	.571		16.50	38.50		55	75
1410	3/4" hub		14	.571		16	38.50		54.50	74.50
1420	FD, 1 gang for variable terminations		14	.571		15.50	38.50		54	74
1450	FS, 2 gang for variable terminations		12	.667		18.75	45		63.75	87
1480	Weatherproof blank cover, FS, 1 gang		64	.125		7.80	8.40		16.20	21

26 05 33.17 Outlet Boxes, Plastic		Crew	Daily Output	Labor-Hours	Unit	Material	Labor	Equipment	Total	Total Incl O&P
						2023 Bare Costs				
1500	2 gang	1 Elec	53	.151	Ea.	8.10	10.15		18.25	24
1510	Weatherproof switch cover, FS, 1 gang		64	.125		18.05	8.40		26.45	32.50
1520	2 gang		53	.151		31	10.15		41.15	49
1530	Weatherproof duplex receptacle cover, FS, 1 gang		64	.125		29.50	8.40		37.90	45
1540	2 gang		53	.151		26.50	10.15		36.65	44
1750	FSC, 1 gang, 1/2" hub		13	.615		15.70	41.50		57.20	79
1760	3/4" hub		13	.615		17	41.50		58.50	80
1770	FSC, 2 gang, 1/2" hub		11	.727		23	49		72	98.50
1780	3/4" hub		11	.727		20.50	49		69.50	95.50
1790	FDC, 1 gang, 1/2" hub		13	.615		16.50	41.50		58	79.50
1800	3/4" hub		13	.615		13.35	41.50		54.85	76
1810	Weatherproof, T box w/3 holes		14	.571		22	38.50		60.50	81.50
1820	4" diameter round w/5 holes		14	.571		20.50	38.50		59	79.50
1850	In-use cover, 1 gang		64	.125		13.45	8.40		21.85	27.50
1870	2 gang		53	.151		16.65	10.15		26.80	33.50

26 05 33.18 Pull Boxes		Crew	Daily Output	Labor-Hours	Unit	Material	Labor	Equipment	Total	Total Incl O&P
0010	**PULL BOXES** R260533-70									
0100	Steel, pull box, NEMA 1, type SC, 6" W x 6" H x 4" D	1 Elec	8	1	Ea.	12.60	67.50		80.10	114
0180	8" W x 6" H x 4" D		8	1		16.95	67.50		84.45	119
0200	8" W x 8" H x 4" D		8	1		17.05	67.50		84.55	119
0210	10" W x 10" H x 4" D		7	1.143		22.50	77		99.50	139
0220	12" W x 12" H x 4" D		6.50	1.231		28.50	83		111.50	155
0230	15" W x 15" H x 4" D		5.20	1.538		54.50	104		158.50	214
0240	18" W x 18" H x 4" D		4.40	1.818		51	122		173	238
0250	6" W x 6" H x 6" D		8	1		14.95	67.50		82.45	116
0260	8" W x 8" H x 6" D		7.50	1.067		20.50	72		92.50	130
0270	10" W x 10" H x 6" D		5.50	1.455		26	98		124	175
0300	10" W x 12" H x 6" D		5.30	1.509		36	102		138	191
0310	12" W x 12" H x 6" D		5.20	1.538		33.50	104		137.50	191
0320	15" W x 15" H x 6" D		4.60	1.739		106	117		223	291
0330	18" W x 18" H x 6" D		4.20	1.905		60	128		188	257
0340	24" W x 24" H x 6" D		3.20	2.500		122	168		290	385
0350	12" W x 12" H x 8" D		5	1.600		41	108		149	205
0360	15" W x 15" H x 8" D		4.50	1.778		61	120		181	246
0370	18" W x 18" H x 8" D		4	2		81.50	135		216.50	290
0380	24" W x 18" H x 6" D		3.70	2.162		117	146		263	345
0400	16" W x 20" H x 8" D		4	2		106	135		241	315
0500	20" W x 24" H x 8" D		3.20	2.500		124	168		292	385
0510	24" W x 24" H x 8" D		3	2.667		131	180		311	410
0600	24" W x 36" H x 8" D		2.70	2.963		195	200		395	510
0610	30" W x 30" H x 8" D		2.70	2.963		259	200		459	580
0620	36" W x 36" H x 8" D		2	4		274	269		543	700
0630	24" W x 24" H x 10" D		2.50	3.200		235	216		451	580
0650	Pull box, hinged, NEMA 1, 6" W x 6" H x 4" D		8	1		17.55	67.50		85.05	119
0660	8" W x 8" H x 4" D		8	1		22	67.50		89.50	125
0670	10" W x 10" H x 4" D		7	1.143		23.50	77		100.50	140
0680	12" W x 12" H x 4" D		6	1.333		38	90		128	175
0690	15" W x 15" H x 4" D		5.20	1.538		42.50	104		146.50	201
0700	18" W x 18" H x 4" D		4.40	1.818		58	122		180	246
0710	6" W x 6" H x 6" D		8	1		19.75	67.50		87.25	122
0720	8" W x 8" H x 6" D		7.50	1.067		29.50	72		101.50	140
0730	10" W x 10" H x 6" D		5.50	1.455		41.50	98		139.50	192

26 05 33.18 Pull Boxes		Crew	Daily Output	Labor-Hours	Unit	2023 Bare Costs Material	Labor	Equipment	Total	Total Incl O&P
0740	12″ W x 12″ H x 6″ D	1 Elec	5.20	1.538	Ea.	49	104		153	208
0800	12″ W x 16″ H x 6″ D		4.70	1.702		99	115		214	279
0820	18″ W x 18″ H x 6″ D		4.20	1.905		80	128		208	279
1000	20″ W x 20″ H x 6″ D		3.60	2.222		261	150		411	510
1010	24″ W x 24″ H x 6″ D		3.20	2.500		173	168		341	440
1020	12″ W x 12″ H x 8″ D		5	1.600		93	108		201	262
1030	15″ W x 15″ H x 8″ D		4.50	1.778		90	120		210	277
1040	18″ W x 18″ H x 8″ D		4	2		127	135		262	340
1200	20″ W x 20″ H x 8″ D		3.20	2.500		171	168		339	440
1210	24″ W x 24″ H x 8″ D		3	2.667		179	180		359	465
1220	30″ W x 30″ H x 8″ D		2.70	2.963		300	200		500	625
1400	24″ W x 36″ H x 8″ D		2.70	2.963		250	200		450	570
1600	24″ W x 42″ H x 8″ D		2	4		370	269		639	805
1610	36″ W x 36″ H x 8″ D		2	4		310	269		579	740
2100	Pull box, NEMA 3R, type SC, raintight & weatherproof									
2150	6″ L x 6″ W x 6″ D	1 Elec	10	.800	Ea.	25	54		79	108
2200	8″ L x 6″ W x 6″ D		8	1		44	67.50		111.50	149
2250	10″ L x 6″ W x 6″ D		7	1.143		32.50	77		109.50	150
2300	12″ L x 12″ W x 6″ D		5	1.600		61.50	108		169.50	228
2350	16″ L x 16″ W x 6″ D		4.50	1.778		92.50	120		212.50	280
2400	20″ L x 20″ W x 6″ D		4	2		89.50	135		224.50	299
2450	24″ L x 18″ W x 8″ D		3	2.667		185	180		365	470
2500	24″ L x 24″ W x 10″ D		2.50	3.200		234	216		450	575
2550	30″ L x 24″ W x 12″ D		2	4		925	269		1,194	1,425
2600	36″ L x 36″ W x 12″ D		1.50	5.333		595	360		955	1,200
2800	Cast iron, pull boxes for surface mounting									
3000	NEMA 4, watertight & dust tight									
3050	6″ L x 6″ W x 6″ D	1 Elec	4	2	Ea.	515	135		650	765
3100	8″ L x 6″ W x 6″ D		3.20	2.500		615	168		783	925
3150	10″ L x 6″ W x 6″ D		2.50	3.200		870	216		1,086	1,275
3200	12″ L x 12″ W x 6″ D		2.30	3.478		1,950	234		2,184	2,475
3250	16″ L x 16″ W x 6″ D		1.30	6.154		2,500	415		2,915	3,375
3300	20″ L x 20″ W x 6″ D		.80	10		4,675	675		5,350	6,150
3350	24″ L x 18″ W x 8″ D		.70	11.429		6,875	770		7,645	8,725
3400	24″ L x 24″ W x 10″ D		.50	16		9,275	1,075		10,350	11,800
3450	30″ L x 24″ W x 12″ D		.40	20		14,800	1,350		16,150	18,300
3500	36″ L x 36″ W x 12″ D		.20	40		19,900	2,700		22,600	25,900
3510	NEMA 4 clamp cover, 6″ L x 6″ W x 4″ D		4	2		345	135		480	580
3520	8″ L x 6″ W x 4″ D		4	2		335	135		470	570
4000	NEMA 7, explosion proof									
4050	6″ L x 6″ W x 6″ D	1 Elec	2	4	Ea.	565	269		834	1,025
4100	8″ L x 6″ W x 6″ D		1.80	4.444		1,725	299		2,024	2,350
4150	10″ L x 6″ W x 6″ D		1.60	5		1,425	335		1,760	2,075
4200	12″ L x 12″ W x 6″ D		1	8		2,950	540		3,490	4,050
4250	16″ L x 14″ W x 6″ D		.60	13.333		3,300	900		4,200	4,950
4300	18″ L x 18″ W x 8″ D		.50	16		7,275	1,075		8,350	9,600
4350	24″ L x 18″ W x 8″ D		.40	20		11,700	1,350		13,050	14,800
4400	24″ L x 24″ W x 10″ D		.30	26.667		9,975	1,800		11,775	13,700
4450	30″ L x 24″ W x 12″ D		.20	40		14,800	2,700		17,500	20,300
5000	NEMA 9, dust tight 6″ L x 6″ W x 6″ D		3.20	2.500		1,075	168		1,243	1,425
5050	8″ L x 6″ W x 6″ D		2.70	2.963		1,025	200		1,225	1,425
5100	10″ L x 6″ W x 6″ D		2	4		1,700	269		1,969	2,250
5150	12″ L x 12″ W x 6″ D		1.60	5		3,275	335		3,610	4,125

26 05 33.18 Pull Boxes		Crew	Daily Output	Labor-Hours	Unit	Material	Labor	Equipment	Total	Total Incl O&P
						2023 Bare Costs				
5200	16" L x 16" W x 6" D	1 Elec	1	8	Ea.	2,150	540		2,690	3,175
5250	18" L x 18" W x 8" D		.70	11.429		3,375	770		4,145	4,850
5300	24" L x 18" W x 8" D		.60	13.333		4,775	900		5,675	6,600
5350	24" L x 24" W x 10" D		.40	20		6,425	1,350		7,775	9,050
5400	30" L x 24" W x 12" D	↓	.30	26.667	↓	9,700	1,800		11,500	13,400
6000	J.I.C. wiring boxes, NEMA 12, dust tight & drip tight									
6050	6" L x 8" W x 4" D	1 Elec	10	.800	Ea.	96.50	54		150.50	186
6100	8" L x 10" W x 4" D		8	1		119	67.50		186.50	231
6150	12" L x 14" W x 6" D		5.30	1.509		202	102		304	375
6200	14" L x 16" W x 6" D		4.70	1.702		237	115		352	430
6250	16" L x 20" W x 6" D		4.40	1.818		315	122		437	525
6300	24" L x 30" W x 6" D		3.20	2.500		460	168		628	755
6350	24" L x 30" W x 8" D		2.90	2.759		470	186		656	795
6400	24" L x 36" W x 8" D		2.70	2.963		525	200		725	875
6450	24" L x 42" W x 8" D		2.30	3.478		595	234		829	1,000
6500	24" L x 48" W x 8" D	↓	2	4	↓	655	269		924	1,125

26 05 33.23 Wireway		Crew	Daily Output	Labor-Hours	Unit	Material	Labor	Equipment	Total	Total Incl O&P
0010	**WIREWAY** to 10' high R260533-60									
0020	For higher elevations, see Section 26 05 36.40									
0100	NEMA 1, screw cover w/fittings and supports, 2-1/2" x 2-1/2"	1 Elec	45	.178	L.F.	16.90	11.95		28.85	36.50
0200	4" x 4"	"	40	.200		20.50	13.45		33.95	42.50
0400	6" x 6"	2 Elec	60	.267		38.50	17.95		56.45	68.50
0600	8" x 8"		40	.400		34.50	27		61.50	78
0620	10" x 10"		30	.533		68	36		104	128
0640	12" x 12"	↓	20	.800	↓	75.50	54		129.50	163
0800	Elbows, 90°, 2-1/2"	1 Elec	24	.333	Ea.	32.50	22.50		55	69
1000	4"		20	.400		39	27		66	82.50
1200	6"		18	.444		41	30		71	90
1400	8"		16	.500		66.50	33.50		100	124
1420	10"		12	.667		133	45		178	213
1440	12"		10	.800		132	54		186	225
1500	Elbows, 45°, 2-1/2"		24	.333		32.50	22.50		55	69
1510	4"		20	.400		39.50	27		66.50	83.50
1520	6"		18	.444		44	30		74	92.50
1530	8"		16	.500		66.50	33.50		100	124
1540	10"		12	.667		112	45		157	191
1550	12"		10	.800		169	54		223	265
1600	"T" box, 2-1/2"		18	.444		37	30		67	85.50
1800	4"		16	.500		48.50	33.50		82	103
2000	6"		14	.571		53	38.50		91.50	116
2200	8"		12	.667		93	45		138	169
2220	10"		10	.800		124	54		178	216
2240	12"		8	1		146	67.50		213.50	261
2300	Cross, 2-1/2"		16	.500		41.50	33.50		75	95.50
2310	4"		14	.571		50.50	38.50		89	113
2320	6"		12	.667		62.50	45		107.50	135
2400	Panel adapter, 2-1/2"		24	.333		8.55	22.50		31.05	43
2600	4"		20	.400		10.05	27		37.05	51
2800	6"		18	.444		16.50	30		46.50	62.50
3000	8"		16	.500		17.75	33.50		51.25	69.50
3020	10"		14	.571		31	38.50		69.50	91
3040	12"	↓	12	.667	↓	45.50	45		90.50	117

26 05 33.23 Wireway		Crew	Daily Output	Labor-Hours	Unit	2023 Bare Costs Material	Labor	Equipment	Total	Total Incl O&P
3200	Reducer, 4" to 2-1/2"	1 Elec	24	.333	Ea.	15.85	22.50		38.35	51
3400	6" to 4"		20	.400		36.50	27		63.50	80
3600	8" to 6"		18	.444		44.50	30		74.50	93.50
3620	10" to 8"		16	.500		73	33.50		106.50	130
3640	12" to 10"		14	.571		67	38.50		105.50	131
3780	End cap, 2-1/2"		24	.333		5.25	22.50		27.75	39.50
3800	4"		20	.400		6	27		33	46.50
4000	6"		18	.444		7.30	30		37.30	52.50
4200	8"		16	.500		9.30	33.50		42.80	60
4220	10"		14	.571		17.50	38.50		56	76.50
4240	12"		12	.667		20.50	45		65.50	89
4300	U-connector, 2-1/2"		200	.040		5.10	2.69		7.79	9.60
4320	4"		200	.040		6.25	2.69		8.94	10.85
4340	6"		180	.044		7.70	2.99		10.69	12.95
4360	8"		170	.047		14.05	3.17		17.22	20
4380	10"		150	.053		46.50	3.59		50.09	56.50
4400	12"		130	.062		25	4.14		29.14	33.50
4420	Hanger, 2-1/2"		100	.080		14.25	5.40		19.65	23.50
4430	4"		100	.080		14.80	5.40		20.20	24.50
4440	6"		80	.100		15.25	6.75		22	27
4450	8"		65	.123		24.50	8.30		32.80	39.50
4460	10"		50	.160		44.50	10.80		55.30	65
4470	12"		40	.200		65	13.45		78.45	91.50
4475	NEMA 3R, screw cover w/fittings and supports, 4" x 4"		36	.222	L.F.	43.50	14.95		58.45	70
4480	6" x 6"	2 Elec	55	.291		63	19.60		82.60	98.50
4485	8" x 8"		36	.444		73	30		103	125
4490	12" x 12"		18	.889		137	60		197	240
4500	Hinged cover, with fittings and supports, 2-1/2" x 2-1/2"	1 Elec	60	.133		23	9		32	39
4520	4" x 4"	"	45	.178		27	11.95		38.95	47.50
4540	6" x 6"	2 Elec	80	.200		39	13.45		52.45	63
4560	8" x 8"		60	.267		52.50	17.95		70.45	84
4580	10" x 10"		50	.320		67.50	21.50		89	106
4600	12" x 12"		24	.667		66.50	45		111.50	140
4700	Elbows 90°, 2-1/2" x 2-1/2"	1 Elec	32	.250	Ea.	45.50	16.85		62.35	75
4720	4"		27	.296		204	19.95		223.95	254
4730	6"		23	.348		238	23.50		261.50	296
4740	8"		18	.444		325	30		355	400
4750	10"		14	.571		167	38.50		205.50	241
4760	12"		12	.667		174	45		219	258
4800	Tee box, hinged cover, 2-1/2" x 2-1/2"		23	.348		67.50	23.50		91	110
4810	4"		20	.400		255	27		282	320
4820	6"		18	.444		285	30		315	360
4830	8"		16	.500		365	33.50		398.50	450
4840	10"		12	.667		158	45		203	241
4860	12"		10	.800		266	54		320	370
4880	Cross box, hinged cover, 2-1/2" x 2-1/2"		18	.444		76	30		106	128
4900	4"		16	.500		335	33.50		368.50	415
4920	6"		13	.615		410	41.50		451.50	510
4940	8"		11	.727		525	49		574	655
4960	10"		10	.800		236	54		290	340
4980	12"		9	.889		226	60		286	340
5000	NEMA 12, hinged cover, 2-1/2" x 2-1/2"		40	.200	L.F.	50	13.45		63.45	75
5020	4" x 4"		35	.229		56.50	15.40		71.90	85.50

26 05 33 – Raceway and Boxes for Electrical Systems

26 05 33.23 Wireway		Crew	Daily Output	Labor-Hours	Unit	Material	2023 Bare Costs Labor	Equipment	Total	Total Incl O&P
5040	6" x 6"	2 Elec	60	.267	L.F.	84	17.95		101.95	119
5060	8" x 8"	"	50	.320		114	21.50		135.50	158
5120	Elbows 90°, flanged, 2-1/2" x 2-1/2"	1 Elec	23	.348	Ea.	128	23.50		151.50	175
5140	4"		20	.400		159	27		186	215
5160	6"		18	.444		201	30		231	267
5180	8"		15	.533		292	36		328	375
5240	Tee box, flanged, 2-1/2" x 2-1/2"		18	.444		178	30		208	241
5260	4"		16	.500		202	33.50		235.50	273
5280	6"		15	.533		265	36		301	345
5300	8"		13	.615		385	41.50		426.50	485
5360	Cross box, flanged, 2-1/2" x 2-1/2"		15	.533		200	36		236	274
5380	4"		13	.615		278	41.50		319.50	365
5400	6"		12	.667		360	45		405	460
5420	8"		10	.800		485	54		539	610
5480	Flange gasket, 2-1/2"		160	.050		6.45	3.37		9.82	12.10
5500	4"		80	.100		8.90	6.75		15.65	19.80
5520	6"		53	.151		11.80	10.15		21.95	28
5530	8"		40	.200		15.25	13.45		28.70	37

26 05 33.25 Conduit Fittings for Rigid Galvanized Steel		Crew	Daily Output	Labor-Hours	Unit	Material	Labor	Equipment	Total	Total Incl O&P
0010	**CONDUIT FITTINGS FOR RIGID GALVANIZED STEEL**									
0050	Standard, locknuts, 1/2" diameter				Ea.	.33			.33	.36
0100	3/4" diameter					.57			.57	.63
0300	1" diameter					.92			.92	1.01
0500	1-1/4" diameter					1.16			1.16	1.28
0700	1-1/2" diameter					1.90			1.90	2.09
1000	2" diameter					2.76			2.76	3.04
1030	2-1/2" diameter					6.95			6.95	7.65
1050	3" diameter					8.95			8.95	9.80
1070	3-1/2" diameter					14.55			14.55	16
1100	4" diameter					18.50			18.50	20.50
1110	5" diameter					38			38	42
1120	6" diameter					69			69	76
1130	Bushings, plastic, 1/2" diameter	1 Elec	40	.200		.19	13.45		13.64	20
1150	3/4" diameter		32	.250		.24	16.85		17.09	25.50
1170	1" diameter		28	.286		.42	19.25		19.67	29
1200	1-1/4" diameter		24	.333		.51	22.50		23.01	34
1230	1-1/2" diameter		18	.444		.80	30		30.80	45.50
1250	2" diameter		15	.533		1.20	36		37.20	55
1270	2-1/2" diameter		13	.615		2.39	41.50		43.89	64
1300	3" diameter		12	.667		2.79	45		47.79	69.50
1330	3-1/2" diameter		11	.727		2.95	49		51.95	76.50
1350	4" diameter		9	.889		3.60	60		63.60	93
1360	5" diameter		7	1.143		26.50	77		103.50	143
1370	6" diameter		5	1.600		62	108		170	229
1390	Steel, 1/2" diameter		40	.200		1.20	13.45		14.65	21.50
1400	3/4" diameter		32	.250		1.78	16.85		18.63	27
1430	1" diameter		28	.286		2.82	19.25		22.07	31.50
1450	Steel insulated, 1-1/4" diameter		24	.333		5.55	22.50		28.05	39.50
1470	1-1/2" diameter		18	.444		7.05	30		37.05	52.50
1500	2" diameter		15	.533		9.90	36		45.90	64.50
1530	2-1/2" diameter		13	.615		19.35	41.50		60.85	83
1550	3" diameter		12	.667		28	45		73	97.50

26 05 33.25 Conduit Fittings for Rigid Galvanized Steel		Crew	Daily Output	Labor-Hours	Unit	Material	Labor	Equipment	Total	Total Incl O&P
						2023 Bare Costs				
1570	3-1/2" diameter	1 Elec	11	.727	Ea.	83	49		132	164
1600	4" diameter		9	.889		47.50	60		107.50	142
1610	5" diameter		7	1.143		78	77		155	200
1620	6" diameter		5	1.600		128	108		236	300
1630	Sealing locknuts, 1/2" diameter		40	.200		2.03	13.45		15.48	22
1650	3/4" diameter		32	.250		2.38	16.85		19.23	27.50
1670	1" diameter		28	.286		3.62	19.25		22.87	32.50
1700	1-1/4" diameter		24	.333		5.40	22.50		27.90	39.50
1730	1-1/2" diameter		18	.444		7.15	30		37.15	52.50
1750	2" diameter		15	.533		8.85	36		44.85	63.50
1760	Grounding bushing, insulated, 1/2" diameter		32	.250		6.40	16.85		23.25	32
1770	3/4" diameter		28	.286		16.45	19.25		35.70	46.50
1780	1" diameter		20	.400		19.35	27		46.35	61.50
1800	1-1/4" diameter		18	.444		30.50	30		60.50	78
1830	1-1/2" diameter		16	.500		31	33.50		64.50	84
1850	2" diameter		13	.615		40	41.50		81.50	106
1870	2-1/2" diameter		12	.667		63.50	45		108.50	136
1900	3" diameter		11	.727		66	49		115	146
1930	3-1/2" diameter		9	.889		100	60		160	199
1950	4" diameter		8	1		130	67.50		197.50	243
1960	5" diameter		6	1.333		220	90		310	375
1970	6" diameter		4	2		325	135		460	560
1990	Coupling, with set screw, 1/2" diameter		50	.160		4.22	10.80		15.02	20.50
2000	3/4" diameter		40	.200		5.55	13.45		19	26
2030	1" diameter		35	.229		9.70	15.40		25.10	33.50
2050	1-1/4" diameter		28	.286		13.95	19.25		33.20	44
2070	1-1/2" diameter		23	.348		18.40	23.50		41.90	55
2090	2" diameter		20	.400		40	27		67	84
2100	2-1/2" diameter		18	.444		79.50	30		109.50	132
2110	3" diameter		15	.533		119	36		155	184
2120	3-1/2" diameter		12	.667		141	45		186	222
2130	4" diameter		10	.800		224	54		278	325
2140	5" diameter		9	.889		385	60		445	510
2150	6" diameter		8	1		505	67.50		572.50	655
2160	Box connector with set screw, plain, 1/2" diameter		70	.114		3.04	7.70		10.74	14.80
2170	3/4" diameter		60	.133		4.04	9		13.04	17.80
2180	1" diameter		50	.160		6.15	10.80		16.95	23
2190	Insulated, 1-1/4" diameter		40	.200		13.10	13.45		26.55	34.50
2200	1-1/2" diameter		30	.267		17.80	17.95		35.75	46
2210	2" diameter		20	.400		37.50	27		64.50	81
2220	2-1/2" diameter		18	.444		98.50	30		128.50	153
2230	3" diameter		15	.533		131	36		167	198
2240	3-1/2" diameter		12	.667		183	45		228	269
2250	4" diameter		10	.800		288	54		342	395
2260	5" diameter		9	.889		655	60		715	810
2270	6" diameter		8	1		615	67.50		682.50	780
2280	LB, LR or LL fittings & covers, 1/2" diameter		16	.500		10.90	33.50		44.40	62
2290	3/4" diameter		13	.615		13	41.50		54.50	76
2300	1" diameter		11	.727		23.50	49		72.50	99
2330	1-1/4" diameter		8	1		33	67.50		100.50	137
2350	1-1/2" diameter		6	1.333		40.50	90		130.50	178
2370	2" diameter	1 Elec	5	1.600	Ea.	67.50	108		175.50	235
2380	2-1/2" diameter		4	2		147	135		282	360

26 05 33.25 Conduit Fittings for Rigid Galvanized Steel		Crew	Daily Output	Labor-Hours	Unit	2023 Bare Costs Material	Labor	Equipment	Total	Total Incl O&P
2390	3" diameter	1 Elec	3.50	2.286	Ea.	188	154		342	435
2400	3-1/2" diameter		3	2.667		365	180		545	665
2410	4" diameter		2.50	3.200		375	216		591	730
2420	T fittings, with cover, 1/2" diameter		12	.667		14.70	45		59.70	82.50
2430	3/4" diameter		11	.727		17.35	49		66.35	92
2440	1" diameter		9	.889		29	60		89	121
2450	1-1/4" diameter		6	1.333		36.50	90		126.50	173
2470	1-1/2" diameter		5	1.600		50.50	108		158.50	216
2500	2" diameter		4	2		67.50	135		202.50	275
2510	2-1/2" diameter		3.50	2.286		117	154		271	360
2520	3" diameter		3	2.667		224	180		404	515
2530	3-1/2" diameter		2.50	3.200		265	216		481	610
2540	4" diameter		2	4		305	269		574	735
2550	Nipples chase, plain, 1/2" diameter		40	.200		1.02	13.45		14.47	21
2560	3/4" diameter		32	.250		3.39	16.85		20.24	28.50
2570	1" diameter		28	.286		2.53	19.25		21.78	31.50
2600	Insulated, 1-1/4" diameter		24	.333		9.75	22.50		32.25	44
2630	1-1/2" diameter		18	.444		9.60	30		39.60	55
2650	2" diameter		15	.533		17.80	36		53.80	73
2660	2-1/2" diameter		12	.667		48	45		93	120
2670	3" diameter		10	.800		54	54		108	140
2680	3-1/2" diameter		9	.889		82.50	60		142.50	180
2690	4" diameter		8	1		115	67.50		182.50	227
2700	5" diameter		7	1.143		315	77		392	465
2710	6" diameter		6	1.333		590	90		680	780
2720	Nipples offset, plain, 1/2" diameter		40	.200		5.25	13.45		18.70	26
2730	3/4" diameter		32	.250		5.80	16.85		22.65	31.50
2740	1" diameter		24	.333		6.80	22.50		29.30	41
2750	Insulated, 1-1/4" diameter		20	.400		9.35	27		36.35	50.50
2760	1-1/2" diameter		18	.444		11.30	30		41.30	57
2770	2" diameter		16	.500		15.90	33.50		49.40	67.50
2780	3" diameter		14	.571		89	38.50		127.50	155
2850	Coupling, expansion, 1/2" diameter		12	.667		70	45		115	144
2880	3/4" diameter		10	.800		79	54		133	167
2900	1" diameter		8	1		98	67.50		165.50	208
2920	1-1/4" diameter		6.40	1.250		133	84		217	271
2940	1-1/2" diameter		5.30	1.509		176	102		278	345
2960	2" diameter		4.60	1.739		272	117		389	475
2980	2-1/2" diameter		3.60	2.222		450	150		600	715
3000	3" diameter		3	2.667		500	180		680	815
3020	3-1/2" diameter		2.80	2.857		755	192		947	1,125
3040	4" diameter		2.40	3.333		900	225		1,125	1,325
3060	5" diameter		2	4		1,550	269		1,819	2,100
3080	6" diameter		1.80	4.444		2,725	299		3,024	3,450
3100	Expansion deflection, 1/2" diameter		12	.667		385	45		430	485
3120	3/4" diameter		12	.667		435	45		480	545
3140	1" diameter		10	.800		500	54		554	630
3160	1-1/4" diameter		6.40	1.250		605	84		689	790
3180	1-1/2" diameter		5.30	1.509		680	102		782	895
3200	2" diameter		4.60	1.739		890	117		1,007	1,150
3220	2-1/2" diameter		3.60	2.222		1,225	150		1,375	1,575
3240	3" diameter		3	2.667		1,600	180		1,780	2,050
3260	3-1/2" diameter		2.80	2.857		1,725	192		1,917	2,175

26 05 33.25 Conduit Fittings for Rigid Galvanized Steel		Crew	Daily Output	Labor-Hours	Unit	Material	Labor	Equipment	Total	Total Incl O&P
						2023 Bare Costs				
3280	4″ diameter	1 Elec	2.40	3.333	Ea.	2,450	225		2,675	3,025
3300	5″ diameter		2	4		3,425	269		3,694	4,175
3320	6″ diameter		1.80	4.444		5,725	299		6,024	6,750
3340	Ericson, 1/2″ diameter		16	.500		6.55	33.50		40.05	57
3360	3/4″ diameter		14	.571		7.90	38.50		46.40	65.50
3380	1″ diameter		11	.727		13.20	49		62.20	87.50
3400	1-1/4″ diameter		8	1		23	67.50		90.50	125
3420	1-1/2″ diameter		7	1.143		30	77		107	147
3440	2″ diameter		5	1.600		62	108		170	228
3460	2-1/2″ diameter		4	2		125	135		260	340
3480	3″ diameter		3.50	2.286		195	154		349	445
3500	3-1/2″ diameter		3	2.667		283	180		463	575
3520	4″ diameter		2.70	2.963		305	200		505	630
3540	5″ diameter		2.50	3.200		505	216		721	875
3560	6″ diameter		2.30	3.478		640	234		874	1,050
3580	Split, 1/2″ diameter		32	.250		4.34	16.85		21.19	30
3600	3/4″ diameter		27	.296		7.45	19.95		27.40	37.50
3620	1″ diameter		20	.400		12.40	27		39.40	53.50
3640	1-1/4″ diameter		16	.500		15.95	33.50		49.45	67.50
3660	1-1/2″ diameter		14	.571		19.30	38.50		57.80	78.50
3680	2″ diameter		12	.667		36	45		81	106
3700	2-1/2″ diameter		10	.800		103	54		157	194
3720	3″ diameter		9	.889		114	60		174	215
3740	3-1/2″ diameter		8	1		186	67.50		253.50	305
3760	4″ diameter		7	1.143		217	77		294	355
3780	5″ diameter		6	1.333		390	90		480	565
3800	6″ diameter		5	1.600		525	108		633	735
4600	Reducing bushings, 3/4″ to 1/2″ diameter		54	.148		2.98	10		12.98	18.15
4620	1″ to 3/4″ diameter		46	.174		2.93	11.70		14.63	20.50
4640	1-1/4″ to 1″ diameter		40	.200		5.55	13.45		19	26
4660	1-1/2″ to 1-1/4″ diameter		36	.222		7.50	14.95		22.45	30.50
4680	2″ to 1-1/2″ diameter		32	.250		13.70	16.85		30.55	40
4740	2-1/2″ to 2″ diameter		30	.267		20	17.95		37.95	48.50
4760	3″ to 2-1/2″ diameter		28	.286		27	19.25		46.25	58
4800	Through-wall seal, 1/2″ diameter		8	1		250	67.50		317.50	375
4820	3/4″ diameter		7.50	1.067		435	72		507	580
4840	1″ diameter		6.50	1.231		410	83		493	575
4860	1-1/4″ diameter		5.50	1.455		415	98		513	600
4880	1-1/2″ diameter		5	1.600		555	108		663	770
4900	2″ diameter		4.20	1.905		570	128		698	820
4920	2-1/2″ diameter		3.50	2.286		655	154		809	950
4940	3″ diameter		3	2.667		730	180		910	1,075
4960	3-1/2″ diameter		2.50	3.200		1,100	216		1,316	1,525
4980	4″ diameter		2	4		1,125	269		1,394	1,650
5000	5″ diameter		1.50	5.333		1,575	360		1,935	2,250
5020	6″ diameter		1	8		1,550	540		2,090	2,525
5100	Cable supports, 2 or more wires									
5120	1-1/2″ diameter	1 Elec	8	1	Ea.	231	67.50		298.50	355
5140	2″ diameter		6	1.333		305	90		395	470
5160	2-1/2″ diameter		4	2		325	135		460	555
5180	3″ diameter		3.50	2.286		400	154		554	670
5200	3-1/2″ diameter		2.60	3.077		575	207		782	940
5220	4″ diameter		2	4		720	269		989	1,200

26 05 33.25 Conduit Fittings for Rigid Galvanized Steel		Crew	Daily Output	Labor-Hours	Unit	Material	2023 Bare Costs Labor	Equipment	Total	Total Incl O&P
5240	5" diameter	1 Elec	1.50	5.333	Ea.	1,400	360		1,760	2,075
5260	6" diameter		1	8		2,525	540		3,065	3,600
5280	Service entrance cap, 1/2" diameter		16	.500		8.25	33.50		41.75	59
5300	3/4" diameter		13	.615		9.90	41.50		51.40	72.50
5320	1" diameter		10	.800		11.75	54		65.75	93
5340	1-1/4" diameter		8	1		7.85	67.50		75.35	109
5360	1-1/2" diameter		6.50	1.231		14.85	83		97.85	139
5380	2" diameter		5.50	1.455		25.50	98		123.50	174
5400	2-1/2" diameter		4	2		85.50	135		220.50	294
5420	3" diameter		3.40	2.353		107	158		265	355
5440	3-1/2" diameter		3	2.667		127	180		307	405
5460	4" diameter		2.70	2.963		183	200		383	500
5750	90° pull elbows steel, female, 1/2" diameter		16	.500		9.65	33.50		43.15	60.50
5760	3/4" diameter		13	.615		11.40	41.50		52.90	74
5780	1" diameter		11	.727		18.95	49		67.95	94
5800	1-1/4" diameter		8	1		24.50	67.50		92	127
5820	1-1/2" diameter		6	1.333		35	90		125	172
5840	2" diameter		5	1.600		56	108		164	222
6000	Explosion proof, flexible coupling									
6010	1/2" diameter, 4" long	1 Elec	12	.667	Ea.	125	45		170	205
6020	6" long		12	.667		139	45		184	219
6050	12" long		12	.667		204	45		249	292
6070	18" long		12	.667		253	45		298	345
6090	24" long		12	.667		280	45		325	375
6110	30" long		12	.667		265	45		310	360
6130	36" long		12	.667		370	45		415	470
6140	3/4" diameter, 4" long		10	.800		153	54		207	248
6150	6" long		10	.800		180	54		234	278
6180	12" long		10	.800		244	54		298	350
6200	18" long		10	.800		320	54		374	435
6220	24" long		10	.800		360	54		414	480
6240	30" long		10	.800		425	54		479	550
6260	36" long		10	.800		485	54		539	615
6270	1" diameter, 6" long		8	1		305	67.50		372.50	435
6300	12" long		8	1		405	67.50		472.50	550
6320	18" long		8	1		485	67.50		552.50	635
6340	24" long		8	1		595	67.50		662.50	755
6360	30" long		8	1		625	67.50		692.50	790
6380	36" long		8	1		740	67.50		807.50	915
6390	1-1/4" diameter, 12" long		6.40	1.250		590	84		674	775
6410	18" long		6.40	1.250		700	84		784	895
6430	24" long		6.40	1.250		840	84		924	1,050
6450	30" long		6.40	1.250		1,050	84		1,134	1,275
6470	36" long		6.40	1.250		1,500	84		1,584	1,775
6480	1-1/2" diameter, 12" long		5.30	1.509		870	102		972	1,100
6500	18" long		5.30	1.509		920	102		1,022	1,150
6520	24" long		5.30	1.509		1,150	102		1,252	1,400
6540	30" long		5.30	1.509		1,475	102		1,577	1,775
6560	36" long		5.30	1.509		1,325	102		1,427	1,625
6570	2" diameter, 12" long		4.60	1.739		960	117		1,077	1,225
6590	18" long		4.60	1.739		1,250	117		1,367	1,550
6610	24" long		4.60	1.739		1,500	117		1,617	1,825
6630	30" long		4.60	1.739		1,925	117		2,042	2,300

26 05 33.25 Conduit Fittings for Rigid Galvanized Steel		Crew	Daily Output	Labor-Hours	Unit	Material	2023 Bare Costs Labor	Equipment	Total	Total Incl O&P
6650	36" long	1 Elec	4.60	1.739	Ea.	2,000	117		2,117	2,375
7000	Close up plug, 1/2" diameter, explosion proof		40	.200		3.08	13.45		16.53	23.50
7010	3/4" diameter		32	.250		3.68	16.85		20.53	29
7020	1" diameter		28	.286		4.28	19.25		23.53	33
7030	1-1/4" diameter		24	.333		4.41	22.50		26.91	38.50
7040	1-1/2" diameter		18	.444		6.15	30		36.15	51.50
7050	2" diameter		15	.533		10.40	36		46.40	65
7060	2-1/2" diameter		13	.615		16.40	41.50		57.90	79.50
7070	3" diameter		12	.667		24.50	45		69.50	93.50
7080	3-1/2" diameter		11	.727		29	49		78	105
7090	4" diameter		9	.889		40	60		100	133
7091	Elbow female, 45°, 1/2"		16	.500		24	33.50		57.50	76.50
7092	3/4"		13	.615		27.50	41.50		69	91.50
7093	1"		11	.727		30.50	49		79.50	107
7094	1-1/4"		8	1		64	67.50		131.50	171
7095	1-1/2"		6	1.333		51	90		141	189
7096	2"		5	1.600		67.50	108		175.50	234
7097	2-1/2"		4.50	1.778		181	120		301	375
7098	3"		4.20	1.905		192	128		320	405
7099	3-1/2"		4	2		248	135		383	475
7100	4"		3.80	2.105		345	142		487	590
7101	90°, 1/2"		16	.500		22.50	33.50		56	74.50
7102	3/4"		13	.615		24	41.50		65.50	88
7103	1"		11	.727		33	49		82	110
7104	1-1/4"		8	1		55.50	67.50		123	161
7105	1-1/2"		6	1.333		80	90		170	221
7106	2"		5	1.600		119	108		227	291
7107	2-1/2"		4.50	1.778		274	120		394	480
7110	Elbows 90°, long male & female, 1/2" diameter, explosion proof		16	.500		33	33.50		66.50	86.50
7120	3/4" diameter		13	.615		36.50	41.50		78	102
7130	1" diameter		11	.727		53.50	49		102.50	132
7140	1-1/4" diameter		8	1		65.50	67.50		133	173
7150	1-1/2" diameter		6	1.333		63	90		153	203
7160	2" diameter		5	1.600		80	108		188	248
7170	Capped elbow, 1/2" diameter, explosion proof		11	.727		34	49		83	111
7180	3/4" diameter		8	1		44.50	67.50		112	149
7190	1" diameter		6	1.333		47.50	90		137.50	186
7200	1-1/4" diameter		5	1.600		93.50	108		201.50	263
7210	Pulling elbow, 1/2" diameter, explosion proof		11	.727		184	49		233	275
7220	3/4" diameter		8	1		320	67.50		387.50	455
7230	1" diameter		6	1.333		460	90		550	640
7240	1-1/4" diameter		5	1.600		510	108		618	720
7250	1-1/2" diameter		5	1.600		560	108		668	780
7260	2" diameter		4	2		740	135		875	1,000
7270	2-1/2" diameter		3.50	2.286		1,875	154		2,029	2,275
7280	3" diameter		3	2.667		2,325	180		2,505	2,825
7290	3-1/2" diameter		2.50	3.200		2,775	216		2,991	3,375
7300	4" diameter		2.20	3.636		3,675	245		3,920	4,425
7310	LB conduit body, 1/2" diameter		11	.727		89	49		138	171
7320	3/4" diameter		8	1		103	67.50		170.50	214
7330	T conduit body, 1/2" diameter		9	.889		94	60		154	192
7340	3/4" diameter		6	1.333		109	90		199	253
7350	Explosion proof, round box w/cover, 3 threaded hubs, 1/2" diameter		8	1		104	67.50		171.50	214

26 05 33.25 Conduit Fittings for Rigid Galvanized Steel		Crew	Daily Output	Labor-Hours	Unit	Material	2023 Bare Costs Labor	Equipment	Total	Total Incl O&P
7351	3/4" diameter	1 Elec	8	1	Ea.	111	67.50		178.50	222
7352	1" diameter		7.50	1.067		137	72		209	257
7353	1-1/4" diameter		7	1.143		222	77		299	360
7354	1-1/2" diameter		7	1.143		242	77		319	380
7355	2" diameter		6	1.333		425	90		515	600
7356	Round box w/cover & mtng flange, 3 threaded hubs, 1/2" diameter		8	1		76	67.50		143.50	184
7357	3/4" diameter		8	1		81.50	67.50		149	190
7358	4 threaded hubs, 1" diameter		7	1.143		80	77		157	202
7400	Unions, 1/2" diameter		20	.400		19.80	27		46.80	62
7410	3/4" - 1/2" diameter		16	.500		25.50	33.50		59	78.50
7420	3/4" diameter		16	.500		29.50	33.50		63	82.50
7430	1" diameter		14	.571		51	38.50		89.50	113
7440	1-1/4" diameter		12	.667		79	45		124	154
7450	1-1/2" diameter		10	.800		97.50	54		151.50	187
7460	2" diameter		8.50	.941		117	63.50		180.50	223
7480	2-1/2" diameter		8	1		266	67.50		333.50	395
7490	3" diameter		7	1.143		310	77		387	455
7500	3-1/2" diameter		6	1.333		675	90		765	880
7510	4" diameter		5	1.600		550	108		658	765
7680	Reducer, 3/4" to 1/2"		54	.148		4.78	10		14.78	20
7690	1" to 1/2"		46	.174		5.95	11.70		17.65	24
7700	1" to 3/4"		46	.174		5.30	11.70		17	23
7710	1-1/4" to 3/4"		40	.200		6.60	13.45		20.05	27.50
7720	1-1/4" to 1"		40	.200		6.75	13.45		20.20	27.50
7730	1-1/2" to 1"		36	.222		12.45	14.95		27.40	35.50
7740	1-1/2" to 1-1/4"		36	.222		10.60	14.95		25.55	33.50
7750	2" to 3/4"		32	.250		17.95	16.85		34.80	45
7760	2" to 1-1/4"		32	.250		13.75	16.85		30.60	40
7770	2" to 1-1/2"		32	.250		15.80	16.85		32.65	42.50
7780	2-1/2" to 1-1/2"		30	.267		31	17.95		48.95	60.50
7790	3" to 2"		30	.267		26.50	17.95		44.45	55.50
7800	3-1/2" to 2-1/2"		28	.286		46.50	19.25		65.75	79.50
7810	4" to 3"		28	.286		54	19.25		73.25	88
7820	Sealing fitting, vertical/horizontal, 1/2" diameter		14.50	.552		19.35	37		56.35	76.50
7830	3/4" diameter		13.30	.602		23	40.50		63.50	85.50
7840	1" diameter		11.40	.702		30	47.50		77.50	103
7850	1-1/4" diameter		10	.800		37	54		91	121
7860	1-1/2" diameter		8.80	.909		54.50	61		115.50	151
7870	2" diameter		8	1		73.50	67.50		141	181
7880	2-1/2" diameter		6.70	1.194		123	80.50		203.50	255
7890	3" diameter		5.70	1.404		139	94.50		233.50	293
7900	3-1/2" diameter		4.70	1.702		365	115		480	570
7910	4" diameter		4	2		565	135		700	825
7920	Sealing hubs, 1" by 1-1/2"		12	.667		61	45		106	134
7930	1-1/4" by 2"		10	.800		65	54		119	152
7940	1-1/2" by 2"		9	.889		123	60		183	224
7950	2" by 2-1/2"		8	1		162	67.50		229.50	278
7960	3" by 4"		7	1.143		261	77		338	400
7970	4" by 5"		6	1.333		630	90		720	830
7980	Drain, 1/2"		32	.250		171	16.85		187.85	213
7990	Breather, 1/2"		32	.250		191	16.85		207.85	235
7991	Explosion proof sealant compound, hub, fittings, 60 min set time, 1lb. pail		48	.167		28	11.25		39.25	47.50
7992	5 lb. pail		48	.167		72	11.25		83.25	95.50

26 05 33.25 Conduit Fittings for Rigid Galvanized Steel		Crew	Daily Output	Labor-Hours	Unit	Material	Labor	Equipment	Total	Total Incl O&P
						2023 Bare Costs				
7993	2 oz. tube	1 Elec	50	.160	Ea.	85	10.80		95.80	110
7994	6 oz. tube		50	.160		177	10.80		187.80	211
7995	2.0 oz. cartridge		50	.160		61	10.80		71.80	83.50
7996	6.0 oz. cartridge		50	.160		126	10.80		136.80	154
7997	2.0 oz. box		50	.160		37	10.80		47.80	56.50
7998	8.0 oz. box		50	.160		125	10.80		135.80	154
7999	1.0 lb. box		50	.160		196	10.80		206.80	232
8000	Plastic coated 40 mil thick									
8010	LB, LR or LL conduit body w/cover, 1/2" diameter	1 Elec	13	.615	Ea.	86	41.50		127.50	156
8020	3/4" diameter		11	.727		95	49		144	178
8030	1" diameter		8	1		125	67.50		192.50	238
8040	1-1/4" diameter		6	1.333		183	90		273	335
8050	1-1/2" diameter		5	1.600		217	108		325	400
8060	2" diameter		4.50	1.778		330	120		450	545
8070	2-1/2" diameter		4	2		550	135		685	810
8080	3" diameter		3.50	2.286		780	154		934	1,075
8090	3-1/2" diameter		3	2.667		1,000	180		1,180	1,375
8100	4" diameter		2.50	3.200		1,250	216		1,466	1,700
8150	T conduit body with cover, 1/2" diameter		11	.727		106	49		155	189
8160	3/4" diameter		9	.889		124	60		184	225
8170	1" diameter		6	1.333		148	90		238	295
8180	1-1/4" diameter		5	1.600		225	108		333	405
8190	1-1/2" diameter		4.50	1.778		246	120		366	450
8200	2" diameter		4	2		425	135		560	665
8210	2-1/2" diameter		3.50	2.286		575	154		729	865
8220	3" diameter		3	2.667		765	180		945	1,100
8230	3-1/2" diameter		2.50	3.200		1,300	216		1,516	1,750
8240	4" diameter		2	4		1,275	269		1,544	1,800
8300	FS conduit body, 1 gang, 3/4" diameter		11	.727		106	49		155	189
8310	1" diameter		10	.800		113	54		167	205
8350	2 gang, 3/4" diameter		9	.889		172	60		232	279
8360	1" diameter		8	1		203	67.50		270.50	325
8400	Duplex receptacle cover		64	.125		71	8.40		79.40	91
8410	Switch cover		64	.125		123	8.40		131.40	148
8420	Switch, vaportight cover		53	.151		435	10.15		445.15	490
8430	Blank, cover		64	.125		69	8.40		77.40	88.50
8520	FSC conduit body, 1 gang, 3/4" diameter		10	.800		130	54		184	223
8530	1" diameter		9	.889		145	60		205	248
8550	2 gang, 3/4" diameter		8	1		238	67.50		305.50	360
8560	1" diameter		7	1.143		223	77		300	360
8590	Conduit hubs, 1/2" diameter		18	.444		67	30		97	118
8600	3/4" diameter		16	.500		72.50	33.50		106	130
8610	1" diameter		14	.571		89.50	38.50		128	156
8620	1-1/4" diameter		12	.667		110	45		155	188
8630	1-1/2" diameter		10	.800		119	54		173	210
8640	2" diameter		8.80	.909		169	61		230	277
8650	2-1/2" diameter		8.50	.941		258	63.50		321.50	380
8660	3" diameter		8	1		360	67.50		427.50	495
8670	3-1/2" diameter		7.50	1.067		515	72		587	670
8680	4" diameter		7	1.143		585	77		662	760
8690	5" diameter		6	1.333		835	90		925	1,050
8700	Plastic coated 40 mil thick									
8710	Pipe strap, stamped 1 hole, 1/2" diameter	1 Elec	470	.017	Ea.	21.50	1.15		22.65	25.50

26 05 33.25 Conduit Fittings for Rigid Galvanized Steel		Crew	Daily Output	Labor-Hours	Unit	Material	Labor	Equipment	Total	Total Incl O&P
						2023 Bare Costs				
8720	3/4" diameter	1 Elec	440	.018	Ea.	19.75	1.22		20.97	23.50
8730	1" diameter		400	.020		21.50	1.35		22.85	25.50
8740	1-1/4" diameter		355	.023		33.50	1.52		35.02	39
8750	1-1/2" diameter		320	.025		33	1.68		34.68	38.50
8760	2" diameter		266	.030		44	2.03		46.03	51.50
8770	2-1/2" diameter		200	.040		65	2.69		67.69	75.50
8780	3" diameter		133	.060		88.50	4.05		92.55	103
8790	3-1/2" diameter		110	.073		167	4.90		171.90	191
8800	4" diameter		90	.089		169	6		175	195
8810	5" diameter		70	.114		191	7.70		198.70	221
8840	Clamp back spacers, 3/4" diameter		440	.018		30	1.22		31.22	35
8850	1" diameter		400	.020		39	1.35		40.35	45
8860	1-1/4" diameter		355	.023		54.50	1.52		56.02	62.50
8870	1-1/2" diameter		320	.025		67	1.68		68.68	76
8880	2" diameter		266	.030		99	2.03		101.03	112
8900	3" diameter		133	.060		234	4.05		238.05	263
8920	4" diameter		90	.089		102	6		108	121
8950	Touch-up plastic coating, spray, 12 oz.					103			103	113
8960	Sealing fittings, 1/2" diameter	1 Elec	11	.727		168	49		217	258
8970	3/4" diameter		9	.889		141	60		201	244
8980	1" diameter		7.50	1.067		163	72		235	287
8990	1-1/4" diameter		6.50	1.231		163	83		246	305
9000	1-1/2" diameter		5.50	1.455		285	98		383	460
9010	2" diameter		4.80	1.667		330	112		442	530
9020	2-1/2" diameter		4	2		390	135		525	630
9030	3" diameter		3.50	2.286		500	154		654	780
9040	3-1/2" diameter		3	2.667		1,250	180		1,430	1,650
9050	4" diameter		2.50	3.200		2,025	216		2,241	2,575
9060	5" diameter		1.70	4.706		2,500	315		2,815	3,225
9070	Unions, 1/2" diameter		18	.444		104	30		134	160
9080	3/4" diameter		15	.533		109	36		145	174
9090	1" diameter		13	.615		135	41.50		176.50	211
9100	1-1/4" diameter		11	.727		210	49		259	305
9110	1-1/2" diameter		9.50	.842		281	56.50		337.50	395
9120	2" diameter		8	1		345	67.50		412.50	480
9130	2-1/2" diameter		7.50	1.067		505	72		577	660
9140	3" diameter		6.80	1.176		495	79		574	665
9150	3-1/2" diameter		5.80	1.379		865	93		958	1,100
9160	4" diameter		4.80	1.667		1,050	112		1,162	1,325
9170	5" diameter		4	2		1,325	135		1,460	1,650

26 05 33.30 Electrical Nonmetallic Tubing (ENT)		Crew	Daily Output	Labor-Hours	Unit	Material	Labor	Equipment	Total	Total Incl O&P
0010	**ELECTRICAL NONMETALLIC TUBING (ENT)**									
0050	Flexible, 1/2" diameter	1 Elec	270	.030	L.F.	1.02	2		3.02	4.09
0100	3/4" diameter		230	.035		.86	2.34		3.20	4.43
0200	1" diameter		145	.055		3.18	3.72		6.90	9
0210	1-1/4" diameter		125	.064		3.02	4.31		7.33	9.70
0220	1-1/2" diameter		100	.080		4.49	5.40		9.89	12.95
0230	2" diameter		75	.107		5.95	7.20		13.15	17.25
0300	Connectors, to outlet box, 1/2" diameter		230	.035	Ea.	1.96	2.34		4.30	5.65
0310	3/4" diameter		210	.038		3.47	2.57		6.04	7.65
0320	1" diameter		200	.040		5	2.69		7.69	9.50
0400	Couplings, to conduit, 1/2" diameter		145	.055		1.73	3.72		5.45	7.40

26 05 33.30 Electrical Nonmetallic Tubing (ENT)		Crew	Daily Output	Labor-Hours	Unit	Material	2023 Bare Costs Labor	Equipment	Total	Total Incl O&P
0410	3/4" diameter	1 Elec	130	.062	Ea.	2.43	4.14		6.57	8.80
0420	1" diameter		125	.064		4.41	4.31		8.72	11.25

26 05 33.33 Raceway/Boxes for Utility Substations

		Crew	Daily Output	Labor-Hours	Unit	Material	Labor	Equipment	Total	Total Incl O&P
0010	**RACEWAY/BOXES FOR UTILITY SUBSTATIONS**									
7000	Conduit, conductors, and insulators									
7100	Conduit, metallic	R-11	560	.100	Lb.	4.36	6.45	4.17	14.98	19
7110	Non-metallic	"	800	.070	"	10.55	4.51	2.92	17.98	21.50
7190	See Section 26 05 33									
7200	Wire and cable	R-11	700	.080	Lb.	13.40	5.15	3.34	21.89	26
7290	See Section 26 05 19									

26 05 33.35 Flexible Metallic Conduit

		Crew	Daily Output	Labor-Hours	Unit	Material	Labor	Equipment	Total	Total Incl O&P
0010	**FLEXIBLE METALLIC CONDUIT**									
0050	Steel, 3/8" diameter	1 Elec	200	.040	L.F.	.57	2.69		3.26	4.63
0100	1/2" diameter		200	.040		.62	2.69		3.31	4.68
0200	3/4" diameter		160	.050		.85	3.37		4.22	5.95
0250	1" diameter		100	.080		1.56	5.40		6.96	9.70
0300	1-1/4" diameter		70	.114		2.01	7.70		9.71	13.65
0350	1-1/2" diameter		50	.160		3.26	10.80		14.06	19.60
0370	2" diameter		40	.200		4.08	13.45		17.53	24.50
0380	2-1/2" diameter		30	.267		4.95	17.95		22.90	32
0390	3" diameter	2 Elec	50	.320		8.40	21.50		29.90	41.50
0400	3-1/2" diameter		40	.400		9.60	27		36.60	50.50
0410	4" diameter		30	.533		10.85	36		46.85	65.50
0420	Connectors, plain, 3/8" diameter	1 Elec	100	.080	Ea.	1.94	5.40		7.34	10.15
0430	1/2" diameter		80	.100		1.86	6.75		8.61	12.05
0440	3/4" diameter		70	.114		2.43	7.70		10.13	14.10
0450	1" diameter		50	.160		4.43	10.80		15.23	21
0452	1-1/4" diameter		45	.178		6.70	11.95		18.65	25
0454	1-1/2" diameter		40	.200		9.15	13.45		22.60	30
0456	2" diameter		28	.286		13.90	19.25		33.15	44
0458	2-1/2" diameter		25	.320		22	21.50		43.50	56.50
0460	3" diameter		20	.400		34.50	27		61.50	77.50
0462	3-1/2" diameter		16	.500		128	33.50		161.50	191
0464	4" diameter		13	.615		137	41.50		178.50	213
0490	Insulated, 1" diameter		40	.200		7.10	13.45		20.55	28
0500	1-1/4" diameter		40	.200		11.80	13.45		25.25	33
0550	1-1/2" diameter		32	.250		29	16.85		45.85	56.50
0600	2" diameter		23	.348		40.50	23.50		64	80
0610	2-1/2" diameter		20	.400		42.50	27		69.50	86.50
0620	3" diameter		17	.471		51.50	31.50		83	104
0630	3-1/2" diameter		13	.615		380	41.50		421.50	480
0640	4" diameter		10	.800		425	54		479	550
0650	Connectors 90°, plain, 3/8" diameter		80	.100		4.58	6.75		11.33	15.05
0660	1/2" diameter		60	.133		9.75	9		18.75	24
0700	3/4" diameter		50	.160		13.75	10.80		24.55	31
0750	1" diameter		40	.200		22.50	13.45		35.95	44.50
0790	Insulated, 1" diameter		40	.200		9.40	13.45		22.85	30.50
0800	1-1/4" diameter		30	.267		20	17.95		37.95	48.50
0850	1-1/2" diameter		23	.348		38	23.50		61.50	77
0900	2" diameter		18	.444		52.50	30		82.50	103
0910	2-1/2" diameter		16	.500		259	33.50		292.50	335
0920	3" diameter		14	.571		175	38.50		213.50	250

26 05 33.35 Flexible Metallic Conduit		Crew	Daily Output	Labor-Hours	Unit	Material	2023 Bare Costs Labor	Equipment	Total	Total Incl O&P
0930	3-1/2" diameter	1 Elec	11	.727	Ea.	435	49		484	550
0940	4" diameter		8	1		1,025	67.50		1,092.50	1,225
0960	Couplings, to flexible conduit, 1/2" diameter		50	.160		1.21	10.80		12.01	17.35
0970	3/4" diameter		40	.200		1.96	13.45		15.41	22
0980	1" diameter		35	.229		3.60	15.40		19	27
0990	1-1/4" diameter		28	.286		6.75	19.25		26	36
1000	1-1/2" diameter		23	.348		8.45	23.50		31.95	44.50
1010	2" diameter		20	.400		15.75	27		42.75	57.50
1020	2-1/2" diameter		18	.444		51.50	30		81.50	101
1030	3" diameter		15	.533		130	36		166	197
1032	Aluminum, 3/8" diameter		210	.038	L.F.	.54	2.57		3.11	4.40
1034	1/2" diameter		210	.038		.62	2.57		3.19	4.49
1036	3/4" diameter		165	.048		.85	3.27		4.12	5.80
1038	1" diameter		105	.076		1.57	5.15		6.72	9.40
1040	1-1/4" diameter		75	.107		2.21	7.20		9.41	13.15
1042	1-1/2" diameter		53	.151		3.16	10.15		13.31	18.60
1044	2" diameter		42	.190		4.08	12.85		16.93	23.50
1046	2-1/2" diameter		32	.250		5.20	16.85		22.05	31
1048	3" diameter	2 Elec	53	.302		8.55	20.50		29.05	39.50
1050	3-1/2" diameter		42	.381		9.70	25.50		35.20	48.50
1052	4" diameter		32	.500		11	33.50		44.50	62
1070	Sealtite, 3/8" diameter	1 Elec	140	.057		1.07	3.85		4.92	6.90
1080	1/2" diameter		140	.057		1.49	3.85		5.34	7.35
1090	3/4" diameter		100	.080		2.02	5.40		7.42	10.20
1100	1" diameter		70	.114		3.46	7.70		11.16	15.25
1200	1-1/4" diameter		50	.160		4.30	10.80		15.10	20.50
1300	1-1/2" diameter		40	.200		5.10	13.45		18.55	25.50
1400	2" diameter		30	.267		5.85	17.95		23.80	33
1410	2-1/2" diameter		27	.296		10.85	19.95		30.80	41.50
1420	3" diameter	2 Elec	50	.320		11.45	21.50		32.95	44.50
1440	4" diameter	"	30	.533		13.90	36		49.90	69
1490	Connectors, plain, 3/8" diameter	1 Elec	70	.114	Ea.	4.05	7.70		11.75	15.90
1500	1/2" diameter		70	.114		5	7.70		12.70	16.95
1700	3/4" diameter		50	.160		6.95	10.80		17.75	23.50
1900	1" diameter		40	.200		9.75	13.45		23.20	30.50
1910	Insulated, 1" diameter		40	.200		11.35	13.45		24.80	32.50
2000	1-1/4" diameter		32	.250		20	16.85		36.85	47
2100	1-1/2" diameter		27	.296		25.50	19.95		45.45	57.50
2200	2" diameter		20	.400		47.50	27		74.50	92
2210	2-1/2" diameter		15	.533		145	36		181	214
2220	3" diameter		12	.667		226	45		271	315
2240	4" diameter		8	1		320	67.50		387.50	450
2290	Connectors, 90°, 3/8" diameter		70	.114		10.30	7.70		18	23
2300	1/2" diameter		70	.114		9.65	7.70		17.35	22
2400	3/4" diameter		50	.160		14.90	10.80		25.70	32.50
2600	1" diameter		40	.200		30.50	13.45		43.95	53.50
2790	Insulated, 1" diameter		40	.200		22.50	13.45		35.95	45
2800	1-1/4" diameter		32	.250		35	16.85		51.85	63.50
3000	1-1/2" diameter		27	.296		43.50	19.95		63.45	77.50
3100	2" diameter		20	.400		61.50	27		88.50	108
3110	2-1/2" diameter		14	.571		275	38.50		313.50	360
3120	3" diameter		11	.727		530	49		579	660
3140	4" diameter		7	1.143		385	77		462	535

26 05 33.35 Flexible Metallic Conduit		Crew	Daily Output	Labor-Hours	Unit	Material	2023 Bare Costs Labor	Equipment	Total	Total Incl O&P
4300	Coupling sealtite to rigid, 1/2" diameter	1 Elec	20	.400	Ea.	6.30	27		33.30	47
4500	3/4" diameter		18	.444		9	30		39	54.50
4800	1" diameter		14	.571		10.40	38.50		48.90	68.50
4900	1-1/4" diameter		12	.667		15.90	45		60.90	84
5000	1-1/2" diameter		11	.727		28	49		77	104
5100	2" diameter		10	.800		39.50	54		93.50	124
5110	2-1/2" diameter		9.50	.842		200	56.50		256.50	305
5120	3" diameter		9	.889		194	60		254	305
5130	3-1/2" diameter		9	.889		225	60		285	335
5140	4" diameter		8.50	.941		255	63.50		318.50	375

26 05 33.95 Cutting and Drilling		Crew	Daily Output	Labor-Hours	Unit	Material	Labor	Equipment	Total	Total Incl O&P
0010	**CUTTING AND DRILLING**									
0100	Hole drilling to 10' high, concrete wall									
0110	8" thick, 1/2" pipe size	R-31	12	.667	Ea.	.30	45	5.10	50.40	72.50
0120	3/4" pipe size		12	.667		.30	45	5.10	50.40	72.50
0130	1" pipe size		9.50	.842		.40	56.50	6.45	63.35	92
0140	1-1/4" pipe size		9.50	.842		.40	56.50	6.45	63.35	92
0150	1-1/2" pipe size		9.50	.842		.40	56.50	6.45	63.35	92
0160	2" pipe size		4.40	1.818		.57	122	13.95	136.52	198
0170	2-1/2" pipe size		4.40	1.818		.57	122	13.95	136.52	198
0180	3" pipe size		4.40	1.818		.57	122	13.95	136.52	198
0190	3-1/2" pipe size		3.30	2.424		.76	163	18.60	182.36	264
0200	4" pipe size		3.30	2.424		.76	163	18.60	182.36	264
0500	12" thick, 1/2" pipe size		9.40	.851		.44	57.50	6.55	64.49	92.50
0520	3/4" pipe size		9.40	.851		.44	57.50	6.55	64.49	92.50
0540	1" pipe size		7.30	1.096		.61	74	8.40	83.01	120
0560	1-1/4" pipe size		7.30	1.096		.61	74	8.40	83.01	120
0570	1-1/2" pipe size		7.30	1.096		.61	74	8.40	83.01	120
0580	2" pipe size		3.60	2.222		.86	150	17.05	167.91	242
0590	2-1/2" pipe size		3.60	2.222		.86	150	17.05	167.91	242
0600	3" pipe size		3.60	2.222		.86	150	17.05	167.91	242
0610	3-1/2" pipe size		2.80	2.857		1.15	192	22	215.15	310
0630	4" pipe size		2.50	3.200		1.15	216	24.50	241.65	350
0650	16" thick, 1/2" pipe size		7.60	1.053		.59	71	8.10	79.69	115
0670	3/4" pipe size		7	1.143		.59	77	8.80	86.39	124
0690	1" pipe size		6	1.333		.81	90	10.25	101.06	145
0710	1-1/4" pipe size		5.50	1.455		.81	98	11.15	109.96	159
0730	1-1/2" pipe size		5.50	1.455		.81	98	11.15	109.96	159
0750	2" pipe size		3	2.667		1.15	180	20.50	201.65	291
0770	2-1/2" pipe size		2.70	2.963		1.15	200	23	224.15	325
0790	3" pipe size		2.50	3.200		1.15	216	24.50	241.65	350
0810	3-1/2" pipe size		2.30	3.478		1.53	234	26.50	262.03	380
0830	4" pipe size		2	4		1.53	269	30.50	301.03	435
0850	20" thick, 1/2" pipe size		6.40	1.250		.74	84	9.60	94.34	136
0870	3/4" pipe size		6	1.333		.74	90	10.25	100.99	145
0890	1" pipe size		5	1.600		1.01	108	12.30	121.31	175
0910	1-1/4" pipe size		4.80	1.667		1.01	112	12.80	125.81	182
0930	1-1/2" pipe size		4.60	1.739		1.01	117	13.35	131.36	190
0950	2" pipe size		2.70	2.963		1.43	200	23	224.43	325
0970	2-1/2" pipe size		2.40	3.333		1.43	225	25.50	251.93	365
0990	3" pipe size		2.20	3.636		1.43	245	28	274.43	395
1010	3-1/2" pipe size		2	4		1.91	269	30.50	301.41	435

26 05 33.95 Cutting and Drilling		Crew	Daily Output	Labor-Hours	Unit	2023 Bare Costs Material	Labor	Equipment	Total	Total Incl O&P
1030	4" pipe size	R-31	1.70	4.706	Ea.	1.91	315	36	352.91	510
1050	24" thick, 1/2" pipe size		5.50	1.455		.89	98	11.15	110.04	159
1070	3/4" pipe size		5.10	1.569		.89	106	12.05	118.94	171
1090	1" pipe size		4.30	1.860		1.21	125	14.30	140.51	203
1110	1-1/4" pipe size		4	2		1.21	135	15.35	151.56	218
1130	1-1/2" pipe size		4	2		1.21	135	15.35	151.56	218
1150	2" pipe size		2.40	3.333		1.72	225	25.50	252.22	365
1170	2-1/2" pipe size		2.20	3.636		1.72	245	28	274.72	395
1190	3" pipe size		2	4		1.72	269	30.50	301.22	435
1210	3-1/2" pipe size		1.80	4.444		2.29	299	34	335.29	485
1230	4" pipe size		1.50	5.333		2.29	360	41	403.29	585
1500	Brick wall, 8" thick, 1/2" pipe size		18	.444		.30	30	3.41	33.71	48.50
1520	3/4" pipe size		18	.444		.30	30	3.41	33.71	48.50
1540	1" pipe size		13.30	.602		.40	40.50	4.62	45.52	65.50
1560	1-1/4" pipe size		13.30	.602		.40	40.50	4.62	45.52	65.50
1580	1-1/2" pipe size		13.30	.602		.40	40.50	4.62	45.52	65.50
1600	2" pipe size		5.70	1.404		.57	94.50	10.80	105.87	152
1620	2-1/2" pipe size		5.70	1.404		.57	94.50	10.80	105.87	152
1640	3" pipe size		5.70	1.404		.57	94.50	10.80	105.87	152
1660	3-1/2" pipe size		4.40	1.818		.76	122	13.95	136.71	198
1680	4" pipe size		4	2		.76	135	15.35	151.11	218
1700	12" thick, 1/2" pipe size		14.50	.552		.44	37	4.24	41.68	60
1720	3/4" pipe size		14.50	.552		.44	37	4.24	41.68	60
1740	1" pipe size		11	.727		.61	49	5.60	55.21	80
1760	1-1/4" pipe size		11	.727		.61	49	5.60	55.21	80
1780	1-1/2" pipe size		11	.727		.61	49	5.60	55.21	80
1800	2" pipe size		5	1.600		.86	108	12.30	121.16	174
1820	2-1/2" pipe size		5	1.600		.86	108	12.30	121.16	174
1840	3" pipe size		5	1.600		.86	108	12.30	121.16	174
1860	3-1/2" pipe size		3.80	2.105		1.15	142	16.15	159.30	230
1880	4" pipe size		3.30	2.424		1.15	163	18.60	182.75	265
1900	16" thick, 1/2" pipe size		12.30	.650		.59	44	5	49.59	71
1920	3/4" pipe size		12.30	.650		.59	44	5	49.59	71
1940	1" pipe size		9.30	.860		.81	58	6.60	65.41	94
1960	1-1/4" pipe size		9.30	.860		.81	58	6.60	65.41	94
1980	1-1/2" pipe size		9.30	.860		.81	58	6.60	65.41	94
2000	2" pipe size		4.40	1.818		1.15	122	13.95	137.10	199
2010	2-1/2" pipe size		4.40	1.818		1.15	122	13.95	137.10	199
2030	3" pipe size		4.40	1.818		1.15	122	13.95	137.10	199
2050	3-1/2" pipe size		3.30	2.424		1.53	163	18.60	183.13	265
2070	4" pipe size		3	2.667		1.53	180	20.50	202.03	291
2090	20" thick, 1/2" pipe size		10.70	.748		.74	50.50	5.75	56.99	82
2110	3/4" pipe size		10.70	.748		.74	50.50	5.75	56.99	82
2130	1" pipe size		8	1		1.01	67.50	7.70	76.21	110
2150	1-1/4" pipe size		8	1		1.01	67.50	7.70	76.21	110
2170	1-1/2" pipe size		8	1		1.01	67.50	7.70	76.21	110
2190	2" pipe size		4	2		1.43	135	15.35	151.78	218
2210	2-1/2" pipe size		4	2		1.43	135	15.35	151.78	218
2230	3" pipe size		4	2		1.43	135	15.35	151.78	218
2250	3-1/2" pipe size		3	2.667		1.91	180	20.50	202.41	292
2270	4" pipe size		2.70	2.963		1.91	200	23	224.91	325
2290	24" thick, 1/2" pipe size		9.40	.851		.89	57.50	6.55	64.94	93
2310	3/4" pipe size		9.40	.851		.89	57.50	6.55	64.94	93

26 05 33 – Raceway and Boxes for Electrical Systems

26 05 33.95 Cutting and Drilling

		Crew	Daily Output	Labor-Hours	Unit	2023 Bare Costs Material	Labor	Equipment	Total	Total Incl O&P
2330	1" pipe size	R-31	7.10	1.127	Ea.	1.21	76	8.65	85.86	124
2350	1-1/4" pipe size		7.10	1.127		1.21	76	8.65	85.86	124
2370	1-1/2" pipe size		7.10	1.127		1.21	76	8.65	85.86	124
2390	2" pipe size		3.60	2.222		1.72	150	17.05	168.77	243
2410	2-1/2" pipe size		3.60	2.222		1.72	150	17.05	168.77	243
2430	3" pipe size		3.60	2.222		1.72	150	17.05	168.77	243
2450	3-1/2" pipe size		2.80	2.857		2.29	192	22	216.29	315
2470	4" pipe size		2.50	3.200		2.29	216	24.50	242.79	350
3000	Knockouts to 8' high, metal boxes & enclosures									
3020	With hole saw, 1/2" pipe size	1 Elec	53	.151	Ea.		10.15		10.15	15.10
3040	3/4" pipe size		47	.170			11.45		11.45	17.05
3050	1" pipe size		40	.200			13.45		13.45	20
3060	1-1/4" pipe size		36	.222			14.95		14.95	22
3070	1-1/2" pipe size		32	.250			16.85		16.85	25
3080	2" pipe size		27	.296			19.95		19.95	29.50
3090	2-1/2" pipe size		20	.400			27		27	40
4010	3" pipe size		16	.500			33.50		33.50	50
4030	3-1/2" pipe size		13	.615			41.50		41.50	61.50
4050	4" pipe size		11	.727			49		49	73

26 05 36 – Cable Trays for Electrical Systems

26 05 36.10 Cable Tray Ladder Type

		Crew	Daily Output	Labor-Hours	Unit	Material	Labor	Equipment	Total	Total Incl O&P
0010	**CABLE TRAY LADDER TYPE** w/ftngs. & supports, 4" dp., to 15' elev.									
0100	For higher elevations, see Section 26 05 36.40									
0160	Galvanized steel tray R260536-10									
0170	4" rung spacing, 6" wide	2 Elec	98	.163	L.F.	17.05	11		28.05	35
0180	9" wide R260536-11		92	.174		18.60	11.70		30.30	38
0200	12" wide		86	.186		20.50	12.55		33.05	41
0400	18" wide		82	.195		24	13.15		37.15	45.50
0600	24" wide		78	.205		27.50	13.80		41.30	50.50
0650	30" wide		68	.235		34.50	15.85		50.35	61.50
0800	6" rung spacing, 6" wide		100	.160		15.55	10.80		26.35	33
0850	9" wide		94	.170		17.05	11.45		28.50	36
0860	12" wide		88	.182		20.50	12.25		32.75	40.50
0870	18" wide		84	.190		20.50	12.85		33.35	41.50
0880	24" wide		80	.200		23	13.45		36.45	45
0890	30" wide		70	.229		27	15.40		42.40	52.50
0910	9" rung spacing, 6" wide		102	.157		14.45	10.55		25	31.50
0920	9" wide		98	.163		14.85	11		25.85	32.50
0930	12" wide		94	.170		17	11.45		28.45	36
0940	18" wide		90	.178		19.25	11.95		31.20	39
0950	24" wide		86	.186		28	12.55		40.55	49.50
0960	30" wide		80	.200		35	13.45		48.45	58.50
0980	12" rung spacing, 6" wide		106	.151		14.25	10.15		24.40	31
0990	9" wide		104	.154		14.60	10.35		24.95	31.50
1000	12" wide		100	.160		47	10.80		57.80	67.50
1010	18" wide		96	.167		16.55	11.25		27.80	35
1020	24" wide		94	.170		17.75	11.45		29.20	36.50
1030	30" wide		88	.182		20	12.25		32.25	40
1041	18" rung spacing, 6" wide		108	.148		14.15	10		24.15	30.50
1042	9" wide		106	.151		14.35	10.15		24.50	31
1043	12" wide		102	.157		15.25	10.55		25.80	32.50
1044	18" wide		98	.163		16.05	11		27.05	34

26 05 36.10 Cable Tray Ladder Type		Crew	Daily Output	Labor-Hours	Unit	2023 Bare Costs Material	Labor	Equipment	Total	Total Incl O&P
1045	24" wide	2 Elec	96	.167	L.F.	16.55	11.25		27.80	35
1046	30" wide		90	.178		17.45	11.95		29.40	37
1050	Elbows horiz. 9" rung spacing, 90°, 12" radius, 6" wide		9.60	1.667	Ea.	65.50	112		177.50	240
1060	9" wide		8.40	1.905		69.50	128		197.50	268
1070	12" wide		7.60	2.105		75.50	142		217.50	294
1080	18" wide		6.20	2.581		99.50	174		273.50	370
1090	24" wide		5.40	2.963		111	200		311	420
1100	30" wide		4.80	3.333		147	225		372	495
1120	90°, 24" radius, 6" wide		9.20	1.739		135	117		252	325
1130	9" wide		8	2		139	135		274	355
1140	12" wide		7.20	2.222		143	150		293	380
1150	18" wide		5.80	2.759		155	186		341	445
1160	24" wide		5	3.200		167	216		383	505
1170	30" wide		4.40	3.636		181	245		426	565
1190	90°, 36" radius, 6" wide		8.80	1.818		149	122		271	345
1200	9" wide		7.60	2.105		157	142		299	385
1210	12" wide		6.80	2.353		165	158		323	420
1220	18" wide		5.40	2.963		189	200		389	505
1230	24" wide		4.60	3.478		207	234		441	580
1240	30" wide		4	4		249	269		518	675
1260	45°, 12" radius, 6" wide		13.20	1.212		51	81.50		132.50	177
1270	9" wide		11	1.455		53	98		151	204
1280	12" wide		9.60	1.667		55	112		167	228
1290	18" wide		7.60	2.105		58	142		200	275
1300	24" wide		6.20	2.581		74.50	174		248.50	340
1310	30" wide		5.40	2.963		95	200		295	400
1330	45°, 24" radius, 6" wide		12.80	1.250		64	84		148	196
1340	9" wide		10.60	1.509		68.50	102		170.50	226
1350	12" wide		9.20	1.739		76.50	117		193.50	259
1360	18" wide		7.20	2.222		78.50	150		228.50	310
1370	24" wide		5.80	2.759		95	186		281	380
1380	30" wide		5	3.200		113	216		329	445
1400	45°, 36" radius, 6" wide		12.40	1.290		92	87		179	230
1410	9" wide		10.20	1.569		97.50	106		203.50	264
1420	12" wide		8.80	1.818		99.50	122		221.50	291
1430	18" wide		6.80	2.353		108	158		266	355
1440	24" wide		5.40	2.963		114	200		314	420
1450	30" wide		4.60	3.478		147	234		381	510
1470	Elbows horizontal, 4" rung spacing, use 9" rung x 1.50									
1480	6" rung spacing, use 9" rung x 1.20									
1490	12" rung spacing, use 9" rung x 0.93									
1500	Elbows vertical, 9" rung spacing, 90°, 12" radius, 6" wide	2 Elec	9.60	1.667	Ea.	90	112		202	266
1510	9" wide		8.40	1.905		92	128		220	292
1520	12" wide		7.60	2.105		95	142		237	315
1530	18" wide		6.20	2.581		99.50	174		273.50	365
1540	24" wide		5.40	2.963		104	200		304	410
1550	30" wide		4.80	3.333		111	225		336	460
1570	24" radius, 6" wide		9.20	1.739		127	117		244	315
1580	9" wide		8	2		131	135		266	345
1590	12" wide		7.20	2.222		135	150		285	370
1600	18" wide		5.80	2.759		143	186		329	435
1610	24" wide		5	3.200		390	216		606	750
1620	30" wide		4.40	3.636		157	245		402	540

26 05 36.10 Cable Tray Ladder Type		Crew	Daily Output	Labor-Hours	Unit	2023 Bare Costs Material	Labor	Equipment	Total	Total Incl O&P
1640	36″ radius, 6″ wide	2 Elec	8.80	1.818	Ea.	171	122		293	370
1650	9″ wide		7.60	2.105		177	142		319	405
1660	12″ wide		6.80	2.353		179	158		337	435
1670	18″ wide		5.40	2.963		195	200		395	510
1680	24″ wide		4.60	3.478		197	234		431	565
1690	30″ wide		4	4		223	269		492	645
1710	Elbows vertical, 4″ rung spacing, use 9″ rung x 1.25									
1720	6″ rung spacing, use 9″ rung x 1.15									
1730	12″ rung spacing, use 9″ rung x 0.90									
1740	Tee horizontal, 9″ rung spacing, 12″ radius, 6″ wide	2 Elec	5	3.200	Ea.	139	216		355	475
1750	9″ wide		4.60	3.478		149	234		383	515
1760	12″ wide		4.40	3.636		157	245		402	540
1770	18″ wide		4	4		179	269		448	595
1780	24″ wide		3.60	4.444		211	299		510	675
1790	30″ wide		3.40	4.706		253	315		568	750
1810	24″ radius, 6″ wide		4.60	3.478		217	234		451	590
1820	9″ wide		4.20	3.810		227	257		484	630
1830	12″ wide		4	4		235	269		504	660
1840	18″ wide		3.60	4.444		255	299		554	725
1850	24″ wide		3.20	5		277	335		612	805
1860	30″ wide		3	5.333		300	360		660	865
1880	36″ radius, 6″ wide		4.20	3.810		325	257		582	735
1890	9″ wide		3.80	4.211		340	284		624	790
1900	12″ wide		3.60	4.444		360	299		659	840
1910	18″ wide		3.20	5		385	335		720	925
1920	24″ wide		2.80	5.714		435	385		820	1,050
1930	30″ wide		2.60	6.154		475	415		890	1,150
1980	Tee vertical, 9″ rung spacing, 12″ radius, 6″ wide		5.40	2.963		237	200		437	560
1990	9″ wide		5.20	3.077		239	207		446	575
2000	12″ wide		5	3.200		241	216		457	585
2010	18″ wide		4.60	3.478		243	234		477	615
2020	24″ wide		4.40	3.636		249	245		494	640
2030	30″ wide		4	4		265	269		534	690
2050	24″ radius, 6″ wide		5	3.200		425	216		641	790
2060	9″ wide		4.80	3.333		430	225		655	810
2070	12″ wide		4.60	3.478		440	234		674	830
2080	18″ wide		4.20	3.810		450	257		707	875
2090	24″ wide		4	4		465	269		734	910
2100	30″ wide		3.60	4.444		475	299		774	970
2120	36″ radius, 6″ wide		4.60	3.478		795	234		1,029	1,225
2130	9″ wide		4.40	3.636		810	245		1,055	1,250
2140	12″ wide		4.20	3.810		820	257		1,077	1,275
2150	18″ wide		3.80	4.211		830	284		1,114	1,325
2160	24″ wide		3.60	4.444		840	299		1,139	1,375
2170	30″ wide		3.20	5		870	335		1,205	1,450
2190	Tee, 4″ rung spacing, use 9″ rung x 1.30									
2200	6″ rung spacing, use 9″ rung x 1.20									
2210	12″ rung spacing, use 9″ rung x 0.90									
2220	Cross horizontal, 9″ rung spacing, 12″ radius, 6″ wide	2 Elec	4	4	Ea.	172	269		441	590
2230	9″ wide		3.80	4.211		180	284		464	620
2240	12″ wide		3.60	4.444		197	299		496	660
2250	18″ wide		3.40	4.706		215	315		530	705
2260	24″ wide		3	5.333		239	360		599	800

26 05 36.10 Cable Tray Ladder Type		Crew	Daily Output	Labor-Hours	Unit	Material	2023 Bare Costs Labor	Equipment	Total	Total Incl O&P
2270	30″ wide	2 Elec	2.80	5.714	Ea.	289	385		674	890
2290	24″ radius, 6″ wide		3.60	4.444		335	299		634	815
2300	9″ wide		3.40	4.706		345	315		660	850
2310	12″ wide		3.20	5		355	335		690	890
2320	18″ wide		3	5.333		380	360		740	950
2330	24″ wide		2.60	6.154		400	415		815	1,050
2340	30″ wide		2.40	6.667		430	450		880	1,125
2360	36″ radius, 6″ wide		3.20	5		465	335		800	1,000
2370	9″ wide		3	5.333		485	360		845	1,075
2380	12″ wide		2.80	5.714		510	385		895	1,125
2390	18″ wide		2.60	6.154		560	415		975	1,225
2400	24″ wide		2.20	7.273		620	490		1,110	1,425
2410	30″ wide		2	8		675	540		1,215	1,550
2430	Cross horizontal, 4″ rung spacing, use 9″ rung x 1.30									
2440	6″ rung spacing, use 9″ rung x 1.20									
2450	12″ rung spacing, use 9″ rung x 0.90									
2460	Reducer, 9″ to 6″ wide tray	2 Elec	13	1.231	Ea.	95.50	83		178.50	228
2470	12″ to 9″ wide tray		12	1.333		97.50	90		187.50	240
2480	18″ to 12″ wide tray		10.40	1.538		97.50	104		201.50	261
2490	24″ to 18″ wide tray		9	1.778		99.50	120		219.50	287
2500	30″ to 24″ wide tray		8	2		102	135		237	310
2510	36″ to 30″ wide tray		7	2.286		113	154		267	355
2511	Reducer, 18″ to 6″ wide tray		10.40	1.538		102	104		206	266
2512	24″ to 12″ wide tray		9	1.778		104	120		224	292
2513	30″ to 18″ wide tray		8	2		105	135		240	315
2514	30″ to 12″ wide tray		8	2		113	135		248	325
2515	36″ to 24″ wide tray		7	2.286		115	154		269	355
2516	36″ to 18″ wide tray		7	2.286		115	154		269	355
2517	36″ to 12″ wide tray		7	2.286		115	154		269	355
2520	Dropout or end plate, 6″ wide		32	.500		10.65	33.50		44.15	62
2530	9″ wide		28	.571		12.55	38.50		51.05	71
2540	12″ wide		26	.615		13.75	41.50		55.25	76.50
2550	18″ wide		22	.727		16.10	49		65.10	90.50
2560	24″ wide		20	.800		19.50	54		73.50	102
2570	30″ wide		18	.889		21.50	60		81.50	113
2590	Tray connector		48	.333		18.90	22.50		41.40	54.50
3200	Aluminum tray, 4″ deep, 6″ rung spacing, 6″ wide		134	.119	L.F.	90	8.05		98.05	111
3210	9″ wide		128	.125		93.50	8.40		101.90	116
3220	12″ wide		124	.129		100	8.70		108.70	123
3230	18″ wide		114	.140		110	9.45		119.45	135
3240	24″ wide		106	.151		123	10.15		133.15	150
3250	30″ wide		100	.160		140	10.80		150.80	170
3270	9″ rung spacing, 6″ wide		140	.114		80	7.70		87.70	99.50
3280	9″ wide		134	.119		16.25	8.05		24.30	30
3290	12″ wide		130	.123		84.50	8.30		92.80	105
3300	18″ wide		122	.131		91.50	8.85		100.35	114
3310	24″ wide		116	.138		100	9.30		109.30	124
3320	30″ wide		108	.148		111	10		121	137
3340	12″ rung spacing, 6″ wide		146	.110		73	7.40		80.40	91.50
3350	9″ wide		140	.114		16.65	7.70		24.35	30
3360	12″ wide		134	.119		77	8.05		85.05	96.50
3370	18″ wide		128	.125		82.50	8.40		90.90	103
3380	24″ wide		124	.129		89.50	8.70		98.20	111

26 05 36.10 Cable Tray Ladder Type		Crew	Daily Output	Labor-Hours	Unit	2023 Bare Costs Material	Labor	Equipment	Total	Total Incl O&P
3390	30″ wide	2 Elec	114	.140	L.F.	97.50	9.45		106.95	121
3401	18″ rung spacing, 6″ wide		150	.107		16.35	7.20		23.55	28.50
3402	9″ wide tray		144	.111		16.55	7.50		24.05	29.50
3403	12″ wide tray		140	.114		17.10	7.70		24.80	30.50
3404	18″ wide tray		134	.119		18.10	8.05		26.15	32
3405	24″ wide tray		130	.123		19.50	8.30		27.80	34
3406	30″ wide tray		120	.133		20	9		29	35.50
3410	Elbows horiz., 9″ rung spacing, 90°, 12″ radius, 6″ wide		9.60	1.667	Ea.	223	112		335	410
3420	9″ wide		8.40	1.905		75	128		203	274
3430	12″ wide		7.60	2.105		278	142		420	515
3440	18″ wide		6.20	2.581		330	174		504	625
3450	24″ wide		5.40	2.963		375	200		575	705
3460	30″ wide		4.80	3.333		132	225		357	480
3480	24″ radius, 6″ wide		9.20	1.739		131	117		248	320
3490	9″ wide		8	2		520	135		655	775
3500	12″ wide		7.20	2.222		142	150		292	380
3510	18″ wide		5.80	2.759		194	186		380	490
3520	24″ wide		5	3.200		229	216		445	570
3530	30″ wide		4.40	3.636		370	245		615	770
3550	90°, 36″ radius, 6″ wide		8.80	1.818		143	122		265	340
3560	9″ wide		7.60	2.105		147	142		289	370
3570	12″ wide		6.80	2.353		165	158		323	415
3580	18″ wide		5.40	2.963		184	200		384	500
3590	24″ wide		4.60	3.478		207	234		441	580
3600	30″ wide		4	4		229	269		498	650
3620	45°, 12″ radius, 6″ wide		13.20	1.212		48.50	81.50		130	174
3630	9″ wide		11	1.455		50	98		148	201
3640	12″ wide		9.60	1.667		52	112		164	224
3650	18″ wide		7.60	2.105		61.50	142		203.50	279
3660	24″ wide		6.20	2.581		76	174		250	340
3670	30″ wide		5.40	2.963		440	200		640	775
3690	45°, 24″ radius, 6″ wide		12.80	1.250		64.50	84		148.50	196
3700	9″ wide		10.60	1.509		73.50	102		175.50	232
3710	12″ wide		9.20	1.739		75	117		192	257
3720	18″ wide		7.20	2.222		80.50	150		230.50	310
3730	24″ wide		5.80	2.759		93	186		279	380
3740	30″ wide		5	3.200		111	216		327	440
3760	45°, 36″ radius, 6″ wide		12.40	1.290		87.50	87		174.50	226
3770	9″ wide		10.20	1.569		89.50	106		195.50	256
3780	12″ wide		8.80	1.818		91	122		213	282
3790	18″ wide		6.80	2.353		100	158		258	345
3800	24″ wide		5.40	2.963		123	200		323	435
3810	30″ wide		4.60	3.478		131	234		365	495
3830	Elbows horizontal, 4″ rung spacing, use 9″ rung x 1.50									
3840	6″ rung spacing, use 9″ rung x 1.20									
3850	12″ rung spacing, use 9″ rung x 0.93									
3860	Elbows vertical, 9″ rung spacing, 90°, 12″ radius, 6″ wide	2 Elec	9.60	1.667	Ea.	102	112		214	279
3870	9″ wide		8.40	1.905		107	128		235	310
3880	12″ wide		7.60	2.105		109	142		251	330
3890	18″ wide		6.20	2.581		113	174		287	380
3900	24″ wide		5.40	2.963		120	200		320	430
3910	30″ wide		4.80	3.333		125	225		350	475
3930	24″ radius, 6″ wide		9.20	1.739		111	117		228	296

26 05 36.10 Cable Tray Ladder Type		Crew	Daily Output	Labor-Hours	Unit	2023 Bare Costs Material	Labor	Equipment	Total	Total Incl O&P
3940	9″ wide	2 Elec	8	2	Ea.	115	135		250	325
3950	12″ wide		7.20	2.222		118	150		268	350
3960	18″ wide		5.80	2.759		665	186		851	1,000
3970	24″ wide		5	3.200		199	216		415	540
3980	30″ wide		4.40	3.636		865	245		1,110	1,325
4000	36″ radius, 6″ wide		8.80	1.818		172	122		294	370
4010	9″ wide		7.60	2.105		175	142		317	405
4020	12″ wide		6.80	2.353		186	158		344	440
4030	18″ wide		5.40	2.963		193	200		393	510
4040	24″ wide		4.60	3.478		200	234		434	570
4050	30″ wide	↓	4	4	↓	216	269		485	640
4070	Elbows vertical, 4″ rung spacing, use 9″ rung x 1.25									
4080	6″ rung spacing, use 9″ rung x 1.15									
4090	12″ rung spacing, use 9″ rung x 0.90									
4100	Tee horizontal, 9″ rung spacing, 12″ radius, 6″ wide	2 Elec	5	3.200	Ea.	655	216		871	1,050
4110	9″ wide		4.60	3.478		122	234		356	485
4120	12″ wide		4.40	3.636		103	245		348	480
4130	18″ wide		4.20	3.810		790	257		1,047	1,250
4140	24″ wide		4	4		161	269		430	575
4150	30″ wide		3.60	4.444		188	299		487	650
4170	24″ radius, 6″ wide		4.60	3.478		193	234		427	560
4180	9″ wide		4.20	3.810		204	257		461	605
4190	12″ wide		4	4		209	269		478	630
4200	18″ wide		3.80	4.211		1,150	284		1,434	1,700
4210	24″ wide		3.60	4.444		1,350	299		1,649	1,950
4220	30″ wide		3.20	5		1,650	335		1,985	2,325
4240	36″ radius, 6″ wide		4.20	3.810		274	257		531	680
4250	9″ wide		3.80	4.211		281	284		565	730
4260	12″ wide		3.60	4.444		310	299		609	785
4270	18″ wide		3.40	4.706		325	315		640	825
4280	24″ wide		3.20	5		360	335		695	895
4290	30″ wide		2.80	5.714		450	385		835	1,075
4310	Tee vertical, 9″ rung spacing, 12″ radius, 6″ wide		5.40	2.963		254	200		454	575
4320	9″ wide		5.20	3.077		263	207		470	600
4330	12″ wide		5	3.200		263	216		479	610
4340	18″ wide		4.60	3.478		270	234		504	645
4350	24″ wide		4.40	3.636		291	245		536	685
4360	30″ wide		4.20	3.810		297	257		554	705
4380	24″ radius, 6″ wide		5	3.200		430	216		646	795
4390	9″ wide		4.80	3.333		435	225		660	815
4400	12″ wide		4.60	3.478		445	234		679	840
4410	18″ wide		4.20	3.810		455	257		712	880
4420	24″ wide		4	4		465	269		734	915
4430	30″ wide		3.80	4.211		480	284		764	945
4450	36″ radius, 6″ wide		4.60	3.478		950	234		1,184	1,400
4460	9″ wide		4.40	3.636		965	245		1,210	1,450
4470	12″ wide		4.20	3.810		1,000	257		1,257	1,475
4480	18″ wide		3.80	4.211		1,025	284		1,309	1,550
4490	24″ wide		3.60	4.444		1,050	299		1,349	1,600
4500	30″ wide	↓	3.40	4.706	↓	1,050	315		1,365	1,625
4520	Tees, 4″ rung spacing, use 9″ rung x 1.30									
4530	6″ rung spacing, use 9″ rung x 1.20									
4540	12″ rung spacing, use 9″ rung x 0.90									

26 05 36 – Cable Trays for Electrical Systems

26 05 36.10 Cable Tray Ladder Type		Crew	Daily Output	Labor-Hours	Unit	Material	Labor	Equipment	Total	Total Incl O&P
						2023 Bare Costs				
4550	Cross horizontal, 9" rung spacing, 12" radius, 6" wide	2 Elec	4.40	3.636	Ea.	157	245		402	540
4560	9" wide		4.20	3.810		175	257		432	575
4570	12" wide		4	4		149	269		418	565
4580	18" wide		3.60	4.444		215	299		514	680
4590	24" wide		3.40	4.706		222	315		537	715
4600	30" wide		3	5.333		261	360		621	820
4620	24" radius, 6" wide		4	4		300	269		569	730
4630	9" wide		3.80	4.211		315	284		599	765
4640	12" wide		3.60	4.444		320	299		619	800
4650	18" wide		3.20	5		340	335		675	870
4660	24" wide		3	5.333		370	360		730	940
4670	30" wide		2.60	6.154		395	415		810	1,050
4690	36" radius, 6" wide		3.60	4.444		360	299		659	840
4700	9" wide		3.40	4.706		370	315		685	880
4710	12" wide		3.20	5		395	335		730	935
4720	18" wide		2.80	5.714		420	385		805	1,025
4730	24" wide		2.60	6.154		520	415		935	1,175
4740	30" wide		2.20	7.273		575	490		1,065	1,375
4760	Cross horizontal, 4" rung spacing, use 9" rung x 1.30									
4770	6" rung spacing, use 9" rung x 1.20									
4780	12" rung spacing, use 9" rung x 0.90									
4790	Reducer, 9" to 6" wide tray	2 Elec	16	1	Ea.	84	67.50		151.50	193
4800	12" to 9" wide tray		14	1.143		87.50	77		164.50	211
4810	18" to 12" wide tray		12.40	1.290		87.50	87		174.50	226
4820	24" to 18" wide tray		10.60	1.509		89.50	102		191.50	250
4830	30" to 24" wide tray		9.20	1.739		350	117		467	560
4840	36" to 30" wide tray		8	2		96.50	135		231.50	305
4841	Reducer, 18" to 6" wide tray		12.40	1.290		87.50	87		174.50	226
4842	24" to 12" wide tray		10.60	1.509		89.50	102		191.50	250
4843	30" to 18" wide tray		9.20	1.739		91	117		208	274
4844	30" to 12" wide tray		9.20	1.739		91	117		208	274
4845	36" to 24" wide tray		8	2		96.50	135		231.50	305
4846	36" to 18" wide tray		8	2		96.50	135		231.50	305
4847	36" to 12" wide tray		8	2		96.50	135		231.50	305
4850	Dropout or end plate, 6" wide		32	.500		11	33.50		44.50	62
4860	9" wide tray		28	.571		11.90	38.50		50.40	70
4870	12" wide tray		26	.615		12.75	41.50		54.25	75.50
4880	18" wide tray		22	.727		33	49		82	109
4890	24" wide tray		20	.800		43.50	54		97.50	128
4900	30" wide tray		18	.889		38	60		98	131
4920	Tray connector		48	.333		18.60	22.50		41.10	54
8000	Elbow 36" radius horiz., 60°, 6" wide tray		10.60	1.509		122	102		224	285
8010	9" wide tray		9	1.778		132	120		252	325
8020	12" wide tray		7.80	2.051		136	138		274	355
8030	18" wide tray		6.20	2.581		145	174		319	415
8040	24" wide tray		5	3.200		170	216		386	505
8050	30" wide tray		4.40	3.636		174	245		419	555
8060	30°, 6" wide tray		14	1.143		93	77		170	216
8070	9" wide tray		11.40	1.404		98.50	94.50		193	248
8080	12" wide tray		9.80	1.633		100	110		210	273
8090	18" wide tray		7.40	2.162		105	146		251	330
8100	24" wide tray		5.80	2.759		129	186		315	420
8110	30" wide tray		4.80	3.333		132	225		357	480

26 05 36.10 Cable Tray Ladder Type		Crew	Daily Output	Labor-Hours	Unit	Material	Labor	Equipment	Total	Total Incl O&P
						2023 Bare Costs				
8120	Adjustable, 6" wide tray	2 Elec	12.40	1.290	Ea.	123	87		210	265
8130	9" wide tray		10.20	1.569		131	106		237	300
8140	12" wide tray		8.80	1.818		132	122		254	330
8150	18" wide tray		6.80	2.353		145	158		303	395
8160	24" wide tray		5.40	2.963		154	200		354	465
8170	30" wide tray		4.60	3.478		172	234		406	540
8180	Wye 36" radius horiz., 45°, 6" wide tray		4.60	3.478		134	234		368	500
8190	9" wide tray		4.40	3.636		141	245		386	520
8200	12" wide tray		4.20	3.810		147	257		404	540
8210	18" wide tray		3.80	4.211		166	284		450	605
8220	24" wide tray		3.60	4.444		186	299		485	650
8230	30" wide tray		3.40	4.706		207	315		522	700
8240	Elbow 36" radius vert. in/outside, 60°, 6" wide tray		10.60	1.509		134	102		236	299
8250	9" wide tray		9	1.778		140	120		260	330
8260	12" wide tray		7.80	2.051		141	138		279	360
8270	18" wide tray		6.20	2.581		147	174		321	420
8280	24" wide tray		5	3.200		156	216		372	490
8290	30" wide tray		4.40	3.636		166	245		411	550
8300	45°, 6" wide tray		12.40	1.290		121	87		208	262
8310	9" wide tray		10.20	1.569		128	106		234	298
8320	12" wide tray		8.80	1.818		130	122		252	325
8330	18" wide tray		6.80	2.353		134	158		292	385
8340	24" wide tray		5.40	2.963		141	200		341	450
8350	30" wide tray		4.60	3.478		145	234		379	510
8360	30°, 6" wide tray		14	1.143		106	77		183	230
8370	9" wide tray		11.40	1.404		108	94.50		202.50	259
8380	12" wide tray		9.80	1.633		115	110		225	290
8390	18" wide tray		7.40	2.162		117	146		263	345
8400	24" wide tray		5.80	2.759		120	186		306	410
8410	30" wide tray		4.80	3.333		126	225		351	475
8660	Adjustable, 6" wide tray		12.40	1.290		121	87		208	262
8670	9" wide tray		10.20	1.569		128	106		234	298
8680	12" wide tray		8.80	1.818		131	122		253	325
8690	18" wide tray		6.80	2.353		145	158		303	395
8700	24" wide tray		5.40	2.963		154	200		354	465
8710	30" wide tray		4.60	3.478		170	234		404	535
8720	Cross, vertical, 24" radius, 6" wide tray		3.60	4.444		880	299		1,179	1,400
8730	9" wide tray		3.40	4.706		895	315		1,210	1,450
8740	12" wide tray		3.20	5		920	335		1,255	1,525
8750	18" wide tray		2.80	5.714		965	385		1,350	1,625
8760	24" wide tray		2.60	6.154		995	415		1,410	1,725
8770	30" wide tray		2.20	7.273		1,050	490		1,540	1,875
9200	Splice plate	1 Elec	48	.167	Pair	25	11.25		36.25	44.50
9210	Expansion joint		48	.167		38.50	11.25		49.75	58.50
9220	Horizontal hinged		48	.167		16.80	11.25		28.05	35
9230	Vertical hinged		48	.167		20	11.25		31.25	38.50
9240	Ladder hanger, vertical		28	.286	Ea.	38.50	19.25		57.75	71
9250	Ladder to channel connector		24	.333		58.50	22.50		81	98
9260	Ladder to box connector, 30" wide		19	.421		58.50	28.50		87	107
9270	24" wide		20	.400		58.50	27		85.50	105
9280	18" wide		21	.381		56.50	25.50		82	101
9290	12" wide		22	.364		53	24.50		77.50	94.50
9300	9" wide		23	.348		47.50	23.50		71	87

26 05 36.10 Cable Tray Ladder Type

	26 05 36.10 Cable Tray Ladder Type		Crew	Daily Output	Labor-Hours	Unit	2023 Bare Costs Material	Labor	Equipment	Total	Total Incl O&P
9310	6" wide		1 Elec	24	.333	Ea.	32.50	22.50		55	69
9320	Ladder floor flange			24	.333		38	22.50		60.50	75.50
9330	Cable roller for tray, 30" wide			10	.800		330	54		384	445
9340	24" wide			11	.727		282	49		331	385
9350	18" wide			12	.667		269	45		314	365
9360	12" wide			13	.615		212	41.50		253.50	295
9370	9" wide			14	.571		188	38.50		226.50	263
9380	6" wide			15	.533		152	36		188	222
9390	Pulley, single wheel			12	.667		345	45		390	445
9400	Triple wheel			10	.800		695	54		749	840
9440	Nylon cable tie, 14" long			80	.100		.61	6.75		7.36	10.65
9450	Ladder, hold down clamp			60	.133		4.30	9		13.30	18.10
9460	Cable clamp			60	.133		10.85	9		19.85	25.50
9470	Wall bracket, 30" wide tray			19	.421		61.50	28.50		90	110
9480	24" wide tray			20	.400		48	27		75	92.50
9490	18" wide tray			21	.381		42.50	25.50		68	85
9500	12" wide tray			22	.364		257	24.50		281.50	320
9510	9" wide tray			23	.348		35	23.50		58.50	73.50
9520	6" wide tray		↓	24	.333	↓	34	22.50		56.50	71

26 05 36.20 Cable Tray Solid Bottom

	26 05 36.20 Cable Tray Solid Bottom		Crew	Daily Output	Labor-Hours	Unit	Material	Labor	Equipment	Total	Total Incl O&P
0010	**CABLE TRAY SOLID BOTTOM** w/ftngs. & supports, 3" deep, to 15' high										
0200	For higher elevations, see Section 26 05 36.40										
0220	Galvanized steel, tray, 6" wide	R260536-10	2 Elec	120	.133	L.F.	13.50	9		22.50	28
0240	12" wide			100	.160		17.35	10.80		28.15	35
0260	18" wide			70	.229		21	15.40		36.40	46
0280	24" wide	R260536-11		60	.267		24.50	17.95		42.45	53.50
0300	30" wide			50	.320	↓	29.50	21.50		51	64.50
0340	Elbow horizontal, 90°, 12" radius, 6" wide			9.60	1.667	Ea.	102	112		214	280
0360	12" wide			6.80	2.353		115	158		273	360
0370	18" wide			5.40	2.963		131	200		331	440
0380	24" wide			4.40	3.636		160	245		405	540
0390	30" wide			3.80	4.211		191	284		475	630
0420	24" radius, 6" wide			9.20	1.739		146	117		263	335
0440	12" wide			6.40	2.500		169	168		337	435
0450	18" wide			5	3.200		197	216		413	535
0460	24" wide			4	4		228	269		497	650
0470	30" wide			3.40	4.706		268	315		583	765
0500	36" radius, 6" wide			8.80	1.818		213	122		335	415
0520	12" wide			6	2.667		240	180		420	530
0530	18" wide			4.60	3.478		293	234		527	675
0540	24" wide			3.60	4.444		315	299		614	795
0550	30" wide			3	5.333		385	360		745	960
0580	Elbow vertical, 90°, 12" radius, 6" wide			9.60	1.667		124	112		236	305
0600	12" wide			6.80	2.353		136	158		294	385
0610	18" wide			5.40	2.963		172	200		372	485
0620	24" wide			4.40	3.636		156	245		401	535
0630	30" wide			3.80	4.211		165	284		449	600
0670	24" radius, 6" wide			9.20	1.739		175	117		292	365
0690	12" wide			6.40	2.500		193	168		361	460
0700	18" wide			5	3.200		209	216		425	550
0710	24" wide			4	4		227	269		496	650
0720	30" wide		↓	3.40	4.706	↓	240	315		555	735

26 05 36 – Cable Trays for Electrical Systems

26 05 36.20 Cable Tray Solid Bottom		Crew	Daily Output	Labor-Hours	Unit	Material	Labor	Equipment	Total	Total Incl O&P
						2023 Bare Costs				
0750	36" radius, 6" wide	2 Elec	8.80	1.818	Ea.	240	122		362	445
0770	12" wide		6.60	2.424		268	163		431	540
0780	18" wide		4.60	3.478		293	234		527	675
0790	24" wide		3.60	4.444		320	299		619	800
0800	30" wide		3	5.333		350	360		710	920
0840	Tee horizontal, 12" radius, 6" wide		5	3.200		144	216		360	480
0860	12" wide		4	4		156	269		425	570
0870	18" wide		3.40	4.706		185	315		500	675
0880	24" wide		2.80	5.714		207	385		592	800
0890	30" wide		2.60	6.154		236	415		651	875
0940	24" radius, 6" wide		4.60	3.478		223	234		457	595
0960	12" wide		3.60	4.444		260	299		559	730
0970	18" wide		3	5.333		290	360		650	855
0980	24" wide		2.40	6.667		390	450		840	1,100
0990	30" wide		2.20	7.273		425	490		915	1,200
1020	36" radius, 6" wide		4.20	3.810		350	257		607	765
1040	12" wide		3.20	5		390	335		725	930
1050	18" wide		2.60	6.154		425	415		840	1,075
1060	24" wide		2.20	7.273		550	490		1,040	1,325
1070	30" wide		2	8		595	540		1,135	1,450
1100	Tee vertical, 12" radius, 6" wide		5	3.200		236	216		452	580
1120	12" wide		4	4		246	269		515	670
1130	18" wide		3.60	4.444		250	299		549	720
1140	24" wide		3.40	4.706		274	315		589	770
1150	30" wide		3	5.333		293	360		653	860
1180	24" radius, 6" wide		4.60	3.478		350	234		584	735
1200	12" wide		3.60	4.444		365	299		664	845
1210	18" wide		3.20	5		380	335		715	920
1220	24" wide		3	5.333		400	360		760	975
1230	30" wide		2.60	6.154		440	415		855	1,100
1260	36" radius, 6" wide		4.20	3.810		545	257		802	980
1280	12" wide		3.20	5		555	335		890	1,100
1290	18" wide		2.80	5.714		595	385		980	1,225
1300	24" wide		2.60	6.154		615	415		1,030	1,300
1310	30" wide		2.20	7.273		715	490		1,205	1,525
1340	Cross horizontal, 12" radius, 6" wide		4	4		171	269		440	590
1360	12" wide		3.40	4.706		187	315		502	675
1370	18" wide		2.80	5.714		219	385		604	810
1380	24" wide		2.40	6.667		246	450		696	935
1390	30" wide		2	8		274	540		814	1,100
1420	24" radius, 6" wide		3.60	4.444		315	299		614	790
1440	12" wide		3	5.333		350	360		710	920
1450	18" wide		2.40	6.667		390	450		840	1,100
1460	24" wide		2	8		500	540		1,040	1,350
1470	30" wide		1.80	8.889		545	600		1,145	1,500
1500	36" radius, 6" wide		3.20	5		510	335		845	1,075
1520	12" wide		2.60	6.154		565	415		980	1,225
1530	18" wide		2	8		615	540		1,155	1,475
1540	24" wide		1.80	8.889		725	600		1,325	1,700
1550	30" wide		1.60	10		790	675		1,465	1,875
1580	Drop out or end plate, 6" wide		32	.500		21	33.50		54.50	73
1600	12" wide		26	.615		26	41.50		67.50	90
1610	18" wide		22	.727		28	49		77	104

26 05 36.20 Cable Tray Solid Bottom		Crew	Daily Output	Labor-Hours	Unit	2023 Bare Costs Material	Labor	Equipment	Total	Total Incl O&P
1620	24" wide	2 Elec	20	.800	Ea.	33	54		87	116
1630	30" wide		18	.889		37	60		97	130
1660	Reducer, 12" to 6" wide		12	1.333		100	90		190	244
1680	18" to 12" wide		10.60	1.509		102	102		204	264
1700	18" to 6" wide		10.60	1.509		102	102		204	264
1720	24" to 18" wide		9.20	1.739		106	117		223	291
1740	24" to 12" wide		9.20	1.739		106	117		223	291
1760	30" to 24" wide		8	2		114	135		249	325
1780	30" to 18" wide		8	2		114	135		249	325
1800	30" to 12" wide		8	2		114	135		249	325
1820	36" to 30" wide		7.20	2.222		118	150		268	350
1840	36" to 24" wide		7.20	2.222		118	150		268	350
1860	36" to 18" wide		7.20	2.222		118	150		268	350
1880	36" to 12" wide		7.20	2.222		118	150		268	350
2000	Aluminum tray, 6" wide		150	.107	L.F.	13.20	7.20		20.40	25.50
2020	12" wide		130	.123		17.35	8.30		25.65	31.50
2030	18" wide		100	.160		22	10.80		32.80	40
2040	24" wide		90	.178		27.50	11.95		39.45	48
2050	30" wide		70	.229		32.50	15.40		47.90	58.50
2080	Elbow horizontal, 90°, 12" radius, 6" wide		9.60	1.667	Ea.	106	112		218	284
2100	12" wide		7.60	2.105		120	142		262	345
2110	18" wide		6.80	2.353		147	158		305	400
2120	24" wide		5.80	2.759		168	186		354	460
2130	30" wide		5	3.200		204	216		420	545
2160	24" radius, 6" wide		9.20	1.739		152	117		269	340
2180	12" wide		7.20	2.222		179	150		329	420
2190	18" wide		6.40	2.500		204	168		372	475
2200	24" wide		5.40	2.963		252	200		452	575
2210	30" wide		4.60	3.478		289	234		523	670
2240	36" radius, 6" wide		8.80	1.818		224	122		346	430
2260	12" wide		6.80	2.353		268	158		426	530
2270	18" wide		6	2.667		320	180		500	615
2280	24" wide		5	3.200		340	216		556	695
2290	30" wide		4.20	3.810		385	257		642	805
2320	Elbow vertical, 90°, 12" radius, 6" wide		9.60	1.667		126	112		238	305
2340	12" wide		7.60	2.105		131	142		273	355
2350	18" wide		6.80	2.353		149	158		307	400
2360	24" wide		5.80	2.759		157	186		343	450
2370	30" wide		5	3.200		166	216		382	505
2400	24" radius, 6" wide		9.20	1.739		179	117		296	370
2420	12" wide		7.20	2.222		195	150		345	435
2430	18" wide		6.40	2.500		209	168		377	480
2440	24" wide		5.40	2.963		227	200		427	545
2450	30" wide		4.60	3.478		241	234		475	615
2480	36" radius, 6" wide		8.80	1.818		236	122		358	440
2500	12" wide		6.80	2.353		265	158		423	530
2510	18" wide		6	2.667		289	180		469	585
2520	24" wide		5	3.200		300	216		516	650
2530	30" wide		4.20	3.810		330	257		587	745
2560	Tee horizontal, 12" radius, 6" wide		5	3.200		165	216		381	500
2580	12" wide		4.40	3.636		200	245		445	585
2590	18" wide		4	4		224	269		493	645
2600	24" wide		3.60	4.444		251	299		550	720

26 05 36.20	Cable Tray Solid Bottom	Crew	Daily Output	Labor-Hours	Unit	Material (2023 Bare Costs)	Labor (2023 Bare Costs)	Equipment (2023 Bare Costs)	Total (2023 Bare Costs)	Total Incl O&P
2610	30" wide	2 Elec	3	5.333	Ea.	289	360		649	855
2640	24" radius, 6" wide		4.60	3.478		271	234		505	650
2660	12" wide		4	4		305	269		574	735
2670	18" wide		3.60	4.444		345	299		644	825
2680	24" wide		3	5.333		425	360		785	1,000
2690	30" wide		2.40	6.667		480	450		930	1,200
2720	36" radius, 6" wide		4.20	3.810		440	257		697	865
2740	12" wide		3.60	4.444		480	299		779	975
2750	18" wide		3.20	5		555	335		890	1,100
2760	24" wide		2.60	6.154		650	415		1,065	1,325
2770	30" wide		2	8		715	540		1,255	1,575
2800	Tee vertical, 12" radius, 6" wide		5	3.200		235	216		451	580
2820	12" wide		4.40	3.636		240	245		485	630
2830	18" wide		4.20	3.810		249	257		506	655
2840	24" wide		4	4		265	269		534	690
2850	30" wide		3.60	4.444		289	299		588	765
2880	24" radius, 6" wide		4.60	3.478		345	234		579	730
2900	12" wide		4	4		365	269		634	800
2910	18" wide		3.80	4.211		390	284		674	850
2920	24" wide		3.60	4.444		425	299		724	910
2930	30" wide		3.20	5		465	335		800	1,000
2960	36" radius, 6" wide		4.20	3.810		540	257		797	975
2980	12" wide		3.40	4.706		565	315		880	1,100
2990	18" wide		3.40	4.706		595	315		910	1,125
3000	24" wide		3.20	5		615	335		950	1,175
3010	30" wide		2.80	5.714		665	385		1,050	1,300
3040	Cross horizontal, 12" radius, 6" wide		4.40	3.636		209	245		454	595
3060	12" wide		4	4		236	269		505	660
3070	18" wide		3.40	4.706		268	315		583	765
3080	24" wide		2.80	5.714		305	385		690	905
3090	30" wide		2.60	6.154		345	415		760	995
3120	24" radius, 6" wide		4	4		365	269		634	800
3140	12" wide		3.60	4.444		425	299		724	910
3150	18" wide		3	5.333		460	360		820	1,050
3160	24" wide		2.40	6.667		555	450		1,005	1,275
3170	30" wide		2.20	7.273		615	490		1,105	1,400
3200	36" radius, 6" wide		3.60	4.444		640	299		939	1,150
3220	12" wide		3.20	5		670	335		1,005	1,250
3230	18" wide		2.60	6.154		745	415		1,160	1,425
3240	24" wide		2	8		815	540		1,355	1,700
3250	30" wide		1.80	8.889		880	600		1,480	1,850
3280	Dropout, or end plate, 6" wide		32	.500		21	33.50		54.50	73
3300	12" wide		26	.615		24	41.50		65.50	87.50
3310	18" wide		22	.727		28.50	49		77.50	105
3320	24" wide		20	.800		31.50	54		85.50	115
3330	30" wide		18	.889		36.50	60		96.50	129
3380	Reducer, 12" to 6" wide		14	1.143		103	77		180	227
3400	18" to 12" wide		12	1.333		106	90		196	250
3420	18" to 6" wide		12	1.333		106	90		196	250
3440	24" to 18" wide		10.60	1.509		113	102		215	275
3460	24" to 12" wide		10.60	1.509		113	102		215	275
3480	30" to 24" wide		9.20	1.739		123	117		240	310
3500	30" to 18" wide		9.20	1.739		123	117		240	310

26 05 36 – Cable Trays for Electrical Systems

26 05 36.20 Cable Tray Solid Bottom		Crew	Daily Output	Labor-Hours	Unit	Material	Labor	Equipment	Total	Total Incl O&P
3520	30″ to 12″ wide	2 Elec	9.20	1.739	Ea.	123	117		240	310
3540	36″ to 30″ wide		8	2		129	135		264	340
3560	36″ to 24″ wide		8	2		131	135		266	345
3580	36″ to 18″ wide		8	2		131	135		266	345
3600	36″ to 12″ wide		8	2		134	135		269	350

2023 Bare Costs: Material, Labor, Equipment, Total

26 05 36.30 Cable Tray Trough		Crew	Daily Output	Labor-Hours	Unit	Material	Labor	Equipment	Total	Total Incl O&P
0010	**CABLE TRAY TROUGH** vented, w/ftngs. & supports, 6″ deep, to 10′ high									
0020	For higher elevations, see Section 26 05 36.40									
0200	Galvanized steel, tray, 6″ wide R260536-10	2 Elec	90	.178	L.F.	18.75	11.95		30.70	38.50
0240	12″ wide		80	.200		22	13.45		35.45	44.50
0260	18″ wide		70	.229		28	15.40		43.40	54
0280	24″ wide R260536-11		60	.267		57.50	17.95		75.45	90
0300	30″ wide		50	.320		54.50	21.50		76	92
0340	Elbow horizontal, 90°, 12″ radius, 6″ wide		7.60	2.105	Ea.	152	142		294	380
0360	12″ wide		5.60	2.857		181	192		373	485
0370	18″ wide		4.40	3.636		208	245		453	595
0380	24″ wide		3.60	4.444		258	299		557	730
0390	30″ wide		3.20	5		291	335		626	820
0420	24″ radius, 6″ wide		7.20	2.222		225	150		375	470
0440	12″ wide		5.20	3.077		260	207		467	595
0450	18″ wide		4	4		315	269		584	745
0460	24″ wide		3.20	5		355	335		690	890
0470	30″ wide		2.80	5.714		410	385		795	1,025
0500	36″ radius, 6″ wide		6.80	2.353		292	158		450	555
0520	12″ wide		4.80	3.333		330	225		555	700
0530	18″ wide		3.60	4.444		400	299		699	885
0540	24″ wide		2.80	5.714		410	385		795	1,025
0550	30″ wide		2.40	6.667		460	450		910	1,175
0580	Elbow vertical, 90°, 12″ radius, 6″ wide		7.60	2.105		165	142		307	395
0600	12″ wide		5.60	2.857		183	192		375	490
0610	18″ wide		4.40	3.636		186	245		431	570
0620	24″ wide		3.60	4.444		213	299		512	680
0630	30″ wide		3.20	5		218	335		553	740
0660	24″ radius, 6″ wide		7.20	2.222		236	150		386	480
0680	12″ wide		5.20	3.077		250	207		457	585
0690	18″ wide		4	4		277	269		546	705
0700	24″ wide		3.20	5		287	335		622	815
0710	30″ wide		2.80	5.714		320	385		705	925
0740	36″ radius, 6″ wide		6.80	2.353		320	158		478	585
0760	12″ wide		4.80	3.333		340	225		565	710
0770	18″ wide		3.60	4.444		375	299		674	860
0780	24″ wide		2.80	5.714		405	385		790	1,025
0790	30″ wide		2.40	6.667		415	450		865	1,125
0820	Tee horizontal, 12″ radius, 6″ wide		4	4		193	269		462	610
0840	12″ wide		3.20	5		216	335		551	735
0850	18″ wide		2.80	5.714		243	385		628	835
0860	24″ wide		2.40	6.667		282	450		732	975
0870	30″ wide		2.20	7.273		320	490		810	1,075
0900	24″ radius, 6″ wide		3.60	4.444		320	299		619	795
0920	12″ wide		2.80	5.714		350	385		735	955
0930	18″ wide		2.40	6.667		390	450		840	1,100
0940	24″ wide		2	8		505	540		1,045	1,350

26 05 36 – Cable Trays for Electrical Systems

26 05 36.30 Cable Tray Trough		Crew	Daily Output	Labor-Hours	Unit	2023 Bare Costs Material	Labor	Equipment	Total	Total Incl O&P
0950	30″ wide	2 Elec	1.80	8.889	Ea.	550	600		1,150	1,500
0980	36″ radius, 6″ wide		3.20	5		460	335		795	1,000
1000	12″ wide		2.40	6.667		525	450		975	1,250
1010	18″ wide		2	8		570	540		1,110	1,425
1020	24″ wide		1.60	10		690	675		1,365	1,750
1030	30″ wide		1.40	11.429		730	770		1,500	1,950
1060	Tee vertical, 12″ radius, 6″ wide		4	4		305	269		574	735
1080	12″ wide		3.20	5		310	335		645	840
1090	18″ wide		3	5.333		320	360		680	885
1100	24″ wide		2.80	5.714		335	385		720	940
1110	30″ wide		2.60	6.154		355	415		770	1,000
1140	24″ radius, 6″ wide		3.60	4.444		410	299		709	895
1160	12″ wide		2.80	5.714		430	385		815	1,050
1170	18″ wide		2.60	6.154		450	415		865	1,100
1180	24″ wide		2.40	6.667		485	450		935	1,200
1190	30″ wide		2.20	7.273		510	490		1,000	1,300
1220	36″ radius, 6″ wide		3.20	5		665	335		1,000	1,225
1240	12″ wide		2.40	6.667		685	450		1,135	1,425
1250	18″ wide		2.20	7.273		705	490		1,195	1,500
1260	24″ wide		2	8		745	540		1,285	1,625
1270	30″ wide		1.80	8.889		870	600		1,470	1,850
1300	Cross horizontal, 12″ radius, 6″ wide		3.20	5		240	335		575	765
1320	12″ wide		2.80	5.714		243	385		628	835
1330	18″ wide		2.40	6.667		271	450		721	965
1340	24″ wide		2	8		285	540		825	1,125
1350	30″ wide		1.80	8.889		320	600		920	1,250
1380	24″ radius, 6″ wide		2.80	5.714		380	385		765	985
1400	12″ wide		2.40	6.667		395	450		845	1,100
1410	18″ wide		2	8		435	540		975	1,275
1420	24″ wide		1.60	10		555	675		1,230	1,600
1430	30″ wide		1.40	11.429		610	770		1,380	1,825
1460	36″ radius, 6″ wide		2.40	6.667		645	450		1,095	1,375
1480	12″ wide		2	8		670	540		1,210	1,525
1490	18″ wide		1.60	10		685	675		1,360	1,750
1500	24″ wide		1.20	13.333		820	900		1,720	2,225
1510	30″ wide		1	16		905	1,075		1,980	2,600
1540	Dropout or end plate, 6″ wide		26	.615		28.50	41.50		70	93
1560	12″ wide		22	.727		35	49		84	112
1580	18″ wide		20	.800		38.50	54		92.50	123
1600	24″ wide		18	.889		44.50	60		104.50	138
1620	30″ wide		16	1		47.50	67.50		115	152
1660	Reducer, 12″ to 6″ wide		9.40	1.702		117	115		232	299
1680	18″ to 12″ wide		8.40	1.905		121	128		249	325
1700	18″ to 6″ wide		8.40	1.905		121	128		249	325
1720	24″ to 18″ wide		7.20	2.222		129	150		279	365
1740	24″ to 12″ wide		7.20	2.222		129	150		279	365
1760	30″ to 24″ wide		6.40	2.500		134	168		302	400
1780	30″ to 18″ wide		6.40	2.500		134	168		302	400
1800	30″ to 12″ wide		6.40	2.500		134	168		302	400
1820	36″ to 30″ wide		5.80	2.759		144	186		330	435
1840	36″ to 24″ wide		5.80	2.759		144	186		330	435
1860	36″ to 18″ wide		5.80	2.759		146	186		332	435
1880	36″ to 12″ wide		5.80	2.759		146	186		332	435

26 05 36.30 Cable Tray Trough		Crew	Daily Output	Labor-Hours	Unit	2023 Bare Costs Material	Labor	Equipment	Total	Total Incl O&P
2000	Aluminum, tray, vented, 6" wide	2 Elec	120	.133	L.F.	21	9		30	36.50
2010	9" wide		110	.145		24	9.80		33.80	40.50
2020	12" wide		100	.160		35	10.80		45.80	55
2030	18" wide		90	.178		32	11.95		43.95	53
2040	24" wide		80	.200		37.50	13.45		50.95	61.50
2050	30" wide		70	.229		50	15.40		65.40	78
2080	Elbow horiz., 90°, 12" radius, 6" wide		7.60	2.105	Ea.	132	142		274	355
2090	9" wide		7	2.286		143	154		297	385
2100	12" wide		6.20	2.581		152	174		326	425
2110	18" wide		5.60	2.857		178	192		370	480
2120	24" wide		4.60	3.478		205	234		439	575
2130	30" wide		4	4		253	269		522	680
2160	24" radius, 6" wide		7.20	2.222		191	150		341	430
2180	12" wide		5.80	2.759		224	186		410	520
2190	18" wide		5.20	3.077		257	207		464	590
2200	24" wide		4.20	3.810		293	257		550	705
2210	30" wide		3.60	4.444		335	299		634	815
2240	36" radius, 6" wide		6.80	2.353		276	158		434	540
2260	12" wide		5.40	2.963		315	200		515	640
2270	18" wide		4.80	3.333		355	225		580	730
2280	24" wide		3.80	4.211		390	284		674	850
2290	30" wide		3.40	4.706		460	315		775	975
2320	Elbow vertical, 90°, 12" radius, 6" wide		7.60	2.105		160	142		302	385
2330	9" wide		7	2.286		171	154		325	415
2340	12" wide		6.20	2.581		172	174		346	450
2350	18" wide		5.60	2.857		178	192		370	480
2360	24" wide		4.60	3.478		196	234		430	565
2370	30" wide		4	4		205	269		474	625
2400	24" radius, 6" wide		7.20	2.222		216	150		366	460
2420	12" wide		5.80	2.759		235	186		421	535
2430	18" wide		5.20	3.077		255	207		462	590
2440	24" wide		4.20	3.810		259	257		516	665
2450	30" wide		3.60	4.444		273	299		572	745
2480	36" radius, 6" wide		6.80	2.353		274	158		432	535
2500	12" wide		5.40	2.963		293	200		493	615
2510	18" wide		4.80	3.333		330	225		555	695
2520	24" wide		3.80	4.211		355	284		639	810
2530	30" wide		3.40	4.706		390	315		705	900
2560	Tee horizontal, 12" radius, 6" wide		4	4		200	269		469	620
2570	9" wide		3.80	4.211		205	284		489	645
2580	12" wide		3.60	4.444		224	299		523	690
2590	18" wide		3.20	5		259	335		594	785
2600	24" wide		2.80	5.714		297	385		682	895
2610	30" wide		2.40	6.667		320	450		770	1,025
2640	24" radius, 6" wide		3.60	4.444		305	299		604	780
2660	12" wide		3.20	5		345	335		680	880
2670	18" wide		2.80	5.714		380	385		765	990
2680	24" wide		2.40	6.667		475	450		925	1,200
2690	30" wide		2	8		515	540		1,055	1,375
2720	36" radius, 6" wide		3.20	5		490	335		825	1,050
2740	12" wide		2.80	5.714		565	385		950	1,200
2750	18" wide		2.40	6.667		640	450		1,090	1,375
2760	24" wide		2	8		745	540		1,285	1,625

26 05 36.30 Cable Tray Trough		Crew	Daily Output	Labor-Hours	Unit	Material	Labor	Equipment	Total	Total Incl O&P
						2023 Bare Costs				
2770	30″ wide	2 Elec	1.60	10	Ea.	790	675		1,465	1,875
2800	Tee vertical, 12″ radius, 6″ wide		4	4		282	269		551	710
2810	9″ wide		3.80	4.211		284	284		568	730
2820	12″ wide		3.60	4.444		305	299		604	780
2830	18″ wide		3.40	4.706		310	315		625	810
2840	24″ wide		3.20	5		315	335		650	845
2850	30″ wide		3	5.333		330	360		690	895
2880	24″ radius, 6″ wide		3.60	4.444		400	299		699	885
2900	12″ wide		3.20	5		430	335		765	975
2910	18″ wide		3	5.333		460	360		820	1,050
2920	24″ wide		2.80	5.714		490	385		875	1,100
2930	30″ wide		2.60	6.154		530	415		945	1,200
2960	36″ radius, 6″ wide		3.20	5		600	335		935	1,150
2980	12″ wide		2.80	5.714		640	385		1,025	1,275
2990	18″ wide		2.60	6.154		660	415		1,075	1,350
3000	24″ wide		2.40	6.667		705	450		1,155	1,450
3010	30″ wide		2.20	7.273		765	490		1,255	1,575
3040	Cross horizontal, 12″ radius, 6″ wide		3.60	4.444		249	299		548	720
3050	9″ wide		3.40	4.706		268	315		583	765
3060	12″ wide		3.20	5		275	335		610	805
3070	18″ wide		2.80	5.714		288	385		673	885
3080	24″ wide		2.40	6.667		320	450		770	1,025
3090	30″ wide		2.20	7.273		410	490		900	1,175
3120	24″ radius, 6″ wide		3.20	5		445	335		780	990
3140	12″ wide		2.80	5.714		490	385		875	1,100
3150	18″ wide		2.40	6.667		530	450		980	1,250
3160	24″ wide		2	8		610	540		1,150	1,475
3170	30″ wide		1.80	8.889		660	600		1,260	1,625
3200	36″ radius, 6″ wide		2.80	5.714		780	385		1,165	1,425
3220	12″ wide		2.40	6.667		815	450		1,265	1,575
3230	18″ wide		2	8		890	540		1,430	1,775
3240	24″ wide		1.60	10		1,025	675		1,700	2,125
3250	30″ wide		1.40	11.429		1,125	770		1,895	2,375
3280	Dropout, or end plate, 6″ wide		26	.615		21.50	41.50		63	85
3300	12″ wide		22	.727		30	49		79	107
3310	18″ wide		20	.800		36.50	54		90.50	120
3320	24″ wide		18	.889		44	60		104	138
3330	30″ wide		16	1		47	67.50		114.50	152
3370	Reducer, 9″ to 6″ wide		12	1.333		125	90		215	271
3380	12″ to 6″ wide		11.40	1.404		131	94.50		225.50	285
3390	12″ to 9″ wide		11.40	1.404		131	94.50		225.50	285
3400	18″ to 12″ wide		9.60	1.667		141	112		253	320
3420	18″ to 6″ wide		9.60	1.667		141	112		253	320
3430	18″ to 9″ wide		9.60	1.667		141	112		253	320
3440	24″ to 18″ wide		8.40	1.905		150	128		278	355
3460	24″ to 12″ wide		8.40	1.905		150	128		278	355
3470	24″ to 9″ wide		8.40	1.905		152	128		280	360
3475	24″ to 6″ wide		8.40	1.905		152	128		280	360
3480	30″ to 24″ wide		7.20	2.222		154	150		304	390
3500	30″ to 18″ wide		7.20	2.222		154	150		304	390
3520	30″ to 12″ wide		7.20	2.222		158	150		308	395
3540	36″ to 30″ wide		6.40	2.500		160	168		328	425
3560	36″ to 24″ wide	↓	6.40	2.500	↓	160	168		328	425

26 05 36.30 Cable Tray Trough		Crew	Daily Output	Labor-Hours	Unit	Material	Labor	Equipment	Total	Total Incl O&P
						2023 Bare Costs				
3580	36" to 18" wide	2 Elec	6.40	2.500	Ea.	160	168		328	425
3600	36" to 12" wide		6.40	2.500		160	168		328	425
3610	Elbow horizontal, 60°, 12" radius, 6" wide		7.80	2.051		109	138		247	325
3620	9" wide		7.20	2.222		119	150		269	355
3630	12" wide		6.40	2.500		131	168		299	395
3640	18" wide		5.80	2.759		147	186		333	440
3650	24" wide		4.80	3.333		173	225		398	525
3680	Elbow horizontal, 45°, 12" radius, 6" wide		8	2		74.50	135		209.50	282
3690	9" wide		7.40	2.162		99.50	146		245.50	325
3700	12" wide		6.60	2.424		105	163		268	360
3710	18" wide		6	2.667		118	180		298	395
3720	24" wide		5	3.200		138	216		354	470
3750	Elbow horizontal, 30°, 12" radius, 6" wide		8.20	1.951		82	131		213	286
3760	9" wide		7.60	2.105		86	142		228	305
3770	12" wide		6.80	2.353		94	158		252	340
3780	18" wide		6.20	2.581		99.50	174		273.50	365
3790	24" wide		5.20	3.077		109	207		316	430
3820	Elbow vertical, 60° in/outside, 12" radius, 6" wide		7.80	2.051		135	138		273	355
3830	9" wide		7.20	2.222		137	150		287	375
3840	12" wide		6.40	2.500		139	168		307	405
3850	18" wide		5.80	2.759		145	186		331	435
3860	24" wide		4.80	3.333		150	225		375	500
3890	Elbow vertical, 45° in/outside, 12" radius, 6" wide		8	2		86.50	135		221.50	296
3900	9" wide		7.40	2.162		111	146		257	340
3910	12" wide		6.60	2.424		119	163		282	375
3920	18" wide		6	2.667		123	180		303	400
3930	24" wide		5	3.200		135	216		351	470
3960	Elbow vertical, 30° in/outside, 12" radius, 6" wide		8.20	1.951		93.50	131		224.50	298
3970	9" wide		7.60	2.105		99.50	142		241.50	320
3980	12" wide		6.80	2.353		101	158		259	350
3990	18" wide		6.20	2.581		106	174		280	375
4000	24" wide		5.20	3.077		107	207		314	430
4250	Reducer, left or right hand, 24" to 18" wide		8.40	1.905		143	128		271	350
4260	24" to 12" wide		8.40	1.905		143	128		271	350
4270	24" to 9" wide		8.40	1.905		143	128		271	350
4280	24" to 6" wide		8.40	1.905		145	128		273	350
4290	18" to 12" wide		9.60	1.667		133	112		245	315
4300	18" to 9" wide		9.60	1.667		133	112		245	315
4310	18" to 6" wide		9.60	1.667		133	112		245	315
4320	12" to 9" wide		11.40	1.404		128	94.50		222.50	280
4330	12" to 6" wide		11.40	1.404		128	94.50		222.50	280
4340	9" to 6" wide		12	1.333		124	90		214	269
4350	Splice plate	1 Elec	48	.167		11.85	11.25		23.10	29.50
4360	Splice plate, expansion joint		48	.167		12.15	11.25		23.40	30
4370	Splice plate, hinged, horizontal		48	.167		9.75	11.25		21	27.50
4380	Vertical		48	.167		13.90	11.25		25.15	32
4390	Trough, hanger, vertical		28	.286		39	19.25		58.25	71.50
4400	Box connector, 24" wide		20	.400		52	27		79	97
4410	18" wide		21	.381		44	25.50		69.50	86.50
4420	12" wide		22	.364		42	24.50		66.50	83
4430	9" wide		23	.348		40	23.50		63.50	79
4440	6" wide		24	.333		38	22.50		60.50	75.50
4450	Floor flange		24	.333		40	22.50		62.50	77.50

26 05 36.30 Cable Tray Trough			Crew	Daily Output	Labor-Hours	Unit	Material	Labor	Equipment	Total	Total Incl O&P
							2023 Bare Costs				
4460	Hold down clamp		1 Elec	60	.133	Ea.	4.59	9		13.59	18.40
4520	Wall bracket, 24" wide tray			20	.400		45.50	27		72.50	90.50
4530	18" wide tray			21	.381		44.50	25.50		70	87
4540	12" wide tray			22	.364		24	24.50		48.50	62.50
4550	9" wide tray			23	.348		21.50	23.50		45	58.50
4560	6" wide tray			24	.333		19.35	22.50		41.85	55
5000	Cable channel aluminum, vented, 1-1/4" deep, 4" wide, straight			80	.100	L.F.	10.40	6.75		17.15	21.50
5010	Elbow horizontal, 36" radius, 90°			5	1.600	Ea.	188	108		296	365
5020	60°			5.50	1.455		144	98		242	305
5030	45°			6	1.333		117	90		207	262
5040	30°			6.50	1.231		100	83		183	233
5050	Adjustable			6	1.333		95.50	90		185.50	238
5060	Elbow vertical, 36" radius, 90°			5	1.600		202	108		310	380
5070	60°			5.50	1.455		155	98		253	315
5080	45°			6	1.333		127	90		217	273
5090	30°			6.50	1.231		113	83		196	247
5100	Adjustable			6	1.333		95.50	90		185.50	238
5110	Splice plate, hinged, horizontal			48	.167		12.05	11.25		23.30	30
5120	Splice plate, hinged, vertical			48	.167		17.05	11.25		28.30	35.50
5130	Hanger, vertical			28	.286		18.80	19.25		38.05	49
5140	Single			28	.286		28.50	19.25		47.75	60
5150	Double			20	.400		29	27		56	72
5160	Channel to box connector			24	.333		39	22.50		61.50	76.50
5170	Hold down clip			80	.100		5.45	6.75		12.20	15.95
5180	Wall bracket, single			28	.286		15.35	19.25		34.60	45.50
5190	Double			20	.400		19.70	27		46.70	61.50
5200	Cable roller			16	.500		241	33.50		274.50	315
5210	Splice plate			48	.167		7.40	11.25		18.65	25

26 05 36.36 Cable Trays for Utility Substations			Crew	Daily Output	Labor-Hours	Unit	Material	Labor	Equipment	Total	Total Incl O&P
0010	**CABLE TRAYS FOR UTILITY SUBSTATIONS**										
7700	Cable tray		R-11	40	1.400	L.F.	28	90	58.50	176.50	229
7790	See Section 26 05 36										

26 05 36.40 Cable Tray, Covers and Dividers			Crew	Daily Output	Labor-Hours	Unit	Material	Labor	Equipment	Total	Total Incl O&P
0010	**CABLE TRAY, COVERS AND DIVIDERS** To 10' high	R260536-10									
0011	For higher elevations, see lines 9900 – 9960										
0100	Covers, ventilated galv. steel, straight, 6" wide tray size		2 Elec	520	.031	L.F.	6.20	2.07		8.27	9.95
0200	9" wide tray size			460	.035		8.40	2.34		10.74	12.75
0300	12" wide tray size	R260536-11		400	.040		10.25	2.69		12.94	15.30
0400	18" wide tray size			300	.053		14.75	3.59		18.34	21.50
0500	24" wide tray size			220	.073		28.50	4.90		33.40	39
0600	30" wide tray size			180	.089		25.50	6		31.50	37
1000	Elbow horizontal, 90°, 12" radius, 6" wide tray size			150	.107	Ea.	45	7.20		52.20	60
1020	9" wide tray size			128	.125		50	8.40		58.40	67.50
1040	12" wide tray size			108	.148		52.50	10		62.50	73
1060	18" wide tray size			84	.190		73	12.85		85.85	99
1080	24" wide tray size			66	.242		88	16.35		104.35	122
1100	30" wide tray size			60	.267		112	17.95		129.95	150
1160	24" radius, 6" wide tray size			136	.118		75	7.90		82.90	94.50
1180	9" wide tray size			116	.138		76.50	9.30		85.80	98.50
1200	12" wide tray size			96	.167		85.50	11.25		96.75	111
1220	18" wide tray size			76	.211		105	14.20		119.20	137
1240	24" wide tray size			60	.267		128	17.95		145.95	168

26 05 36 – Cable Trays for Electrical Systems

26 05 36.40 Cable Tray, Covers and Dividers		Crew	Daily Output	Labor-Hours	Unit	Material	Labor	Equipment	Total	Total Incl O&P
						2023 Bare Costs				
1260	30" wide tray size	2 Elec	52	.308	Ea.	169	20.50		189.50	216
1320	36" radius, 6" wide tray size		120	.133		112	9		121	136
1340	9" wide tray size		104	.154		123	10.35		133.35	151
1360	12" wide tray size		84	.190		132	12.85		144.85	164
1380	18" wide tray size		72	.222		167	14.95		181.95	206
1400	24" wide tray size		52	.308		199	20.50		219.50	250
1420	30" wide tray size		46	.348		237	23.50		260.50	296
1480	Elbow horizontal, 45°, 12" radius, 6" wide tray size		150	.107		33.50	7.20		40.70	47.50
1500	9" wide tray size		128	.125		40.50	8.40		48.90	57
1520	12" wide tray size		108	.148		44	10		54	63
1540	18" wide tray size		88	.182		53.50	12.25		65.75	77
1560	24" wide tray size		76	.211		62.50	14.20		76.70	89.50
1580	30" wide tray size		66	.242		73.50	16.35		89.85	106
1640	24" radius, 6" wide tray size		136	.118		47	7.90		54.90	63.50
1660	9" wide tray size		116	.138		52.50	9.30		61.80	72
1680	12" wide tray size		96	.167		59.50	11.25		70.75	81.50
1700	18" wide tray size		80	.200		69	13.45		82.45	96
1720	24" wide tray size		70	.229		78.50	15.40		93.90	110
1740	30" wide tray size		60	.267		99.50	17.95		117.45	137
1800	36" radius, 6" wide tray size		120	.133		69.50	9		78.50	90
1820	9" wide tray size		104	.154		78.50	10.35		88.85	101
1840	12" wide tray size		84	.190		86	12.85		98.85	114
1860	18" wide tray size		76	.211		99	14.20		113.20	130
1880	24" wide tray size		62	.258		120	17.40		137.40	158
1900	30" wide tray size		52	.308		131	20.50		151.50	175
1960	Elbow vertical, 90°, 12" radius, 6" wide tray size		150	.107		39.50	7.20		46.70	54
1980	9" wide tray size		128	.125		40.50	8.40		48.90	57
2000	12" wide tray size		108	.148		43.50	10		53.50	63
2020	18" wide tray size		88	.182		49.50	12.25		61.75	72.50
2040	24" wide tray size		68	.235		50.50	15.85		66.35	79
2060	30" wide tray size		60	.267		55.50	17.95		73.45	87.50
2120	24" radius, 6" wide tray size		136	.118		48.50	7.90		56.40	65.50
2140	9" wide tray size		116	.138		53.50	9.30		62.80	73
2160	12" wide tray size		96	.167		55.50	11.25		66.75	77.50
2180	18" wide tray size		80	.200		73.50	13.45		86.95	101
2200	24" wide tray size		62	.258		82.50	17.40		99.90	117
2220	30" wide tray size		52	.308		91	20.50		111.50	131
2280	36" radius, 6" wide tray size		120	.133		55	9		64	74
2300	9" wide tray size		104	.154		70.50	10.35		80.85	93
2320	12" wide tray size		84	.190		78.50	12.85		91.35	105
2340	18" wide tray size		76	.211		99	14.20		113.20	130
2350	24" wide tray size		54	.296		109	19.95		128.95	150
2360	30" wide tray size		46	.348		131	23.50		154.50	179
2400	Tee horizontal, 12" radius, 6" wide tray size		92	.174		71.50	11.70		83.20	96.50
2410	9" wide tray size		80	.200		73.50	13.45		86.95	101
2420	12" wide tray size		68	.235		83.50	15.85		99.35	115
2430	18" wide tray size		60	.267		101	17.95		118.95	138
2440	24" wide tray size		52	.308		127	20.50		147.50	171
2460	30" wide tray size		36	.444		149	30		179	209
2500	24" radius, 6" wide tray size		88	.182		115	12.25		127.25	145
2510	9" wide tray size		76	.211		123	14.20		137.20	156
2520	12" wide tray size		64	.250		126	16.85		142.85	164
2530	18" wide tray size	↓	56	.286	↓	162	19.25		181.25	207

26 05 36.40 Cable Tray, Covers and Dividers		Crew	Daily Output	Labor-Hours	Unit	2023 Bare Costs Material	Labor	Equipment	Total	Total Incl O&P
2540	24" wide tray size	2 Elec	48	.333	Ea.	249	22.50		271.50	310
2560	30" wide tray size		32	.500		284	33.50		317.50	360
2600	36" radius, 6" wide tray size		84	.190		198	12.85		210.85	236
2610	9" wide tray size		72	.222		201	14.95		215.95	243
2620	12" wide tray size		60	.267		224	17.95		241.95	273
2630	18" wide tray size		52	.308		261	20.50		281.50	320
2640	24" wide tray size		44	.364		345	24.50		369.50	415
2660	30" wide tray size		28	.571		375	38.50		413.50	465
2700	Cross horizontal, 12" radius, 6" wide tray size		68	.235		107	15.85		122.85	142
2710	9" wide tray size		64	.250		113	16.85		129.85	149
2720	12" wide tray size		60	.267		126	17.95		143.95	166
2730	18" wide tray size		52	.308		149	20.50		169.50	195
2740	24" wide tray size		36	.444		177	30		207	240
2760	30" wide tray size		30	.533		201	36		237	275
2800	24" radius, 6" wide tray size		64	.250		193	16.85		209.85	238
2810	9" wide tray size		60	.267		210	17.95		227.95	258
2820	12" wide tray size		56	.286		227	19.25		246.25	278
2830	18" wide tray size		48	.333		271	22.50		293.50	330
2840	24" wide tray size		32	.500		330	33.50		363.50	415
2860	30" wide tray size		26	.615		365	41.50		406.50	460
2900	36" radius, 6" wide tray size		60	.267		330	17.95		347.95	390
2910	9" wide tray size		56	.286		330	19.25		349.25	390
2920	12" wide tray size		52	.308		360	20.50		380.50	425
2930	18" wide tray size		44	.364		405	24.50		429.50	480
2940	24" wide tray size		28	.571		505	38.50		543.50	615
2960	30" wide tray size		22	.727		545	49		594	675
3000	Reducer, 9" to 6" wide tray size		128	.125		46	8.40		54.40	63
3010	12" to 6" wide tray size		108	.148		48	10		58	67.50
3020	12" to 9" wide tray size		108	.148		48	10		58	67.50
3030	18" to 12" wide tray size		88	.182		51	12.25		63.25	74
3050	18" to 6" wide tray size		88	.182		51	12.25		63.25	74
3060	24" to 18" wide tray size		80	.200		71.50	13.45		84.95	98.50
3070	24" to 12" wide tray size		80	.200		65.50	13.45		78.95	92
3090	30" to 24" wide tray size		70	.229		75.50	15.40		90.90	106
3100	30" to 18" wide tray size		70	.229		75.50	15.40		90.90	106
3110	30" to 12" wide tray size		70	.229		65.50	15.40		80.90	95
3140	36" to 30" wide tray size		64	.250		82.50	16.85		99.35	116
3150	36" to 24" wide tray size		64	.250		82.50	16.85		99.35	116
3160	36" to 18" wide tray size		64	.250		82.50	16.85		99.35	116
3170	36" to 12" wide tray size		64	.250		82.50	16.85		99.35	116
3250	Covers, aluminum, straight, 6" wide tray size		520	.031	L.F.	4	2.07		6.07	7.50
3270	9" wide tray size		460	.035		4.82	2.34		7.16	8.80
3290	12" wide tray size		400	.040		5.75	2.69		8.44	10.35
3310	18" wide tray size		320	.050		7.60	3.37		10.97	13.35
3330	24" wide tray size		260	.062		9.50	4.14		13.64	16.60
3350	30" wide tray size		200	.080		10.50	5.40		15.90	19.55
3400	Elbow horizontal, 90°, 12" radius, 6" wide tray size		150	.107	Ea.	30	7.20		37.20	43.50
3410	9" wide tray size		128	.125		31	8.40		39.40	47
3420	12" wide tray size		108	.148		33.50	10		43.50	52
3430	18" wide tray size		88	.182		58	12.25		70.25	82
3440	24" wide tray size		70	.229		73.50	15.40		88.90	104
3460	30" wide tray size		64	.250		88	16.85		104.85	122
3500	24" radius, 6" wide tray size		136	.118		51	7.90		58.90	68

26 05 36.40 Cable Tray, Covers and Dividers		Crew	Daily Output	Labor-Hours	Unit	2023 Bare Costs Material	Labor	Equipment	Total	Total Incl O&P
3510	9" wide tray size	2 Elec	116	.138	Ea.	63	9.30		72.30	83.50
3520	12" wide tray size		96	.167		69.50	11.25		80.75	92.50
3530	18" wide tray size		80	.200		82	13.45		95.45	111
3540	24" wide tray size		64	.250		102	16.85		118.85	137
3560	30" wide tray size		56	.286		124	19.25		143.25	165
3600	36" radius, 6" wide tray size		120	.133		89.50	9		98.50	111
3610	9" wide tray size		104	.154		97.50	10.35		107.85	122
3620	12" wide tray size		84	.190		111	12.85		123.85	141
3630	18" wide tray size		76	.211		132	14.20		146.20	166
3640	24" wide tray size		56	.286		160	19.25		179.25	205
3660	30" wide tray size		50	.320		184	21.50		205.50	235
3700	Elbow horizontal, 45°, 12" radius, 6" wide tray size		150	.107		29	7.20		36.20	42.50
3710	9" wide tray size		128	.125		30	8.40		38.40	45.50
3720	12" wide tray size		108	.148		33.50	10		43.50	52
3730	18" wide tray size		88	.182		38.50	12.25		50.75	60
3740	24" wide tray size		80	.200		42.50	13.45		55.95	67
3760	30" wide tray size		70	.229		54	15.40		69.40	82
3800	24" radius, 6" wide tray size		136	.118		32	7.90		39.90	47
3810	9" wide tray size		116	.138		40.50	9.30		49.80	58.50
3820	12" wide tray size		96	.167		42	11.25		53.25	62.50
3830	18" wide tray size		80	.200		51	13.45		64.45	76
3840	24" wide tray size		72	.222		63	14.95		77.95	91.50
3860	30" wide tray size		64	.250		72.50	16.85		89.35	105
3900	36" radius, 6" wide tray size		120	.133		56	9		65	75.50
3910	9" wide tray size		104	.154		61	10.35		71.35	83
3920	12" wide tray size		84	.190		64.50	12.85		77.35	90
3930	18" wide tray size		76	.211		77.50	14.20		91.70	107
3940	24" wide tray size		64	.250		94	16.85		110.85	129
3960	30" wide tray size		56	.286		107	19.25		126.25	147
3970	36" wide tray size		50	.320		122	21.50		143.50	166
4000	Elbow vertical, 90°, 12" radius, 6" wide tray size		150	.107		33.50	7.20		40.70	47.50
4010	9" wide tray size		128	.125		33.50	8.40		41.90	49.50
4020	12" wide tray size		108	.148		36.50	10		46.50	55.50
4030	18" wide tray size		88	.182		42.50	12.25		54.75	65
4040	24" wide tray size		70	.229		44.50	15.40		59.90	71.50
4060	30" wide tray size		64	.250		45.50	16.85		62.35	75
4070	36" wide tray size		54	.296		54.50	19.95		74.45	89.50
4100	24" radius, 6" wide tray size		136	.118		38.50	7.90		46.40	54
4110	9" wide tray size		116	.138		42	9.30		51.30	60
4120	12" wide tray size		96	.167		45.50	11.25		56.75	66.50
4130	18" wide tray size		80	.200		54.50	13.45		67.95	80
4140	24" wide tray size		64	.250		59.50	16.85		76.35	90.50
4160	30" wide tray size		56	.286		72.50	19.25		91.75	109
4170	36" wide tray size		48	.333		79	22.50		101.50	121
4200	36" radius, 6" wide tray size		120	.133		43	9		52	60.50
4210	9" wide tray size		104	.154		53	10.35		63.35	73.50
4220	12" wide tray size		84	.190		61	12.85		73.85	86.50
4230	18" wide tray size		76	.211		74.50	14.20		88.70	103
4240	24" wide tray size		56	.286		87.50	19.25		106.75	125
4260	30" wide tray size		50	.320		111	21.50		132.50	154
4270	36" wide tray size		44	.364		119	24.50		143.50	168
4300	Tee horizontal, 12" radius, 6" wide tray size		108	.148		54.50	10		64.50	75
4310	9" wide tray size		88	.182		58	12.25		70.25	82

26 05 36.40 Cable Tray, Covers and Dividers		Crew	Daily Output	Labor-Hours	Unit	Material	2023 Bare Costs Labor	Equipment	Total	Total Incl O&P
4320	12" wide tray size	2 Elec	80	.200	Ea.	65	13.45		78.45	91
4330	18" wide tray size		68	.235		76.50	15.85		92.35	108
4340	24" wide tray size		56	.286		97	19.25		116.25	136
4360	30" wide tray size		44	.364		114	24.50		138.50	163
4370	36" wide tray size		36	.444		138	30		168	197
4400	24" radius, 6" wide tray size		96	.167		88.50	11.25		99.75	114
4410	9" wide tray size		80	.200		93.50	13.45		106.95	123
4420	12" wide tray size		72	.222		105	14.95		119.95	137
4430	18" wide tray size		60	.267		123	17.95		140.95	162
4440	24" wide tray size		48	.333		195	22.50		217.50	249
4460	30" wide tray size		40	.400		216	27		243	277
4470	36" wide tray size		32	.500		240	33.50		273.50	315
4500	36" radius, 6" wide tray size		88	.182		157	12.25		169.25	191
4510	9" wide tray size		72	.222		160	14.95		174.95	198
4520	12" wide tray size		64	.250		176	16.85		192.85	219
4530	18" wide tray size		56	.286		200	19.25		219.25	249
4540	24" wide tray size		44	.364		254	24.50		278.50	315
4560	30" wide tray size		36	.444		286	30		316	360
4570	36" wide tray size		28	.571		320	38.50		358.50	410
4600	Cross horizontal, 12" radius, 6" wide tray size		80	.200		83.50	13.45		96.95	112
4610	9" wide tray size		72	.222		88.50	14.95		103.45	120
4620	12" wide tray size		64	.250		98.50	16.85		115.35	133
4630	18" wide tray size		56	.286		120	19.25		139.25	161
4640	24" wide tray size		48	.333		138	22.50		160.50	185
4660	30" wide tray size		40	.400		164	27		191	220
4670	36" wide tray size		32	.500		188	33.50		221.50	257
4700	24" radius, 6" wide tray size		72	.222		155	14.95		169.95	193
4710	9" wide tray size		64	.250		166	16.85		182.85	208
4720	12" wide tray size		56	.286		178	19.25		197.25	225
4730	18" wide tray size		48	.333		208	22.50		230.50	263
4740	24" wide tray size		40	.400		248	27		275	315
4760	30" wide tray size		32	.500		290	33.50		323.50	370
4770	36" wide tray size		24	.667		315	45		360	410
4800	36" radius, 6" wide tray size		64	.250		254	16.85		270.85	305
4810	9" wide tray size		56	.286		265	19.25		284.25	320
4820	12" wide tray size		50	.320		292	21.50		313.50	350
4830	18" wide tray size		44	.364		320	24.50		344.50	390
4840	24" wide tray size		36	.444		395	30		425	480
4860	30" wide tray size		28	.571		455	38.50		493.50	555
4870	36" wide tray size		22	.727		495	49		544	620
4900	Reducer, 9" to 6" wide tray size		128	.125		32	8.40		40.40	47.50
4910	12" to 6" wide tray size		108	.148		33	10		43	51.50
4920	12" to 9" wide tray size		108	.148		33	10		43	51.50
4930	18" to 12" wide tray size		88	.182		36.50	12.25		48.75	58
4950	18" to 6" wide tray size		88	.182		36.50	12.25		48.75	58
4960	24" to 18" wide tray size		80	.200		46.50	13.45		59.95	71.50
4970	24" to 12" wide tray size		80	.200		40	13.45		53.45	64
4990	30" to 24" wide tray size		70	.229		48.50	15.40		63.90	76.50
5000	30" to 18" wide tray size		70	.229		48.50	15.40		63.90	76.50
5010	30" to 12" wide tray size		70	.229		48.50	15.40		63.90	76.50
5040	36" to 30" wide tray size		64	.250		54	16.85		70.85	84.50
5050	36" to 24" wide tray size		64	.250		54	16.85		70.85	84.50
5060	36" to 18" wide tray size	↓	64	.250	↓	54	16.85		70.85	84.50

26 05 36.40 Cable Tray, Covers and Dividers		Crew	Daily Output	Labor-Hours	Unit	2023 Bare Costs Material	Labor	Equipment	Total	Total Incl O&P
5070	36" to 12" wide tray size	2 Elec	64	.250	Ea.	54	16.85		70.85	84.50
5710	Tray cover hold down clamp	1 Elec	60	.133		4.09	9		13.09	17.85
8000	Divider strip, straight, galvanized, 3" deep		200	.040	L.F.	5.70	2.69		8.39	10.30
8020	4" deep		180	.044		6.95	2.99		9.94	12.10
8040	6" deep		160	.050		9.10	3.37		12.47	15.05
8060	Aluminum, straight, 3" deep		210	.038		5.70	2.57		8.27	10.10
8080	4" deep		190	.042		7.05	2.84		9.89	12
8100	6" deep		170	.047		9	3.17		12.17	14.60
8110	Divider strip, vertical fitting, 3" deep									
8120	12" radius, galvanized, 30°	1 Elec	28	.286	Ea.	27.50	19.25		46.75	59
8140	45°		27	.296		34.50	19.95		54.45	67.50
8160	60°		26	.308		36.50	20.50		57	71.50
8180	90°		25	.320		46	21.50		67.50	82.50
8200	Aluminum, 30°		29	.276		14.85	18.60		33.45	44
8220	45°		28	.286		17.55	19.25		36.80	48
8240	60°		27	.296		27	19.95		46.95	59
8260	90°		26	.308		34	20.50		54.50	68.50
8280	24" radius, galvanized, 30°		25	.320		41.50	21.50		63	77.50
8300	45°		24	.333		44	22.50		66.50	82
8320	60°		23	.348		55.50	23.50		79	96
8340	90°		22	.364		75.50	24.50		100	120
8360	Aluminum, 30°		26	.308		30.50	20.50		51	65
8380	45°		25	.320		35.50	21.50		57	71
8400	60°		24	.333		44.50	22.50		67	82.50
8420	90°		23	.348		60.50	23.50		84	102
8440	36" radius, galvanized, 30°		22	.364		52.50	24.50		77	94.50
8460	45°		21	.381		61.50	25.50		87	106
8480	60°		20	.400		72	27		99	119
8500	90°		19	.421		99.50	28.50		128	152
8520	Aluminum, 30°		23	.348		47	23.50		70.50	86.50
8540	45°		22	.364		60.50	24.50		85	103
8560	60°		21	.381		78	25.50		103.50	124
8570	90°		20	.400		102	27		129	153
8590	Divider strip, vertical fitting, 4" deep									
8600	12" radius, galvanized, 30°	1 Elec	27	.296	Ea.	33	19.95		52.95	66
8610	45°		26	.308		38.50	20.50		59	73
8620	60°		25	.320		43	21.50		64.50	79.50
8630	90°		24	.333		52.50	22.50		75	91.50
8640	Aluminum, 30°		28	.286		26.50	19.25		45.75	57.50
8650	45°		27	.296		30.50	19.95		50.45	63
8660	60°		26	.308		35	20.50		55.50	69
8670	90°		25	.320		41	21.50		62.50	77
8680	24" radius, galvanized, 30°		24	.333		52.50	22.50		75	91.50
8690	45°		23	.348		66	23.50		89.50	108
8700	60°		22	.364		75	24.50		99.50	119
8710	90°		21	.381		99.50	25.50		125	148
8720	Aluminum, 30°		25	.320		41	21.50		62.50	77
8730	45°		24	.333		50	22.50		72.50	88.50
8740	60°		23	.348		59	23.50		82.50	100
8750	90°		22	.364		80.50	24.50		105	125
8760	36" radius, galvanized, 30°		23	.348		62.50	23.50		86	104
8770	45°		22	.364		71.50	24.50		96	115
8780	60°		21	.381		90	25.50		115.50	137

26 05 36 – Cable Trays for Electrical Systems

26 05 36.40 Cable Tray, Covers and Dividers		Crew	Daily Output	Labor-Hours	Unit	2023 Bare Costs Material	Labor	Equipment	Total	Total Incl O&P
8790	90°	1 Elec	20	.400	Ea.	120	27		147	172
8800	Aluminum, 30°		24	.333		64.50	22.50		87	105
8810	45°		23	.348		82.50	23.50		106	126
8820	60°		22	.364		101	24.50		125.50	148
8830	90°		21	.381		127	25.50		152.50	178
8840	Divider strip, vertical fitting, 6" deep									
8850	12" radius, galvanized, 30°	1 Elec	24	.333	Ea.	38	22.50		60.50	75
8860	45°		23	.348		42.50	23.50		66	81.50
8870	60°		22	.364		48.50	24.50		73	90
8880	90°		21	.381		60.50	25.50		86	105
8890	Aluminum, 30°		25	.320		30	21.50		51.50	65
8900	45°		24	.333		35.50	22.50		58	73
8910	60°		23	.348		37.50	23.50		61	76.50
8920	90°		22	.364		44.50	24.50		69	85
8930	24" radius, galvanized, 30°		23	.348		52.50	23.50		76	93
8940	45°		22	.364		66	24.50		90.50	110
8950	60°		21	.381		75.50	25.50		101	122
8960	90°		20	.400		99.50	27		126.50	150
8970	Aluminum, 30°		24	.333		42	22.50		64.50	79.50
8980	45°		23	.348		57	23.50		80.50	98
8990	60°		22	.364		63	24.50		87.50	106
9000	90°		21	.381		85.50	25.50		111	132
9010	36" radius, galvanized, 30°		22	.364		61.50	24.50		86	104
9020	45°		21	.381		75.50	25.50		101	122
9030	60°		20	.400		99.50	27		126.50	150
9040	90°		19	.421		131	28.50		159.50	186
9050	Aluminum, 30°		23	.348		65.50	23.50		89	107
9060	45°		22	.364		87.50	24.50		112	133
9070	60°		21	.381		103	25.50		128.50	152
9080	90°		20	.400		124	27		151	176
9120	Divider strip, horizontal fitting, galvanized, 3" deep		33	.242		37.50	16.35		53.85	66
9130	4" deep		30	.267		42	17.95		59.95	73
9140	6" deep		27	.296		54	19.95		73.95	88.50
9150	Aluminum, 3" deep		35	.229		30	15.40		45.40	56
9160	4" deep		32	.250		33	16.85		49.85	61.50
9170	6" deep		29	.276		44	18.60		62.60	75.50
9300	Divider strip protector		300	.027	L.F.	2.88	1.80		4.68	5.85
9310	Fastener, ladder tray				Ea.	.51			.51	.56
9320	Trough or solid bottom tray				"	.40			.40	.44
9900	Add to labor for higher elevated installation									
9905	10' to 14.5' high, add						10%			
9910	15' to 20' high, add						20%			
9920	20' to 25' high, add						25%			
9930	25' to 30' high, add						35%			
9940	30' to 35' high, add						40%			
9950	35' to 40' high, add						50%			
9960	Over 40' high, add						55%			

26 05 39 – Underfloor Raceways for Electrical Systems

26 05 39.30 Conduit In Concrete Slab		Crew	Daily Output	Labor-Hours	Unit	2023 Bare Costs Material	Labor	Equipment	Total	Total Incl O&P
0010	**CONDUIT IN CONCRETE SLAB** Including terminations, R260539-30									
0020	fittings and supports									
3230	PVC, schedule 40, 1/2" diameter	1 Elec	270	.030	L.F.	1.32	2		3.32	4.42
3250	3/4" diameter		230	.035		1.47	2.34		3.81	5.10
3270	1" diameter		200	.040		2	2.69		4.69	6.20
3300	1-1/4" diameter		170	.047		2.92	3.17		6.09	7.90
3330	1-1/2" diameter		140	.057		3.38	3.85		7.23	9.40
3350	2" diameter		120	.067		4.17	4.49		8.66	11.25
3370	2-1/2" diameter		90	.089		6.85	6		12.85	16.45
3400	3" diameter	2 Elec	160	.100		8.60	6.75		15.35	19.45
3430	3-1/2" diameter		120	.133		10.95	9		19.95	25.50
3440	4" diameter		100	.160		11.95	10.80		22.75	29
3450	5" diameter		80	.200		17.35	13.45		30.80	39
3460	6" diameter		60	.267		23	17.95		40.95	52
3530	Sweeps, 1" diameter, 30" radius	1 Elec	32	.250	Ea.	35	16.85		51.85	63.50
3550	1-1/4" diameter		24	.333		9.95	22.50		32.45	44.50
3570	1-1/2" diameter		21	.381		80.50	25.50		106	127
3600	2" diameter		18	.444		141	30		171	200
3630	2-1/2" diameter		14	.571		106	38.50		144.50	174
3650	3" diameter		10	.800		80.50	54		134.50	169
3670	3-1/2" diameter		8	1		65.50	67.50		133	172
3700	4" diameter		7	1.143		81.50	77		158.50	204
3710	5" diameter		6	1.333		135	90		225	282
3730	Couplings, 1/2" diameter					.23			.23	.25
3750	3/4" diameter					.28			.28	.31
3770	1" diameter					.45			.45	.50
3800	1-1/4" diameter					.67			.67	.74
3830	1-1/2" diameter					.84			.84	.92
3850	2" diameter					1.12			1.12	1.23
3870	2-1/2" diameter					2.02			2.02	2.22
3900	3" diameter					3.26			3.26	3.59
3930	3-1/2" diameter					3.66			3.66	4.03
3950	4" diameter					4.90			4.90	5.40
3960	5" diameter					11.50			11.50	12.65
3970	6" diameter					15.45			15.45	17
4030	End bells, 1" diameter, PVC	1 Elec	60	.133		5.45	9		14.45	19.35
4050	1-1/4" diameter		53	.151		8.60	10.15		18.75	24.50
4100	1-1/2" diameter		48	.167		5.40	11.25		16.65	22.50
4150	2" diameter		34	.235		8.10	15.85		23.95	32.50
4170	2-1/2" diameter		27	.296		6.45	19.95		26.40	36.50
4200	3" diameter		20	.400		9.95	27		36.95	51
4250	3-1/2" diameter		16	.500		12.45	33.50		45.95	63.50
4300	4" diameter		14	.571		11.35	38.50		49.85	69.50
4310	5" diameter		12	.667		18.70	45		63.70	87
4320	6" diameter		9	.889		18.60	60		78.60	110
4350	Rigid galvanized steel, 1/2" diameter		200	.040	L.F.	4.47	2.69		7.16	8.90
4400	3/4" diameter		170	.047		4.61	3.17		7.78	9.80
4450	1" diameter		130	.062		6.95	4.14		11.09	13.80
4500	1-1/4" diameter		110	.073		10.10	4.90		15	18.40
4600	1-1/2" diameter		100	.080		11.25	5.40		16.65	20.50
4800	2" diameter		90	.089		13.85	6		19.85	24

26 05 39 – Underfloor Raceways for Electrical Systems

26 05 39.40 Conduit In Trench		Crew	Daily Output	Labor-Hours	Unit	Material	Labor	Equipment	Total	Total Incl O&P
						2023 Bare Costs				
0010	**CONDUIT IN TRENCH** Includes terminations and fittings R260539-40									
0020	Does not include excavation or backfill, see Section 31 23 16									
0200	Rigid galvanized steel, 2" diameter	1 Elec	150	.053	L.F.	13.35	3.59		16.94	20
0400	2-1/2" diameter	"	100	.080		27	5.40		32.40	38
0600	3" diameter	2 Elec	160	.100		30.50	6.75		37.25	43.50
0800	3-1/2" diameter		140	.114		40.50	7.70		48.20	56
1000	4" diameter		100	.160		42	10.80		52.80	62
1200	5" diameter		80	.200		84.50	13.45		97.95	113
1400	6" diameter		60	.267		116	17.95		133.95	154

26 05 43 – Underground Ducts and Raceways for Electrical Systems

26 05 43.10 Trench Duct		Crew	Daily Output	Labor-Hours	Unit	Material	Labor	Equipment	Total	Total Incl O&P
0010	**TRENCH DUCT** Steel with cover									
0020	Standard adjustable, depths to 4"									
0100	Straight, single compartment, 9" wide	2 Elec	40	.400	L.F.	385	27		412	465
0200	12" wide		32	.500		455	33.50		488.50	555
0400	18" wide		26	.615		560	41.50		601.50	675
0600	24" wide		22	.727		645	49		694	785
0700	27" wide		21	.762		232	51.50		283.50	330
0800	30" wide		20	.800		249	54		303	355
1000	36" wide		16	1		276	67.50		343.50	405
1020	Two compartment, 9" wide		38	.421		133	28.50		161.50	188
1030	12" wide		30	.533		156	36		192	226
1040	18" wide		24	.667		221	45		266	310
1050	24" wide		20	.800		274	54		328	380
1060	30" wide		18	.889		350	60		410	475
1070	36" wide		14	1.143		385	77		462	540
1090	Three compartment, 9" wide		36	.444		168	30		198	230
1100	12" wide		28	.571		195	38.50		233.50	271
1110	18" wide		22	.727		237	49		286	335
1120	24" wide		18	.889		296	60		356	415
1130	30" wide		16	1		370	67.50		437.50	505
1140	36" wide		12	1.333		420	90		510	595
1200	Horizontal elbow, 9" wide		5.40	2.963	Ea.	450	200		650	790
1400	12" wide		4.60	3.478		475	234		709	870
1600	18" wide		4	4		640	269		909	1,100
1800	24" wide		3.20	5		900	335		1,235	1,500
1900	27" wide		3	5.333		1,075	360		1,435	1,700
2000	30" wide		2.60	6.154		1,325	415		1,740	2,075
2200	36" wide		2.40	6.667		1,575	450		2,025	2,400
2220	Two compartment, 9" wide		3.80	4.211		730	284		1,014	1,225
2230	12" wide		3	5.333		805	360		1,165	1,425
2240	18" wide		2.40	6.667		970	450		1,420	1,750
2250	24" wide		2	8		1,300	540		1,840	2,225
2260	30" wide		1.80	8.889		1,750	600		2,350	2,825
2270	36" wide		1.60	10		2,100	675		2,775	3,325
2290	Three compartment, 9" wide		3.60	4.444		805	299		1,104	1,325
2300	12" wide		2.80	5.714		905	385		1,290	1,575
2310	18" wide		2.20	7.273		1,100	490		1,590	1,925
2320	24" wide		1.80	8.889		1,400	600		2,000	2,425
2330	30" wide		1.60	10		1,800	675		2,475	3,000
2350	36" wide		1.40	11.429		2,200	770		2,970	3,575
2400	Vertical elbow, 9" wide		5.40	2.963		201	200		401	520

26 05 43.10 Trench Duct		Crew	Daily Output	Labor-Hours	Unit	Material	2023 Bare Costs Labor	Equipment	Total	Total Incl O&P
2600	12″ wide	2 Elec	4.60	3.478	Ea.	171	234		405	540
2800	18″ wide		4	4		196	269		465	615
3000	24″ wide		3.20	5		244	335		579	770
3100	27″ wide		3	5.333		254	360		614	815
3200	30″ wide		2.60	6.154		269	415		684	910
3400	36″ wide		2.40	6.667		296	450		746	990
3600	Cross, 9″ wide		4	4		740	269		1,009	1,200
3800	12″ wide		3.20	5		780	335		1,115	1,350
4000	18″ wide		2.60	6.154		935	415		1,350	1,650
4200	24″ wide		2.20	7.273		1,175	490		1,665	2,000
4300	27″ wide		2.20	7.273		1,475	490		1,965	2,350
4400	30″ wide		2	8		1,625	540		2,165	2,600
4600	36″ wide		1.80	8.889		2,050	600		2,650	3,150
4620	Two compartment, 9″ wide		3.80	4.211		815	284		1,099	1,325
4630	12″ wide		3	5.333		780	360		1,140	1,400
4640	18″ wide		2.40	6.667		1,025	450		1,475	1,825
4650	24″ wide		2	8		1,325	540		1,865	2,250
4660	30″ wide		1.80	8.889		1,750	600		2,350	2,825
4670	36″ wide		1.60	10		2,100	675		2,775	3,325
4690	Three compartment, 9″ wide		3.60	4.444		830	299		1,129	1,350
4700	12″ wide		2.80	5.714		945	385		1,330	1,625
4710	18″ wide		2.20	7.273		1,125	490		1,615	1,950
4720	24″ wide		1.80	8.889		1,400	600		2,000	2,450
4730	30″ wide		1.60	10		1,650	675		2,325	2,825
4740	36″ wide		1.40	11.429		2,050	770		2,820	3,400
4800	End closure, 9″ wide		14.40	1.111		49	75		124	165
5000	12″ wide		12	1.333		56	90		146	195
5200	18″ wide		10	1.600		86	108		194	255
5400	24″ wide		8	2		113	135		248	325
5500	27″ wide		7	2.286		131	154		285	375
5600	30″ wide		6.60	2.424		176	163		339	435
5800	36″ wide		5.80	2.759		168	186		354	460
6000	Tees, 9″ wide		4	4		475	269		744	925
6200	12″ wide		3.60	4.444		550	299		849	1,050
6400	18″ wide		3.20	5		705	335		1,040	1,275
6600	24″ wide		3	5.333		1,025	360		1,385	1,650
6700	27″ wide		2.80	5.714		1,125	385		1,510	1,800
6800	30″ wide		2.60	6.154		1,325	415		1,740	2,075
7000	36″ wide		2	8		1,725	540		2,265	2,700
7020	Two compartment, 9″ wide		3.80	4.211		550	284		834	1,025
7030	12″ wide		3.40	4.706		595	315		910	1,125
7040	18″ wide		3	5.333		795	360		1,155	1,400
7050	24″ wide		2.80	5.714		1,075	385		1,460	1,750
7060	30″ wide		2.40	6.667		1,450	450		1,900	2,275
7070	36″ wide		1.90	8.421		1,825	565		2,390	2,850
7090	Three compartment, 9″ wide		3.60	4.444		630	299		929	1,150
7100	12″ wide		3.20	5		660	335		995	1,225
7110	18″ wide		2.80	5.714		840	385		1,225	1,500
7120	24″ wide		2.60	6.154		1,150	415		1,565	1,900
7130	30″ wide		2.20	7.273		1,500	490		1,990	2,375
7140	36″ wide		1.80	8.889		1,925	600		2,525	3,025
7200	Riser, and cabinet connector, 9″ wide		5.40	2.963		208	200		408	525
7400	12″ wide		4.60	3.478		242	234		476	615

26 05 43.10 Trench Duct

	26 05 43.10 Trench Duct	Crew	Daily Output	Labor-Hours	Unit	2023 Bare Costs Material	Labor	Equipment	Total	Total Incl O&P
7600	18" wide	2 Elec	4	4	Ea.	257	269		526	685
7800	24" wide		3.20	5		360	335		695	895
7900	27" wide		3	5.333		305	360		665	870
8000	30" wide		2.60	6.154		415	415		830	1,075
8200	36" wide		2	8		480	540		1,020	1,325
8400	Insert assembly, cell to conduit adapter, 1-1/4"	1 Elec	16	.500		75.50	33.50		109	133
8500	Adjustable partition	"	320	.025	L.F.	29.50	1.68		31.18	34.50
8600	Depth of duct over 4", per 1", add					12.05			12.05	13.25
8700	Support post	1 Elec	240	.033		27.50	2.25		29.75	34
8800	Cover double tile trim, 2 sides					42.50			42.50	47
8900	4 sides					134			134	147
9160	Trench duct 3-1/2" x 4-1/2", add					11.40			11.40	12.55
9170	Trench duct 4" x 5", add					11.40			11.40	12.55
9200	For carpet trim, add					39			39	42.50
9210	For double carpet trim, add					118			118	130

26 05 43.20 Underfloor Duct

	26 05 43.20 Underfloor Duct	Crew	Daily Output	Labor-Hours	Unit	2023 Bare Costs Material	Labor	Equipment	Total	Total Incl O&P
0010	**UNDERFLOOR DUCT** R260543-50									
0100	Duct, 1-3/8" x 3-1/8" blank, standard	2 Elec	160	.100	L.F.	14	6.75		20.75	25.50
0200	1-3/8" x 7-1/4" blank, super duct		120	.133		33	9		42	49.50
0400	7/8" or 1-3/8" insert type, 24" OC, 1-3/8" x 3-1/8", std.		140	.114		22	7.70		29.70	35.50
0600	1-3/8" x 7-1/4", super duct		100	.160		38.50	10.80		49.30	58.50
0800	Junction box, single duct, 1 level, 3-1/8"	1 Elec	4	2	Ea.	490	135		625	735
0820	3-1/8" x 7-1/4"		4	2		630	135		765	895
0840	2 level, 3-1/8" upper & lower		3.20	2.500		575	168		743	880
0860	3-1/8" upper, 7-1/4" lower		2.70	2.963		555	200		755	905
0880	Carpet pan for above		80	.100		405	6.75		411.75	455
0900	Terrazzo pan for above		67	.119		965	8.05		973.05	1,075
1000	Junction box, single duct, 1 level, 7-1/4"		2.70	2.963		565	200		765	920
1020	2 level, 7-1/4" upper & lower		2.70	2.963		650	200		850	1,000
1040	2 duct, two 3-1/8" upper & lower		3.20	2.500		880	168		1,048	1,225
1200	1 level, 2 duct, 3-1/8"		3.20	2.500		650	168		818	965
1220	Carpet pan for above boxes		80	.100		395	6.75		401.75	445
1240	Terrazzo pan for above boxes		67	.119		925	8.05		933.05	1,025
1260	Junction box, 1 level, two 3-1/8" x one 3-1/8" + one 7-1/4"		2.30	3.478		1,075	234		1,309	1,550
1280	2 level, two 3-1/8" upper, one 3-1/8" + one 7-1/4" lower		2	4		1,175	269		1,444	1,700
1300	Carpet pan for above boxes		80	.100		395	6.75		401.75	445
1320	Terrazzo pan for above boxes		67	.119		925	8.05		933.05	1,025
1400	Junction box, 1 level, 2 duct, 7-1/4"		2.30	3.478		1,600	234		1,834	2,100
1420	Two 3-1/8" + one 7-1/4"		2	4		1,625	269		1,894	2,200
1440	Carpet pan for above		80	.100		395	6.75		401.75	445
1460	Terrazzo pan for above		67	.119		925	8.05		933.05	1,025
1580	Junction box, 1 level, one 3-1/8" + one 7-1/4" x same		2.30	3.478		1,100	234		1,334	1,575
1600	Triple duct, 3-1/8"		2.30	3.478		1,100	234		1,334	1,575
1700	Junction box, 1 level, one 3-1/8" + two 7-1/4"		2	4		1,825	269		2,094	2,400
1720	Carpet pan for above		80	.100		395	6.75		401.75	445
1740	Terrazzo pan for above		67	.119		925	8.05		933.05	1,025
1800	Insert to conduit adapter, 3/4" & 1"		32	.250		40	16.85		56.85	69
2000	Support, single cell		27	.296		59.50	19.95		79.45	94.50
2200	Super duct		16	.500		60	33.50		93.50	116
2400	Double cell		16	.500		60	33.50		93.50	117
2600	Triple cell		11	.727		68	49		117	148
2800	Vertical elbow, standard duct		10	.800		107	54		161	198

26 05 43 – Underground Ducts and Raceways for Electrical Systems

26 05 43.20 Underfloor Duct		Crew	Daily Output	Labor-Hours	Unit	Material	Labor	Equipment	Total	Total Incl O&P
						2023 Bare Costs				
3000	Super duct	1 Elec	8	1	Ea.	107	67.50		174.50	218
3200	Cabinet connector, standard duct		32	.250		86	16.85		102.85	120
3400	Super duct		27	.296		84	19.95		103.95	122
3600	Conduit adapter, 1" to 1-1/4"		32	.250		80.50	16.85		97.35	114
3800	2" to 1-1/4"		27	.296		96	19.95		115.95	136
4000	Outlet, low tension (tele, computer, etc.)		8	1		113	67.50		180.50	225
4200	High tension, receptacle (120 volt)		8	1		115	67.50		182.50	227
4300	End closure, standard duct		160	.050		4.85	3.37		8.22	10.35
4310	Super duct		160	.050		9.20	3.37		12.57	15.10
4350	Elbow, horiz., standard duct		26	.308		275	20.50		295.50	335
4360	Super duct		26	.308		256	20.50		276.50	310
4380	Elbow, offset, standard duct		26	.308		107	20.50		127.50	149
4390	Super duct		26	.308		109	20.50		129.50	151
4400	Marker screw assembly for inserts		50	.160		21	10.80		31.80	39.50
4410	Y take off, standard duct		26	.308		168	20.50		188.50	215
4420	Super duct		26	.308		168	20.50		188.50	215
4430	Box opening plug, standard duct		160	.050		20.50	3.37		23.87	27.50
4440	Super duct		160	.050		20.50	3.37		23.87	27.50
4450	Sleeve coupling, standard duct		160	.050		54	3.37		57.37	64.50
4460	Super duct		160	.050		54	3.37		57.37	64.50
4470	Conduit adapter, standard duct, 3/4"		32	.250		87	16.85		103.85	121
4480	1" or 1-1/4"		32	.250		83	16.85		99.85	116
4500	1-1/2"		32	.250		80.50	16.85		97.35	114

26 05 83 – Wiring Connections

26 05 83.10 Motor Connections

		Crew	Daily Output	Labor-Hours	Unit	Material	Labor	Equipment	Total	Total Incl O&P
0010	**MOTOR CONNECTIONS**									
0020	Flexible conduit and fittings, 115 volt, 1 phase, up to 1 HP motor	1 Elec	8	1	Ea.	6.60	67.50		74.10	107
0050	2 HP motor R260580-75		6.50	1.231		13.85	83		96.85	138
0100	3 HP motor		5.50	1.455		12.10	98		110.10	159
0110	230 volt, 3 phase, 3 HP motor		6.78	1.180		8	79.50		87.50	127
0112	5 HP motor		5.47	1.463		6.85	98.50		105.35	154
0114	7-1/2 HP motor		4.61	1.735		12.05	117		129.05	187
0120	10 HP motor		4.20	1.905		21.50	128		149.50	215
0150	15 HP motor		3.30	2.424		21.50	163		184.50	267
0200	25 HP motor		2.70	2.963		32	200		232	330
0400	50 HP motor		2.20	3.636		66.50	245		311.50	440
0600	100 HP motor		1.50	5.333		151	360		511	700
1500	460 volt, 5 HP motor, 3 phase		8	1		7.25	67.50		74.75	108
1520	10 HP motor		8	1		7.25	67.50		74.75	108
1530	25 HP motor		6	1.333		15.10	90		105.10	150
1540	30 HP motor		6	1.333		15.10	90		105.10	150
1550	40 HP motor		5	1.600		20	108		128	182
1560	50 HP motor		5	1.600		24	108		132	187
1570	60 HP motor		3.80	2.105		27.50	142		169.50	241
1580	75 HP motor		3.50	2.286		40.50	154		194.50	274
1590	100 HP motor		2.50	3.200		58	216		274	385
1600	125 HP motor		2	4		74.50	269		343.50	480
1610	150 HP motor		1.80	4.444		77.50	299		376.50	530
1620	200 HP motor		1.50	5.333		130	360		490	680
2005	460 volt, 5 HP motor, 3 phase, w/sealtite		8	1		14.90	67.50		82.40	116
2010	10 HP motor		8	1		14.90	67.50		82.40	116
2015	25 HP motor		6	1.333		26	90		116	162

26 05 83 – Wiring Connections

26 05 83.10 Motor Connections		Crew	Daily Output	Labor-Hours	Unit	Material	Labor	Equipment	Total	Total Incl O&P
2020	30 HP motor	1 Elec	6	1.333	Ea.	26	90		116	162
2025	40 HP motor		5	1.600		39	108		147	203
2030	50 HP motor		5	1.600		40.50	108		148.50	205
2035	60 HP motor		3.80	2.105		64	142		206	282
2040	75 HP motor		3.50	2.286		71	154		225	305
2045	100 HP motor		2.50	3.200		93	216		309	425
2055	150 HP motor		1.80	4.444		101	299		400	555
2060	200 HP motor		1.50	5.333		385	360		745	960

Material, Labor, Equipment and Total columns: 2023 Bare Costs.

26 05 90 – Residential Applications

26 05 90.10 Residential Wiring

		Crew	Daily Output	Labor-Hours	Unit	Material	Labor	Equipment	Total	Total Incl O&P
0010	**RESIDENTIAL WIRING**									
0020	20' avg. runs and #14/2 wiring incl. unless otherwise noted									
1000	Service & panel, includes 24' SE-AL cable, service eye, meter,									
1010	Socket, panel board, main bkr., ground rod, 15 or 20 amp									
1020	1-pole circuit breakers, and misc. hardware									
1100	100 amp, with 10 branch breakers	1 Elec	1.19	6.723	Ea.	605	455		1,060	1,350
1110	With PVC conduit and wire		.92	8.696		695	585		1,280	1,625
1120	With RGS conduit and wire		.73	10.959		975	740		1,715	2,175
1150	150 amp, with 14 branch breakers		1.03	7.767		915	525		1,440	1,775
1170	With PVC conduit and wire		.82	9.756		1,075	655		1,730	2,175
1180	With RGS conduit and wire		.67	11.940		1,650	805		2,455	3,025
1200	200 amp, with 18 branch breakers	2 Elec	1.80	8.889		1,550	600		2,150	2,600
1220	With PVC conduit and wire		1.46	10.959		1,725	740		2,465	2,975
1230	With RGS conduit and wire		1.24	12.903		2,400	870		3,270	3,925
1800	Lightning surge suppressor	1 Elec	32	.250		93	16.85		109.85	128
2000	Switch devices									
2100	Single pole, 15 amp, ivory, with a 1-gang box, cover plate,									
2110	Type NM (Romex) cable	1 Elec	17.10	.468	Ea.	12.90	31.50		44.40	61
2120	Type MC cable		14.30	.559		23	37.50		60.50	81
2130	EMT & wire		5.71	1.401		54.50	94.50		149	200
2150	3-way, #14/3, type NM cable		14.55	.550		15.70	37		52.70	72.50
2170	Type MC cable		12.31	.650		30.50	44		74.50	98.50
2180	EMT & wire		5	1.600		59.50	108		167.50	225
2200	4-way, #14/3, type NM cable		14.55	.550		24	37		61	81.50
2220	Type MC cable		12.31	.650		38.50	44		82.50	108
2230	EMT & wire		5	1.600		67.50	108		175.50	234
2250	S.P., 20 amp, #12/2, type NM cable		13.33	.600		19.25	40.50		59.75	81
2270	Type MC cable		11.43	.700		27.50	47		74.50	100
2280	EMT & wire		4.85	1.649		59	111		170	230
2290	S.P. rotary dimmer, 600 W, no wiring		17	.471		30.50	31.50		62	80.50
2300	S.P. rotary dimmer, 600 W, type NM cable		14.55	.550		40	37		77	99
2320	Type MC cable		12.31	.650		50	44		94	120
2330	EMT & wire		5	1.600		86	108		194	255
2350	3-way rotary dimmer, type NM cable		13.33	.600		42.50	40.50		83	107
2370	Type MC cable		11.43	.700		52.50	47		99.50	128
2380	EMT & wire		4.85	1.649		88.50	111		199.50	262
2400	Interval timer wall switch, 20 amp, 1-30 min., #12/2									
2410	Type NM cable	1 Elec	14.55	.550	Ea.	91	37		128	155
2420	Type MC cable		12.31	.650		92	44		136	166
2430	EMT & wire		5	1.600		131	108		239	305
2500	Decorator style									
2510	S.P., 15 amp, type NM cable	1 Elec	17.10	.468	Ea.	19.40	31.50		50.90	68.50

26 05 90.10 Residential Wiring		Crew	Daily Output	Labor-Hours	Unit	Material	Labor	Equipment	Total	Total Incl O&P
						2023 Bare Costs				
2520	Type MC cable	1 Elec	14.30	.559	Ea.	29.50	37.50		67	88.50
2530	EMT & wire		5.71	1.401		61	94.50		155.50	207
2550	3-way, #14/3, type NM cable		14.55	.550		22	37		59	79.50
2570	Type MC cable		12.31	.650		37	44		81	106
2580	EMT & wire		5	1.600		66	108		174	233
2600	4-way, #14/3, type NM cable		14.55	.550		30.50	37		67.50	88.50
2620	Type MC cable		12.31	.650		45	44		89	115
2630	EMT & wire		5	1.600		74	108		182	242
2650	S.P., 20 amp, #12/2, type NM cable		13.33	.600		26	40.50		66.50	88.50
2670	Type MC cable		11.43	.700		34	47		81	107
2680	EMT & wire		4.85	1.649		65.50	111		176.50	237
2700	S.P., slide dimmer, type NM cable		17.10	.468		44	31.50		75.50	95.50
2720	Type MC cable		14.30	.559		54.50	37.50		92	116
2730	EMT & wire		5.71	1.401		90	94.50		184.50	239
2750	S.P., touch dimmer, type NM cable		17.10	.468		38	31.50		69.50	88.50
2770	Type MC cable		14.30	.559		48	37.50		85.50	109
2780	EMT & wire		5.71	1.401		84	94.50		178.50	232
2800	3-way touch dimmer, type NM cable		13.33	.600		40	40.50		80.50	104
2820	Type MC cable		11.43	.700		50	47		97	125
2830	EMT & wire	↓	4.85	1.649	↓	86	111		197	260
3000	Combination devices									
3100	S.P. switch/15 amp recpt., ivory, 1-gang box, plate									
3110	Type NM cable	1 Elec	11.43	.700	Ea.	28	47		75	101
3120	Type MC cable		10	.800		38	54		92	122
3130	EMT & wire		4.40	1.818		74	122		196	263
3150	S.P. switch/pilot light, type NM cable		11.43	.700		29.50	47		76.50	103
3170	Type MC cable		10	.800		39.50	54		93.50	124
3180	EMT & wire		4.43	1.806		75.50	122		197.50	264
3190	2-S.P. switches, 2-#14/2, no wiring		14	.571		5.35	38.50		43.85	63
3200	2-S.P. switches, 2-#14/2, type NM cables		10	.800		34.50	54		88.50	118
3220	Type MC cable		8.89	.900		43	60.50		103.50	138
3230	EMT & wire		4.10	1.951		84	131		215	288
3250	3-way switch/15 amp recpt., #14/3, type NM cable		10	.800		37.50	54		91.50	122
3270	Type MC cable		8.89	.900		52.50	60.50		113	148
3280	EMT & wire		4.10	1.951		81.50	131		212.50	285
3300	2-3 way switches, 2-#14/3, type NM cables		8.89	.900		49	60.50		109.50	144
3320	Type MC cable		8	1		67	67.50		134.50	174
3330	EMT & wire		4	2		94	135		229	305
3350	S.P. switch/20 amp recpt., #12/2, type NM cable		10	.800		41.50	54		95.50	126
3370	Type MC cable		8.89	.900		42.50	60.50		103	137
3380	EMT & wire	↓	4.10	1.951	↓	81.50	131		212.50	285
3400	Decorator style									
3410	S.P. switch/15 amp recpt., type NM cable	1 Elec	11.43	.700	Ea.	34.50	47		81.50	108
3420	Type MC cable		10	.800		44.50	54		98.50	129
3430	EMT & wire		4.40	1.818		80.50	122		202.50	271
3450	S.P. switch/pilot light, type NM cable		11.43	.700		36	47		83	110
3470	Type MC cable		10	.800		46	54		100	131
3480	EMT & wire		4.40	1.818		82	122		204	273
3500	2-S.P. switches, 2-#14/2, type NM cables		10	.800		41	54		95	125
3520	Type MC cable		8.89	.900		49.50	60.50		110	145
3530	EMT & wire		4.10	1.951		90.50	131		221.50	295
3550	3-way/15 amp recpt., #14/3, type NM cable		10	.800		44.50	54		98.50	129
3570	Type MC cable	↓	8.89	.900	↓	59	60.50		119.50	155

26 05 90.10 Residential Wiring		Crew	Daily Output	Labor-Hours	Unit	Material	Labor	Equipment	Total	Total Incl O&P
						2023 Bare Costs				
3580	EMT & wire	1 Elec	4.10	1.951	Ea.	88	131		219	292
3650	2-3 way switches, 2-#14/3, type NM cables		8.89	.900		55.50	60.50		116	151
3670	Type MC cable		8	1		73.50	67.50		141	181
3680	EMT & wire		4	2		101	135		236	310
3700	S.P. switch/20 amp recpt., #12/2, type NM cable		10	.800		48	54		102	133
3720	Type MC cable		8.89	.900		49	60.50		109.50	144
3730	EMT & wire		4.10	1.951		88	131		219	292
4000	Receptacle devices									
4010	Duplex outlet, 15 amp recpt., ivory, 1-gang box, plate									
4015	Type NM cable	1 Elec	14.55	.550	Ea.	13.45	37		50.45	70
4020	Type MC cable		12.31	.650		23.50	44		67.50	91
4030	EMT & wire		5.33	1.501		55	101		156	211
4050	With #12/2, type NM cable		12.31	.650		16.55	44		60.55	83
4070	Type MC cable		10.67	.750		24.50	50.50		75	102
4080	EMT & wire		4.71	1.699		56.50	114		170.50	232
4100	20 amp recpt., #12/2, type NM cable		12.31	.650		28	44		72	95.50
4120	Type MC cable		10.67	.750		36	50.50		86.50	115
4130	EMT & wire		4.71	1.699		68	114		182	245
4140	For GFI see Section 26 05 90.10 line 4300 below									
4150	Decorator style, 15 amp recpt., type NM cable	1 Elec	14.55	.550	Ea.	19.95	37		56.95	77
4170	Type MC cable		12.31	.650		30	44		74	98
4180	EMT & wire		5.33	1.501		61.50	101		162.50	218
4200	With #12/2, type NM cable		12.31	.650		23	44		67	90.50
4220	Type MC cable		10.67	.750		31	50.50		81.50	109
4230	EMT & wire		4.71	1.699		63	114		177	239
4250	20 amp recpt., #12/2, type NM cable		12.31	.650		34.50	44		78.50	103
4270	Type MC cable		10.67	.750		42.50	50.50		93	122
4280	EMT & wire		4.71	1.699		74.50	114		188.50	252
4300	GFI, 15 amp recpt., type NM cable		12.31	.650		32.50	44		76.50	101
4320	Type MC cable		10.67	.750		43	50.50		93.50	122
4330	EMT & wire		4.71	1.699		74.50	114		188.50	252
4350	GFI with #12/2, type NM cable		10.67	.750		36	50.50		86.50	115
4370	Type MC cable		9.20	.870		44	58.50		102.50	135
4380	EMT & wire		4.21	1.900		75.50	128		203.50	273
4400	20 amp recpt., #12/2, type NM cable		10.67	.750		53.50	50.50		104	134
4420	Type MC cable		9.20	.870		61.50	58.50		120	155
4430	EMT & wire		4.21	1.900		93.50	128		221.50	293
4500	Weather-proof cover for above receptacles, add		32	.250		4.48	16.85		21.33	30
4550	Air conditioner outlet, 20 amp-240 volt recpt.									
4560	30′ of #12/2, 2 pole circuit breaker									
4570	Type NM cable	1 Elec	10	.800	Ea.	94.50	54		148.50	184
4580	Type MC cable		9	.889		101	60		161	200
4590	EMT & wire		4	2		133	135		268	345
4600	Decorator style, type NM cable		10	.800		101	54		155	191
4620	Type MC cable		9	.889		108	60		168	207
4630	EMT & wire		4	2		140	135		275	355
4650	Dryer outlet, 30 amp-240 volt recpt., 20′ of #10/3									
4660	2 pole circuit breaker									
4670	Type NM cable	1 Elec	6.41	1.248	Ea.	90.50	84		174.50	225
4680	Type MC cable		5.71	1.401		79.50	94.50		174	228
4690	EMT & wire		3.48	2.299		128	155		283	370
4700	Range outlet, 50 amp-240 volt recpt., 30′ of #8/3									
4710	Type NM cable	1 Elec	4.21	1.900	Ea.	163	128		291	370

26 05 90 – Residential Applications

26 05 90.10 Residential Wiring		Crew	Daily Output	Labor-Hours	Unit	Material	Labor	Equipment	Total	Total Incl O&P
4720	Type MC cable	1 Elec	4	2	Ea.	141	135		276	355
4730	EMT & wire		2.96	2.703		174	182		356	460
4750	Central vacuum outlet, type NM cable		6.40	1.250		93	84		177	227
4770	Type MC cable		5.71	1.401		90	94.50		184.50	240
4780	EMT & wire	↓	3.48	2.299	↓	145	155		300	390
4800	30 amp-110 volt locking recpt., #10/2 circ. bkr.									
4810	Type NM cable	1 Elec	6.20	1.290	Ea.	114	87		201	255
4820	Type MC cable		5.40	1.481		103	100		203	261
4830	EMT & wire	↓	3.20	2.500	↓	173	168		341	440
4900	Low voltage outlets									
4910	Telephone recpt., 20′ of 4/C phone wire	1 Elec	26	.308	Ea.	10.55	20.50		31.05	42.50
4920	TV recpt., 20′ of RG59U coax wire, F type connector	"	16	.500	"	18.75	33.50		52.25	70.50
4950	Door bell chime, transformer, 2 buttons, 60′ of bellwire									
4970	Economy model	1 Elec	11.50	.696	Ea.	72	47		119	149
4980	Custom model		11.50	.696		120	47		167	202
4990	Luxury model, 3 buttons	↓	9.50	.842	↓	208	56.50		264.50	315
6000	Lighting outlets									
6050	Wire only (for fixture), type NM cable	1 Elec	32	.250	Ea.	13.45	16.85		30.30	40
6070	Type MC cable		24	.333		13	22.50		35.50	48
6080	EMT & wire		10	.800		43.50	54		97.50	128
6100	Box (4″) and wire (for fixture), type NM cable		25	.320		23	21.50		44.50	57
6120	Type MC cable		20	.400		22.50	27		49.50	64.50
6130	EMT & wire	↓	11	.727	↓	53	49		102	132
6200	Fixtures (use with line 6050 or 6100 above)									
6210	Canopy style, economy grade	1 Elec	40	.200	Ea.	24.50	13.45		37.95	47
6220	Custom grade		40	.200		63.50	13.45		76.95	89.50
6250	Dining room chandelier, economy grade		19	.421		101	28.50		129.50	153
6260	Custom grade		19	.421		385	28.50		413.50	460
6270	Luxury grade		15	.533		3,200	36		3,236	3,575
6310	Kitchen fixture (fluorescent), economy grade		30	.267		90.50	17.95		108.45	126
6320	Custom grade		25	.320		220	21.50		241.50	274
6350	Outdoor, wall mounted, economy grade		30	.267		45	17.95		62.95	75.50
6360	Custom grade		30	.267		139	17.95		156.95	180
6370	Luxury grade		25	.320		248	21.50		269.50	305
6410	Outdoor PAR floodlights, 1 lamp, 150 watt		20	.400		17.85	27		44.85	59.50
6420	2 lamp, 150 watt each		20	.400		28.50	27		55.50	71.50
6425	Motion sensing, 2 lamp, 150 watt each		20	.400		127	27		154	180
6430	For infrared security sensor, add		32	.250		114	16.85		130.85	150
6450	Outdoor, quartz-halogen, 300 watt flood		20	.400		48	27		75	93
6600	Recessed downlight, round, pre-wired, 50 or 75 watt trim		30	.267		56.50	17.95		74.45	89
6610	With shower light trim		30	.267		86.50	17.95		104.45	122
6620	With wall washer trim		28	.286		87	19.25		106.25	124
6630	With eye-ball trim		28	.286		36	19.25		55.25	68.50
6700	Porcelain lamp holder		40	.200		3.12	13.45		16.57	23.50
6710	With pull switch		40	.200		13.55	13.45		27	35
6750	Fluorescent strip, 2-20 watt tube, wrap around diffuser, 24″		24	.333		52	22.50		74.50	90.50
6760	1-34 watt tube, 48″		24	.333		131	22.50		153.50	178
6770	2-34 watt tubes, 48″		20	.400		149	27		176	204
6800	Bathroom heat lamp, 1-250 watt		28	.286		41	19.25		60.25	73.50
6810	2-250 watt lamps	↓	28	.286	↓	72	19.25		91.25	108
6820	For timer switch, see Section 26 05 90.10 line 2400									
6900	Outdoor post lamp, incl. post, fixture, 35′ of #14/2									
6910	Type NM cable	1 Elec	3.50	2.286	Ea.	405	154		559	675

Material, Labor, Equipment and Total columns are under "2023 Bare Costs".

26 05 90.10 Residential Wiring		Crew	Daily Output	Labor-Hours	Unit	2023 Bare Costs Material	Labor	Equipment	Total	Total Incl O&P
6920	Photo-eye, add	1 Elec	27	.296	Ea.	15.20	19.95		35.15	46
6950	Clock dial time switch, 24 hr., w/enclosure, type NM cable		11.43	.700		93	47		140	173
6970	Type MC cable		11	.727		103	49		152	187
6980	EMT & wire	↓	4.85	1.649	↓	135	111		246	315
7000	Alarm systems									
7050	Smoke detectors, box, #14/3, type NM cable	1 Elec	14.55	.550	Ea.	40.50	37		77.50	99.50
7070	Type MC cable		12.31	.650		47.50	44		91.50	118
7080	EMT & wire	↓	5	1.600		76.50	108		184.50	244
7090	For relay output to security system, add				↓	10.70			10.70	11.75
8000	Residential equipment									
8050	Disposal hook-up, incl. switch, outlet box, 3′ of flex									
8060	20 amp-1 pole circ. bkr., and 25′ of #12/2									
8070	Type NM cable	1 Elec	10	.800	Ea.	40	54		94	124
8080	Type MC cable		8	1		47.50	67.50		115	152
8090	EMT & wire	↓	5	1.600	↓	86	108		194	255
8100	Trash compactor or dishwasher hook-up, incl. outlet box,									
8110	3′ of flex, 15 amp-1 pole circ. bkr., and 25′ of #14/2									
8120	Type NM cable	1 Elec	10	.800	Ea.	34	54		88	117
8130	Type MC cable		8	1		45	67.50		112.50	150
8140	EMT & wire	↓	5	1.600	↓	79.50	108		187.50	248
8150	Hot water sink dispenser hook-up, use line 8100									
8200	Vent/exhaust fan hook-up, type NM cable	1 Elec	32	.250	Ea.	13.45	16.85		30.30	40
8220	Type MC cable		24	.333		13	22.50		35.50	48
8230	EMT & wire	↓	10	.800	↓	43.50	54		97.50	128
8250	Bathroom vent fan, 50 CFM (use with above hook-up)									
8260	Economy model	1 Elec	15	.533	Ea.	23.50	36		59.50	79
8270	Low noise model		15	.533		60	36		96	120
8280	Custom model	↓	12	.667	↓	120	45		165	199
8300	Bathroom or kitchen vent fan, 110 CFM									
8310	Economy model	1 Elec	15	.533	Ea.	75	36		111	136
8320	Low noise model	"	15	.533	"	121	36		157	187
8350	Paddle fan, variable speed (w/o lights)									
8360	Economy model (AC motor)	1 Elec	10	.800	Ea.	157	54		211	253
8362	With light kit		10	.800		201	54		255	300
8370	Custom model (AC motor)		10	.800		385	54		439	500
8372	With light kit		10	.800		425	54		479	550
8380	Luxury model (DC motor)		8	1		299	67.50		366.50	430
8382	With light kit		8	1		340	67.50		407.50	475
8390	Remote speed switch for above, add	↓	12	.667	↓	48.50	45		93.50	120
8500	Whole house exhaust fan, ceiling mount, 36″, variable speed									
8510	Remote switch, incl. shutters, 20 amp-1 pole circ. bkr.									
8520	30′ of #12/2, type NM cable	1 Elec	4	2	Ea.	1,675	135		1,810	2,025
8530	Type MC cable		3.50	2.286		1,675	154		1,829	2,075
8540	EMT & wire	↓	3	2.667	↓	1,725	180		1,905	2,175
8600	Whirlpool tub hook-up, incl. timer switch, outlet box									
8610	3′ of flex, 20 amp-1 pole GFI circ. bkr.									
8620	30′ of #12/2, type NM cable	1 Elec	5	1.600	Ea.	266	108		374	455
8630	Type MC cable		4.20	1.905		268	128		396	485
8640	EMT & wire	↓	3.40	2.353	↓	300	158		458	565
8650	Hot water heater hook-up, incl. 1-2 pole circ. bkr., box;									
8660	3′ of flex, 20′ of #10/2, type NM cable	1 Elec	5	1.600	Ea.	48.50	108		156.50	213
8670	Type MC cable		4.20	1.905		51	128		179	247
8680	EMT & wire	↓	3.40	2.353	↓	78.50	158		236.50	320

26 05 Common Work Results for Electrical

26 05 90 – Residential Applications

26 05 90.10 Residential Wiring		Crew	Daily Output	Labor-Hours	Unit	Material	2023 Bare Costs Labor	Equipment	Total	Total Incl O&P
9000	Heating/air conditioning									
9050	Furnace/boiler hook-up, incl. firestat, local on-off switch									
9060	Emergency switch, and 40' of type NM cable	1 Elec	4	2	Ea.	82	135		217	290
9070	Type MC cable		3.50	2.286		90.50	154		244.50	330
9080	EMT & wire		1.50	5.333		155	360		515	705
9100	Air conditioner hook-up, incl. local 60 amp disc. switch									
9110	3' sealtite, 40 amp, 2 pole circuit breaker									
9130	40' of #8/2, type NM cable	1 Elec	3.50	2.286	Ea.	239	154		393	490
9140	Type MC cable		3	2.667		224	180		404	515
9150	EMT & wire		1.30	6.154		285	415		700	930
9200	Heat pump hook-up, 1-40 & 1-100 amp 2 pole circ. bkr.									
9210	Local disconnect switch, 3' sealtite									
9220	40' of #8/2 & 30' of #3/2									
9230	Type NM cable	1 Elec	1.30	6.154	Ea.	810	415		1,225	1,500
9240	Type MC cable		1.08	7.407		525	500		1,025	1,325
9250	EMT & wire		.94	8.511		765	575		1,340	1,700
9500	Thermostat hook-up, using low voltage wire									
9520	Heating only, 25' of #18-3	1 Elec	24	.333	Ea.	14	22.50		36.50	49
9530	Heating/cooling, 25' of #18-4	"	20	.400	"	15.05	27		42.05	56.50

26 09 Instrumentation and Control for Electrical Systems

26 09 13 – Electrical Power Monitoring

26 09 13.10 Switchboard Instruments		Crew	Daily Output	Labor-Hours	Unit	Material	Labor	Equipment	Total	Total Incl O&P
0010	**SWITCHBOARD INSTRUMENTS** 3 phase, 4 wire R260913-80									
0100	AC indicating, ammeter & switch	1 Elec	8	1	Ea.	5,600	67.50		5,667.50	6,275
0200	Voltmeter & switch		8	1		4,550	67.50		4,617.50	5,100
0300	Wattmeter		8	1		3,225	67.50		3,292.50	3,625
0400	AC recording, ammeter		4	2		5,725	135		5,860	6,500
0500	Voltmeter		4	2		5,725	135		5,860	6,500
0600	Ground fault protection, zero sequence		2.70	2.963		5,050	200		5,250	5,850
0700	Ground return path		2.70	2.963		5,050	200		5,250	5,850
0800	3 current transformers, 5 to 800 amp		2	4		2,350	269		2,619	3,000
0900	1,000 to 1,500 amp		1.30	6.154		3,375	415		3,790	4,350
1200	2,000 to 4,000 amp		1	8		4,000	540		4,540	5,200
1300	Fused potential transformer, maximum 600 volt		8	1		885	67.50		952.50	1,075
26 09 13.20 Voltage Monitor Systems										
0010	**VOLTAGE MONITOR SYSTEMS** (test equipment)									
0100	AC voltage monitor system, 120/240 V, one-channel				Ea.	2,300			2,300	2,525
0110	Modem adapter					287			287	315
0120	Add-on detector only					1,200			1,200	1,325
0150	AC voltage remote monitor sys., 3 channel, 120, 230, or 480 V					4,175			4,175	4,600
0160	With internal modem					4,400			4,400	4,850
0170	Combination temperature and humidity probe					645			645	710
0180	Add-on detector only					3,025			3,025	3,325
0190	With internal modem					3,300			3,300	3,625
26 09 13.30 Smart Metering										
0010	**SMART METERING**, In panel									
0100	Single phase, 120/208 volt, 100 amp G	1 Elec	8.78	.911	Ea.	430	61.50		491.50	560
0120	200 amp G		8.78	.911		470	61.50		531.50	605
0200	277 volt, 100 amp G		8.78	.911		480	61.50		541.50	620

26 09 Instrumentation and Control for Electrical Systems

26 09 13 – Electrical Power Monitoring

26 09 13.30 Smart Metering			Crew	Daily Output	Labor-Hours	Unit	Material	2023 Bare Costs Labor	Equipment	Total	Total Incl O&P
0220	200 amp	G	1 Elec	8.78	.911	Ea.	485	61.50		546.50	620
1100	Three phase, 120/208 volt, 100 amp	G		4.69	1.706		900	115		1,015	1,150
1120	200 amp	G		4.69	1.706		900	115		1,015	1,150
1130	400 amp	G		4.69	1.706		1,050	115		1,165	1,325
1140	800 amp	G		4.69	1.706		1,075	115		1,190	1,350
1150	1,600 amp	G		4.69	1.706		1,075	115		1,190	1,350
1200	277/480 volt, 100 amp	G		4.69	1.706		1,000	115		1,115	1,275
1220	200 amp	G		4.69	1.706		1,000	115		1,115	1,275
1230	400 amp	G		4.69	1.706		1,000	115		1,115	1,275
1240	800 amp	G		4.69	1.706		1,175	115		1,290	1,450
1250	1,600 amp	G		4.69	1.706		1,175	115		1,290	1,450
2000	Data recorder, 8 meters	G		10.97	.729		2,350	49		2,399	2,675
2100	16 meters	G	↓	8.53	.938		3,425	63		3,488	3,875
3000	Software package, per meter, basic	G					202			202	222
3100	Premium	G				↓	530			530	585

26 09 23 – Lighting Control Devices

26 09 23.10 Energy Saving Lighting Devices			Crew	Daily Output	Labor-Hours	Unit	Material	Labor	Equipment	Total	Total Incl O&P
0010	**ENERGY SAVING LIGHTING DEVICES**										
0100	Occupancy sensors, passive infrared ceiling mounted	G	1 Elec	7	1.143	Ea.	68.50	77		145.50	190
0110	Ultrasonic ceiling mounted	G		7	1.143		65	77		142	186
0120	Dual technology ceiling mounted	G		6.50	1.231		111	83		194	245
0150	Automatic wall switches	G		24	.333		80	22.50		102.50	122
0160	Daylighting sensor, manual control, ceiling mounted	G		7	1.143		157	77		234	287
0170	Remote and dimming control with remote controller	G		6.50	1.231		221	83		304	365
0200	Passive infrared ceiling mounted			6.50	1.231		46.50	83		129.50	174
0400	Remote power pack	G		10	.800		46.50	54		100.50	131
0450	Photoelectric control, S.P.S.T. 120 V	G		8	1		17.60	67.50		85.10	119
0500	S.P.S.T. 208 V/277 V	G		8	1		28	67.50		95.50	131
0550	D.P.S.T. 120 V	G		6	1.333		162	90		252	310
0600	D.P.S.T. 208 V/277 V	G		6	1.333		184	90		274	335
0650	S.P.D.T. 208 V/277 V	G		6	1.333		178	90		268	330
0660	Daylight level sensor, wall mounted, on/off or dimming	G	↓	8	1	↓	135	67.50		202.50	249

26 09 26 – Lighting Control Panelboards

26 09 26.10 Lighting Control Relay Panel			Crew	Daily Output	Labor-Hours	Unit	Material	Labor	Equipment	Total	Total Incl O&P
0010	**LIGHTING CONTROL RELAY PANEL** with timeclock										
0100	4 Relay	G	1 Elec	2.50	3.200	Ea.	1,425	216		1,641	1,900
0110	8 Relay	G		2.30	3.478		1,925	234		2,159	2,475
0120	16 Relay	G		1.80	4.444		1,400	299		1,699	2,000
0130	24 Relay	G		1.50	5.333		1,925	360		2,285	2,625
0140	48 Relay	G	↓	1	8	↓	1,625	540		2,165	2,575
0200	Room Controller, switching only										
0210	1 Relay	G	1 Elec	3	2.667	Ea.	123	180		303	400
0220	2 Relay	G		3	2.667		186	180		366	470
0230	3 Relay	G	↓	3	2.667	↓	1,625	180		1,805	2,050
0240	Dimming										
0250	1 Relay	G	1 Elec	3	2.667	Ea.	1,000	180		1,180	1,375
0260	2 Relay	G		3	2.667		1,050	180		1,230	1,425
0270	3 Relay	G	↓	3	2.667	↓	1,625	180		1,805	2,050

26 09 Instrumentation and Control for Electrical Systems

26 09 36 – Modular Dimming Controls

26 09 36.13 Manual Modular Dimming Controls		Crew	Daily Output	Labor-Hours	Unit	Material	Labor	Equipment	Total	Total Incl O&P
						2023 Bare Costs				
0010	MANUAL MODULAR DIMMING CONTROLS									
2000	Lighting control module G	1 Elec	2	4	Ea.	395	269		664	835

26 12 Medium-Voltage Transformers

26 12 19 – Pad-Mounted, Liquid-Filled, Medium-Voltage Transformers

26 12 19.10 Transformer, Oil-Filled

		Crew	Daily Output	Labor-Hours	Unit	Material	Labor	Equipment	Total	Total Incl O&P
0010	**TRANSFORMER, OIL-FILLED** primary delta or Y, R262213-60									
0050	Pad mounted 5 kV or 15 kV, with taps, 277/480 V secondary, 3 phase									
0100	150 kVA	R-3	.65	30.769	Ea.	27,500	2,075	297	29,872	33,600
0110	225 kVA		.55	36.364		36,200	2,450	350	39,000	43,800
0200	300 kVA		.45	44.444		40,300	3,000	430	43,730	49,200
0300	500 kVA		.40	50		64,000	3,375	485	67,860	76,000
0400	750 kVA		.38	52.632		80,000	3,550	510	84,060	94,000
0500	1,000 kVA		.26	76.923		80,500	5,175	740	86,415	97,000
0600	1,500 kVA		.23	86.957		107,000	5,850	840	113,690	127,000
0700	2,000 kVA		.20	100		119,500	6,725	965	127,190	142,500
0710	2,500 kVA		.19	105		138,500	7,100	1,025	146,625	163,500
0720	3,000 kVA		.17	118		140,000	7,925	1,125	149,050	166,500
0800	3,750 kVA		.16	125		160,500	8,425	1,200	170,125	190,500
1990	Pole mounted distribution type, single phase									
2000	13.8 kV primary, 120/240 V secondary, 10 kVA	R-15	7.45	6.443	Ea.	3,925	425	46.50	4,396.50	5,000
2010	50 kVA		3.70	12.973		5,275	860	93.50	6,228.50	7,175
2020	100 kVA		2.75	17.455		8,700	1,150	126	9,976	11,400
2030	167 kVA		2.15	22.326		11,300	1,475	161	12,936	14,800
2900	2,400 V primary, 120/240 V secondary, 10 kVA		7.45	6.443		3,450	425	46.50	3,921.50	4,450
2910	15 kVA		6.70	7.164		3,500	475	51.50	4,026.50	4,625
2920	25 kVA		6	8		3,875	530	57.50	4,462.50	5,100
2930	37.5 kVA		4.30	11.163		5,250	740	80.50	6,070.50	6,975
2940	50 kVA		3.70	12.973		6,150	860	93.50	7,103.50	8,150
2950	75 kVA		3	16		8,050	1,050	115	9,215	10,600
2960	100 kVA		2.75	17.455		10,100	1,150	126	11,376	13,000

26 12 19.20 Transformer, Liquid-Filled

		Crew	Daily Output	Labor-Hours	Unit	Material	Labor	Equipment	Total	Total Incl O&P
0010	**TRANSFORMER, LIQUID-FILLED** Pad mounted									
0020	5 kV or 15 kV primary, 277/480 volt secondary, 3 phase									
0050	225 kVA	R-3	.55	36.364	Ea.	35,500	2,450	350	38,300	43,000
0100	300 kVA		.45	44.444		40,300	3,000	430	43,730	49,200
0200	500 kVA		.40	50		61,500	3,375	485	65,360	73,000
0250	750 kVA		.38	52.632		76,500	3,550	510	80,560	90,000
0300	1,000 kVA		.26	76.923		80,500	5,175	740	86,415	97,000
0350	1,500 kVA		.23	86.957		136,500	5,850	840	143,190	159,500
0400	2,000 kVA		.20	100		139,500	6,725	965	147,190	164,500
0450	2,500 kVA		.19	105		151,000	7,100	1,025	159,125	177,500

26 13 16 – Medium-Voltage Fusible Interrupter Switchgear

26 13 16.10 Switchgear		Crew	Daily Output	Labor-Hours	Unit	2023 Bare Costs Material	Labor	Equipment	Total	Total Incl O&P
0010	**SWITCHGEAR**, Incorporate switch with cable connections, transformer,									
0100	& low voltage section									
0200	Load interrupter switch, 600 amp, 2 position									
0300	NEMA 1, 4.8 kV, 300 kVA & below w/CLF fuses	R-3	.40	50	Ea.	19,500	3,375	485	23,360	26,900
0400	400 kVA & above w/CLF fuses		.38	52.632		22,600	3,550	510	26,660	30,700
0500	Non fusible		.41	48.780		17,600	3,275	470	21,345	24,700
0600	13.8 kV, 300 kVA & below w/CLF fuses		.38	52.632		29,900	3,550	510	33,960	38,700
0700	400 kVA & above w/CLF fuses		.36	55.556		29,900	3,750	535	34,185	39,000
0800	Non fusible		.40	50		19,300	3,375	485	23,160	26,700
0900	Cable lugs for 2 feeders 4.8 kV or 13.8 kV	1 Elec	8	1		735	67.50		802.50	910
1000	Pothead, one 3 conductor or three 1 conductor		4	2		3,525	135		3,660	4,075
1100	Two 3 conductor or six 1 conductor		2	4		6,975	269		7,244	8,075
1200	Key interlocks		8	1		730	67.50		797.50	905
1300	Lightning arresters, distribution class (no charge)									
1400	Intermediate class or line type 4.8 kV	1 Elec	2.70	2.963	Ea.	3,950	200		4,150	4,650
1500	13.8 kV		2	4		5,250	269		5,519	6,175
1600	Station class, 4.8 kV		2.70	2.963		6,800	200		7,000	7,775
1700	13.8 kV		2	4		11,700	269		11,969	13,200
1800	Transformers, 4,800 volts to 480/277 volts, 75 kVA	R-3	.68	29.412		25,400	1,975	284	27,659	31,200
1900	112.5 kVA		.65	30.769		27,400	2,075	297	29,772	33,600
2000	150 kVA		.57	35.088		30,500	2,375	340	33,215	37,500
2100	225 kVA		.48	41.667		35,900	2,800	400	39,100	44,100
2200	300 kVA		.41	48.780		38,000	3,275	470	41,745	47,200
2300	500 kVA		.36	55.556		41,100	3,750	535	45,385	51,500
2400	750 kVA		.29	68.966		47,300	4,650	665	52,615	59,500
2500	13,800 volts to 480/277 volts, 75 kVA		.61	32.787		24,200	2,200	315	26,715	30,200
2600	112.5 kVA		.55	36.364		26,700	2,450	350	29,500	33,400
2700	150 kVA		.49	40.816		29,600	2,750	395	32,745	37,000
2800	225 kVA		.41	48.780		35,000	3,275	470	38,745	43,900
2900	300 kVA		.37	54.054		37,100	3,650	520	41,270	46,800
3000	500 kVA		.31	64.516		40,100	4,350	625	45,075	51,000
3100	750 kVA		.26	76.923		45,800	5,175	740	51,715	59,000
3200	Forced air cooling & temperature alarm	1 Elec	1	8		4,500	540		5,040	5,750
3300	Low voltage components									
3400	Maximum panel height 49-1/2", single or twin row									
3500	Breaker heights, type FA or FH, 6"									
3600	type KA or KH, 8"									
3700	type LA, 11"									
3800	type MA, 14"									
3900	Breakers, 2 pole, 15 to 60 amp, type FA	1 Elec	5.60	1.429	Ea.	760	96		856	985
4000	70 to 100 amp, type FA		4.20	1.905		570	128		698	820
4100	15 to 60 amp, type FH		5.60	1.429		955	96		1,051	1,200
4200	70 to 100 amp, type FH		4.20	1.905		695	128		823	955
4300	125 to 225 amp, type KA		3.40	2.353		4,375	158		4,533	5,050
4400	125 to 225 amp, type KH		3.40	2.353		4,375	158		4,533	5,050
4500	125 to 400 amp, type LA		2.50	3.200		3,325	216		3,541	3,975
4600	125 to 600 amp, type MA		1.80	4.444		6,875	299		7,174	8,000
4700	700 & 800 amp, type MA		1.50	5.333		4,775	360		5,135	5,775
4800	3 pole, 15 to 60 amp, type FA		5.30	1.509		780	102		882	1,000
4900	70 to 100 amp, type FA		4	2		710	135		845	980
5000	15 to 60 amp, type FH		5.30	1.509		865	102		967	1,100
5100	70 to 100 amp, type FH		4	2		825	135		960	1,100
5200	125 to 225 amp, type KA		3.20	2.500		4,775	168		4,943	5,500

26 13 Medium-Voltage Switchgear

26 13 16 – Medium-Voltage Fusible Interrupter Switchgear

26 13 16.10 Switchgear		Crew	Daily Output	Labor-Hours	Unit	2023 Bare Costs Material	Labor	Equipment	Total	Total Incl O&P
5300	125 to 225 amp, type KH	1 Elec	3.20	2.500	Ea.	4,775	168		4,943	5,500
5400	125 to 400 amp, type LA		2.30	3.478		3,500	234		3,734	4,200
5500	125 to 600 amp, type MA		1.60	5		4,725	335		5,060	5,700
5600	700 & 800 amp, type MA		1.30	6.154		6,050	415		6,465	7,275

26 22 Low-Voltage Transformers

26 22 13 – Low-Voltage Distribution Transformers

26 22 13.10 Transformer, Dry-Type

		Crew	Daily Output	Labor-Hours	Unit	Material	Labor	Equipment	Total	Total Incl O&P
0010	**TRANSFORMER, DRY-TYPE** R262213-10									
0050	Single phase, 240/480 volt primary, 120/240 volt secondary									
0100	1 kVA R262213-60	1 Elec	2	4	Ea.	685	269		954	1,150
0300	2 kVA		1.60	5		1,025	335		1,360	1,625
0500	3 kVA		1.40	5.714		1,300	385		1,685	2,000
0700	5 kVA		1.20	6.667		1,525	450		1,975	2,350
0900	7.5 kVA	2 Elec	2.20	7.273		1,950	490		2,440	2,875
1100	10 kVA		1.60	10		2,625	675		3,300	3,875
1300	15 kVA		1.20	13.333		2,950	900		3,850	4,575
1500	25 kVA		1	16		3,450	1,075		4,525	5,400
1700	37.5 kVA		.80	20		4,100	1,350		5,450	6,525
1900	50 kVA		.70	22.857		4,900	1,550		6,450	7,675
2100	75 kVA		.65	24.615		8,500	1,650		10,150	11,800
2110	100 kVA	R-3	.90	22.222		9,325	1,500	214	11,039	12,800
2120	167 kVA	"	.80	25		23,700	1,675	241	25,616	28,900
2190	480 V primary, 120/240 V secondary, nonvent., 15 kVA	2 Elec	1.20	13.333		3,800	900		4,700	5,525
2200	25 kVA		.90	17.778		3,975	1,200		5,175	6,125
2210	37 kVA		.75	21.333		11,200	1,425		12,625	14,500
2220	50 kVA		.65	24.615		16,800	1,650		18,450	21,000
2230	75 kVA		.60	26.667		17,600	1,800		19,400	22,100
2240	100 kVA		.50	32		22,300	2,150		24,450	27,700
2250	Low operating temperature (80°C), 25 kVA		1	16		5,875	1,075		6,950	8,050
2260	37 kVA		.80	20		6,325	1,350		7,675	8,950
2270	50 kVA		.70	22.857		8,250	1,550		9,800	11,400
2280	75 kVA		.65	24.615		13,100	1,650		14,750	16,900
2290	100 kVA		.55	29.091		13,700	1,950		15,650	17,900
2300	3 phase, 480 volt primary, 120/208 volt secondary									
2310	Ventilated, 3 kVA	1 Elec	1	8	Ea.	1,150	540		1,690	2,075
2700	6 kVA		.80	10		2,400	675		3,075	3,625
2900	9 kVA		.70	11.429		2,700	770		3,470	4,125
3100	15 kVA	2 Elec	1.10	14.545		1,550	980		2,530	3,175
3300	30 kVA		.90	17.778		1,925	1,200		3,125	3,875
3500	45 kVA		.80	20		2,325	1,350		3,675	4,550
3700	75 kVA		.70	22.857		3,375	1,550		4,925	6,025
3900	112.5 kVA	R-3	.90	22.222		4,125	1,500	214	5,839	6,975
4100	150 kVA		.85	23.529		5,825	1,575	227	7,627	9,000
4300	225 kVA		.65	30.769		7,675	2,075	297	10,047	11,900
4500	300 kVA		.55	36.364		15,500	2,450	350	18,300	21,000
4700	500 kVA		.45	44.444		18,900	3,000	430	22,330	25,700
4800	750 kVA		.35	57.143		24,800	3,850	550	29,200	33,500
4820	1,000 kVA		.32	62.500		31,800	4,200	605	36,605	41,800
4850	K-4 rated, 15 kVA	2 Elec	1.10	14.545		3,150	980		4,130	4,900
4855	30 kVA		.90	17.778		4,100	1,200		5,300	6,275

26 22 13.10 Transformer, Dry-Type		Crew	Daily Output	Labor-Hours	Unit	2023 Bare Costs Material	Labor	Equipment	Total	Total Incl O&P
4860	45 kVA	2 Elec	.80	20	Ea.	4,400	1,350		5,750	6,850
4865	75 kVA		.70	22.857		6,725	1,550		8,275	9,700
4870	112.5 kVA	R-3	.90	22.222		8,350	1,500	214	10,064	11,600
4875	150 kVA		.85	23.529		11,100	1,575	227	12,902	14,800
4880	225 kVA		.65	30.769		16,200	2,075	297	18,572	21,200
4885	300 kVA		.55	36.364		24,300	2,450	350	27,100	30,700
4890	500 kVA		.45	44.444		47,500	3,000	430	50,930	57,500
4900	K-13 rated, 15 kVA	2 Elec	1.10	14.545		3,425	980		4,405	5,200
4905	30 kVA		.90	17.778		4,450	1,200		5,650	6,650
4910	45 kVA		.80	20		4,775	1,350		6,125	7,250
4915	75 kVA		.70	22.857		7,300	1,550		8,850	10,400
4920	112.5 kVA	R-3	.90	22.222		9,075	1,500	214	10,789	12,400
4925	150 kVA		.85	23.529		12,100	1,575	227	13,902	15,900
4930	225 kVA		.65	30.769		17,500	2,075	297	19,872	22,700
4935	300 kVA		.55	36.364		30,000	2,450	350	32,800	37,000
4940	500 kVA		.45	44.444		43,800	3,000	430	47,230	53,000
5020	480 volt primary, 120/208 volt secondary									
5030	Nonventilated, 15 kVA	2 Elec	1.10	14.545	Ea.	3,475	980		4,455	5,275
5040	30 kVA		.80	20		5,075	1,350		6,425	7,600
5050	45 kVA		.70	22.857		7,100	1,550		8,650	10,100
5060	75 kVA		.65	24.615		10,900	1,650		12,550	14,400
5070	112.5 kVA	R-3	.85	23.529		28,700	1,575	227	30,502	34,200
5081	150 kVA		.85	23.529		36,900	1,575	227	38,702	43,100
5090	225 kVA		.60	33.333		50,000	2,250	320	52,570	59,000
5100	300 kVA		.50	40		55,000	2,700	385	58,085	65,000
5200	Low operating temperature (80°C), 30 kVA	2 Elec	.90	17.778		5,750	1,200		6,950	8,100
5210	45 kVA		.80	20		6,900	1,350		8,250	9,600
5220	75 kVA		.70	22.857		11,300	1,550		12,850	14,700
5230	112.5 kVA	R-3	.90	22.222		13,900	1,500	214	15,614	17,800
5240	150 kVA		.85	23.529		17,800	1,575	227	19,602	22,200
5250	225 kVA		.65	30.769		24,100	2,075	297	26,472	29,900
5260	300 kVA		.55	36.364		39,800	2,450	350	42,600	47,700
5270	500 kVA		.45	44.444		43,700	3,000	430	47,130	53,000
5380	3 phase, 5 kV primary, 277/480 volt secondary									
5400	High voltage, 112.5 kVA	R-3	.85	23.529	Ea.	9,100	1,575	227	10,902	12,600
5410	150 kVA		.65	30.769		11,600	2,075	297	13,972	16,200
5420	225 kVA		.55	36.364		13,000	2,450	350	15,800	18,300
5430	300 kVA		.45	44.444		16,700	3,000	430	20,130	23,200
5440	500 kVA		.35	57.143		22,300	3,850	550	26,700	30,800
5450	750 kVA		.32	62.500		30,800	4,200	605	35,605	40,700
5460	1,000 kVA		.30	66.667		41,800	4,500	645	46,945	53,500
5470	1,500 kVA		.27	74.074		57,500	5,000	715	63,215	71,000
5480	2,000 kVA		.25	80		117,000	5,375	770	123,145	137,500
5490	2,500 kVA		.20	100		131,500	6,725	965	139,190	156,000
5500	3,000 kVA		.18	111		172,500	7,475	1,075	181,050	202,000
5590	15 kV primary, 277/480 volt secondary									
5600	High voltage, 112.5 kVA	R-3	.85	23.529	Ea.	18,600	1,575	227	20,402	23,000
5610	150 kVA		.65	30.769		26,500	2,075	297	28,872	32,600
5620	225 kVA		.55	36.364		31,300	2,450	350	34,100	38,500
5630	300 kVA		.45	44.444		34,400	3,000	430	37,830	42,800
5640	500 kVA		.35	57.143		37,600	3,850	550	42,000	47,700
5650	750 kVA		.32	62.500		40,300	4,200	605	45,105	51,000
5660	1,000 kVA		.30	66.667		47,100	4,500	645	52,245	59,500

26 22 Low-Voltage Transformers

26 22 13 – Low-Voltage Distribution Transformers

26 22 13.10 Transformer, Dry-Type		Crew	Daily Output	Labor-Hours	Unit	2023 Bare Costs Material	Labor	Equipment	Total	Total Incl O&P
5670	1,500 kVA	R-3	.27	74.074	Ea.	56,500	5,000	715	62,215	70,000
5680	2,000 kVA		.25	80		65,000	5,375	770	71,145	80,500
5690	2,500 kVA		.20	100		71,500	6,725	965	79,190	89,500
5700	3,000 kVA		.18	111		74,500	7,475	1,075	83,050	94,500
6000	2400 volt primary, 480 volt secondary, 300 kVA		.45	44.444		9,000	3,000	430	12,430	14,800
6010	500 kVA		.35	57.143		14,800	3,850	550	19,200	22,600
6020	750 kVA		.32	62.500		19,300	4,200	605	24,105	28,200
9300	Energy efficient transformer 3 ph									
9400	15 kVA, 480VAC delta, 208Y/120VAC	R-3	1.50	13.333	Ea.	1,525	900	129	2,554	3,150
9405	30 kVA, 480VAC delta, 208Y/120VAC		1.50	13.333		1,975	900	129	3,004	3,650
9410	45 kVA, 480VAC delta, 208Y/120VAC		1.50	13.333		2,275	900	129	3,304	3,975
9415	75 kVA, 480VAC delta, 208Y/120VAC		1.25	16		3,175	1,075	154	4,404	5,275
9420	112 kVA, 480VAC delta, 208Y/120VAC		1.25	16		4,350	1,075	154	5,579	6,550
9425	150 kVA, 480VAC delta, 208Y/120VAC		1.25	16		5,625	1,075	154	6,854	7,975
9430	225 kVA, 480VAC delta, 208Y/120VAC		1.25	16		7,500	1,075	154	8,729	10,000
9435	300 kVA, 480VAC delta, 208Y/120VAC		1.25	16		14,500	1,075	154	15,729	17,800

26 22 13.20 Isolating Panels		Crew	Daily Output	Labor-Hours	Unit	Material	Labor	Equipment	Total	Total Incl O&P
0010	**ISOLATING PANELS** used with isolating transformers									
0020	For hospital applications									
0100	Critical care area, 8 circuit, 3 kVA	1 Elec	.58	13.793	Ea.	8,850	930		9,780	11,100
0200	5 kVA		.54	14.815		7,225	1,000		8,225	9,425
0400	7.5 kVA		.52	15.385		3,725	1,025		4,750	5,650
0600	10 kVA		.44	18.182		10,500	1,225		11,725	13,400
0800	Operating room power & lighting, 8 circuit, 3 kVA		.58	13.793		6,750	930		7,680	8,775
1000	5 kVA		.54	14.815		7,325	1,000		8,325	9,525
1200	7.5 kVA		.52	15.385		3,050	1,025		4,075	4,900
1400	10 kVA		.44	18.182		3,375	1,225		4,600	5,550
1600	X-ray systems, 15 kVA, 90 amp		.44	18.182		10,700	1,225		11,925	13,600
1800	25 kVA, 125 amp		.36	22.222		9,450	1,500		10,950	12,600

26 22 13.30 Isolating Transformer		Crew	Daily Output	Labor-Hours	Unit	Material	Labor	Equipment	Total	Total Incl O&P
0010	**ISOLATING TRANSFORMER**									
0100	Single phase, 120/240 volt primary, 120/240 volt secondary									
0200	0.50 kVA R262213-60	1 Elec	4	2	Ea.	545	135		680	795
0400	1 kVA		2	4		1,100	269		1,369	1,600
0600	2 kVA		1.60	5		1,750	335		2,085	2,425
0800	3 kVA		1.40	5.714		1,900	385		2,285	2,650
1000	5 kVA		1.20	6.667		2,425	450		2,875	3,325
1200	7.5 kVA		1.10	7.273		3,225	490		3,715	4,275
1400	10 kVA		.80	10		4,000	675		4,675	5,400
1600	15 kVA		.60	13.333		5,000	900		5,900	6,825
1800	25 kVA		.50	16		10,300	1,075		11,375	12,900
1810	37.5 kVA	2 Elec	.80	20		7,300	1,350		8,650	10,000
1820	75 kVA	"	.65	24.615		11,000	1,650		12,650	14,600
1830	3 phase, 120/240 V primary, 120/240 V secondary, 112.5 kVA	R-3	.90	22.222		11,800	1,500	214	13,514	15,500
1840	150 kVA		.85	23.529		15,000	1,575	227	16,802	19,100
1850	225 kVA		.65	30.769		20,900	2,075	297	23,272	26,400
1860	300 kVA		.55	36.364		27,800	2,450	350	30,600	34,600
1870	500 kVA		.45	44.444		46,300	3,000	430	49,730	56,000
1880	750 kVA		.35	57.143		46,700	3,850	550	51,100	58,000

26 22 Low-Voltage Transformers

26 22 13 – Low-Voltage Distribution Transformers

26 22 13.90 Transformer Handling		Crew	Daily Output	Labor-Hours	Unit	Material	2023 Bare Costs Labor	Equipment	Total	Total Incl O&P
0010	**TRANSFORMER HANDLING** Add to normal labor cost in restricted areas									
5000	Transformers									
5150	15 kVA, approximately 200 pounds	2 Elec	2.70	5.926	Ea.		400		400	595
5160	25 kVA, approximately 300 pounds		2.50	6.400			430		430	640
5170	37.5 kVA, approximately 400 pounds		2.30	6.957			470		470	695
5180	50 kVA, approximately 500 pounds		2	8			540		540	800
5190	75 kVA, approximately 600 pounds		1.80	8.889			600		600	890
5200	100 kVA, approximately 700 pounds		1.60	10			675		675	1,000
5210	112.5 kVA, approximately 800 pounds	3 Elec	2.20	10.909			735		735	1,100
5220	125 kVA, approximately 900 pounds		2	12			810		810	1,200
5230	150 kVA, approximately 1,000 pounds		1.80	13.333			900		900	1,325
5240	167 kVA, approximately 1,200 pounds		1.60	15			1,000		1,000	1,500
5250	200 kVA, approximately 1,400 pounds		1.40	17.143			1,150		1,150	1,725
5260	225 kVA, approximately 1,600 pounds		1.30	18.462			1,250		1,250	1,850
5270	250 kVA, approximately 1,800 pounds		1.10	21.818			1,475		1,475	2,175
5280	300 kVA, approximately 2,000 pounds		1	24			1,625		1,625	2,400
5290	500 kVA, approximately 3,000 pounds		.75	32			2,150		2,150	3,200
5300	600 kVA, approximately 3,500 pounds		.67	35.821			2,425		2,425	3,575
5310	750 kVA, approximately 4,000 pounds		.60	40			2,700		2,700	4,000
5320	1,000 kVA, approximately 5,000 pounds		.50	48			3,225		3,225	4,800

26 22 16 – Low-Voltage Buck-Boost Transformers

26 22 16.10 Buck-Boost Transformer		Crew	Daily Output	Labor-Hours	Unit	Material	Labor	Equipment	Total	Total Incl O&P
0010	**BUCK-BOOST TRANSFORMER** R262213-60									
0100	Single phase, 120/240 V primary, 12/24 V secondary									
0200	0.10 kVA	1 Elec	8	1	Ea.	200	67.50		267.50	320
0400	0.25 kVA		5.70	1.404		283	94.50		377.50	450
0600	0.50 kVA		4	2		370	135		505	610
0800	0.75 kVA		3.10	2.581		505	174		679	815
1000	1.0 kVA		2	4		595	269		864	1,050
1200	1.5 kVA		1.80	4.444		645	299		944	1,150
1400	2.0 kVA		1.60	5		1,050	335		1,385	1,650
1600	3.0 kVA		1.40	5.714		1,300	385		1,685	2,000
1800	5.0 kVA		1.20	6.667		3,725	450		4,175	4,775
2000	3 phase, 240 V primary, 208/120 V secondary, 15 kVA	2 Elec	2.40	6.667		860	450		1,310	1,625
2200	30 kVA		1.60	10		3,675	675		4,350	5,050
2400	45 kVA		1.40	11.429		4,425	770		5,195	6,000
2600	75 kVA		1.20	13.333		5,350	900		6,250	7,200
2800	112.5 kVA	R-3	1.40	14.286		6,650	960	138	7,748	8,875
3000	150 kVA		1.10	18.182		8,825	1,225	175	10,225	11,700
3200	225 kVA		1	20		11,500	1,350	193	13,043	14,900
3400	300 kVA		.90	22.222		15,600	1,500	214	17,314	19,700

26 24 13.10 Incoming Switchboards		Crew	Daily Output	Labor-Hours	Unit	Material	2023 Bare Costs Labor	Equipment	Total	Total Incl O&P
0010	**INCOMING SWITCHBOARDS** main service section R262419-84									
0100	Aluminum bus bars, not including CT's or PT's									
0200	No main disconnect, includes CT compartment									
0300	120/208 volt, 4 wire, 600 amp	2 Elec	1	16	Ea.	4,975	1,075		6,050	7,075
0400	800 amp		.88	18.182		4,975	1,225		6,200	7,300
0500	1,000 amp		.80	20		5,975	1,350		7,325	8,575
0600	1,200 amp		.72	22.222		5,975	1,500		7,475	8,800
0700	1,600 amp		.66	24.242		5,975	1,625		7,600	9,000
0800	2,000 amp		.62	25.806		6,550	1,750		8,300	9,775
1000	3,000 amp		.56	28.571		8,625	1,925		10,550	12,400
1200	277/480 volt, 4 wire, 600 amp		1	16		4,975	1,075		6,050	7,075
1300	800 amp		.88	18.182		4,975	1,225		6,200	7,300
1400	1,000 amp		.80	20		6,325	1,350		7,675	8,950
1500	1,200 amp		.72	22.222		6,325	1,500		7,825	9,175
1600	1,600 amp		.66	24.242		6,325	1,625		7,950	9,375
1700	2,000 amp		.62	25.806		6,550	1,750		8,300	9,775
1800	3,000 amp		.56	28.571		8,625	1,925		10,550	12,400
1900	4,000 amp		.52	30.769		10,500	2,075		12,575	14,700
2000	Fused switch & CT compartment									
2100	120/208 volt, 4 wire, 400 amp	2 Elec	1.12	14.286	Ea.	2,925	960		3,885	4,650
2200	600 amp		.94	17.021		3,475	1,150		4,625	5,525
2300	800 amp		.84	19.048		13,500	1,275		14,775	16,700
2400	1,200 amp		.68	23.529		17,500	1,575		19,075	21,700
2500	277/480 volt, 4 wire, 400 amp		1.14	14.035		9,525	945		10,470	11,900
2600	600 amp		.94	17.021		14,900	1,150		16,050	18,000
2700	800 amp		.84	19.048		13,500	1,275		14,775	16,700
2800	1,200 amp		.68	23.529		17,500	1,575		19,075	21,700
2900	Pressure switch & CT compartment									
3000	120/208 volt, 4 wire, 800 amp	2 Elec	.80	20	Ea.	12,100	1,350		13,450	15,300
3100	1,200 amp		.66	24.242		23,800	1,625		25,425	28,500
3200	1,600 amp		.62	25.806		25,300	1,750		27,050	30,400
3300	2,000 amp		.56	28.571		26,400	1,925		28,325	32,000
3310	2,500 amp		.50	32		33,000	2,150		35,150	39,600
3320	3,000 amp		.44	36.364		43,900	2,450		46,350	52,000
3330	4,000 amp		.40	40		57,000	2,700		59,700	67,000
3340	120/208 volt, 4 wire, 800 amp, with ground fault		.80	20		20,000	1,350		21,350	24,000
3350	1,200 amp, with ground fault		.66	24.242		25,800	1,625		27,425	30,800
3360	1,600 amp, with ground fault		.62	25.806		28,500	1,750		30,250	33,900
3370	2,000 amp, with ground fault		.56	28.571		30,700	1,925		32,625	36,700
3400	277/480 volt, 4 wire, 800 amp, with ground fault		.80	20		20,000	1,350		21,350	24,000
3600	1,200 amp, with ground fault		.66	24.242		25,800	1,625		27,425	30,800
4000	1,600 amp, with ground fault		.62	25.806		28,500	1,750		30,250	33,900
4200	2,000 amp, with ground fault		.56	28.571		30,700	1,925		32,625	36,700
4400	Circuit breaker, molded case & CT compartment									
4600	3 pole, 4 wire, 600 amp	2 Elec	.94	17.021	Ea.	12,500	1,150		13,650	15,400
4800	800 amp		.84	19.048		19,000	1,275		20,275	22,800
5000	1,200 amp		.68	23.529		17,000	1,575		18,575	21,100
5100	Copper bus bars, not incl. CT's or PT's, add, minimum					15%				

26 24 13.20 In Plant Distribution Switchboards		Crew	Daily Output	Labor-Hours	Unit	Material	Labor	Equipment	Total	Total Incl O&P
0010	**IN PLANT DISTRIBUTION SWITCHBOARDS**									
0100	Main lugs only, to 600 volt, 3 pole, 3 wire, 200 amp	2 Elec	1.20	13.333	Ea.	1,275	900		2,175	2,725
0110	400 amp		1.20	13.333		1,350	900		2,250	2,825

26 24 13.20 In Plant Distribution Switchboards		Crew	Daily Output	Labor-Hours	Unit	Material	2023 Bare Costs Labor	Equipment	Total	Total Incl O&P
0120	600 amp	2 Elec	1.20	13.333	Ea.	1,300	900		2,200	2,750
0130	800 amp		1.08	14.815		1,425	1,000		2,425	3,025
0140	1,200 amp		.92	17.391		1,725	1,175		2,900	3,625
0150	1,600 amp		.86	18.605		2,250	1,250		3,500	4,325
0160	2,000 amp		.82	19.512		2,500	1,325		3,825	4,700
0250	To 480 volt, 3 pole, 4 wire, 200 amp		1.20	13.333		1,100	900		2,000	2,525
0260	400 amp		1.20	13.333		1,275	900		2,175	2,725
0270	600 amp		1.20	13.333		1,375	900		2,275	2,850
0280	800 amp		1.08	14.815		1,500	1,000		2,500	3,125
0290	1,200 amp		.92	17.391		1,850	1,175		3,025	3,775
0300	1,600 amp		.86	18.605		2,125	1,250		3,375	4,200
0310	2,000 amp		.82	19.512		2,475	1,325		3,800	4,675
0400	Main circuit breaker, to 600 volt, 3 pole, 3 wire, 200 amp		1.20	13.333		2,700	900		3,600	4,275
0410	400 amp		1.14	14.035		3,000	945		3,945	4,700
0420	600 amp		1.10	14.545		4,675	980		5,655	6,575
0430	800 amp		1.04	15.385		7,800	1,025		8,825	10,100
0440	1,200 amp		.88	18.182		10,200	1,225		11,425	13,000
0450	1,600 amp		.84	19.048		16,400	1,275		17,675	19,900
0460	2,000 amp		.80	20		17,500	1,350		18,850	21,200
0550	277/480 volt, 3 pole, 4 wire, 200 amp		1.20	13.333		3,925	900		4,825	5,650
0560	400 amp		1.14	14.035		5,850	945		6,795	7,825
0570	600 amp		1.10	14.545		9,125	980		10,105	11,500
0580	800 amp		1.04	15.385		13,500	1,025		14,525	16,500
0590	1,200 amp		.88	18.182		10,600	1,225		11,825	13,500
0600	1,600 amp		.84	19.048		16,500	1,275		17,775	20,000
0610	2,000 amp		.80	20		17,600	1,350		18,950	21,300
0700	Main fusible switch w/fuse, 208/240 volt, 3 pole, 3 wire, 200 amp		1.20	13.333		4,050	900		4,950	5,800
0710	400 amp		1.14	14.035		3,300	945		4,245	5,050
0720	600 amp		1.10	14.545		4,700	980		5,680	6,625
0730	800 amp		1.04	15.385		25,000	1,025		26,025	29,100
0740	1,200 amp		.88	18.182		11,800	1,225		13,025	14,700
0800	120/208, 120/240 volt, 3 pole, 4 wire, 200 amp		1.20	13.333		3,650	900		4,550	5,350
0810	400 amp		1.14	14.035		3,300	945		4,245	5,050
0820	600 amp		1.10	14.545		7,000	980		7,980	9,150
0830	800 amp		1.04	15.385		25,000	1,025		26,025	29,100
0840	1,200 amp		.88	18.182		8,700	1,225		9,925	11,400
0900	480 or 600 volt, 3 pole, 3 wire, 200 amp		1.20	13.333		3,900	900		4,800	5,625
0910	400 amp		1.14	14.035		3,175	945		4,120	4,900
0920	600 amp		1.10	14.545		4,700	980		5,680	6,625
0930	800 amp		1.04	15.385		7,250	1,025		8,275	9,525
0940	1,200 amp		.88	18.182		8,550	1,225		9,775	11,200
1000	277 or 480 volt, 3 pole, 4 wire, 200 amp		1.20	13.333		4,125	900		5,025	5,850
1010	400 amp		1.14	14.035		3,925	945		4,870	5,725
1020	600 amp		1.10	14.545		6,150	980		7,130	8,200
1030	800 amp		1.04	15.385		7,500	1,025		8,525	9,800
1040	1,200 amp		.88	18.182		8,700	1,225		9,925	11,400
1120	1,600 amp		.76	21.053		15,900	1,425		17,325	19,600
1130	2,000 amp		.68	23.529		20,900	1,575		22,475	25,400
1150	Pressure switch, bolted, 3 pole, 208/240 volt, 3 wire, 800 amp		.96	16.667		11,800	1,125		12,925	14,700
1160	1,200 amp		.80	20		15,000	1,350		16,350	18,500
1170	1,600 amp		.76	21.053		17,400	1,425		18,825	21,300
1180	2,000 amp		.68	23.529		19,600	1,575		21,175	23,900
1200	120/208 or 120/240 volt, 3 pole, 4 wire, 800 amp		.96	16.667		9,300	1,125		10,425	11,900

26 24 13.20 In Plant Distribution Switchboards		Crew	Daily Output	Labor-Hours	Unit	2023 Bare Costs Material	Labor	Equipment	Total	Total Incl O&P
1210	1,200 amp	2 Elec	.80	20	Ea.	10,900	1,350		12,250	14,000
1220	1,600 amp		.76	21.053		17,400	1,425		18,825	21,300
1230	2,000 amp		.68	23.529		19,600	1,575		21,175	23,900
1300	480 or 600 volt, 3 wire, 800 amp		.96	16.667		11,800	1,125		12,925	14,700
1310	1,200 amp		.80	20		16,700	1,350		18,050	20,400
1320	1,600 amp		.76	21.053		18,600	1,425		20,025	22,500
1330	2,000 amp		.68	23.529		20,900	1,575		22,475	25,400
1400	277/480 volt, 4 wire, 800 amp		.96	16.667		11,800	1,125		12,925	14,700
1410	1,200 amp		.80	20		16,700	1,350		18,050	20,400
1420	1,600 amp		.76	21.053		18,600	1,425		20,025	22,500
1430	2,000 amp		.68	23.529		20,900	1,575		22,475	25,400
1500	Main ground fault protector, 1,200-2,000 amp		5.40	2.963		3,400	200		3,600	4,050
1600	Busway connection, 200 amp		5.40	2.963		545	200		745	895
1610	400 amp		4.60	3.478		545	234		779	950
1620	600 amp		4	4		545	269		814	1,000
1630	800 amp		3.20	5		545	335		880	1,100
1640	1,200 amp		2.60	6.154		545	415		960	1,225
1650	1,600 amp		2.40	6.667		1,125	450		1,575	1,925
1660	2,000 amp		2	8		1,125	540		1,665	2,050
1700	Shunt trip for remote operation, 200 amp		8	2		660	135		795	930
1710	400 amp		8	2		1,050	135		1,185	1,375
1720	600 amp		8	2		1,250	135		1,385	1,575
1730	800 amp		8	2		1,600	135		1,735	1,975
1740	1,200-2,000 amp		8	2		3,500	135		3,635	4,050
1800	Motor operated main breaker, 200 amp		8	2		3,925	135		4,060	4,525
1810	400 amp		8	2		4,000	135		4,135	4,600
1820	600 amp		8	2		3,700	135		3,835	4,275
1830	800 amp		8	2		3,150	135		3,285	3,675
1840	1,200-2,000 amp		8	2		3,450	135		3,585	4,000
1900	Current/potential transformer metering compartment, 200-800 amp		5.40	2.963		2,150	200		2,350	2,675
1940	1,200 amp		5.40	2.963		6,150	200		6,350	7,075
1950	1,600-2,000 amp		5.40	2.963		9,825	200		10,025	11,100
2000	With watt meter, 200-800 amp		4	4		10,100	269		10,369	11,500
2040	1,200 amp		4	4		10,200	269		10,469	11,600
2050	1,600-2,000 amp		4	4		12,300	269		12,569	13,900
2100	Split bus, 60-200 amp	1 Elec	5.30	1.509		205	102		307	375
2130	400 amp	2 Elec	4.60	3.478		345	234		579	730
2140	600 amp		3.60	4.444		425	299		724	910
2150	800 amp		2.60	6.154		540	415		955	1,200
2170	1,200 amp		2	8		615	540		1,155	1,475
2250	Contactor control, 60 amp	1 Elec	2	4		1,350	269		1,619	1,875
2260	100 amp		1.50	5.333		1,475	360		1,835	2,150
2270	200 amp		1	8		2,225	540		2,765	3,250
2280	400 amp	2 Elec	1	16		6,925	1,075		8,000	9,200
2290	600 amp		.84	19.048		7,750	1,275		9,025	10,400
2300	800 amp		.72	22.222		8,950	1,500		10,450	12,100
2500	Modifier, two distribution sections, add		.80	20		2,950	1,350		4,300	5,250
2520	Three distribution sections, add		.40	40		4,450	2,700		7,150	8,900
2560	Auxiliary pull section, 20", add		2	8		1,125	540		1,665	2,025
2580	24", add		1.80	8.889		1,125	600		1,725	2,125
2600	30", add		1.60	10		1,125	675		1,800	2,225
2620	36", add		1.40	11.429		1,350	770		2,120	2,625
2640	Dog house, 12", add		2.40	6.667		231	450		681	920

26 24 13 – Switchboards

26 24 13.20 In Plant Distribution Switchboards		Crew	Daily Output	Labor-Hours	Unit	Material	Labor	Equipment	Total	Total Incl O&P
2660	18", add	2 Elec	2	8	Ea.	460	540		1,000	1,300
3000	Transition section between switchboard and transformer									
3050	or motor control center, 4 wire alum. bus, 600 amp	2 Elec	1.14	14.035	Ea.	2,200	945		3,145	3,825
3100	800 amp		1	16		2,475	1,075		3,550	4,325
3150	1,000 amp		.88	18.182		2,775	1,225		4,000	4,875
3200	1,200 amp		.80	20		3,050	1,350		4,400	5,375
3250	1,600 amp		.72	22.222		3,625	1,500		5,125	6,200
3300	2,000 amp		.66	24.242		4,150	1,625		5,775	7,000
3350	2,500 amp		.62	25.806		4,850	1,750		6,600	7,900
3400	3,000 amp		.56	28.571		5,575	1,925		7,500	8,975
4000	Weatherproof construction, per vertical section	↓	1.76	9.091	↓	2,725	610		3,335	3,900

26 24 13.30 Distribution Switchboards Section

		Crew	Daily Output	Labor-Hours	Unit	Material	Labor	Equipment	Total	Total Incl O&P
0010	**DISTRIBUTION SWITCHBOARDS SECTION** R262419-80									
0100	Aluminum bus bars, not including breakers									
0160	Subfeed lug-rated at 60 amp	2 Elec	1.30	12.308	Ea.	1,225	830		2,055	2,575
0170	100 amp		1.26	12.698		1,275	855		2,130	2,675
0180	200 amp		1.20	13.333		1,625	900		2,525	3,125
0190	400 amp		1.10	14.545		1,200	980		2,180	2,750
0195	120/208 or 277/480 volt, 4 wire, 400 amp		1.10	14.545		1,675	980		2,655	3,300
0200	600 amp		1	16		1,600	1,075		2,675	3,350
0300	800 amp		.88	18.182		2,000	1,225		3,225	4,050
0400	1,000 amp		.80	20		2,550	1,350		3,900	4,800
0500	1,200 amp		.72	22.222		3,025	1,500		4,525	5,550
0600	1,600 amp		.66	24.242		4,725	1,625		6,350	7,625
0700	2,000 amp		.62	25.806		6,000	1,750		7,750	9,175
0800	2,500 amp		.60	26.667		6,350	1,800		8,150	9,650
0900	3,000 amp		.56	28.571		8,600	1,925		10,525	12,300
0950	4,000 amp	↓	.52	30.769	↓	8,050	2,075		10,125	12,000

26 24 13.40 Switchboards Feeder Section

		Crew	Daily Output	Labor-Hours	Unit	Material	Labor	Equipment	Total	Total Incl O&P
0010	**SWITCHBOARDS FEEDER SECTION** group mounted devices R262419-82									
0030	Circuit breakers									
0160	FA frame, 15 to 60 amp, 240 volt, 1 pole	1 Elec	8	1	Ea.	137	67.50		204.50	250
0170	2 pole		7	1.143		450	77		527	610
0180	3 pole		5.30	1.509		480	102		582	675
0210	480 volt, 1 pole		8	1		173	67.50		240.50	291
0220	2 pole		7	1.143		380	77		457	535
0230	3 pole		5.30	1.509		625	102		727	840
0260	600 volt, 2 pole		7	1.143		820	77		897	1,025
0270	3 pole		5.30	1.509		630	102		732	840
0280	FA frame, 70 to 100 amp, 240 volt, 1 pole		7	1.143		229	77		306	365
0310	2 pole		5	1.600		530	108		638	740
0320	3 pole		4	2		645	135		780	910
0330	480 volt, 1 pole		7	1.143		655	77		732	840
0360	2 pole		5	1.600		920	108		1,028	1,150
0370	3 pole		4	2		1,150	135		1,285	1,475
0380	600 volt, 2 pole		5	1.600		825	108		933	1,075
0410	3 pole		4	2		1,050	135		1,185	1,350
0420	KA frame, 70 to 225 amp		3.20	2.500		1,450	168		1,618	1,850
0430	LA frame, 125 to 400 amp		2.30	3.478		4,350	234		4,584	5,150
0460	MA frame, 450 to 600 amp		1.60	5		6,025	335		6,360	7,125
0470	700 to 800 amp		1.30	6.154		6,100	415		6,515	7,325
0480	MAL frame, 1,000 amp	↓	1	8	↓	8,125	540		8,665	9,725

26 24 13 – Switchboards

26 24 13.40 Switchboards Feeder Section		Crew	Daily Output	Labor-Hours	Unit	Material	Labor	Equipment	Total	Total Incl O&P
						2023 Bare Costs				
0490	PA frame, 1,200 amp	1 Elec	.80	10	Ea.	16,500	675		17,175	19,100
0500	Branch circuit, fusible switch, 600 volt, double 30/30 amp		4	2		895	135		1,030	1,175
0550	60/60 amp		3.20	2.500		920	168		1,088	1,250
0600	100/100 amp		2.70	2.963		1,175	200		1,375	1,600
0650	Single, 30 amp		5.30	1.509		845	102		947	1,075
0700	60 amp		4.70	1.702		890	115		1,005	1,150
0750	100 amp		4	2		1,550	135		1,685	1,925
0800	200 amp		2.70	2.963		1,300	200		1,500	1,725
0850	400 amp		2.30	3.478		2,325	234		2,559	2,925
0900	600 amp		1.80	4.444		2,875	299		3,174	3,625
0950	800 amp		1.30	6.154		4,875	415		5,290	5,975
1000	1,200 amp		.80	10		5,525	675		6,200	7,075
1080	Branch circuit, circuit breakers, high interrupting capacity									
1100	60 amp, 240, 480 or 600 volt, 1 pole	1 Elec	8	1	Ea.	380	67.50		447.50	520
1120	2 pole		7	1.143		1,025	77		1,102	1,250
1140	3 pole		5.30	1.509		1,075	102		1,177	1,325
1150	100 amp, 240, 480 or 600 volt, 1 pole		7	1.143		400	77		477	555
1160	2 pole		5	1.600		1,250	108		1,358	1,525
1180	3 pole		4	2		1,400	135		1,535	1,750
1200	225 amp, 240, 480 or 600 volt, 2 pole		3.50	2.286		4,200	154		4,354	4,850
1220	3 pole		3.20	2.500		4,925	168		5,093	5,675
1240	400 amp, 240, 480 or 600 volt, 2 pole		2.50	3.200		7,750	216		7,966	8,850
1260	3 pole		2.30	3.478		2,950	234		3,184	3,600
1280	600 amp, 240, 480 or 600 volt, 2 pole		1.80	4.444		3,500	299		3,799	4,300
1300	3 pole		1.60	5		3,500	335		3,835	4,350
1320	800 amp, 240, 480 or 600 volt, 2 pole		1.50	5.333		4,475	360		4,835	5,450
1340	3 pole		1.30	6.154		5,475	415		5,890	6,650
1360	1,000 amp, 240, 480 or 600 volt, 2 pole		1.10	7.273		5,600	490		6,090	6,875
1380	3 pole		1	8		6,025	540		6,565	7,425
1400	1,200 amp, 240, 480 or 600 volt, 2 pole		.90	8.889		7,950	600		8,550	9,625
1420	3 pole		.80	10		7,600	675		8,275	9,350
1700	Fusible switch, 240 V, 60 amp, 2 pole		3.20	2.500		500	168		668	800
1720	3 pole		3	2.667		690	180		870	1,025
1740	100 amp, 2 pole		2.70	2.963		510	200		710	855
1760	3 pole		2.50	3.200		775	216		991	1,175
1780	200 amp, 2 pole		2	4		1,075	269		1,344	1,575
1800	3 pole		1.90	4.211		1,250	284		1,534	1,800
1820	400 amp, 2 pole		1.50	5.333		2,000	360		2,360	2,725
1840	3 pole		1.30	6.154		2,500	415		2,915	3,375
1860	600 amp, 2 pole		1	8		2,850	540		3,390	3,925
1880	3 pole		.90	8.889		3,500	600		4,100	4,750
1900	240-600 V, 800 amp, 2 pole		.70	11.429		6,350	770		7,120	8,125
1920	3 pole		.60	13.333		7,775	900		8,675	9,875
2000	600 V, 60 amp, 2 pole		3.20	2.500		760	168		928	1,075
2040	100 amp, 2 pole		2.70	2.963		785	200		985	1,150
2080	200 amp, 2 pole		2	4		1,350	269		1,619	1,900
2120	400 amp, 2 pole		1.50	5.333		2,700	360		3,060	3,500
2160	600 amp, 2 pole		1	8		3,275	540		3,815	4,400
2500	Branch circuit, circuit breakers, 60 amp, 600 volt, 3 pole		5.30	1.509		915	102		1,017	1,150
2520	240, 480 or 600 volt, 1 pole		8	1		187	67.50		254.50	305
2540	240 volt, 2 pole		7	1.143		395	77		472	550
2560	480 or 600 volt, 2 pole		7	1.143		430	77		507	590
2580	240 volt, 3 pole		5.30	1.509		610	102		712	820

26 24 Switchboards and Panelboards

26 24 13 – Switchboards

26 24 13.40 Switchboards Feeder Section		Crew	Daily Output	Labor-Hours	Unit	Material (2023 Bare Costs)	Labor (2023 Bare Costs)	Equipment (2023 Bare Costs)	Total (2023 Bare Costs)	Total Incl O&P
2600	480 volt, 3 pole	1 Elec	5.30	1.509	Ea.	630	102		732	845
2620	100 amp, 600 volt, 2 pole		5	1.600		560	108		668	775
2640	3 pole		4	2		705	135		840	975
2660	480 volt, 2 pole		5	1.600		560	108		668	775
2680	240 volt, 2 pole		5	1.600		445	108		553	650
2700	3 pole		4	2		655	135		790	920
2720	480 volt, 3 pole		4	2		655	135		790	920
2740	225 amp, 240, 480 or 600 volt, 2 pole		3.50	2.286		2,050	154		2,204	2,475
2760	3 pole		3.20	2.500		985	168		1,153	1,325
2780	400 amp, 240, 480 or 600 volt, 2 pole		2.50	3.200		3,650	216		3,866	4,350
2800	3 pole		2.30	3.478		4,700	234		4,934	5,500
2820	600 amp, 240 or 480 volt, 2 pole		1.80	4.444		5,725	299		6,024	6,750
2840	3 pole		1.60	5		7,100	335		7,435	8,300
2860	800 amp, 240, 480 or 600 volt, 2 pole		1.50	5.333		7,400	360		7,760	8,675
2880	3 pole		1.30	6.154		9,525	415		9,940	11,100
2900	1,000 amp, 240, 480 or 600 volt, 2 pole		1.10	7.273		14,700	490		15,190	16,900
2920	480 or 600 volt, 3 pole		1	8		15,400	540		15,940	17,700
2940	1,200 amp, 240, 480 or 600 volt, 2 pole		.90	8.889		14,700	600		15,300	17,100
2960	3 pole		.80	10		15,700	675		16,375	18,300
2980	600 volt, 3 pole		.80	10		8,175	675		8,850	10,000

26 24 16 – Panelboards

26 24 16.10 Load Centers		Crew	Daily Output	Labor-Hours	Unit	Material	Labor	Equipment	Total	Total Incl O&P
0010	**LOAD CENTERS** (residential type) R262416-50									
0100	3 wire, 120/240 V, 1 phase, including 1 pole plug-in breakers									
0200	100 amp main lugs, indoor, 8 circuits	1 Elec	1.40	5.714	Ea.	206	385		591	795
0300	12 circuits		1.20	6.667		275	450		725	970
0400	Rainproof, 8 circuits		1.40	5.714		241	385		626	835
0500	12 circuits		1.20	6.667		310	450		760	1,000
0600	200 amp main lugs, indoor, 16 circuits	R-1A	1.80	8.889		470	540		1,010	1,325
0700	20 circuits		1.50	10.667		455	645		1,100	1,450
0800	24 circuits		1.30	12.308		660	745		1,405	1,825
0900	30 circuits		1.20	13.333		760	810		1,570	2,025
1000	40 circuits		.80	20		1,050	1,225		2,275	2,950
1200	Rainproof, 16 circuits		1.80	8.889		475	540		1,015	1,325
1300	20 circuits		1.50	10.667		625	645		1,270	1,650
1400	24 circuits		1.30	12.308		670	745		1,415	1,850
1500	30 circuits		1.20	13.333		895	810		1,705	2,175
1600	40 circuits		.80	20		1,200	1,225		2,425	3,125
1800	400 amp main lugs, indoor, 42 circuits		.72	22.222		2,175	1,350		3,525	4,400
1900	Rainproof, 42 circuits		.72	22.222		2,300	1,350		3,650	4,525
2200	Plug in breakers, 20 amp, 1 pole, 4 wire, 120/208 volts									
2210	125 amp main lugs, indoor, 12 circuits	1 Elec	1.20	6.667	Ea.	385	450		835	1,100
2300	18 circuits		.80	10		510	675		1,185	1,550
2400	Rainproof, 12 circuits		1.20	6.667		500	450		950	1,225
2500	18 circuits		.80	10		585	675		1,260	1,650
2600	200 amp main lugs, indoor, 24 circuits	R-1A	1.30	12.308		760	745		1,505	1,925
2700	30 circuits		1.20	13.333		845	810		1,655	2,125
2800	36 circuits		1	16		825	970		1,795	2,350
2900	42 circuits		.80	20		1,150	1,225		2,375	3,075
3000	Rainproof, 24 circuits		1.30	12.308		805	745		1,550	1,975
3100	30 circuits		1.20	13.333		955	810		1,765	2,250
3200	36 circuits		1	16		945	970		1,915	2,500

26 24 16 – Panelboards

26 24 16.10 Load Centers		Crew	Daily Output	Labor-Hours	Unit	Material	Labor	Equipment	Total	Total Incl O&P
						2023 Bare Costs				
3300	42 circuits	R-1A	.80	20	Ea.	1,200	1,225		2,425	3,125
3500	400 amp main lugs, indoor, 42 circuits		.72	22.222		2,250	1,350		3,600	4,475
3600	Rainproof, 42 circuits		.72	22.222		2,750	1,350		4,100	5,025
3700	Plug-in breakers, 20 amp, 1 pole, 3 wire, 120/240 volts									
3800	100 amp main breaker, indoor, 12 circuits	1 Elec	1.20	6.667	Ea.	340	450		790	1,050
3900	18 circuits	"	.80	10		445	675		1,120	1,500
4000	200 amp main breaker, indoor, 20 circuits	R-1A	1.50	10.667		675	645		1,320	1,700
4200	24 circuits		1.30	12.308		745	745		1,490	1,925
4300	30 circuits		1.20	13.333		900	810		1,710	2,200
4400	40 circuits		.90	17.778		1,075	1,075		2,150	2,775
4500	Rainproof, 20 circuits		1.50	10.667		740	645		1,385	1,775
4600	24 circuits		1.30	12.308		740	745		1,485	1,925
4700	30 circuits		1.20	13.333		1,125	810		1,935	2,425
4800	40 circuits		.90	17.778		1,375	1,075		2,450	3,100
5000	400 amp main breaker, indoor, 42 circuits		.72	22.222		4,175	1,350		5,525	6,575
5100	Rainproof, 42 circuits		.72	22.222		4,150	1,350		5,500	6,575
5300	Plug in breakers, 20 amp, 1 pole, 4 wire, 120/208 volts									
5400	200 amp main breaker, indoor, 30 circuits	R-1A	1.20	13.333	Ea.	1,325	810		2,135	2,675
5500	42 circuits		.80	20		1,650	1,225		2,875	3,625
5600	Rainproof, 30 circuits		1.20	13.333		1,425	810		2,235	2,775
5700	42 circuits		.80	20		1,750	1,225		2,975	3,725

26 24 16.20 Panelboard and Load Center Circuit Breakers

		Crew	Daily Output	Labor-Hours	Unit	Material	Labor	Equipment	Total	Total Incl O&P
0010	**PANELBOARD AND LOAD CENTER CIRCUIT BREAKERS** R262416-50									
0050	Bolt-on, 10,000 amp I.C., 120 volt, 1 pole									
0100	15-50 amp	1 Elec	10	.800	Ea.	25	54		79	108
0200	60 amp		8	1		28.50	67.50		96	131
0300	70 amp		8	1		24	67.50		91.50	127
0350	240 volt, 2 pole									
0400	15-50 amp	1 Elec	8	1	Ea.	78	67.50		145.50	186
0500	60 amp		7.50	1.067		57.50	72		129.50	171
0600	80-100 amp		5	1.600		143	108		251	315
0700	3 pole, 15-60 amp		6.20	1.290		187	87		274	335
0800	70 amp		5	1.600		213	108		321	395
0900	80-100 amp		3.60	2.222		264	150		414	515
1000	22,000 amp I.C., 240 volt, 2 pole, 70-225 amp		2.70	2.963		278	200		478	600
1100	3 pole, 70-225 amp		2.30	3.478		515	234		749	920
1200	14,000 amp I.C., 277 volts, 1 pole, 15-30 amp		8	1		105	67.50		172.50	215
1300	22,000 amp I.C., 480 volts, 2 pole, 70-225 amp		2.70	2.963		230	200		430	550
1400	3 pole, 70-225 amp		2.30	3.478		1,000	234		1,234	1,450
2000	Plug-in panel or load center, 120/240 volt, to 60 amp, 1 pole		12	.667		17.35	45		62.35	85.50
2004	Circuit breaker, 120/240 volt, 20 A, 1 pole with NM cable		6.50	1.231		30	83		113	156
2006	30 A, 1 pole with NM cable		6.50	1.231		30	83		113	156
2010	2 pole		9	.889		35.50	60		95.50	128
2014	50 A, 2 pole with NM cable		5.50	1.455		48	98		146	199
2020	3 pole		7.50	1.067		91.50	72		163.50	207
2030	100 amp, 2 pole		6	1.333		59.50	90		149.50	199
2040	3 pole		4.50	1.778		137	120		257	330
2050	150-200 amp, 2 pole		3	2.667		171	180		351	455
2060	Plug-in tandem, 120/240 V, 2-15 A, 1 pole		11	.727		23	49		72	98.50
2070	1-15 A & 1-20 A		11	.727		22.50	49		71.50	98
2080	2-20 A		11	.727		23	49		72	98.50
2082	Arc fault circuit interrupter, 120/240 V, 1-15 A & 1-20 A, 1 pole		11	.727		56	49		105	135

26 24 16.20 Panelboard and Load Center Circuit Breakers		Crew	Daily Output	Labor-Hours	Unit	Material	Labor (2023 Bare Costs)	Equipment	Total	Total Incl O&P
2100	High interrupting capacity, 120/240 volt, plug-in, 30 amp, 1 pole	1 Elec	12	.667	Ea.	26	45		71	95
2110	60 amp, 2 pole		9	.889		52	60		112	146
2120	3 pole		7.50	1.067		145	72		217	266
2130	100 amp, 2 pole		6	1.333		116	90		206	260
2140	3 pole		4.50	1.778		212	120		332	410
2150	125 amp, 2 pole		3	2.667		390	180		570	695
2200	Bolt-on, 30 amp, 1 pole		10	.800		65.50	54		119.50	152
2210	60 amp, 2 pole		7.50	1.067		155	72		227	277
2220	3 pole		6.20	1.290		400	87		487	570
2230	100 amp, 2 pole		5	1.600		355	108		463	550
2240	3 pole		3.60	2.222		570	150		720	845
2300	Ground fault, 240 volt, 30 amp, 1 pole		7	1.143		209	77		286	345
2310	2 pole		6	1.333		370	90		460	545
2350	Key operated, 240 volt, 1 pole, 30 amp		7	1.143		142	77		219	270
2360	Switched neutral, 240 volt, 30 amp, 2 pole		6	1.333		96.50	90		186.50	239
2370	3 pole		5.50	1.455		144	98		242	305
2400	Shunt trip, for 240 volt breaker, 60 amp, 1 pole		4	2		83.50	135		218.50	292
2410	2 pole		3.50	2.286		83.50	154		237.50	320
2420	3 pole		3	2.667		83.50	180		263.50	360
2430	100 amp, 2 pole		3	2.667		83.50	180		263.50	360
2440	3 pole		2.50	3.200		83.50	216		299.50	410
2450	150 amp, 2 pole		2	4		242	269		511	665
2500	Auxiliary switch, for 240 volt breaker, 60 amp, 1 pole		4	2		92.50	135		227.50	300
2510	2 pole		3.50	2.286		92.50	154		246.50	330
2520	3 pole		3	2.667		92.50	180		272.50	370
2530	100 amp, 2 pole		3	2.667		92.50	180		272.50	370
2540	3 pole		2.50	3.200		92.50	216		308.50	420
2550	150 amp, 2 pole		2	4		126	269		395	540
2600	Panel or load center, 277/480 volt, plug-in, 30 amp, 1 pole		12	.667		73	45		118	147
2610	60 amp, 2 pole		9	.889		224	60		284	335
2620	3 pole		7.50	1.067		330	72		402	465
2650	Bolt-on, 60 amp, 2 pole		7.50	1.067		224	72		296	355
2660	3 pole		6.20	1.290		610	87		697	800
2700	I-line, 277/480 volt, 30 amp, 1 pole		8	1		233	67.50		300.50	355
2710	60 amp, 2 pole		7.50	1.067		520	72		592	680
2720	3 pole		6.20	1.290		625	87		712	820
2730	100 amp, 1 pole		7.50	1.067		237	72		309	365
2740	2 pole		5	1.600		595	108		703	815
2750	3 pole		3.50	2.286		765	154		919	1,075
2800	High interrupting capacity, 277/480 volt, plug-in, 30 amp, 1 pole		12	.667		430	45		475	540
2810	60 amp, 2 pole		9	.889		665	60		725	820
2820	3 pole		7	1.143		775	77		852	965
2830	Bolt-on, 30 amp, 1 pole		8	1		360	67.50		427.50	495
2840	60 amp, 2 pole		7.50	1.067		600	72		672	765
2850	3 pole		6.20	1.290		1,200	87		1,287	1,450
2900	I-line, 30 amp, 1 pole		8	1		435	67.50		502.50	580
2910	60 amp, 2 pole		7.50	1.067		870	72		942	1,050
2920	3 pole		6.20	1.290		1,075	87		1,162	1,300
2930	100 amp, 1 pole		7.50	1.067		530	72		602	690
2940	2 pole		5	1.600		830	108		938	1,075
2950	3 pole		3.60	2.222		1,075	150		1,225	1,425
2960	Shunt trip, 277/480 volt breaker, remote oper., 30 amp, 1 pole		4	2		450	135		585	695
2970	60 amp, 2 pole		3.50	2.286		660	154		814	955

26 24 16.20 Panelboard and Load Center Circuit Breakers		Crew	Daily Output	Labor-Hours	Unit	Material	Labor	Equipment	Total	Total Incl O&P
						2023 Bare Costs				
2980	3 pole	1 Elec	3	2.667	Ea.	1,700	180		1,880	2,150
2990	100 amp, 1 pole		3.50	2.286		540	154		694	825
3000	2 pole		3	2.667		750	180		930	1,100
3010	3 pole		2.50	3.200		1,925	216		2,141	2,425
3050	Under voltage trip, 277/480 volt breaker, 30 amp, 1 pole		4	2		450	135		585	695
3060	60 amp, 2 pole		3.50	2.286		660	154		814	955
3070	3 pole		3	2.667		750	180		930	1,100
3080	100 amp, 1 pole		3.50	2.286		540	154		694	825
3090	2 pole		3	2.667		750	180		930	1,100
3100	3 pole		2.50	3.200		690	216		906	1,075
3150	Motor operated, 277/480 volt breaker, 30 amp, 1 pole		4	2		800	135		935	1,075
3160	60 amp, 2 pole		3.50	2.286		840	154		994	1,150
3170	3 pole		3	2.667		1,650	180		1,830	2,100
3180	100 amp, 1 pole		3.50	2.286		900	154		1,054	1,225
3190	2 pole		3	2.667		1,125	180		1,305	1,525
3200	3 pole		2.50	3.200		1,825	216		2,041	2,350
3250	Panelboard spacers, per pole		40	.200		1.94	13.45		15.39	22
5110	NEMA 1 enclosure only, 600V, 3 p, 14k AIC, 100A	↓	2.20	3.636	↓	112	245		357	490

26 24 16.30 Panelboards Commercial Applications		Crew	Daily Output	Labor-Hours	Unit	Material	Labor	Equipment	Total	Total Incl O&P
0010	**PANELBOARDS COMMERCIAL APPLICATIONS** R262416-50									
0050	NQ, w/20 amp 1 pole bolt-on circuit breakers									
0100	3 wire, 120/240 volts, 100 amp main lugs									
0150	10 circuits	1 Elec	1	8	Ea.	1,225	540		1,765	2,150
0200	14 circuits		.88	9.091		1,325	610		1,935	2,350
0250	18 circuits		.75	10.667		1,425	720		2,145	2,650
0300	20 circuits	↓	.65	12.308		1,575	830		2,405	2,950
0350	225 amp main lugs, 24 circuits	2 Elec	1.20	13.333		1,725	900		2,625	3,225
0400	30 circuits		.90	17.778		1,875	1,200		3,075	3,825
0450	36 circuits		.80	20		2,125	1,350		3,475	4,325
0500	38 circuits		.72	22.222		2,175	1,500		3,675	4,600
0550	42 circuits	↓	.66	24.242		2,600	1,625		4,225	5,300
0600	4 wire, 120/208 volts, 100 amp main lugs, 12 circuits	1 Elec	1	8		1,325	540		1,865	2,250
0650	16 circuits		.75	10.667		1,425	720		2,145	2,650
0700	20 circuits		.65	12.308		1,600	830		2,430	3,000
0750	24 circuits		.60	13.333		1,750	900		2,650	3,250
0800	30 circuits	↓	.53	15.094		1,850	1,025		2,875	3,550
0850	225 amp main lugs, 32 circuits	2 Elec	.90	17.778		2,075	1,200		3,275	4,050
0900	34 circuits		.84	19.048		2,175	1,275		3,450	4,275
0950	36 circuits		.80	20		3,325	1,350		4,675	5,675
1000	42 circuits		.68	23.529		3,475	1,575		5,050	6,175
1010	400 amp main lugs, 42 circs		.68	23.529		1,650	1,575		3,225	4,150
1040	225 amp main lugs, NEMA 7, 12 circuits		1	16		6,450	1,075		7,525	8,700
1100	24 circuits	↓	.40	40	↓	7,800	2,700		10,500	12,600
1200	NF, w/20 amp, 1 pole bolt-on circuit breakers									
1250	4 wire, 277/480 volts, 100 amp main lugs, 12 circuits	1 Elec	.88	9.091	Ea.	3,050	610		3,660	4,250
1300	20 circuits	"	.60	13.333		4,100	900		5,000	5,850
1350	225 amp main lugs, 24 circuits	2 Elec	.90	17.778		4,825	1,200		6,025	7,075
1400	30 circuits		.80	20		5,450	1,350		6,800	8,000
1448	32 circuits		4.90	3.265		2,675	220		2,895	3,275
1450	36 circuits		.72	22.222		6,350	1,500		7,850	9,200
1500	42 circuits		.60	26.667		6,975	1,800		8,775	10,400
1510	225 amp main lugs, NEMA 7, 12 circuits	↓	.90	17.778	↓	6,625	1,200		7,825	9,050

26 24 16.30 Panelboards Commercial Applications		Crew	Daily Output	Labor-Hours	Unit	Material	Labor	Equipment	Total	Total Incl O&P
						2023 Bare Costs				
1590	24 circuits	2 Elec	.30	53.333	Ea.	9,475	3,600		13,075	15,800
1600	NQ panel, w/20 amp, 1 pole, circuit breakers									
1650	3 wire, 120/240 volt with main circuit breaker									
1700	100 amp main, 12 circuits	1 Elec	.80	10	Ea.	1,900	675		2,575	3,100
1750	20 circuits	"	.60	13.333		2,300	900		3,200	3,875
1800	225 amp main, 30 circuits	2 Elec	.68	23.529		2,200	1,575		3,775	4,775
1801	225 amp main, 32 circuits		5	3.200		355	216		571	710
1850	42 circuits		.52	30.769		2,650	2,075		4,725	5,975
1900	400 amp main, 30 circuits		.54	29.630		5,850	2,000		7,850	9,400
1950	42 circuits		.50	32		6,150	2,150		8,300	9,975
2000	4 wire, 120/208 volts with main circuit breaker									
2050	100 amp main, 24 circuits	1 Elec	.47	17.021	Ea.	2,450	1,150		3,600	4,400
2100	30 circuits	"	.40	20		2,600	1,350		3,950	4,850
2200	225 amp main, 32 circuits	2 Elec	.72	22.222		2,775	1,500		4,275	5,275
2250	42 circuits		.56	28.571		3,075	1,925		5,000	6,225
2300	400 amp main, 42 circuits		.48	33.333		6,700	2,250		8,950	10,700
2350	600 amp main, 42 circuits		.40	40		9,825	2,700		12,525	14,800
2400	NF, with 20 amp, 1 pole circuit breaker									
2450	4 wire, 277/480 volts with main circuit breaker									
2500	100 amp main, 24 circuits	1 Elec	.42	19.048	Ea.	5,475	1,275		6,750	7,925
2550	30 circuits	"	.38	21.053		6,100	1,425		7,525	8,800
2600	225 amp main, 30 circuits	2 Elec	.72	22.222		6,750	1,500		8,250	9,650
2650	42 circuits		.56	28.571		8,200	1,925		10,125	11,900
2700	400 amp main, 42 circuits		.46	34.783		11,700	2,350		14,050	16,400
2750	600 amp main, 42 circuits		.38	42.105		14,400	2,825		17,225	20,100
2900	Note: the following line items don't include branch circuit breakers									
2910	For branch circuit breakers information, see Section 26 24 16.20									
3010	Main lug, no main breaker, 240 volt, 1 pole, 3 wire, 100 amp	1 Elec	2.30	3.478	Ea.	1,075	234		1,309	1,525
3020	225 amp	2 Elec	2.40	6.667		1,200	450		1,650	2,000
3030	400 amp	"	1.80	8.889		1,575	600		2,175	2,625
3060	3 pole, 3 wire, 100 amp	1 Elec	2.30	3.478		2,025	234		2,259	2,575
3070	225 amp	2 Elec	2.40	6.667		2,325	450		2,775	3,225
3080	400 amp		1.80	8.889		2,725	600		3,325	3,900
3090	600 amp		1.60	10		3,975	675		4,650	5,375
3110	3 pole, 4 wire, 100 amp	1 Elec	2.30	3.478		2,025	234		2,259	2,575
3120	225 amp	2 Elec	2.40	6.667		2,325	450		2,775	3,225
3130	400 amp		1.80	8.889		2,725	600		3,325	3,900
3140	600 amp		1.60	10		3,975	675		4,650	5,375
3160	480 volt, 3 pole, 3 wire, 100 amp	1 Elec	2.30	3.478		2,025	234		2,259	2,575
3170	225 amp	2 Elec	2.40	6.667		2,325	450		2,775	3,225
3180	400 amp		1.80	8.889		2,725	600		3,325	3,900
3190	600 amp		1.60	10		3,975	675		4,650	5,375
3210	277/480 volt, 3 pole, 4 wire, 100 amp	1 Elec	2.30	3.478		2,025	234		2,259	2,575
3220	225 amp	2 Elec	2.40	6.667		2,325	450		2,775	3,225
3230	400 amp		1.80	8.889		3,375	600		3,975	4,600
3240	600 amp		1.60	10		3,975	675		4,650	5,375
3260	Main circuit breaker, 240 volt, 1 pole, 3 wire, 100 amp	1 Elec	2	4		1,800	269		2,069	2,400
3270	225 amp	2 Elec	2	8		1,600	540		2,140	2,550
3280	400 amp	"	1.60	10		5,100	675		5,775	6,600
3310	3 pole, 3 wire, 100 amp	1 Elec	2	4		2,750	269		3,019	3,425
3320	225 amp	2 Elec	2	8		3,650	540		4,190	4,825
3330	400 amp		1.60	10		6,775	675		7,450	8,450
3360	120/208 volt, 3 pole, 4 wire, 100 amp		4	4		1,850	269		2,119	2,425

26 24 16 – Panelboards

26 24 16.30 Panelboards Commercial Applications		Crew	Daily Output	Labor-Hours	Unit	Material	Labor	Equipment	Total	Total Incl O&P
						2023 Bare Costs				
3370	225 amp	2 Elec	2	8	Ea.	3,100	540		3,640	4,200
3380	400 amp		1.60	10		5,650	675		6,325	7,225
3410	480 volt, 3 pole, 3 wire, 100 amp	1 Elec	2	4		2,950	269		3,219	3,650
3420	225 amp	2 Elec	2	8		3,600	540		4,140	4,775
3430	400 amp		1.60	10		6,775	675		7,450	8,450
3460	277/480 volt, 3 pole, 4 wire, 100 amp		4	4		2,950	269		3,219	3,650
3470	225 amp		2	8		3,800	540		4,340	4,975
3480	400 amp		1.60	10		6,925	675		7,600	8,625
3510	Main circuit breaker, HIC, 240 volt, 1 pole, 3 wire, 100 amp	1 Elec	2	4		2,325	269		2,594	2,950
3520	225 amp	2 Elec	2	8		2,225	540		2,765	3,250
3530	400 amp	"	1.60	10		8,275	675		8,950	10,100
3560	3 pole, 3 wire, 100 amp	1 Elec	2	4		3,275	269		3,544	4,000
3570	225 amp	2 Elec	2	8		6,325	540		6,865	7,750
3580	400 amp	"	1.60	10		9,425	675		10,100	11,400
3610	120/208 volt, 3 pole, 4 wire, 100 amp	1 Elec	2	4		2,350	269		2,619	3,000
3620	225 amp	2 Elec	2	8		3,975	540		4,515	5,150
3630	400 amp	"	1.60	10		8,325	675		9,000	10,200
3660	480 volt, 3 pole, 3 wire, 100 amp	1 Elec	2	4		3,275	269		3,544	4,000
3670	225 amp	2 Elec	2	8		6,150	540		6,690	7,550
3680	400 amp	"	1.60	10		9,425	675		10,100	11,400
3710	277/480 volt, 3 pole, 4 wire, 100 amp	1 Elec	2	4		3,275	269		3,544	4,000
3720	225 amp	2 Elec	2	8		6,325	540		6,865	7,775
3730	400 amp	"	1.60	10		9,575	675		10,250	11,500
3760	Main circuit breaker, shunt trip, 100 amp	1 Elec	1.20	6.667		1,225	450		1,675	2,025
3770	225 amp	2 Elec	1.60	10		2,825	675		3,500	4,100
3780	400 amp	"	1.40	11.429		4,075	770		4,845	5,650

26 24 19 – Motor-Control Centers

26 24 19.20 Motor Control Center Components		Crew	Daily Output	Labor-Hours	Unit	Material	Labor	Equipment	Total	Total Incl O&P
0010	**MOTOR CONTROL CENTER COMPONENTS** R262419-60									
0100	Starter, size 1, FVNR, NEMA 1, type A, fusible	1 Elec	2.70	2.963	Ea.	1,625	200		1,825	2,075
0120	Circuit breaker		2.70	2.963		1,750	200		1,950	2,225
0140	Type B, fusible		2.70	2.963		1,775	200		1,975	2,250
0160	Circuit breaker		2.70	2.963		1,925	200		2,125	2,425
0180	NEMA 12, type A, fusible		2.60	3.077		1,650	207		1,857	2,100
0200	Circuit breaker		2.60	3.077		1,775	207		1,982	2,250
0220	Type B, fusible		2.60	3.077		1,800	207		2,007	2,275
0240	Circuit breaker		2.60	3.077		1,950	207		2,157	2,450
0300	Starter, size 1, FVR, NEMA 1, type A, fusible		2	4		2,325	269		2,594	2,950
0320	Circuit breaker		2	4		2,325	269		2,594	2,950
0340	Type B, fusible		2	4		2,550	269		2,819	3,200
0360	Circuit breaker		2	4		2,550	269		2,819	3,200
0380	NEMA 12, type A, fusible		1.90	4.211		2,350	284		2,634	3,000
0400	Circuit breaker		1.90	4.211		2,350	284		2,634	3,000
0420	Type B, fusible		1.90	4.211		2,575	284		2,859	3,250
0440	Circuit breaker		1.90	4.211		2,575	284		2,859	3,250
0490	Starter size 1, 2 speed, separate winding									
0500	NEMA 1, type A, fusible	1 Elec	2.60	3.077	Ea.	3,050	207		3,257	3,650
0520	Circuit breaker		2.60	3.077		3,050	207		3,257	3,650
0540	Type B, fusible		2.60	3.077		3,350	207		3,557	4,000
0560	Circuit breaker		2.60	3.077		3,350	207		3,557	4,000
0580	NEMA 12, type A, fusible		2.50	3.200		3,100	216		3,316	3,750
0600	Circuit breaker		2.50	3.200		3,100	216		3,316	3,750

26 24 19 – Motor-Control Centers

26 24 19.20 Motor Control Center Components		Crew	Daily Output	Labor-Hours	Unit	Material	Labor	Equipment	Total	Total Incl O&P
						2023 Bare Costs				
0620	Type B, fusible	1 Elec	2.50	3.200	Ea.	3,400	216		3,616	4,075
0640	Circuit breaker		2.50	3.200		3,400	216		3,616	4,075
0650	Starter size 1, 2 speed, consequent pole									
0660	NEMA 1, type A, fusible	1 Elec	2.60	3.077	Ea.	3,050	207		3,257	3,650
0680	Circuit breaker		2.60	3.077		3,050	207		3,257	3,650
0700	Type B, fusible		2.60	3.077		3,350	207		3,557	4,000
0720	Circuit breaker		2.60	3.077		3,350	207		3,557	4,000
0740	NEMA 12, type A, fusible		2.50	3.200		3,100	216		3,316	3,750
0760	Circuit breaker		2.50	3.200		3,100	216		3,316	3,750
0780	Type B, fusible		2.50	3.200		3,400	216		3,616	4,050
0800	Circuit breaker		2.50	3.200		3,400	216		3,616	4,075
0810	Starter size 1, 2 speed, space only									
0820	NEMA 1, type A, fusible	1 Elec	16	.500	Ea.	685	33.50		718.50	805
0840	Circuit breaker		16	.500		685	33.50		718.50	805
0860	Type B, fusible		16	.500		685	33.50		718.50	805
0880	Circuit breaker		16	.500		685	33.50		718.50	805
0900	NEMA 12, type A, fusible		15	.533		715	36		751	840
0920	Circuit breaker		15	.533		715	36		751	840
0940	Type B, fusible		15	.533		715	36		751	840
0960	Circuit breaker		15	.533		715	36		751	840
1100	Starter size 2, FVNR, NEMA 1, type A, fusible	2 Elec	4	4		1,825	269		2,094	2,400
1120	Circuit breaker		4	4		2,000	269		2,269	2,600
1140	Type B, fusible		4	4		2,000	269		2,269	2,600
1160	Circuit breaker		4	4		2,175	269		2,444	2,800
1180	NEMA 12, type A, fusible		3.80	4.211		1,850	284		2,134	2,475
1200	Circuit breaker		3.80	4.211		2,025	284		2,309	2,650
1220	Type B, fusible		3.80	4.211		2,025	284		2,309	2,650
1240	Circuit breaker		3.80	4.211		2,225	284		2,509	2,850
1300	FVR, NEMA 1, type A, fusible		3.20	5		3,100	335		3,435	3,900
1320	Circuit breaker		3.20	5		3,100	335		3,435	3,900
1340	Type B, fusible		3.20	5		3,400	335		3,735	4,250
1360	Circuit breaker		3.20	5		3,400	335		3,735	4,250
1380	NEMA type 12, type A, fusible		3	5.333		3,150	360		3,510	3,975
1400	Circuit breaker		3	5.333		3,150	360		3,510	3,975
1420	Type B, fusible		3	5.333		3,450	360		3,810	4,325
1440	Circuit breaker		3	5.333		3,450	360		3,810	4,325
1490	Starter size 2, 2 speed, separate winding									
1500	NEMA 1, type A, fusible	2 Elec	3.80	4.211	Ea.	3,450	284		3,734	4,225
1520	Circuit breaker		3.80	4.211		3,450	284		3,734	4,225
1540	Type B, fusible		3.80	4.211		3,800	284		4,084	4,600
1560	Circuit breaker		3.80	4.211		3,800	284		4,084	4,600
1570	NEMA 12, type A, fusible		3.60	4.444		3,500	299		3,799	4,300
1580	Circuit breaker		3.60	4.444		3,500	299		3,799	4,300
1600	Type B, fusible		3.60	4.444		3,850	299		4,149	4,675
1620	Circuit breaker		3.60	4.444		3,850	299		4,149	4,675
1630	Starter size 2, 2 speed, consequent pole									
1640	NEMA 1, type A, fusible	2 Elec	3.80	4.211	Ea.	3,925	284		4,209	4,725
1660	Circuit breaker		3.80	4.211		3,925	284		4,209	4,725
1680	Type B, fusible		3.80	4.211		4,150	284		4,434	4,975
1700	Circuit breaker		3.80	4.211		4,150	284		4,434	4,975
1720	NEMA 12, type A, fusible		3.80	4.211		3,925	284		4,209	4,750
1740	Circuit breaker		3.60	4.444		3,975	299		4,274	4,825
1760	Type B, fusible		3.60	4.444		4,200	299		4,499	5,075

26 24 19 – Motor-Control Centers

26 24 19.20 Motor Control Center Components	Crew	Daily Output	Labor-Hours	Unit	Material	Labor	Equipment	Total	Total Incl O&P
					2023 Bare Costs				
1780 Circuit breaker	2 Elec	3.60	4.444	Ea.	4,200	299		4,499	5,075
1830 Starter size 2, autotransformer									
1840 NEMA 1, type A, fusible	2 Elec	3.40	4.706	Ea.	6,100	315		6,415	7,200
1860 Circuit breaker		3.40	4.706		6,250	315		6,565	7,350
1880 Type B, fusible		3.40	4.706		6,675	315		6,990	7,800
1900 Circuit breaker		3.40	4.706		6,675	315		6,990	7,800
1920 NEMA 12, type A, fusible		3.20	5		6,225	335		6,560	7,350
1940 Circuit breaker		3.20	5		6,225	335		6,560	7,350
1960 Type B, fusible		3.20	5		6,775	335		7,110	7,950
1980 Circuit breaker		3.20	5		6,775	335		7,110	7,950
2030 Starter size 2, space only									
2040 NEMA 1, type A, fusible	1 Elec	16	.500	Ea.	685	33.50		718.50	805
2060 Circuit breaker		16	.500		685	33.50		718.50	805
2080 Type B, fusible		16	.500		685	33.50		718.50	805
2100 Circuit breaker		16	.500		685	33.50		718.50	805
2120 NEMA 12, type A, fusible		15	.533		715	36		751	840
2140 Circuit breaker		15	.533		715	36		751	840
2160 Type B, fusible		15	.533		715	36		751	840
2180 Circuit breaker		15	.533		715	36		751	840
2300 Starter size 3, FVNR, NEMA 1, type A, fusible	2 Elec	2	8		3,475	540		4,015	4,625
2320 Circuit breaker		2	8		3,100	540		3,640	4,200
2340 Type B, fusible		2	8		3,825	540		4,365	5,000
2360 Circuit breaker		2	8		3,400	540		3,940	4,550
2380 NEMA 12, type A, fusible		1.90	8.421		3,550	565		4,115	4,750
2400 Circuit breaker		1.90	8.421		3,150	565		3,715	4,300
2420 Type B, fusible		1.90	8.421		3,950	565		4,515	5,200
2440 Circuit breaker		1.90	8.421		3,450	565		4,015	4,650
2500 Starter size 3, FVR, NEMA 1, type A, fusible		1.60	10		4,750	675		5,425	6,225
2520 Circuit breaker		1.60	10		4,525	675		5,200	5,975
2540 Type B, fusible		1.60	10		5,150	675		5,825	6,675
2560 Circuit breaker		1.60	10		4,950	675		5,625	6,450
2580 NEMA 12, type A, fusible		1.50	10.667		4,850	720		5,570	6,400
2600 Circuit breaker		1.50	10.667		4,625	720		5,345	6,150
2620 Type B, fusible		1.50	10.667		5,250	720		5,970	6,850
2640 Circuit breaker		1.50	10.667		5,450	720		6,170	7,075
2690 Starter size 3, 2 speed, separate winding									
2700 NEMA 1, type A, fusible	2 Elec	2	8	Ea.	5,450	540		5,990	6,800
2720 Circuit breaker		2	8		4,825	540		5,365	6,100
2740 Type B, fusible		2	8		5,975	540		6,515	7,375
2760 Circuit breaker		2	8		5,275	540		5,815	6,600
2780 NEMA 12, type A, fusible		1.90	8.421		5,575	565		6,140	6,975
2800 Circuit breaker		1.90	8.421		4,900	565		5,465	6,250
2820 Type B, fusible		1.90	8.421		6,075	565		6,640	7,550
2840 Circuit breaker		1.90	8.421		5,375	565		5,940	6,750
2850 Starter size 3, 2 speed, consequent pole									
2860 NEMA 1, type A, fusible	2 Elec	2	8	Ea.	6,075	540		6,615	7,500
2880 Circuit breaker		2	8		5,450	540		5,990	6,800
2900 Type B, fusible		2	8		6,600	540		7,140	8,050
2920 Circuit breaker		2	8		5,900	540		6,440	7,275
2940 NEMA 12, type A, fusible		1.90	8.421		6,200	565		6,765	7,675
2960 Circuit breaker		1.90	8.421		5,550	565		6,115	6,950
2980 Type B, fusible		1.90	8.421		6,700	565		7,265	8,225
3000 Circuit breaker		1.90	8.421		6,000	565		6,565	7,450

26 24 19 – Motor-Control Centers

26 24 19.20 Motor Control Center Components		Crew	Daily Output	Labor-Hours	Unit	2023 Bare Costs Material	Labor	Equipment	Total	Total Incl O&P
3100	Starter size 3, autotransformer, NEMA 1, type A, fusible	2 Elec	1.60	10	Ea.	8,050	675		8,725	9,850
3120	Circuit breaker		1.60	10		7,575	675		8,250	9,325
3140	Type B, fusible		1.60	10		8,275	675		8,950	10,100
3160	Circuit breaker		1.60	10		8,275	675		8,950	10,100
3180	NEMA 12, type A, fusible		1.50	10.667		7,700	720		8,420	9,550
3200	Circuit breaker		1.50	10.667		7,700	720		8,420	9,550
3220	Type B, fusible		1.50	10.667		8,400	720		9,120	10,300
3240	Circuit breaker		1.50	10.667		8,400	720		9,120	10,300
3260	Starter size 3, space only, NEMA 1, type A, fusible	1 Elec	15	.533		1,175	36		1,211	1,350
3280	Circuit breaker		15	.533		915	36		951	1,050
3300	Type B, fusible		15	.533		1,175	36		1,211	1,350
3320	Circuit breaker		15	.533		915	36		951	1,050
3340	NEMA 12, type A, fusible		14	.571		1,250	38.50		1,288.50	1,425
3360	Circuit breaker		14	.571		970	38.50		1,008.50	1,125
3380	Type B, fusible		14	.571		1,250	38.50		1,288.50	1,425
3400	Circuit breaker		14	.571		970	38.50		1,008.50	1,125
3500	Starter size 4, FVNR, NEMA 1, type A, fusible	2 Elec	1.60	10		4,525	675		5,200	5,975
3520	Circuit breaker		1.60	10		4,100	675		4,775	5,525
3540	Type B, fusible		1.60	10		4,950	675		5,625	6,450
3560	Circuit breaker		1.60	10		4,525	675		5,200	5,975
3580	NEMA 12, type A, fusible		1.50	10.667		4,650	720		5,370	6,175
3600	Circuit breaker		1.50	10.667		4,175	720		4,895	5,675
3620	Type B, fusible		1.50	10.667		5,050	720		5,770	6,650
3640	Circuit breaker		1.50	10.667		4,600	720		5,320	6,125
3700	Starter size 4, FVR, NEMA 1, type A, fusible		1.20	13.333		6,200	900		7,100	8,125
3720	Circuit breaker		1.20	13.333		5,575	900		6,475	7,475
3740	Type B, fusible		1.20	13.333		6,750	900		7,650	8,750
3760	Circuit breaker		1.20	13.333		6,150	900		7,050	8,075
3780	NEMA 12, type A, fusible		1.16	13.793		6,325	930		7,255	8,350
3800	Circuit breaker		1.16	13.793		5,675	930		6,605	7,600
3820	Type B, fusible		1.16	13.793		5,725	930		6,655	7,675
3840	Circuit breaker		1.16	13.793		6,225	930		7,155	8,225
3890	Starter size 4, 2 speed, separate windings									
3900	NEMA 1, type A, fusible	2 Elec	1.60	10	Ea.	7,825	675		8,500	9,600
3920	Circuit breaker		1.60	10		5,875	675		6,550	7,450
3940	Type B, fusible		1.60	10		8,575	675		9,250	10,500
3960	Circuit breaker		1.60	10		6,425	675		7,100	8,075
3980	NEMA 12, type A, fusible		1.50	10.667		7,950	720		8,670	9,825
4000	Circuit breaker		1.50	10.667		5,975	720		6,695	7,650
4020	Type B, fusible		1.50	10.667		8,725	720		9,445	10,700
4040	Circuit breaker		1.50	10.667		6,525	720		7,245	8,250
4050	Starter size 4, 2 speed, consequent pole									
4060	NEMA 1, type A, fusible	2 Elec	1.60	10	Ea.	9,125	675		9,800	11,000
4080	Circuit breaker		1.60	10		6,800	675		7,475	8,475
4100	Type B, fusible		1.60	10		10,000	675		10,675	12,000
4120	Circuit breaker		1.60	10		7,450	675		8,125	9,175
4140	NEMA 12, type A, fusible		1.50	10.667		9,275	720		9,995	11,300
4160	Circuit breaker		1.50	10.667		6,900	720		7,620	8,650
4180	Type B, fusible		1.50	10.667		10,200	720		10,920	12,300
4200	Circuit breaker		1.50	10.667		7,550	720		8,270	9,375
4300	Starter size 4, autotransformer, NEMA 1, type A, fusible		1.30	12.308		8,975	830		9,805	11,100
4320	Circuit breaker		1.30	12.308		9,050	830		9,880	11,200
4340	Type B, fusible		1.30	12.308		9,900	830		10,730	12,100

26 24 19.20 Motor Control Center Components		Crew	Daily Output	Labor-Hours	Unit	Material	2023 Bare Costs Labor	Equipment	Total	Total Incl O&P
4360	Circuit breaker	2 Elec	1.30	12.308	Ea.	9,900	830		10,730	12,100
4380	NEMA 12, type A, fusible		1.24	12.903		9,150	870		10,020	11,400
4400	Circuit breaker		1.24	12.903		9,175	870		10,045	11,400
4420	Type B, fusible		1.24	12.903		10,100	870		10,970	12,400
4440	Circuit breaker		1.24	12.903		10,000	870		10,870	12,300
4500	Starter size 4, space only, NEMA 1, type A, fusible	1 Elec	14	.571		1,625	38.50		1,663.50	1,850
4520	Circuit breaker		14	.571		1,175	38.50		1,213.50	1,350
4540	Type B, fusible		14	.571		1,625	38.50		1,663.50	1,850
4560	Circuit breaker		14	.571		1,175	38.50		1,213.50	1,350
4580	NEMA 12, type A, fusible		13	.615		1,725	41.50		1,766.50	1,950
4600	Circuit breaker		13	.615		1,250	41.50		1,291.50	1,425
4620	Type B, fusible		13	.615		1,725	41.50		1,766.50	1,950
4640	Circuit breaker		13	.615		1,250	41.50		1,291.50	1,425
4800	Starter size 5, FVNR, NEMA 1, type A, fusible	2 Elec	1	16		9,350	1,075		10,425	11,900
4820	Circuit breaker		1	16		6,625	1,075		7,700	8,900
4840	Type B, fusible		1	16		10,300	1,075		11,375	12,900
4860	Circuit breaker		1	16		7,300	1,075		8,375	9,625
4880	NEMA 12, type A, fusible		.96	16.667		9,475	1,125		10,600	12,100
4900	Circuit breaker		.96	16.667		6,750	1,125		7,875	9,100
4920	Type B, fusible		.96	16.667		10,400	1,125		11,525	13,100
4940	Circuit breaker		.96	16.667		7,425	1,125		8,550	9,850
5000	Starter size 5, FVR, NEMA 1, type A, fusible		.80	20		13,800	1,350		15,150	17,200
5020	Circuit breaker		.80	20		10,800	1,350		12,150	13,900
5040	Type B, fusible		.80	20		15,100	1,350		16,450	18,600
5060	Circuit breaker		.80	20		11,900	1,350		13,250	15,100
5080	NEMA 12, type A, fusible		.76	21.053		14,000	1,425		15,425	17,600
5100	Circuit breaker		.76	21.053		11,000	1,425		12,425	14,200
5120	Type B, fusible		.76	21.053		15,400	1,425		16,825	19,000
5140	Circuit breaker		.76	21.053		12,000	1,425		13,425	15,300
5190	Starter size 5, 2 speed, separate windings									
5200	NEMA 1, type A, fusible	2 Elec	1	16	Ea.	19,000	1,075		20,075	22,500
5220	Circuit breaker		1	16		14,200	1,075		15,275	17,200
5240	Type B, fusible		1	16		20,900	1,075		21,975	24,500
5260	Circuit breaker		1	16		15,600	1,075		16,675	18,700
5280	NEMA 12, type A, fusible		.96	16.667		19,300	1,125		20,425	22,900
5300	Circuit breaker		.96	16.667		14,300	1,125		15,425	17,500
5320	Type B, fusible		.96	16.667		21,100	1,125		22,225	24,900
5340	Circuit breaker		.96	16.667		15,700	1,125		16,825	19,000
5400	Starter size 5, autotransformer, NEMA 1, type A, fusible		.70	22.857		15,500	1,550		17,050	19,400
5420	Circuit breaker		.70	22.857		12,900	1,550		14,450	16,500
5440	Type B, fusible		.70	22.857		17,100	1,550		18,650	21,100
5460	Circuit breaker		.70	22.857		14,200	1,550		15,750	17,900
5480	NEMA 12, type A, fusible		.68	23.529		15,700	1,575		17,275	19,700
5500	Circuit breaker		.68	23.529		13,000	1,575		14,575	16,700
5520	Type B, fusible		.68	23.529		17,200	1,575		18,775	21,400
5540	Circuit breakers		.68	23.529		14,300	1,575		15,875	18,100
5600	Starter size 5, space only, NEMA 1, type A, fusible	1 Elec	12	.667		2,100	45		2,145	2,375
5620	Circuit breaker		12	.667		2,100	45		2,145	2,375
5640	Type B, fusible		12	.667		2,100	45		2,145	2,375
5660	Circuit breaker		12	.667		1,375	45		1,420	1,575
5680	NEMA 12, type A, fusible		11	.727		2,225	49		2,274	2,500
5700	Circuit breaker		11	.727		1,450	49		1,499	1,675
5720	Type B, fusible		11	.727		2,225	49		2,274	2,500

26 24 Switchboards and Panelboards

26 24 19 – Motor-Control Centers

26 24 19.20 Motor Control Center Components		Crew	Daily Output	Labor-Hours	Unit	Material	2023 Bare Costs Labor	Equipment	Total	Total Incl O&P
5740	Circuit breaker	1 Elec	11	.727	Ea.	1,450	49		1,499	1,675
5800	Fuse, light contactor NEMA 1, type A, 30 amp		2.70	2.963		1,575	200		1,775	2,025
5820	60 amp		2	4		1,775	269		2,044	2,350
5840	100 amp		1	8		3,375	540		3,915	4,500
5860	200 amp		.80	10		7,825	675		8,500	9,625
5880	Type B, 30 amp		2.70	2.963		1,700	200		1,900	2,175
5900	60 amp		2	4		1,900	269		2,169	2,500
5920	100 amp		1	8		3,725	540		4,265	4,875
5940	200 amp	2 Elec	1.60	10		8,575	675		9,250	10,500
5960	NEMA 12, type A, 30 amp	1 Elec	2.60	3.077		1,600	207		1,807	2,050
5980	60 amp		1.90	4.211		1,800	284		2,084	2,400
6000	100 amp		.95	8.421		3,450	565		4,015	4,625
6020	200 amp	2 Elec	1.50	10.667		7,950	720		8,670	9,825
6040	Type B, 30 amp	1 Elec	2.60	3.077		1,725	207		1,932	2,200
6060	60 amp		1.90	4.211		1,925	284		2,209	2,550
6080	100 amp		.95	8.421		3,775	565		4,340	5,000
6100	200 amp	2 Elec	1.50	10.667		8,725	720		9,445	10,700
6200	Circuit breaker, light contactor NEMA 1, type A, 30 amp	1 Elec	2.70	2.963		1,700	200		1,900	2,175
6220	60 amp		2	4		1,950	269		2,219	2,525
6240	100 amp		1	8		3,000	540		3,540	4,100
6260	200 amp	2 Elec	1.60	10		6,500	675		7,175	8,150
6280	Type B, 30 amp	1 Elec	2.70	2.963		1,875	200		2,075	2,350
6300	60 amp		2	4		2,150	269		2,419	2,750
6320	100 amp		1	8		3,275	540		3,815	4,400
6340	200 amp	2 Elec	1.60	10		7,075	675		7,750	8,800
6360	NEMA 12, type A, 30 amp	1 Elec	2.60	3.077		1,725	207		1,932	2,200
6380	60 amp		1.90	4.211		1,975	284		2,259	2,600
6400	100 amp		.95	8.421		3,050	565		3,615	4,200
6420	200 amp	2 Elec	1.50	10.667		6,525	720		7,245	8,250
6440	Type B, 30 amp	1 Elec	2.60	3.077		2,025	207		2,232	2,550
6460	60 amp		1.90	4.211		2,175	284		2,459	2,825
6480	100 amp		.95	8.421		3,325	565		3,890	4,500
6500	200 amp	2 Elec	1.50	10.667		7,175	720		7,895	8,950
6600	Fusible switch, NEMA 1, type A, 30 amp	1 Elec	5.30	1.509		1,075	102		1,177	1,325
6620	60 amp		5	1.600		1,150	108		1,258	1,400
6640	100 amp		4	2		1,275	135		1,410	1,600
6660	200 amp		3.20	2.500		2,175	168		2,343	2,650
6680	400 amp	2 Elec	4.60	3.478		5,125	234		5,359	6,000
6700	600 amp		3.20	5		5,550	335		5,885	6,600
6720	800 amp		2.60	6.154		15,200	415		15,615	17,300
6740	NEMA 12, type A, 30 amp	1 Elec	5.20	1.538		1,100	104		1,204	1,350
6760	60 amp		4.90	1.633		1,175	110		1,285	1,450
6780	100 amp		3.90	2.051		1,300	138		1,438	1,625
6800	200 amp		3.10	2.581		2,225	174		2,399	2,700
6820	400 amp	2 Elec	4.40	3.636		5,250	245		5,495	6,125
6840	600 amp		3	5.333		5,700	360		6,060	6,800
6860	800 amp		2.40	6.667		15,400	450		15,850	17,600
6900	Circuit breaker, NEMA 1, type A, 30 amp	1 Elec	5.30	1.509		985	102		1,087	1,225
6920	60 amp		5	1.600		985	108		1,093	1,225
6940	100 amp		4	2		985	135		1,120	1,275
6960	225 amp		3.20	2.500		1,750	168		1,918	2,175
6980	400 amp	2 Elec	4.60	3.478		3,325	234		3,559	4,025
7000	600 amp		3.20	5		3,900	335		4,235	4,775

26 24 19 – Motor-Control Centers

26 24 19.20 Motor Control Center Components		Crew	Daily Output	Labor-Hours	Unit	Material	Labor	Equipment	Total	Total Incl O&P
						2023 Bare Costs				
7020	800 amp	2 Elec	2.60	6.154	Ea.	8,150	415		8,565	9,575
7040	NEMA 12, type A, 30 amp	1 Elec	5.20	1.538		1,000	104		1,104	1,250
7060	60 amp		4.90	1.633		1,000	110		1,110	1,275
7080	100 amp		3.90	2.051		1,000	138		1,138	1,300
7100	225 amp		3.10	2.581		1,775	174		1,949	2,200
7120	400 amp	2 Elec	4.40	3.636		3,400	245		3,645	4,100
7140	600 amp		3	5.333		3,950	360		4,310	4,875
7160	800 amp		2.40	6.667		8,300	450		8,750	9,800
7300	Incoming line, main lug only, 600 amp, alum., NEMA 1		1.60	10		1,250	675		1,925	2,375
7320	NEMA 12		1.50	10.667		1,275	720		1,995	2,475
7340	Copper, NEMA 1		1.60	10		1,300	675		1,975	2,450
7360	800 amp, alum., NEMA 1		1.50	10.667		3,125	720		3,845	4,500
7380	NEMA 12		1.40	11.429		3,175	770		3,945	4,625
7400	Copper, NEMA 1		1.50	10.667		3,250	720		3,970	4,650
7420	1,200 amp, copper, NEMA 1		1.40	11.429		3,350	770		4,120	4,850
7440	Incoming line, fusible switch, 400 amp, alum., NEMA 1		1.20	13.333		4,275	900		5,175	6,050
7460	NEMA 12		1.10	14.545		4,375	980		5,355	6,250
7480	Copper, NEMA 1		1.20	13.333		4,350	900		5,250	6,125
7500	600 amp, alum., NEMA 1		1.10	14.545		5,250	980		6,230	7,200
7520	NEMA 12		1	16		5,325	1,075		6,400	7,450
7540	Copper, NEMA 1		1.10	14.545		5,300	980		6,280	7,275
7560	Incoming line, circuit breaker, 225 amp, alum., NEMA 1		1.20	13.333		2,225	900		3,125	3,775
7580	NEMA 12		1.10	14.545		2,275	980		3,255	3,950
7600	Copper, NEMA 1		1.20	13.333		2,300	900		3,200	3,850
7620	400 amp, alum., NEMA 1		1.20	13.333		3,325	900		4,225	5,000
7640	NEMA 12		1.10	14.545		3,400	980		4,380	5,175
7660	Copper, NEMA 1		1.20	13.333		3,400	900		4,300	5,075
7680	600 amp, alum., NEMA 1		1.10	14.545		3,900	980		4,880	5,725
7700	NEMA 12		1	16		3,950	1,075		5,025	5,950
7720	Copper, NEMA 1		1.10	14.545		3,975	980		4,955	5,800
7740	800 amp, copper, NEMA 1		.90	17.778		8,150	1,200		9,350	10,700
7760	Incoming line, for copper bus, add					123			123	135
7780	For 65,000 amp bus bracing, add					183			183	201
7800	For NEMA 3R enclosure, add					5,725			5,725	6,300
7820	For NEMA 12 enclosure, add					158			158	174
7840	For 1/4" x 1" ground bus, add	1 Elec	16	.500		102	33.50		135.50	162
7860	For 1/4" x 2" ground bus, add	"	12	.667		102	45		147	179
7900	Main rating basic section, alum., NEMA 1, 800 amp	2 Elec	1.40	11.429		335	770		1,105	1,525
7920	1,200 amp	"	1.20	13.333		655	900		1,555	2,050
7940	For copper bus, add					490			490	540
7960	For 65,000 amp bus bracing, add					330			330	365
7980	For NEMA 3R enclosure, add					5,725			5,725	6,300
8000	For NEMA 12, enclosure, add					158			158	174
8020	For 1/4" x 1" ground bus, add	1 Elec	16	.500		102	33.50		135.50	162
8040	For 1/4" x 2" ground bus, add		12	.667		102	45		147	179
8060	Unit devices, pilot light, standard		16	.500		88	33.50		121.50	147
8080	Pilot light, push to test		16	.500		123	33.50		156.50	185
8100	Pilot light, standard, and push button		12	.667		211	45		256	299
8120	Pilot light, push to test, and push button		12	.667		246	45		291	335
8140	Pilot light, standard, and select switch		12	.667		211	45		256	299
8160	Pilot light, push to test, and select switch		12	.667		246	45		291	335

26 24 19 – Motor-Control Centers

26 24 19.30 Motor Control Center		Crew	Daily Output	Labor-Hours	Unit	Material	2023 Bare Costs Labor	Equipment	Total	Total Incl O&P
0010	**MOTOR CONTROL CENTER** Consists of starters & structures R262419-60									
0050	Starters, class 1, type B, comb. MCP, FVNR, with									
0100	control transformer, 10 HP, size 1, 12" high	1 Elec	2.70	2.963	Ea.	1,750	200		1,950	2,225
0200	25 HP, size 2, 18" high	2 Elec	4	4		2,000	269		2,269	2,600
0300	50 HP, size 3, 24" high		2	8		3,100	540		3,640	4,200
0350	75 HP, size 4, 24" high		1.60	10		4,100	675		4,775	5,525
0400	100 HP, size 4, 30" high		1.40	11.429		5,425	770		6,195	7,125
0500	200 HP, size 5, 48" high		1	16		8,100	1,075		9,175	10,500
0600	400 HP, size 6, 72" high		.80	20		16,600	1,350		17,950	20,300
0800	Structures, 600 amp, 22,000 rms, takes any									
0900	combination of starters up to 72" high	2 Elec	1.60	10	Ea.	1,900	675		2,575	3,100
1000	Back to back, 72" front & 66" back	"	1.20	13.333		2,625	900		3,525	4,200
1100	For copper bus, add per structure					270			270	297
1200	For NEMA 12, add per structure					156			156	172
1300	For 42,000 rms, add per structure					217			217	239
1400	For 100,000 rms, size 1 & 2, add					695			695	760
1500	Size 3, add					1,125			1,125	1,225
1600	Size 4, add					900			900	990
1700	For pilot lights, add per starter	1 Elec	16	.500		121	33.50		154.50	183
1800	For push button, add per starter		16	.500		121	33.50		154.50	183
1900	For auxiliary contacts, add per starter		16	.500		251	33.50		284.50	325

26 24 19.40 Motor Starters and Controls		Crew	Daily Output	Labor-Hours	Unit	Material	Labor	Equipment	Total	Total Incl O&P
0010	**MOTOR STARTERS AND CONTROLS** R262419-65									
0050	Magnetic, FVNR, with enclosure and heaters, 480 volt									
0080	2 HP, size 00	1 Elec	3.50	2.286	Ea.	151	154		305	395
0100	5 HP, size 0		2.30	3.478		460	234		694	855
0200	10 HP, size 1		1.60	5		214	335		549	735
0300	25 HP, size 2 R263413-33	2 Elec	2.20	7.273		425	490		915	1,200
0400	50 HP, size 3		1.80	8.889		705	600		1,305	1,675
0500	100 HP, size 4		1.20	13.333		1,600	900		2,500	3,075
0600	200 HP, size 5		.90	17.778		3,650	1,200		4,850	5,800
0610	400 HP, size 6		.80	20		10,600	1,350		11,950	13,600
0620	NEMA 7, 5 HP, size 0	1 Elec	1.60	5		2,575	335		2,910	3,350
0630	10 HP, size 1	"	1.10	7.273		2,700	490		3,190	3,700
0640	25 HP, size 2	2 Elec	1.80	8.889		4,350	600		4,950	5,700
0650	50 HP, size 3		1.20	13.333		6,550	900		7,450	8,525
0660	100 HP, size 4		.90	17.778		8,450	1,200		9,650	11,100
0670	200 HP, size 5		.50	32		13,700	2,150		15,850	18,300
0700	Combination, with motor circuit protectors, 5 HP, size 0	1 Elec	1.80	4.444		1,475	299		1,774	2,075
0800	10 HP, size 1	"	1.30	6.154		1,550	415		1,965	2,325
0900	25 HP, size 2	2 Elec	2	8		2,150	540		2,690	3,150
1000	50 HP, size 3		1.32	12.121		3,125	815		3,940	4,650
1200	100 HP, size 4		.80	20		6,850	1,350		8,200	9,525
1220	NEMA 7, 5 HP, size 0	1 Elec	1.30	6.154		3,450	415		3,865	4,425
1230	10 HP, size 1	"	1	8		3,550	540		4,090	4,700
1240	25 HP, size 2	2 Elec	1.32	12.121		4,725	815		5,540	6,425
1250	50 HP, size 3		.80	20		7,800	1,350		9,150	10,600
1260	100 HP, size 4		.60	26.667		12,200	1,800		14,000	16,100
1270	200 HP, size 5		.40	40		26,400	2,700		29,100	33,000
1400	Combination, with fused switch, 5 HP, size 0	1 Elec	1.80	4.444		1,400	299		1,699	1,975
1600	10 HP, size 1	"	1.30	6.154		1,400	415		1,815	2,150
1800	25 HP, size 2	2 Elec	2	8		2,300	540		2,840	3,325

26 24 19.40 Motor Starters and Controls		Crew	Daily Output	Labor-Hours	Unit	Material	Labor	Equipment	Total	Total Incl O&P
						2023 Bare Costs				
2000	50 HP, size 3	2 Elec	1.32	12.121	Ea.	3,725	815		4,540	5,325
2200	100 HP, size 4		.80	20		7,400	1,350		8,750	10,200
2610	NEMA 4, with start-stop push button, size 1	1 Elec	1.30	6.154		1,575	415		1,990	2,350
2620	Size 2	2 Elec	2	8		2,100	540		2,640	3,125
2630	Size 3		1.32	12.121		3,350	815		4,165	4,900
2640	Size 4		.80	20		5,125	1,350		6,475	7,650
2650	NEMA 4, FVNR, including control transformer									
2660	Size 1	2 Elec	2.60	6.154	Ea.	1,675	415		2,090	2,475
2670	Size 2		2	8		2,400	540		2,940	3,425
2680	Size 3		1.32	12.121		3,825	815		4,640	5,425
2690	Size 4		.80	20		5,875	1,350		7,225	8,475
2710	Magnetic, FVR, control circuit transformer, NEMA 1, size 1	1 Elec	1.30	6.154		990	415		1,405	1,725
2720	Size 2	2 Elec	2	8		1,575	540		2,115	2,550
2730	Size 3		1.32	12.121		2,400	815		3,215	3,875
2740	Size 4		.80	20		5,225	1,350		6,575	7,750
2760	NEMA 4, size 1	1 Elec	1.10	7.273		1,425	490		1,915	2,300
2770	Size 2	2 Elec	1.60	10		2,275	675		2,950	3,525
2780	Size 3		1.20	13.333		3,450	900		4,350	5,100
2790	Size 4		.70	22.857		7,075	1,550		8,625	10,100
2820	NEMA 12, size 1	1 Elec	1.10	7.273		1,175	490		1,665	2,000
2830	Size 2	2 Elec	1.60	10		1,850	675		2,525	3,025
2840	Size 3		1.20	13.333		2,900	900		3,800	4,525
2850	Size 4		.70	22.857		5,975	1,550		7,525	8,875
2870	Combination FVR, fused, w/control XFMR & PB, NEMA 1, size 1	1 Elec	1	8		1,700	540		2,240	2,675
2880	Size 2	2 Elec	1.50	10.667		2,425	720		3,145	3,750
2890	Size 3		1.10	14.545		3,600	980		4,580	5,425
2900	Size 4		.70	22.857		7,325	1,550		8,875	10,400
2910	NEMA 4, size 1	1 Elec	.90	8.889		2,525	600		3,125	3,675
2920	Size 2	2 Elec	1.40	11.429		3,675	770		4,445	5,200
2930	Size 3		1	16		5,825	1,075		6,900	8,000
2940	Size 4		.60	26.667		9,650	1,800		11,450	13,300
2950	NEMA 12, size 1	1 Elec	1	8		1,925	540		2,465	2,925
2960	Size 2	2 Elec	1.40	11.429		2,725	770		3,495	4,150
2970	Size 3		1	16		4,000	1,075		5,075	6,000
2980	Size 4		.60	26.667		7,950	1,800		9,750	11,400
3010	Manual, single phase, w/pilot, 1 pole, 120 V, NEMA 1	1 Elec	6.40	1.250		165	84		249	305
3020	NEMA 4		4	2		400	135		535	640
3030	2 pole, 120/240 V, NEMA 1		6.40	1.250		139	84		223	278
3040	NEMA 4		4	2		450	135		585	695
3041	3 phase, 3 pole, 600 V, NEMA 1		5.50	1.455		85	98		183	240
3042	NEMA 4		3.50	2.286		237	154		391	490
3043	NEMA 12		3.50	2.286		615	154		769	905
3070	Auxiliary contact, normally open					101			101	111
3500	Magnetic FVNR with NEMA 12, enclosure & heaters, 480 volt									
3600	5 HP, size 0	1 Elec	2.20	3.636	Ea.	260	245		505	650
3700	10 HP, size 1	"	1.50	5.333		390	360		750	965
3800	25 HP, size 2	2 Elec	2	8		735	540		1,275	1,600
3900	50 HP, size 3		1.60	10		1,125	675		1,800	2,250
4000	100 HP, size 4		1	16		2,700	1,075		3,775	4,575
4100	200 HP, size 5		.80	20		6,475	1,350		7,825	9,125
4200	Combination, with motor circuit protectors, 5 HP, size 0	1 Elec	1.70	4.706		860	315		1,175	1,425
4300	10 HP, size 1	"	1.20	6.667		895	450		1,345	1,650
4400	25 HP, size 2	2 Elec	1.80	8.889		1,350	600		1,950	2,375

26 24 19.40 Motor Starters and Controls		Crew	Daily Output	Labor-Hours	Unit	Material	Labor	Equipment	Total	Total Incl O&P
						2023 Bare Costs				
4500	50 HP, size 3	2 Elec	1.20	13.333	Ea.	2,175	900		3,075	3,725
4600	100 HP, size 4	↓	.74	21.622		4,925	1,450		6,375	7,600
4700	Combination, with fused switch, 5 HP, size 0	1 Elec	1.70	4.706		710	315		1,025	1,250
4800	10 HP, size 1	"	1.20	6.667		735	450		1,185	1,475
4900	25 HP, size 2	2 Elec	1.80	8.889		1,125	600		1,725	2,125
5000	50 HP, size 3		1.20	13.333		1,800	900		2,700	3,300
5100	100 HP, size 4	↓	.74	21.622	↓	3,650	1,450		5,100	6,200
5200	Factory installed controls, adders to size 0 thru 5									
5300	Start-stop push button	1 Elec	32	.250	Ea.	54.50	16.85		71.35	85
5400	Hand-off-auto-selector switch		32	.250		54.50	16.85		71.35	85
5500	Pilot light		32	.250		102	16.85		118.85	137
5600	Start-stop-pilot		32	.250		157	16.85		173.85	197
5700	Auxiliary contact, NO or NC		32	.250		75	16.85		91.85	108
5800	NO-NC		32	.250		150	16.85		166.85	190
5810	Magnetic FVR, NEMA 7, w/heaters, size 1	↓	.66	12.121		4,025	815		4,840	5,675
5830	Size 2	2 Elec	1.10	14.545		5,525	980		6,505	7,525
5840	Size 3		.70	22.857		8,875	1,550		10,425	12,100
5850	Size 4	↓	.60	26.667		11,600	1,800		13,400	15,500
5860	Combination w/circuit breakers, heaters, control XFMR PB, size 1	1 Elec	.60	13.333		1,625	900		2,525	3,125
5870	Size 2	2 Elec	.80	20		2,100	1,350		3,450	4,300
5880	Size 3		.50	32		2,800	2,150		4,950	6,275
5890	Size 4	↓	.40	40		5,550	2,700		8,250	10,100
5900	Manual, 240 volt, 0.75 HP motor	1 Elec	4	2		58	135		193	264
5910	2 HP motor		4	2		157	135		292	370
6000	Magnetic, 240 volt, 1 or 2 pole, 0.75 HP motor		4	2		380	135		515	615
6020	2 HP motor		4	2		430	135		565	675
6040	5 HP motor		3	2.667		685	180		865	1,025
6060	10 HP motor		2.30	3.478		770	234		1,004	1,200
6100	3 pole, 0.75 HP motor		3	2.667		380	180		560	680
6120	5 HP motor		2.30	3.478		455	234		689	850
6140	10 HP motor		1.60	5		1,050	335		1,385	1,650
6160	15 HP motor		1.60	5		1,050	335		1,385	1,650
6180	20 HP motor	↓	1.10	7.273		1,825	490		2,315	2,750
6200	25 HP motor	2 Elec	2.20	7.273		1,825	490		2,315	2,750
6210	30 HP motor		1.80	8.889		1,825	600		2,425	2,925
6220	40 HP motor		1.80	8.889		4,125	600		4,725	5,450
6230	50 HP motor		1.80	8.889		4,125	600		4,725	5,450
6240	60 HP motor		1.20	13.333		9,725	900		10,625	12,000
6250	75 HP motor		1.20	13.333		9,725	900		10,625	12,000
6260	100 HP motor		1.20	13.333		10,100	900		11,000	12,400
6270	125 HP motor		.90	17.778		16,900	1,200		18,100	20,400
6280	150 HP motor		.90	17.778		16,900	1,200		18,100	20,400
6290	200 HP motor	↓	.90	17.778		16,900	1,200		18,100	20,400
6400	Starter & nonfused disconnect, 240 volt, 1-2 pole, 0.75 HP motor	1 Elec	2	4		445	269		714	890
6410	2 HP motor		2	4		500	269		769	950
6420	5 HP motor		1.80	4.444		750	299		1,049	1,275
6430	10 HP motor		1.40	5.714		860	385		1,245	1,525
6440	3 pole, 0.75 HP motor		1.60	5		445	335		780	990
6450	5 HP motor		1.40	5.714		525	385		910	1,150
6460	10 HP motor		1.10	7.273		1,150	490		1,640	1,975
6470	15 HP motor	↓	1	8		1,150	540		1,690	2,050
6480	20 HP motor	2 Elec	1.50	10.667		2,050	720		2,770	3,325
6490	25 HP motor	↓	1.50	10.667	↓	2,050	720		2,770	3,325

26 24 19.40 Motor Starters and Controls		Crew	Daily Output	Labor-Hours	Unit	2023 Bare Costs Material	Labor	Equipment	Total	Total Incl O&P
6500	30 HP motor	2 Elec	1.30	12.308	Ea.	2,050	830		2,880	3,475
6510	40 HP motor		1.24	12.903		4,500	870		5,370	6,250
6520	50 HP motor		1.12	14.286		4,500	960		5,460	6,375
6530	60 HP motor		.90	17.778		10,100	1,200		11,300	12,900
6540	75 HP motor		.76	21.053		10,100	1,425		11,525	13,200
6550	100 HP motor		.70	22.857		10,500	1,550		12,050	13,800
6560	125 HP motor		.60	26.667		17,900	1,800		19,700	22,400
6570	150 HP motor		.52	30.769		17,900	2,075		19,975	22,800
6580	200 HP motor		.50	32		17,900	2,150		20,050	22,900
6600	Starter & fused disconnect, 240 volt, 1-2 pole, 0.75 HP motor	1 Elec	2	4		465	269		734	910
6610	2 HP motor		2	4		515	269		784	970
6620	5 HP motor		1.80	4.444		770	299		1,069	1,300
6630	10 HP motor		1.40	5.714		915	385		1,300	1,575
6640	3 pole, 0.75 HP motor		1.60	5		465	335		800	1,000
6650	5 HP motor		1.40	5.714		540	385		925	1,175
6660	10 HP motor		1.10	7.273		1,200	490		1,690	2,025
6690	15 HP motor		1	8		1,200	540		1,740	2,100
6700	20 HP motor	2 Elec	1.60	10		2,075	675		2,750	3,275
6710	25 HP motor		1.60	10		2,075	675		2,750	3,275
6720	30 HP motor		1.40	11.429		2,075	770		2,845	3,425
6730	40 HP motor		1.20	13.333		4,650	900		5,550	6,450
6740	50 HP motor		1.20	13.333		4,650	900		5,550	6,450
6750	60 HP motor		.90	17.778		10,200	1,200		11,400	13,100
6760	75 HP motor		.90	17.778		10,200	1,200		11,400	13,100
6770	100 HP motor		.70	22.857		10,600	1,550		12,150	14,000
6780	125 HP motor		.54	29.630		18,200	2,000		20,200	23,100
6790	Combination starter & nonfusible disconnect									
6800	240 volt, 1-2 pole, 0.75 HP motor	1 Elec	2	4	Ea.	745	269		1,014	1,225
6810	2 HP motor		2	4		655	269		924	1,125
6820	5 HP motor		1.50	5.333		655	360		1,015	1,250
6830	10 HP motor		1.20	6.667		1,025	450		1,475	1,800
6840	3 pole, 0.75 HP motor		1.80	4.444		620	299		919	1,125
6850	5 HP motor		1.30	6.154		655	415		1,070	1,325
6860	10 HP motor		1	8		1,025	540		1,565	1,925
6870	15 HP motor		1	8		1,025	540		1,565	1,925
6880	20 HP motor	2 Elec	1.32	12.121		1,675	815		2,490	3,075
6890	25 HP motor		1.32	12.121		1,675	815		2,490	3,075
6900	30 HP motor		1.32	12.121		1,675	815		2,490	3,075
6910	40 HP motor		.80	20		3,200	1,350		4,550	5,525
6920	50 HP motor		.80	20		3,200	1,350		4,550	5,525
6930	60 HP motor		.70	22.857		7,150	1,550		8,700	10,200
6940	75 HP motor		.70	22.857		7,150	1,550		8,700	10,200
6950	100 HP motor		.70	22.857		7,150	1,550		8,700	10,200
6960	125 HP motor		.60	26.667		18,800	1,800		20,600	23,400
6970	150 HP motor		.60	26.667		18,800	1,800		20,600	23,400
6980	200 HP motor		.60	26.667		18,800	1,800		20,600	23,400
6990	Combination starter and fused disconnect									
7000	240 volt, 1-2 pole, 0.75 HP motor	1 Elec	2	4	Ea.	625	269		894	1,075
7010	2 HP motor		2	4		625	269		894	1,075
7020	5 HP motor		1.50	5.333		655	360		1,015	1,250
7030	10 HP motor		1.20	6.667		1,025	450		1,475	1,800
7040	3 pole, 0.75 HP motor		1.80	4.444		625	299		924	1,125
7050	5 HP motor		1.30	6.154		1,350	415		1,765	2,100

26 24 19.40 Motor Starters and Controls		Crew	Daily Output	Labor-Hours	Unit	2023 Bare Costs Material	Labor	Equipment	Total	Total Incl O&P
7060	10 HP motor	1 Elec	1	8	Ea.	1,025	540		1,565	1,925
7070	15 HP motor	↓	1	8		1,025	540		1,565	1,925
7080	20 HP motor	2 Elec	1.32	12.121		1,700	815		2,515	3,075
7090	25 HP motor		1.32	12.121		1,700	815		2,515	3,075
7100	30 HP motor		1.32	12.121		1,700	815		2,515	3,075
7110	40 HP motor		.80	20		3,225	1,350		4,575	5,550
7120	50 HP motor		.80	20		3,225	1,350		4,575	5,550
7130	60 HP motor		.80	20		7,200	1,350		8,550	9,900
7140	75 HP motor		.70	22.857		7,200	1,550		8,750	10,200
7150	100 HP motor		.70	22.857		7,200	1,550		8,750	10,200
7160	125 HP motor		.70	22.857		19,000	1,550		20,550	23,200
7170	150 HP motor		.60	26.667		19,000	1,800		20,800	23,600
7180	200 HP motor	↓	.60	26.667	↓	19,000	1,800		20,800	23,600
7190	Combination starter & circuit breaker disconnect									
7200	240 volt, 1-2 pole, 0.75 HP motor	1 Elec	2	4	Ea.	645	269		914	1,100
7210	2 HP motor		2	4		645	269		914	1,100
7220	5 HP motor		1.50	5.333		680	360		1,040	1,275
7230	10 HP motor		1.20	6.667		1,050	450		1,500	1,825
7240	3 pole, 0.75 HP motor		1.80	4.444		665	299		964	1,175
7250	5 HP motor		1.30	6.154		700	415		1,115	1,375
7260	10 HP motor		1	8		1,050	540		1,590	1,975
7270	15 HP motor	↓	1	8		2,525	540		3,065	3,600
7280	20 HP motor	2 Elec	1.32	12.121		1,800	815		2,615	3,200
7290	25 HP motor		1.32	12.121		1,800	815		2,615	3,200
7300	30 HP motor		1.32	12.121		3,775	815		4,590	5,375
7310	40 HP motor		.80	20		3,925	1,350		5,275	6,300
7320	50 HP motor		.80	20		3,925	1,350		5,275	6,300
7330	60 HP motor		.80	20		9,050	1,350		10,400	12,000
7340	75 HP motor		.70	22.857		9,050	1,550		10,600	12,300
7350	100 HP motor		.70	22.857		9,050	1,550		10,600	12,300
7360	125 HP motor		.70	22.857		19,600	1,550		21,150	23,900
7370	150 HP motor		.60	26.667		19,600	1,800		21,400	24,300
7380	200 HP motor	↓	.60	26.667	↓	19,600	1,800		21,400	24,300
7400	Magnetic FVNR with enclosure & heaters, 2 pole,									
7410	230 volt, 1 HP, size 00	1 Elec	4	2	Ea.	178	135		313	395
7420	2 HP, size 0		4	2		198	135		333	420
7430	3 HP, size 1		3	2.667		228	180		408	515
7440	5 HP, size 1P		3	2.667		292	180		472	585
7450	115 volt, 1/3 HP, size 00		4	2		178	135		313	395
7460	1 HP, size 0		4	2		198	135		333	420
7470	2 HP, size 1		3	2.667		228	180		408	515
7480	3 HP, size 1P	↓	3	2.667		283	180		463	575
7500	3 pole, 480 volt, 600 HP, size 7	2 Elec	.70	22.857	↓	15,100	1,550		16,650	18,900
7590	Magnetic FVNR with heater, NEMA 1									
7600	600 volt, 3 pole, 5 HP motor	1 Elec	2.30	3.478	Ea.	605	234		839	1,025
7610	10 HP motor	"	1.60	5		695	335		1,030	1,275
7620	25 HP motor	2 Elec	2.20	7.273		1,250	490		1,740	2,100
7630	30 HP motor		1.80	8.889		1,575	600		2,175	2,625
7640	40 HP motor		1.80	8.889		2,000	600		2,600	3,100
7650	50 HP motor		1.80	8.889		2,000	600		2,600	3,100
7660	60 HP motor		1.20	13.333		3,750	900		4,650	5,450
7670	75 HP motor		1.20	13.333		3,750	900		4,650	5,450
7680	100 HP motor	↓	1.20	13.333	↓	4,425	900		5,325	6,200

26 24 19.40 Motor Starters and Controls		Crew	Daily Output	Labor-Hours	Unit	Material	Labor	Equipment	Total	Total Incl O&P
						2023 Bare Costs				
7690	125 HP motor	2 Elec	.90	17.778	Ea.	5,325	1,200		6,525	7,625
7700	150 HP motor		.90	17.778		5,325	1,200		6,525	7,625
7710	200 HP motor		.90	17.778		5,325	1,200		6,525	7,625
7750	Starter & nonfused disconnect, 600 volt, 3 pole, 5 HP motor	1 Elec	1.40	5.714		725	385		1,110	1,375
7760	10 HP motor	"	1.10	7.273		815	490		1,305	1,625
7770	25 HP motor	2 Elec	1.50	10.667		1,375	720		2,095	2,575
7780	30 HP motor		1.30	12.308		1,800	830		2,630	3,200
7790	40 HP motor		1.30	12.308		2,200	830		3,030	3,650
7800	50 HP motor		1.30	12.308		2,200	830		3,030	3,650
7810	60 HP motor		.92	17.391		4,100	1,175		5,275	6,250
7820	75 HP motor		.92	17.391		4,100	1,175		5,275	6,250
7830	100 HP motor		.84	19.048		4,750	1,275		6,025	7,125
7840	125 HP motor		.70	22.857		5,825	1,550		7,375	8,700
7850	150 HP motor		.70	22.857		5,825	1,550		7,375	8,700
7860	200 HP motor		.60	26.667		5,825	1,800		7,625	9,075
7870	Starter & fused disconnect, 600 volt, 3 pole, 5 HP motor	1 Elec	1.40	5.714		835	385		1,220	1,500
7880	10 HP motor	"	1.10	7.273		925	490		1,415	1,750
7890	25 HP motor	2 Elec	1.50	10.667		1,475	720		2,195	2,700
7900	30 HP motor		1.30	12.308		1,850	830		2,680	3,250
7910	40 HP motor		1.30	12.308		2,275	830		3,105	3,725
7920	50 HP motor		1.30	12.308		2,275	830		3,105	3,725
7930	60 HP motor		.92	17.391		4,250	1,175		5,425	6,425
7940	75 HP motor		.92	17.391		4,250	1,175		5,425	6,425
7950	100 HP motor		.84	19.048		4,925	1,275		6,200	7,325
7960	125 HP motor		.70	22.857		6,025	1,550		7,575	8,925
7970	150 HP motor		.70	22.857		6,025	1,550		7,575	8,925
7980	200 HP motor		.60	26.667		6,025	1,800		7,825	9,300
7990	Combination starter and nonfusible disconnect									
8000	600 volt, 3 pole, 5 HP motor	1 Elec	1.80	4.444	Ea.	1,225	299		1,524	1,800
8010	10 HP motor	"	1.30	6.154		1,300	415		1,715	2,050
8020	25 HP motor	2 Elec	2	8		1,000	540		1,540	1,900
8030	30 HP motor		1.32	12.121		1,750	815		2,565	3,150
8040	40 HP motor		1.32	12.121		1,750	815		2,565	3,150
8050	50 HP motor		1.32	12.121		2,000	815		2,815	3,425
8060	60 HP motor		.80	20		3,325	1,350		4,675	5,650
8070	75 HP motor		.80	20		3,325	1,350		4,675	5,650
8080	100 HP motor		.80	20		3,950	1,350		5,300	6,350
8090	125 HP motor		.70	22.857		7,550	1,550		9,100	10,600
8100	150 HP motor		.70	22.857		8,675	1,550		10,225	11,900
8110	200 HP motor		.70	22.857		7,650	1,550		9,200	10,700
8140	Combination starter and fused disconnect									
8150	600 volt, 3 pole, 5 HP motor	1 Elec	1.80	4.444	Ea.	625	299		924	1,125
8160	10 HP motor	"	1.30	6.154		1,375	415		1,790	2,125
8170	25 HP motor	2 Elec	2	8		2,150	540		2,690	3,175
8180	30 HP motor		1.32	12.121		1,725	815		2,540	3,125
8190	40 HP motor		1.32	12.121		1,850	815		2,665	3,275
8200	50 HP motor		1.32	12.121		3,725	815		4,540	5,325
8210	60 HP motor		.80	20		3,250	1,350		4,600	5,575
8220	75 HP motor		.80	20		3,250	1,350		4,600	5,575
8230	100 HP motor		.80	20		3,250	1,350		4,600	5,575
8240	125 HP motor		.70	22.857		7,200	1,550		8,750	10,200
8250	150 HP motor		.70	22.857		7,200	1,550		8,750	10,200
8260	200 HP motor		.70	22.857		7,200	1,550		8,750	10,200

26 24 19.40 Motor Starters and Controls		Crew	Daily Output	Labor-Hours	Unit	Material	Labor	Equipment	Total	Total Incl O&P
						2023 Bare Costs				
8290	Combination starter & circuit breaker disconnect									
8300	600 volt, 3 pole, 5 HP motor	1 Elec	1.80	4.444	Ea.	1,600	299		1,899	2,200
8310	10 HP motor	"	1.30	6.154		910	415		1,325	1,625
8320	25 HP motor	2 Elec	2	8		2,525	540		3,065	3,600
8330	30 HP motor		1.32	12.121		1,800	815		2,615	3,200
8340	40 HP motor		1.32	12.121		1,800	815		2,615	3,200
8350	50 HP motor		1.32	12.121		1,775	815		2,590	3,175
8360	60 HP motor		.80	20		3,925	1,350		5,275	6,300
8370	75 HP motor		.80	20		3,925	1,350		5,275	6,300
8380	100 HP motor		.80	20		3,875	1,350		5,225	6,250
8390	125 HP motor		.70	22.857		9,050	1,550		10,600	12,300
8400	150 HP motor		.70	22.857		8,850	1,550		10,400	12,100
8410	200 HP motor		.70	22.857		8,925	1,550		10,475	12,100
8430	Starter & circuit breaker disconnect									
8440	600 volt, 3 pole, 5 HP motor	1 Elec	1.40	5.714	Ea.	1,150	385		1,535	1,825
8450	10 HP motor	"	1.10	7.273		1,225	490		1,715	2,075
8460	25 HP motor	2 Elec	1.50	10.667		1,775	720		2,495	3,025
8470	30 HP motor		1.30	12.308		2,200	830		3,030	3,650
8480	40 HP motor		1.30	12.308		2,625	830		3,455	4,100
8490	50 HP motor		1.30	12.308		2,625	830		3,455	4,100
8500	60 HP motor		.92	17.391		4,725	1,175		5,900	6,950
8510	75 HP motor		.92	17.391		4,725	1,175		5,900	6,950
8520	100 HP motor		.84	19.048		5,400	1,275		6,675	7,850
8530	125 HP motor		.70	22.857		6,300	1,550		7,850	9,225
8540	150 HP motor		.70	22.857		6,300	1,550		7,850	9,225
8550	200 HP motor		.60	26.667		9,850	1,800		11,650	13,500
8900	240 volt, 1-2 pole, 0.75 HP motor	1 Elec	2	4		915	269		1,184	1,400
8910	2 HP motor		2	4		965	269		1,234	1,475
8920	5 HP motor		1.80	4.444		1,225	299		1,524	1,800
8930	10 HP motor		1.40	5.714		1,400	385		1,785	2,100
8950	3 pole, 0.75 HP motor		1.60	5		915	335		1,250	1,500
8970	5 HP motor		1.40	5.714		990	385		1,375	1,675
8980	10 HP motor		1.10	7.273		1,675	490		2,165	2,575
8990	15 HP motor		1	8		1,675	540		2,215	2,650
9100	20 HP motor	2 Elec	1.50	10.667		2,475	720		3,195	3,800
9110	25 HP motor		1.50	10.667		2,475	720		3,195	3,800
9120	30 HP motor		1.30	12.308		2,475	830		3,305	3,950
9130	40 HP motor		1.24	12.903		5,100	870		5,970	6,925
9140	50 HP motor		1.12	14.286		5,100	960		6,060	7,050
9150	60 HP motor		.90	17.778		14,300	1,200		15,500	17,500
9160	75 HP motor		.76	21.053		14,300	1,425		15,725	17,800
9170	100 HP motor		.70	22.857		14,600	1,550		16,150	18,400
9180	125 HP motor		.60	26.667		24,000	1,800		25,800	29,100
9190	150 HP motor		.52	30.769		24,000	2,075		26,075	29,500
9200	200 HP motor		.50	32		24,000	2,150		26,150	29,600

26 25 13 – Low-Voltage Busways

26 25 13.10 Aluminum Bus Duct		Crew	Daily Output	Labor-Hours	Unit	2023 Bare Costs Material	Labor	Equipment	Total	Total Incl O&P
0010	**ALUMINUM BUS DUCT** 10 ft. long R262513-10									
0050	Indoor 3 pole 4 wire, plug-in, straight section, 225 amp	2 Elec	44	.364	L.F.	705	24.50		729.50	810
0100	400 amp		36	.444		1,150	30		1,180	1,325
0150	600 amp		32	.500		1,000	33.50		1,033.50	1,150
0200	800 amp		26	.615		925	41.50		966.50	1,075
0250	1,000 amp		24	.667		1,125	45		1,170	1,300
0270	1,200 amp		23	.696		1,400	47		1,447	1,600
0300	1,350 amp		22	.727		1,675	49		1,724	1,900
0310	1,600 amp		18	.889		1,925	60		1,985	2,225
0320	2,000 amp		16	1		2,375	67.50		2,442.50	2,700
0330	2,500 amp		14	1.143		2,900	77		2,977	3,325
0340	3,000 amp		12	1.333		3,375	90		3,465	3,825
0350	Feeder, 600 amp		34	.471		795	31.50		826.50	920
0400	800 amp		28	.571		940	38.50		978.50	1,075
0450	1,000 amp		26	.615		1,075	41.50		1,116.50	1,225
0455	1,200 amp		25	.640		1,350	43		1,393	1,550
0500	1,350 amp		24	.667		1,675	45		1,720	1,900
0550	1,600 amp		20	.800		1,975	54		2,029	2,250
0600	2,000 amp		18	.889		2,300	60		2,360	2,650
0620	2,500 amp		14	1.143		3,000	77		3,077	3,425
0630	3,000 amp		12	1.333		3,225	90		3,315	3,675
0640	4,000 amp		10	1.600		760	108		868	995
0650	Elbow, 225 amp		4.40	3.636	Ea.	2,075	245		2,320	2,650
0700	400 amp		3.80	4.211		2,200	284		2,484	2,850
0750	600 amp		3.40	4.706		2,475	315		2,790	3,200
0800	800 amp		3	5.333		2,650	360		3,010	3,450
0850	1,000 amp		2.80	5.714		3,500	385		3,885	4,425
0870	1,200 amp		2.70	5.926		3,900	400		4,300	4,875
0900	1,350 amp		2.60	6.154		6,525	415		6,940	7,800
0950	1,600 amp		2.40	6.667		9,175	450		9,625	10,800
1000	2,000 amp		2	8		8,825	540		9,365	10,500
1020	2,500 amp		1.80	8.889		13,300	600		13,900	15,500
1030	3,000 amp		1.60	10		15,200	675		15,875	17,700
1040	4,000 amp		1.40	11.429		14,200	770		14,970	16,900
1100	Cable tap box end, 225 amp		3.60	4.444		1,975	299		2,274	2,625
1150	400 amp		3.20	5		2,475	335		2,810	3,225
1200	600 amp		2.60	6.154		3,650	415		4,065	4,650
1250	800 amp		2.20	7.273		10,600	490		11,090	12,400
1300	1,000 amp		2	8		11,300	540		11,840	13,200
1320	1,200 amp		2	8		11,900	540		12,440	13,900
1350	1,350 amp		1.60	10		13,200	675		13,875	15,500
1400	1,600 amp		1.40	11.429		13,100	770		13,870	15,600
1450	2,000 amp		1.20	13.333		14,500	900		15,400	17,200
1460	2,500 amp		1	16		17,700	1,075		18,775	21,000
1470	3,000 amp		.80	20		19,500	1,350		20,850	23,400
1480	4,000 amp		.60	26.667		23,000	1,800		24,800	27,900
1500	Switchboard stub, 225 amp		5.80	2.759		870	186		1,056	1,225
1550	400 amp		5.40	2.963		1,850	200		2,050	2,350
1600	600 amp		4.60	3.478		2,050	234		2,284	2,625
1650	800 amp		4	4		2,100	269		2,369	2,725
1700	1,000 amp		3.20	5		1,850	335		2,185	2,525
1720	1,200 amp		3.10	5.161		1,900	350		2,250	2,600
1750	1,350 amp		3	5.333		1,875	360		2,235	2,575

26 25 13.10 Aluminum Bus Duct		Crew	Daily Output	Labor-Hours	Unit	Material	Labor	Equipment	Total	Total Incl O&P
						2023 Bare Costs				
1800	1,600 amp	2 Elec	2.60	6.154	Ea.	2,900	415		3,315	3,825
1850	2,000 amp		2.40	6.667		3,450	450		3,900	4,475
1860	2,500 amp		2.20	7.273		2,450	490		2,940	3,425
1870	3,000 amp		2	8		3,225	540		3,765	4,350
1880	4,000 amp		1.80	8.889		2,075	600		2,675	3,200
1890	Tee fittings, 225 amp		3.20	5		3,725	335		4,060	4,600
1900	400 amp		2.80	5.714		7,350	385		7,735	8,675
1950	600 amp		2.60	6.154		3,725	415		4,140	4,725
2000	800 amp		2.40	6.667		1,075	450		1,525	1,850
2050	1,000 amp		2.20	7.273		1,125	490		1,615	1,975
2070	1,200 amp		2.10	7.619		1,325	515		1,840	2,225
2100	1,350 amp		2	8		1,825	540		2,365	2,800
2150	1,600 amp		1.60	10		2,200	675		2,875	3,425
2200	2,000 amp		1.20	13.333		2,425	900		3,325	4,000
2220	2,500 amp		1	16		2,900	1,075		3,975	4,800
2230	3,000 amp		.80	20		3,325	1,350		4,675	5,650
2240	4,000 amp		.60	26.667		5,525	1,800		7,325	8,750
2300	Wall flange, 600 amp		20	.800		825	54		879	990
2310	800 amp		16	1		825	67.50		892.50	1,000
2320	1,000 amp		13	1.231		825	83		908	1,025
2325	1,200 amp		12	1.333		825	90		915	1,050
2330	1,350 amp		10.80	1.481		825	100		925	1,050
2340	1,600 amp		9	1.778		825	120		945	1,100
2350	2,000 amp		8	2		825	135		960	1,100
2360	2,500 amp		6.60	2.424		825	163		988	1,150
2370	3,000 amp		5.40	2.963		1,200	200		1,400	1,625
2380	4,000 amp		4	4		1,200	269		1,469	1,725
2390	5,000 amp		3	5.333		1,200	360		1,560	1,850
2400	Vapor barrier		8	2		520	135		655	770
2420	Roof flange kit		4	4		1,075	269		1,344	1,575
2600	Expansion fitting, 225 amp		10	1.600		1,675	108		1,783	1,975
2610	400 amp		8	2		1,675	135		1,810	2,050
2620	600 amp		6	2.667		1,675	180		1,855	2,125
2630	800 amp		4.60	3.478		1,875	234		2,109	2,400
2640	1,000 amp		4	4		2,150	269		2,419	2,750
2650	1,350 amp		3.60	4.444		2,325	299		2,624	3,000
2660	1,600 amp		3.20	5		2,800	335		3,135	3,575
2670	2,000 amp		2.80	5.714		3,100	385		3,485	4,000
2680	2,500 amp		2.40	6.667		3,750	450		4,200	4,800
2690	3,000 amp		2	8		4,325	540		4,865	5,550
2700	4,000 amp		1.60	10		5,700	675		6,375	7,250
2800	Reducer nonfused, 400 amp		8	2		995	135		1,130	1,300
2810	600 amp		6	2.667		995	180		1,175	1,375
2820	800 amp		4.60	3.478		1,200	234		1,434	1,675
2830	1,000 amp		4	4		1,400	269		1,669	1,925
2840	1,350 amp		3.60	4.444		1,825	299		2,124	2,450
2850	1,600 amp		3.20	5		2,475	335		2,810	3,225
2860	2,000 amp		2.80	5.714		2,825	385		3,210	3,700
2870	2,500 amp		2.40	6.667		3,575	450		4,025	4,600
2880	3,000 amp		2	8		4,125	540		4,665	5,350
2890	4,000 amp		1.60	10		5,500	675		6,175	7,075
2950	Reducer fuse included, 225 amp		4.40	3.636		2,925	245		3,170	3,575
2960	400 amp		4.20	3.810		2,975	257		3,232	3,625

26 25 13.10 Aluminum Bus Duct		Crew	Daily Output	Labor-Hours	Unit	Material	Labor	Equipment	Total	Total Incl O&P
						2023 Bare Costs				
2970	600 amp	2 Elec	3.60	4.444	Ea.	3,500	299		3,799	4,300
2980	800 amp		3.20	5		5,575	335		5,910	6,625
2990	1,000 amp		3	5.333		6,375	360		6,735	7,525
3000	1,200 amp		2.80	5.714		6,375	385		6,760	7,575
3010	1,600 amp		2.20	7.273		14,500	490		14,990	16,700
3020	2,000 amp		1.80	8.889		16,100	600		16,700	18,600
3100	Reducer circuit breaker, 225 amp		4.40	3.636		2,875	245		3,120	3,525
3110	400 amp		4.20	3.810		3,500	257		3,757	4,225
3120	600 amp		3.60	4.444		4,950	299		5,249	5,900
3130	800 amp		3.20	5		5,825	335		6,160	6,900
3140	1,000 amp		3	5.333		6,600	360		6,960	7,775
3150	1,200 amp		2.80	5.714		7,925	385		8,310	9,300
3160	1,600 amp		2.20	7.273		11,700	490		12,190	13,600
3170	2,000 amp		1.80	8.889		12,900	600		13,500	15,000
3250	Reducer circuit breaker, 75,000 AIC, 225 amp		4.40	3.636		4,500	245		4,745	5,300
3260	400 amp		4.20	3.810		4,500	257		4,757	5,300
3270	600 amp		3.60	4.444		6,000	299		6,299	7,050
3280	800 amp		3.20	5		6,600	335		6,935	7,750
3290	1,000 amp		3	5.333		10,600	360		10,960	12,200
3300	1,200 amp		2.80	5.714		10,600	385		10,985	12,300
3310	1,600 amp		2.20	7.273		11,700	490		12,190	13,600
3320	2,000 amp		1.80	8.889		12,900	600		13,500	15,000
3400	Reducer circuit breaker CLF 225 amp		4.40	3.636		4,625	245		4,870	5,450
3410	400 amp		4.20	3.810		5,475	257		5,732	6,400
3420	600 amp		3.60	4.444		8,200	299		8,499	9,475
3430	800 amp		3.20	5		8,575	335		8,910	9,925
3440	1,000 amp		3	5.333		8,925	360		9,285	10,400
3450	1,200 amp		2.80	5.714		11,700	385		12,085	13,400
3460	1,600 amp		2.20	7.273		11,700	490		12,190	13,600
3470	2,000 amp		1.80	8.889		12,900	600		13,500	15,000
3550	Ground bus added to bus duct, 225 amp		320	.050	L.F.	37.50	3.37		40.87	46
3560	400 amp		320	.050		37.50	3.37		40.87	46
3570	600 amp		280	.057		37.50	3.85		41.35	46.50
3580	800 amp		240	.067		37.50	4.49		41.99	47.50
3590	1,000 amp		200	.080		37.50	5.40		42.90	49
3600	1,350 amp		180	.089		37.50	6		43.50	50
3610	1,600 amp		160	.100		37.50	6.75		44.25	51
3620	2,000 amp		160	.100		37.50	6.75		44.25	51
3630	2,500 amp		140	.114		37.50	7.70		45.20	52.50
3640	3,000 amp		120	.133		37.50	9		46.50	54.50
3650	4,000 amp		100	.160		37.50	10.80		48.30	57
3810	High short circuit, 400 amp		36	.444		225	30		255	292
3820	600 amp		32	.500		390	33.50		423.50	480
3830	800 amp		26	.615		455	41.50		496.50	560
3840	1,000 amp		24	.667		570	45		615	690
3850	1,350 amp		22	.727		211	49		260	305
3860	1,600 amp		18	.889		243	60		303	355
3870	2,000 amp		16	1		285	67.50		352.50	415
3880	2,500 amp		14	1.143		475	77		552	635
3890	3,000 amp		12	1.333		540	90		630	725
3920	Cross, 225 amp		5.60	2.857	Ea.	1,500	192		1,692	1,925
3930	400 amp		4.60	3.478		1,500	234		1,734	2,000
3940	600 amp		4	4		1,500	269		1,769	2,050

26 25 13 – Low-Voltage Busways

26 25 13.10 Aluminum Bus Duct		Crew	Daily Output	Labor-Hours	Unit	Material	Labor	Equipment	Total	Total Incl O&P
						2023 Bare Costs				
3950	800 amp	2 Elec	3.40	4.706	Ea.	1,575	315		1,890	2,200
3960	1,000 amp		3	5.333		1,650	360		2,010	2,350
3970	1,350 amp		2.80	5.714		2,675	385		3,060	3,525
3980	1,600 amp		2.20	7.273		3,200	490		3,690	4,225
3990	2,000 amp		1.80	8.889		3,500	600		4,100	4,750
4000	2,500 amp		1.60	10		4,150	675		4,825	5,575
4010	3,000 amp		1.20	13.333		4,775	900		5,675	6,575
4020	4,000 amp		1	16		7,300	1,075		8,375	9,625
4040	Cable tap box center, 225 amp		3.60	4.444		3,325	299		3,624	4,100
4050	400 amp		3.20	5		3,800	335		4,135	4,675
4060	600 amp		2.60	6.154		5,075	415		5,490	6,200
4070	800 amp		2.20	7.273		5,600	490		6,090	6,900
4080	1,000 amp		2	8		7,125	540		7,665	8,625
4090	1,350 amp		1.60	10		10,500	675		11,175	12,600
4100	1,600 amp		1.40	11.429		10,500	770		11,270	12,800
4110	2,000 amp		1.20	13.333		2,100	900		3,000	3,625
4120	2,500 amp		1	16		2,550	1,075		3,625	4,400
4130	3,000 amp		.80	20		2,800	1,350		4,150	5,100
4140	4,000 amp		.60	26.667		3,725	1,800		5,525	6,775
4500	Weatherproof 3 pole 4 wire, feeder, 600 amp		30	.533	L.F.	152	36		188	221
4520	800 amp		24	.667		178	45		223	262
4540	1,000 amp		22	.727		202	49		251	296
4550	1,200 amp		21	.762		280	51.50		331.50	385
4560	1,350 amp		20	.800		315	54		369	430
4580	1,600 amp		17	.941		365	63.50		428.50	500
4600	2,000 amp		16	1		430	67.50		497.50	575
4620	2,500 amp		12	1.333		555	90		645	750
4640	3,000 amp		10	1.600		635	108		743	855
4660	4,000 amp		8	2		910	135		1,045	1,200
5000	Indoor 3 pole, 3 wire, feeder, 600 amp		40	.400		116	27		143	168
5010	800 amp		32	.500		700	33.50		733.50	820
5020	1,000 amp		30	.533		780	36		816	915
5025	1,200 amp		29	.552		1,050	37		1,087	1,200
5030	1,350 amp		28	.571		201	38.50		239.50	278
5040	1,600 amp		24	.667		1,500	45		1,545	1,725
5050	2,000 amp		20	.800		1,775	54		1,829	2,025
5060	2,500 amp		16	1		2,175	67.50		2,242.50	2,500
5070	3,000 amp		14	1.143		2,475	77		2,552	2,850
5080	4,000 amp		12	1.333		550	90		640	740
5200	Plug-in type, 225 amp		50	.320		151	21.50		172.50	199
5210	400 amp		42	.381		186	25.50		211.50	243
5220	600 amp		36	.444		231	30		261	299
5230	800 amp		30	.533		325	36		361	410
5240	1,000 amp		28	.571		365	38.50		403.50	460
5245	1,200 amp		27	.593		495	40		535	600
5250	1,350 amp		26	.615		211	41.50		252.50	294
5260	1,600 amp		20	.800		840	54		894	1,000
5270	2,000 amp		18	.889		1,975	60		2,035	2,275
5280	2,500 amp		16	1		1,225	67.50		1,292.50	1,450
5290	3,000 amp		14	1.143		1,300	77		1,377	1,550
5300	4,000 amp		12	1.333		560	90		650	750
5330	High short circuit, 400 amp		42	.381		223	25.50		248.50	283
5340	600 amp		36	.444		277	30		307	350

26 25 13.10 Aluminum Bus Duct		Crew	Daily Output	Labor-Hours	Unit	2023 Bare Costs Material	Labor	Equipment	Total	Total Incl O&P
5350	800 amp	2 Elec	30	.533	L.F.	390	36		426	480
5360	1,000 amp		28	.571		440	38.50		478.50	540
5370	1,350 amp		26	.615		211	41.50		252.50	294
5380	1,600 amp		20	.800		243	54		297	345
5390	2,000 amp		18	.889		285	60		345	405
5400	2,500 amp		16	1		450	67.50		517.50	595
5410	3,000 amp		14	1.143		465	77		542	625
5440	Elbow, 225 amp		5	3.200	Ea.	1,975	216		2,191	2,500
5450	400 amp		4.40	3.636		1,800	245		2,045	2,375
5460	600 amp		4	4		1,950	269		2,219	2,550
5470	800 amp		3.40	4.706		2,225	315		2,540	2,925
5480	1,000 amp		3.20	5		805	335		1,140	1,400
5485	1,200 amp		3.10	5.161		860	350		1,210	1,450
5490	1,350 amp		3	5.333		815	360		1,175	1,425
5500	1,600 amp		2.80	5.714		7,475	385		7,860	8,775
5510	2,000 amp		2.40	6.667		8,825	450		9,275	10,400
5520	2,500 amp		2	8		10,700	540		11,240	12,600
5530	3,000 amp		1.80	8.889		12,200	600		12,800	14,300
5540	4,000 amp		1.60	10		18,700	675		19,375	21,600
5560	Tee fittings, 225 amp		3.60	4.444		3,050	299		3,349	3,825
5570	400 amp		3.20	5		3,350	335		3,685	4,175
5580	600 amp		3	5.333		6,050	360		6,410	7,175
5590	800 amp		2.80	5.714		960	385		1,345	1,625
5600	1,000 amp		2.60	6.154		995	415		1,410	1,725
5605	1,200 amp		2.50	6.400		1,050	430		1,480	1,825
5610	1,350 amp		2.40	6.667		1,475	450		1,925	2,300
5620	1,600 amp		1.80	8.889		1,725	600		2,325	2,800
5630	2,000 amp		1.40	11.429		1,925	770		2,695	3,275
5640	2,500 amp		1.20	13.333		2,400	900		3,300	3,975
5650	3,000 amp		1	16		2,825	1,075		3,900	4,700
5660	4,000 amp		.70	22.857		4,125	1,550		5,675	6,850
5680	Cross, 225 amp		6.40	2.500		1,450	168		1,618	1,850
5690	400 amp		5.40	2.963		1,450	200		1,650	1,900
5700	600 amp		4.60	3.478		1,450	234		1,684	1,950
5710	800 amp		4	4		1,525	269		1,794	2,100
5720	1,000 amp		3.60	4.444		1,575	299		1,874	2,175
5730	1,350 amp		3.20	5		2,350	335		2,685	3,075
5740	1,600 amp		2.60	6.154		2,750	415		3,165	3,650
5750	2,000 amp		2.20	7.273		3,000	490		3,490	4,025
5760	2,500 amp		1.80	8.889		3,625	600		4,225	4,900
5770	3,000 amp		1.40	11.429		4,325	770		5,095	5,900
5780	4,000 amp		1.20	13.333		6,025	900		6,925	7,950
5800	Expansion fitting, 225 amp		11.60	1.379		1,275	93		1,368	1,550
5810	400 amp		9.20	1.739		1,275	117		1,392	1,575
5820	600 amp		7	2.286		1,275	154		1,429	1,625
5830	800 amp		5.20	3.077		1,500	207		1,707	1,950
5840	1,000 amp		4.60	3.478		1,650	234		1,884	2,150
5850	1,350 amp		4.20	3.810		1,650	257		1,907	2,200
5860	1,600 amp		3.60	4.444		2,050	299		2,349	2,700
5870	2,000 amp		3.20	5		2,425	335		2,760	3,175
5880	2,500 amp		2.80	5.714		2,750	385		3,135	3,600
5890	3,000 amp		2.40	6.667		3,200	450		3,650	4,200
5900	4,000 amp		1.80	8.889		4,400	600		5,000	5,750

26 25 13.10 Aluminum Bus Duct		Crew	Daily Output	Labor-Hours	Unit	Material	2023 Bare Costs Labor	Equipment	Total	Total Incl O&P
5940	Reducer, nonfused, 400 amp	2 Elec	9.20	1.739	Ea.	855	117		972	1,125
5950	600 amp		7	2.286		855	154		1,009	1,175
5960	800 amp		5.20	3.077		895	207		1,102	1,300
5970	1,000 amp		4.60	3.478		1,100	234		1,334	1,550
5980	1,350 amp		4.20	3.810		1,625	257		1,882	2,175
5990	1,600 amp		3.60	4.444		1,850	299		2,149	2,500
6000	2,000 amp		3.20	5		2,175	335		2,510	2,900
6010	2,500 amp		2.80	5.714		2,775	385		3,160	3,625
6020	3,000 amp		2.20	7.273		3,250	490		3,740	4,300
6030	4,000 amp		1.80	8.889		4,450	600		5,050	5,800
6050	Reducer, fuse included, 225 amp		5	3.200		2,225	216		2,441	2,775
6060	400 amp		4.80	3.333		2,975	225		3,200	3,575
6070	600 amp		4.20	3.810		3,800	257		4,057	4,550
6080	800 amp		3.60	4.444		5,875	299		6,174	6,925
6090	1,000 amp		3.40	4.706		6,425	315		6,740	7,525
6100	1,350 amp		3.20	5		11,700	335		12,035	13,400
6110	1,600 amp		2.60	6.154		13,900	415		14,315	15,900
6120	2,000 amp		2	8		16,100	540		16,640	18,500
6160	Reducer, circuit breaker, 225 amp		5	3.200		2,750	216		2,966	3,350
6170	400 amp		4.80	3.333		3,375	225		3,600	4,025
6180	600 amp		4.20	3.810		4,825	257		5,082	5,700
6190	800 amp		3.60	4.444		5,650	299		5,949	6,650
6200	1,000 amp		3.40	4.706		6,425	315		6,740	7,525
6210	1,350 amp		3.20	5		7,750	335		8,085	9,025
6220	1,600 amp		2.60	6.154		11,600	415		12,015	13,300
6230	2,000 amp		2	8		12,600	540		13,140	14,700
6270	Cable tap box center, 225 amp		4.20	3.810		3,325	257		3,582	4,050
6280	400 amp		3.60	4.444		1,150	299		1,449	1,725
6290	600 amp		3	5.333		1,150	360		1,510	1,800
6300	800 amp		2.60	6.154		1,250	415		1,665	2,025
6310	1,000 amp		2.40	6.667		1,350	450		1,800	2,150
6320	1,350 amp		1.80	8.889		9,200	600		9,800	11,000
6330	1,600 amp		1.60	10		9,200	675		9,875	11,100
6340	2,000 amp		1.40	11.429		1,800	770		2,570	3,150
6350	2,500 amp		1.20	13.333		2,250	900		3,150	3,800
6360	3,000 amp		1	16		2,550	1,075		3,625	4,425
6370	4,000 amp		.70	22.857		3,025	1,550		4,575	5,625
6390	Cable tap box end, 225 amp		4.20	3.810		1,800	257		2,057	2,350
6400	400 amp		3.60	4.444		2,175	299		2,474	2,825
6410	600 amp		3	5.333		705	360		1,065	1,300
6420	800 amp		2.60	6.154		775	415		1,190	1,475
6430	1,000 amp		2.40	6.667		835	450		1,285	1,575
6435	1,200 amp		2.10	7.619		905	515		1,420	1,750
6440	1,350 amp		1.80	8.889		880	600		1,480	1,850
6450	1,600 amp		1.60	10		11,400	675		12,075	13,600
6460	2,000 amp		1.40	11.429		12,400	770		13,170	14,800
6470	2,500 amp		1.20	13.333		14,700	900		15,600	17,400
6480	3,000 amp		1	16		15,800	1,075		16,875	19,000
6490	4,000 amp		.70	22.857		1,850	1,550		3,400	4,325
7000	Weatherproof 3 pole 3 wire, feeder, 600 amp		34	.471	L.F.	150	31.50		181.50	212
7020	800 amp		28	.571		165	38.50		203.50	239
7040	1,000 amp		26	.615		178	41.50		219.50	257
7050	1,200 amp		25	.640		207	43		250	292

26 25 Low-Voltage Enclosed Bus Assemblies

26 25 13 – Low-Voltage Busways

26 25 13.10 Aluminum Bus Duct		Crew	Daily Output	Labor-Hours	Unit	Material	2023 Bare Costs Labor	Equipment	Total	Total Incl O&P
7060	1,350 amp	2 Elec	24	.667	L.F.	241	45		286	330
7080	1,600 amp		20	.800		278	54		332	385
7100	2,000 amp		18	.889		330	60		390	450
7120	2,500 amp		14	1.143		455	77		532	615
7140	3,000 amp		12	1.333		545	90		635	735
7160	4,000 amp		10	1.600		660	108		768	885

26 25 13.20 Bus Duct		Crew	Daily Output	Labor-Hours	Unit	Material	Labor	Equipment	Total	Total Incl O&P
0010	**BUS DUCT** 100 amp and less, aluminum or copper, plug-in									
0080	Bus duct, 3 pole 3 wire, 100 amp	1 Elec	42	.190	L.F.	89.50	12.85		102.35	117
0110	Elbow		4	2	Ea.	144	135		279	360
0120	Tee		2	4		204	269		473	625
0130	Wall flange		8	1		31.50	67.50		99	135
0140	Ground kit		16	.500		61	33.50		94.50	118
0180	3 pole 4 wire, 100 amp		40	.200	L.F.	98	13.45		111.45	128
0200	Cable tap box		3.10	2.581	Ea.	294	174		468	585
0300	End closure		16	.500		39	33.50		72.50	93
0400	Elbow		4	2		246	135		381	470
0500	Tee		2	4		355	269		624	790
0600	Hangers		10	.800		65	54		119	152
0700	Circuit breakers, 15 to 50 amp, 1 pole		8	1		251	67.50		318.50	375
0800	15 to 60 amp, 2 pole		6.70	1.194		420	80.50		500.50	580
0900	3 pole		5.30	1.509		515	102		617	720
1000	60 to 100 amp, 1 pole		6.70	1.194		2,025	80.50		2,105.50	2,350
1100	70 to 100 amp, 2 pole		5.30	1.509		2,025	102		2,127	2,375
1200	3 pole		4.50	1.778		2,025	120		2,145	2,400
1220	Switch, nonfused, 3 pole, 4 wire		8	1		248	67.50		315.50	375
1240	Fused, 3 fuses, 4 wire, 30 amp		8	1		395	67.50		462.50	535
1260	60 amp		5.30	1.509		460	102		562	655
1280	100 amp		4.50	1.778		620	120		740	865
1300	Plug, fusible, 3 pole 250 volt, 30 amp		5.30	1.509		605	102		707	820
1310	60 amp		5.30	1.509		685	102		787	900
1320	100 amp		4.50	1.778		920	120		1,040	1,175
1330	3 pole 480 volt, 30 amp		5.30	1.509		610	102		712	820
1340	60 amp		5.30	1.509		660	102		762	875
1350	100 amp		4.50	1.778		955	120		1,075	1,225
1360	Circuit breaker, 3 pole 250 volt, 60 amp		5.30	1.509		1,075	102		1,177	1,350
1370	3 pole 480 volt, 100 amp		4.50	1.778		1,075	120		1,195	1,375
2000	Bus duct, 2 wire, 250 volt, 30 amp		60	.133	L.F.	9.50	9		18.50	24
2100	60 amp		50	.160		9.50	10.80		20.30	26.50
2200	300 volt, 30 amp		60	.133		9.50	9		18.50	24
2300	60 amp		50	.160		9.50	10.80		20.30	26.50
2400	3 wire, 250 volt, 30 amp		60	.133		12.20	9		21.20	27
2500	60 amp		50	.160		11.95	10.80		22.75	29
2600	480/277 volt, 30 amp		60	.133		12.20	9		21.20	27
2700	60 amp		50	.160		12.20	10.80		23	29.50
2750	End feed, 300 volt 2 wire max. 30 amp		6	1.333	Ea.	85	90		175	227
2800	60 amp		5.50	1.455		85	98		183	240
2850	30 amp miniature		6	1.333		85	90		175	227
2900	3 wire, 30 amp		6	1.333		107	90		197	251
2950	60 amp		5.50	1.455		107	98		205	264
3000	30 amp miniature		6	1.333		107	90		197	251
3050	Center feed, 300 volt 2 wire, 30 amp		6	1.333		118	90		208	262

26 25 13 – Low-Voltage Busways

26 25 13.20 Bus Duct		Crew	Daily Output	Labor-Hours	Unit	Material	2023 Bare Costs Labor	Equipment	Total	Total Incl O&P
3100	60 amp	1 Elec	5.50	1.455	Ea.	118	98		216	275
3150	3 wire, 30 amp		6	1.333		134	90		224	280
3200	60 amp		5.50	1.455		134	98		232	293
3220	Elbow, 30 amp		6	1.333		46.50	90		136.50	184
3240	60 amp		5.50	1.455		46.50	98		144.50	197
3260	End cap		40	.200		11.25	13.45		24.70	32.50
3280	Strength beam, 10′		15	.533		27.50	36		63.50	83.50
3300	Hanger		24	.333		5.85	22.50		28.35	40
3320	Tap box, nonfusible		6.30	1.270		95.50	85.50		181	232
3340	Fusible switch 30 amp, 1 fuse		6	1.333		505	90		595	690
3360	2 fuse		6	1.333		530	90		620	720
3380	3 fuse		6	1.333		600	90		690	795
3400	Circuit breaker handle on cover, 1 pole		6	1.333		68	90		158	208
3420	2 pole		6	1.333		690	90		780	895
3440	3 pole		6	1.333		845	90		935	1,075
3460	Circuit breaker external operhandle, 1 pole		6	1.333		81	90		171	222
3480	2 pole		6	1.333		890	90		980	1,125
3500	3 pole		6	1.333		975	90		1,065	1,200
3520	Terminal plug only		16	.500		108	33.50		141.50	169
3540	Terminal with receptacle		16	.500		118	33.50		151.50	180
3560	Fixture plug		16	.500		80.50	33.50		114	139
4000	Copper bus duct, lighting, 2 wire 300 volt, 20 amp		70	.114	L.F.	8.55	7.70		16.25	21
4020	35 amp		60	.133		8.55	9		17.55	23
4040	50 amp		55	.145		8.55	9.80		18.35	24
4060	60 amp		50	.160		8.55	10.80		19.35	25.50
4080	3 wire 300 volt, 20 amp		70	.114		8.40	7.70		16.10	20.50
4100	35 amp		60	.133		8.10	9		17.10	22.50
4120	50 amp		55	.145		8.40	9.80		18.20	24
4140	60 amp		50	.160		8.40	10.80		19.20	25
4160	Feeder in box, end, 1 circuit		6	1.333	Ea.	105	90		195	249
4180	2 circuit		5.50	1.455		110	98		208	267
4200	Center, 1 circuit		6	1.333		146	90		236	293
4220	2 circuit		5.50	1.455		151	98		249	310
4240	End cap		40	.200		17.80	13.45		31.25	39.50
4260	Hanger, surface mount		24	.333		10.60	22.50		33.10	45
4280	Coupling		40	.200		13.55	13.45		27	35

26 25 13.30 Copper Bus Duct		Crew	Daily Output	Labor-Hours	Unit	Material	Labor	Equipment	Total	Total Incl O&P
0010	**COPPER BUS DUCT**									
0100	Weatherproof 3 pole 4 wire, feeder duct, 600 amp	2 Elec	24	.667	L.F.	340	45		385	435
0110	800 amp		18	.889		645	60		705	800
0120	1,000 amp		17	.941		545	63.50		608.50	695
0125	1,200 amp		16.50	.970		595	65.50		660.50	750
0130	1,350 amp		16	1		660	67.50		727.50	830
0140	1,600 amp		12	1.333		700	90		790	905
0150	2,000 amp		10	1.600		850	108		958	1,100
0160	2,500 amp		7	2.286		970	154		1,124	1,300
0170	3,000 amp		5	3.200		1,275	216		1,491	1,750
0180	4,000 amp		3.60	4.444		1,975	299		2,274	2,625
0200	Indoor 3 pole 4 wire, plug-in, bus duct high short circuit, 400 amp		32	.500		490	33.50		523.50	590
0210	600 amp		26	.615		560	41.50		601.50	675
0220	800 amp		20	.800		815	54		869	975
0230	1,000 amp		18	.889		950	60		1,010	1,150

26 25 13 – Low-Voltage Busways

26 25 13.30 Copper Bus Duct		Crew	Daily Output	Labor-Hours	Unit	2023 Bare Costs Material	Labor	Equipment	Total	Total Incl O&P
0240	1,350 amp	2 Elec	16	1	L.F.	610	67.50		677.50	770
0250	1,600 amp		12	1.333		690	90		780	895
0260	2,000 amp		10	1.600		875	108		983	1,125
0270	2,500 amp		8	2		1,075	135		1,210	1,375
0280	3,000 amp		6	2.667		1,150	180		1,330	1,550
0310	Cross, 225 amp		3	5.333	Ea.	4,000	360		4,360	4,925
0320	400 amp		2.80	5.714		4,000	385		4,385	4,975
0330	600 amp		2.60	6.154		4,000	415		4,415	5,025
0340	800 amp		2.20	7.273		4,325	490		4,815	5,500
0350	1,000 amp		2	8		4,825	540		5,365	6,125
0360	1,350 amp		1.80	8.889		5,275	600		5,875	6,700
0370	1,600 amp		1.70	9.412		5,875	635		6,510	7,400
0380	2,000 amp		1.60	10		9,650	675		10,325	11,600
0390	2,500 amp		1.40	11.429		11,700	770		12,470	14,000
0400	3,000 amp		1.20	13.333		11,900	900		12,800	14,400
0410	4,000 amp		1	16		15,500	1,075		16,575	18,700
0430	Expansion fitting, 225 amp		5.40	2.963		2,475	200		2,675	3,025
0440	400 amp		4.60	3.478		2,800	234		3,034	3,425
0450	600 amp		4	4		3,475	269		3,744	4,225
0460	800 amp		3.40	4.706		4,075	315		4,390	4,950
0470	1,000 amp		3	5.333		4,700	360		5,060	5,675
0480	1,350 amp		2.80	5.714		4,800	385		5,185	5,875
0490	1,600 amp		2.60	6.154		6,700	415		7,115	8,000
0500	2,000 amp		2.20	7.273		7,725	490		8,215	9,225
0510	2,500 amp		1.80	8.889		9,400	600		10,000	11,200
0520	3,000 amp		1.60	10		9,825	675		10,500	11,800
0530	4,000 amp		1.20	13.333		12,700	900		13,600	15,200
0550	Reducer nonfused, 225 amp		5.40	2.963		2,350	200		2,550	2,900
0560	400 amp		4.60	3.478		2,350	234		2,584	2,950
0570	600 amp		4	4		2,350	269		2,619	3,000
0580	800 amp		3.40	4.706		2,850	315		3,165	3,625
0590	1,000 amp		3	5.333		3,425	360		3,785	4,300
0600	1,350 amp		2.80	5.714		5,175	385		5,560	6,275
0610	1,600 amp		2.60	6.154		5,950	415		6,365	7,175
0620	2,000 amp		2.20	7.273		7,150	490		7,640	8,600
0630	2,500 amp		1.80	8.889		9,025	600		9,625	10,800
0640	3,000 amp		1.60	10		9,275	675		9,950	11,200
0650	4,000 amp		1.20	13.333		12,100	900		13,000	14,600
0670	Reducer fuse included, 225 amp		4.40	3.636		5,050	245		5,295	5,925
0680	400 amp		4.20	3.810		6,325	257		6,582	7,325
0690	600 amp		3.60	4.444		7,775	299		8,074	9,025
0700	800 amp		3.20	5		11,000	335		11,335	12,600
0710	1,000 amp		3	5.333		13,800	360		14,160	15,700
0720	1,350 amp		2.80	5.714		17,000	385		17,385	19,300
0730	1,600 amp		2.20	7.273		30,400	490		30,890	34,200
0740	2,000 amp		1.80	8.889		34,200	600		34,800	38,600
0790	Reducer, circuit breaker, 225 amp		4.40	3.636		6,400	245		6,645	7,400
0800	400 amp		4.20	3.810		7,450	257		7,707	8,575
0810	600 amp		3.60	4.444		10,600	299		10,899	12,000
0820	800 amp		3.20	5		12,400	335		12,735	14,200
0830	1,000 amp		3	5.333		14,100	360		14,460	16,000
0840	1,350 amp		2.80	5.714		16,900	385		17,285	19,100
0850	1,600 amp		2.20	7.273		24,900	490		25,390	28,100

26 25 13 – Low-Voltage Busways

26 25 13.30 Copper Bus Duct		Crew	Daily Output	Labor-Hours	Unit	2023 Bare Costs Material	Labor	Equipment	Total	Total Incl O&P
0860	2,000 amp	2 Elec	1.80	8.889	Ea.	27,300	600		27,900	30,900
0910	Cable tap box, center, 225 amp		3.20	5		3,925	335		4,260	4,825
0920	400 amp		2.60	6.154		5,600	415		6,015	6,775
0930	600 amp		2.20	7.273		6,525	490		7,015	7,900
0940	800 amp		2	8		2,550	540		3,090	3,600
0950	1,000 amp		1.60	10		2,750	675		3,425	4,025
0960	1,350 amp		1.40	11.429		3,525	770		4,295	5,025
0970	1,600 amp		1.20	13.333		3,950	900		4,850	5,650
0980	2,000 amp		1	16		4,750	1,075		5,825	6,825
1040	2,500 amp		.80	20		5,625	1,350		6,975	8,175
1060	3,000 amp		.60	26.667		5,750	1,800		7,550	9,000
1080	4,000 amp		.40	40		7,225	2,700		9,925	12,000
1800	Weatherproof 3 pole 3 wire, feeder duct, 600 amp		28	.571	L.F.	355	38.50		393.50	445
1820	800 amp		22	.727		430	49		479	550
1840	1,000 amp		20	.800		480	54		534	610
1850	1,200 amp		19	.842		495	56.50		551.50	630
1860	1,350 amp		18	.889		685	60		745	840
1880	1,600 amp		14	1.143		780	77		857	975
1900	2,000 amp		12	1.333		1,000	90		1,090	1,225
1920	2,500 amp		8	2		1,250	135		1,385	1,575
1940	3,000 amp		6	2.667		1,350	180		1,530	1,750
1960	4,000 amp		4	4		1,775	269		2,044	2,350
2000	Indoor 3 pole 3 wire, feeder duct, 600 amp		32	.500		295	33.50		328.50	375
2010	800 amp		26	.615		1,150	41.50		1,191.50	1,300
2020	1,000 amp		24	.667		1,350	45		1,395	1,550
2025	1,200 amp		22	.727		1,750	49		1,799	2,000
2030	1,350 amp		20	.800		570	54		624	705
2040	1,600 amp		16	1		2,100	67.50		2,167.50	2,425
2050	2,000 amp		14	1.143		2,700	77		2,777	3,075
2060	2,500 amp		10	1.600		1,025	108		1,133	1,300
2070	3,000 amp		8	2		1,075	135		1,210	1,400
2080	4,000 amp		6	2.667		1,475	180		1,655	1,900
2090	5,000 amp		5	3.200		1,800	216		2,016	2,300
2200	Indoor 3 pole 3 wire, bus duct plug-in, 225 amp		46	.348		187	23.50		210.50	241
2210	400 amp		36	.444		283	30		313	355
2220	600 amp		30	.533		365	36		401	455
2230	800 amp		24	.667		530	45		575	650
2240	1,000 amp		20	.800		490	54		544	620
2250	1,350 amp		18	.889		870	60		930	1,050
2260	1,600 amp		14	1.143		925	77		1,002	1,150
2270	2,000 amp		12	1.333		3,000	90		3,090	3,425
2280	2,500 amp		10	1.600		1,075	108		1,183	1,325
2290	3,000 amp		8	2		1,150	135		1,285	1,475
2330	High short circuit, 400 amp		36	.444		340	30		370	420
2340	600 amp		30	.533		435	36		471	535
2350	800 amp		24	.667		635	45		680	765
2360	1,000 amp		20	.800		690	54		744	840
2370	1,350 amp		18	.889		1,050	60		1,110	1,250
2380	1,600 amp		14	1.143		1,100	77		1,177	1,350
2390	2,000 amp		12	1.333		875	90		965	1,100
2400	2,500 amp		10	1.600		1,075	108		1,183	1,325
2410	3,000 amp		8	2		1,150	135		1,285	1,475
2440	Elbows, 225 amp		4.60	3.478	Ea.	1,850	234		2,084	2,375

26 25 13.30 Copper Bus Duct		Crew	Daily Output	Labor-Hours	Unit	Material	Labor	Equipment	Total	Total Incl O&P
						2023 Bare Costs				
2450	400 amp	2 Elec	4.20	3.810	Ea.	2,125	257		2,382	2,725
2460	600 amp		3.60	4.444		2,375	299		2,674	3,050
2470	800 amp		3.20	5		2,900	335		3,235	3,675
2480	1,000 amp		3	5.333		3,125	360		3,485	3,950
2485	1,200 amp		2.90	5.517		6,725	370		7,095	7,950
2490	1,350 amp		2.80	5.714		4,325	385		4,710	5,325
2500	1,600 amp		2.60	6.154		4,475	415		4,890	5,550
2510	2,000 amp		2	8		8,900	540		9,440	10,600
2520	2,500 amp		1.80	8.889		11,400	600		12,000	13,500
2530	3,000 amp		1.60	10		11,500	675		12,175	13,700
2540	4,000 amp		1.40	11.429		5,675	770		6,445	7,400
2560	Tee fittings, 225 amp		2.80	5.714		3,550	385		3,935	4,475
2570	400 amp		2.40	6.667		2,000	450		2,450	2,850
2580	600 amp		2	8		6,925	540		7,465	8,425
2590	800 amp		1.80	8.889		2,175	600		2,775	3,275
2600	1,000 amp		1.60	10		2,425	675		3,100	3,650
2605	1,200 amp		1.50	10.667		2,575	720		3,295	3,925
2610	1,350 amp		1.40	11.429		2,750	770		3,520	4,175
2620	1,600 amp		1.20	13.333		3,200	900		4,100	4,825
2630	2,000 amp		1	16		5,300	1,075		6,375	7,425
2640	2,500 amp		.70	22.857		6,225	1,550		7,775	9,125
2650	3,000 amp		.60	26.667		6,400	1,800		8,200	9,700
2660	4,000 amp		.50	32		8,250	2,150		10,400	12,300
2680	Cross, 225 amp		3.60	4.444		3,025	299		3,324	3,775
2690	400 amp		3.20	5		3,025	335		3,360	3,825
2700	600 amp		3	5.333		3,025	360		3,385	3,850
2710	800 amp		2.60	6.154		3,625	415		4,040	4,600
2720	1,000 amp		2.40	6.667		3,800	450		4,250	4,850
2730	1,350 amp		2.20	7.273		4,400	490		4,890	5,550
2740	1,600 amp		2	8		4,725	540		5,265	6,000
2750	2,000 amp		1.80	8.889		7,475	600		8,075	9,125
2760	2,500 amp		1.60	10		8,700	675		9,375	10,600
2770	3,000 amp		1.40	11.429		8,900	770		9,670	10,900
2780	4,000 amp		1	16		11,400	1,075		12,475	14,100
2800	Expansion fitting, 225 amp		6.40	2.500		2,600	168		2,768	3,100
2810	400 amp		5.40	2.963		5,275	200		5,475	6,100
2820	600 amp		4.60	3.478		2,600	234		2,834	3,200
2830	800 amp		4	4		3,100	269		3,369	3,825
2840	1,000 amp		3.60	4.444		3,400	299		3,699	4,200
2850	1,350 amp		3.20	5		3,725	335		4,060	4,600
2860	1,600 amp		3	5.333		4,075	360		4,435	5,000
2870	2,000 amp		2.60	6.154		5,075	415		5,490	6,200
2880	2,500 amp		2.20	7.273		7,075	490		7,565	8,525
2890	3,000 amp		1.80	8.889		7,400	600		8,000	9,025
2900	4,000 amp		1.40	11.429		9,425	770		10,195	11,600
2920	Reducer nonfused, 225 amp		6.40	2.500		1,925	168		2,093	2,375
2930	400 amp		5.40	2.963		1,925	200		2,125	2,425
2940	600 amp		4.60	3.478		1,925	234		2,159	2,475
2950	800 amp		4	4		2,250	269		2,519	2,875
2960	1,000 amp		3.60	4.444		2,550	299		2,849	3,250
2970	1,350 amp		3.20	5		3,350	335		3,685	4,175
2980	1,600 amp		3	5.333		3,800	360		4,160	4,700
2990	2,000 amp		2.60	6.154		4,550	415		4,965	5,625

26 25 13.30 Copper Bus Duct		Crew	Daily Output	Labor-Hours	Unit	Material	2023 Bare Costs Labor	Equipment	Total	Total Incl O&P
3000	2,500 amp	2 Elec	2.20	7.273	Ea.	6,650	490		7,140	8,050
3010	3,000 amp		1.80	8.889		6,800	600		7,400	8,375
3020	4,000 amp		1.40	11.429		8,825	770		9,595	10,900
3040	Reducer fuse included, 225 amp		5	3.200		4,575	216		4,791	5,375
3050	400 amp		4.80	3.333		6,100	225		6,325	7,025
3060	600 amp		4.20	3.810		7,275	257		7,532	8,375
3070	800 amp		3.60	4.444		10,400	299		10,699	11,800
3080	1,000 amp		3.40	4.706		12,300	315		12,615	14,000
3090	1,350 amp		3.20	5		12,400	335		12,735	14,200
3100	1,600 amp		2.60	6.154		29,000	415		29,415	32,500
3110	2,000 amp		2	8		32,800	540		33,340	36,900
3160	Reducer circuit breaker, 225 amp		5	3.200		5,850	216		6,066	6,775
3170	400 amp		4.80	3.333		7,175	225		7,400	8,225
3180	600 amp		4.20	3.810		10,300	257		10,557	11,700
3190	800 amp		3.60	4.444		12,000	299		12,299	13,600
3200	1,000 amp		3.40	4.706		13,700	315		14,015	15,600
3210	1,350 amp		3.20	5		16,500	335		16,835	18,600
3220	1,600 amp		2.60	6.154		24,600	415		25,015	27,600
3230	2,000 amp		2	8		26,800	540		27,340	30,300
3280	3 pole, 3 wire, cable tap box center, 225 amp		3.60	4.444		2,250	299		2,549	2,925
3290	400 amp		3	5.333		4,250	360		4,610	5,200
3300	600 amp		2.60	6.154		7,975	415		8,390	9,400
3310	800 amp		2.40	6.667		7,250	450		7,700	8,650
3320	1,000 amp		1.80	8.889		7,625	600		8,225	9,300
3330	1,350 amp		1.60	10		11,200	675		11,875	13,300
3340	1,600 amp		1.40	11.429		11,800	770		12,570	14,200
3350	2,000 amp		1.20	13.333		5,625	900		6,525	7,500
3360	2,500 amp		1	16		6,700	1,075		7,775	8,975
3370	3,000 amp		.70	22.857		6,900	1,550		8,450	9,875
3380	4,000 amp		.50	32		8,750	2,150		10,900	12,800
3400	Cable tap box end, 225 amp		3.60	4.444		2,300	299		2,599	2,975
3410	400 amp		3	5.333		2,775	360		3,135	3,575
3420	600 amp		2.60	6.154		4,075	415		4,490	5,100
3430	800 amp		2.40	6.667		9,775	450		10,225	11,500
3440	1,000 amp		1.80	8.889		10,100	600		10,700	12,000
3445	1,200 amp		1.70	9.412		10,900	635		11,535	12,800
3450	1,350 amp		1.60	10		2,075	675		2,750	3,300
3460	1,600 amp		1.40	11.429		12,000	770		12,770	14,400
3470	2,000 amp		1.20	13.333		13,200	900		14,100	15,800
3480	2,500 amp		1	16		8,450	1,075		9,525	10,900
3490	3,000 amp		.70	22.857		3,550	1,550		5,100	6,225
3500	4,000 amp		.50	32		4,525	2,150		6,675	8,175
4600	Plug-in, fusible switch w/3 fuses, 3 pole, 250 volt, 30 amp	1 Elec	4	2		575	135		710	830
4610	60 amp		3.60	2.222		1,050	150		1,200	1,375
4620	100 amp		2.70	2.963		1,400	200		1,600	1,825
4630	200 amp	2 Elec	3.20	5		2,725	335		3,060	3,475
4640	400 amp		1.40	11.429		6,050	770		6,820	7,800
4650	600 amp		.90	17.778		8,450	1,200		9,650	11,100
4700	4 pole, 120/208 volt, 30 amp	1 Elec	3.90	2.051		785	138		923	1,075
4710	60 amp		3.50	2.286		845	154		999	1,150
4720	100 amp		2.60	3.077		1,450	207		1,657	1,875
4730	200 amp	2 Elec	3	5.333		2,700	360		3,060	3,475
4740	400 amp		1.30	12.308		6,450	830		7,280	8,300

26 25 13 – Low-Voltage Busways

26 25 13.30 Copper Bus Duct		Crew	Daily Output	Labor-Hours	Unit	Material	2023 Bare Costs Labor	Equipment	Total	Total Incl O&P
4750	600 amp	2 Elec	.80	20	Ea.	6,500	1,350		7,850	9,150
4800	3 pole, 480 volt, 30 amp	1 Elec	4	2		1,150	135		1,285	1,475
4810	60 amp		3.60	2.222		620	150		770	905
4820	100 amp		2.70	2.963		1,675	200		1,875	2,125
4830	200 amp	2 Elec	3.20	5		2,400	335		2,735	3,125
4840	400 amp		1.40	11.429		6,050	770		6,820	7,800
4850	600 amp		.90	17.778		5,975	1,200		7,175	8,350
4860	800 amp		.66	24.242		15,800	1,625		17,425	19,700
4870	1,000 amp		.60	26.667		21,900	1,800		23,700	26,800
4880	1,200 amp		.50	32		28,500	2,150		30,650	34,600
4890	1,600 amp		.44	36.364		28,700	2,450		31,150	35,300
4900	4 pole, 277/480 volt, 30 amp	1 Elec	3.90	2.051		850	138		988	1,150
4910	60 amp		3.50	2.286		905	154		1,059	1,225
4920	100 amp		2.60	3.077		1,775	207		1,982	2,250
4930	200 amp	2 Elec	3	5.333		2,850	360		3,210	3,650
4940	400 amp		1.30	12.308		6,475	830		7,305	8,350
4950	600 amp		.80	20		6,775	1,350		8,125	9,450
5050	800 amp		.60	26.667		17,800	1,800		19,600	22,300
5060	1,000 amp		.56	28.571		28,700	1,925		30,625	34,400
5070	1,200 amp		.48	33.333		30,200	2,250		32,450	36,500
5080	1,600 amp		.42	38.095		30,000	2,575		32,575	36,800
5150	Fusible with starter, 3 pole 250 volt, 30 amp	1 Elec	3.50	2.286		3,950	154		4,104	4,575
5160	60 amp		3.20	2.500		4,175	168		4,343	4,850
5170	100 amp		2.50	3.200		4,725	216		4,941	5,525
5180	200 amp	2 Elec	2.80	5.714		7,800	385		8,185	9,150
5200	3 pole 480 volt, 30 amp	1 Elec	3.50	2.286		3,950	154		4,104	4,575
5210	60 amp		3.20	2.500		4,175	168		4,343	4,850
5220	100 amp		2.50	3.200		4,725	216		4,941	5,525
5230	200 amp	2 Elec	2.80	5.714		7,800	385		8,185	9,150
5300	Fusible with contactor, 3 pole 250 volt, 30 amp	1 Elec	3.50	2.286		3,850	154		4,004	4,450
5310	60 amp		3.20	2.500		4,900	168		5,068	5,625
5320	100 amp		2.50	3.200		6,850	216		7,066	7,850
5330	200 amp	2 Elec	2.80	5.714		7,850	385		8,235	9,200
5400	3 pole 480 volt, 30 amp	1 Elec	3.50	2.286		4,150	154		4,304	4,775
5410	60 amp		3.20	2.500		5,850	168		6,018	6,675
5420	100 amp		2.50	3.200		8,025	216		8,241	9,150
5430	200 amp	2 Elec	2.80	5.714		8,200	385		8,585	9,600
5450	Fusible with capacitor, 3 pole 250 volt, 30 amp	1 Elec	3	2.667		10,000	180		10,180	11,300
5460	60 amp		2	4		11,600	269		11,869	13,200
5500	3 pole 480 volt, 30 amp		3	2.667		8,375	180		8,555	9,475
5510	60 amp		2	4		10,500	269		10,769	11,900
5600	Circuit breaker, 3 pole, 250 volt, 60 amp		4.50	1.778		1,925	120		2,045	2,300
5610	100 amp		3.20	2.500		990	168		1,158	1,350
5650	4 pole, 120/208 volt, 60 amp		4.40	1.818		910	122		1,032	1,175
5660	100 amp		3.10	2.581		1,075	174		1,249	1,450
5700	3 pole, 4 wire 277/480 volt, 60 amp		4.30	1.860		2,150	125		2,275	2,550
5710	100 amp		3	2.667		2,950	180		3,130	3,500
5720	225 amp	2 Elec	3.20	5		3,025	335		3,360	3,825
5730	400 amp		1.20	13.333		9,775	900		10,675	12,000
5740	600 amp		.96	16.667		16,000	1,125		17,125	19,300
5750	700 amp		.60	26.667		10,700	1,800		12,500	14,500
5760	800 amp		.60	26.667		10,700	1,800		12,500	14,500
5770	900 amp		.54	29.630		14,100	2,000		16,100	18,500

26 25 Low-Voltage Enclosed Bus Assemblies

26 25 13 – Low-Voltage Busways

26 25 13.30 Copper Bus Duct		Crew	Daily Output	Labor-Hours	Unit	2023 Bare Costs Material	Labor	Equipment	Total	Total Incl O&P
5780	1,000 amp	2 Elec	.54	29.630	Ea.	14,100	2,000		16,100	18,500
5790	1,200 amp		.42	38.095		16,900	2,575		19,475	22,400
5810	Circuit breaker w/HIC fuses, 3 pole 480 volt, 60 amp	1 Elec	4.40	1.818		1,550	122		1,672	1,875
5820	100 amp	″	3.10	2.581		1,700	174		1,874	2,125
5830	225 amp	2 Elec	3.40	4.706		5,400	315		5,715	6,425
5840	400 amp		1.40	11.429		8,575	770		9,345	10,600
5850	600 amp		1	16		8,675	1,075		9,750	11,200
5860	700 amp		.64	25		11,500	1,675		13,175	15,200
5870	800 amp		.64	25		11,500	1,675		13,175	15,200
5880	900 amp		.56	28.571		24,900	1,925		26,825	30,300
5890	1,000 amp		.56	28.571		24,900	1,925		26,825	30,300
5950	3 pole 4 wire 277/480 volt, 60 amp	1 Elec	4.30	1.860		1,550	125		1,675	1,875
5960	100 amp	″	3	2.667		1,700	180		1,880	2,150
5970	225 amp	2 Elec	3	5.333		5,400	360		5,760	6,475
5980	400 amp		1.10	14.545		8,575	980		9,555	10,900
5990	600 amp		.94	17.021		8,675	1,150		9,825	11,300
6000	700 amp		.58	27.586		11,500	1,850		13,350	15,500
6010	800 amp		.58	27.586		11,500	1,850		13,350	15,500
6020	900 amp		.52	30.769		24,900	2,075		26,975	30,500
6030	1,000 amp		.52	30.769		24,900	2,075		26,975	30,500
6040	1,200 amp		.40	40		24,900	2,700		27,600	31,400
6100	Circuit breaker with starter, 3 pole 250 volt, 60 amp	1 Elec	3.20	2.500		2,025	168		2,193	2,475
6110	100 amp	″	2.50	3.200		3,350	216		3,566	4,000
6120	225 amp	2 Elec	3	5.333		4,975	360		5,335	6,000
6130	3 pole 480 volt, 60 amp	1 Elec	3.20	2.500		2,425	168		2,593	2,900
6140	100 amp	″	2.50	3.200		3,350	216		3,566	4,000
6150	225 amp	2 Elec	3	5.333		4,175	360		4,535	5,125
6200	Circuit breaker with contactor, 3 pole 250 volt, 60 amp	1 Elec	3.20	2.500		2,275	168		2,443	2,775
6210	100 amp	″	2.50	3.200		3,100	216		3,316	3,750
6220	225 amp	2 Elec	3	5.333		4,625	360		4,985	5,600
6250	3 pole 480 volt, 60 amp	1 Elec	3.20	2.500		2,275	168		2,443	2,775
6260	100 amp	″	2.50	3.200		3,100	216		3,316	3,750
6270	225 amp	2 Elec	3	5.333		4,000	360		4,360	4,925
6300	Circuit breaker with capacitor, 3 pole 250 volt, 60 amp	1 Elec	2	4		13,100	269		13,369	14,800
6310	3 pole 480 volt, 60 amp		2	4		12,600	269		12,869	14,200
6400	Add control transformer with pilot light to above starter		16	.500		685	33.50		718.50	805
6410	Switch, fusible, mechanically held contactor optional		16	.500		1,825	33.50		1,858.50	2,050
6430	Circuit breaker, mechanically held contactor optional		16	.500		1,825	33.50		1,858.50	2,050
6450	Ground neutralizer, 3 pole		16	.500		83.50	33.50		117	142

26 25 13.40 Copper Bus Duct		Crew	Daily Output	Labor-Hours	Unit	Material	Labor	Equipment	Total	Total Incl O&P
0010	**COPPER BUS DUCT** 10′ long									
0050	Indoor 3 pole 4 wire, plug-in, straight section, 225 amp	2 Elec	40	.400	L.F.	243	27		270	305
1000	400 amp		32	.500		198	33.50		231.50	268
1500	600 amp		26	.615		465	41.50		506.50	570
2400	800 amp		20	.800		680	54		734	825
2450	1,000 amp		18	.889		335	60		395	455
2470	1,200 amp		17	.941		2,325	63.50		2,388.50	2,650
2500	1,350 amp		16	1		440	67.50		507.50	585
2510	1,600 amp		12	1.333		3,150	90		3,240	3,575
2520	2,000 amp		10	1.600		3,875	108		3,983	4,400
2530	2,500 amp		8	2		780	135		915	1,050
2540	3,000 amp		6	2.667		3,050	180		3,230	3,650

26 25 13.40 Copper Bus Duct		Crew	Daily Output	Labor-Hours	Unit	2023 Bare Costs Material	Labor	Equipment	Total	Total Incl O&P
2550	Feeder, 600 amp	2 Elec	28	.571	L.F.	221	38.50		259.50	300
2600	800 amp		22	.727		1,725	49		1,774	1,975
2700	1,000 amp		20	.800		2,025	54		2,079	2,300
2750	1,200 amp		19	.842		2,100	56.50		2,156.50	2,375
2800	1,350 amp		18	.889		415	60		475	545
2900	1,600 amp		14	1.143		2,825	77		2,902	3,250
3000	2,000 amp		12	1.333		4,000	90		4,090	4,525
3010	2,500 amp		8	2		750	135		885	1,025
3020	3,000 amp		6	2.667		910	180		1,090	1,275
3030	4,000 amp		4	4		1,200	269		1,469	1,725
3040	5,000 amp		2	8		1,475	540		2,015	2,400
3100	Elbows, 225 amp		4	4	Ea.	2,275	269		2,544	2,900
3200	400 amp		3.60	4.444		2,775	299		3,074	3,500
3300	600 amp		3.20	5		2,950	335		3,285	3,725
3400	800 amp		2.80	5.714		3,900	385		4,285	4,875
3500	1,000 amp		2.60	6.154		4,175	415		4,590	5,225
3550	1,200 amp		2.50	6.400		9,550	430		9,980	11,100
3600	1,350 amp		2.40	6.667		10,100	450		10,550	11,800
3700	1,600 amp		2.20	7.273		11,200	490		11,690	13,000
3800	2,000 amp		1.80	8.889		13,300	600		13,900	15,500
3810	2,500 amp		1.60	10		9,300	675		9,975	11,200
3820	3,000 amp		1.40	11.429		21,000	770		21,770	24,300
3830	4,000 amp		1.20	13.333		32,500	900		33,400	37,100
3840	5,000 amp		1	16		21,200	1,075		22,275	24,900
4000	End box, 225 amp		34	.471		82	31.50		113.50	138
4100	400 amp		32	.500		205	33.50		238.50	275
4200	600 amp		28	.571		205	38.50		243.50	282
4300	800 amp		26	.615		205	41.50		246.50	287
4400	1,000 amp		24	.667		121	45		166	200
4410	1,200 amp		23	.696		205	47		252	295
4500	1,350 amp		22	.727		191	49		240	284
4600	1,600 amp		20	.800		191	54		245	291
4700	2,000 amp		18	.889		235	60		295	345
4710	2,500 amp		16	1		235	67.50		302.50	360
4720	3,000 amp		14	1.143		234	77		311	370
4730	4,000 amp		12	1.333		283	90		373	445
4740	5,000 amp		10	1.600		283	108		391	470
4800	Cable tap box end, 225 amp		3.20	5		2,575	335		2,910	3,325
5000	400 amp		2.60	6.154		3,100	415		3,515	4,050
5100	600 amp		2.20	7.273		4,550	490		5,040	5,725
5200	800 amp		2	8		4,775	540		5,315	6,050
5300	1,000 amp		1.60	10		4,825	675		5,500	6,325
5350	1,200 amp		1.50	10.667		2,125	720		2,845	3,400
5400	1,350 amp		1.40	11.429		2,500	770		3,270	3,900
5500	1,600 amp		1.20	13.333		2,800	900		3,700	4,400
5600	2,000 amp		1	16		3,025	1,075		4,100	4,950
5610	2,500 amp		.80	20		3,375	1,350		4,725	5,700
5620	3,000 amp		.60	26.667		4,175	1,800		5,975	7,275
5630	4,000 amp		.40	40		4,700	2,700		7,400	9,150
5640	5,000 amp		.20	80		5,825	5,400		11,225	14,400
5700	Switchboard stub, 225 amp		5.40	2.963		1,275	200		1,475	1,700
5800	400 amp		4.60	3.478		1,425	234		1,659	1,900
5900	600 amp		4	4		1,500	269		1,769	2,050

26 25 13.40 Copper Bus Duct		Crew	Daily Output	Labor-Hours	Unit	2023 Bare Costs Material	Labor	Equipment	Total	Total Incl O&P
6000	800 amp	2 Elec	3.20	5	Ea.	1,825	335		2,160	2,500
6100	1,000 amp		3	5.333		2,125	360		2,485	2,850
6150	1,200 amp		2.80	5.714		2,475	385		2,860	3,300
6200	1,350 amp		2.60	6.154		2,550	415		2,965	3,425
6300	1,600 amp		2.40	6.667		2,875	450		3,325	3,850
6400	2,000 amp		2	8		3,500	540		4,040	4,650
6410	2,500 amp		1.80	8.889		4,250	600		4,850	5,575
6420	3,000 amp		1.60	10		4,950	675		5,625	6,425
6430	4,000 amp		1.40	11.429		6,425	770		7,195	8,225
6440	5,000 amp		1.20	13.333		7,875	900		8,775	10,000
6490	Tee fittings, 225 amp		2.40	6.667		3,675	450		4,125	4,725
6500	400 amp		2	8		3,675	540		4,215	4,850
6600	600 amp		1.80	8.889		3,675	600		4,275	4,950
6700	800 amp		1.60	10		2,525	675		3,200	3,775
6750	1,000 amp		1.40	11.429		2,800	770		3,570	4,225
6770	1,200 amp		1.30	12.308		3,150	830		3,980	4,675
6800	1,350 amp		1.20	13.333		3,250	900		4,150	4,900
7000	1,600 amp		1	16		3,700	1,075		4,775	5,675
7100	2,000 amp		.80	20		4,400	1,350		5,750	6,825
7110	2,500 amp		.60	26.667		5,400	1,800		7,200	8,625
7120	3,000 amp		.50	32		6,250	2,150		8,400	10,100
7130	4,000 amp		.40	40		8,025	2,700		10,725	12,800
7140	5,000 amp		.20	80		9,475	5,400		14,875	18,400
7200	Plug-in fusible switches w/3 fuses, 600 volt, 3 pole, 30 amp	1 Elec	4	2		895	135		1,030	1,175
7300	60 amp		3.60	2.222		1,000	150		1,150	1,325
7400	100 amp		2.70	2.963		2,375	200		2,575	2,925
7500	200 amp	2 Elec	3.20	5		3,725	335		4,060	4,600
7600	400 amp		1.40	11.429		8,050	770		8,820	10,000
7700	600 amp		.90	17.778		7,850	1,200		9,050	10,400
7800	800 amp		.66	24.242		13,000	1,625		14,625	16,700
7900	1,200 amp		.50	32		24,400	2,150		26,550	30,100
7910	1,600 amp		.44	36.364		23,900	2,450		26,350	30,000
8000	Plug-in circuit breakers, molded case, 15 to 50 amp	1 Elec	4.40	1.818		850	122		972	1,125
8100	70 to 100 amp	"	3.10	2.581		940	174		1,114	1,275
8200	150 to 225 amp	2 Elec	3.40	4.706		2,550	315		2,865	3,275
8300	250 to 400 amp		1.40	11.429		4,475	770		5,245	6,075
8400	500 to 600 amp		1	16		6,050	1,075		7,125	8,250
8500	700 to 800 amp		.64	25		7,450	1,675		9,125	10,700
8600	900 to 1,000 amp		.56	28.571		10,700	1,925		12,625	14,600
8700	1,200 amp		.44	36.364		12,800	2,450		15,250	17,800
8720	1,400 amp		.40	40		18,400	2,700		21,100	24,200
8730	1,600 amp		.40	40		20,200	2,700		22,900	26,200
8750	Circuit breakers, with current limiting fuse, 15 to 50 amp	1 Elec	4.40	1.818		1,700	122		1,822	2,050
8760	70 to 100 amp	"	3.10	2.581		2,000	174		2,174	2,475
8770	150 to 225 amp	2 Elec	3.40	4.706		4,325	315		4,640	5,225
8780	250 to 400 amp		1.40	11.429		6,675	770		7,445	8,500
8790	500 to 600 amp		1	16		7,700	1,075		8,775	10,100
8800	700 to 800 amp		.64	25		12,600	1,675		14,275	16,400
8810	900 to 1,000 amp		.56	28.571		14,400	1,925		16,325	18,800
8850	Combination starter FVNR, fusible switch, NEMA size 0, 30 amp	1 Elec	2	4		2,275	269		2,544	2,900
8860	NEMA size 1, 60 amp		1.80	4.444		2,425	299		2,724	3,100
8870	NEMA size 2, 100 amp		1.30	6.154		3,050	415		3,465	3,975
8880	NEMA size 3, 200 amp	2 Elec	2	8		4,875	540		5,415	6,150

26 25 Low-Voltage Enclosed Bus Assemblies

26 25 13 – Low-Voltage Busways

26 25 13.40 Copper Bus Duct		Crew	Daily Output	Labor-Hours	Unit	Material	2023 Bare Costs Labor	Equipment	Total	Total Incl O&P
8900	Circuit breaker, NEMA size 0, 30 amp	1 Elec	2	4	Ea.	2,350	269		2,619	2,975
8910	NEMA size 1, 60 amp		1.80	4.444		2,425	299		2,724	3,125
8920	NEMA size 2, 100 amp		1.30	6.154		3,500	415		3,915	4,475
8930	NEMA size 3, 200 amp	2 Elec	2	8		4,450	540		4,990	5,675
8950	Combination contactor, fusible switch, NEMA size 0, 30 amp	1 Elec	2	4		1,325	269		1,594	1,875
8960	NEMA size 1, 60 amp		1.80	4.444		1,375	299		1,674	1,975
8970	NEMA size 2, 100 amp		1.30	6.154		2,050	415		2,465	2,875
8980	NEMA size 3, 200 amp	2 Elec	2	8		2,350	540		2,890	3,400
9000	Circuit breaker, NEMA size 0, 30 amp	1 Elec	2	4		1,525	269		1,794	2,075
9010	NEMA size 1, 60 amp		1.80	4.444		1,575	299		1,874	2,175
9020	NEMA size 2, 100 amp		1.30	6.154		2,425	415		2,840	3,300
9030	NEMA size 3, 200 amp	2 Elec	2	8		2,950	540		3,490	4,050
9050	Control transformer for above, NEMA size 0, 30 amp	1 Elec	8	1		259	67.50		326.50	385
9060	NEMA size 1, 60 amp		8	1		259	67.50		326.50	385
9070	NEMA size 2, 100 amp		7	1.143		360	77		437	515
9080	NEMA size 3, 200 amp	2 Elec	14	1.143		505	77		582	670
9100	Comb. fusible switch & lighting control, electrically held, 30 amp	1 Elec	2	4		1,050	269		1,319	1,575
9110	60 amp		1.80	4.444		1,525	299		1,824	2,125
9120	100 amp		1.30	6.154		1,975	415		2,390	2,775
9130	200 amp	2 Elec	2	8		4,825	540		5,365	6,125
9150	Mechanically held, 30 amp	1 Elec	2	4		1,325	269		1,594	1,850
9160	60 amp		1.80	4.444		1,975	299		2,274	2,625
9170	100 amp		1.30	6.154		2,550	415		2,965	3,425
9180	200 amp	2 Elec	2	8		5,175	540		5,715	6,500
9200	Ground bus added to bus duct, 225 amp		320	.050	L.F.	48.50	3.37		51.87	58
9210	400 amp		240	.067		48.50	4.49		52.99	59.50
9220	600 amp		240	.067		48.50	4.49		52.99	59.50
9230	800 amp		160	.100		56.50	6.75		63.25	72
9240	1,000 amp		160	.100		64.50	6.75		71.25	81
9250	1,350 amp		140	.114		90.50	7.70		98.20	111
9260	1,600 amp		120	.133		98	9		107	121
9270	2,000 amp		110	.145		128	9.80		137.80	156
9280	2,500 amp		100	.160		158	10.80		168.80	190
9290	3,000 amp		90	.178		187	11.95		198.95	224
9300	4,000 amp		80	.200		247	13.45		260.45	292
9310	5,000 amp		70	.229		297	15.40		312.40	350
9320	High short circuit bracing, add					19.90			19.90	22

26 25 13.60 Copper or Aluminum Bus Duct Fittings		Crew	Daily Output	Labor-Hours	Unit	Material	Labor	Equipment	Total	Total Incl O&P
0010	**COPPER OR ALUMINUM BUS DUCT FITTINGS**									
0100	Flange, wall, with vapor barrier, 225 amp	2 Elec	6.20	2.581	Ea.	945	174		1,119	1,300
0110	400 amp		6	2.667		840	180		1,020	1,200
0120	600 amp		5.80	2.759		945	186		1,131	1,325
0130	800 amp		5.40	2.963		945	200		1,145	1,350
0140	1,000 amp		5	3.200		945	216		1,161	1,375
0145	1,200 amp		4.80	3.333		945	225		1,170	1,375
0150	1,350 amp		4.60	3.478		945	234		1,179	1,400
0160	1,600 amp		4.20	3.810		945	257		1,202	1,425
0170	2,000 amp		4	4		945	269		1,214	1,450
0180	2,500 amp		3.60	4.444		945	299		1,244	1,500
0190	3,000 amp		3.20	5		945	335		1,280	1,550
0200	4,000 amp		2.60	6.154		910	415		1,325	1,625
0300	Roof, 225 amp		6.20	2.581		1,200	174		1,374	1,550

26 25 Low-Voltage Enclosed Bus Assemblies

26 25 13 – Low-Voltage Busways

26 25 13.60 Copper or Aluminum Bus Duct Fittings		Crew	Daily Output	Labor-Hours	Unit	2023 Bare Costs Material	Labor	Equipment	Total	Total Incl O&P
0310	400 amp	2 Elec	6	2.667	Ea.	1,200	180		1,380	1,575
0320	600 amp		5.80	2.759		1,200	186		1,386	1,575
0330	800 amp		5.40	2.963		1,200	200		1,400	1,600
0340	1,000 amp		5	3.200		1,200	216		1,416	1,625
0345	1,200 amp		4.80	3.333		1,200	225		1,425	1,625
0350	1,350 amp		4.60	3.478		1,200	234		1,434	1,650
0360	1,600 amp		4.20	3.810		1,200	257		1,457	1,675
0370	2,000 amp		4	4		1,200	269		1,469	1,700
0380	2,500 amp		3.60	4.444		1,200	299		1,499	1,750
0390	3,000 amp		3.20	5		1,200	335		1,535	1,800
0400	4,000 amp		2.60	6.154		1,200	415		1,615	1,925
0420	Support, floor mounted, 225 amp		20	.800		188	54		242	287
0430	400 amp		20	.800		188	54		242	287
0440	600 amp		18	.889		188	60		248	296
0450	800 amp		16	1		188	67.50		255.50	305
0460	1,000 amp		13	1.231		188	83		271	330
0465	1,200 amp		11.80	1.356		188	91.50		279.50	345
0470	1,350 amp		10.60	1.509		188	102		290	360
0480	1,600 amp		9.20	1.739		188	117		305	380
0490	2,000 amp		8	2		188	135		323	405
0500	2,500 amp		6.40	2.500		188	168		356	455
0510	3,000 amp		5.40	2.963		188	200		388	505
0520	4,000 amp		4	4		188	269		457	605
0540	Weather stop, 225 amp		12	1.333		560	90		650	750
0550	400 amp		10	1.600		560	108		668	775
0560	600 amp		9	1.778		560	120		680	795
0570	800 amp		8	2		560	135		695	815
0580	1,000 amp		6.40	2.500		560	168		728	865
0585	1,200 amp		5.90	2.712		560	183		743	885
0590	1,350 amp		5.40	2.963		560	200		760	910
0600	1,600 amp		4.60	3.478		560	234		794	965
0610	2,000 amp		4	4		560	269		829	1,025
0620	2,500 amp		3.20	5		560	335		895	1,125
0630	3,000 amp		2.60	6.154		560	415		975	1,225
0640	4,000 amp		2	8		560	540		1,100	1,425
0660	End closure, 225 amp		34	.471		900	31.50		931.50	1,025
0670	400 amp		32	.500		1,125	33.50		1,158.50	1,275
0680	600 amp		28	.571		880	38.50		918.50	1,025
0690	800 amp		26	.615		192	41.50		233.50	273
0700	1,000 amp		24	.667		850	45		895	1,000
0705	1,200 amp		23	.696		890	47		937	1,050
0710	1,350 amp		22	.727		790	49		839	945
0720	1,600 amp		20	.800		900	54		954	1,075
0730	2,000 amp		18	.889		1,175	60		1,235	1,375
0740	2,500 amp		16	1		1,025	67.50		1,092.50	1,225
0750	3,000 amp		14	1.143		1,000	77		1,077	1,225
0760	4,000 amp		12	1.333		1,300	90		1,390	1,550
0780	Switchboard stub, 3 pole 3 wire, 225 amp		6	2.667		1,125	180		1,305	1,525
0790	400 amp		5.20	3.077		1,125	207		1,332	1,550
0800	600 amp		4.60	3.478		1,125	234		1,359	1,600
0810	800 amp		3.60	4.444		1,375	299		1,674	1,950
0820	1,000 amp		3.40	4.706		1,600	315		1,915	2,225
0825	1,200 amp		3.20	5		1,600	335		1,935	2,250

26 25 13.60 Copper or Aluminum Bus Duct Fittings		Crew	Daily Output	Labor-Hours	Unit	2023 Bare Costs Material	Labor	Equipment	Total	Total Incl O&P
0830	1,350 amp	2 Elec	3	5.333	Ea.	1,900	360		2,260	2,625
0840	1,600 amp		2.80	5.714		2,250	385		2,635	3,050
0850	2,000 amp		2.40	6.667		2,625	450		3,075	3,550
0860	2,500 amp		2	8		3,200	540		3,740	4,325
0870	3,000 amp		1.80	8.889		3,650	600		4,250	4,900
0880	4,000 amp		1.60	10		4,700	675		5,375	6,175
0890	5,000 amp		1.40	11.429		5,825	770		6,595	7,575
0900	3 pole 4 wire, 225 amp		5.40	2.963		1,400	200		1,600	1,850
0910	400 amp		4.60	3.478		1,400	234		1,634	1,900
0920	600 amp		4	4		1,400	269		1,669	1,950
0930	800 amp		3.20	5		1,675	335		2,010	2,350
0940	1,000 amp		3	5.333		1,975	360		2,335	2,700
0950	1,350 amp		2.60	6.154		2,525	415		2,940	3,400
0960	1,600 amp		2.40	6.667		2,875	450		3,325	3,850
0970	2,000 amp		2	8		3,450	540		3,990	4,600
0980	2,500 amp		1.80	8.889		4,250	600		4,850	5,575
0990	3,000 amp		1.60	10		4,925	675		5,600	6,425
1000	4,000 amp		1.40	11.429		6,450	770		7,220	8,250
1050	Service head, weatherproof, 3 pole 3 wire, 225 amp		3	5.333		1,900	360		2,260	2,625
1060	400 amp		2.80	5.714		1,900	385		2,285	2,675
1070	600 amp		2.60	6.154		1,900	415		2,315	2,725
1080	800 amp		2.40	6.667		2,150	450		2,600	3,025
1090	1,000 amp		2	8		2,325	540		2,865	3,350
1100	1,350 amp		1.80	8.889		3,000	600		3,600	4,200
1110	1,600 amp		1.60	10		3,375	675		4,050	4,700
1120	2,000 amp		1.40	11.429		4,125	770		4,895	5,700
1130	2,500 amp		1.20	13.333		4,925	900		5,825	6,750
1140	3,000 amp		.90	17.778		5,700	1,200		6,900	8,025
1150	4,000 amp		.70	22.857		7,250	1,550		8,800	10,300
1200	3 pole 4 wire, 225 amp		2.60	6.154		2,125	415		2,540	2,975
1210	400 amp		2.40	6.667		2,125	450		2,575	3,025
1220	600 amp		2.20	7.273		2,125	490		2,615	3,075
1230	800 amp		2	8		2,475	540		3,015	3,525
1240	1,000 amp		1.70	9.412		2,850	635		3,485	4,100
1250	1,350 amp		1.50	10.667		3,400	720		4,120	4,800
1260	1,600 amp		1.40	11.429		3,725	770		4,495	5,250
1270	2,000 amp		1.20	13.333		4,950	900		5,850	6,775
1280	2,500 amp		1	16		6,100	1,075		7,175	8,300
1290	3,000 amp		.80	20		7,200	1,350		8,550	9,925
1300	4,000 amp		.60	26.667		9,250	1,800		11,050	12,900
1350	Flanged end, 3 pole 3 wire, 225 amp		6	2.667		1,050	180		1,230	1,425
1360	400 amp		5.20	3.077		1,050	207		1,257	1,450
1370	600 amp		4.60	3.478		1,050	234		1,284	1,500
1380	800 amp		3.60	4.444		1,150	299		1,449	1,725
1390	1,000 amp		3.40	4.706		1,300	315		1,615	1,900
1395	1,200 amp		3.20	5		1,450	335		1,785	2,100
1400	1,350 amp		3	5.333		1,550	360		1,910	2,225
1410	1,600 amp		2.80	5.714		1,750	385		2,135	2,525
1420	2,000 amp		2.40	6.667		2,100	450		2,550	2,975
1430	2,500 amp		2	8		2,425	540		2,965	3,475
1440	3,000 amp		1.80	8.889		2,775	600		3,375	3,950
1450	4,000 amp		1.60	10		3,425	675		4,100	4,775
1500	3 pole 4 wire, 225 amp		5.40	2.963		1,200	200		1,400	1,625

26 25 13 – Low-Voltage Busways

26 25 13.60 Copper or Aluminum Bus Duct Fittings		Crew	Daily Output	Labor-Hours	Unit	2023 Bare Costs Material	Labor	Equipment	Total	Total Incl O&P
1510	400 amp	2 Elec	4.60	3.478	Ea.	1,200	234		1,434	1,675
1520	600 amp		4	4		1,200	269		1,469	1,725
1530	800 amp		3.20	5		1,425	335		1,760	2,050
1540	1,000 amp		3	5.333		1,575	360		1,935	2,250
1545	1,200 amp		2.80	5.714		1,800	385		2,185	2,550
1550	1,350 amp		2.60	6.154		1,925	415		2,340	2,725
1560	1,600 amp		2.40	6.667		2,200	450		2,650	3,100
1570	2,000 amp		2	8		2,600	540		3,140	3,675
1580	2,500 amp		1.80	8.889		3,075	600		3,675	4,300
1590	3,000 amp		1.60	10		3,550	675		4,225	4,900
1600	4,000 amp		1.40	11.429		4,600	770		5,370	6,200
1650	Hanger, standard, 225 amp		64	.250		130	16.85		146.85	168
1660	400 amp		48	.333		134	22.50		156.50	181
1670	600 amp		40	.400		129	27		156	182
1680	800 amp		32	.500		165	33.50		198.50	231
1690	1,000 amp		24	.667		130	45		175	210
1695	1,200 amp		22	.727		126	49		175	211
1700	1,350 amp		20	.800		63	54		117	150
1710	1,600 amp		20	.800		114	54		168	205
1720	2,000 amp		18	.889		130	60		190	232
1730	2,500 amp		16	1		114	67.50		181.50	225
1740	3,000 amp		16	1		114	67.50		181.50	225
1750	4,000 amp		16	1		109	67.50		176.50	220
1800	Spring type, 225 amp		16	1		97.50	67.50		165	208
1810	400 amp		14	1.143		97.50	77		174.50	222
1820	600 amp		14	1.143		97.50	77		174.50	222
1830	800 amp		14	1.143		97.50	77		174.50	222
1840	1,000 amp		14	1.143		97.50	77		174.50	222
1845	1,200 amp		14	1.143		97.50	77		174.50	222
1850	1,350 amp		14	1.143		97.50	77		174.50	222
1860	1,600 amp		12	1.333		97.50	90		187.50	241
1870	2,000 amp		12	1.333		97.50	90		187.50	241
1880	2,500 amp		12	1.333		97.50	90		187.50	241
1890	3,000 amp		10	1.600		97.50	108		205.50	268
1900	4,000 amp		10	1.600		97.50	108		205.50	268

26 25 13.70 Feedrail		Crew	Daily Output	Labor-Hours	Unit	Material	Labor	Equipment	Total	Total Incl O&P
0010	**FEEDRAIL**, 12′ mounting									
0050	Trolley busway, 3 pole									
0100	300 volt 60 amp, plain, 10′ lengths	1 Elec	50	.160	L.F.	24.50	10.80		35.30	43
0300	Door track		50	.160		47	10.80		57.80	68
0500	Curved track		30	.267		22.50	17.95		40.45	51
0700	Coupling				Ea.	15			15	16.50
0900	Center feed	1 Elec	5.30	1.509		50.50	102		152.50	207
1100	End feed		5.30	1.509		45	102		147	201
1300	Hanger set		24	.333		3.11	22.50		25.61	37
3000	600 volt 100 amp, plain, 10′ lengths		35	.229	L.F.	66.50	15.40		81.90	96
3300	Door track		35	.229	"	102	15.40		117.40	136
3700	Coupling				Ea.	53.50			53.50	58.50
4000	End cap	1 Elec	40	.200		71.50	13.45		84.95	98.50
4200	End feed		4	2		242	135		377	465
4500	Trolley, 600 volt, 20 amp		5.30	1.509		293	102		395	470
4700	30 amp		5.30	1.509		293	102		395	470

26 25 Low-Voltage Enclosed Bus Assemblies

26 25 13 – Low-Voltage Busways

26 25 13.70 Feedrail		Crew	Daily Output	Labor-Hours	Unit	Material	2023 Bare Costs Labor	Equipment	Total	Total Incl O&P
4900	Duplex, 40 amp	1 Elec	4	2	Ea.	900	135		1,035	1,200
5000	60 amp		4	2		890	135		1,025	1,175
5300	Fusible, 20 amp		4	2		670	135		805	935
5500	30 amp		4	2		670	135		805	935
5900	300 volt, 20 amp		5.30	1.509		275	102		377	455
6000	30 amp		5.30	1.509		370	102		472	555
6300	Fusible, 20 amp		4.70	1.702		385	115		500	590
6500	30 amp		4.70	1.702		535	115		650	755
7300	Busway, 250 volt 50 amp, 2 wire		70	.114	L.F.	22	7.70		29.70	35.50
7330	Coupling				Ea.	48			48	52.50
7340	Center feed	1 Elec	6	1.333		565	90		655	755
7350	End feed		6	1.333		131	90		221	277
7360	End cap		40	.200		32	13.45		45.45	55
7370	Hanger set		24	.333		3.68	22.50		26.18	37.50
7400	125/250 volt 50 amp, 3 wire		60	.133	L.F.	22.50	9		31.50	38
7430	Coupling		6	1.333	Ea.	66.50	90		156.50	206
7440	Center feed		6	1.333		555	90		645	745
7450	End feed		6	1.333		125	90		215	271
7460	End cap		40	.200		31.50	13.45		44.95	55
7470	Hanger set		24	.333		5.25	22.50		27.75	39.50
7480	Trolley, 250 volt, 2 pole, 20 amp		6	1.333		44.50	90		134.50	182
7490	30 amp		6	1.333		44.50	90		134.50	182
7500	125/250 volt, 3 pole, 20 amp		6	1.333		39.50	90		129.50	177
7510	30 amp		6	1.333		39.50	90		129.50	177
8000	Cleaning tools, 300 volt, dust remover					117			117	128
8100	Bus bar cleaner					218			218	240
8300	600 volt, dust remover, 60 amp					335			335	370
8400	100 amp					870			870	955
8600	Bus bar cleaner, 60 amp					825			825	905
8700	100 amp					1,075			1,075	1,175

26 27 Low-Voltage Distribution Equipment

26 27 13 – Electricity Metering

26 27 13.10 Meter Centers and Sockets

		Crew	Daily Output	Labor-Hours	Unit	Material	Labor	Equipment	Total	Total Incl O&P
0010	**METER CENTERS AND SOCKETS**									
0100	Sockets, single position, 4 terminal, 100 amp	1 Elec	3.20	2.500	Ea.	85.50	168		253.50	345
0200	150 amp		2.30	3.478		76	234		310	435
0300	200 amp		1.90	4.211		225	284		509	665
0400	Transformer rated, 20 amp		3.20	2.500		271	168		439	550
0500	Double position, 4 terminal, 100 amp		2.80	2.857		360	192		552	685
0600	150 amp		2.10	3.810		380	257		637	800
0700	200 amp		1.70	4.706		735	315		1,050	1,275
0800	Trans-socket, 13 terminal, 3 CT mounts, 400 amp		1	8		1,525	540		2,065	2,475
0900	800 amp	2 Elec	1.20	13.333		2,025	900		2,925	3,550
1100	Meter centers and sockets, three phase, single pos, 7 terminal, 100 amp	1 Elec	2.80	2.857		183	192		375	485
1200	200 amp		2.10	3.810		370	257		627	785
1400	400 amp		1.70	4.706		3,300	315		3,615	4,100
2000	Meter center, main fusible switch, 1P 3W 120/240 V									
2030	400 amp	2 Elec	1.60	10	Ea.	1,550	675		2,225	2,725
2040	600 amp		1.10	14.545		2,550	980		3,530	4,275
2050	800 amp		.90	17.778		3,125	1,200		4,325	5,200

26 27 13 – Electricity Metering

26 27 13.10 Meter Centers and Sockets		Crew	Daily Output	Labor-Hours	Unit	Material	2023 Bare Costs Labor	Equipment	Total	Total Incl O&P
2060	Rainproof 1P 3W 120/240 V, 400 A	2 Elec	1.60	10	Ea.	1,525	675		2,200	2,675
2070	600 amp		1.10	14.545		2,650	980		3,630	4,375
2080	800 amp		.90	17.778		3,400	1,200		4,600	5,525
2100	3P 4W 120/208 V, 400 amp		1.60	10		1,625	675		2,300	2,800
2110	600 amp		1.10	14.545		2,875	980		3,855	4,625
2120	800 amp		.90	17.778		3,700	1,200		4,900	5,850
2130	Rainproof 3P 4W 120/208 V, 400 amp		1.60	10		1,700	675		2,375	2,875
2140	600 amp		1.10	14.545		3,175	980		4,155	4,950
2150	800 amp		.90	17.778		4,400	1,200		5,600	6,600
2170	Main circuit breaker, 1P 3W 120/240 V									
2180	400 amp	2 Elec	1.60	10	Ea.	1,850	675		2,525	3,050
2190	600 amp		1.10	14.545		2,425	980		3,405	4,100
2200	800 amp		.90	17.778		4,900	1,200		6,100	7,175
2210	1,000 amp		.80	20		6,125	1,350		7,475	8,725
2220	1,200 amp		.76	21.053		6,325	1,425		7,750	9,050
2230	1,600 amp		.68	23.529		9,500	1,575		11,075	12,900
2240	Rainproof 1P 3W 120/240 V, 400 amp		1.60	10		2,350	675		3,025	3,575
2250	600 amp		1.10	14.545		3,250	980		4,230	5,025
2260	800 amp		.90	17.778		4,325	1,200		5,525	6,525
2270	1,000 amp		.80	20		6,000	1,350		7,350	8,600
2280	1,200 amp		.76	21.053		7,725	1,425		9,150	10,600
2300	3P 4W 120/208 V, 400 amp		1.60	10		2,525	675		3,200	3,775
2310	600 amp		1.10	14.545		3,900	980		4,880	5,725
2320	800 amp		.90	17.778		5,175	1,200		6,375	7,475
2330	1,000 amp		.80	20		6,475	1,350		7,825	9,100
2340	1,200 amp		.76	21.053		8,775	1,425		10,200	11,800
2350	1,600 amp		.68	23.529		14,600	1,575		16,175	18,500
2360	Rainproof 3P 4W 120/208 V, 400 amp		1.60	10		2,525	675		3,200	3,775
2370	600 amp		1.10	14.545		3,900	980		4,880	5,725
2380	800 amp		.90	17.778		5,175	1,200		6,375	7,475
2390	1,000 amp		.76	21.053		6,475	1,425		7,900	9,200
2400	1,200 amp		.68	23.529		8,775	1,575		10,350	12,000
2420	Main lugs terminal box, 1P 3W 120/240 V									
2430	800 amp	2 Elec	.94	17.021	Ea.	750	1,150		1,900	2,525
2440	1,200 amp		.72	22.222		1,300	1,500		2,800	3,675
2450	Rainproof 1P 3W 120/240 V, 225 amp		2.40	6.667		305	450		755	1,000
2460	800 amp		.94	17.021		470	1,150		1,620	2,225
2470	1,200 amp		.72	22.222		1,375	1,500		2,875	3,725
2500	3P 4W 120/208 V, 800 amp		.94	17.021		550	1,150		1,700	2,300
2510	1,200 amp		.72	22.222		1,875	1,500		3,375	4,300
2520	Rainproof 3P 4W 120/208 V, 225 amp		2.40	6.667		385	450		835	1,100
2530	800 amp		.94	17.021		550	1,150		1,700	2,300
2540	1,200 amp		.72	22.222		1,375	1,500		2,875	3,725
2590	Basic meter device									
2600	1P 3W 120/240 V 4 jaw 125A sockets, 3 meter	2 Elec	1	16	Ea.	575	1,075		1,650	2,225
2610	4 meter		.90	17.778		775	1,200		1,975	2,625
2620	5 meter		.80	20		1,125	1,350		2,475	3,225
2630	6 meter		.60	26.667		965	1,800		2,765	3,725
2640	7 meter		.56	28.571		2,125	1,925		4,050	5,175
2650	8 meter		.52	30.769		2,300	2,075		4,375	5,625
2660	10 meter		.48	33.333		2,900	2,250		5,150	6,500
2680	Rainproof 1P 3W 120/240 V 4 jaw 125A sockets									
2690	3 meter	2 Elec	1	16	Ea.	550	1,075		1,625	2,200

26 27 13.10 Meter Centers and Sockets		Crew	Daily Output	Labor-Hours	Unit	Material	Labor	Equipment	Total	Total Incl O&P
						2023 Bare Costs				
2700	4 meter	2 Elec	.90	17.778	Ea.	730	1,200		1,930	2,575
2710	6 meter		.60	26.667		1,050	1,800		2,850	3,850
2720	7 meter		.56	28.571		2,125	1,925		4,050	5,175
2730	8 meter		.52	30.769		2,300	2,075		4,375	5,625
2750	1P 3W 120/240 V 4 jaw sockets									
2760	with 125A circuit breaker, 3 meter	2 Elec	1	16	Ea.	1,800	1,075		2,875	3,575
2770	4 meter		.90	17.778		2,275	1,200		3,475	4,275
2780	5 meter		.80	20		2,850	1,350		4,200	5,125
2790	6 meter		.60	26.667		3,350	1,800		5,150	6,350
2800	7 meter		.56	28.571		4,075	1,925		6,000	7,350
2810	8 meter		.52	30.769		4,550	2,075		6,625	8,075
2820	10 meter		.48	33.333		5,700	2,250		7,950	9,600
2830	Rainproof 1P 3W 120/240 V 4 jaw sockets									
2840	with 125A circuit breaker, 3 meter	2 Elec	1	16	Ea.	1,800	1,075		2,875	3,575
2850	4 meter		.90	17.778		2,275	1,200		3,475	4,275
2870	6 meter		.60	26.667		3,350	1,800		5,150	6,350
2880	7 meter		.56	28.571		4,075	1,925		6,000	7,350
2890	8 meter		.52	30.769		4,550	2,075		6,625	8,075
2920	1P 3W on 3P 4W 120/208 V system 5 jaw									
2930	125A sockets, 3 meter	2 Elec	1	16	Ea.	965	1,075		2,040	2,650
2940	4 meter		.90	17.778		775	1,200		1,975	2,625
2950	5 meter		.80	20		985	1,350		2,335	3,075
2960	6 meter		.60	26.667		1,150	1,800		2,950	3,925
2970	7 meter		.56	28.571		2,125	1,925		4,050	5,175
2980	8 meter		.52	30.769		2,300	2,075		4,375	5,625
2990	10 meter		.48	33.333		2,900	2,250		5,150	6,500
3000	Rainproof 1P 3W on 3P 4W 120/208 V system									
3020	5 jaw 125A sockets, 3 meter	2 Elec	1	16	Ea.	965	1,075		2,040	2,650
3030	4 meter		.90	17.778		1,150	1,200		2,350	3,050
3050	6 meter		.60	26.667		1,675	1,800		3,475	4,500
3060	7 meter		.56	28.571		2,125	1,925		4,050	5,175
3070	8 meter		.52	30.769		2,300	2,075		4,375	5,625
3090	1P 3W on 3P 4W 120/208 V system 5 jaw sockets									
3100	With 125A circuit breaker, 3 meter	2 Elec	1	16	Ea.	1,800	1,075		2,875	3,575
3110	4 meter		.90	17.778		2,275	1,200		3,475	4,275
3120	5 meter		.80	20		2,850	1,350		4,200	5,125
3130	6 meter		.60	26.667		3,350	1,800		5,150	6,350
3140	7 meter		.56	28.571		4,075	1,925		6,000	7,350
3150	8 meter		.52	30.769		4,550	2,075		6,625	8,075
3160	10 meter		.48	33.333		5,700	2,250		7,950	9,600
3170	Rainproof 1P 3W on 3P 4W 120/208 V system									
3180	5 jaw sockets w/125A circuit breaker, 3 meter	2 Elec	1	16	Ea.	1,800	1,075		2,875	3,575
3190	4 meter		.90	17.778		2,275	1,200		3,475	4,275
3210	6 meter		.60	26.667		3,350	1,800		5,150	6,350
3220	7 meter		.56	28.571		4,075	1,925		6,000	7,350
3230	8 meter		.52	30.769		4,550	2,075		6,625	8,075
3250	1P 3W 120/240 V 4 jaw sockets									
3260	with 200A circuit breaker, 3 meter	2 Elec	1	16	Ea.	2,700	1,075		3,775	4,575
3270	4 meter		.90	17.778		3,650	1,200		4,850	5,800
3290	6 meter		.60	26.667		5,425	1,800		7,225	8,625
3300	7 meter		.56	28.571		6,375	1,925		8,300	9,850
3310	8 meter		.56	28.571		7,325	1,925		9,250	10,900
3330	Rainproof 1P 3W 120/240 V 4 jaw sockets									

26 27 13.10 Meter Centers and Sockets		Crew	Daily Output	Labor-Hours	Unit	Material	2023 Bare Costs Labor	Equipment	Total	Total Incl O&P
3350	with 200A circuit breaker, 3 meter	2 Elec	1	16	Ea.	2,700	1,075		3,775	4,575
3360	4 meter		.90	17.778		3,650	1,200		4,850	5,800
3380	6 meter		.60	26.667		5,425	1,800		7,225	8,625
3390	7 meter		.56	28.571		6,375	1,925		8,300	9,850
3400	8 meter		.52	30.769		7,325	2,075		9,400	11,100
3420	1P 3W on 3P 4W 120/208 V 5 jaw sockets									
3430	with 200A circuit breaker, 3 meter	2 Elec	1	16	Ea.	2,700	1,075		3,775	4,575
3440	4 meter		.90	17.778		3,650	1,200		4,850	5,800
3460	6 meter		.60	26.667		5,425	1,800		7,225	8,650
3470	7 meter		.56	28.571		6,375	1,925		8,300	9,850
3480	8 meter		.52	30.769		7,325	2,075		9,400	11,100
3500	Rainproof 1P 3W on 3P 4W 120/208 V 5 jaw socket									
3510	with 200A circuit breaker, 3 meter	2 Elec	1	16	Ea.	2,700	1,075		3,775	4,575
3520	4 meter		.90	17.778		3,650	1,200		4,850	5,800
3540	6 meter		.60	26.667		5,425	1,800		7,225	8,625
3550	7 meter		.56	28.571		6,375	1,925		8,300	9,850
3560	8 meter		.52	30.769		7,325	2,075		9,400	11,100
3600	Automatic circuit closing, add					105			105	115
3610	Manual circuit closing, add					106			106	117
3650	Branch meter device									
3660	3P 4W 208/120 or 240/120 V 7 jaw sockets									
3670	with 200A circuit breaker, 2 meter	2 Elec	.90	17.778	Ea.	4,525	1,200		5,725	6,750
3680	3 meter		.80	20		6,775	1,350		8,125	9,475
3690	4 meter		.70	22.857		9,050	1,550		10,600	12,300
3700	Main circuit breaker 42,000 rms, 400 amp		1.60	10		3,500	675		4,175	4,850
3710	600 amp		1.10	14.545		4,200	980		5,180	6,075
3720	800 amp		.90	17.778		4,825	1,200		6,025	7,075
3730	Rainproof main circ. breaker 42,000 rms, 400 amp		1.60	10		4,450	675		5,125	5,900
3740	600 amp		1.10	14.545		3,500	980		4,480	5,325
3750	800 amp		.90	17.778		5,925	1,200		7,125	8,300
3760	Main circuit breaker 65,000 rms, 400 amp		1.60	10		5,375	675		6,050	6,900
3770	600 amp		1.10	14.545		7,550	980		8,530	9,750
3780	800 amp		.90	17.778		8,550	1,200		9,750	11,200
3790	1,000 amp		.80	20		11,200	1,350		12,550	14,400
3800	1,200 amp		.76	21.053		14,400	1,425		15,825	17,900
3810	1,600 amp		.68	23.529		29,500	1,575		31,075	34,900
3820	Rainproof main circ. breaker 65,000 rms, 400 amp		1.60	10		5,375	675		6,050	6,900
3830	600 amp		1.10	14.545		7,550	980		8,530	9,750
3840	800 amp		.90	17.778		8,550	1,200		9,750	11,200
3850	1,000 amp		.80	20		11,200	1,350		12,550	14,400
3860	1,200 amp		.76	21.053		14,400	1,425		15,825	17,900
3880	Main circuit breaker 100,000 rms, 400 amp		1.60	10		5,375	675		6,050	6,900
3890	600 amp		1.10	14.545		7,550	980		8,530	9,750
3900	800 amp		.90	17.778		8,875	1,200		10,075	11,500
3910	Rainproof main circ. breaker 100,000 rms, 400 amp		1.60	10		5,375	675		6,050	6,900
3920	600 amp		1.10	14.545		7,550	980		8,530	9,750
3930	800 amp		.90	17.778		8,875	1,200		10,075	11,500
3940	Main lugs terminal box, 800 amp		.94	17.021		935	1,150		2,085	2,725
3950	1,600 amp		.72	22.222		4,425	1,500		5,925	7,100
3960	Rainproof, 800 amp		.94	17.021		935	1,150		2,085	2,725
3970	1,600 amp		.72	22.222		4,450	1,500		5,950	7,125

26 27 16 – Electrical Cabinets and Enclosures

26 27 16.10 Cabinets		Crew	Daily Output	Labor-Hours	Unit	2023 Bare Costs Material	Labor	Equipment	Total	Total Incl O&P
0010	**CABINETS** R260533-70									
7000	Cabinets, current transformer									
7050	Single door, 24" H x 24" W x 10" D R262716-40	1 Elec	1.60	5	Ea.	167	335		502	685
7100	30" H x 24" W x 10" D		1.30	6.154		184	415		599	820
7150	36" H x 24" W x 10" D		1.10	7.273		580	490		1,070	1,375
7200	30" H x 30" W x 10" D		1	8		330	540		870	1,150
7250	36" H x 30" W x 10" D		.90	8.889		400	600		1,000	1,325
7300	36" H x 36" W x 10" D		.80	10		455	675		1,130	1,500
7500	Double door, 48" H x 36" W x 10" D		.60	13.333		830	900		1,730	2,225
7550	24" H x 24" W x 12" D		1	8		243	540		783	1,075
8000	NEMA 12, double door, floor mounted									
8020	54" H x 42" W x 8" D	2 Elec	6	2.667	Ea.	1,975	180		2,155	2,450
8040	60" H x 48" W x 8" D		5.40	2.963		2,650	200		2,850	3,225
8060	60" H x 48" W x 10" D		5.40	2.963		2,675	200		2,875	3,250
8080	60" H x 60" W x 10" D		5	3.200		3,075	216		3,291	3,700
8100	72" H x 60" W x 10" D		4	4		3,550	269		3,819	4,325
8120	72" H x 72" W x 10" D		3.40	4.706		3,850	315		4,165	4,725
8140	60" H x 48" W x 12" D		3.40	4.706		2,750	315		3,065	3,475
8160	60" H x 60" W x 12" D		3.20	5		3,050	335		3,385	3,850
8180	72" H x 60" W x 12" D		3	5.333		3,500	360		3,860	4,375
8200	72" H x 72" W x 12" D		3	5.333		3,900	360		4,260	4,825
8220	60" H x 48" W x 16" D		3.20	5		2,900	335		3,235	3,700
8240	72" H x 72" W x 16" D		2.60	6.154		4,175	415		4,590	5,225
8260	60" H x 48" W x 20" D		3	5.333		3,150	360		3,510	4,000
8280	72" H x 72" W x 20" D		2.20	7.273		4,475	490		4,965	5,650
8300	60" H x 48" W x 24" D		2.60	6.154		3,275	415		3,690	4,225
8320	72" H x 72" W x 24" D		2	8		4,700	540		5,240	5,975
8340	Pushbutton enclosure, oiltight									
8360	3-1/2" H x 3-1/4" W x 2-3/4" D, for 1 P.B.	1 Elec	12	.667	Ea.	86.50	45		131.50	162
8380	5-3/4" H x 3-1/4" W x 2-3/4" D, for 2 P.B.		11	.727		100	49		149	183
8400	8" H x 3-1/4" W x 2-3/4" D, for 3 P.B.		10.50	.762		113	51.50		164.50	202
8420	10-1/4" H x 3-1/4" W x 2-3/4" D, for 4 P.B.		10.50	.762		128	51.50		179.50	218
8460	12-1/2" H x 3-1/4" W x 3" D, for 5 P.B.		9	.889		140	60		200	243
8480	9-1/2" H x 6-1/4" W x 3" D, for 6 P.B.		8.50	.941		161	63.50		224.50	271
8500	9-1/2" H x 8-1/2" W x 3" D, for 9 P.B.		8	1		190	67.50		257.50	310
8510	11-3/4" H x 8-1/2" W x 3" D, for 12 P.B.		7	1.143		214	77		291	350
8520	11-3/4" H x 10-3/4" W x 3" D, for 16 P.B.		6.50	1.231		246	83		329	395
8540	14" H x 10-3/4" W x 3" D, for 20 P.B.		5	1.600		179	108		287	355
8560	14" H x 13" W x 3" D, for 25 P.B.		4.50	1.778		195	120		315	390
8580	Sloping front pushbutton enclosures									
8600	3-1/2" H x 7-3/4" W x 4-7/8" D, for 3 P.B.	1 Elec	10	.800	Ea.	155	54		209	250
8620	7-1/4" H x 8-1/2" W x 6-3/4" D, for 6 P.B.		8	1		225	67.50		292.50	345
8640	9-1/2" H x 8-1/2" W x 7-7/8" D, for 9 P.B.		7	1.143		267	77		344	410
8660	11-1/4" H x 8-1/2" W x 9" D, for 12 P.B.		5	1.600		310	108		418	500
8680	11-3/4" H x 10" W x 9" D, for 16 P.B.		5	1.600		330	108		438	525
8700	11-3/4" H x 13" W x 9" D, for 20 P.B.		5	1.600		380	108		488	580
8720	14" H x 13" W x 10-1/8" D, for 25 P.B.		4.50	1.778		435	120		555	660
8740	Pedestals, not including P.B. enclosure or base									
8760	Straight column 4" x 4"	1 Elec	4.50	1.778	Ea.	390	120		510	605
8780	6" x 6"		4	2		580	135		715	840
8800	Angled column 4" x 4"		4.50	1.778		460	120		580	685
8820	6" x 6"		4	2		680	135		815	950

26 27 16 – Electrical Cabinets and Enclosures

26 27 16.10 Cabinets		Crew	Daily Output	Labor-Hours	Unit	Material	2023 Bare Costs Labor	Equipment	Total	Total Incl O&P
8840	Pedestal, base 18″ x 18″	1 Elec	10	.800	Ea.	239	54		293	345
8860	24″ x 24″		9	.889		535	60		595	680
8900	Electronic rack enclosures									
8920	72″ H x 19″ W x 24″ D	1 Elec	1.50	5.333	Ea.	2,225	360		2,585	2,975
8940	72″ H x 23″ W x 24″ D		1.50	5.333		2,500	360		2,860	3,275
8960	72″ H x 19″ W x 30″ D		1.30	6.154		2,675	415		3,090	3,550
8980	72″ H x 19″ W x 36″ D		1.20	6.667		3,175	450		3,625	4,150
9000	72″ H x 23″ W x 36″ D		1.20	6.667		3,500	450		3,950	4,525
9020	NEMA 12 & 4 enclosure panels									
9040	12″ x 24″	1 Elec	20	.400	Ea.	56.50	27		83.50	102
9060	16″ x 12″		20	.400		40.50	27		67.50	84.50
9080	20″ x 16″		20	.400		59	27		86	105
9100	20″ x 20″		19	.421		70.50	28.50		99	120
9120	24″ x 20″		18	.444		92	30		122	146
9140	24″ x 24″		17	.471		107	31.50		138.50	165
9160	30″ x 20″		16	.500		185	33.50		218.50	253
9180	30″ x 24″		16	.500		131	33.50		164.50	194
9200	36″ x 24″		15	.533		155	36		191	224
9220	36″ x 30″		15	.533		208	36		244	282
9240	42″ x 24″		15	.533		187	36		223	259
9260	42″ x 30″		14	.571		241	38.50		279.50	320
9280	42″ x 36″		14	.571		275	38.50		313.50	360
9300	48″ x 24″		14	.571		216	38.50		254.50	295
9320	48″ x 30″		14	.571		263	38.50		301.50	345
9340	48″ x 36″		13	.615		310	41.50		351.50	400
9360	60″ x 36″		12	.667		380	45		425	480
9400	Wiring trough steel JIC, clamp cover									
9490	4″ x 4″, 12″ long	1 Elec	12	.667	Ea.	142	45		187	223
9510	24″ long		10	.800		180	54		234	278
9530	36″ long		8	1		221	67.50		288.50	345
9540	48″ long		7	1.143		260	77		337	400
9550	60″ long		6	1.333		300	90		390	465
9560	6″ x 6″, 12″ long		11	.727		184	49		233	275
9580	24″ long		9	.889		241	60		301	355
9600	36″ long		7	1.143		297	77		374	440
9610	48″ long		6	1.333		365	90		455	535
9620	60″ long		5	1.600		425	108		533	625

26 27 16.20 Cabinets and Enclosures

		Crew	Daily Output	Labor-Hours	Unit	Material	Labor	Equipment	Total	Total Incl O&P
0010	**CABINETS AND ENCLOSURES** Nonmetallic									
0080	Enclosures fiberglass NEMA 4X									
0100	Wall mount, quick release latch door, 20″ H x 16″ W x 6″ D	1 Elec	4.80	1.667	Ea.	930	112		1,042	1,200
0110	20″ H x 20″ W x 6″ D		4.50	1.778		1,125	120		1,245	1,400
0120	24″ H x 20″ W x 6″ D		4.20	1.905		1,175	128		1,303	1,500
0130	20″ H x 16″ W x 8″ D		4.50	1.778		1,050	120		1,170	1,325
0140	20″ H x 20″ W x 8″ D		4.20	1.905		1,175	128		1,303	1,500
0150	24″ H x 24″ W x 8″ D		3.80	2.105		1,300	142		1,442	1,625
0160	30″ H x 24″ W x 8″ D		3.20	2.500		1,450	168		1,618	1,850
0170	36″ H x 30″ W x 8″ D		3	2.667		2,050	180		2,230	2,525
0180	20″ H x 16″ W x 10″ D		3.50	2.286		1,200	154		1,354	1,550
0190	20″ H x 20″ W x 10″ D		3.20	2.500		1,300	168		1,468	1,675
0200	24″ H x 20″ W x 10″ D		3	2.667		1,375	180		1,555	1,800
0210	30″ H x 24″ W x 10″ D		2.80	2.857		1,550	192		1,742	2,000

26 27 16.20 Cabinets and Enclosures		Crew	Daily Output	Labor-Hours	Unit	Material (2023 Bare Costs)	Labor (2023 Bare Costs)	Equipment (2023 Bare Costs)	Total (2023 Bare Costs)	Total Incl O&P
0220	20″ H x 16″ W x 12″ D	1 Elec	3	2.667	Ea.	1,350	180		1,530	1,750
0230	20″ H x 20″ W x 12″ D		2.80	2.857		1,425	192		1,617	1,850
0240	24″ H x 24″ W x 12″ D		2.60	3.077		1,550	207		1,757	2,000
0250	30″ H x 24″ W x 12″ D		2.40	3.333		1,700	225		1,925	2,200
0260	36″ H x 30″ W x 12″ D		2.20	3.636		2,350	245		2,595	2,950
0270	36″ H x 36″ W x 12″ D		2.10	3.810		2,550	257		2,807	3,200
0280	48″ H x 36″ W x 12″ D		2	4		3,050	269		3,319	3,750
0290	60″ H x 36″ W x 12″ D		1.80	4.444		3,350	299		3,649	4,150
0300	30″ H x 24″ W x 16″ D		1.40	5.714		2,000	385		2,385	2,800
0310	48″ H x 36″ W x 16″ D		1.20	6.667		3,350	450		3,800	4,350
0320	60″ H x 36″ W x 16″ D		1	8		3,775	540		4,315	4,950
0480	Freestanding, one door, 72″ H x 25″ W x 25″ D		.80	10		6,650	675		7,325	8,325
0490	Two doors with two panels, 72″ H x 49″ W x 24″ D		.50	16		15,600	1,075		16,675	18,700
0500	Floor stand kits, for NEMA 4 & 12, 20″ W or more, 6″ H x 8″ D		24	.333		240	22.50		262.50	298
0510	6″ H x 10″ D		24	.333		265	22.50		287.50	325
0520	6″ H x 12″ D		24	.333		300	22.50		322.50	365
0530	6″ H x 18″ D		24	.333		360	22.50		382.50	430
0540	12″ H x 8″ D		22	.364		315	24.50		339.50	380
0550	12″ H x 10″ D		22	.364		335	24.50		359.50	405
0560	12″ H x 12″ D		22	.364		360	24.50		384.50	430
0570	12″ H x 16″ D		22	.364		400	24.50		424.50	475
0580	12″ H x 18″ D		22	.364		430	24.50		454.50	505
0590	12″ H x 20″ D		22	.364		450	24.50		474.50	530
0600	18″ H x 8″ D		20	.400		380	27		407	460
0610	18″ H x 10″ D		20	.400		400	27		427	480
0620	18″ H x 12″ D		20	.400		425	27		452	510
0630	18″ H x 16″ D		20	.400		470	27		497	560
0640	24″ H x 8″ D		16	.500		450	33.50		483.50	545
0650	24″ H x 10″ D		16	.500		470	33.50		503.50	570
0660	24″ H x 12″ D		16	.500		495	33.50		528.50	595
0670	24″ H x 16″ D		16	.500		545	33.50		578.50	650
0680	Small, screw cover, 5-1/2″ H x 4″ W x 4-15/16″ D		12	.667		160	45		205	243
0690	7-1/2″ H x 4″ W x 4-15/16″ D		12	.667		166	45		211	250
0700	7-1/2″ H x 6″ W x 5-3/16″ D		10	.800		192	54		246	291
0710	9-1/2″ H x 6″ W x 5-11/16″ D		10	.800		201	54		255	300
0720	11-1/2″ H x 8″ W x 6-11/16″ D		8	1		292	67.50		359.50	420
0730	13-1/2″ H x 10″ W x 7-3/16″ D		7	1.143		360	77		437	510
0740	15-1/2″ H x 12″ W x 8-3/16″ D		6	1.333		460	90		550	640
0750	17-1/2″ H x 14″ W x 8-11/16″ D		5	1.600		555	108		663	770
0760	Screw cover with window, 6″ H x 4″ W x 5″ D		12	.667		208	45		253	296
0770	8″ H x 4″ W x 5″ D		11	.727		275	49		324	375
0780	8″ H x 6″ W x 5″ D		11	.727		390	49		439	505
0790	10″ H x 6″ W x 6″ D		10	.800		420	54		474	540
0800	12″ H x 8″ W x 7″ D		8	1		535	67.50		602.50	685
0810	14″ H x 10″ W x 7″ D		7	1.143		630	77		707	810
0820	16″ H x 12″ W x 8″ D		6	1.333		760	90		850	970
0830	18″ H x 14″ W x 9″ D		5	1.600		905	108		1,013	1,150
0840	Quick-release latch cover, 5-1/2″ H x 4″ W x 5″ D		12	.667		207	45		252	295
0850	7-1/2″ H x 4″ W x 5″ D		12	.667		219	45		264	310
0860	7-1/2″ H x 6″ W x 5-1/4″ D		10	.800		249	54		303	355
0870	9-1/2″ H x 6″ W x 5-3/4″ D		10	.800		261	54		315	365
0880	11-1/2″ H x 8″ W x 6-3/4″ D		8	1		375	67.50		442.50	510
0890	13-1/2″ H x 10″ W x 7-1/4″ D		7	1.143		465	77		542	625

26 27 16.20 Cabinets and Enclosures		Crew	Daily Output	Labor-Hours	Unit	Material	Labor (2023 Bare Costs)	Equipment	Total	Total Incl O&P
0900	15-1/2" H x 12" W x 8-1/4" D	1 Elec	6	1.333	Ea.	585	90		675	780
0910	17-1/2" H x 14" W x 8-3/4" D		5	1.600		710	108		818	940
0920	Pushbutton, 1 hole 5-1/2" H x 4" W x 4-15/16" D		12	.667		585	45		630	705
0930	2 hole 7-1/2" H x 4" W x 4-15/16" D		11	.727		805	49		854	960
0940	4 hole 7-1/2" H x 6" W x 5-3/16" D		10.50	.762		570	51.50		621.50	700
0950	6 hole 9-1/2" H x 6" W x 5-11/16" D		9	.889		785	60		845	955
0960	8 hole 11-1/2" H x 8" W x 6-11/16" D		8.50	.941		1,000	63.50		1,063.50	1,200
0970	12 hole 13-1/2" H x 10" W x 7-3/16" D		8	1		1,150	67.50		1,217.50	1,375
0980	20 hole 15-1/2" H x 12" W x 8-3/16" D		5	1.600		1,075	108		1,183	1,325
0990	30 hole 17-1/2" H x 14" W x 8-11/16" D	↓	4.50	1.778	↓	1,275	120		1,395	1,575
1450	Enclosures polyester NEMA 4X									
1460	Small, screw cover,									
1500	3-15/16" H x 3-15/16" W x 3-1/16" D	1 Elec	12	.667	Ea.	88	45		133	164
1510	5-3/16" H x 3-5/16" W x 3-1/16" D		12	.667		86.50	45		131.50	162
1520	5-7/8" H x 3-7/8" W x 4-3/16" D		12	.667		91.50	45		136.50	168
1530	5-7/8" H x 5-7/8" W x 4-3/16" D		12	.667		103	45		148	180
1540	7-5/8" H x 3-5/16" W x 3-1/16" D		12	.667		94.50	45		139.50	171
1550	10-3/16" H x 3-5/16" W x 3-1/16" D		10	.800		118	54		172	210
1560	Clear cover, 3-15/16" H x 3-15/16" W x 2-7/8" D		12	.667		99.50	45		144.50	176
1570	5-3/16" H x 3-5/16" W x 2-7/8" D		12	.667		106	45		151	183
1580	5-7/8" H x 3-7/8" W x 4" D		12	.667		132	45		177	212
1590	5-7/8" H x 5-7/8" W x 4" D		12	.667		162	45		207	245
1600	7-5/8" H x 3-5/16" W x 2-7/8" D		12	.667		119	45		164	198
1610	10-3/16" H x 3-5/16" W x 2-7/8" D		10	.800		149	54		203	244
1620	Pushbutton, 1 hole, 5-5/16" H x 3-5/16" W x 3-1/16" D		12	.667		81	45		126	156
1630	2 hole, 7-5/8" H x 3-5/16" W x 3-1/8" D		11	.727		87.50	49		136.50	169
1640	3 hole, 10-3/16" H x 3-5/16" W x 3-1/16" D		10.50	.762		104	51.50		155.50	191
8000	Wireway fiberglass, straight sect. screwcover, 12" L, 4" W x 4" D		40	.200		293	13.45		306.45	340
8010	6" W x 6" D		30	.267		390	17.95		407.95	455
8020	24" L, 4" W x 4" D		20	.400		375	27		402	455
8030	6" W x 6" D		15	.533		565	36		601	680
8040	36" L, 4" W x 4" D		13.30	.602		455	40.50		495.50	560
8050	6" W x 6" D		10	.800		720	54		774	870
8060	48" L, 4" W x 4" D		10	.800		540	54		594	670
8070	6" W x 6" D		7.50	1.067		860	72		932	1,050
8080	60" L, 4" W x 4" D		8	1		620	67.50		687.50	785
8090	6" W x 6" D		6	1.333		1,000	90		1,090	1,225
8100	Elbow, 90°, 4" W x 4" D		20	.400		287	27		314	355
8110	6" W x 6" D		18	.444		590	30		620	695
8120	Elbow, 45°, 4" W x 4" D		20	.400		286	27		313	355
8130	6" W x 6" D		18	.444		575	30		605	680
8140	Tee, 4" W x 4" D		16	.500		380	33.50		413.50	465
8150	6" W x 6" D		14	.571		670	38.50		708.50	790
8160	Cross, 4" W x 4" D		14	.571		505	38.50		543.50	610
8170	6" W x 6" D		12	.667		945	45		990	1,100
8180	Cut-off fitting, w/flange & adhesive, 4" W x 4" D		18	.444		229	30		259	297
8190	6" W x 6" D		16	.500		460	33.50		493.50	555
8200	Flexible ftng., hvy. neoprene coated nylon, 4" W x 4" D		20	.400		415	27		442	500
8210	6" W x 6" D		18	.444		620	30		650	730
8220	Closure plate, fiberglass, 4" W x 4" D		20	.400		79.50	27		106.50	128
8230	6" W x 6" D		18	.444		89.50	30		119.50	143
8240	Box connector, stainless steel type 304, 4" W x 4" D		20	.400		144	27		171	199
8250	6" W x 6" D	↓	18	.444	↓	158	30		188	219

26 27 Low-Voltage Distribution Equipment

26 27 16 – Electrical Cabinets and Enclosures

26 27 16.20 Cabinets and Enclosures		Crew	Daily Output	Labor-Hours	Unit	Material	Labor	Equipment	Total	Total Incl O&P
						2023 Bare Costs				
8260	Hanger, 4" W x 4" D	1 Elec	100	.080	Ea.	35	5.40		40.40	46.50
8270	6" W x 6" D		80	.100		42	6.75		48.75	56
8280	Straight tube section fiberglass, 4" W x 4" D, 12" long		40	.200		256	13.45		269.45	300
8290	24" long		20	.400		294	27		321	365
8300	36" long		13.30	.602		370	40.50		410.50	470
8310	48" long		10	.800		405	54		459	525
8320	60" long		8	1		460	67.50		527.50	610
8330	120" long		4	2		690	135		825	960

26 27 19 – Multi-Outlet Assemblies

26 27 19.10 Wiring Duct		Crew	Daily Output	Labor-Hours	Unit	Material	Labor	Equipment	Total	Total Incl O&P
0010	**WIRING DUCT** Plastic									
1250	PVC, snap-in slots, adhesive backed									
1270	1-1/2" W x 2" H	2 Elec	120	.133	L.F.	8.30	9		17.30	22.50
1280	1-1/2" W x 3" H		120	.133		9.55	9		18.55	24
1290	1-1/2" W x 4" H		120	.133		11.65	9		20.65	26
1300	2" W x 1" H		120	.133		7.15	9		16.15	21.50
1310	2" W x 1-1/2" H		120	.133		7.70	9		16.70	22
1320	2" W x 2" H		120	.133		7.30	9		16.30	21.50
1340	2" W x 3" H		120	.133		9.20	9		18.20	23.50
1350	2" W x 4" H		120	.133		11.45	9		20.45	26
1360	2-1/2" W x 3" H		120	.133		7.85	9		16.85	22
1370	3" W x 1" H		110	.145		5.30	9.80		15.10	20.50
1390	3" W x 2" H		110	.145		11.30	9.80		21.10	27
1400	3" W x 3" H		110	.145		11.30	9.80		21.10	27
1410	3" W x 4" H		110	.145		14.75	9.80		24.55	31
1420	3" W x 5" H		110	.145		20	9.80		29.80	36.50
1430	4" W x 1-1/2" H		100	.160		7.30	10.80		18.10	24
1440	4" W x 2" H		100	.160		11.80	10.80		22.60	29
1450	4" W x 3" H		100	.160		13.10	10.80		23.90	30.50
1460	4" W x 4" H		100	.160		17.25	10.80		28.05	35
1470	4" W x 5" H		100	.160		23.50	10.80		34.30	42
1550	Cover, 1-1/2" W		200	.080		1.58	5.40		6.98	9.75
1560	2" W		200	.080		1.94	5.40		7.34	10.15
1570	2-1/2" W		200	.080		2.46	5.40		7.86	10.70
1580	3" W		200	.080		2.92	5.40		8.32	11.20
1590	4" W		200	.080		3.52	5.40		8.92	11.85

26 27 23 – Indoor Service Poles

26 27 23.40 Surface Raceway		Crew	Daily Output	Labor-Hours	Unit	Material	Labor	Equipment	Total	Total Incl O&P
0010	**SURFACE RACEWAY**									
0090	Metal, straight section									
0100	No. 500	1 Elec	100	.080	L.F.	1.36	5.40		6.76	9.50
0110	No. 700		100	.080		1.50	5.40		6.90	9.65
0200	No. 1000		90	.089		2.32	6		8.32	11.45
0400	No. 1500, small pancake		90	.089		2.99	6		8.99	12.20
0600	No. 2000, base & cover, blank		90	.089		2.94	6		8.94	12.15
0610	Receptacle, 6" OC		40	.200		16.45	13.45		29.90	38
0620	12" OC		44	.182		10.15	12.25		22.40	29.50
0630	18" OC		46	.174		8.45	11.70		20.15	26.50
0650	30" OC		50	.160		7.95	10.80		18.75	24.50
0660	60" OC		50	.160		5.55	10.80		16.35	22
0670	No. 2400, base & cover, blank		80	.100		3.12	6.75		9.87	13.45
0680	Receptacle, 6" OC		42	.190		50	12.85		62.85	74

26 27 23 – Indoor Service Poles

26 27 23.40 Surface Raceway		Crew	Daily Output	Labor-Hours	Unit	Material	Labor	Equipment	Total	Total Incl O&P
						2023 Bare Costs				
0690	12" OC	1 Elec	53	.151	L.F.	55.50	10.15		65.65	76
0700	18" OC		55	.145		60.50	9.80		70.30	81
0710	24" OC		57	.140		12.65	9.45		22.10	28
0720	30" OC		59	.136		9.05	9.15		18.20	23.50
0730	60" OC		61	.131		8.40	8.85		17.25	22.50
0800	No. 3000, base & cover, blank		75	.107		5.70	7.20		12.90	16.95
0810	Receptacle, 6" OC		45	.178		59.50	11.95		71.45	83.50
0820	12" OC		62	.129		33.50	8.70		42.20	50
0830	18" OC		64	.125		27	8.40		35.40	42.50
0840	24" OC		66	.121		20.50	8.15		28.65	34.50
0850	30" OC		68	.118		18.35	7.90		26.25	32
0860	60" OC		70	.114		13.40	7.70		21.10	26
1000	No. 4000, base & cover, blank		65	.123		9.05	8.30		17.35	22.50
1010	Receptacle, 6" OC		41	.195		62.50	13.15		75.65	88
1020	12" OC		52	.154		49.50	10.35		59.85	70
1030	18" OC		54	.148		40.50	10		50.50	59.50
1040	24" OC		56	.143		33.50	9.60		43.10	51
1050	30" OC		58	.138		31.50	9.30		40.80	48.50
1060	60" OC		60	.133		23	9		32	39
1200	No. 6000, base & cover, blank		50	.160		15.15	10.80		25.95	32.50
1210	Receptacle, 6" OC		30	.267		76.50	17.95		94.45	111
1220	12" OC		37	.216		65	14.55		79.55	93
1230	18" OC		39	.205		55	13.80		68.80	80.50
1240	24" OC		41	.195		45	13.15		58.15	69
1250	30" OC		43	.186		42.50	12.55		55.05	65.50
1260	60" OC		45	.178		33	11.95		44.95	54.50
2400	Fittings, elbows, No. 500		40	.200	Ea.	2.53	13.45		15.98	23
2800	Elbow cover, No. 2000		40	.200		5.05	13.45		18.50	25.50
2880	Tee, No. 500		42	.190		4.86	12.85		17.71	24.50
2900	No. 2000		27	.296		16.05	19.95		36	47
3000	Switch box, No. 500		16	.500		17.50	33.50		51	69.50
3400	Telephone outlet, No. 1500		16	.500		21.50	33.50		55	73.50
3600	Junction box, No. 1500		16	.500		12.90	33.50		46.40	64
3800	Plugmold wired sections, No. 2000									
4000	1 circuit, 6 outlets, 3' long	1 Elec	8	1	Ea.	49	67.50		116.50	154
4100	2 circuits, 8 outlets, 6' long		5.30	1.509		81	102		183	241
4110	Tele-power pole, alum, w/2 recept, 10'		4	2		294	135		429	525
4120	12'		3.85	2.078		360	140		500	605
4130	15'		3.70	2.162		470	146		616	735
4140	Steel, w/2 recept, 10'		4	2		192	135		327	410
4150	One phone fitting, 10'		4	2		216	135		351	435
4160	Alum, 4 outlets, 10'		3.70	2.162		455	146		601	715
4300	Overhead distribution systems, 125 volt									
4800	No. 2000, entrance end fitting	1 Elec	20	.400	Ea.	7.40	27		34.40	48
5000	Blank end fitting		40	.200		3.47	13.45		16.92	24
5200	Supporting clip		40	.200		1.69	13.45		15.14	22
5800	No. 3000, entrance end fitting		20	.400		14.65	27		41.65	56
6000	Blank end fitting		40	.200		3.57	13.45		17.02	24
6020	Internal elbow		20	.400		19.20	27		46.20	61
6030	External elbow		20	.400		27	27		54	70
6040	Device bracket		53	.151		6.50	10.15		16.65	22.50
6400	Hanger clamp		32	.250		9.90	16.85		26.75	36
7000	No. 4000 base		90	.089	L.F.	7	6		13	16.60

26 27 23 – Indoor Service Poles

26 27 23.40 Surface Raceway		Crew	Daily Output	Labor-Hours	Unit	Material	Labor	Equipment	Total	Total Incl O&P
						2023 Bare Costs				
7200	Divider	1 Elec	100	.080	L.F.	1.17	5.40		6.57	9.30
7400	Entrance end fitting		16	.500	Ea.	32	33.50		65.50	85
7600	Blank end fitting		40	.200		8.45	13.45		21.90	29.50
7610	Recpt. & tele. cover		53	.151		16.75	10.15		26.90	33.50
7620	External elbow		16	.500		55	33.50		88.50	111
7630	Coupling		53	.151		8.35	10.15		18.50	24.50
7640	Divider clip & coupling		80	.100		1.66	6.75		8.41	11.85
7650	Panel connector		16	.500		35	33.50		68.50	88.50
7800	Take off connector		16	.500		115	33.50		148.50	177
8000	No. 6000, take off connector		16	.500		137	33.50		170.50	201
8100	Take off fitting		16	.500		102	33.50		135.50	162
8200	Hanger clamp	↓	32	.250		26	16.85		42.85	53.50
8230	Coupling					11.75			11.75	12.90
8240	One gang device plate	1 Elec	53	.151		13.15	10.15		23.30	29.50
8250	Two gang device plate		40	.200		16.10	13.45		29.55	37.50
8260	Blank end fitting		40	.200		14.55	13.45		28	36
8270	Combination elbow		14	.571		57	38.50		95.50	120
8300	Panel connector	↓	16	.500	↓	25	33.50		58.50	77.50
8500	Chan-L-Wire system installed in 1-5/8" x 1-5/8" strut. Strut									
8600	not incl., 30 amp, 4 wire, 3 phase	1 Elec	200	.040	L.F.	6.35	2.69		9.04	10.95
8700	Junction box		8	1	Ea.	42	67.50		109.50	147
8800	Insulating end cap		40	.200		11.25	13.45		24.70	32.50
8900	Strut splice plate		40	.200		14.90	13.45		28.35	36.50
9000	Tap		40	.200		30.50	13.45		43.95	53.50
9100	Fixture hanger	↓	60	.133		13.20	9		22.20	28
9200	Pulling tool				↓	114			114	125
9300	Non-metallic, straight section									
9310	7/16" x 7/8", base & cover, blank	1 Elec	160	.050	L.F.	2.72	3.37		6.09	8
9320	Base & cover w/adhesive		160	.050		2.35	3.37		5.72	7.60
9340	7/16" x 1-5/16", base & cover, blank		145	.055		2.99	3.72		6.71	8.80
9350	Base & cover w/adhesive		145	.055		2.72	3.72		6.44	8.50
9370	11/16" x 2-1/4", base & cover, blank		130	.062		3.62	4.14		7.76	10.15
9380	Base & cover w/adhesive		130	.062		3.73	4.14		7.87	10.25
9385	1-11/16" x 5-1/4", two compartment base & cover w/screws		80	.100	↓	13.20	6.75		19.95	24.50
9400	Fittings, elbows, 7/16" x 7/8"		50	.160	Ea.	2.32	10.80		13.12	18.55
9410	7/16" x 1-5/16"		45	.178		2.48	11.95		14.43	20.50
9420	11/16" x 2-1/4"		40	.200		2.58	13.45		16.03	23
9425	1-11/16" x 5-1/4"		28	.286		13.25	19.25		32.50	43
9430	Tees, 7/16" x 7/8"		35	.229		2.97	15.40		18.37	26.50
9440	7/16" x 1-5/16"		32	.250		3.02	16.85		19.87	28.50
9450	11/16" x 2-1/4"		30	.267		3.04	17.95		20.99	30
9455	1-11/16" x 5-1/4"		24	.333		22	22.50		44.50	57.50
9460	Cover clip, 7/16" x 7/8"		80	.100		.60	6.75		7.35	10.65
9470	7/16" x 1-5/16"		72	.111		.54	7.50		8.04	11.70
9480	11/16" x 2-1/4"		64	.125		.94	8.40		9.34	13.55
9484	1-11/16" x 5-1/4"		42	.190		3.20	12.85		16.05	22.50
9486	Wire clip, 1-11/16" x 5-1/4"		68	.118		.54	7.90		8.44	12.40
9490	Blank end, 7/16" x 7/8"		50	.160		.85	10.80		11.65	16.95
9500	7/16" x 1-5/16"		45	.178		.98	11.95		12.93	18.90
9510	11/16" x 2-1/4"		40	.200		1.44	13.45		14.89	21.50
9515	1-11/16" x 5-1/4"		38	.211		6.60	14.20		20.80	28.50
9520	Round fixture box, 5.5" diam. x 1"		25	.320		13.70	21.50		35.20	47
9530	Device box, 1 gang	↓	30	.267	↓	6.15	17.95		24.10	33.50

26 27 23 – Indoor Service Poles

26 27 23.40 Surface Raceway		Crew	Daily Output	Labor-Hours	Unit	2023 Bare Costs Material	Labor	Equipment	Total	Total Incl O&P
9540	2 gang	1 Elec	25	.320	Ea.	9.15	21.50		30.65	42

26 27 26 – Wiring Devices

26 27 26.10 Low Voltage Switching

		Crew	Daily Output	Labor-Hours	Unit	Material	Labor	Equipment	Total	Total Incl O&P
0010	**LOW VOLTAGE SWITCHING**									
3600	Relays, 120 V or 277 V standard	1 Elec	12	.667	Ea.	40	45		85	111
3800	Flush switch, standard		40	.200		18.70	13.45		32.15	40.50
4000	Interchangeable		40	.200		24.50	13.45		37.95	47
4100	Surface switch, standard		40	.200		10.85	13.45		24.30	32
4200	Transformer 115 V to 25 V		12	.667		163	45		208	246
4400	Master control, 12 circuit, manual		4	2		166	135		301	380
4500	25 circuit, motorized		4	2		211	135		346	430
4600	Rectifier, silicon		12	.667		66	45		111	139
4800	Switchplates, 1 gang, 1, 2 or 3 switch, plastic		80	.100		6.45	6.75		13.20	17.10
5000	Stainless steel		80	.100		14.40	6.75		21.15	26
5400	2 gang, 3 switch, stainless steel		53	.151		30	10.15		40.15	48
5500	4 switch, plastic		53	.151		13.30	10.15		23.45	30
5600	2 gang, 4 switch, stainless steel		53	.151		29.50	10.15		39.65	47.50
5700	6 switch, stainless steel		53	.151		57	10.15		67.15	78
5800	3 gang, 9 switch, stainless steel		32	.250		90	16.85		106.85	124
5900	Receptacle, triple, 1 return, 1 feed		26	.308		56	20.50		76.50	92.50
6000	2 feed		20	.400		56	27		83	102
6100	Relay gang boxes, flush or surface, 6 gang		5.30	1.509		123	102		225	286
6200	12 gang		4.70	1.702		147	115		262	330
6400	18 gang		4	2		150	135		285	365
6500	Frame, to hold up to 6 relays		12	.667		121	45		166	200
7200	Control wire, 2 conductor		6.30	1.270	C.L.F.	26.50	85.50		112	156
7400	3 conductor		5	1.600		39.50	108		147.50	204
7600	19 conductor		2.50	3.200		415	216		631	780
7800	26 conductor		2	4		565	269		834	1,025
8000	Weatherproof, 3 conductor		5	1.600		82.50	108		190.50	251

26 27 26.20 Wiring Devices Elements

		Crew	Daily Output	Labor-Hours	Unit	Material	Labor	Equipment	Total	Total Incl O&P
0010	**WIRING DEVICES ELEMENTS** R262726-90									
0200	Toggle switch, quiet type, single pole, 15 amp	1 Elec	40	.200	Ea.	2.61	13.45		16.06	23
0500	20 amp		27	.296		4.23	19.95		24.18	34
0510	30 amp		23	.348		22.50	23.50		46	59.50
0530	Lock handle, 20 amp		27	.296		33.50	19.95		53.45	66.50
0540	Security key, 20 amp		26	.308		100	20.50		120.50	141
0550	Rocker, 15 amp		40	.200		3.78	13.45		17.23	24
0560	20 amp		27	.296		7.10	19.95		27.05	37.50
0600	3 way, 15 amp		23	.348		1.96	23.50		25.46	37
0800	20 amp		18	.444		6.45	30		36.45	51.50
0810	30 amp		9	.889		22	60		82	113
0830	Lock handle, 20 amp		18	.444		40	30		70	88.50
0840	Security key, 20 amp		17	.471		95.50	31.50		127	152
0850	Rocker, 15 amp		23	.348		10.95	23.50		34.45	47
0860	20 amp		18	.444		10.15	30		40.15	55.50
0900	4 way, 15 amp		15	.533		9.80	36		45.80	64.50
1000	20 amp		11	.727		64	49		113	144
1020	Lock handle, 20 amp		11	.727		53	49		102	132
1030	Rocker, 15 amp		15	.533		11.65	36		47.65	66.50
1040	20 amp		11	.727		22.50	49		71.50	97.50
1100	Toggle switch, quiet type, double pole, 15 amp		15	.533		19.40	36		55.40	75

26 27 26.20 Wiring Devices Elements		Crew	Daily Output	Labor-Hours	Unit	Material	Labor	Equipment	Total	Total Incl O&P
						2023 Bare Costs				
1200	20 amp	1 Elec	11	.727	Ea.	33	49		82	109
1210	30 amp		9	.889		49	60		109	143
1230	Lock handle, 20 amp		11	.727		34	49		83	111
1250	Security key, 20 amp		10	.800		99	54		153	189
1420	Toggle switch quiet type, 1 pole, 2 throw center off, 15 amp		23	.348		63.50	23.50		87	105
1440	20 amp		18	.444		90	30		120	144
1460	2 pole, 2 throw center off, lock handle, 20 amp		11	.727		109	49		158	193
1480	1 pole, momentary contact, 15 amp		23	.348		28	23.50		51.50	65.50
1500	20 amp		18	.444		26	30		56	73
1520	Momentary contact, lock handle, 20 amp		18	.444		39	30		69	87.50
1650	Dimmer switch, 120 volt, incandescent, 600 watt, 1 pole G		16	.500		21.50	33.50		55	73.50
1700	600 watt, 3 way G		12	.667		24	45		69	92.50
1750	1,000 watt, 1 pole G		16	.500		81	33.50		114.50	139
1800	1,000 watt, 3 way G		12	.667		95	45		140	171
2000	1,500 watt, 1 pole G		11	.727		141	49		190	228
2100	2,000 watt, 1 pole G		8	1		310	67.50		377.50	440
2110	Fluorescent, 600 watt G		15	.533		143	36		179	211
2120	1,000 watt G		15	.533		199	36		235	273
2130	1,500 watt G		10	.800		370	54		424	485
2160	Explosion proof, toggle switch, wall, single pole 20 amp		5.30	1.509		365	102		467	555
2180	Receptacle, single outlet, 20 amp		5.30	1.509		780	102		882	1,000
2190	30 amp		4	2		1,250	135		1,385	1,575
2290	60 amp		2.50	3.200		1,125	216		1,341	1,550
2360	Plug, 20 amp		16	.500		370	33.50		403.50	455
2370	30 amp		12	.667		645	45		690	775
2380	60 amp		8	1		610	67.50		677.50	770
2410	Furnace, thermal cutoff switch with plate		26	.308		28.50	20.50		49	62
2460	Receptacle, duplex, 120 volt, grounded, 15 amp		40	.200		1.54	13.45		14.99	21.50
2470	20 amp		27	.296		12.90	19.95		32.85	43.50
2480	Ground fault interrupting, 15 amp		27	.296		21	19.95		40.95	52.50
2482	20 amp		27	.296		38.50	19.95		58.45	72
2486	Clock receptacle, 15 amp		40	.200		38	13.45		51.45	62
2490	Dryer, 30 amp		15	.533		5.10	36		41.10	59
2500	Range, 50 amp		11	.727		18.70	49		67.70	93.50
2530	Surge suppressor receptacle, duplex, 20 amp		27	.296		91.50	19.95		111.45	131
2532	Quad, 20 amp		20	.400		134	27		161	187
2540	Isolated ground receptacle, duplex, 20 amp		27	.296		39	19.95		58.95	72.50
2542	Quad, 20 amp		20	.400		54	27		81	99.50
2550	Simplex, 20 amp		27	.296		39	19.95		58.95	72.50
2560	Simplex, 30 amp		15	.533		52	36		88	111
2570	Cable reel w/receptacle 50′ w/3#12, 120 V, 20 A	2 Elec	2.67	5.999		1,525	405		1,930	2,275
2600	Wall plates, stainless steel, 1 gang	1 Elec	80	.100		1.72	6.75		8.47	11.90
2800	2 gang		53	.151		14.80	10.15		24.95	31.50
3000	3 gang		32	.250		13.10	16.85		29.95	39.50
3100	4 gang		27	.296		14.25	19.95		34.20	45
3110	Brown plastic, 1 gang		80	.100		.39	6.75		7.14	10.45
3120	2 gang		53	.151		.83	10.15		10.98	16
3130	3 gang		32	.250		1.86	16.85		18.71	27
3140	4 gang		27	.296		3.78	19.95		23.73	33.50
3150	Brushed brass, 1 gang		80	.100		6.90	6.75		13.65	17.60
3160	Anodized aluminum, 1 gang		80	.100		4.46	6.75		11.21	14.90
3170	Switch cover, weatherproof, 1 gang		60	.133		8.95	9		17.95	23
3180	Vandal proof lock, 1 gang		60	.133		18.85	9		27.85	34.50

26 27 26.20 Wiring Devices Elements		Crew	Daily Output	Labor-Hours	Unit	Material	Labor	Equipment	Total	Total Incl O&P
						2023 Bare Costs				
3200	Lampholder, keyless	1 Elec	26	.308	Ea.	28.50	20.50		49	62
3400	Pullchain with receptacle		22	.364		27.50	24.50		52	66.50
3500	Pilot light, neon with jewel		27	.296		12.40	19.95		32.35	43
3600	Receptacle, 20 amp, 250 volt, NEMA 6		27	.296		37.50	19.95		57.45	70.50
3620	277 volt NEMA 7		27	.296		29.50	19.95		49.45	62
3640	125/250 volt NEMA 10		27	.296		30.50	19.95		50.45	63
3680	125/250 volt NEMA 14		25	.320		41	21.50		62.50	77
3700	3 pole, 250 volt NEMA 15		25	.320		42.50	21.50		64	79
3720	120/208 volt NEMA 18		25	.320		44	21.50		65.50	80
3740	30 amp, 125 volt NEMA 5		15	.533		33	36		69	89.50
3760	250 volt NEMA 6		15	.533		36.50	36		72.50	93.50
3780	277 volt NEMA 7		15	.533		44	36		80	102
3820	125/250 volt NEMA 14		14	.571		78.50	38.50		117	144
3840	3 pole, 250 volt NEMA 15		14	.571		80.50	38.50		119	146
3880	50 amp, 125 volt NEMA 5		11	.727		41	49		90	118
3900	250 volt NEMA 6		11	.727		41.50	49		90.50	119
3920	277 volt NEMA 7		11	.727		47.50	49		96.50	126
3960	125/250 volt NEMA 14		10	.800		111	54		165	202
3980	3 pole, 250 volt NEMA 15		10	.800		108	54		162	199
4020	60 amp, 125/250 volt, NEMA 14		8	1		123	67.50		190.50	236
4040	3 pole, 250 volt NEMA 15		8	1		129	67.50		196.50	242
4060	120/208 volt NEMA 18		8	1		114	67.50		181.50	225
4100	Receptacle locking, 20 amp, 125 volt NEMA L5		27	.296		29.50	19.95		49.45	62
4120	250 volt NEMA L6		27	.296		28.50	19.95		48.45	61
4140	277 volt NEMA L7		27	.296		26.50	19.95		46.45	58.50
4150	3 pole, 250 volt, NEMA L11		27	.296		29	19.95		48.95	61
4160	20 amp, 480 volt NEMA L8		27	.296		31	19.95		50.95	63.50
4180	600 volt NEMA L9		27	.296		42	19.95		61.95	75.50
4200	125/250 volt NEMA L10		27	.296		36	19.95		55.95	69
4230	125/250 volt NEMA L14		25	.320		65	21.50		86.50	104
4280	250 volt NEMA L15		25	.320		64.50	21.50		86	103
4300	480 volt NEMA L16		25	.320		63.50	21.50		85	102
4320	3 phase, 120/208 volt NEMA L18		25	.320		40.50	21.50		62	76.50
4340	277/480 volt NEMA L19		25	.320		46	21.50		67.50	82.50
4360	347/600 volt NEMA L20		25	.320		45.50	21.50		67	82.50
4380	120/208 volt NEMA L21		23	.348		48.50	23.50		72	88
4400	277/480 volt NEMA L22		23	.348		47.50	23.50		71	87
4420	347/600 volt NEMA L23		23	.348		59.50	23.50		83	101
4440	30 amp, 125 volt NEMA L5		15	.533		41	36		77	99
4460	250 volt NEMA L6		15	.533		44	36		80	102
4480	277 volt NEMA L7		15	.533		42.50	36		78.50	100
4500	480 volt NEMA L8		15	.533		45	36		81	103
4520	600 volt NEMA L9		15	.533		48	36		84	106
4540	125/250 volt NEMA L10		15	.533		53	36		89	112
4560	3 phase, 250 volt NEMA L11		15	.533		32.50	36		68.50	89
4620	125/250 volt NEMA L14		14	.571		62.50	38.50		101	126
4640	250 volt NEMA L15		14	.571		64	38.50		102.50	128
4660	480 volt NEMA L16		14	.571		66	38.50		104.50	130
4680	600 volt NEMA L17		14	.571		61.50	38.50		100	125
4700	120/208 volt NEMA L18		14	.571		65.50	38.50		104	130
4720	277/480 volt NEMA L19		14	.571		65	38.50		103.50	129
4740	347/600 volt NEMA L20		14	.571		67.50	38.50		106	132
4760	120/208 volt NEMA L21		13	.615		64	41.50		105.50	132

26 27 26.20 Wiring Devices Elements		Crew	Daily Output	Labor-Hours	Unit	Material	Labor	Equipment	Total	Total Incl O&P
4780	277/480 volt NEMA L22	1 Elec	13	.615	Ea.	60	41.50		101.50	127
4800	347/600 volt NEMA L23		13	.615		77	41.50		118.50	147
4840	Receptacle, corrosion resistant, 15 or 20 amp, 125 volt NEMA L5		27	.296		35	19.95		54.95	68
4860	250 volt NEMA L6		27	.296		27	19.95		46.95	59
4870	Receptacle box assembly, cast aluminum, 60A, 4P5W, 3P, 120/208V, NEMA PR4		22	.364		1,725	24.50		1,749.50	1,925
4875	100A, 4P5W, 3P, 347/600V, NEMA PR4		22	.364		2,075	24.50		2,099.50	2,300
4880	200A, 4P5W, 3P, 347/600V, NEMA PR4		22	.364		4,450	24.50		4,474.50	4,925
4900	Receptacle, cover plate, phenolic plastic, NEMA 5 & 6		80	.100		.49	6.75		7.24	10.55
4910	NEMA 7-23		80	.100		.76	6.75		7.51	10.85
4920	Stainless steel, NEMA 5 & 6		80	.100		1.53	6.75		8.28	11.70
4930	NEMA 7-23		80	.100		5.45	6.75		12.20	16
4940	Brushed brass NEMA 5 & 6		80	.100		7.50	6.75		14.25	18.25
4950	NEMA 7-23		80	.100		7.65	6.75		14.40	18.45
4960	Anodized aluminum, NEMA 5 & 6		80	.100		4.60	6.75		11.35	15.05
4970	NEMA 7-23		80	.100		7.60	6.75		14.35	18.35
4980	Weatherproof NEMA 7-23		60	.133		58	9		67	77
5000	Duplex receptacle, combo 15A/125V, 3 wire w/2-5V 0.7A, port USB, AL		27	.296		27	19.95		46.95	59
5002	15A/125V, 3 wire w/2-5V 0.7A, port USB, BK		27	.296		22	19.95		41.95	53.50
5004	15A/125V, 3 wire w/2-5V 0.7A, port USB, LA		27	.296		25.50	19.95		45.45	57.50
5006	15A/125V, 3 wire w/2-5V 0.7A, port USB, IV		27	.296		25.50	19.95		45.45	58
5008	15A/125V, 3 wire w/2-5V 0.7A, port USB, WH		27	.296		22.50	19.95		42.45	54
5010	Duplex receptacle, combo 15A/125V, 3 wire w/2-5V 2.1A, port USB, AL		27	.296		44	19.95		63.95	77.50
5012	15A/125V, 3 wire w/2-5V 2.1A, port USB, BK		27	.296		44	19.95		63.95	77.50
5014	15A/125V, 3 wire w/2-5V 2.1A, port USB, LA		27	.296		44	19.95		63.95	77.50
5016	15A/125V, 3 wire w/2-5V 2.1A, port USB, IV		27	.296		44	19.95		63.95	77.50
5018	15A/125V, 3 wire w/2-5V 2.1A, port USB, WH		27	.296		44	19.95		63.95	77.50
5020	Duplex receptacle, combo 20A/125V, 3 wire w/2-5V 2.1A, port USB, AL		27	.296		46	19.95		65.95	80
5022	20A/125V, 3 wire w/2-5V 2.1A, port USB, BK		27	.296		40	19.95		59.95	73.50
5024	20A/125V, 3 wire w/2-5V 2.1A, port USB, LA		27	.296		43	19.95		62.95	77
5026	20A/125V, 3 wire w/2-5V 2.1A, port USB, IV		27	.296		41	19.95		60.95	74.50
5028	20A/125V, 3 wire w/2-5V 2.1A, port USB, WH		27	.296		37	19.95		56.95	70
5100	Plug, 20 amp, 250 volt NEMA 6		30	.267		26.50	17.95		44.45	55.50
5110	277 volt NEMA 7		30	.267		28.50	17.95		46.45	58
5120	3 pole, 120/250 volt NEMA 10		26	.308		34	20.50		54.50	68.50
5130	125/250 volt NEMA 14		26	.308		64	20.50		84.50	101
5140	250 volt NEMA 15		26	.308		67.50	20.50		88	105
5150	120/208 volt NEMA 8		26	.308		70	20.50		90.50	108
5160	30 amp, 125 volt NEMA 5		13	.615		67	41.50		108.50	136
5170	250 volt NEMA 6		13	.615		69	41.50		110.50	138
5180	277 volt NEMA 7		13	.615		115	41.50		156.50	189
5190	125/250 volt NEMA 14		13	.615		65.50	41.50		107	134
5200	3 pole, 250 volt NEMA 15		12	.667		79	45		124	153
5210	50 amp, 125 volt NEMA 5		9	.889		100	60		160	199
5220	250 volt NEMA 6		9	.889		105	60		165	204
5230	277 volt NEMA 7		9	.889		112	60		172	212
5240	125/250 volt NEMA 14		9	.889		92.50	60		152.50	191
5250	3 pole, 250 volt NEMA 15		8	1		96	67.50		163.50	206
5260	60 amp, 125/250 volt NEMA 14		7	1.143		104	77		181	228
5270	3 pole, 250 volt NEMA 15		7	1.143		109	77		186	234
5280	120/208 volt NEMA 18		7	1.143		134	77		211	262
5300	Plug angle, 20 amp, 250 volt NEMA 6		30	.267		39	17.95		56.95	69.50
5310	30 amp, 125 volt NEMA 5		13	.615		78.50	41.50		120	148
5320	250 volt NEMA 6		13	.615		80	41.50		121.50	150

26 27 26.20 Wiring Devices Elements		Crew	Daily Output	Labor-Hours	Unit	Material	Labor	Equipment	Total	Total Incl O&P
						2023 Bare Costs				
5330	277 volt NEMA 7	1 Elec	13	.615	Ea.	84	41.50		125.50	154
5340	125/250 volt NEMA 14		13	.615		85	41.50		126.50	155
5350	3 pole, 250 volt NEMA 15		12	.667		87.50	45		132.50	163
5360	50 amp, 125 volt NEMA 5		9	.889		82	60		142	179
5370	250 volt NEMA 6		9	.889		83	60		143	181
5380	277 volt NEMA 7		9	.889		93	60		153	191
5390	125/250 volt NEMA 14		9	.889		98.50	60		158.50	198
5400	3 pole, 250 volt NEMA 15		8	1		106	67.50		173.50	217
5410	60 amp, 125/250 volt NEMA 14		7	1.143		122	77		199	248
5420	3 pole, 250 volt NEMA 15		7	1.143		119	77		196	244
5430	120/208 volt NEMA 18		7	1.143		126	77		203	253
5500	Plug, locking, 20 amp, 125 volt NEMA L5		30	.267		23	17.95		40.95	51.50
5510	250 volt NEMA L6		30	.267		23	17.95		40.95	52
5520	277 volt NEMA L7		30	.267		22.50	17.95		40.45	51
5530	480 volt NEMA L8		30	.267		24.50	17.95		42.45	53.50
5540	600 volt NEMA L9		30	.267		26	17.95		43.95	55
5550	3 pole, 125/250 volt NEMA L10		26	.308		30	20.50		50.50	63.50
5560	250 volt NEMA L11		26	.308		30	20.50		50.50	63.50
5570	480 volt NEMA L12		26	.308		35	20.50		55.50	69.50
5580	125/250 volt NEMA L14		26	.308		34.50	20.50		55	69
5590	250 volt NEMA L15		26	.308		38	20.50		58.50	73
5600	480 volt NEMA L16		26	.308		38.50	20.50		59	73.50
5610	4 pole, 120/208 volt NEMA L18		24	.333		39	22.50		61.50	76.50
5620	277/480 volt NEMA L19		24	.333		41.50	22.50		64	79
5630	347/600 volt NEMA L20		24	.333		43.50	22.50		66	81.50
5640	120/208 volt NEMA L21		24	.333		41	22.50		63.50	78.50
5650	277/480 volt NEMA L22		24	.333		46.50	22.50		69	85
5660	347/600 volt NEMA L23		24	.333		53.50	22.50		76	92
5670	30 amp, 125 volt NEMA L5		13	.615		35	41.50		76.50	100
5680	250 volt NEMA L6		13	.615		35.50	41.50		77	101
5690	277 volt NEMA L7		13	.615		33	41.50		74.50	98
5700	480 volt NEMA L8		13	.615		34.50	41.50		76	99.50
5710	600 volt NEMA L9		13	.615		35	41.50		76.50	100
5720	3 pole, 125/250 volt NEMA L10		11	.727		33	49		82	109
5730	250 volt NEMA L11		11	.727		32.50	49		81.50	109
5760	125/250 volt NEMA L14		11	.727		47.50	49		96.50	126
5770	250 volt NEMA L15		11	.727		48	49		97	126
5780	480 volt NEMA L16		11	.727		47	49		96	125
5790	600 volt NEMA L17		11	.727		46	49		95	124
5800	4 pole, 120/208 volt NEMA L18		10	.800		51	54		105	136
5810	120/208 volt NEMA L19		10	.800		48.50	54		102.50	133
5820	347/600 volt NEMA L20		10	.800		51.50	54		105.50	137
5830	120/208 volt NEMA L21		10	.800		48.50	54		102.50	133
5840	277/480 volt NEMA L22		10	.800		49.50	54		103.50	135
5850	347/600 volt NEMA L23		10	.800		55.50	54		109.50	141
6000	Connector, 20 amp, 250 volt NEMA 6		30	.267		40	17.95		57.95	70.50
6010	277 volt NEMA 7		30	.267		40	17.95		57.95	70.50
6020	3 pole, 120/250 volt NEMA 10		26	.308		45	20.50		65.50	80.50
6030	125/250 volt NEMA 14		26	.308		45	20.50		65.50	80.50
6040	250 volt NEMA 15		26	.308		45.50	20.50		66	81
6050	120/208 volt NEMA 18		26	.308		49.50	20.50		70	85.50
6060	30 amp, 125 volt NEMA 5		13	.615		78.50	41.50		120	148
6070	250 volt NEMA 6		13	.615		78.50	41.50		120	148

26 27 26.20 Wiring Devices Elements		Crew	Daily Output	Labor-Hours	Unit	Material	Labor	Equipment	Total	Total Incl O&P
						2023 Bare Costs				
6080	277 volt NEMA 7	1 Elec	13	.615	Ea.	78.50	41.50		120	148
6110	50 amp, 125 volt NEMA 5		9	.889		108	60		168	208
6120	250 volt NEMA 6		9	.889		108	60		168	208
6130	277 volt NEMA 7		9	.889		108	60		168	208
6200	Connector, locking, 20 amp, 125 volt NEMA L5		30	.267		35	17.95		52.95	65
6210	250 volt NEMA L6		30	.267		35.50	17.95		53.45	65.50
6220	277 volt NEMA L7		30	.267		31.50	17.95		49.45	61.50
6230	480 volt NEMA L8		30	.267		36.50	17.95		54.45	67
6240	600 volt NEMA L9		30	.267		40.50	17.95		58.45	71
6250	3 pole, 125/250 volt NEMA L10		26	.308		46.50	20.50		67	82
6260	250 volt NEMA L11		26	.308		46.50	20.50		67	82
6280	125/250 volt NEMA L14		26	.308		48	20.50		68.50	84
6290	250 volt NEMA L15		26	.308		49	20.50		69.50	85
6300	480 volt NEMA L16		26	.308		49	20.50		69.50	85
6310	4 pole, 120/208 volt NEMA L18		24	.333		56	22.50		78.50	95
6320	277/480 volt NEMA L19		24	.333		60	22.50		82.50	99.50
6330	347/600 volt NEMA L20		24	.333		57.50	22.50		80	97
6340	120/208 volt NEMA L21		24	.333		70	22.50		92.50	111
6350	277/480 volt NEMA L22		24	.333		72.50	22.50		95	113
6360	347/600 volt NEMA L23		24	.333		93.50	22.50		116	137
6370	30 amp, 125 volt NEMA L5		13	.615		67	41.50		108.50	135
6380	250 volt NEMA L6		13	.615		69.50	41.50		111	138
6390	277 volt NEMA L7		13	.615		75	41.50		116.50	144
6400	480 volt NEMA L8		13	.615		75	41.50		116.50	144
6410	600 volt NEMA L9		13	.615		83	41.50		124.50	153
6420	3 pole, 125/250 volt NEMA L10		11	.727		89.50	49		138.50	172
6430	250 volt NEMA L11		11	.727		89.50	49		138.50	172
6460	125/250 volt NEMA L14		11	.727		91	49		140	173
6470	250 volt NEMA L15		11	.727		94.50	49		143.50	177
6480	480 volt NEMA L16		11	.727		99.50	49		148.50	183
6490	600 volt NEMA L17		11	.727		103	49		152	186
6500	4 pole, 120/208 volt NEMA L18		10	.800		99.50	54		153.50	190
6510	120/208 volt NEMA L19		10	.800		102	54		156	192
6520	347/600 volt NEMA L20		10	.800		107	54		161	198
6530	120/208 volt NEMA L21		10	.800		80	54		134	168
6540	277/480 volt NEMA L22		10	.800		105	54		159	195
6550	347/600 volt NEMA L23		10	.800		105	54		159	195
7000	Receptacle computer, 250 volt, 15 amp, 3 pole 4 wire		8	1		126	67.50		193.50	238
7010	20 amp, 2 pole 3 wire		8	1		148	67.50		215.50	262
7020	30 amp, 2 pole 3 wire		6.50	1.231		240	83		323	390
7030	30 amp, 3 pole 4 wire		6.50	1.231		261	83		344	410
7040	60 amp, 3 pole 4 wire		4.50	1.778		440	120		560	665
7050	100 amp, 3 pole 4 wire		3	2.667		530	180		710	850
7100	Connector computer, 250 volt, 15 amp, 3 pole 4 wire		27	.296		194	19.95		213.95	243
7110	20 amp, 2 pole 3 wire		27	.296		209	19.95		228.95	260
7120	30 amp, 2 pole 3 wire		15	.533		305	36		341	390
7130	30 amp, 3 pole 4 wire		15	.533		335	36		371	425
7140	60 amp, 3 pole 4 wire		8	1		550	67.50		617.50	705
7150	100 amp, 3 pole 4 wire		4	2		745	135		880	1,025
7200	Plug, computer, 250 volt, 15 amp, 3 pole 4 wire		27	.296		173	19.95		192.95	220
7210	20 amp, 2 pole 3 wire		27	.296		185	19.95		204.95	234
7220	30 amp, 2 pole 3 wire		15	.533		281	36		317	365
7230	30 amp, 3 pole 4 wire		15	.533		274	36		310	355

26 27 Low-Voltage Distribution Equipment

26 27 26 – Wiring Devices

26 27 26.20 Wiring Devices Elements		Crew	Daily Output	Labor-Hours	Unit	2023 Bare Costs Material	Labor	Equipment	Total	Total Incl O&P
7240	60 amp, 3 pole 4 wire	1 Elec	8	1	Ea.	390	67.50		457.50	530
7250	100 amp, 3 pole 4 wire		4	2		490	135		625	740
7300	Connector adapter to flexible conduit, 1/2"		60	.133		6.45	9		15.45	20.50
7310	3/4"		50	.160		9.10	10.80		19.90	26
7320	1-1/4"		30	.267		27	17.95		44.95	56.50
7330	1-1/2"		23	.348		38	23.50		61.50	76.50
8100	Pin/sleeve, 20A, 480V, DSN1, male inlet, 3 pole, 3 phase, 4 wire		16	.500		58.50	33.50		92	115
8110	20A, 125V, DSN20, male inlet, 3 pole, 3 phase, 3 wire		16	.500		51	33.50		84.50	106
8120	60A, 480V, DS60, male inlet, 3 pole, 3 phase, 3 wire		16	.500		485	33.50		518.50	585
8130	Pin/sleeve, 20A, 480V, DSN10, female RCPT, 3P, 3 phase, 4 wire		16	.500		106	33.50		139.50	166
8140	30A, 480V, DS30, female RCPT, 3P, 3 phase, 4 wire		16	.500		430	33.50		463.50	525
8500	Wiring device terminal strip, 2 pole, 12-2AWG, 300VAC, CSA, 600VAC, 10A		36	.222		4.31	14.95		19.26	26.50
8505	4 pole, 12-2AWG, 300VAC, CSA, 600VAC, 10A		36	.222		6.10	14.95		21.05	28.50
8510	6 pole, 12-2AWG, 300VAC, CSA, 600VAC, 10A		36	.222		6.85	14.95		21.80	29.50
8515	8 pole, 12-2AWG, 300VAC, CSA, 600VAC, 10A		30	.267		7.75	17.95		25.70	35
8520	10 pole, 12-2AWG, 300VAC, CSA, 600VAC, 10A		30	.267		8.55	17.95		26.50	36
8525	12 pole, 12-2AWG, 300VAC, CSA, 600VAC, 10A		30	.267		9.40	17.95		27.35	37
8530	Wiring device terminal strip jumper, 10A		36	.222		.99	14.95		15.94	23
8535	Wiring device terminal strip, 2 pole, 12-22AWG, 300VAC, CSA, 600VAC, 20A		34	.235		4.65	15.85		20.50	28.50
8540	4 pole, 12-22AWG, 300VAC, CSA, 600VAC, 20A		34	.235		6.40	15.85		22.25	30.50
8545	6 pole, 12-22AWG, 300VAC, CSA, 600VAC, 20A		34	.235		7.30	15.85		23.15	31.50
8550	8 pole, 12-22AWG, 300VAC, CSA, 600VAC, 20A		30	.267		8.15	17.95		26.10	35.50
8555	10 pole, 12-22AWG, 300VAC, CSA, 600VAC, 20A		30	.267		9	17.95		26.95	36.50
8560	12 pole, 12-22AWG, 300VAC, CSA, 600VAC, 20A		30	.267		9.90	17.95		27.85	37.50
8565	Wiring device terminal strip jumper, 20A		34	.235		1.23	15.85		17.08	25
8570	Wiring device terminal shorting type no cover, 4 pole, 6-10AWG, 600VAC, 50A		30	.267		17.25	17.95		35.20	45.50
8575	6 pole, 6-10AWG, 600VAC, 50A		30	.267		22	17.95		39.95	51
8580	8 pole, 6-10AWG, 600VAC, 50A		30	.267		40.50	17.95		58.45	71
8585	12 pole, 6-10AWG, 600VAC, 50A		30	.267		28.50	17.95		46.45	57.50
8590	Wiring device terminal 2 shorting pin 1/2 cover, 2 pole, 8-4AWG, 600V, 45A		30	.267		17.85	17.95		35.80	46
8595	4 pole, 8-4AWG, 600V, 45A		30	.267		22.50	17.95		40.45	51
8600	6 pole, 8-4AWG, 600V, 45A		30	.267		49	17.95		66.95	80.50
8605	8 pole, 8-4AWG, 600V, 45A		30	.267		40	17.95		57.95	71
8610	12 pole, 8-4AWG, 600V, 45A		30	.267		84	17.95		101.95	119
8615	Wiring device terminal 2 shorting pin W/cover, 4 pole, 8-4AWG, 600V, 45A		30	.267		30.50	17.95		48.45	60
8620	6 pole, 8-4AWG, 600V, 45A		30	.267		54	17.95		71.95	86
8625	8 pole, 8-4AWG, 600V, 45A		30	.267		48.50	17.95		66.45	80
8630	12 pole, 8-4AWG, 600V, 45A		30	.267		57.50	17.95		75.45	90

26 27 33 – Power Distribution Units

26 27 33.10 Power Distribution Unit Cabinet

		Crew	Daily Output	Labor-Hours	Unit	Material	Labor	Equipment	Total	Total Incl O&P
0010	**POWER DISTRIBUTION UNIT CABINET**									
0100	Power distribution unit, single cabinet, 50 kVA output, 480/208 input	1 Elec	2	4	Ea.	11,600	269		11,869	13,200
0110	75 kVA output, 480/208 input		2	4		12,600	269		12,869	14,300
0120	100 kVA output, 480/208 input		2	4		13,800	269		14,069	15,500
0130	125 kVA output, 480/208 input		1.50	5.333		15,100	360		15,460	17,100
0140	150 kVA output, 480/208 input		1.50	5.333		18,300	360		18,660	20,700
0150	200 kVA output, 480/208 input		1	8		20,200	540		20,740	23,000
0160	225 kVA output, 480/208 input		1	8		21,400	540		21,940	24,300

26 27 Low-Voltage Distribution Equipment

26 27 33 – Power Distribution Units

26 27 33.20 Power Distribution Unit		Crew	Daily Output	Labor-Hours	Unit	2023 Bare Costs Material	Labor	Equipment	Total	Total Incl O&P
0010	**POWER DISTRIBUTION UNIT**									
0050	3PH, 60 kVA, PDU									
0100	208V-208V/120V	2 Elec	2	8	Ea.	17,600	540		18,140	20,200
0110	480V-208V/120V		2	8		17,600	540		18,140	20,200
0120	600V-208V/120V		2	8		17,600	540		18,140	20,200
0125	3PH, 80 kVA, PDU									
0130	208V-208V/120V	2 Elec	2	8	Ea.	26,800	540		27,340	30,300
0140	480V-208V/120V		2	8		28,600	540		29,140	32,300
0150	600V-208V/120V		2	8		28,300	540		28,840	32,000
0200	3PH, 15 kVA, 480-208/120V, 208-208/120V		3	5.333		11,800	360		12,160	13,500
0210	30 kVA, 400-208/120V, 208-208/120V		3	5.333		19,500	360		19,860	21,900
0250	50 kVA, 480-208/120V, 208-208/120V		2.50	6.400		10,700	430		11,130	12,300
0260	75 kVA, 480-208/120V, 208-208/120V		2.50	6.400		12,000	430		12,430	13,800
0270	100 kVA, 480-208/120V, 208-208/120V		2	8		12,900	540		13,440	15,000
0280	125 kVA, 480-208/120V, 208-208/120V		2	8		13,900	540		14,440	16,100
0290	150 kVA, 480-208/120V, 208-208/120V		2	8		12,700	540		13,240	14,800
0300	200 kVA, 480-208/120V, 208-208/120V		1.50	10.667		14,000	720		14,720	16,500
0310	225 kVA, 480-208/120V, 208-208/120V		1.50	10.667		14,800	720		15,520	17,400

26 27 73 – Door Chimes

26 27 73.10 Doorbell System		Crew	Daily Output	Labor-Hours	Unit	Material	Labor	Equipment	Total	Total Incl O&P
0010	**DOORBELL SYSTEM**, incl. transformer, button & signal									
0100	6" bell	1 Elec	4	2	Ea.	204	135		339	425
0200	Buzzer		4	2		164	135		299	380
1000	Door chimes, 2 notes		16	.500		41.50	33.50		75	95.50
1020	with ambient light		12	.667		125	45		170	205
1100	Tube type, 3 tube system		12	.667		305	45		350	400
1180	4 tube system		10	.800		485	54		539	610
1900	For transformer & button, add		5	1.600		20	108		128	182
3000	For push button only		24	.333		1.16	22.50		23.66	35
3200	Bell transformer		16	.500		37	33.50		70.50	90.50

26 28 Low-Voltage Circuit Protective Devices

26 28 13 – Fuses

26 28 13.10 Fuse Elements		Crew	Daily Output	Labor-Hours	Unit	Material	Labor	Equipment	Total	Total Incl O&P
0010	**FUSE ELEMENTS**									
0020	Cartridge, nonrenewable									
0050	250 volt, 30 amp	1 Elec	50	.160	Ea.	2.74	10.80		13.54	19
0100	60 amp		50	.160		4.42	10.80		15.22	21
0150	100 amp		40	.200		19.75	13.45		33.20	41.50
0200	200 amp		36	.222		42.50	14.95		57.45	69
0250	400 amp		30	.267		80	17.95		97.95	115
0300	600 amp		24	.333		129	22.50		151.50	176
0400	600 volt, 30 amp		40	.200		15.60	13.45		29.05	37
0450	60 amp		40	.200		19.40	13.45		32.85	41.50
0500	100 amp		36	.222		36.50	14.95		51.45	62
0550	200 amp		30	.267		76.50	17.95		94.45	111
0600	400 amp		24	.333		162	22.50		184.50	212
0650	600 amp		20	.400		288	27		315	355
0800	Dual element, time delay, 250 volt, 30 amp		50	.160		26	10.80		36.80	45
0840	50 amp		50	.160		16.30	10.80		27.10	34

26 28 13 – Fuses

26 28 13.10 Fuse Elements		Crew	Daily Output	Labor-Hours	Unit	Material	Labor	Equipment	Total	Total Incl O&P
						2023 Bare Costs				
0850	60 amp	1 Elec	50	.160	Ea.	31	10.80		41.80	50.50
0900	100 amp		40	.200		54	13.45		67.45	79.50
0950	200 amp		36	.222		116	14.95		130.95	149
1000	400 amp		30	.267		287	17.95		304.95	340
1050	600 amp		24	.333		153	22.50		175.50	203
1300	600 volt, 15 to 30 amp		40	.200		43.50	13.45		56.95	67.50
1350	35 to 60 amp		40	.200		84	13.45		97.45	112
1400	70 to 100 amp		36	.222		144	14.95		158.95	181
1450	110 to 200 amp		30	.267		277	17.95		294.95	330
1500	225 to 400 amp		24	.333		650	22.50		672.50	750
1550	600 amp		20	.400		810	27		837	930
1800	Class RK1, high capacity, 250 volt, 30 amp		50	.160		9.05	10.80		19.85	26
1850	60 amp		50	.160		16.90	10.80		27.70	34.50
1900	100 amp		40	.200		32.50	13.45		45.95	55.50
1950	200 amp		36	.222		74	14.95		88.95	103
2000	400 amp		30	.267		138	17.95		155.95	179
2050	600 amp		24	.333		225	22.50		247.50	282
2200	600 volt, 30 amp		40	.200		17.30	13.45		30.75	39
2250	60 amp		40	.200		25.50	13.45		38.95	48
2300	100 amp		36	.222		54	14.95		68.95	81.50
2350	200 amp		30	.267		107	17.95		124.95	145
2400	400 amp		24	.333		214	22.50		236.50	270
2450	600 amp		20	.400		420	27		447	505
2700	Class J, current limiting, 250 or 600 volt, 30 amp		40	.200		23.50	13.45		36.95	45.50
2750	60 amp		40	.200		38	13.45		51.45	61.50
2800	100 amp		36	.222		68	14.95		82.95	96.50
2850	200 amp		30	.267		115	17.95		132.95	154
2900	400 amp		24	.333		266	22.50		288.50	325
2950	600 amp		20	.400		415	27		442	495
3100	Class L, current limiting, 250 or 600 volt, 601 to 1,200 amp		16	.500		630	33.50		663.50	745
3150	1,500 to 1,600 amp		13	.615		920	41.50		961.50	1,050
3200	1,800 to 2,000 amp		10	.800		1,150	54		1,204	1,350
3250	2,500 amp		10	.800		1,700	54		1,754	1,950
3300	3,000 amp		8	1		1,925	67.50		1,992.50	2,225
3350	3,500 to 4,000 amp		8	1		2,700	67.50		2,767.50	3,075
3400	4,500 to 5,000 amp		6.70	1.194		2,725	80.50		2,805.50	3,125
3450	6,000 amp		5.70	1.404		4,225	94.50		4,319.50	4,775
3600	Plug, 120 volt, 1 to 10 amp		50	.160		5.10	10.80		15.90	21.50
3650	15 to 30 amp		50	.160		5.05	10.80		15.85	21.50
3700	Dual element 0.3 to 14 amp		50	.160		8.60	10.80		19.40	25.50
3750	15 to 30 amp		50	.160		8.50	10.80		19.30	25.50
3800	Fustat, 120 volt, 15 to 30 amp		50	.160		9.90	10.80		20.70	27
3850	0.3 to 14 amp		50	.160		10.20	10.80		21	27
3900	Adapters 0.3 to 10 amp		50	.160		8.65	10.80		19.45	25.50
3950	15 to 30 amp		50	.160		11	10.80		21.80	28
4000	F-frame current limiting fuse, 14 to 2 AWG, 3 ampere, 3P, aluminum terminal		40	.200		2,500	13.45		2,513.45	2,775
4010	7 ampere, 3P, aluminum terminal		40	.200		2,675	13.45		2,688.45	2,975
4020	15 AMP, 3P, aluminum terminal		40	.200		2,575	13.45		2,588.45	2,850
4030	30 AMP, 3P, aluminum terminal		40	.200		2,600	13.45		2,613.45	2,900
4040	50 AMP, 3P, aluminum terminal		40	.200		2,525	13.45		2,538.45	2,800
4050	F-frame current limiting fuse, 1 to 4/0 AWG, 100 AMP, 3P, aluminum terminal		40	.200		2,700	13.45		2,713.45	3,000
4060	150 AMP, 3P, aluminum terminal	↓	40	.200	↓	3,200	13.45		3,213.45	3,550

26 28 16 – Enclosed Switches and Circuit Breakers

26 28 16.10 Circuit Breakers		Crew	Daily Output	Labor-Hours	Unit	Material	Labor	Equipment	Total	Total Incl O&P
						2023 Bare Costs				
0010	CIRCUIT BREAKERS (in enclosure)									
0100	Enclosed (NEMA 1), 600 volt, 3 pole, 30 amp	1 Elec	3.20	2.500	Ea.	535	168		703	840
0200	60 amp		2.80	2.857		625	192		817	970
0400	100 amp		2.30	3.478		650	234		884	1,075
0500	200 amp		1.50	5.333		1,150	360		1,510	1,800
0600	225 amp		1.50	5.333		985	360		1,345	1,600
0700	400 amp	2 Elec	1.60	10		4,525	675		5,200	5,975
0800	600 amp		1.20	13.333		7,100	900		8,000	9,125
1000	800 amp		.94	17.021		8,700	1,150		9,850	11,300
1200	1,000 amp		.84	19.048		16,700	1,275		17,975	20,300
1220	1,200 amp		.80	20		17,900	1,350		19,250	21,700
1240	1,600 amp		.72	22.222		21,500	1,500		23,000	25,800
1260	2,000 amp		.64	25		26,100	1,675		27,775	31,300
1400	1,200 amp with ground fault		.80	20		23,100	1,350		24,450	27,400
1600	1,600 amp with ground fault		.72	22.222		27,400	1,500		28,900	32,300
1800	2,000 amp with ground fault		.64	25		29,300	1,675		30,975	34,800
2000	Disconnect, 240 volt 3 pole, 5 HP motor	1 Elec	3.20	2.500		115	168		283	375
2020	10 HP motor		3.20	2.500		224	168		392	495
2040	15 HP motor		2.80	2.857		735	192		927	1,100
2060	20 HP motor		2.30	3.478		795	234		1,029	1,225
2080	25 HP motor		2.30	3.478		715	234		949	1,150
2100	30 HP motor		2.30	3.478		1,075	234		1,309	1,550
2120	40 HP motor		2	4		1,525	269		1,794	2,075
2140	50 HP motor		1.50	5.333		1,525	360		1,885	2,200
2160	60 HP motor		1.50	5.333		3,500	360		3,860	4,375
2180	75 HP motor	2 Elec	2	8		3,500	540		4,040	4,650
2200	100 HP motor		1.60	10		3,500	675		4,175	4,850
2220	125 HP motor		1.60	10		3,500	675		4,175	4,850
2240	150 HP motor		1.20	13.333		6,850	900		7,750	8,850
2260	200 HP motor		1.20	13.333		8,925	900		9,825	11,100
2300	Enclosed (NEMA 7), explosion proof, 600 volt 3 pole, 50 amp	1 Elec	2.30	3.478		2,950	234		3,184	3,600
2350	100 amp		1.50	5.333		3,075	360		3,435	3,900
2400	150 amp		1	8		3,650	540		4,190	4,800
2450	250 amp	2 Elec	1.60	10		9,225	675		9,900	11,100
2500	400 amp	"	1.20	13.333		9,275	900		10,175	11,500

26 28 16.13 Circuit Breakers		Crew	Daily Output	Labor-Hours	Unit	Material	Labor	Equipment	Total	Total Incl O&P
0010	CIRCUIT BREAKERS									
0100	Circuit breaker current limiter, 225 to 400, ampere, 1 pole	1 Elec	48	.167	Ea.	1,300	11.25		1,311.25	1,450
0200	Circuit breaker current limiter, 200 to 500, ampere, 1 pole, thermal magnet		46	.174		1,700	11.70		1,711.70	1,900
0300	300 to 500, ampere, 1 pole, thermal magnet		46	.174		1,400	11.70		1,411.70	1,575
0400	Circuit breaker current limiter, 600 to 1000, ampere, 1 pole, tri pac		46	.174		1,950	11.70		1,961.70	2,175

26 28 16.20 Safety Switches		Crew	Daily Output	Labor-Hours	Unit	Material	Labor	Equipment	Total	Total Incl O&P
0010	SAFETY SWITCHES R262816-80									
0100	General duty 240 volt, 3 pole NEMA 1, fusible, 30 amp	1 Elec	3.20	2.500	Ea.	84.50	168		252.50	345
0200	60 amp		2.30	3.478		142	234		376	505
0300	100 amp		1.90	4.211		242	284		526	685
0400	200 amp		1.30	6.154		525	415		940	1,200
0500	400 amp	2 Elec	1.80	8.889		1,300	600		1,900	2,325
0600	600 amp	"	1.20	13.333		2,375	900		3,275	3,925
0610	Nonfusible, 30 amp	1 Elec	3.20	2.500		68	168		236	325
0650	60 amp		2.30	3.478		89	234		323	450
0700	100 amp		1.90	4.211		208	284		492	650

26 28 16.20 Safety Switches		Crew	Daily Output	Labor-Hours	Unit	2023 Bare Costs Material	Labor	Equipment	Total	Total Incl O&P
0750	200 amp	1 Elec	1.30	6.154	Ea.	385	415		800	1,050
0800	400 amp	2 Elec	1.80	8.889		950	600		1,550	1,950
0850	600 amp	"	1.20	13.333		1,725	900		2,625	3,225
1100	Heavy duty, 600 volt, 3 pole NEMA 1 nonfused									
1110	30 amp	1 Elec	3.20	2.500	Ea.	122	168		290	385
1500	60 amp		2.30	3.478		214	234		448	585
1700	100 amp		1.90	4.211		335	284		619	790
1900	200 amp		1.30	6.154		515	415		930	1,175
2100	400 amp	2 Elec	1.80	8.889		1,175	600		1,775	2,200
2300	600 amp		1.20	13.333		2,100	900		3,000	3,650
2500	800 amp		.94	17.021		3,900	1,150		5,050	6,000
2700	1,200 amp		.80	20		5,500	1,350		6,850	8,050
2900	Heavy duty, 240 volt, 3 pole NEMA 1 fusible									
2910	30 amp	1 Elec	3.20	2.500	Ea.	139	168		307	405
3000	60 amp		2.30	3.478		227	234		461	600
3300	100 amp		1.90	4.211		350	284		634	805
3500	200 amp		1.30	6.154		610	415		1,025	1,275
3700	400 amp	2 Elec	1.80	8.889		1,350	600		1,950	2,400
3900	600 amp		1.20	13.333		2,925	900		3,825	4,525
4100	800 amp		.94	17.021		6,050	1,150		7,200	8,350
4300	1,200 amp		.80	20		8,675	1,350		10,025	11,600
4340	2 pole fusible, 30 amp	1 Elec	3.50	2.286		105	154		259	345
4350	600 volt, 3 pole, fusible, 30 amp		3.20	2.500		230	168		398	505
4380	60 amp		2.30	3.478		276	234		510	655
4400	100 amp		1.90	4.211		505	284		789	975
4420	200 amp		1.30	6.154		720	415		1,135	1,400
4440	400 amp	2 Elec	1.80	8.889		1,875	600		2,475	2,950
4450	600 amp		1.20	13.333		3,300	900		4,200	4,975
4460	800 amp		.94	17.021		6,050	1,150		7,200	8,350
4480	1,200 amp		.80	20		8,675	1,350		10,025	11,600
4500	240 volt 3 pole NEMA 3R (no hubs), fusible									
4510	30 amp	1 Elec	3.10	2.581	Ea.	235	174		409	515
4700	60 amp		2.20	3.636		375	245		620	780
4900	100 amp		1.80	4.444		565	299		864	1,075
5100	200 amp		1.20	6.667		745	450		1,195	1,475
5300	400 amp	2 Elec	1.60	10		1,600	675		2,275	2,775
5500	600 amp	"	1	16		3,225	1,075		4,300	5,150
5510	Heavy duty, 600 volt, 3 pole 3 ph. NEMA 3R fusible, 30 amp	1 Elec	3.10	2.581		380	174		554	675
5520	60 amp		2.20	3.636		475	245		720	890
5530	100 amp		1.80	4.444		685	299		984	1,200
5540	200 amp		1.20	6.667		935	450		1,385	1,700
5550	400 amp	2 Elec	1.60	10		2,250	675		2,925	3,475
5700	600 volt, 3 pole NEMA 3R nonfused									
5710	30 amp	1 Elec	3.10	2.581	Ea.	212	174		386	490
5900	60 amp		2.20	3.636		370	245		615	775
6100	100 amp		1.80	4.444		520	299		819	1,025
6300	200 amp		1.20	6.667		630	450		1,080	1,350
6500	400 amp	2 Elec	1.60	10		1,600	675		2,275	2,775
6700	600 amp	"	1	16		3,200	1,075		4,275	5,125
6900	600 volt, 6 pole NEMA 3R nonfused, 30 amp	1 Elec	2.70	2.963		1,425	200		1,625	1,850
7100	60 amp		2	4		1,800	269		2,069	2,375
7300	100 amp		1.50	5.333		2,425	360		2,785	3,175
7500	200 amp		1.20	6.667		4,750	450		5,200	5,900

26 28 Low-Voltage Circuit Protective Devices

26 28 16 – Enclosed Switches and Circuit Breakers

26 28 16.20 Safety Switches		Crew	Daily Output	Labor-Hours	Unit	2023 Bare Costs Material	Labor	Equipment	Total	Total Incl O&P
7600	600 volt, 3 pole NEMA 7 explosion proof nonfused									
7610	30 amp	1 Elec	2.20	3.636	Ea.	1,800	245		2,045	2,350
7620	60 amp		1.80	4.444		2,150	299		2,449	2,825
7630	100 amp		1.20	6.667		3,600	450		4,050	4,650
7640	200 amp		.80	10		7,750	675		8,425	9,525
7710	600 volt 6 pole, NEMA 3R fusible, 30 amp		2.70	2.963		1,850	200		2,050	2,350
7900	60 amp		2	4		2,650	269		2,919	3,300
8100	100 amp		1.50	5.333		2,725	360		3,085	3,525
8110	240 volt 3 pole, NEMA 12 fusible, 30 amp		3.10	2.581		310	174		484	600
8120	60 amp		2.20	3.636		510	245		755	925
8130	100 amp		1.80	4.444		705	299		1,004	1,225
8140	200 amp		1.20	6.667		915	450		1,365	1,675
8150	400 amp	2 Elec	1.60	10		1,950	675		2,625	3,150
8160	600 amp	"	1	16		3,700	1,075		4,775	5,675
8180	600 volt 3 pole, NEMA 12 fusible, 30 amp	1 Elec	3.10	2.581		465	174		639	770
8190	60 amp		2.20	3.636		555	245		800	975
8200	100 amp		1.80	4.444		790	299		1,089	1,325
8210	200 amp		1.20	6.667		1,100	450		1,550	1,875
8220	400 amp	2 Elec	1.60	10		2,725	675		3,400	4,000
8230	600 amp	"	1	16		4,625	1,075		5,700	6,675
8240	600 volt 3 pole, NEMA 12 nonfused, 30 amp	1 Elec	3.10	2.581		292	174		466	580
8250	60 amp		2.20	3.636		395	245		640	800
8260	100 amp		1.80	4.444		585	299		884	1,100
8270	200 amp		1.20	6.667		705	450		1,155	1,450
8280	400 amp	2 Elec	1.60	10		1,750	675		2,425	2,925
8290	600 amp	"	1	16		3,550	1,075		4,625	5,500
8310	600 volt, 3 pole NEMA 4 fusible, 30 amp	1 Elec	3	2.667		1,100	180		1,280	1,500
8320	60 amp		2.20	3.636		1,175	245		1,420	1,675
8330	100 amp		1.80	4.444		2,450	299		2,749	3,150
8340	200 amp		1.20	6.667		3,300	450		3,750	4,300
8350	400 amp	2 Elec	1.60	10		6,800	675		7,475	8,475
8360	600 volt 3 pole NEMA 4 nonfused, 30 amp	1 Elec	3	2.667		945	180		1,125	1,325
8370	60 amp		2.20	3.636		1,075	245		1,320	1,550
8380	100 amp		1.80	4.444		2,200	299		2,499	2,875
8390	200 amp		1.20	6.667		2,975	450		3,425	3,950
8400	400 amp	2 Elec	1.60	10		5,550	675		6,225	7,100
8490	Motor starters, manual, single phase, NEMA 1	1 Elec	6.40	1.250		128	84		212	266
8500	NEMA 4		4	2		320	135		455	550
8700	NEMA 7		4	2		365	135		500	605
8900	NEMA 1 with pilot		6.40	1.250		143	84		227	282
8920	3 pole, NEMA 1, 230/460 volt, 5 HP, size 0		3.50	2.286		254	154		408	510
8940	10 HP, size 1		2	4		300	269		569	730
9010	Disc. switch, 600 volt 3 pole fusible, 30 amp, to 10 HP motor		3.20	2.500		450	168		618	745
9050	60 amp, to 30 HP motor		2.30	3.478		1,025	234		1,259	1,500
9070	100 amp, to 60 HP motor		1.90	4.211		1,025	284		1,309	1,575
9100	200 amp, to 125 HP motor		1.30	6.154		1,550	415		1,965	2,325
9110	400 amp, to 200 HP motor	2 Elec	1.80	8.889		3,925	600		4,525	5,200

26 28 16.40 Time Switches		Crew	Daily Output	Labor-Hours	Unit	Material	Labor	Equipment	Total	Total Incl O&P
0010	**TIME SWITCHES**									
0100	Single pole, single throw, 24 hour dial	1 Elec	4	2	Ea.	172	135		307	390
0200	24 hour dial with reserve power		3.60	2.222		930	150		1,080	1,250
0300	Astronomic dial		3.60	2.222		320	150		470	575

26 28 Low-Voltage Circuit Protective Devices

26 28 16 – Enclosed Switches and Circuit Breakers

26 28 16.40 Time Switches		Crew	Daily Output	Labor-Hours	Unit	Material	Labor	Equipment	Total	Total Incl O&P
						2023 Bare Costs				
0400	Astronomic dial with reserve power	1 Elec	3.30	2.424	Ea.	1,200	163		1,363	1,575
0500	7 day calendar dial		3.30	2.424		268	163		431	540
0600	7 day calendar dial with reserve power		3.20	2.500		230	168		398	505
0700	Photo cell 2,000 watt		8	1		28	67.50		95.50	131
1080	Load management device, 4 loads		2	4		1,450	269		1,719	1,975
1100	8 loads		1	8		3,250	540		3,790	4,375

26 28 16.50 Meter Socket Entry Hub		Crew	Daily Output	Labor-Hours	Unit	Material	Labor	Equipment	Total	Total Incl O&P
0010	**METER SOCKET ENTRY HUB**									
0100	Meter socket entry hub closing cap, 3/4 to 4 inch	1 Elec	40	.200	Ea.	2.10	13.45		15.55	22.50
0110	Meter socket entry hub, 3/4 conduit		40	.200		10.65	13.45		24.10	31.50
0120	1 inch conduit		40	.200		10.65	13.45		24.10	31.50
0130	1.25 inch conduit		40	.200		10.55	13.45		24	31.50
0140	1.50 inch conduit		40	.200		10.60	13.45		24.05	31.50
0150	2 inch conduit		40	.200		31.50	13.45		44.95	54.50
0160	2.50 inch conduit		40	.200		40	13.45		53.45	64
0170	3 inch conduit		40	.200		72.50	13.45		85.95	100

26 29 Low-Voltage Controllers

26 29 13 – Enclosed Controllers

26 29 13.10 Contactors, AC		Crew	Daily Output	Labor-Hours	Unit	Material	Labor	Equipment	Total	Total Incl O&P
0010	**CONTACTORS, AC** Enclosed (NEMA 1)									
0050	Lighting, 600 volt 3 pole, electrically held									
0100	20 amp	1 Elec	4	2	Ea.	555	135		690	810
0200	30 amp		3.60	2.222		360	150		510	615
0300	60 amp		3	2.667		780	180		960	1,125
0400	100 amp		2.50	3.200		1,300	216		1,516	1,750
0500	200 amp		1.40	5.714		3,250	385		3,635	4,150
0600	300 amp	2 Elec	1.60	10		10,600	675		11,275	12,700
0800	600 volt 3 pole, mechanically held, 30 amp	1 Elec	3.60	2.222		680	150		830	965
0900	60 amp		3	2.667		1,425	180		1,605	1,825
1000	75 amp		2.80	2.857		1,850	192		2,042	2,300
1100	100 amp		2.50	3.200		1,850	216		2,066	2,350
1200	150 amp		2	4		4,525	269		4,794	5,375
1300	200 amp		1.40	5.714		5,175	385		5,560	6,275
1500	Magnetic with auxiliary contact, size 00, 9 amp		4	2		273	135		408	500
1600	Size 0, 18 amp		4	2		325	135		460	555
1700	Size 1, 27 amp		3.60	2.222		540	150		690	815
1800	Size 2, 45 amp		3	2.667		875	180		1,055	1,225
1900	Size 3, 90 amp		2.50	3.200		1,100	216		1,316	1,525
2000	Size 4, 135 amp		2.30	3.478		2,525	234		2,759	3,125
2100	Size 5, 270 amp	2 Elec	1.80	8.889		5,275	600		5,875	6,725
2200	Size 6, 540 amp		1.20	13.333		15,500	900		16,400	18,300
2300	Size 7, 810 amp		1	16		20,800	1,075		21,875	24,500
2310	Size 8, 1,215 amp		.80	20		32,400	1,350		33,750	37,700
2500	Magnetic, 240 volt, 1-2 pole, 0.75 HP motor	1 Elec	4	2		218	135		353	440
2520	2 HP motor		3.60	2.222		455	150		605	720
2540	5 HP motor		2.50	3.200		595	216		811	970
2560	10 HP motor		1.40	5.714		975	385		1,360	1,650
2600	240 volt or less, 3 pole, 0.75 HP motor		4	2		218	135		353	440
2620	5 HP motor		3.60	2.222		270	150		420	520
2640	10 HP motor		3.60	2.222		315	150		465	565

26 29 13 – Enclosed Controllers

26 29 13.10 Contactors, AC		Crew	Daily Output	Labor-Hours	Unit	2023 Bare Costs Material	Labor	Equipment	Total	Total Incl O&P
2660	15 HP motor	1 Elec	2.50	3.200	Ea.	630	216		846	1,000
2700	25 HP motor	↓	2.50	3.200		630	216		846	1,000
2720	30 HP motor	2 Elec	2.80	5.714		1,050	385		1,435	1,725
2740	40 HP motor		2.80	5.714		1,050	385		1,435	1,725
2760	50 HP motor		1.60	10		1,050	675		1,725	2,150
2800	75 HP motor		1.60	10		2,450	675		3,125	3,700
2820	100 HP motor		1	16		2,450	1,075		3,525	4,300
2860	150 HP motor		1	16		5,225	1,075		6,300	7,350
2880	200 HP motor	↓	1	16		5,225	1,075		6,300	7,350
3000	600 volt, 3 pole, 5 HP motor	1 Elec	4	2		270	135		405	495
3020	10 HP motor		3.60	2.222		315	150		465	565
3040	25 HP motor		3	2.667		630	180		810	955
3100	50 HP motor	↓	2.50	3.200		1,050	216		1,266	1,475
3160	100 HP motor	2 Elec	2.80	5.714		2,450	385		2,835	3,275
3220	200 HP motor	"	1.60	10	↓	5,225	675		5,900	6,750

26 29 13.20 Control Stations		Crew	Daily Output	Labor-Hours	Unit	Material	Labor	Equipment	Total	Total Incl O&P
0010	**CONTROL STATIONS**									
0050	NEMA 1, heavy duty, stop/start	1 Elec	8	1	Ea.	335	67.50		402.50	470
0100	Stop/start, pilot light		6.20	1.290		370	87		457	540
0200	Hand/off/automatic		6.20	1.290		375	87		462	540
0400	Stop/start/reverse		5.30	1.509		485	102		587	685
0500	NEMA 7, heavy duty, stop/start		6	1.333		470	90		560	650
0600	Stop/start, pilot light		4	2		680	135		815	950
0700	NEMA 7 or 9, 1 element		6	1.333		655	90		745	855
0800	2 element		6	1.333		845	90		935	1,075
0900	3 element		4	2		1,200	135		1,335	1,525
0910	Selector switch, 2 position		6	1.333		720	90		810	930
0920	3 position		4	2		720	135		855	995
0930	Oiltight, 1 element		8	1		270	67.50		337.50	395
0940	2 element		6.20	1.290		272	87		359	430
0950	3 element		5.30	1.509		370	102		472	555
0960	Selector switch, 2 position		6.20	1.290		287	87		374	445
0970	3 position	↓	5.30	1.509	↓	246	102		348	420

26 29 13.30 Control Switches		Crew	Daily Output	Labor-Hours	Unit	Material	Labor	Equipment	Total	Total Incl O&P
0010	**CONTROL SWITCHES** Field installed									
6000	Push button 600 V 10A, momentary contact									
6150	Standard operator with colored button	1 Elec	34	.235	Ea.	50	15.85		65.85	78.50
6160	With single block 1NO 1NC		18	.444		69	30		99	121
6170	With double block 2NO 2NC		15	.533		106	36		142	171
6180	Std operator w/mushroom button 1-9/16" diam.	↓	34	.235	↓	80.50	15.85		96.35	112
6190	Std operator w/mushroom button 2-1/4" diam.									
6200	With single block 1NO 1NC	1 Elec	18	.444	Ea.	68	30		98	119
6210	With double block 2NO 2NC		15	.533		91	36		127	154
6500	Maintained contact, selector operator		34	.235		68	15.85		83.85	98
6510	With single block 1NO 1NC		18	.444		91	30		121	145
6520	With double block 2NO 2NC		15	.533		114	36		150	180
6560	Spring-return selector operator		34	.235		68	15.85		83.85	98
6570	With single block 1NO 1NC		18	.444		91	30		121	145
6580	With double block 2NO 2NC	↓	15	.533	↓	114	36		150	180
6620	Transformer operator w/illuminated									
6630	button 6 V #12 lamp	1 Elec	32	.250	Ea.	114	16.85		130.85	151
6640	With single block 1NO 1NC w/guard	↓	16	.500	↓	138	33.50		171.50	202

26 29 Low-Voltage Controllers

26 29 13 – Enclosed Controllers

26 29 13.30 Control Switches

26 29 13.30 Control Switches		Crew	Daily Output	Labor-Hours	Unit	Material (2023 Bare Costs)	Labor (2023 Bare Costs)	Equipment (2023 Bare Costs)	Total (2023 Bare Costs)	Total Incl O&P
6650	With double block 2NO 2NC w/guard	1 Elec	13	.615	Ea.	161	41.50		202.50	239
6690	Combination operator		34	.235		68	15.85		83.85	98
6700	With single block 1NO 1NC		18	.444		91	30		121	145
6710	With double block 2NO 2NC		15	.533		114	36		150	180
9000	Indicating light unit, full voltage									
9010	110-125 V front mount	1 Elec	32	.250	Ea.	101	16.85		117.85	136
9020	130 V resistor type		32	.250		73.50	16.85		90.35	106
9030	6 V transformer type		32	.250		83.50	16.85		100.35	117

26 29 13.40 Relays

26 29 13.40 Relays		Crew	Daily Output	Labor-Hours	Unit	Material	Labor	Equipment	Total	Total Incl O&P
0010	**RELAYS** Enclosed (NEMA 1)									
0050	600 volt AC, 1 pole, 12 amp	1 Elec	5.30	1.509	Ea.	117	102		219	279
0100	2 pole, 12 amp		5	1.600		145	108		253	320
0200	4 pole, 10 amp		4.50	1.778		193	120		313	390
0500	250 volt DC, 1 pole, 15 amp		5.30	1.509		153	102		255	320
0600	2 pole, 10 amp		5	1.600		265	108		373	450
0700	4 pole, 4 amp		4.50	1.778		315	120		435	525

26 29 23 – Variable-Frequency Motor Controllers

26 29 23.10 Variable Frequency Drives/Adj. Frequency Drives

26 29 23.10 Variable Frequency Drives/Adj. Frequency Drives			Crew	Daily Output	Labor-Hours	Unit	Material	Labor	Equipment	Total	Total Incl O&P
0010	**VARIABLE FREQUENCY DRIVES/ADJ. FREQUENCY DRIVES**										
0100	Enclosed (NEMA 1), 460 volt, for 3 HP motor size	G	1 Elec	.80	10	Ea.	1,750	675		2,425	2,925
0110	5 HP motor size	G		.80	10		1,975	675		2,650	3,175
0120	7.5 HP motor size	G		.67	11.940		2,400	805		3,205	3,850
0130	10 HP motor size	G		.67	11.940		2,650	805		3,455	4,100
0140	15 HP motor size	G	2 Elec	.89	17.978		3,400	1,200		4,600	5,525
0150	20 HP motor size	G		.89	17.978		4,275	1,200		5,475	6,500
0160	25 HP motor size	G		.67	23.881		5,075	1,600		6,675	7,975
0170	30 HP motor size	G		.67	23.881		6,150	1,600		7,750	9,175
0180	40 HP motor size	G		.67	23.881		7,125	1,600		8,725	10,200
0190	50 HP motor size	G		.53	30.189		9,375	2,025		11,400	13,300
0200	60 HP motor size	G	R-3	.56	35.714		11,800	2,400	345	14,545	16,900
0210	75 HP motor size	G		.56	35.714		13,600	2,400	345	16,345	18,900
0220	100 HP motor size	G		.50	40		16,400	2,700	385	19,485	22,500
0230	125 HP motor size	G		.50	40		17,800	2,700	385	20,885	24,000
0240	150 HP motor size	G		.50	40		23,300	2,700	385	26,385	30,000
0250	200 HP motor size	G		.42	47.619		32,900	3,200	460	36,560	41,500
1100	Custom-engineered, 460 volt, for 3 HP motor size	G	1 Elec	.56	14.286		4,325	960		5,285	6,200
1110	5 HP motor size	G		.56	14.286		4,400	960		5,360	6,250
1120	7.5 HP motor size	G		.47	17.021		3,725	1,150		4,875	5,800
1130	10 HP motor size	G		.47	17.021		3,950	1,150		5,100	6,050
1140	15 HP motor size	G	2 Elec	.62	25.806		5,975	1,750		7,725	9,125
1150	20 HP motor size	G		.62	25.806		3,675	1,750		5,425	6,625
1160	25 HP motor size	G		.47	34.043		6,875	2,300		9,175	11,000
1170	30 HP motor size	G		.47	34.043		7,975	2,300		10,275	12,200
1180	40 HP motor size	G		.47	34.043		9,000	2,300		11,300	13,300
1190	50 HP motor size	G		.37	43.243		13,300	2,900		16,200	18,900
1200	60 HP motor size	G	R-3	.39	51.282		20,000	3,450	495	23,945	27,600
1210	75 HP motor size	G		.39	51.282		16,700	3,450	495	20,645	24,100
1220	100 HP motor size	G		.35	57.143		23,400	3,850	550	27,800	32,100
1230	125 HP motor size	G		.35	57.143		25,100	3,850	550	29,500	33,900
1240	150 HP motor size	G		.35	57.143		28,400	3,850	550	32,800	37,600
1250	200 HP motor size	G		.29	68.966		32,700	4,650	665	38,015	43,500
2000	For complex & special design systems to meet specific										

26 29 Low-Voltage Controllers

26 29 23 – Variable-Frequency Motor Controllers

26 29 23.10 Variable Frequency Drives/Adj. Frequency Drives			Crew	Daily Output	Labor-Hours	Unit	2023 Bare Costs Material	Labor	Equipment	Total	Total Incl O&P
2010	requirements, obtain quote from vendor.										

26 31 Photovoltaic Collectors

26 31 13 – Photovoltaics

26 31 13.50 Solar Energy - Photovoltaics

			Crew	Daily Output	Labor-Hours	Unit	Material	Labor	Equipment	Total	Total Incl O&P
0010	**SOLAR ENERGY - PHOTOVOLTAICS**										
0220	Alt. energy source, photovoltaic module, 6 watt, 15 V	G	1 Elec	8	1	Ea.	61	67.50		128.50	167
0230	10 watt, 16.3 V	G		8	1		122	67.50		189.50	234
0240	20 watt, 14.5 V	G		8	1		96	67.50		163.50	205
0250	36 watt, 17 V	G		8	1		193	67.50		260.50	315
0260	55 watt, 17 V	G		8	1		142	67.50		209.50	256
0270	75 watt, 17 V	G		8	1		450	67.50		517.50	595
0280	130 watt, 33 V	G		8	1		425	67.50		492.50	565
0290	140 watt, 33 V	G		8	1		515	67.50		582.50	665
0300	150 watt, 24 V	G		8	1		245	67.50		312.50	370
0304	300 watt, 37 V	G		8	1		198	67.50		265.50	320
0306	350 watt, 37 V	G		8	1		259	67.50		326.50	385
0307	400 watt, 37 V	G		8	1		277	67.50		344.50	405
0308	450 watt, 37 V	G		8	1		310	67.50		377.50	445
0310	DC to AC inverter for, 12 V, 2,000 watt	G		4	2		1,625	135		1,760	1,975
0320	12 V, 2,500 watt	G		4	2		1,225	135		1,360	1,525
0330	24 V, 2,500 watt	G		4	2		1,750	135		1,885	2,125
0340	12 V, 3,000 watt	G		3	2.667		1,375	180		1,555	1,775
0350	24 V, 3,000 watt	G		3	2.667		1,250	180		1,430	1,650
0360	24 V, 4,000 watt	G		2	4		1,475	269		1,744	2,025
0370	48 V, 4,000 watt	G		2	4		3,300	269		3,569	4,025
0380	48 V, 5,500 watt	G		2	4		2,925	269		3,194	3,625
0390	PV components, combiner box, 10 lug, NEMA 3R enclosure	G		4	2		315	135		450	545
0400	Fuse, 15 A for combiner box	G		40	.200		43.50	13.45		56.95	67.50
0410	Battery charger controller w/temperature sensor	G		4	2		465	135		600	710
0420	Digital readout panel, displays hours, volts, amps, etc.	G		4	2		165	135		300	380
0430	Deep cycle solar battery, 6 V, 180 Ah (C/20)	G		8	1		365	67.50		432.50	500
0440	Battery interconn, 15" AWG #2/0, sealed w/copper ring lugs	G		16	.500		24.50	33.50		58	76.50
0442	Battery interconn, 24" AWG #2/0, sealed w/copper ring lugs	G		16	.500		27.50	33.50		61	80.50
0444	Battery interconn, 60" AWG #2/0, sealed w/copper ring lugs	G		16	.500		51.50	33.50		85	107
0446	Batt temp computer probe, RJ11 jack, 15' cord	G		16	.500		23.50	33.50		57	75.50
0450	System disconnect, DC 175 amp circuit breaker	G		8	1		123	67.50		190.50	236
0460	Conduit box for inverter	G		8	1		59	67.50		126.50	165
0470	Low voltage disconnect	G		8	1		340	67.50		407.50	475
0480	Vented battery enclosure, wood	G	1 Carp	2	4		299	234		533	680
0490	PV rack system, roof, non-penetrating ballast, 1 panel	G	R-1A	30.50	.525		44.50	32		76.50	96.50
0500	Penetrating surface mount, on steel framing, 1 panel			5.13	3.122		29	189		218	315
0510	On wood framing, 1 panel			11	1.455		32.50	88		120.50	167
0520	With standoff, 1 panel			11	1.455		37	88		125	172
0530	Ground, ballast, fixed, 3 panel			20.50	.780		385	47.50		432.50	490
0540	4 panel			20.50	.780		1,600	47.50		1,647.50	1,825
0550	5 panel			20.50	.780		2,100	47.50		2,147.50	2,400
0560	6 panel			20.50	.780		2,425	47.50		2,472.50	2,750
0570	Adjustable, 3 panel			20.50	.780		1,225	47.50		1,272.50	1,425
0580	4 panel			20.50	.780		1,700	47.50		1,747.50	1,950
0590	5 panel			20.50	.780		2,250	47.50		2,297.50	2,550

26 31 Photovoltaic Collectors

26 31 13 – Photovoltaics

26 31 13.50 Solar Energy - Photovoltaics		Crew	Daily Output	Labor-Hours	Unit	2023 Bare Costs Material	Labor	Equipment	Total	Total Incl O&P
0600	6 panel	R-1A	20.50	.780	Ea.	2,575	47.50		2,622.50	2,900
0605	Top of Pole, see 26 56 13.10 3800+, 5400+ & 33 71 16.33 7400+ for poles									
0610	Passive tracking, 1 panel	R-1A	20.50	.780	Ea.	400	47.50		447.50	510
0620	2 panel		20.50	.780		450	47.50		497.50	565
0630	3 panel		20.50	.780		575	47.50		622.50	705
0640	4 panel		20.50	.780		1,175	47.50		1,222.50	1,375
0650	6 panel		20.50	.780		1,800	47.50		1,847.50	2,050
0660	8 panel		20.50	.780		2,375	47.50		2,422.50	2,700
1020	Photovoltaic module, Thin film	1 Elec	8	1		96	67.50		163.50	205
1040	Photovoltaic module, Cadium telluride		8	1		142	67.50		209.50	256
1060	Photovoltaic module, Polycrystalline		8	1		96	67.50		163.50	205
1080	Photovoltaic module, Monocrystalline		8	1		425	67.50		492.50	565

26 32 Packaged Generator Assemblies

26 32 13 – Engine Generators

26 32 13.13 Diesel-Engine-Driven Generator Sets

		Crew	Daily Output	Labor-Hours	Unit	Material	Labor	Equipment	Total	Total Incl O&P
0010	**DIESEL-ENGINE-DRIVEN GENERATOR SETS**									
2000	Diesel engine, including battery, charger,									
2010	muffler & day tank, 30 kW	R-3	.55	36.364	Ea.	16,200	2,450	350	19,000	21,800
2100	50 kW		.42	47.619		18,600	3,200	460	22,260	25,700
2110	60 kW		.39	51.282		26,200	3,450	495	30,145	34,500
2200	75 kW		.35	57.143		30,700	3,850	550	35,100	40,100
2300	100 kW		.31	64.516		35,900	4,350	625	40,875	46,500
2400	125 kW		.29	68.966		32,300	4,650	665	37,615	43,100
2500	150 kW		.26	76.923		24,300	5,175	740	30,215	35,200
2501	Generator set, dsl eng in alum encl, incl btry, chgr, muf & day tank,150 kW		.26	76.923		47,600	5,175	740	53,515	61,000
2600	175 kW		.25	80		42,100	5,375	770	48,245	55,000
2700	200 kW		.24	83.333		71,000	5,600	805	77,405	87,000
2800	250 kW		.23	86.957		57,500	5,850	840	64,190	72,500
2850	275 kW		.22	90.909		77,500	6,125	875	84,500	95,000
2900	300 kW		.22	90.909		64,500	6,125	875	71,500	80,500
3000	350 kW		.20	100		79,000	6,725	965	86,690	98,000
3100	400 kW		.19	105		76,000	7,100	1,025	84,125	95,000
3200	500 kW		.18	111		86,000	7,475	1,075	94,550	107,000
3220	600 kW		.17	118		155,500	7,925	1,125	164,550	184,000
3230	650 kW	R-13	.38	111		226,500	7,225	1,600	235,325	261,500
3240	750 kW		.38	111		226,000	7,225	1,600	234,825	261,000
3250	800 kW		.36	117		207,500	7,625	1,675	216,800	241,000
3260	900 kW		.31	135		276,000	8,850	1,950	286,800	319,000
3270	1,000 kW		.27	156		256,000	10,200	2,250	268,450	299,000

26 32 13.16 Gas-Engine-Driven Generator Sets

		Crew	Daily Output	Labor-Hours	Unit	Material	Labor	Equipment	Total	Total Incl O&P
0010	**GAS-ENGINE-DRIVEN GENERATOR SETS**									
0020	Gas or gasoline operated, includes battery,									
0050	charger & muffler									
0200	7.5 kW	R-3	.83	24.096	Ea.	8,175	1,625	233	10,033	11,700
0300	11.5 kW		.71	28.169		11,600	1,900	272	13,772	15,900
0400	20 kW		.63	31.746		11,800	2,150	305	14,255	16,500
0460	25 kW, steel enclosure		.63	31.746		11,900	2,150	305	14,355	16,600
0470	27 kW, aluminum enclosure		.63	31.746		12,400	2,150	305	14,855	17,100
0480	30 kW, steel enclosure		.63	31.746		19,100	2,150	305	21,555	24,500
0485	120/208 V, 30kW		.63	31.746		20,700	2,150	305	23,155	26,200

26 32 Packaged Generator Assemblies

26 32 13 – Engine Generators

26 32 13.16 Gas-Engine-Driven Generator Sets		Crew	Daily Output	Labor-Hours	Unit	Material	Labor (2023 Bare Costs)	Equipment	Total	Total Incl O&P
0500	35 kW	R-3	.55	36.364	Ea.	16,700	2,450	350	19,500	22,400
0510	45 kW, steel enclosure		.50	40		36,900	2,700	385	39,985	45,000
0515	48 kW, aluminum enclosure		.50	40		17,800	2,700	385	20,885	24,000
0520	60 kW	↓	.50	40		16,100	2,700	385	19,185	22,200
0550	70 kW, aluminum enclosure	R-13	.46	91.304		45,900	5,975	1,325	53,200	61,000
0600	80 kW		.40	105		26,500	6,850	1,525	34,875	41,100
0700	100 kW		.33	127		29,000	8,300	1,850	39,150	46,300
0800	125 kW		.28	150		31,700	9,800	2,175	43,675	52,000
0850	130 kW, aluminum enclosure		.28	150		70,500	9,800	2,175	82,475	94,500
0875	150 kW, aluminum enclosure		.25	168		86,500	11,000	2,425	99,925	114,000
0900	185 kW	↓	.25	168	↓	79,000	11,000	2,425	92,425	106,000

26 33 Battery Equipment

26 33 19 – Battery Units

26 33 19.10 Battery Units		Crew	Daily Output	Labor-Hours	Unit	Material	Labor	Equipment	Total	Total Incl O&P
0010	**BATTERY UNITS**									
0500	Salt water battery, 2.1 kWA, 24V, 750W, 30A, wired in crate, IP22 rated	1 Elec	16.25	.492	Ea.	945	33		978	1,100
0510	2.2 kWh, 48V, 800W, 17A, wired in crate, IP22 rated		16.25	.492		1,175	33		1,208	1,350
0520	25.9 kWh, 48V, 11700W, 240A, wired in crate, IP2X rated		16.25	.492		14,100	33		14,133	15,600
0700	Nickel iron nife battery, deep cycle, 100Ah, 12V, 10 cells		14.25	.561		1,025	38		1,063	1,175
0710	24V, 10 cells		14.25	.561		2,175	38		2,213	2,425
0720	48V, 10 cells		14.25	.561		4,050	38		4,088	4,525
0730	Nickel iron nife battery, deep cycle, 300Ah, 12V, 10 cells		12.25	.653		3,000	44		3,044	3,375
0740	24V, 10 cells		12.25	.653		5,975	44		6,019	6,650
0750	48V, 10 cells	↓	12.25	.653	↓	12,500	44		12,544	13,900

26 33 43 – Battery Chargers

26 33 43.55 Electric Vehicle Charging		Crew	Daily Output	Labor-Hours	Unit	Material	Labor	Equipment	Total	Total Incl O&P
0010	**ELECTRIC VEHICLE CHARGING**									
0020	Level 2, wall mounted									
2200	Heavy duty G	R-1A	15.36	1.042	Ea.	800	63		863	975
2210	with RFID G		12.29	1.302		4,525	79		4,604	5,100
2300	Free standing, single connector G		10.24	1.563		4,325	94.50		4,419.50	4,900
2310	with RFID G		8.78	1.822		4,675	110		4,785	5,325
2320	Double connector G		7.68	2.083		4,375	126		4,501	5,000
2330	with RFID G	↓	6.83	2.343	↓	9,100	142		9,242	10,200

26 33 53 – Static Uninterruptible Power Supply

26 33 53.10 Uninterruptible Power Supply/Conditioner Trans.		Crew	Daily Output	Labor-Hours	Unit	Material	Labor	Equipment	Total	Total Incl O&P
0010	**UNINTERRUPTIBLE POWER SUPPLY/CONDITIONER TRANSFORMERS**									
0100	Volt. regulating, isolating transf., w/invert. & 10 min. battery pack									
0110	Single-phase, 120 V, 0.35 kVA R263353-80	1 Elec	2.29	3.493	Ea.	1,225	235		1,460	1,700
0120	0.5 kVA		2	4		1,275	269		1,544	1,800
0130	For additional 55 min. battery, add to 0.35 kVA		2.29	3.493		720	235		955	1,150
0140	Add to 0.5 kVA		1.14	7.018		755	475		1,230	1,525
0150	Single-phase, 120 V, 0.75 kVA		.80	10		1,625	675		2,300	2,775
0160	1.0 kVA	↓	.80	10		2,325	675		3,000	3,550
0170	1.5 kVA	2 Elec	1.14	14.035		3,975	945		4,920	5,775
0180	2 kVA	"	.89	17.978		4,325	1,200		5,525	6,550
0190	3 kVA	R-3	.63	31.746		5,325	2,150	305	7,780	9,350
0200	5 kVA		.42	47.619		7,600	3,200	460	11,260	13,600
0210	7.5 kVA	↓	.33	60.606	↓	9,675	4,075	585	14,335	17,400

26 33 Battery Equipment

26 33 53 – Static Uninterruptible Power Supply

26 33 53.10 Uninterruptible Power Supply/Conditioner Trans.		Crew	Daily Output	Labor-Hours	Unit	Material	2023 Bare Costs Labor	Equipment	Total	Total Incl O&P
0220	10 kVA	R-3	.28	71.429	Ea.	10,800	4,800	690	16,290	19,700
0230	15 kVA		.22	90.909		15,400	6,125	875	22,400	27,000
0240	3 phase, 120/208 V input 120/208 V output, 20 kVA, incl 17 min. battery		.21	95.238		29,200	6,425	920	36,545	42,700
0242	30 kVA, incl 11 min. battery		.20	100		32,700	6,725	965	40,390	47,100
0250	40 kVA, incl 15 min. battery		.20	100		43,700	6,725	965	51,390	59,000
0260	480 V input 277/480 V output, 60 kVA, incl 6 min. battery		.19	105		49,100	7,100	1,025	57,225	65,500
0262	80 kVA, incl 4 min. battery		.19	105		58,500	7,100	1,025	66,625	76,000
0400	For additional 34 min./15 min. battery, add to 40 kVA	▼	.71	28.011	▼	15,200	1,875	270	17,345	19,900
0600	For complex & special design systems to meet specific									
0610	requirements, obtain quote from vendor									

26 35 Power Filters and Conditioners

26 35 13 – Capacitors

26 35 13.10 Capacitors Indoor		Crew	Daily Output	Labor-Hours	Unit	Material	Labor	Equipment	Total	Total Incl O&P
0010	**CAPACITORS INDOOR**									
0020	240 volts, single & 3 phase, 0.5 kVAR	1 Elec	2.70	2.963	Ea.	630	200		830	990
0100	1.0 kVAR		2.70	2.963		470	200		670	815
0150	2.5 kVAR		2	4		860	269		1,129	1,350
0200	5.0 kVAR		1.80	4.444		825	299		1,124	1,350
0250	7.5 kVAR		1.60	5		1,575	335		1,910	2,250
0300	10 kVAR		1.50	5.333		1,825	360		2,185	2,525
0350	15 kVAR		1.30	6.154		1,375	415		1,790	2,150
0400	20 kVAR		1.10	7.273		2,850	490		3,340	3,850
0450	25 kVAR		1	8		3,275	540		3,815	4,400
1000	480 volts, single & 3 phase, 1 kVAR		2.70	2.963		575	200		775	925
1050	2 kVAR		2.70	2.963		660	200		860	1,025
1100	5 kVAR		2	4		835	269		1,104	1,325
1150	7.5 kVAR		2	4		900	269		1,169	1,400
1200	10 kVAR		2	4		1,275	269		1,544	1,800
1250	15 kVAR		2	4		1,500	269		1,769	2,050
1300	20 kVAR		1.60	5		1,650	335		1,985	2,300
1350	30 kVAR		1.50	5.333		1,450	360		1,810	2,125
1400	40 kVAR		1.20	6.667		2,450	450		2,900	3,375
1450	50 kVAR		1.10	7.273		2,875	490		3,365	3,900
2000	600 volts, single & 3 phase, 1 kVAR		2.70	2.963		595	200		795	950
2050	2 kVAR		2.70	2.963		680	200		880	1,050
2100	5 kVAR		2	4		835	269		1,104	1,325
2150	7.5 kVAR		2	4		900	269		1,169	1,400
2200	10 kVAR		2	4		1,275	269		1,544	1,800
2250	15 kVAR		1.60	5		1,500	335		1,835	2,150
2300	20 kVAR		1.60	5		1,650	335		1,985	2,300
2350	25 kVAR		1.50	5.333		1,800	360		2,160	2,525
2400	35 kVAR		1.40	5.714		2,225	385		2,610	3,025
2450	50 kVAR	▼	1.30	6.154	▼	2,900	415		3,315	3,800

26 35 26 – Harmonic Filters

26 35 26.10 Computer Isolation Transformer		Crew	Daily Output	Labor-Hours	Unit	Material	Labor	Equipment	Total	Total Incl O&P
0010	**COMPUTER ISOLATION TRANSFORMER**									
0100	Computer grade									
0110	Single-phase, 120/240 V, 0.5 kVA	1 Elec	4	2	Ea.	485	135		620	735
0120	1.0 kVA	▼	2.67	2.996	▼	690	202		892	1,050

26 35 26 – Harmonic Filters

26 35 26.10 Computer Isolation Transformer

	26 35 26.10 Computer Isolation Transformer	Crew	Daily Output	Labor-Hours	Unit	2023 Bare Costs Material	Labor	Equipment	Total	Total Incl O&P
0130	2.5 kVA	1 Elec	2	4	Ea.	1,050	269		1,319	1,550
0140	5 kVA		1.14	7.018		1,200	475		1,675	2,025

26 35 26.20 Computer Regulator Transformer

	26 35 26.20 Computer Regulator Transformer	Crew	Daily Output	Labor-Hours	Unit	Material	Labor	Equipment	Total	Total Incl O&P
0010	**COMPUTER REGULATOR TRANSFORMER**									
0100	Ferro-resonant, constant voltage, variable transformer									
0110	Single-phase, 240 V, 0.5 kVA	1 Elec	2.67	2.996	Ea.	600	202		802	960
0120	1.0 kVA		2	4		825	269		1,094	1,300
0130	2.0 kVA		1	8		2,875	540		3,415	3,975
0210	Plug-in unit 120 V, 0.14 kVA		8	1		345	67.50		412.50	480
0220	0.25 kVA		8	1		405	67.50		472.50	545
0230	0.5 kVA		8	1		600	67.50		667.50	760
0240	1.0 kVA		5.33	1.501		825	101		926	1,050
0250	2.0 kVA		4	2		2,875	135		3,010	3,375

26 35 26.30 Power Conditioner Transformer

	26 35 26.30 Power Conditioner Transformer	Crew	Daily Output	Labor-Hours	Unit	Material	Labor	Equipment	Total	Total Incl O&P
0010	**POWER CONDITIONER TRANSFORMER**									
0100	Electronic solid state, buck-boost, transformer, w/tap switch									
0110	Single-phase, 115 V, 3.0 kVA, + or - 3% accuracy	2 Elec	1.60	10	Ea.	4,125	675		4,800	5,525
0120	208, 220, 230, or 240 V, 5.0 kVA, + or - 1.5% accuracy	3 Elec	1.60	15		6,025	1,000		7,025	8,125
0130	5.0 kVA, + or - 6% accuracy	2 Elec	1.14	14.035		3,750	945		4,695	5,525
0140	7.5 kVA, + or - 1.5% accuracy	3 Elec	1.50	16		5,325	1,075		6,400	7,450
0150	7.5 kVA, + or - 6% accuracy		1.60	15		4,425	1,000		5,425	6,375
0160	10.0 kVA, + or - 1.5% accuracy		1.33	18.045		7,100	1,225		8,325	9,600
0170	10.0 kVA, + or - 6% accuracy		1.41	17.021		6,025	1,150		7,175	8,350

26 35 26.40 Transient Voltage Suppressor Transformer

	26 35 26.40 Transient Voltage Suppressor Transformer	Crew	Daily Output	Labor-Hours	Unit	Material	Labor	Equipment	Total	Total Incl O&P
0010	**TRANSIENT VOLTAGE SUPPRESSOR TRANSFORMER**									
0110	Single-phase, 120 V, 1.8 kVA	1 Elec	4	2	Ea.	1,575	135		1,710	1,950
0120	3.6 kVA		4	2		2,275	135		2,410	2,700
0130	7.2 kVA		3.20	2.500		3,325	168		3,493	3,925
0150	240 V, 3.6 kVA		4	2		3,650	135		3,785	4,225
0160	7.2 kVA		4	2		3,925	135		4,060	4,525
0170	14.4 kVA		3.20	2.500		6,300	168		6,468	7,175
0210	Plug-in unit, 120 V, 1.8 kVA		8	1		1,300	67.50		1,367.50	1,550

26 35 53 – Voltage Regulators

26 35 53.10 Automatic Voltage Regulators

	26 35 53.10 Automatic Voltage Regulators	Crew	Daily Output	Labor-Hours	Unit	Material	Labor	Equipment	Total	Total Incl O&P
0010	**AUTOMATIC VOLTAGE REGULATORS**									
0100	Computer grade, solid state, variable transf. volt. regulator									
0110	Single-phase, 120 V, 8.6 kVA	2 Elec	1.33	12.030	Ea.	6,775	810		7,585	8,650
0120	17.3 kVA		1.14	14.035		8,025	945		8,970	10,200
0130	208/240 V, 7.5/8.6 kVA		1.33	12.030		6,775	810		7,585	8,650
0140	13.5/15.6 kVA		1.33	12.030		8,025	810		8,835	10,000
0150	27.0/31.2 kVA		1.14	14.035		10,100	945		11,045	12,500
0210	Two-phase, single control, 208/240 V, 15.0/17.3 kVA		1.14	14.035		8,025	945		8,970	10,200
0220	Individual phase control, 15.0/17.3 kVA		1.14	14.035		8,025	945		8,970	10,200
0230	30.0/34.6 kVA	3 Elec	1.33	18.045		10,100	1,225		11,325	12,900
0310	Three-phase single control, 208/240 V, 26/30 kVA	2 Elec	1	16		8,025	1,075		9,100	10,400
0320	380/480 V, 24/30 kVA	"	1	16		8,025	1,075		9,100	10,400
0330	43/54 kVA	3 Elec	1.33	18.045		14,600	1,225		15,825	17,800
0340	Individual phase control, 208 V, 26 kVA	"	1.33	18.045		8,025	1,225		9,250	10,600
0350	52 kVA	R-3	.91	21.978		10,100	1,475	212	11,787	13,500
0360	340/480 V, 24/30 kVA	2 Elec	1	16		8,025	1,075		9,100	10,400
0370	43/54 kVA	"	1	16		10,100	1,075		11,175	12,700

26 35 53 – Voltage Regulators

26 35 53.10 Automatic Voltage Regulators

	26 35 53.10 Automatic Voltage Regulators	Crew	Daily Output	Labor-Hours	Unit	2023 Bare Costs Material	Labor	Equipment	Total	Total Incl O&P
0380	48/60 kVA	3 Elec	1.33	18.045	Ea.	14,700	1,225		15,925	17,900
0390	86/108 kVA	R-3	.91	21.978		16,300	1,475	212	17,987	20,300
0500	Standard grade, solid state, variable transformer volt. regulator									
0510	Single-phase, 115 V, 2.3 kVA	1 Elec	2.29	3.493	Ea.	2,525	235		2,760	3,125
0520	4.2 kVA		2	4		4,050	269		4,319	4,850
0530	6.6 kVA		1.14	7.018		4,975	475		5,450	6,175
0540	13.0 kVA		1.14	7.018		7,975	475		8,450	9,475
0550	16.6 kVA	2 Elec	1.23	13.008		9,425	875		10,300	11,700
0610	230 V, 8.3 kVA		1.33	12.030		7,975	810		8,785	9,975
0620	21.4 kVA		1.23	13.008		9,425	875		10,300	11,700
0630	29.9 kVA		1.23	13.008		9,425	875		10,300	11,700
0710	460 V, 9.2 kVA		1.33	12.030		7,975	810		8,785	9,975
0720	20.7 kVA		1.23	13.008		9,425	875		10,300	11,700
0810	Three-phase, 230 V, 13.1 kVA	3 Elec	1.41	17.021		7,975	1,150		9,125	10,500
0820	19.1 kVA		1.41	17.021		9,425	1,150		10,575	12,100
0830	25.1 kVA		1.23	19.512		9,425	1,325		10,750	12,400
0840	57.8 kVA	R-3	.95	21.053		17,100	1,425	203	18,728	21,100
0850	74.9 kVA	"	.91	21.978		17,100	1,475	212	18,787	21,200
0910	460 V, 14.3 kVA	3 Elec	1.41	17.021		7,975	1,150		9,125	10,500
0920	19.1 kVA		1.41	17.021		9,425	1,150		10,575	12,100
0930	27.9 kVA		1.23	19.512		9,425	1,325		10,750	12,400
0940	59.8 kVA	R-3	1	20		17,100	1,350	193	18,643	21,000
0950	79.7 kVA		.95	21.053		19,200	1,425	203	20,828	23,400
0960	118 kVA		.95	21.053		20,200	1,425	203	21,828	24,500
1000	Laboratory grade, precision, electronic voltage regulator									
1110	Single-phase, 115 V, 0.5 kVA	1 Elec	2.29	3.493	Ea.	1,675	235		1,910	2,175
1120	1.0 kVA		2	4		1,775	269		2,044	2,350
1130	3.0 kVA		.80	10		2,475	675		3,150	3,725
1140	6.0 kVA	2 Elec	1.46	10.959		4,600	740		5,340	6,150
1150	10.0 kVA	3 Elec	1	24		5,975	1,625		7,600	8,950
1160	15.0 kVA	"	1.50	16		6,800	1,075		7,875	9,100
1210	230 V, 3.0 kVA	1 Elec	.80	10		2,800	675		3,475	4,075
1220	6.0 kVA	2 Elec	1.46	10.959		4,675	740		5,415	6,250
1230	10.0 kVA	3 Elec	1.71	14.035		6,225	945		7,170	8,250
1240	15.0 kVA	"	1.60	15		7,050	1,000		8,050	9,250

26 35 53.30 Transient Suppressor/Voltage Regulator

	26 35 53.30 Transient Suppressor/Voltage Regulator	Crew	Daily Output	Labor-Hours	Unit	Material	Labor	Equipment	Total	Total Incl O&P
0010	**TRANSIENT SUPPRESSOR/VOLTAGE REGULATOR** (without isolation)									
0110	Single-phase, 115 V, 1.0 kVA	1 Elec	2.67	2.996	Ea.	1,200	202		1,402	1,600
0120	2.0 kVA		2.29	3.493		1,625	235		1,860	2,125
0130	4.0 kVA		2.13	3.756		2,000	253		2,253	2,575
0140	220 V, 1.0 kVA		2.67	2.996		1,200	202		1,402	1,600
0150	2.0 kVA		2.29	3.493		2,300	235		2,535	2,875
0160	4.0 kVA		2.13	3.756		2,100	253		2,353	2,700
0210	Plug-in unit, 120 V, 1.0 kVA		8	1		1,125	67.50		1,192.50	1,350
0220	2.0 kVA		8	1		1,600	67.50		1,667.50	1,850

26 36 13 – Manual Transfer Switches

26 36 13.10 Non-Automatic Transfer Switches		Crew	Daily Output	Labor-Hours	Unit	2023 Bare Costs Material	Labor	Equipment	Total	Total Incl O&P
0010	**NON-AUTOMATIC TRANSFER SWITCHES** enclosed									
0100	Manual operated, 480 volt 3 pole, 30 amp	1 Elec	2.30	3.478	Ea.	2,750	234		2,984	3,375
0150	60 amp		1.90	4.211		3,825	284		4,109	4,650
0200	100 amp		1.30	6.154		4,875	415		5,290	5,975
0250	200 amp	2 Elec	2	8		6,175	540		6,715	7,600
0300	400 amp		1.60	10		14,300	675		14,975	16,700
0350	600 amp		1	16		9,075	1,075		10,150	11,600
1000	250 volt 3 pole, 30 amp	1 Elec	2.30	3.478		1,600	234		1,834	2,125
1100	60 amp		1.90	4.211		2,925	284		3,209	3,650
1150	100 amp		1.30	6.154		4,100	415		4,515	5,125
1200	200 amp	2 Elec	2	8		7,350	540		7,890	8,900
1300	600 amp	″	1	16		15,800	1,075		16,875	19,000
1500	Electrically operated, 480 volt 3 pole, 60 amp	1 Elec	1.90	4.211		2,650	284		2,934	3,325
1600	100 amp	″	1.30	6.154		2,650	415		3,065	3,525
1650	200 amp	2 Elec	2	8		4,350	540		4,890	5,600
1700	400 amp		1.60	10		6,100	675		6,775	7,700
1750	600 amp		1	16		8,775	1,075		9,850	11,300
2000	250 volt 3 pole, 30 amp	1 Elec	2.30	3.478		515	234		749	915
2050	60 amp	″	1.90	4.211		645	284		929	1,125
2150	200 amp	2 Elec	2	8		2,450	540		2,990	3,500
2200	400 amp		1.60	10		4,975	675		5,650	6,475
2250	600 amp		1	16		9,275	1,075		10,350	11,800
2500	NEMA 3R, 480 volt 3 pole, 60 amp	1 Elec	1.80	4.444		4,375	299		4,674	5,250
2550	100 amp	″	1.20	6.667		5,500	450		5,950	6,725
2600	200 amp	2 Elec	1.80	8.889		8,450	600		9,050	10,200
2650	400 amp	″	1.40	11.429		6,675	770		7,445	8,475
2800	NEMA 3R, 250 volt 3 pole solid state, 100 amp	1 Elec	1.20	6.667		5,950	450		6,400	7,225
2850	150 amp	2 Elec	1.80	8.889		7,900	600		8,500	9,600
2900	250 volt 2 pole solid state, 100 amp	1 Elec	1.30	6.154		5,775	415		6,190	6,975
2950	150 amp	2 Elec	2	8		7,675	540		8,215	9,250

26 36 23 – Automatic Transfer Switches

26 36 23.10 Automatic Transfer Switch Devices

Line	Description	Crew	Daily Output	Labor-Hours	Unit	Material	Labor	Equipment	Total	Total Incl O&P
0010	**AUTOMATIC TRANSFER SWITCH DEVICES** R263623-60									
0015	Switches, enclosed 120/240 volt, 2 pole, 30 amp	1 Elec	2.40	3.333	Ea.	2,075	225		2,300	2,600
0020	70 amp		2	4		2,075	269		2,344	2,675
0030	100 amp		1.35	5.926		1,650	400		2,050	2,425
0040	225 amp	2 Elec	2.10	7.619		1,925	515		2,440	2,900
0050	400 amp		1.70	9.412		5,450	635		6,085	6,950
0060	600 amp		1.06	15.094		4,700	1,025		5,725	6,675
0070	800 amp		.84	19.048		4,800	1,275		6,075	7,200
0100	Switches, enclosed 480 volt, 3 pole, 30 amp	1 Elec	2.30	3.478		3,575	234		3,809	4,275
0200	60 amp		1.90	4.211		3,575	284		3,859	4,350
0300	100 amp		1.30	6.154		1,675	415		2,090	2,450
0400	150 amp	2 Elec	2.40	6.667		1,800	450		2,250	2,650
0500	225 amp		2	8		2,075	540		2,615	3,100
0600	260 amp		2	8		2,250	540		2,790	3,275
0700	400 amp		1.60	10		4,875	675		5,550	6,375
0800	600 amp		1	16		5,675	1,075		6,750	7,825
0900	800 amp		.80	20		5,125	1,350		6,475	7,625
1000	1,000 amp		.76	21.053		17,900	1,425		19,325	21,800
1100	1,200 amp		.70	22.857		23,200	1,550		24,750	27,800
1200	1,600 amp		.60	26.667		26,600	1,800		28,400	32,000

26 36 Transfer Switches

26 36 23 – Automatic Transfer Switches

26 36 23.10 Automatic Transfer Switch Devices		Crew	Daily Output	Labor-Hours	Unit	2023 Bare Costs Material	Labor	Equipment	Total	Total Incl O&P
1300	2,000 amp	2 Elec	.50	32	Ea.	29,300	2,150		31,450	35,500
1500	Switches, enclosed 480 V, 4 pole, Bypass/Iso. SW 150 A		2.40	6.667		18,800	450		19,250	21,400
1510	260 A		2	8		19,900	540		20,440	22,600
1520	400 A		1.60	10		25,100	675		25,775	28,600
1530	600 A		1	16		32,400	1,075		33,475	37,200
1600	Accessories, time delay on engine starting					262			262	288
1700	Adjustable time delay on retransfer					262			262	288
1800	Shunt trips for customer connections					470			470	515
1900	Maintenance select switch					107			107	117
2000	Auxiliary contact when normal fails					106			106	116
2100	Pilot light-emergency					107			107	117
2200	Pilot light-normal					107			107	117
2300	Auxiliary contact-closed on normal					123			123	136
2400	Auxiliary contact-closed on emergency					123			123	136
2500	Emergency source sensing, frequency relay					540			540	595

26 41 Facility Lightning Protection

26 41 13 – Lightning Protection for Structures

26 41 13.13 Lightning Protection for Buildings		Crew	Daily Output	Labor-Hours	Unit	Material	Labor	Equipment	Total	Total Incl O&P
0010	LIGHTNING PROTECTION FOR BUILDINGS									
0200	Air terminals & base, copper									
0400	3/8" diameter x 10" (to 75' high)	1 Elec	8	1	Ea.	60	67.50		127.50	166
0500	1/2" diameter x 12" (over 75' high)		8	1		67.50	67.50		135	174
0520	1/2" diameter x 24"		7.30	1.096		86.50	74		160.50	206
0540	1/2" diameter x 60"		6.70	1.194		155	80.50		235.50	290
1000	Aluminum, 1/2" diameter x 12" (to 75' high)		8	1		25.50	67.50		93	128
1020	1/2" diameter x 24"		7.30	1.096		29	74		103	142
1040	1/2" diameter x 60"		6.70	1.194		38.50	80.50		119	162
1100	5/8" diameter x 12" (over 75' high)		8	1		28	67.50		95.50	131
2000	Cable, copper, 220 lb. per thousand ft. (to 75' high)		320	.025	L.F.	6.40	1.68		8.08	9.55
2100	375 lb. per thousand ft. (over 75' high)		230	.035		7.10	2.34		9.44	11.30
2500	Aluminum, 101 lb. per thousand ft. (to 75' high)		280	.029		1.99	1.92		3.91	5.05
2600	199 lb. per thousand ft. (over 75' high)		240	.033		2.89	2.25		5.14	6.50
3000	Arrester, 175 volt AC to ground		8	1	Ea.	77.50	67.50		145	186
3100	650 volt AC to ground		6.70	1.194	"	49.50	80.50		130	175
4000	Air terminals, copper									
4010	3/8" x 10"	1 Elec	50	.160	Ea.	13.10	10.80		23.90	30.50
4020	1/2" x 12"		38	.211		20.50	14.20		34.70	43.50
4030	5/8" x 12"		33	.242		29.50	16.35		45.85	57
4040	1/2" x 24"		30	.267		39.50	17.95		57.45	70
4050	1/2" x 60"		19	.421		108	28.50		136.50	160
4060	Air terminals, aluminum									
4070	3/8" x 10"	1 Elec	50	.160	Ea.	5.55	10.80		16.35	22
4080	1/2" x 12"		38	.211		6.15	14.20		20.35	28
4090	5/8" x 12"		33	.242		8.50	16.35		24.85	34
4100	1/2" x 24"		30	.267		9.50	17.95		27.45	37
4110	1/2" x 60"		19	.421		18.85	28.50		47.35	62.50
4200	Air terminal bases, copper									
4210	Adhesive bases, 1/2"	1 Elec	15	.533	Ea.	59.50	36		95.50	119
4215	Adhesive base, lightning air terminal					59.50			59.50	65.50
4220	Bolted bases	1 Elec	9	.889		47	60		107	141

26 41 13 – Lightning Protection for Structures

26 41 13.13 Lightning Protection for Buildings		Crew	Daily Output	Labor-Hours	Unit	Material	Labor	Equipment	Total	Total Incl O&P
						2023 Bare Costs				
4230	Hinged bases	1 Elec	7	1.143	Ea.	52.50	77		129.50	172
4240	Side mounted bases		9	.889		50.50	60		110.50	145
4250	Offset point support		9	.889		52.50	60		112.50	147
4260	Concealed base assembly		5	1.600		25	108		133	188
4270	Tee connector base		13	.615		145	41.50		186.50	222
4280	Tripod base, 36" for 60" air terminal		7	1.143		40	77		117	158
4290	Intermediate base, 1/2"		15	.533		94	36		130	158
4300	Air terminal bases, aluminum									
4310	Adhesive bases, 1/2"	1 Elec	15	.533	Ea.	23.50	36		59.50	79.50
4320	Bolted bases		9	.889		19.45	60		79.45	111
4330	Hinged bases		7	1.143		36	77		113	154
4340	Side mounted bases		9	.889		27.50	60		87.50	119
4350	Offset point support		9	.889		31	60		91	123
4360	Concealed base assembly		5	1.600		26.50	108		134.50	190
4370	Tee connector base		13	.615		21.50	41.50		63	85
4380	Tripod base, 36" for 60" air terminal		7	1.143		56.50	77		133.50	176
4390	Intermediate base, 1/2"		15	.533		25	36		61	81
4400	Connector cable, copper									
4410	Through wall connector	1 Elec	7	1.143	Ea.	167	77		244	298
4420	Through roof connector		5	1.600		122	108		230	294
4430	Beam connector		7	1.143		65	77		142	186
4440	Double bolt connector		38	.211		20	14.20		34.20	43
4450	Bar, copper		40	.200		24	13.45		37.45	46.50
4500	Connector cable, aluminum									
4510	Through wall connector	1 Elec	7	1.143	Ea.	46.50	77		123.50	165
4520	Through roof connector		5	1.600		33.50	108		141.50	197
4530	Beam connector		7	1.143		30	77		107	147
4540	Double bolt connector		38	.211		9.30	14.20		23.50	31.50
4600	Bonding plates, copper									
4610	I-beam, 8" square	1 Elec	7	1.143	Ea.	59.50	77		136.50	180
4620	Purlin, 8" square		7	1.143		38	77		115	156
4630	Large heavy duty, 16" square		5	1.600		59	108		167	225
4640	Aluminum, I-beam, 8" square		7	1.143		30	77		107	147
4650	Purlin, 8" square		7	1.143		30.50	77		107.50	148
4660	Large heavy duty, 16" square		5	1.600		31.50	108		139.50	195
4700	Cable support, copper, loop fastener		38	.211		.79	14.20		14.99	22
4710	Adhesive cable holder		38	.211		2.33	14.20		16.53	23.50
4720	Aluminum, loop fastener		38	.211		1.37	14.20		15.57	22.50
4730	Adhesive cable holder		38	.211		1.06	14.20		15.26	22
4740	Bonding strap, copper, 3/4" x 9-1/2"		15	.533		18.40	36		54.40	73.50
4750	Aluminum, 3/4" x 9-1/2"		15	.533		8.25	36		44.25	62.50
4760	Swivel adapter, copper, 1/2"		73	.110		21.50	7.40		28.90	34.50
4770	Aluminum, 1/2"		73	.110		15	7.40		22.40	27.50

26 51 13 – Interior Lighting Fixtures, Lamps, and Ballasts

26 51 13.10 Fixture Hangers		Crew	Daily Output	Labor-Hours	Unit	2023 Bare Costs Material	Labor	Equipment	Total	Total Incl O&P
0010	FIXTURE HANGERS									
0220	Box hub cover	1 Elec	32	.250	Ea.	3.99	16.85		20.84	29.50
0240	Canopy		12	.667		9.20	45		54.20	76.50
0260	Connecting block		40	.200		2.83	13.45		16.28	23
0280	Cushion hanger		16	.500		23.50	33.50		57	75.50
0300	Box hanger, with mounting strap		8	1		13.35	67.50		80.85	115
0320	Connecting block		40	.200		2.70	13.45		16.15	23
0340	Flexible, 1/2" diameter, 4" long		12	.667		16.80	45		61.80	85
0360	6" long		12	.667		18.25	45		63.25	86.50
0380	8" long		12	.667		20	45		65	89
0400	10" long		12	.667		21.50	45		66.50	90.50
0420	12" long		12	.667		23	45		68	91.50
0440	15" long		12	.667		24	45		69	92.50
0460	18" long		12	.667		28	45		73	97.50
0480	3/4" diameter, 4" long		10	.800		19.95	54		73.95	102
0500	6" long		10	.800		22	54		76	105
0520	8" long		10	.800		23	54		77	106
0540	10" long		10	.800		23.50	54		77.50	106
0560	12" long		10	.800		25	54		79	108
0580	15" long		10	.800		28	54		82	111
0600	18" long		10	.800		30.50	54		84.50	114

26 51 13.40 Interior HID Fixtures		Crew	Daily Output	Labor-Hours	Unit	Material	Labor	Equipment	Total	Total Incl O&P
0010	INTERIOR HID FIXTURES Incl. lamps and mounting hardware									
0700	High pressure sodium, recessed, round, 70 watt	1 Elec	3.50	2.286	Ea.	560	154		714	845
0720	100 watt		3.50	2.286		720	154		874	1,025
0740	150 watt		3.20	2.500		755	168		923	1,075
0760	Square, 70 watt		3.60	2.222		690	150		840	980
0780	100 watt		3.60	2.222		725	150		875	1,025
0820	250 watt		3	2.667		850	180		1,030	1,200
0840	1,000 watt	2 Elec	4.80	3.333		1,700	225		1,925	2,200
0860	Surface, round, 70 watt	1 Elec	3	2.667		865	180		1,045	1,225
0880	100 watt		3	2.667		885	180		1,065	1,250
0900	150 watt		2.70	2.963		1,050	200		1,250	1,450
0920	Square, 70 watt		3	2.667		875	180		1,055	1,225
0940	100 watt		3	2.667		855	180		1,035	1,200
0980	250 watt		2.50	3.200		755	216		971	1,150
1040	Pendent, round, 70 watt		3	2.667		965	180		1,145	1,325
1060	100 watt		3	2.667		850	180		1,030	1,200
1080	150 watt		2.70	2.963		940	200		1,140	1,325
1100	Square, 70 watt		3	2.667		935	180		1,115	1,300
1120	100 watt		3	2.667		945	180		1,125	1,325
1140	150 watt		2.70	2.963		970	200		1,170	1,375
1160	250 watt		2.50	3.200		1,300	216		1,516	1,775
1180	400 watt		2.40	3.333		1,375	225		1,600	1,850
1220	Wall, round, 70 watt		3	2.667		885	180		1,065	1,250
1240	100 watt		3	2.667		880	180		1,060	1,225
1260	150 watt		2.70	2.963		890	200		1,090	1,275
1300	Square, 70 watt		3	2.667		740	180		920	1,075
1320	100 watt		3	2.667		870	180		1,050	1,225
1340	150 watt		2.70	2.963		915	200		1,115	1,300
1360	250 watt		2.50	3.200		825	216		1,041	1,225
1380	400 watt	2 Elec	4.80	3.333		1,025	225		1,250	1,450

26 51 13 – Interior Lighting Fixtures, Lamps, and Ballasts

26 51 13.40 Interior HID Fixtures		Crew	Daily Output	Labor-Hours	Unit	Material	Labor (2023 Bare Costs)	Equipment (2023 Bare Costs)	Total (2023 Bare Costs)	Total Incl O&P
1400	1,000 watt	2 Elec	3.60	4.444	Ea.	1,375	299		1,674	1,975
1500	Metal halide, recessed, round, 175 watt	1 Elec	3.40	2.353		465	158		623	745
1520	250 watt	"	3.20	2.500		640	168		808	955
1540	400 watt	2 Elec	5.80	2.759		1,025	186		1,211	1,400
1580	Square, 175 watt	1 Elec	3.40	2.353		475	158		633	760
1640	Surface, round, 175 watt		2.90	2.759		625	186		811	965
1660	250 watt		2.70	2.963		1,275	200		1,475	1,700
1680	400 watt	2 Elec	4.80	3.333		1,550	225		1,775	2,050
1720	Square, 175 watt	1 Elec	2.90	2.759		680	186		866	1,025
1800	Pendent, round, 175 watt		2.90	2.759		1,025	186		1,211	1,400
1820	250 watt		2.70	2.963		1,400	200		1,600	1,825
1840	400 watt	2 Elec	4.80	3.333		1,250	225		1,475	1,700
1880	Square, 175 watt	1 Elec	2.90	2.759		530	186		716	860
1900	250 watt	"	2.70	2.963		770	200		970	1,150
1920	400 watt	2 Elec	4.80	3.333		1,475	225		1,700	1,950
1980	Wall, round, 175 watt	1 Elec	2.90	2.759		1,150	186		1,336	1,550
2000	250 watt	"	2.70	2.963		1,200	200		1,400	1,625
2020	400 watt	2 Elec	4.80	3.333		1,075	225		1,300	1,500
2060	Square, 175 watt	1 Elec	2.90	2.759		540	186		726	870
2080	250 watt	"	2.70	2.963		745	200		945	1,125
2100	400 watt	2 Elec	4.80	3.333		1,050	225		1,275	1,500
2800	High pressure sodium, vaporproof, recessed, 70 watt	1 Elec	3.50	2.286		790	154		944	1,100
2820	100 watt		3.50	2.286		805	154		959	1,125
2840	150 watt		3.20	2.500		825	168		993	1,150
2900	Surface, 70 watt		3	2.667		890	180		1,070	1,250
2920	100 watt		3	2.667		930	180		1,110	1,300
2940	150 watt		2.70	2.963		970	200		1,170	1,375
3000	Pendent, 70 watt		3	2.667		880	180		1,060	1,225
3020	100 watt		3	2.667		905	180		1,085	1,250
3040	150 watt		2.70	2.963		960	200		1,160	1,350
3100	Wall, 70 watt		3	2.667		945	180		1,125	1,325
3120	100 watt		3	2.667		990	180		1,170	1,375
3140	150 watt		2.70	2.963		1,025	200		1,225	1,425
3200	Metal halide, vaporproof, recessed, 175 watt		3.40	2.353		780	158		938	1,100
3220	250 watt		3.20	2.500		740	168		908	1,075
3240	400 watt	2 Elec	5.80	2.759		930	186		1,116	1,300
3260	1,000 watt	"	4.80	3.333		1,700	225		1,925	2,200
3280	Surface, 175 watt	1 Elec	2.90	2.759		1,225	186		1,411	1,625
3300	250 watt	"	2.70	2.963		1,050	200		1,250	1,475
3320	400 watt	2 Elec	4.80	3.333		1,300	225		1,525	1,775
3340	1,000 watt	"	3.60	4.444		1,925	299		2,224	2,550
3360	Pendent, 175 watt	1 Elec	2.90	2.759		1,350	186		1,536	1,750
3380	250 watt	"	2.70	2.963		1,100	200		1,300	1,500
3400	400 watt	2 Elec	4.80	3.333		1,300	225		1,525	1,750
3420	1,000 watt	"	3.60	4.444		2,100	299		2,399	2,750
3440	Wall, 175 watt	1 Elec	2.90	2.759		540	186		726	870
3460	250 watt	"	2.70	2.963		1,150	200		1,350	1,575
3480	400 watt	2 Elec	4.80	3.333		1,350	225		1,575	1,825
3500	1,000 watt	"	3.60	4.444		2,175	299		2,474	2,850

26 51 13 – Interior Lighting Fixtures, Lamps, and Ballasts

26 51 13.50 Interior Lighting Fixtures		Crew	Daily Output	Labor-Hours	Unit	2023 Bare Costs Material	Labor	Equipment	Total	Total Incl O&P
0010	**INTERIOR LIGHTING FIXTURES** Including lamps, mounting R265113-40									
0030	hardware and connections									
0100	Fluorescent, C.W. lamps, troffer, recess mounted in grid, RS									
0130	Grid ceiling mount									
0200	Acrylic lens, 1′ W x 4′ L, two 40 watt	1 Elec	5.70	1.404	Ea.	85	94.50		179.50	234
0210	1′ W x 4′ L, three 40 watt		5.40	1.481		123	100		223	283
0300	2′ W x 2′ L, two U40 watt		5.70	1.404		154	94.50		248.50	310
0400	2′ W x 4′ L, two 40 watt		5.30	1.509		77	102		179	236
0500	2′ W x 4′ L, three 40 watt		5	1.600		81	108		189	249
0600	2′ W x 4′ L, four 40 watt		4.70	1.702		116	115		231	298
0700	4′ W x 4′ L, four 40 watt	2 Elec	6.40	2.500		310	168		478	595
0800	4′ W x 4′ L, six 40 watt		6.20	2.581		325	174		499	620
0900	4′ W x 4′ L, eight 40 watt		5.80	2.759		515	186		701	845
0910	Acrylic lens, 1′ W x 4′ L, two 32 watt T8 G	1 Elec	5.70	1.404		178	94.50		272.50	335
0930	2′ W x 2′ L, two U32 watt T8 G		5.70	1.404		193	94.50		287.50	355
0940	2′ W x 4′ L, two 32 watt T8 G		5.30	1.509		233	102		335	405
0950	2′ W x 4′ L, three 32 watt T8 G		5	1.600		95.50	108		203.50	265
0960	2′ W x 4′ L, four 32 watt T8 G		4.70	1.702		205	115		320	395
1000	Surface mounted, RS									
1030	Acrylic lens with hinged & latched door frame									
1100	1′ W x 4′ L, two 40 watt	1 Elec	7	1.143	Ea.	157	77		234	287
1110	1′ W x 4′ L, three 40 watt		6.70	1.194		76	80.50		156.50	204
1200	2′ W x 2′ L, two U40 watt		7	1.143		100	77		177	224
1300	2′ W x 4′ L, two 40 watt		6.20	1.290		158	87		245	305
1400	2′ W x 4′ L, three 40 watt		5.70	1.404		89	94.50		183.50	238
1500	2′ W x 4′ L, four 40 watt		5.30	1.509		223	102		325	395
1501	2′ W x 4′ L, six 40 watt T8		5.20	1.538		223	104		327	400
1600	4′ W x 4′ L, four 40 watt	2 Elec	7.20	2.222		450	150		600	715
1700	4′ W x 4′ L, six 40 watt		6.60	2.424		490	163		653	780
1800	4′ W x 4′ L, eight 40 watt		6.20	2.581		510	174		684	820
1900	2′ W x 8′ L, four 40 watt		6.40	2.500		180	168		348	450
2000	2′ W x 8′ L, eight 40 watt		6.20	2.581		193	174		367	470
2010	Acrylic wrap around lens									
2020	6″ W x 4′ L, one 40 watt	1 Elec	8	1	Ea.	103	67.50		170.50	213
2030	6″ W x 8′ L, two 40 watt	2 Elec	8	2		203	135		338	425
2040	11″ W x 4′ L, two 40 watt	1 Elec	7	1.143		49	77		126	168
2050	11″ W x 8′ L, four 40 watt	2 Elec	6.60	2.424		81	163		244	330
2060	16″ W x 4′ L, four 40 watt	1 Elec	5.30	1.509		81	102		183	240
2070	16″ W x 8′ L, eight 40 watt	2 Elec	6.40	2.500		177	168		345	445
2080	2′ W x 2′ L, two U40 watt	1 Elec	7	1.143		99	77		176	223
2100	Strip fixture									
2130	Surface mounted									
2200	4′ long, one 40 watt, RS	1 Elec	8.50	.941	Ea.	111	63.50		174.50	216
2300	4′ long, two 40 watt, RS		8	1		147	67.50		214.50	262
2310	4′ long, two 32 watt T8, RS G		8	1		66.50	67.50		134	173
2400	4′ long, one 40 watt, SL		8	1		56	67.50		123.50	162
2500	4′ long, two 40 watt, SL		7	1.143		147	77		224	276
2580	8′ long, one 60 watt T8, SL G	2 Elec	13.40	1.194		117	80.50		197.50	248
2590	8′ long, two 60 watt T8, SL G		12.40	1.290		120	87		207	261
2600	8′ long, one 75 watt, SL		13.40	1.194		106	80.50		186.50	237
2700	8′ long, two 75 watt, SL		12.40	1.290		121	87		208	262
2800	4′ long, two 60 watt, HO	1 Elec	6.70	1.194		116	80.50		196.50	248

26 51 13 – Interior Lighting Fixtures, Lamps, and Ballasts

26 51 13.50 Interior Lighting Fixtures			Crew	Daily Output	Labor-Hours	Unit	2023 Bare Costs Material	Labor	Equipment	Total	Total Incl O&P
2810	4′ long, two 54 watt, T5HO	G	1 Elec	6.70	1.194	Ea.	183	80.50		263.50	320
2900	8′ long, two 110 watt, HO		2 Elec	10.60	1.509		113	102		215	275
2910	4′ long, two 115 watt, VHO		1 Elec	6.50	1.231		149	83		232	286
2920	8′ long, two 215 watt, VHO		2 Elec	10.40	1.538		161	104		265	330
2950	High bay pendent mounted, 16″ W x 4′ L, four 54 watt, T5HO	G		8.90	1.798		290	121		411	500
2952	2′ W x 4′ L, six 54 watt, T5HO	G		8.50	1.882		315	127		442	540
2954	2′ W x 4′ L, six 32 watt, T8	G		8.50	1.882		184	127		311	390
3000	Strip, pendent mounted, industrial, white porcelain enamel										
3100	4′ long, two 40 watt, RS		1 Elec	5.70	1.404	Ea.	55	94.50		149.50	201
3110	4′ long, two 32 watt T8, RS	G		5.70	1.404		233	94.50		327.50	395
3200	4′ long, two 60 watt, HO			5	1.600		85.50	108		193.50	254
3290	8′ long, two 60 watt T8, SL	G	2 Elec	8.80	1.818		126	122		248	320
3300	8′ long, two 75 watt, SL			8.80	1.818		104	122		226	297
3400	8′ long, two 110 watt, HO			8	2		134	135		269	345
3410	Acrylic finish, 4′ long, two 40 watt, RS		1 Elec	5.70	1.404		90	94.50		184.50	239
3420	4′ long, two 60 watt, HO			5	1.600		167	108		275	345
3430	4′ long, two 115 watt, VHO			4.80	1.667		220	112		332	410
3440	8′ long, two 75 watt, SL		2 Elec	8.80	1.818		180	122		302	380
3450	8′ long, two 110 watt, HO			8	2		208	135		343	430
3460	8′ long, two 215 watt, VHO			7.60	2.105		294	142		436	535
3470	Troffer, air handling, 2′ W x 4′ L with four 32 watt T8	G	1 Elec	4	2		123	135		258	335
3480	2′ W x 2′ L with two U32 watt T8	G		5.50	1.455		126	98		224	284
3490	Air connector insulated, 5″ diameter			20	.400		72	27		99	119
3500	6″ diameter			20	.400		71	27		98	118
3502	Troffer, direct/indirect, 2′ W x 4′ L with two 32 W T8	G		5.30	1.509		213	102		315	385
3510	Troffer parabolic lay-in, 1′ W x 4′ L with one 32 W T8	G		5.70	1.404		122	94.50		216.50	274
3520	1′ W x 4′ L with two 32 W T8	G		5.30	1.509		89.50	102		191.50	250
3525	2′ W x 2′ L with two U32 W T8	G		5.70	1.404		127	94.50		221.50	280
3530	2′ W x 4′ L with three 32 W T8	G		5	1.600		132	108		240	305
3531	Intr fxtr, fluor, troffer prismatic lay-in, 2′ W x 4′l w/three 32 W T8			5	1.600		155	108		263	330
3535	Downlight, recess mounted	G		8	1		154	67.50		221.50	269
3540	Wall wash reflector, recess mounted	G		8	1		121	67.50		188.50	234
3550	Direct/indirect, 4′ long, stl., pendent mtd.	G		5	1.600		168	108		276	345
3560	4′ long, alum., pendent mtd.	G		5	1.600		345	108		453	540
3565	Prefabricated cove, 4′ long, stl. continuous row	G		5	1.600		216	108		324	400
3570	4′ long, alum. continuous row	G		5	1.600		360	108		468	555
3580	Wet location, recess mounted, 2′ W x 4′ L with two 32 watt T8	G		5.30	1.509		249	102		351	425
3590	Pendent mounted, 2′ W x 4′ L with two 32 watt T8	G		5.70	1.404		400	94.50		494.50	580
4000	Induction lamp, integral ballast, ceiling mounted										
4110	High bay, aluminum reflector, 160 watt		1 Elec	3.20	2.500	Ea.	965	168		1,133	1,300
4120	320 watt		"	3	2.667		1,725	180		1,905	2,175
4130	480 watt		2 Elec	5.80	2.759		2,625	186		2,811	3,175
4150	Low bay, aluminum reflector, 250 watt		1 Elec	3.20	2.500		980	168		1,148	1,325
4170	Garage, aluminum reflector, 80 watt			3.60	2.222		875	150		1,025	1,175
4180	Vandalproof, aluminum reflector, 100 watt			3.20	2.500		645	168		813	960
4220	Metal halide, integral ballast, ceiling, recess mounted										
4230	prismatic glass lens, floating door										
4240	2′ W x 2′ L, 250 watt		1 Elec	3.20	2.500	Ea.	380	168		548	670
4250	2′ W x 2′ L, 400 watt		2 Elec	5.80	2.759		390	186		576	700
4260	Surface mounted, 2′ W x 2′ L, 250 watt		1 Elec	2.70	2.963		355	200		555	685
4270	400 watt		2 Elec	4.80	3.333		420	225		645	795
4280	High bay, aluminum reflector,										
4290	Single unit, 400 watt		2 Elec	4.60	3.478	Ea.	380	234		614	765

26 51 13 – Interior Lighting Fixtures, Lamps, and Ballasts

26 51 13.50 Interior Lighting Fixtures		Crew	Daily Output	Labor-Hours	Unit	Material	Labor	Equipment	Total	Total Incl O&P
						2023 Bare Costs				
4300	Single unit, 1,000 watt	2 Elec	4	4	Ea.	835	269		1,104	1,325
4310	Twin unit, 400 watt		3.20	5		850	335		1,185	1,425
4320	Low bay, aluminum reflector, 250W DX lamp	1 Elec	3.20	2.500		375	168		543	665
4330	400 watt lamp	2 Elec	5	3.200		560	216		776	935
4340	High pressure sodium integral ballast ceiling, recess mounted									
4350	prismatic glass lens, floating door									
4360	2' W x 2' L, 150 watt lamp	1 Elec	3.20	2.500	Ea.	410	168		578	700
4370	2' W x 2' L, 400 watt lamp	2 Elec	5.80	2.759		490	186		676	815
4380	Surface mounted, 2' W x 2' L, 150 watt lamp	1 Elec	2.70	2.963		500	200		700	845
4390	400 watt lamp	2 Elec	4.80	3.333		560	225		785	955
4400	High bay, aluminum reflector,									
4410	Single unit, 400 watt lamp	2 Elec	4.60	3.478	Ea.	405	234		639	795
4430	Single unit, 1,000 watt lamp	"	4	4		565	269		834	1,025
4440	Low bay, aluminum reflector, 150 watt lamp	1 Elec	3.20	2.500		350	168		518	635
4445	High bay H.I.D. quartz restrike	"	16	.500		174	33.50		207.50	241
4450	Incandescent, high hat can, round alzak reflector, prewired									
4470	100 watt	1 Elec	8	1	Ea.	70.50	67.50		138	178
4480	150 watt		8	1		108	67.50		175.50	218
4500	300 watt		6.70	1.194		249	80.50		329.50	395
4520	Round with reflector and baffles, 150 watt		8	1		55.50	67.50		123	161
4540	Round with concentric louver, 150 watt PAR		8	1		81	67.50		148.50	190
4600	Square glass lens with metal trim, prewired									
4630	100 watt	1 Elec	6.70	1.194	Ea.	56.50	80.50		137	183
4680	150 watt		6.70	1.194		101	80.50		181.50	231
4700	200 watt		6.70	1.194		101	80.50		181.50	231
4800	300 watt		5.70	1.404		151	94.50		245.50	305
4810	500 watt		5	1.600		297	108		405	485
4900	Ceiling/wall, surface mounted, metal cylinder, 75 watt		10	.800		48.50	54		102.50	134
4920	150 watt		10	.800		89	54		143	178
4930	300 watt		8	1		178	67.50		245.50	296
5000	500 watt		6.70	1.194		380	80.50		460.50	535
5010	Square, 100 watt		8	1		124	67.50		191.50	236
5020	150 watt		8	1		127	67.50		194.50	240
5030	300 watt		7	1.143		340	77		417	490
5040	500 watt		6	1.333		370	90		460	545
5200	Ceiling, surface mounted, opal glass drum									
5300	8", one 60 watt lamp	1 Elec	10	.800	Ea.	135	54		189	229
5400	10", two 60 watt lamps		8	1		43	67.50		110.50	148
5500	12", four 60 watt lamps		6.70	1.194		105	80.50		185.50	235
5510	Pendent, round, 100 watt		8	1		167	67.50		234.50	284
5520	150 watt		8	1		125	67.50		192.50	237
5530	300 watt		6.70	1.194		178	80.50		258.50	315
5540	500 watt		5.50	1.455		340	98		438	520
5550	Square, 100 watt		6.70	1.194		157	80.50		237.50	293
5560	150 watt		6.70	1.194		167	80.50		247.50	305
5570	300 watt		5.70	1.404		244	94.50		338.50	410
5580	500 watt		5	1.600		330	108		438	525
5600	Wall, round, 100 watt		8	1		67.50	67.50		135	174
5620	300 watt		8	1		138	67.50		205.50	252
5630	500 watt		6.70	1.194		400	80.50		480.50	565
5640	Square, 100 watt		8	1		135	67.50		202.50	248
5650	150 watt		8	1		112	67.50		179.50	223
5660	300 watt		7	1.143		175	77		252	305

26 51 13 – Interior Lighting Fixtures, Lamps, and Ballasts

26 51 13.50 Interior Lighting Fixtures		Crew	Daily Output	Labor-Hours	Unit	2023 Bare Costs Material	Labor	Equipment	Total	Total Incl O&P
5670	500 watt	1 Elec	6	1.333	Ea.	288	90		378	450
6010	Vapor tight, incandescent, ceiling mounted, 200 watt		6.20	1.290		59	87		146	194
6020	Recessed, 200 watt		6.70	1.194		129	80.50		209.50	262
6030	Pendent, 200 watt		6.70	1.194		72.50	80.50		153	200
6040	Wall, 200 watt		8	1		86.50	67.50		154	195
6100	Fluorescent, surface mounted, 2 lamps, 4′ L, RS, 40 watt		3.20	2.500		123	168		291	385
6110	Industrial, 2 lamps, 4′ L in tandem, 430 MA		2.20	3.636		219	245		464	605
6130	2 lamps, 4′ L, 800 MA		1.90	4.211		187	284		471	625
6160	Pendent, indust, 2 lamps, 4′ L in tandem, 430 MA		1.90	4.211		255	284		539	700
6170	2 lamps, 4′ L, 430 MA		2.30	3.478		171	234		405	540
6180	2 lamps, 4′ L, 800 MA		1.70	4.706		216	315		531	705
6850	Vandalproof, surface mounted, fluorescent, two 32 watt T8 G		3.20	2.500		277	168		445	555
6860	Incandescent, one 150 watt		8	1		103	67.50		170.50	214
6900	Mirror light, fluorescent, RS, acrylic enclosure, two 40 watt		8	1		142	67.50		209.50	256
6910	One 40 watt		8	1		104	67.50		171.50	214
6920	One 20 watt		12	.667		90	45		135	166
7000	Low bay, aluminum reflector, 70 watt, high pressure sodium		4	2		279	135		414	505
7010	250 watt		3.20	2.500		380	168		548	670
7020	400 watt	2 Elec	5	3.200		425	216		641	790
7500	Ballast replacement, by weight of ballast, to 15′ high									
7520	Indoor fluorescent, less than 2 lb.	1 Elec	10	.800	Ea.	40	54		94	124
7540	Two 40W, watt reducer, 2 to 5 lb.		9.40	.851		57	57.50		114.50	148
7560	Two F96 slimline, over 5 lb.		8	1		53	67.50		120.50	159
7580	Vaportite ballast, less than 2 lb.		9.40	.851		40	57.50		97.50	129
7600	2 lb. to 5 lb.		8.90	.899		57	60.50		117.50	153
7620	Over 5 lb.		7.60	1.053		53	71		124	164
7630	Electronic ballast for two tubes		8	1		17.95	67.50		85.45	120
7640	Dimmable ballast one-lamp G		8	1		109	67.50		176.50	220
7650	Dimmable ballast two-lamp G		7.60	1.053		114	71		185	230
7660	Dimmable ballast three-lamp		6.90	1.159		130	78		208	259
7690	Emergency ballast (factory installed in fixture)					125			125	138
7990	Decorator									
8000	Pendent RLM in colors, shallow dome, 12″ diam., 100 watt	1 Elec	8	1	Ea.	83	67.50		150.50	191
8010	Regular dome, 12″ diam., 100 watt		8	1		85.50	67.50		153	194
8020	16″ diam., 200 watt		7	1.143		87	77		164	210
8030	18″ diam., 300 watt		6	1.333		95.50	90		185.50	238
8100	Picture framing light		16	.500		92	33.50		125.50	151
8150	Miniature low voltage, recessed, pinhole		8	1		139	67.50		206.50	252
8160	Star		8	1		138	67.50		205.50	251
8170	Adjustable cone		8	1		175	67.50		242.50	292
8180	Eyeball		8	1		109	67.50		176.50	220
8190	Cone		8	1		134	67.50		201.50	247
8200	Coilex baffle		8	1		188	67.50		255.50	305
8210	Surface mounted, adjustable cylinder		8	1		144	67.50		211.50	258
8250	Chandeliers, incandescent									
8260	24″ diam. x 42″ high, 6 light candle	1 Elec	6	1.333	Ea.	485	90		575	670
8270	24″ diam. x 42″ high, 6 light candle w/glass shade		6	1.333		445	90		535	625
8280	17″ diam. x 12″ high, 8 light w/glass panels		8	1		284	67.50		351.50	410
8300	27″ diam. x 29″ high, 10 light bohemian lead crystal		4	2		705	135		840	975
8310	21″ diam. x 9″ high, 6 light sculptured ice crystal		8	1		380	67.50		447.50	515
8500	Accent lights, on floor or edge, 0.5 W low volt incandescent									
8520	incl. transformer & fastenings, based on 100′ lengths									
8550	Lights in clear tubing, 12″ OC	1 Elec	230	.035	L.F.	8.80	2.34		11.14	13.20

26 51 Interior Lighting

26 51 13 – Interior Lighting Fixtures, Lamps, and Ballasts

26 51 13.50 Interior Lighting Fixtures

Line	Description	Crew	Daily Output	Labor-Hours	Unit	Material (2023 Bare Costs)	Labor (2023 Bare Costs)	Equipment (2023 Bare Costs)	Total (2023 Bare Costs)	Total Incl O&P
8560	6″ OC	1 Elec	160	.050	L.F.	11.50	3.37		14.87	17.65
8570	4″ OC		130	.062		17.55	4.14		21.69	25.50
8580	3″ OC		125	.064		19.50	4.31		23.81	28
8590	2″ OC		100	.080		28.50	5.40		33.90	39
8600	Carpet, lights both sides 6″ OC, in alum. extrusion		270	.030		26.50	2		28.50	32
8610	In bronze extrusion		270	.030		30	2		32	36
8620	Carpet-bare floor, lights 18″ OC, in alum. extrusion		270	.030		21	2		23	26.50
8630	In bronze extrusion		270	.030		25	2		27	30.50
8640	Carpet edge-wall, lights 6″ OC in alum. extrusion		270	.030		26.50	2		28.50	32
8650	In bronze extrusion		270	.030		30	2		32	36
8660	Bare floor, lights 18″ OC, in alum. extrusion		300	.027		21	1.80		22.80	26
8670	In bronze extrusion		300	.027		25	1.80		26.80	30
8680	Bare floor conduit, alum. extrusion		300	.027		7.05	1.80		8.85	10.40
8690	In bronze extrusion		300	.027		14.05	1.80		15.85	18.10
8700	Step edge to 36″, lights 6″ OC, in alum. extrusion		100	.080	Ea.	71	5.40		76.40	86
8710	In bronze extrusion		100	.080		73.50	5.40		78.90	89
8720	Step edge to 54″, lights 6″ OC, in alum. extrusion		100	.080		106	5.40		111.40	125
8730	In bronze extrusion		100	.080		112	5.40		117.40	131
8740	Step edge to 72″, lights 6″ OC, in alum. extrusion		100	.080		141	5.40		146.40	164
8750	In bronze extrusion		100	.080		154	5.40		159.40	178
8760	Connector, male		32	.250		2.63	16.85		19.48	28
8770	Female with pigtail		32	.250		5.50	16.85		22.35	31
8780	Clamps		400	.020		.53	1.35		1.88	2.58
8790	Transformers, 50 watt		8	1		106	67.50		173.50	216
8800	250 watt		4	2		325	135		460	560
8810	1,000 watt		2.70	2.963		370	200		570	700

26 51 13.55 Interior LED Fixtures

Line	Description		Crew	Daily Output	Labor-Hours	Unit	Material	Labor	Equipment	Total	Total Incl O&P
0010	**INTERIOR LED FIXTURES** Incl. lamps and mounting hardware										
0100	Downlight, recess mounted, 7.5″ diameter, 25 watt	G	1 Elec	8	1	Ea.	360	67.50		427.50	495
0120	10″ diameter, 36 watt	G		8	1		375	67.50		442.50	515
0160	cylinder, 10 watts	G		8	1		63	67.50		130.50	170
0180	20 watts	G		8	1		89	67.50		156.50	198
0900	Interior LED fixts, troffer, recess mounted, 2′ x 2′, 3,500K			8.50	.941		150	63.50		213.50	258
0910	2′ x 2′, 4,000K			8.50	.941		164	63.50		227.50	274
1000	Troffer, recess mounted, 2′ x 4′, 3,200 lumens	G		5.30	1.509		182	102		284	350
1010	4,800 lumens	G		5	1.600		161	108		269	340
1020	6,400 lumens	G		4.70	1.702		197	115		312	385
1100	Troffer retrofit lamp, 38 watt	G		21	.381		62.50	25.50		88	107
1110	60 watt	G		20	.400		126	27		153	178
1120	100 watt	G		18	.444		147	30		177	207
1200	Troffer, volumetric recess mounted, 2′ x 2′	G		5.70	1.404		425	94.50		519.50	610
2000	Strip, surface mounted, one light bar 4′ long, 3,500 K	G		8.50	.941		320	63.50		383.50	450
2010	5,000 K	G		8	1		278	67.50		345.50	405
2020	Two light bar 4′ long, 5,000 K	G		7	1.143		435	77		512	595
3000	Linear, suspended mounted, one light bar 4′ long, 37 watt	G		6.70	1.194		183	80.50		263.50	320
3010	One light bar 8′ long, 74 watt	G	2 Elec	12.20	1.311		330	88.50		418.50	495
3020	Two light bar 4′ long, 74 watt	G	1 Elec	5.70	1.404		455	94.50		549.50	640
3030	Two light bar 8′ long, 148 watt	G	2 Elec	8.80	1.818		380	122		502	595
4000	High bay, surface mounted, round, 150 watts	G		5.41	2.959		330	199		529	655
4010	2 bars, 164 watts	G		5.41	2.959		244	199		443	565
4020	3 bars, 246 watts	G		5.01	3.197		535	215		750	905
4030	4 bars, 328 watts	G		4.60	3.478		630	234		864	1,050

26 51 13 – Interior Lighting Fixtures, Lamps, and Ballasts

26 51 13.55 Interior LED Fixtures

	26 51 13.55 Interior LED Fixtures	Crew	Daily Output	Labor-Hours	Unit	2023 Bare Costs Material	Labor	Equipment	Total	Total Incl O&P
4040	5 bars, 410 watts G	3 Elec	4.20	5.716	Ea.	860	385		1,245	1,525
4050	6 bars, 492 watts G		3.80	6.324		1,175	425		1,600	1,900
4060	7 bars, 574 watts G		3.39	7.075		1,150	475		1,625	1,975
4070	8 bars, 656 watts G		2.99	8.029		1,500	540		2,040	2,450
5000	Track, lighthead, 6 watt G	1 Elec	32	.250		57.50	16.85		74.35	88
5010	9 watt G	"	32	.250		65	16.85		81.85	96.50
6000	Garage, surface mounted, 103 watts G	2 Elec	6.50	2.462		1,025	166		1,191	1,375
6100	pendent mounted, 80 watts G		6.50	2.462		770	166		936	1,100
6200	95 watts G		6.50	2.462		855	166		1,021	1,175
6300	125 watts G		6.50	2.462		870	166		1,036	1,200
7000	Downlight, recess mtd., low profile, 4" diam., 9W, 3,000K	1 Elec	8.50	.941		25	63.50		88.50	122
7010	4,000K		8.50	.941		24	63.50		87.50	120
7020	5,000K		8.50	.941		18.35	63.50		81.85	114

26 51 13.70 Residential Fixtures

	26 51 13.70 Residential Fixtures	Crew	Daily Output	Labor-Hours	Unit	Material	Labor	Equipment	Total	Total Incl O&P
0010	**RESIDENTIAL FIXTURES**									
0400	Fluorescent, interior, surface, circline, 32 watt & 40 watt	1 Elec	20	.400	Ea.	187	27		214	246
0500	2' x 2', two U-tube 32 watt T8		8	1		130	67.50		197.50	243
0700	Shallow under cabinet, two 20 watt		16	.500		90.50	33.50		124	150
0900	Wall mounted, 4' L, two 32 watt T8, with baffle		10	.800		168	54		222	265
2000	Incandescent, exterior lantern, wall mounted, 60 watt		16	.500		71	33.50		104.50	128
2100	Post light, 150 W, with 7' post		4	2		330	135		465	565
2500	Lamp holder, weatherproof with 150 W PAR		16	.500		36.50	33.50		70	90.50
2550	With reflector and guard		12	.667		80	45		125	155
2600	Interior pendent, globe with shade, 150 W		20	.400		186	27		213	244

26 51 13.90 Ballast, Replacement HID

	26 51 13.90 Ballast, Replacement HID	Crew	Daily Output	Labor-Hours	Unit	Material	Labor	Equipment	Total	Total Incl O&P
0010	**BALLAST, REPLACEMENT HID**									
7510	Multi-tap 120/208/240/277 V									
7550	High pressure sodium, 70 watt	1 Elec	10	.800	Ea.	120	54		174	211
7560	100 watt		9.40	.851		63	57.50		120.50	155
7570	150 watt		9	.889		48.50	60		108.50	143
7580	250 watt		8.50	.941		136	63.50		199.50	243
7590	400 watt		7	1.143		162	77		239	293
7600	1,000 watt		6	1.333		222	90		312	375
7610	Metal halide, 175 watt		8	1		81	67.50		148.50	189
7620	250 watt		8	1		95.50	67.50		163	205
7630	400 watt		7	1.143		98	77		175	222
7640	1,000 watt		6	1.333		174	90		264	325
7650	1,500 watt		5	1.600		310	108		418	500

26 51 19 – LED Interior Lighting

26 51 19.10 LED Interior Lighting

	26 51 19.10 LED Interior Lighting	Crew	Daily Output	Labor-Hours	Unit	Material	Labor	Equipment	Total	Total Incl O&P
0010	**LED INTERIOR LIGHTING**									
7000	Interior LED fixts, tape rope kit, 120V, 3' strip, 4W, w/5' cord, 3,000K	1 Elec	24	.333	Ea.	18.80	22.50		41.30	54
7010	5,000K		24	.333		11.30	22.50		33.80	46
7020	Interior LED fixts, tape rope kit, 120V, 6' strip, 8W, w/5' cord, 3,000K		23	.348		15.45	23.50		38.95	52
7030	5,000K		23	.348		23	23.50		46.50	60
7040	Interior LED fixts, tape rope kit, 120V, 13' strip, 15W, w/5' cord, 3,000K		22	.364		26.50	24.50		51	66
7050	5,000K		22	.364		28.50	24.50		53	68
7060	Interior LED fixts, tape rope kit, 120V, 20' strip, 22W, w/5' cord, 3,000K		21	.381		41.50	25.50		67	83.50
7070	5,000K		21	.381		41.50	25.50		67	83.50
7080	Interior LED fixts, tape rope kit, 120V, 33' strip, 37W, w/5' cord, 3,000K		20	.400		60.50	27		87.50	107
7090	5,000K		20	.400		61	27		88	107
7100	Interior LED fixts, tape rope kit, 120V, 50' strip, 55W, w/5' cord, 3,000K		19	.421		92	28.50		120.50	143

26 51 Interior Lighting

26 51 19 – LED Interior Lighting

26 51 19.10 LED Interior Lighting		Crew	Daily Output	Labor-Hours	Unit	2023 Bare Costs Material	Labor	Equipment	Total	Total Incl O&P
7110	5,000K	1 Elec	19	.421	Ea.	132	28.50		160.50	187
7120	Interior LED tape light, starstrand, dimmable, 12V, super star, 2", 3,000K		25	.320		11.30	21.50		32.80	44.50
7130	Ultra star, 2", 3,000K		25	.320		14.10	21.50		35.60	47.50
7140	Rainbow star, 2", 3,000K		25	.320		11.30	21.50		32.80	44.50
7150	Interior LED tape light, starstrand, dimmable, 24V, elite star, 4", 35K		25	.320		5.20	21.50		26.70	37.50
7160	12", 35K		25	.320		19.35	21.50		40.85	53.50
7170	60", 35K		23	.348		53	23.50		76.50	93
7180	120", 35K		21	.381		145	25.50		170.50	198
7190	240", 35K		18	.444		310	30		340	385
7200	Interior LED tape lighting channel , 36", AL flex, starstrand, elite star	↓	48	.167	↓	11.60	11.25		22.85	29.50

26 52 Safety Lighting

26 52 13 – Emergency and Exit Lighting

26 52 13.10 Emergency Lighting and Battery Units		Crew	Daily Output	Labor-Hours	Unit	Material	Labor	Equipment	Total	Total Incl O&P
0010	**EMERGENCY LIGHTING AND BATTERY UNITS**									
0300	Emergency light units, battery operated									
0350	Twin sealed beam light, 25 W, 6 V each									
0500	Lead battery operated	1 Elec	4	2	Ea.	145	135		280	360
0700	Nickel cadmium battery operated		4	2		350	135		485	585
0780	Additional remote mount, sealed beam, 25 W 6 V		26.70	.300		21	20		41	53
0790	Twin sealed beam light, 25 W 6 V each		26.70	.300		65	20		85	102
0900	Self-contained fluorescent lamp pack	↓	10	.800	↓	237	54		291	340

26 52 13.16 Exit Signs		Crew	Daily Output	Labor-Hours	Unit	Material	Labor	Equipment	Total	Total Incl O&P
0010	**EXIT SIGNS**									
0080	Exit light ceiling or wall mount, incandescent, single face	1 Elec	8	1	Ea.	61.50	67.50		129	168
0100	Double face		6.70	1.194		61.50	80.50		142	188
0120	Explosion proof		3.80	2.105		550	142		692	815
0150	Fluorescent, single face		8	1		96	67.50		163.50	205
0160	Double face		6.70	1.194		83	80.50		163.50	211
0200	LED standard, single face G		8	1		47.50	67.50		115	152
0220	Double face G		6.70	1.194		51	80.50		131.50	176
0230	LED vandal-resistant, single face G		7.27	1.100		310	74		384	450
0240	LED w/battery unit, single face G		4.40	1.818		335	122		457	545
0260	Double face G		4	2		405	135		540	645
0262	LED w/battery unit, vandal-resistant, single face G		4.40	1.818		350	122		472	565
0270	Combination emergency light units and exit sign		4	2		176	135		311	395
0290	LED retrofit kits G	↓	60	.133		97	9		106	120
1500	Exit sign, 12 V, 1 face, remote end mounted (Type 602A1)	R-19	18	1.111		78	75		153	197
1780	With emergency battery, explosion proof	"	7.70	2.597	↓	3,900	175		4,075	4,525

26 54 Classified Location Lighting

26 54 13 – Incandescent Classified Location Lighting

26 54 13.20 Explosion Proof		Crew	Daily Output	Labor-Hours	Unit	2023 Bare Costs Material	Labor	Equipment	Total	Total Incl O&P
0010	**EXPLOSION PROOF**, incl. lamps, mounting hardware and connections									
6310	Metal halide with ballast, ceiling, surface mounted, 175 watt	1 Elec	2.90	2.759	Ea.	1,600	186		1,786	2,050
6320	250 watt	″	2.70	2.963		1,925	200		2,125	2,425
6330	400 watt	2 Elec	4.80	3.333		2,075	225		2,300	2,600
6340	Ceiling, pendent mounted, 175 watt	1 Elec	2.60	3.077		1,525	207		1,732	1,975
6350	250 watt	″	2.40	3.333		1,850	225		2,075	2,375
6360	400 watt	2 Elec	4.20	3.810		2,000	257		2,257	2,575
6370	Wall, surface mounted, 175 watt	1 Elec	2.90	2.759		1,725	186		1,911	2,175
6380	250 watt	″	2.70	2.963		2,050	200		2,250	2,550
6390	400 watt	2 Elec	4.80	3.333		2,200	225		2,425	2,725
6400	High pressure sodium, ceiling surface mounted, 70 watt	1 Elec	3	2.667		2,525	180		2,705	3,050
6410	100 watt		3	2.667		2,625	180		2,805	3,150
6420	150 watt		2.70	2.963		2,900	200		3,100	3,500
6430	Pendent mounted, 70 watt		2.70	2.963		2,400	200		2,600	2,950
6440	100 watt		2.70	2.963		2,500	200		2,700	3,050
6450	150 watt		2.40	3.333		2,325	225		2,550	2,875
6460	Wall mounted, 70 watt		3	2.667		2,700	180		2,880	3,250
6470	100 watt		3	2.667		3,000	180		3,180	3,575
6480	150 watt		2.70	2.963		2,875	200		3,075	3,475
6510	Incandescent, ceiling mounted, 200 watt		4	2		2,000	135		2,135	2,375
6520	Pendent mounted, 200 watt		3.50	2.286		1,700	154		1,854	2,100
6530	Wall mounted, 200 watt		4	2		1,975	135		2,110	2,375
6600	Fluorescent, RS, 4′ long, ceiling mounted, two 40 watt		2.70	2.963		5,775	200		5,975	6,675
6610	Three 40 watt		2.20	3.636		8,375	245		8,620	9,600
6620	Four 40 watt		1.90	4.211		10,800	284		11,084	12,200
6630	Pendent mounted, two 40 watt		2.30	3.478		6,700	234		6,934	7,725
6640	Three 40 watt		1.90	4.211		9,500	284		9,784	10,900
6650	Four 40 watt		1.70	4.706		12,500	315		12,815	14,300

26 55 Special Purpose Lighting

26 55 33 – Hazard Warning Lighting

26 55 33.10 Warning Beacons

		Crew	Daily Output	Labor-Hours	Unit	Material	Labor	Equipment	Total	Total Incl O&P
0010	**WARNING BEACONS**									
0015	Surface mount with colored or clear lens									
0100	Rotating beacon									
0110	120V, 40 watt halogen	1 Elec	3.50	2.286	Ea.	285	154		439	545
0120	24V, 20 watt halogen	″	3.50	2.286	″	335	154		489	600
0200	Steady beacon									
0210	120V, 40 watt halogen	1 Elec	3.50	2.286	Ea.	315	154		469	575
0220	24V, 20 watt		3.50	2.286		340	154		494	605
0230	12V DC, incandescent		3.50	2.286		120	154		274	360
0300	Flashing beacon									
0310	120V, 40 watt halogen	1 Elec	3.50	2.286	Ea.	267	154		421	520
0320	24V, 20 watt halogen		3.50	2.286		315	154		469	575
0410	12V DC with two 6V lantern batteries		7	1.143		249	77		326	390

26 55 59 – Display Lighting

26 55 59.10 Track Lighting

		Crew	Daily Output	Labor-Hours	Unit	Material	Labor	Equipment	Total	Total Incl O&P
0010	**TRACK LIGHTING**									
0080	Track, 1 circuit, 4′ section	1 Elec	6.70	1.194	Ea.	72	80.50		152.50	199
0100	8′ section	2 Elec	10.60	1.509		64.50	102		166.50	222

26 55 59 – Display Lighting

26 55 59.10 Track Lighting		Crew	Daily Output	Labor-Hours	Unit	2023 Bare Costs Material	Labor	Equipment	Total	Total Incl O&P
0200	12′ section	2 Elec	8.80	1.818	Ea.	135	122		257	330
0300	3 circuits, 4′ section	1 Elec	6.70	1.194		127	80.50		207.50	259
0400	8′ section	2 Elec	10.60	1.509		197	102		299	370
0500	12′ section	"	8.80	1.818		226	122		348	430
1000	Feed kit, surface mounting	1 Elec	16	.500		23.50	33.50		57	76
1100	End cover		24	.333		10.55	22.50		33.05	45
1200	Feed kit, stem mounting, 1 circuit		16	.500		62.50	33.50		96	119
1300	3 circuit		16	.500		62.50	33.50		96	119
2000	Electrical joiner, for continuous runs, 1 circuit		32	.250		43.50	16.85		60.35	73
2100	3 circuit		32	.250		97	16.85		113.85	132
2200	Fixtures, spotlight, 75 W PAR halogen		16	.500		99.50	33.50		133	159
2210	50 W MR16 halogen		16	.500		272	33.50		305.50	350
3000	Wall washer, 250 W tungsten halogen		16	.500		173	33.50		206.50	240
3100	Low voltage, 25/50 W, 1 circuit		16	.500		174	33.50		207.50	242
3120	3 circuit		16	.500		248	33.50		281.50	325

26 55 61 – Theatrical Lighting

26 55 61.10 Lights		Crew	Daily Output	Labor-Hours	Unit	Material	Labor	Equipment	Total	Total Incl O&P
0010	**LIGHTS**									
2000	Lights, border, quartz, reflector, vented,									
2100	colored or white	1 Elec	20	.400	L.F.	550	27		577	645
2500	Spotlight, follow spot, with transformer, 2,100 watt	"	4	2	Ea.	4,325	135		4,460	4,950
2600	For no transformer, deduct					980			980	1,075
3000	Stationary spot, fresnel quartz, 6″ lens	1 Elec	4	2		550	135		685	805
3100	8″ lens		4	2		248	135		383	475
3500	Ellipsoidal quartz, 1,000 watt, 6″ lens		4	2		365	135		500	600
3600	12″ lens		4	2		650	135		785	915
4000	Strobe light, 1 to 15 flashes per second, quartz		3	2.667		920	180		1,100	1,275
4500	Color wheel, portable, five hole, motorized		4	2		226	135		361	450

26 55 63 – Detention Lighting

26 55 63.10 Detention Lighting Fixtures		Crew	Daily Output	Labor-Hours	Unit	Material	Labor	Equipment	Total	Total Incl O&P
0010	**DETENTION LIGHTING FIXTURES**									
1000	Surface mounted, cold rolled steel, 14 ga., 1′ x 4′	1 Elec	5.40	1.481	Ea.	1,125	100		1,225	1,400
1010	2′ x 2′		5.40	1.481		1,100	100		1,200	1,350
1020	2′ x 4′		5	1.600		1,325	108		1,433	1,600
1100	12 ga., 1′ x 4′		5.40	1.481		1,400	100		1,500	1,700
1110	2′ x 2′		5.40	1.481		1,100	100		1,200	1,350
1120	2′ x 4′		5	1.600		1,425	108		1,533	1,700
3000	Fluorescent vandal resistant light fixture, high abuse troffer		5.40	1.481		292	100		392	470
3010	50″ L x 8″ W x 4″ H		5.40	1.481		219	100		319	390
3020	32W		5.40	1.481		370	100		470	555
3030	T8/32W		5.40	1.481		235	100		335	405
3040	No lamp		5.60	1.429		440	96		536	630
3050	Lamp included		5.40	1.481		510	100		610	710
3060	16 ga. cold rolled steel		5.40	1.481		505	100		605	705
3070	16 ga. cold rolled steel, ceiling/wall mount		5.40	1.481		425	100		525	615
3080	w/lamp, white		5.40	1.481		330	100		430	515
3090	wo/lamp, bronze		5.60	1.429		293	96		389	465
3100	w/lamp 6″ L x 4-1/2″ W x 8-1/2″ H		5.40	1.481		42.50	100		142.50	195
3110	w/lamp 5-7/8″ W x 4-1/2″ D x 8-1/2″ H clear		5.40	1.481		133	100		233	294
3120	w/lamp white		5.40	1.481		660	100		760	880
3130	Tall wallpack, w/lamp, bronze		5.40	1.481		155	100		255	320
3140	Tall wallpack, w/lamp, white		5.40	1.481		132	100		232	293

26 56 Exterior Lighting

26 56 13 – Lighting Poles and Standards

26 56 13.10 Lighting Poles		Crew	Daily Output	Labor-Hours	Unit	2023 Bare Costs Material	Labor	Equipment	Total	Total Incl O&P
0010	LIGHTING POLES									
0100	Exterior, light poles, concrete, 30′ above 5′ below, 13.5″ Base, 5.5″ Tip	2 Elec	4.60	3.478	Ea.	1,950	234		2,184	2,500
0110	39′ above 6′ below, 15.5″ Base, 5.25″ Tip		4.60	3.478		2,300	234		2,534	2,875
0120	43′ above 7′ below, 17.25″ Base, 6.5″ Tip		4.60	3.478		2,325	234		2,559	2,925
0130	43′ above 7′ below, 19.5″ Base, 8.25″ Tip		4.60	3.478		2,375	234		2,609	2,950
2800	Light poles, anchor base									
2820	not including concrete bases									
2840	Aluminum pole, 8′ high	1 Elec	4	2	Ea.	455	135		590	705
2850	10′ high		4	2		630	135		765	895
2860	12′ high		3.80	2.105		495	142		637	750
2870	14′ high		3.40	2.353		530	158		688	815
2880	16′ high		3	2.667		575	180		755	895
3000	20′ high	R-3	2.90	6.897		745	465	66.50	1,276.50	1,575
3200	30′ high		2.60	7.692		1,650	520	74	2,244	2,675
3400	35′ high		2.30	8.696		2,325	585	84	2,994	3,550
3600	40′ high		2	10		2,675	675	96.50	3,446.50	4,050
3800	Bracket arms, 1 arm	1 Elec	8	1		580	67.50		647.50	740
4000	2 arms		8	1		1,150	67.50		1,217.50	1,375
4200	3 arms		5.30	1.509		465	102		567	660
4400	4 arms		4.80	1.667		590	112		702	815
4500	Steel pole, galvanized, 8′ high		3.80	2.105		885	142		1,027	1,175
4510	10′ high		3.70	2.162		665	146		811	945
4520	12′ high		3.40	2.353		680	158		838	985
4530	14′ high		3.10	2.581		730	174		904	1,050
4540	16′ high		2.90	2.759		840	186		1,026	1,200
4550	18′ high		2.70	2.963		805	200		1,005	1,175
4600	20′ high	R-3	2.60	7.692		1,325	520	74	1,919	2,300
4800	30′ high		2.30	8.696		1,775	585	84	2,444	2,925
5000	35′ high		2.20	9.091		1,700	610	87.50	2,397.50	2,850
5200	40′ high		1.70	11.765		2,475	790	114	3,379	4,025
5400	Bracket arms, 1 arm	1 Elec	8	1		440	67.50		507.50	585
5600	2 arms		8	1		810	67.50		877.50	990
5800	3 arms		5.30	1.509		915	102		1,017	1,150
6000	4 arms		5.30	1.509		1,125	102		1,227	1,375
6100	Fiberglass pole, 1 or 2 fixtures, 20′ high	R-3	4	5		1,125	335	48.50	1,508.50	1,775
6200	30′ high		3.60	5.556		1,375	375	53.50	1,803.50	2,125
6300	35′ high		3.20	6.250		2,900	420	60.50	3,380.50	3,900
6400	40′ high		2.80	7.143		3,100	480	69	3,649	4,225
6420	Wood pole, 4-1/2″ x 5-1/8″, 8′ high	1 Elec	6	1.333		775	90		865	990
6430	10′ high		6	1.333		925	90		1,015	1,150
6440	12′ high		5.70	1.404		1,075	94.50		1,169.50	1,325
6450	15′ high		5	1.600		1,275	108		1,383	1,550
6460	20′ high		4	2		1,475	135		1,610	1,825
6461	Light poles, anchor base, w/o conc base, pwdr ct stl, 16′ H	2 Elec	3.10	5.161		840	350		1,190	1,450
6462	20′ high	R-3	2.90	6.897		1,325	465	66.50	1,856.50	2,225
6463	30′ high		2.30	8.696		1,775	585	84	2,444	2,925
6464	35′ high		2.40	8.333		1,700	560	80.50	2,340.50	2,775
6470	Light pole conc base, max 6′ buried, 2′ exposed, 18″ diam., average cost	C-6	6	8		246	390	9.90	645.90	860
7300	Transformer bases, not including concrete bases									
7320	Maximum pole size, steel, 40′ high	1 Elec	2	4	Ea.	675	269		944	1,150
7340	Cast aluminum, 30′ high		3	2.667		770	180		950	1,100
7350	40′ high		2.50	3.200		1,000	216		1,216	1,425
8000	Line cover protective devices									

26 56 Exterior Lighting

26 56 13 – Lighting Poles and Standards

26 56 13.10 Lighting Poles		Crew	Daily Output	Labor-Hours	Unit	2023 Bare Costs Material	Labor	Equipment	Total	Total Incl O&P
8010	line cover									
8015	Refer to 26 01 02.20 for labor adjustment factors as they apply									
8100	MVLC 1" W x 1-1/2" H, 14/5'	1 Elec	60	.133	Ea.	5.60	9		14.60	19.50
8110	8'		58	.138		6.25	9.30		15.55	20.50
8120	MVLC 1" W x 1-1/2" H, 18/5'		60	.133		7.10	9		16.10	21
8130	8'		58	.138		11.95	9.30		21.25	27
8140	MVLC 1" W x 1-1/2" H, 38/5'		60	.133		13.15	9		22.15	28
8150	8'		58	.138		15.35	9.30		24.65	30.50

26 56 19 – LED Exterior Lighting

26 56 19.55 Roadway LED Luminaire		Crew	Daily Output	Labor-Hours	Unit	Material	Labor	Equipment	Total	Total Incl O&P
0010	**ROADWAY LED LUMINAIRE**									
0100	LED fixture, 72 LEDs, 120 V AC or 12 V DC, equal to 60 watt G	1 Elec	2.70	2.963	Ea.	650	200		850	1,000
0110	108 LEDs, 120 V AC or 12 V DC, equal to 90 watt G		2.70	2.963		865	200		1,065	1,250
0120	144 LEDs, 120 V AC or 12 V DC, equal to 120 watt G		2.70	2.963		1,075	200		1,275	1,475
0130	252 LEDs, 120 V AC or 12 V DC, equal to 210 watt G	2 Elec	4.40	3.636		1,475	245		1,720	2,000
0140	Replaces high pressure sodium fixture, 75 watt G	1 Elec	2.70	2.963		315	200		515	640
0150	125 watt G		2.70	2.963		288	200		488	610
0160	150 watt G		2.70	2.963		575	200		775	930
0170	175 watt G		2.70	2.963		455	200		655	795
0180	200 watt G		2.70	2.963		500	200		700	845
0190	250 watt G	2 Elec	4.40	3.636		730	245		975	1,175
0200	320 watt G		4.40	3.636		725	245		970	1,175
2000	Exterior fixtures, LED roadway, type 2, 50W, neutral slipfitter bronze		5.20	3.077		915	207		1,122	1,300
2010	3, 50W, neutral slipfitter bronze		5.20	3.077		955	207		1,162	1,350
2020	4, 50W, neutral slipfitter bronze		5.20	3.077		955	207		1,162	1,350
2030	Exterior fixtures, LED roadway, type 2, 78W, neutral slipfitter bronze		5.20	3.077		920	207		1,127	1,325
2040	3, 78W, neutral slipfitter bronze		5.20	3.077		875	207		1,082	1,275
2050	4, 78W, neutral slipfitter bronze		5.20	3.077		960	207		1,167	1,350
2060	Exterior fixtures, LED roadway, type 2, 105W, neutral slipfitter bronze		5.20	3.077		1,125	207		1,332	1,550
2070	3, 105W, neutral slipfitter bronze		5.20	3.077		1,125	207		1,332	1,550
2080	4, 105W, neutral slipfitter bronze		5.20	3.077		1,125	207		1,332	1,550
2090	Exterior fixtures, LED roadway, type 2, 125W, neutral slipfitter bronze		5.20	3.077		1,125	207		1,332	1,550
3010	LED Street lighting, Solar, pole mounting, 10 Watt, 900 lm,12 Hrs		5.20	3.077		295	207		502	635
3020	20 Watt, 2200 lm		5.20	3.077		495	207		702	855
3030	30 Watt, 3300 lm		5.20	3.077		700	207		907	1,075
3220	LED Street lighting, Solar, Commercial, pole, 20 Watt, 4000 lm, 10 Hrs		5.20	3.077		700	207		907	1,075
3230	30 Watt, 6000 lm		5.20	3.077		1,400	207		1,607	1,850
3250	50 Watt, 9000 lm		5.20	3.077		1,400	207		1,607	1,850

26 56 19.60 Parking LED Lighting		Crew	Daily Output	Labor-Hours	Unit	Material	Labor	Equipment	Total	Total Incl O&P
0010	**PARKING LED LIGHTING**									
0100	Round pole mounting, 88 lamp watts G	1 Elec	2	4	Ea.	1,400	269		1,669	1,950
2020	LED Parking lighting, Solar powered, pole mounting, 20W, 2000 Lumens, 5 Hrs		2	4		330	269		599	765
2040	40W, 4000 Lumens		2	4		470	269		739	915
2060	60W, 6000 Lumens		2	4		670	269		939	1,125
2080	80W, 8000 Lumens		2	4		870	269		1,139	1,350
2100	100W, 10000 Lumens		2	4		1,000	269		1,269	1,500
2120	120W, 12000 Lumens		2	4		1,125	269		1,394	1,650

26 56 21 – HID Exterior Lighting

26 56 21.20 Roadway Luminaire		Crew	Daily Output	Labor-Hours	Unit	Material	2023 Bare Costs Labor	Equipment	Total	Total Incl O&P
0010	**ROADWAY LUMINAIRE**									
2650	Roadway area luminaire, low pressure sodium, 135 watt	1 Elec	2	4	Ea.	850	269		1,119	1,325
2700	180 watt	"	2	4		1,025	269		1,294	1,525
2750	Metal halide, 400 watt	2 Elec	4.40	3.636		805	245		1,050	1,250
2760	1,000 watt		4	4		1,125	269		1,394	1,650
2780	High pressure sodium, 400 watt		4.40	3.636		435	245		680	840
2790	1,000 watt	↓	4	4	↓	1,100	269		1,369	1,625

26 56 23 – Area Lighting

26 56 23.10 Exterior Fixtures		Crew	Daily Output	Labor-Hours	Unit	Material	Labor	Equipment	Total	Total Incl O&P
0010	**EXTERIOR FIXTURES** With lamps									
0200	Wall mounted, incandescent, 100 watt	1 Elec	8	1	Ea.	72	67.50		139.50	179
0400	Quartz, 500 watt		5.30	1.509		115	102		217	278
0420	1,500 watt		4.20	1.905		169	128		297	375
1100	Wall pack, low pressure sodium, 35 watt		4	2		172	135		307	390
1150	55 watt		4	2		202	135		337	420
1160	High pressure sodium, 70 watt		4	2		129	135		264	340
1170	150 watt		4	2		268	135		403	495
1175	High pressure sodium, 250 watt		4	2		268	135		403	495
1180	Metal halide, 175 watt		4	2		201	135		336	420
1190	250 watt		4	2		210	135		345	430
1195	400 watt		4	2		500	135		635	750
1250	Induction lamp, 40 watt		4	2		185	135		320	405
1260	80 watt		4	2		197	135		332	415
1278	LED, poly lens, 26 watt		4	2		172	135		307	390
1280	110 watt		4	2		765	135		900	1,050
1500	LED, glass lens, 13 watt	↓	4	2	↓	172	135		307	390

26 56 23.55 Exterior LED Fixtures		Crew	Daily Output	Labor-Hours	Unit	Material	Labor	Equipment	Total	Total Incl O&P
0010	**EXTERIOR LED FIXTURES**									
0100	Wall mounted, indoor/outdoor, 12 watt G	1 Elec	10	.800	Ea.	320	54		374	430
0110	32 watt G		10	.800		410	54		464	530
0120	66 watt G		10	.800		335	54		389	450
0200	outdoor, 110 watt G		10	.800		229	54		283	330
0210	220 watt G		10	.800		365	54		419	485
0300	modular, type IV, 120 V, 50 lamp watts G		9	.889		1,500	60		1,560	1,750
0310	101 lamp watts G		9	.889		455	60		515	590
0320	126 lamp watts G		9	.889		460	60		520	595
0330	202 lamp watts G		9	.889		1,525	60		1,585	1,775
0340	240 V, 50 lamp watts G		8	1		1,325	67.50		1,392.50	1,550
0350	101 lamp watts G		8	1		1,100	67.50		1,167.50	1,300
0360	126 lamp watts G		8	1		1,200	67.50		1,267.50	1,425
0370	202 lamp watts G		8	1		1,550	67.50		1,617.50	1,800
0400	wall pack, glass, 13 lamp watts G		4	2		395	135		530	635
0410	poly w/photocell, 26 lamp watts G		4	2		250	135		385	475
0420	50 lamp watts G		4	2		745	135		880	1,025
0430	replacement, 40 watts G		4	2		76	135		211	284
0440	60 watts G	↓	4	2	↓	137	135		272	350

26 56 26 – Landscape Lighting

26 56 26.20 Landscape Fixtures		Crew	Daily Output	Labor-Hours	Unit	Material	2023 Bare Costs Labor	Equipment	Total	Total Incl O&P
0010	LANDSCAPE FIXTURES									
7380	Landscape recessed uplight, incl. housing, ballast, transformer									
7390	& reflector, not incl. conduit, wire, trench									
7420	Incandescent, 250 watt	1 Elec	5	1.600	Ea.	730	108		838	965
7440	Quartz, 250 watt		5	1.600		695	108		803	925
7460	500 watt		4	2		715	135		850	985

26 56 26.50 Landscape LED Fixtures		Crew	Daily Output	Labor-Hours	Unit	Material	Labor	Equipment	Total	Total Incl O&P
0010	LANDSCAPE LED FIXTURES									
0100	12 volt alum bullet hooded-BLK	1 Elec	5	1.600	Ea.	49	108		157	214
0200	12 volt alum bullet hooded-BRZ		5	1.600		136	108		244	310
0300	12 volt alum bullet hooded-GRN		5	1.600		136	108		244	310
1000	12 volt alum large bullet hooded-BLK		5	1.600		100	108		208	270
1100	12 volt alum large bullet hooded-BRZ		5	1.600		100	108		208	270
1200	12 volt alum large bullet hooded-GRN		5	1.600		100	108		208	270
2000	12 volt large bullet landscape light fixture		5	1.600		100	108		208	270
2100	12 volt alum light large bullet		5	1.600		100	108		208	270
2200	12 volt alum bullet light		5	1.600		100	108		208	270

26 56 33 – Walkway Lighting

26 56 33.10 Walkway Luminaire		Crew	Daily Output	Labor-Hours	Unit	Material	Labor	Equipment	Total	Total Incl O&P
0010	WALKWAY LUMINAIRE									
6500	Bollard light, lamp & ballast, 42" high with polycarbonate lens									
6800	Metal halide, 175 watt	1 Elec	3	2.667	Ea.	1,050	180		1,230	1,425
6900	High pressure sodium, 70 watt		3	2.667		950	180		1,130	1,325
7000	100 watt		3	2.667		950	180		1,130	1,325
7100	150 watt		3	2.667		1,325	180		1,505	1,725
7200	Incandescent, 150 watt		3	2.667		930	180		1,110	1,300
7810	Walkway luminaire, square 16", metal halide 250 watt		2.70	2.963		440	200		640	775
7820	High pressure sodium, 70 watt		3	2.667		950	180		1,130	1,325
7830	100 watt		3	2.667		970	180		1,150	1,350
7840	150 watt		3	2.667		970	180		1,150	1,350
7850	200 watt		3	2.667		975	180		1,155	1,350
7910	Round 19", metal halide, 250 watt		2.70	2.963		1,325	200		1,525	1,750
7920	High pressure sodium, 70 watt		3	2.667		1,450	180		1,630	1,875
7930	100 watt		3	2.667		1,450	180		1,630	1,875
7940	150 watt		3	2.667		1,475	180		1,655	1,900
7950	250 watt		2.70	2.963		1,400	200		1,600	1,850
8000	Sphere 14" opal, incandescent, 200 watt		4	2		425	135		560	665
8020	Sphere 18" opal, incandescent, 300 watt		3.50	2.286		510	154		664	790
8040	Sphere 16" clear, high pressure sodium, 70 watt		3	2.667		885	180		1,065	1,250
8050	100 watt		3	2.667		945	180		1,125	1,300
8100	Cube 16" opal, incandescent, 300 watt		3.50	2.286		560	154		714	845
8120	High pressure sodium, 70 watt		3	2.667		815	180		995	1,150
8130	100 watt		3	2.667		835	180		1,015	1,175
8230	Lantern, high pressure sodium, 70 watt		3	2.667		545	180		725	865
8240	100 watt		3	2.667		790	180		970	1,125
8250	150 watt		3	2.667		740	180		920	1,075
8260	250 watt		2.70	2.963		1,025	200		1,225	1,450
8270	Incandescent, 300 watt		3.50	2.286		545	154		699	830
8330	Reflector 22" w/globe, high pressure sodium, 70 watt		3	2.667		535	180		715	855
8340	100 watt		3	2.667		625	180		805	950
8350	150 watt		3	2.667		715	180		895	1,050

26 56 33 – Walkway Lighting

26 56 33.10 Walkway Luminaire		Crew	Daily Output	Labor-Hours	Unit	Material	2023 Bare Costs Labor	Equipment	Total	Total Incl O&P
8360	250 watt	1 Elec	2.70	2.963	Ea.	745	200		945	1,125

26 56 33.55 Walkway LED Luminaire

			Crew	Daily Output	Labor-Hours	Unit	Material	Labor	Equipment	Total	Total Incl O&P
0010	**WALKWAY LED LUMINAIRE**										
0100	Pole mounted, 86 watts, 4,350 lumens	G	1 Elec	3	2.667	Ea.	1,425	180		1,605	1,850
0110	4,630 lumens	G		3	2.667		2,375	180		2,555	2,875
0120	80 watts, 4,000 lumens	G		3	2.667		2,200	180		2,380	2,675
0600	LED bollard pole, 6″ diam. x 36″ H, cast alum, surf. mtd., 8W, 6,000K, 120V			8.50	.941		450	63.50		513.50	590
0610	6″ diam. x 42″ H, cast alum, surf. mtd., 12W, 5,100K,120V			8.50	.941		790	63.50		853.50	960
0620	6″ diam. x 42″ H, cast alum, surf. mtd., 18W, 5,100K,120V			8.50	.941		795	63.50		858.50	970
0630	6″ diam. x 42″ H, cast alum, surf. mtd., 24W, 5,100K,120V			8.50	.941		825	63.50		888.50	1,000
0640	9.5″ square x 42″ H, cast resin, surf. mtd., A19, 9W, 120V			8.50	.941		655	63.50		718.50	815
0650	9.75″ diam. x 42″ H, cast resin, side mount, dome, 9W, 120V			8.50	.941		750	63.50		813.50	920
0660	9.75″ diam. x 43″ H, cast resin, burial base, dome, 9W, 120V			8.50	.941		750	63.50		813.50	920
0670	8″ diam. x 36″ H, concrete security base, w/rebar, 8W, HID			8	1		1,100	67.50		1,167.50	1,325
0680	10″ diam. x 49″ H, concrete base, w/Sch 40 Steel pipe, 8W			6.75	1.185		1,250	80		1,330	1,500
0690	12″ diam. x 48″ H, concrete base, w/Sch 40 Steel pipe, 8W			6.75	1.185		1,450	80		1,530	1,700
0700	8″ diam. x 36″ H, concrete, cast aluminum dome, 90 degree, 4.1W			7	1.143		1,125	77		1,202	1,350
0710	8″ diam. x 36″ H, concrete, cast aluminum dome, 180 degree, 4.1W			7	1.143		1,375	77		1,452	1,625
0720	8″ diam. x 48″ H, concrete, cast aluminum dome, 360 degree, 4.1W			7	1.143		1,675	77		1,752	1,975

26 56 36 – Flood Lighting

26 56 36.20 Floodlights

			Crew	Daily Output	Labor-Hours	Unit	Material	Labor	Equipment	Total	Total Incl O&P
0010	**FLOODLIGHTS** with ballast and lamp,										
1290	floor mtd, mount with swivel bracket										
1300	Induction lamp, 40 watt		1 Elec	3	2.667	Ea.	505	180		685	820
1310	80 watt			3	2.667		310	180		490	605
1320	150 watt			3	2.667		1,050	180		1,230	1,425
1400	Pole mounted, pole not included										
1950	Metal halide, 175 watt		1 Elec	2.70	2.963	Ea.	270	200		470	595
2000	400 watt		2 Elec	4.40	3.636		395	245		640	800
2200	1,000 watt			4	4		940	269		1,209	1,425
2210	1,500 watt			3.70	4.324		590	291		881	1,075
2250	Low pressure sodium, 55 watt		1 Elec	2.70	2.963		395	200		595	730
2270	90 watt			2	4		565	269		834	1,025
2290	180 watt			2	4		590	269		859	1,050
2340	High pressure sodium, 70 watt			2.70	2.963		296	200		496	620
2360	100 watt			2.70	2.963		146	200		346	455
2380	150 watt			2.70	2.963		226	200		426	545
2400	400 watt		2 Elec	4.40	3.636		480	245		725	890
2600	1,000 watt		"	4	4		480	269		749	925
9005	Solar powered floodlight, w/motion det, incl. batt pack for cloudy days	G	1 Elec	8	1		90	67.50		157.50	199
9020	Replacement battery pack	G	"	8	1		18.90	67.50		86.40	121

26 56 36.55 LED Floodlights

			Crew	Daily Output	Labor-Hours	Unit	Material	Labor	Equipment	Total	Total Incl O&P
0010	**LED FLOODLIGHTS** with ballast and lamp,										
0020	Pole mounted, pole not included										
0100	11 watt	G	1 Elec	4	2	Ea.	187	135		322	405
0110	46 watt	G		4	2		256	135		391	480
0120	90 watt	G		4	2		480	135		615	725
0130	288 watt	G		4	2		890	135		1,025	1,175

26 61 Lighting Systems and Accessories

26 61 13 – Lighting Accessories

26 61 13.30 Fixture Whips		Crew	Daily Output	Labor-Hours	Unit	2023 Bare Costs Material	Labor	Equipment	Total	Total Incl O&P
0010	**FIXTURE WHIPS**									
0080	3/8" Greenfield, 2 connectors, 6' long									
0100	TFFN wire, three #18	1 Elec	32	.250	Ea.	8.70	16.85		25.55	34.50
0150	Four #18		28	.286		11.10	19.25		30.35	41
0200	Three #16		32	.250		13.30	16.85		30.15	39.50
0250	Four #16		28	.286		11.55	19.25		30.80	41
0300	THHN wire, three #14		32	.250		10.95	16.85		27.80	37
0350	Four #14		28	.286		12.95	19.25		32.20	42.50
0360	Three #12		32	.250		12.30	16.85		29.15	38.50

26 61 23 – Lamps Applications

26 61 23.10 Lamps		Crew	Daily Output	Labor-Hours	Unit	Material	Labor	Equipment	Total	Total Incl O&P
0010	**LAMPS**									
0080	Fluorescent, rapid start, cool white, 2' long, 20 watt	1 Elec	1	8	C	430	540		970	1,275
0100	4' long, 40 watt		.90	8.889		495	600		1,095	1,425
0120	3' long, 30 watt		.90	8.889		550	600		1,150	1,500
0125	3' long, 25 watt energy saver R265723-10 G		.90	8.889		1,125	600		1,725	2,125
0150	U-40 watt		.80	10		1,775	675		2,450	2,950
0155	U-34 watt energy saver G		.80	10		16.15	675		691.15	1,025
0170	4' long, 34 watt energy saver G		.90	8.889		5.95	600		605.95	895
0176	2' long, T8, 17 watt energy saver G		1	8		495	540		1,035	1,350
0178	3' long, T8, 25 watt energy saver G		.90	8.889		495	600		1,095	1,425
0180	4' long, T8, 32 watt energy saver G		.90	8.889		815	600		1,415	1,775
0200	Slimline, 4' long, 40 watt		.90	8.889		1,175	600		1,775	2,175
0210	4' long, 30 watt energy saver G		.90	8.889		1,175	600		1,775	2,175
0300	8' long, 75 watt		.80	10		1,675	675		2,350	2,850
0350	8' long, 60 watt energy saver G		.80	10		540	675		1,215	1,600
0400	High output, 4' long, 60 watt		.90	8.889		955	600		1,555	1,950
0410	8' long, 95 watt energy saver G		.80	10		1,225	675		1,900	2,350
0500	8' long, 110 watt		.80	10		1,225	675		1,900	2,350
0512	2' long, T5, 14 watt energy saver G		1	8		320	540		860	1,150
0514	3' long, T5, 21 watt energy saver G		.90	8.889		555	600		1,155	1,500
0516	4' long, T5, 28 watt energy saver G		.90	8.889		490	600		1,090	1,425
0517	4' long, T5, 54 watt energy saver G		.90	8.889		515	600		1,115	1,450
0520	Very high output, 4' long, 110 watt		.90	8.889		3,250	600		3,850	4,475
0525	8' long, 195 watt energy saver G		.70	11.429		2,550	770		3,320	3,950
0550	8' long, 215 watt		.70	11.429		2,100	770		2,870	3,475
0554	Full spectrum, 4' long, 60 watt		.90	8.889		975	600		1,575	1,975
0556	6' long, 85 watt		.90	8.889		1,025	600		1,625	2,025
0558	8' long, 110 watt		.80	10		1,250	675		1,925	2,375
0560	Twin tube compact lamp G		.90	8.889		450	600		1,050	1,375
0570	Double twin tube compact lamp G		.80	10		930	675		1,605	2,025
0600	Mercury vapor, mogul base, deluxe white, 100 watt		.30	26.667		18,300	1,800		20,100	22,800
0650	175 watt		.30	26.667		2,975	1,800		4,775	5,925
0700	250 watt		.30	26.667		14,700	1,800		16,500	18,800
0800	400 watt		.30	26.667		13,400	1,800		15,200	17,500
0900	1,000 watt		.20	40		10,100	2,700		12,800	15,100
1000	Metal halide, mogul base, 175 watt		.30	26.667		1,775	1,800		3,575	4,625
1100	250 watt		.30	26.667		3,225	1,800		5,025	6,225
1200	400 watt		.30	26.667		2,550	1,800		4,350	5,475
1300	1,000 watt		.20	40		4,950	2,700		7,650	9,450
1320	1,000 watt, 125,000 initial lumens		.20	40		8,850	2,700		11,550	13,700
1330	1,500 watt		.20	40		8,375	2,700		11,075	13,200

26 61 23.10 Lamps		Crew	Daily Output	Labor-Hours	Unit	Material	Labor (2023 Bare Costs)	Equipment	Total	Total Incl O&P
1350	High pressure sodium, 70 watt	1 Elec	.30	26.667	C	2,450	1,800		4,250	5,375
1360	100 watt		.30	26.667		2,325	1,800		4,125	5,250
1370	150 watt		.30	26.667		2,200	1,800		4,000	5,100
1380	250 watt		.30	26.667		2,375	1,800		4,175	5,300
1400	400 watt		.30	26.667		2,300	1,800		4,100	5,200
1450	1,000 watt		.20	40		6,475	2,700		9,175	11,100
1500	Low pressure sodium, 35 watt		.30	26.667		5,150	1,800		6,950	8,350
1550	55 watt		.30	26.667		6,800	1,800		8,600	10,200
1600	90 watt		.30	26.667		20,000	1,800		21,800	24,700
1650	135 watt		.20	40		12,600	2,700		15,300	17,800
1700	180 watt		.20	40		25,500	2,700		28,200	32,000
1750	Quartz line, clear, 500 watt		1.10	7.273		905	490		1,395	1,725
1760	1,500 watt		.20	40		2,000	2,700		4,700	6,200
1762	Spot, MR 16, 50 watt		1.30	6.154		2,900	415		3,315	3,825
1770	Tungsten halogen, T4, 400 watt		1.10	7.273		735	490		1,225	1,550
1775	T3, 1,200 watt		.30	26.667		2,900	1,800		4,700	5,875
1778	PAR 30, 50 watt		1.30	6.154		1,425	415		1,840	2,175
1780	PAR 38, 90 watt		1.30	6.154		4,300	415		4,715	5,350
1800	Incandescent, interior, A21, 100 watt		1.60	5		550	335		885	1,100
1900	A21, 150 watt		1.60	5		350	335		685	885
2000	A23, 200 watt		1.60	5		460	335		795	1,000
2200	PS 35, 300 watt		1.60	5		775	335		1,110	1,350
2210	PS 35, 500 watt		1.60	5		720	335		1,055	1,300
2230	PS 52, 1,000 watt		1.30	6.154		4,250	415		4,665	5,300
2240	PS 52, 1,500 watt		1.30	6.154		2,525	415		2,940	3,400
2300	R30, 75 watt		1.30	6.154		1,025	415		1,440	1,750
2400	R40, 100 watt		1.30	6.154		2,450	415		2,865	3,325
2500	Exterior, PAR 38, 75 watt		1.30	6.154		1,400	415		1,815	2,175
2600	PAR 38, 150 watt		1.30	6.154		2,100	415		2,515	2,925
2700	PAR 46, 200 watt		1.10	7.273		2,400	490		2,890	3,375
2800	PAR 56, 300 watt		1.10	7.273		1,825	490		2,315	2,725
3000	Guards, fluorescent lamp, 4′ long		100	.080	Ea.	13.90	5.40		19.30	23.50
3200	8′ long		90	.089	"	28	6		34	39.50

26 61 23.55 LED Lamps		Crew	Daily Output	Labor-Hours	Unit	Material	Labor (2023 Bare Costs)	Equipment	Total	Total Incl O&P
0010	**LED LAMPS**									
0100	LED lamp, interior, shape A60, equal to 60 W [G]	1 Elec	160	.050	Ea.	24	3.37		27.37	31.50
0110	7 W LED decorative c, ca, f, g shape		160	.050		6.85	3.37		10.22	12.55
0120	12V mini lamp LED		160	.050		6.80	3.37		10.17	12.45
0200	Globe frosted A60, equal to 60 W [G]		160	.050		4.39	3.37		7.76	9.85
0205	LED lamp, interior, globe		160	.050		13.05	3.37		16.42	19.35
0210	2.2 W LED LMP		160	.050		82	3.37		85.37	95
0220	2.2 W LED replacement decorative lamp		160	.050		11.05	3.37		14.42	17.15
0230	3.5 W LED replacement decorative lamp		160	.050		9.70	3.37		13.07	15.70
0240	4.5 W 120V LED replacement decorative lamp		160	.050		13.40	3.37		16.77	19.70
0250	4.5 W 120V LED, 2700k replacement decorative lamp		160	.050		16.40	3.37		19.77	23
0260	4.9 W 120V LED, 2700k replacement decorative lamp candelabra base		160	.050		12.40	3.37		15.77	18.65
0270	4.9 W 120V LED, 3000k replacement decorative lamp candelabra base		160	.050		3.75	3.37		7.12	9.15
0280	5 W LED PAR 20 parabolic reflector lamp FL		140	.057		74.50	3.85		78.35	87
0300	Globe earth, equal to 100 W [G]		140	.057		3.47	3.85		7.32	9.50
0305	7 W LED reflector lamp 3000k DIM		140	.057		5.55	3.85		9.40	11.80
0310	10 W omni LED warm white light bulb E26 medium base 120 volt card		140	.057		25	3.85		28.85	33
0315	7 W LED reflector lamp WFL 2700k DIM		140	.057		5.55	3.85		9.40	11.80

26 61 23 – Lamps Applications

26 61 23.55 LED Lamps		Crew	Daily Output	Labor-Hours	Unit	Material	2023 Bare Costs Labor	Equipment	Total	Total Incl O&P
0320	9 W omni LED warm white light bulb E26 medium base 120 volt card	1 Elec	140	.057	Ea.	13.15	3.85		17	20
0500	8 W LED, A19 lamp, equal to 40 W		140	.057		7.30	3.85		11.15	13.75
0505	9 W LED, A19 lamp, 5000K dimmable, equal to 60 W		140	.057		9.10	3.85		12.95	15.70
0510	10.5 W LED, A19 lamp, dimmable, equal to 60 W		140	.057		10.35	3.85		14.20	17.10
0515	10 W LED, A19 lamp, frosted, dimmable, equal to 60 W		140	.057		4.33	3.85		8.18	10.45
0520	10 W LED, A19 lamp, omni-directional, dimmable, equal to 60 W		140	.057		9.60	3.85		13.45	16.25
0525	12 W LED, A19 lamp, dimmable, equal to 75 W		140	.057		8.85	3.85		12.70	15.45
1100	MR16, 3 W, replacement of halogen lamp 25 W G		130	.062		24	4.14		28.14	32.50
1200	6 W replacement of halogen lamp 45 W G		130	.062		25	4.14		29.14	33.50
2100	10 W, PAR20, equal to 60 W G		130	.062		33	4.14		37.14	42.50
2200	15 W, PAR30, equal to 100 W G		130	.062		63	4.14		67.14	75
2210	50 W LED lamp		130	.062		715	4.14		719.14	790
2220	11 Watt reflector dimmable warm white LED light bulb with medium base		130	.062		51.50	4.14		55.64	62.50
2221	12 W A-Line LED lamp DIM		130	.062		96.50	4.14		100.64	112
2225	13 Watt reflector LED warm white e26 with medium base 120 volt box		130	.062		48.50	4.14		52.64	59.50
2226	13 W br30 LED lamp		130	.062		84	4.14		88.14	98.50
2227	15 W 120V br30 inc LED lamp, 2700k		130	.062		78.50	4.14		82.64	92
2228	15 W 120V br30 inc LED lamp, 4000k		130	.062		74.50	4.14		78.64	87.50
2230	3 Watt dimmable warm white decorative LED lamp with medium base		160	.050		15.15	3.37		18.52	21.50
2240	.43 W night light LED daylight bulb E12 candelabra base 120 volt 2 pack		160	.050		5.85	3.37		9.22	11.40
2250	15 W omni-directional LED warm white e26 medium base 120 volt box		160	.050		49.50	3.37		52.87	59.50
2251	11 W omni-directional LED warm white e26 medium base 120 volt box		160	.050		35.50	3.37		38.87	44
2252	10 W omni-directional LED warm white e26 medium base 120 volt box		160	.050		34.50	3.37		37.87	43
2253	7 W omni A19 LED warm white e26 medium base 120 volt box		160	.050		23	3.37		26.37	30.50
2255	8 PAR 20 parabolic reflector 2700 LED lamp		160	.050		23.50	3.37		26.87	30.50
2256	8 PAR 20 parabolic reflector 3000 LED lamp		160	.050		23	3.37		26.37	30.50
2260	12 W PAR 38 120V LED 15 degree directional lamp		160	.050		251	3.37		254.37	281
2270	12 W PAR 38 120V LED 25 degree directional lamp		160	.050		39	3.37		42.37	47.50
2280	12 W PAR 38 120V LED 40 degree directional lamp		160	.050		251	3.37		254.37	281
2285	16 W PAR 38 120V 2700k LED parabolic reflector lamp		160	.050		38	3.37		41.37	46.50
2290	16 W PAR 38 120V 3000k LED parabolic reflector lamp		160	.050		28.50	3.37		31.87	36.50
3000	15 W PAR 30 LED daylight E26 medium base 120V box		160	.050		74.50	3.37		77.87	87
3100	17 W LED 3000k PAR 38 100 W replacement		160	.050		58	3.37		61.37	68.50
3110	17 W LED PAR 38 100 W replacement		160	.050		43.50	3.37		46.87	52.50
3120	17 W LED PAR 38 100 W replacement parabolic reflector		160	.050		45.50	3.37		48.87	55
3130	24 W LED T8 PW straight fluorescent lamp		8.89	.900		355	60.50		415.50	485
3135	Linear fluorescent LED lamp 120V		8.89	.900		164	60.50		224.50	270
3200	30 W LED 2700K recessed 8055E PAR 38 high power		160	.050		98.50	3.37		101.87	113
3210	30 W LED 4200K 120 degree 8055E PAR 38 high power		160	.050		106	3.37		109.37	122
3220	30 W LED 5700K 8055E PAR 38 high power		160	.050		64	3.37		67.37	75.50
3230	50 W LED 2700K 8045M PAR 38 277V high power		160	.050		420	3.37		423.37	470
3240	50 W LED 4200K 8045M PAR 38 277V high power retro fit		160	.050		82	3.37		85.37	95
3250	50 W LED 5700K 8045M PAR 38 277V high power retro fit		160	.050		420	3.37		423.37	470
8000	10 W LED PAR 30/fl 10 pk		160	.050		119	3.37		122.37	136
8010	Gen 3 PAR 30 15 W short neck power LED 120 VAC E26 80 +cri 300k dimm		160	.050		16	3.37		19.37	22.50
8020	12 PAR 30 2700K parabolic reflector LED lamp		160	.050		52	3.37		55.37	62
8030	12 PAR 30 3000K parabolic reflector LED lamp		160	.050		39.50	3.37		42.87	48.50
8040	3500K LED advantage T8 9 W 800LM 2ft linear 2 BD frosted		69	.116		10.90	7.80		18.70	23.50
8050	3500K LED litespan T8 9 W 900LM 2ft linear frosted		69	.116		16.35	7.80		24.15	29.50
8060	4000K LED advantage T8 9 W 800LM 2ft linear 2BD frosted		69	.116		15.55	7.80		23.35	28.50
8070	4000K LED litespan T8 9 W 900LM 2ft linear frosted		69	.116		17.10	7.80		24.90	30.50
8080	5000K LED advantage T8 9 W 800LM 2ft linear 2BD frosted		69	.116		10.15	7.80		17.95	23
8090	5000K LED litespan T8 9 W 900LM 2ft linear frosted		69	.116		13.60	7.80		21.40	26.50

26 61 Lighting Systems and Accessories

26 61 23 – Lamps Applications

26 61 23.55 LED Lamps		Crew	Daily Output	Labor-Hours	Unit	Material	2023 Bare Costs Labor	Equipment	Total	Total Incl O&P
8100	3500K LED advantage T8 18 W 1600LM 4ft linear 2 BD frosted	1 Elec	69	.116	Ea.	12.80	7.80		20.60	25.50
8105	18 W LED 4ft T8 4000K frost 1600L linear lamp		69	.116		23	7.80		30.80	36.50
8108	18 W LED 48 inch T8 4100K 1890LM linear lamp		69	.116		70.50	7.80		78.30	89
8110	3500K LED advantage T8 18 W 1800LM 4ft linear 2 BD frosted		69	.116		36.50	7.80		44.30	51.50
8120	4000K LED advantage T8 18 W 1600LM 4ft linear 2 BD frosted		69	.116		25	7.80		32.80	39
8130	4000K LED litespan T8 18 W 1800LM 4ft linear frosted		69	.116		34.50	7.80		42.30	49.50
8140	5000K LED advantage T8 18 W 1600LM 4ft linear 2BD frosted		69	.116		16.35	7.80		24.15	29.50
8150	5000K LED litespan T8 18 W 1800LM 4ft linear 2BD frosted		69	.116		26	7.80		33.80	40
8200	16.5 T8 3000 IF-6U U-shape fluorescent LED lamp		65	.123		26.50	8.30		34.80	41.50
8210	16.5 T8 3500 IF-6U U-shape fluorescent LED lamp		65	.123		27	8.30		35.30	42.50
8220	16.5 T8 4000 IF-6U U-shape fluorescent LED lamp		65	.123		24	8.30		32.30	39
8230	16.5 T8 5000 IF-6U U-shape fluorescent LED lamp		65	.123		26.50	8.30		34.80	41.50
8240	18 W 6 inch T8 4100K U-shape frosted fluorescent LED lamp		60	.133		14.85	9		23.85	29.50
8250	18 W 6 inch T8 5000K U-shape frosted fluorescent LED lamp		60	.133		14.85	9		23.85	29.50
8260	Circular 12 W linear fluorescent LED 2700K MOD lamp		62.40	.128		375	8.65		383.65	425
8270	Circular 12 W linear fluorescent LED 3000K MOD lamp		62.40	.128		375	8.65		383.65	425
8280	Circular 12 W linear fluorescent LED 3500K MOD lamp		62.40	.128		340	8.65		348.65	385
8290	Circular 18 W linear fluorescent LED 3000K MOD lamp		62.40	.128		460	8.65		468.65	520
8300	Circular 18 W linear fluorescent LED 3500K MOD lamp		62.40	.128		510	8.65		518.65	575
8310	Circular 18 W linear fluorescent LED 5000K MOD lamp		62.40	.128		460	8.65		468.65	520
8320	Circular 18 W linear fluorescent LED 4100K MOD lamp	↓	62.40	.128	↓	490	8.65		498.65	555

26 71 Electrical Machines

26 71 13 – Motors Applications

26 71 13.10 Handling		Crew	Daily Output	Labor-Hours	Unit	Material	Labor	Equipment	Total	Total Incl O&P
0010	**HANDLING** Add to normal labor cost for restricted areas									
5000	Motors									
5100	1/2 HP, 23 pounds	1 Elec	4	2	Ea.		135		135	200
5110	3/4 HP, 28 pounds		4	2			135		135	200
5120	1 HP, 33 pounds		4	2			135		135	200
5130	1-1/2 HP, 44 pounds		3.20	2.500			168		168	250
5140	2 HP, 56 pounds		3	2.667			180		180	267
5150	3 HP, 71 pounds		2.30	3.478			234		234	350
5160	5 HP, 82 pounds		1.90	4.211			284		284	420
5170	7-1/2 HP, 124 pounds		1.50	5.333			360		360	535
5180	10 HP, 144 pounds		1.20	6.667			450		450	665
5190	15 HP, 185 pounds	↓	1	8			540		540	800
5200	20 HP, 214 pounds	2 Elec	1.50	10.667			720		720	1,075
5210	25 HP, 266 pounds		1.40	11.429			770		770	1,150
5220	30 HP, 310 pounds		1.20	13.333			900		900	1,325
5230	40 HP, 400 pounds		1	16			1,075		1,075	1,600
5240	50 HP, 450 pounds		.90	17.778			1,200		1,200	1,775
5250	75 HP, 680 pounds	↓	.80	20			1,350		1,350	2,000
5260	100 HP, 870 pounds	3 Elec	1	24			1,625		1,625	2,400
5270	125 HP, 940 pounds		.80	30			2,025		2,025	3,000
5280	150 HP, 1,200 pounds		.70	34.286			2,300		2,300	3,425
5290	175 HP, 1,300 pounds		.60	40			2,700		2,700	4,000
5300	200 HP, 1,400 pounds	↓	.50	48	↓		3,225		3,225	4,800

26 71 13 – Motors Applications

26 71 13.20 Motors		Crew	Daily Output	Labor-Hours	Unit	Material	Labor	Equipment	Total	Total Incl O&P
						2023 Bare Costs				
0010	**MOTORS** 230/460 V, 60 HZ R263413-30									
0050	Dripproof, premium efficiency, 1.15 service factor									
0060	1,800 RPM, 1/4 HP	1 Elec	5.33	1.501	Ea.	241	101		342	415
0070	1/3 HP		5.33	1.501		195	101		296	365
0080	1/2 HP		5.33	1.501		288	101		389	465
0090	3/4 HP		5.33	1.501		305	101		406	485
0100	1 HP		4.50	1.778		340	120		460	555
0150	2 HP		4.50	1.778		305	120		425	515
0200	3 HP		4.50	1.778		705	120		825	955
0250	5 HP		4.50	1.778		940	120		1,060	1,200
0300	7.5 HP		4.20	1.905		1,325	128		1,453	1,650
0350	10 HP		4	2		1,700	135		1,835	2,075
0400	15 HP		3.20	2.500		2,400	168		2,568	2,900
0450	20 HP	2 Elec	5.20	3.077		3,000	207		3,207	3,600
0500	25 HP		5	3.200		3,650	216		3,866	4,350
0550	30 HP		4.80	3.333		4,000	225		4,225	4,725
0600	40 HP		4	4		5,350	269		5,619	6,300
0650	50 HP		3.20	5		5,750	335		6,085	6,825
0700	60 HP		2.80	5.714		7,250	385		7,635	8,550
0750	75 HP		2.40	6.667		9,125	450		9,575	10,700
0800	100 HP	3 Elec	2.70	8.889		9,875	600		10,475	11,800
0850	125 HP		2.10	11.429		8,675	770		9,445	10,700
0900	150 HP		1.80	13.333		14,500	900		15,400	17,200
0950	200 HP		1.50	16		15,900	1,075		16,975	19,100
1000	1,200 RPM, 1 HP	1 Elec	4.50	1.778		780	120		900	1,025
1050	2 HP		4.50	1.778		930	120		1,050	1,200
1100	3 HP		4.50	1.778		1,175	120		1,295	1,475
1150	5 HP		4.50	1.778		1,550	120		1,670	1,875
1200	3,600 RPM, 2 HP		4.50	1.778		770	120		890	1,025
1250	3 HP		4.50	1.778		865	120		985	1,125
1300	5 HP		4.50	1.778		920	120		1,040	1,200
1350	Totally enclosed, premium efficiency 1.15 service factor									
1360	1,800 RPM, 1/4 HP	1 Elec	5.33	1.501	Ea.	231	101		332	405
1370	1/3 HP		5.33	1.501		330	101		431	510
1380	1/2 HP		5.33	1.501		355	101		456	540
1390	3/4 HP		5.33	1.501		355	101		456	540
1400	1 HP		4.50	1.778		885	120		1,005	1,150
1450	2 HP		4.50	1.778		1,025	120		1,145	1,300
1500	3 HP		4.50	1.778		1,225	120		1,345	1,525
1550	5 HP		4.50	1.778		1,450	120		1,570	1,750
1600	7.5 HP		4.20	1.905		1,725	128		1,853	2,100
1650	10 HP		4	2		2,175	135		2,310	2,575
1700	15 HP		3.20	2.500		3,000	168		3,168	3,550
1750	20 HP	2 Elec	5.20	3.077		4,125	207		4,332	4,850
1800	25 HP		5	3.200		4,700	216		4,916	5,475
1850	30 HP		4.80	3.333		6,200	225		6,425	7,150
1900	40 HP		4	4		6,600	269		6,869	7,650
1950	50 HP		3.20	5		8,000	335		8,335	9,300
2000	60 HP		2.80	5.714		4,850	385		5,235	5,925
2050	75 HP		2.40	6.667		8,725	450		9,175	10,300
2100	100 HP	3 Elec	2.70	8.889		10,700	600		11,300	12,600
2150	125 HP		2.10	11.429		14,700	770		15,470	17,400

26 71 13.20 Motors		Crew	Daily Output	Labor-Hours	Unit	Material	2023 Bare Costs Labor	Equipment	Total	Total Incl O&P
2200	150 HP	3 Elec	1.80	13.333	Ea.	15,800	900		16,700	18,700
2250	200 HP		1.50	16		21,100	1,075		22,175	24,800
2300	1,200 RPM, 1 HP	1 Elec	4.50	1.778		505	120		625	740
2350	2 HP		4.50	1.778		645	120		765	890
2400	3 HP		4.50	1.778		865	120		985	1,125
2450	5 HP		4.50	1.778		1,025	120		1,145	1,300
2500	3,600 RPM, 2 HP		4.50	1.778		860	120		980	1,125
2550	3 HP		4.50	1.778		565	120		685	800
2600	5 HP		4.50	1.778		810	120		930	1,075

26 71 13.40 Motors Explosion Proof		Crew	Daily Output	Labor-Hours	Unit	Material	Labor	Equipment	Total	Total Incl O&P
0010	**MOTORS EXPLOSION PROOF**, 208-230/460 V, 60 HZ									
0020	1,800 RPM, 1/4 HP	1 Elec	5	1.600	Ea.	775	108		883	1,025
0030	1/3 HP		5	1.600		615	108		723	835
0040	1/2 HP		5	1.600		1,150	108		1,258	1,425
0050	3/4 HP		5.33	1.501		1,100	101		1,201	1,350
0060	1 HP		4.20	1.905		560	128		688	805
0070	2 HP		4.20	1.905		645	128		773	900
0080	3 HP		4.20	1.905		725	128		853	985
0090	5 HP		4.20	1.905		890	128		1,018	1,175
0100	7.5 HP		4	2		1,100	135		1,235	1,400
0110	10 HP		3.70	2.162		1,300	146		1,446	1,650
0120	15 HP		3.20	2.500		1,700	168		1,868	2,125
0130	20 HP	2 Elec	5	3.200		2,125	216		2,341	2,650
0140	25 HP		4.80	3.333		2,550	225		2,775	3,125
0150	30 HP		4.40	3.636		2,950	245		3,195	3,625
0160	40 HP		3.80	4.211		3,775	284		4,059	4,575
0170	50 HP		3.20	5		4,600	335		4,935	5,575
0180	60 HP		2.60	6.154		6,000	415		6,415	7,225
0190	75 HP		2	8		7,400	540		7,940	8,925
0200	100 HP	3 Elec	2.50	9.600		9,675	645		10,320	11,700
0210	125 HP		2.20	10.909		12,300	735		13,035	14,600
0220	150 HP		1.60	15		14,600	1,000		15,600	17,500
0230	200 HP		1.20	20		17,800	1,350		19,150	21,600
1000	1,200 RPM, 1 HP	1 Elec	4.20	1.905		660	128		788	915
1010	2 HP		4.20	1.905		810	128		938	1,075
1020	3 HP		4.20	1.905		990	128		1,118	1,300
1030	5 HP		4.20	1.905		1,400	128		1,528	1,750
2000	3,600 RPM, 1/4 HP		5	1.600		520	108		628	730
2010	1/3 HP		5	1.600		545	108		653	760
2020	1/2 HP		5	1.600		775	108		883	1,000
2030	3/4 HP		5	1.600		795	108		903	1,025
2040	1 HP		4.20	1.905		745	128		873	1,000
2050	2 HP		4.20	1.905		670	128		798	925
2060	3 HP		4.20	1.905		730	128		858	995
2070	5 HP		4.20	1.905		975	128		1,103	1,275
2080	7.5 HP		4	2		1,100	135		1,235	1,400
2090	10 HP		3.70	2.162		1,275	146		1,421	1,625
2100	15 HP		3.20	2.500		1,725	168		1,893	2,150
2110	20 HP	2 Elec	5	3.200		2,150	216		2,366	2,675
2120	25 HP		4.80	3.333		2,650	225		2,875	3,250
2130	30 HP		4.40	3.636		3,100	245		3,345	3,775
2140	40 HP		3.80	4.211		3,925	284		4,209	4,750

26 71 13.40 Motors Explosion Proof		Crew	Daily Output	Labor-Hours	Unit	Material (2023 Bare Costs)	Labor (2023 Bare Costs)	Equipment (2023 Bare Costs)	Total (2023 Bare Costs)	Total Incl O&P
2150	50 HP	2 Elec	3.20	5	Ea.	5,000	335		5,335	6,000
2160	60 HP		2.60	6.154		6,075	415		6,490	7,300
2170	75 HP		2	8		7,400	540		7,940	8,950
2180	100 HP	3 Elec	2.50	9.600		10,400	645		11,045	12,500
2190	125 HP		2.20	10.909		12,700	735		13,435	15,100
2200	150 HP		1.60	15		15,600	1,000		16,600	18,700
2210	200 HP		1.20	20		20,000	1,350		21,350	24,000
2220	250 HP		1.20	20		24,400	1,350		25,750	28,900

Division Notes

		CREW	DAILY OUTPUT	LABOR-HOURS	UNIT	BARE COSTS MAT.	BARE COSTS LABOR	BARE COSTS EQUIP.	BARE COSTS TOTAL	TOTAL INCL O&P

Estimating Tips

27 20 00 Data Communications
27 30 00 Voice Communications
27 40 00 Audio-Video Communications

- When estimating material costs for special systems, it is always prudent to obtain manufacturers' quotations for equipment prices and special installation requirements that may affect the total cost.
- For cost modifications for elevated tray installation, add the percentages to labor according to the height of the installation and only to the quantities exceeding the different height levels, not to the total tray quantities. Refer to subdivision 26 01 02.20 for labor adjustment factors.
- Do not overlook the costs for equipment used in the installation. If scissor lifts and boom lifts are available in the field, contractors may use them in lieu of the proposed ladders and rolling staging.

Reference Numbers

Reference numbers are shown at the beginning of some major classifications. These numbers refer to related items in the Reference Section. The reference information may be an estimating procedure, an alternate pricing method, or technical information.

Note: Not all subdivisions listed here necessarily appear. ■

Note: Trade Service, in part, has been used as a reference source for some of the material prices used in Division 27.

27 01 Operation and Maintenance of Communications Systems

27 01 30 – Operation and Maintenance of Voice Communications

27 01 30.51 Operation and Maintenance of Voice Equipment		Crew	Daily Output	Labor-Hours	Unit	2023 Bare Costs Material	Labor	Equipment	Total	Total Incl O&P
0010	**OPERATION AND MAINTENANCE OF VOICE EQUIPMENT**									
3400	Remove and replace (reinstall), speaker	1 Elec	6	1.333	Ea.		90		90	133

27 05 Common Work Results for Communications

27 05 05 – Selective Demolition for Communications

27 05 05.20 Electrical Demolition, Communications

		Crew	Daily Output	Labor-Hours	Unit	Material	Labor	Equipment	Total	Total Incl O&P
0010	**ELECTRICAL DEMOLITION, COMMUNICATIONS** R024119-10									
0100	Fiber optics									
0120	Cable R260105-30	1 Elec	2400	.003	L.F.		.22		.22	.33
0160	Multi-channel rack enclosure		6	1.333	Ea.		90		90	133
0180	Patch panel		18	.444	"		30		30	44.50
0200	Communication cables & fittings									
0220	Voice/data outlet	1 Elec	140	.057	Ea.		3.85		3.85	5.70
0240	Telephone cable		2800	.003	L.F.		.19		.19	.29
0260	Phone jack		135	.059	Ea.		3.99		3.99	5.95
0280	Data jack		135	.059	"		3.99		3.99	5.95
0300	High performance cable, 2 pair		3000	.003	L.F.		.18		.18	.27
0320	4 pair		2100	.004			.26		.26	.38
0340	25 pair		900	.009			.60		.60	.89
0400	Terminal cabinet		5	1.600	Ea.		108		108	160
1000	Nurse call system									
1020	Station	1 Elec	24	.333	Ea.		22.50		22.50	33.50
1040	Standard call button		24	.333			22.50		22.50	33.50
1060	Corridor dome light or zone indicator		24	.333			22.50		22.50	33.50
1080	Master control station	2 Elec	2	8			540		540	800

27 05 05.30 Electrical Demolition, Sound and Video

		Crew	Daily Output	Labor-Hours	Unit	Material	Labor	Equipment	Total	Total Incl O&P
0010	**ELECTRICAL DEMOLITION, SOUND & VIDEO** R024119-10									
0100	Cables									
0120	TV antenna lead-in cable R260105-30	1 Elec	2100	.004	L.F.		.26		.26	.38
0140	Sound cable		2400	.003			.22		.22	.33
0160	Microphone cable		2400	.003			.22		.22	.33
0180	Coaxial cable		2400	.003			.22		.22	.33
0200	Doorbell system, not including wires, cables, and conduit		16	.500	Ea.		33.50		33.50	50
0220	Door chime or devices		36	.222	"		14.95		14.95	22
0300	Public address system, not including wires, cables, and conduit									
0320	Conventional office	1 Elec	16	.500	Speaker		33.50		33.50	50
0340	Conventional industrial	"	8	1	"		67.50		67.50	100
0352	PA cabinet/panel	2 Elec	5	3.200	Ea.		216		216	320
0400	Sound system, not including wires, cables, and conduit									
0410	Components	1 Elec	24	.333	Ea.		22.50		22.50	33.50
0412	Speaker		24	.333			22.50		22.50	33.50
0416	Volume control		24	.333			22.50		22.50	33.50
0420	Intercom, master station		6	1.333			90		90	133
0440	Remote station		24	.333			22.50		22.50	33.50
0460	Intercom outlets		24	.333			22.50		22.50	33.50
0480	Handset		12	.667			45		45	66.50
0500	Emergency call system, not including wires, cables, and conduit									
0520	Annunciator	1 Elec	4	2	Ea.		135		135	200
0540	Devices	"	16	.500			33.50		33.50	50
0600	Master door, buzzer type unit	2 Elec	1.60	10			675		675	1,000
0800	TV system, not including wires, cables, and conduit									

27 05 Common Work Results for Communications

27 05 05 – Selective Demolition for Communications

27 05 05.30 Electrical Demolition, Sound and Video		Crew	Daily Output	Labor-Hours	Unit	2023 Bare Costs Material	Labor	Equipment	Total	Total Incl O&P
0820	Master TV antenna system, per outlet	1 Elec	39	.205	Outlet		13.80		13.80	20.50
0840	School application, per outlet		16	.500	"		33.50		33.50	50
0860	Amplifier		12	.667	Ea.		45		45	66.50
0880	Antenna		6	1.333	"		90		90	133
0900	One camera & one monitor	2 Elec	7.80	2.051	Total		138		138	205
0920	One camera	1 Elec	8	1	Ea.		67.50		67.50	100

27 05 29 – Hangers and Supports for Communications Systems

27 05 29.10 Cable Support		Crew	Daily Output	Labor-Hours	Unit	Material	Labor	Equipment	Total	Total Incl O&P
0010	**CABLE SUPPORT**									
0110	J-hook, single tier, single sided, 1" diam.	1 Elec	68.57	.117	Ea.	3.38	7.85		11.23	15.40
0120	1-1/2" diam.		67.80	.118		4.19	7.95		12.14	16.40
0130	2" diam.		67.30	.119		5.05	8		13.05	17.45
0140	4" diam.		66.80	.120		10	8.05		18.05	23
0330	Double tier, single sided, 2" diam.		67	.119		23.50	8.05		31.55	38
0340	4" diam.		66.20	.121		35	8.15		43.15	50.50
0430	Double sided, 2" diam.		65.80	.122		38	8.20		46.20	54
0440	4" diam.		65.40	.122		50	8.25		58.25	67.50
0530	Triple tier, single sided, 2" diam.		66.40	.120		29.50	8.10		37.60	44.50
0540	4" diam.		65.85	.121		49.50	8.20		57.70	66.50
0630	Double sided, 2" diam.		65.10	.123		49	8.30		57.30	66
0640	4" diam.		64.70	.124		61	8.35		69.35	80

27 11 Communications Equipment Room Fittings

27 11 16 – Communications Cabinets, Racks, Frames and Enclosures

27 11 16.10 Public Phone		Crew	Daily Output	Labor-Hours	Unit	Material	Labor	Equipment	Total	Total Incl O&P
0010	**PUBLIC PHONE**									
7600	Telephone with wood backboard									
7620	Single door, 12" H x 12" W x 4" D	1 Elec	5.30	1.509	Ea.	183	102		285	350
7650	18" H x 12" W x 4" D		4.70	1.702		213	115		328	405
7700	24" H x 12" W x 4" D		4.20	1.905		254	128		382	470
7720	18" H x 18" W x 4" D		4.20	1.905		272	128		400	490
7750	24" H x 18" W x 4" D		4	2		405	135		540	650
7780	36" H x 36" W x 4" D		3.60	2.222		435	150		585	700
7800	24" H x 24" W x 6" D		3.60	2.222		520	150		670	795
7820	30" H x 24" W x 6" D		3.20	2.500		585	168		753	895
7850	30" H x 30" W x 6" D		2.70	2.963		700	200		900	1,075
7880	36" H x 30" W x 6" D		2.50	3.200		820	216		1,036	1,225
7900	48" H x 36" W x 6" D		2.20	3.636		1,025	245		1,270	1,500
7920	Double door, 48" H x 36" W x 6" D		2	4		1,250	269		1,519	1,750

27 11 16.20 Rack Mount Cabinet		Crew	Daily Output	Labor-Hours	Unit	Material	Labor	Equipment	Total	Total Incl O&P
0010	**RACK MOUNT CABINET**									
0100	80" H x 24" W x 40" D									
0110	No sides	1 Elec	9.60	.833	Ea.	1,350	56		1,406	1,575
0120	One side		8	1		1,425	67.50		1,492.50	1,675
0130	Two sides		7.86	1.018		1,525	68.50		1,593.50	1,775
0200	80" H x 24" W x 42" D									
0210	No sides	1 Elec	9.60	.833	Ea.	1,375	56		1,431	1,600
0220	One side		8	1		1,425	67.50		1,492.50	1,675
0230	Two sides		7.86	1.018		1,475	68.50		1,543.50	1,725
0300	80" H x 24" W x 48" D									

27 11 Communications Equipment Room Fittings

27 11 16 – Communications Cabinets, Racks, Frames and Enclosures

27 11 16.20 Rack Mount Cabinet		Crew	Daily Output	Labor-Hours	Unit	Material	Labor (2023 Bare Costs)	Equipment	Total	Total Incl O&P
0310	No sides	1 Elec	9.60	.833	Ea.	1,600	56		1,656	1,825
0320	One side		8	1		1,700	67.50		1,767.50	1,975
0330	Two sides		7.86	1.018		1,775	68.50		1,843.50	2,050
0400	80″ H x 30″ W x 40″ D									
0410	No sides	1 Elec	9.60	.833	Ea.	1,700	56		1,756	1,950
0420	One side		8	1		1,575	67.50		1,642.50	1,825
0430	Two sides		7.86	1.018		1,625	68.50		1,693.50	1,900
0500	80″ H x 30″ W x 42″ D									
0510	No sides	1 Elec	9.60	.833	Ea.	1,525	56		1,581	1,750
0520	One side		8	1		1,575	67.50		1,642.50	1,825
0530	Two sides		7.86	1.018		1,600	68.50		1,668.50	1,875
0600	80″ H x 30″ W x 48″ D									
0610	No sides	1 Elec	9.60	.833	Ea.	1,700	56		1,756	1,950
0620	One side		8	1		1,800	67.50		1,867.50	2,075
0630	Two sides		7.86	1.018		1,925	68.50		1,993.50	2,200
0700	80″ H x 32″ W x 32″ D									
0710	No sides	1 Elec	9.60	.833	Ea.	1,400	56		1,456	1,600
0720	One side		8	1		1,425	67.50		1,492.50	1,675
0730	Two sides		7.86	1.018		1,450	68.50		1,518.50	1,700
0800	80″ H x 32″ W x 40″ D									
0810	No sides	1 Elec	9.60	.833	Ea.	1,575	56		1,631	1,800
0820	One side		8	1		1,625	67.50		1,692.50	1,900
0830	Two sides		7.86	1.018		1,700	68.50		1,768.50	1,975
0900	80″ H x 32″ W x 42″ D									
0910	No sides	1 Elec	9.60	.833	Ea.	1,525	56		1,581	1,750
0920	One side		8	1		1,550	67.50		1,617.50	1,800
0930	Two sides		7.86	1.018		1,575	68.50		1,643.50	1,850
1000	80″ H x 32″ W x 48″ D									
1010	No sides	1 Elec	9.60	.833	Ea.	1,775	56		1,831	2,025
1020	One side		8	1		1,875	67.50		1,942.50	2,150
1030	Two sides		7.86	1.018		1,975	68.50		2,043.50	2,275
1200	Freestanding cabinet with front and rear doors									
1300	84″ H x 19″ W x 24″ D, gray									
1310	No sides	1 Elec	9.60	.833	Ea.	2,475	56		2,531	2,800
1320	One side		9.60	.833		2,475	56		2,531	2,800
1330	Two sides		9.60	.833		2,350	56		2,406	2,675
1400	84″ H x 19″ W x 24″ D, white									
1410	No sides	1 Elec	9.60	.833	Ea.	2,100	56		2,156	2,375
1420	One side		9.60	.833		2,100	56		2,156	2,375
1430	Two sides		9.60	.833		2,000	56		2,056	2,250
1500	84″ H x 19″ W x 24″ D, black									
1510	No sides	1 Elec	9.60	.833	Ea.	2,475	56		2,531	2,800
1520	One side		9.60	.833		2,475	56		2,531	2,800
1530	Two sides		9.60	.833		2,350	56		2,406	2,675
1600	84″ H x 28″ W x 34″ D front glass, rear louvered door		9.60	.833		1,425	56		1,481	1,650

27 11 19 – Communications Termination Blocks and Patch Panels

27 11 19.10 Termination Blocks and Patch Panels		Crew	Daily Output	Labor-Hours	Unit	Material	Labor (2023 Bare Costs)	Equipment	Total	Total Incl O&P
0010	TERMINATION BLOCKS AND PATCH PANELS									
2960	Patch panel, RJ-45/110 type, 24 ports	2 Elec	6	2.667	Ea.	239	180		419	530
3000	48 ports	3 Elec	6	4		380	269		649	815
3040	96 ports	″	4	6		765	405		1,170	1,450
3100	Punch down termination per port	1 Elec	107	.075			5.05		5.05	7.50

27 13 23 – Communications Optical Fiber Backbone Cabling

27 13 23.13 Communications Optical Fiber		Crew	Daily Output	Labor-Hours	Unit	2023 Bare Costs Material	Labor	Equipment	Total	Total Incl O&P
0010	**COMMUNICATIONS OPTICAL FIBER**									
0040	Specialized tools & techniques cause installation costs to vary.									
0070	Fiber optic, cable, bulk simplex, single mode R271323-40	1 Elec	8	1	C.L.F.	22.50	67.50		90	125
0080	Multi mode		8	1		33.50	67.50		101	137
0090	4 strand, single mode		7.34	1.090		38	73.50		111.50	151
0095	Multi mode		7.34	1.090		50.50	73.50		124	165
0100	12 strand, single mode		6.67	1.199		114	81		195	246
0105	Multi mode	↓	6.67	1.199	↓	96.50	81		177.50	226
0150	Jumper				Ea.	56.50			56.50	62.50
0200	Pigtail					37			37	41
0300	Connector	1 Elec	24	.333		34.50	22.50		57	71.50
0350	Finger splice		32	.250		51	16.85		67.85	81.50
0400	Transceiver (low cost bi-directional)		8	1		605	67.50		672.50	765
0450	Rack housing, 4 rack spaces, 12 panels (144 fibers)		2	4		1,475	269		1,744	2,025
0500	Patch panel, 12 ports		6	1.333		430	90		520	610
0600	Cable connector panel, 6 fiber	↓	40	.200	↓	76	13.45		89.45	104
1000	Cable, 62.5 microns, direct burial, 4 fiber	R-15	1200	.040	L.F.	1.05	2.65	.29	3.99	5.40
1020	Indoor, 2 fiber	R-19	1000	.020		.39	1.35		1.74	2.44
1040	Outdoor, aerial/duct	"	1670	.012		.88	.81		1.69	2.17
1060	50 microns, direct burial, 8 fiber	R-22	4000	.009		1.76	.57		2.33	2.79
1080	12 fiber		4000	.009		2.11	.57		2.68	3.17
1100	Indoor, 12 fiber	↓	759	.049	↓	1.26	3.03		4.29	5.90
1120	Connectors, 62.5 micron cable, transmission	R-19	40	.500	Ea.	20.50	33.50		54	72.50
1140	Cable splice		40	.500		24	33.50		57.50	76
1160	125 micron cable, transmission		16	1.250		21.50	84.50		106	149
1180	Receiver, 1.2 mile range		20	1		465	67.50		532.50	615
1200	1.9 mile range		20	1		310	67.50		377.50	440
1220	6.2 mile range		5	4		515	270		785	965
1240	Transmitter, 1.2 mile range		20	1		515	67.50		582.50	665
1260	1.9 mile range		20	1		390	67.50		457.50	530
1280	6.2 mile range		5	4		1,600	270		1,870	2,175
1300	Modem, 1.2 mile range		5	4		273	270		543	700
1320	6.2 mile range		5	4		515	270		785	965
1340	1.9 mile range, 12 channel		5	4		2,875	270		3,145	3,575
1360	Repeater, 1.2 mile range		10	2		465	135		600	715
1380	1.9 mile range		10	2		685	135		820	950
1400	6.2 mile range		5	4		1,225	270		1,495	1,750
1420	1.2 mile range, digital		5	4		630	270		900	1,100
1440	Transceiver, 1.9 mile range		5	4		585	270		855	1,050
1460	1.2 mile range, digital		5	4		570	270		840	1,025
1480	Cable enclosure, interior NEMA 13		7	2.857		212	193		405	520
1500	Splice w/enclosure encapsulant		16	1.250	↓	315	84.50		399.50	470
1510	1/4", black, non-metallic, flexible, tube, liquid tight		8	2.500	C.L.F.	340	169		509	625
1520	3/8"		8	2.500		224	169		393	500
1530	1/2"		7.34	2.725		229	184		413	525
1540	3/4"		7.34	2.725		395	184		579	710
1550	1"		7.34	2.725		630	184		814	965
1560	1-1/4"		6.67	2.999		1,075	202		1,277	1,500
1570	1-1/2"		6.67	2.999		1,200	202		1,402	1,625
1580	2"		6.35	3.150	↓	1,850	212		2,062	2,375
2000	Fiber optic cable, 48 strand, single mode, indoor/outdoor		1.67	11.976	M.L.F.	3,750	810		4,560	5,325
2002	72 strand		1.50	13.307		6,700	900		7,600	8,700
2004	96 strand	↓	1.42	14.085	↓	8,950	950		9,900	11,300

27 13 Communications Backbone Cabling

27 13 23 – Communications Optical Fiber Backbone Cabling

27 13 23.13 Communications Optical Fiber		Crew	Daily Output	Labor-Hours	Unit	Material	Labor (2023 Bare Costs)	Equipment	Total	Total Incl O&P
2006	144 strand	R-19	1.34	14.970	M.L.F.	13,400	1,000		14,400	16,300
2010	Fiber optic cable, 48 strand, Single mode, Indoor, Plenum		1.67	11.976		4,475	810		5,285	6,125
2012	72 strand		1.50	13.307		8,175	900		9,075	10,300
2014	96 strand		1.42	14.085		11,200	950		12,150	13,700
2020	Fiber optic cable, 48 strand, Single mode, Indoor, Riser		1.67	11.976		4,000	810		4,810	5,600
2030	Armored		1.67	11.976		5,400	810		6,210	7,150
2040	Fiber optic cable, 48 strand, single mode, armored, Plenum		1.67	11.976		5,050	810		5,860	6,750
2042	72 strand		1.50	13.307		8,575	900		9,475	10,800
2044	96 strand		1.42	14.085		19,700	950		20,650	23,100
2046	144 strand		1.50	13.307		22,800	900		23,700	26,400
2060	Fiber optic cable 48 strand Single mode Armored Gel Filled Dry Block Burial		1.35	14.815		910	1,000		1,910	2,475
2062	72 strand		1.22	16.461		2,800	1,100		3,900	4,725
2064	96 strand		1.15	17.422		3,175	1,175		4,350	5,225
2066	144 strand		1.08	18.519		4,175	1,250		5,425	6,425
2070	Fiber optic cable 48 strand single mode gel filled dry block outdoor duct		1.25	16		1,150	1,075		2,225	2,875
2090	Armored		1	20		2,000	1,350		3,350	4,200
2100	Aerial. Self-Supported		.95	21.053		920	1,425		2,345	3,100

27 15 Communications Horizontal Cabling

27 15 01 – Communications Horizontal Cabling Applications

27 15 01.19 Fire Alarm Communications Conductors & Cables

		Crew	Daily Output	Labor-Hours	Unit	Material	Labor	Equipment	Total	Total Incl O&P
0010	**FIRE ALARM COMMUNICATIONS CONDUCTORS AND CABLES**									
1500	Fire alarm FEP teflon 150 V to 200°C									
1550	#22, 1 pair	1 Elec	10	.800	C.L.F.	203	54		257	305
1600	2 pair		8	1		415	67.50		482.50	555
1650	4 pair		7	1.143		970	77		1,047	1,200
1700	6 pair		6	1.333		790	90		880	1,000
1750	8 pair		5.50	1.455		360	98		458	540
1800	10 pair		5	1.600		1,150	108		1,258	1,425
1850	#18, 1 pair	2 Elec	16	1		74	67.50		141.50	182
1900	2 pair		13	1.231		385	83		468	550
1950	4 pair		9.60	1.667		300	112		412	495
2000	6 pair		8	2		310	135		445	545
2050	8 pair		7	2.286		470	154		624	750
2100	10 pair		6	2.667		705	180		885	1,050

27 15 01.23 Audio-Video Communications Horizontal Cabling

		Crew	Daily Output	Labor-Hours	Unit	Material	Labor	Equipment	Total	Total Incl O&P
0010	**AUDIO-VIDEO COMMUNICATIONS HORIZONTAL CABLING**									
3000	S-video cable, MD4, 1M Pro interconnects, 3′	1 Elec	38	.211	Ea.	26.50	14.20		40.70	50.50
3010	6′		38	.211		37.50	14.20		51.70	62.50
3020	9′		38	.211		38	14.20		52.20	63
3030	16′		36	.222		63.50	14.95		78.45	92
3040	22′		36	.222		74.50	14.95		89.45	104
3300	HDMI cable, coaxial, HDMI/HDMI, Non plenum, 3′, 24 kt terminations		40	.200		14.35	13.45		27.80	36
3310	6′, 24 kt terminations		40	.200		16.95	13.45		30.40	38.50
3320	HDMI cable, coaxial, HDMI/HDMI metal, Non plenum, 3′, 24 kt terminations		40	.200		16.40	13.45		29.85	38
3330	6′, 24 kt terminations		40	.200		19.05	13.45		32.50	41
3340	15′, 24 kt terminations		38	.211		26.50	14.20		40.70	50
3350	25′, 24 kt terminations		38	.211		34.50	14.20		48.70	59

27 15 Communications Horizontal Cabling

27 15 10 – Special Communications Cabling

27 15 10.23 Sound and Video Cables and Fittings		Crew	Daily Output	Labor-Hours	Unit	Material	Labor	Equipment	Total	Total Incl O&P
0010	SOUND AND VIDEO CABLES & FITTINGS									
0900	TV antenna lead-in, 300 ohm, #20-2 conductor	1 Elec	7	1.143	C.L.F.	34	77		111	152
0950	Coaxial, feeder outlet		7	1.143		20.50	77		97.50	137
1000	Coaxial, main riser		6	1.333		13.05	90		103.05	147
1100	Sound, shielded with drain, #22-2 conductor		8	1		13.20	67.50		80.70	115
1150	#22-3 conductor		7.50	1.067		21	72		93	130
1200	#22-4 conductor		6.50	1.231		27.50	83		110.50	154
1250	Nonshielded, #22-2 conductor		10	.800		19.75	54		73.75	102
1300	#22-3 conductor		9	.889		39	60		99	132
1350	#22-4 conductor		8	1		42.50	67.50		110	147
1400	Microphone cable		8	1		28.50	67.50		96	132

(2023 Bare Costs: Material, Labor, Equipment, Total)

27 15 13 – Communications Copper Horizontal Cabling

27 15 13.13 Communication Cables and Fittings		Crew	Daily Output	Labor-Hours	Unit	Material	Labor	Equipment	Total	Total Incl O&P
0010	COMMUNICATION CABLES AND FITTINGS									
2200	Telephone twisted, PVC insulation, #22-2 conductor	1 Elec	10	.800	C.L.F.	10.40	54		64.40	91.50
2250	#22-3 conductor		9	.889		16.20	60		76.20	107
2300	#22-4 conductor		8	1		17.60	67.50		85.10	119
2350	#18-2 conductor		9	.889		47	60		107	141
2370	Telephone jack, eight pins		32	.250	Ea.	4.39	16.85		21.24	30
5000	High performance unshielded twisted pair (UTP)									
5100	Cable, category 3, #24, 2 pair solid, PVC jacket R271513-75	1 Elec	10	.800	C.L.F.	9.85	54		63.85	91
5200	4 pair solid, PVC jacket		7	1.143		64	77		141	185
5300	25 pair solid, PVC jacket		3	2.667		135	180		315	415
5400	2 pair solid, plenum		10	.800		14.25	54		68.25	95.50
5500	4 pair solid, plenum		7	1.143		14.15	77		91.15	130
5600	25 pair solid, plenum		3	2.667		173	180		353	455
5700	4 pair stranded, PVC jacket		7	1.143		17.85	77		94.85	134
7000	Category 5, #24, 4 pair solid, PVC jacket		7	1.143		76	77		153	198
7100	4 pair solid, plenum		7	1.143		21	77		98	137
7200	4 pair stranded, PVC jacket		7	1.143		34	77		111	152
7210	Category 5e, #24, 4 pair solid, PVC jacket		7	1.143		25.50	77		102.50	142
7212	4 pair solid, plenum		7	1.143		33.50	77		110.50	151
7214	4 pair stranded, PVC jacket		7	1.143		24	77		101	141
7240	Category 6, #24, 4 pair solid, PVC jacket		7	1.143		69	77		146	190
7242	4 pair solid, plenum		7	1.143		14.95	77		91.95	130
7244	4 pair stranded, PVC jacket		7	1.143		24.50	77		101.50	141
7300	Connector, RJ45, category 5		80	.100	Ea.	.93	6.75		7.68	11
7302	Shielded RJ45, category 5		72	.111		1.75	7.50		9.25	13.05
7310	Jack, UTP RJ45, category 3		72	.111		.67	7.50		8.17	11.85
7312	Category 5		65	.123		8	8.30		16.30	21
7314	Category 5e		65	.123		6.35	8.30		14.65	19.30
7316	Category 6		65	.123		4.71	8.30		13.01	17.50
7322	Jack, shielded RJ45, category 5		60	.133		7	9		16	21
7324	Category 5e		60	.133		7	9		16	21
7326	Category 6		60	.133		8.30	9		17.30	22.50
7400	Voice/data expansion module, category 5e		8	1		37.50	67.50		105	142
7401	Modular jack, cat 6 keystone, RJ45, office white		16.50	.485		7.65	32.50		40.15	57
7402	RJ45, green		16.50	.485		7.15	32.50		39.65	56.50
7404	RJ45, grey		16.50	.485		6.55	32.50		39.05	55.50
7408	RJ45, orange		16.50	.485		6.55	32.50		39.05	55.50
7420	5M, RJ45, 568B, cord set		16.50	.485		42.50	32.50		75	95.50
7422	3M, RJ45, 568B, cord set		16.50	.485		31.50	32.50		64	83.50

27 15 13 – Communications Copper Horizontal Cabling

27 15 13.13 Communication Cables and Fittings		Crew	Daily Output	Labor-Hours	Unit	Material	2023 Bare Costs Labor	Equipment	Total	Total Incl O&P
7424	1M, RJ45, 568B, cord set	1 Elec	16.50	.485	Ea.	31.50	32.50		64	83.50
7450	M12 TO RJ45, 2M ultra-loch D-mode, cord set		15.50	.516		41	35		76	97
8000	Multipair unshielded non-plenum cable, 150 V PVC jacket									
8002	#22, 2 pair	1 Elec	8.40	.952	C.L.F.	117	64		181	225
8003	3 pair		8	1		170	67.50		237.50	287
8004	4 pair		7.30	1.096		203	74		277	335
8006	6 pair		6.20	1.290		315	87		402	475
8008	8 pair		5.70	1.404		620	94.50		714.50	820
8010	10 pair		5.30	1.509		78	102		180	237
8012	12 pair		4.20	1.905		160	128		288	365
8015	15 pair		3.80	2.105		715	142		857	1,000
8020	20 pair	2 Elec	6.60	2.424		1,375	163		1,538	1,775
8025	25 pair		6	2.667		1,700	180		1,880	2,125
8030	30 pair		5.60	2.857		605	192		797	950
8040	40 pair		5.20	3.077		520	207		727	885
8050	50 pair		4.90	3.265		745	220		965	1,150
8100	Multipair unshielded non-plenum cable, 300 V PVC jacket									
8102	#20, 2 pair	1 Elec	7.30	1.096	C.L.F.	281	74		355	420
8103	3 pair		6.70	1.194		365	80.50		445.50	520
8104	4 pair		6	1.333		455	90		545	635
8106	6 pair		5.30	1.509		630	102		732	840
8108	8 pair		4.40	1.818		795	122		917	1,050
8110	10 pair	2 Elec	7.30	2.192		123	148		271	355
8112	12 pair		6.20	2.581		153	174		327	425
8115	15 pair		5.90	2.712		192	183		375	485
8201	#18, 1 pair	1 Elec	8	1		147	67.50		214.50	261
8202	2 pair		6.50	1.231		220	83		303	365
8203	3 pair		5.60	1.429		325	96		421	505
8204	4 pair		5	1.600		445	108		553	650
8206	6 pair		4.40	1.818		795	122		917	1,050
8208	8 pair		4	2		1,000	135		1,135	1,300
8215	15 pair	2 Elec	5	3.200		805	216		1,021	1,200
8300	Multipair shielded non-plenum cable, 300 V PVC jacket									
8303	#22, 3 pair	1 Elec	6.70	1.194	C.L.F.	310	80.50		390.50	460
8306	6 pair		5.70	1.404		480	94.50		574.50	665
8309	9 pair		5	1.600		435	108		543	640
8312	12 pair	2 Elec	8	2		620	135		755	885
8315	15 pair		7.30	2.192		680	148		828	970
8317	17 pair		6.80	2.353		1,125	158		1,283	1,475
8319	19 pair		6.40	2.500		905	168		1,073	1,250
8327	27 pair		5.90	2.712		1,575	183		1,758	2,000
8402	#20, 2 pair	1 Elec	6.70	1.194		118	80.50		198.50	249
8403	3 pair		6.20	1.290		150	87		237	294
8406	6 pair		4.40	1.818		380	122		502	595
8409	9 pair		3.60	2.222		278	150		428	525
8412	12 pair	2 Elec	5.90	2.712		870	183		1,053	1,225
8415	15 pair	"	5.70	2.807		470	189		659	795
8502	#18, 2 pair	1 Elec	6.20	1.290		168	87		255	315
8503	3 pair		5.30	1.509		214	102		316	385
8504	4 pair		4.70	1.702		410	115		525	620
8506	6 pair		4	2		400	135		535	640
8509	9 pair		3.40	2.353		595	158		753	890
8515	15 pair	2 Elec	4.80	3.333		1,200	225		1,425	1,650

27 15 Communications Horizontal Cabling

27 15 33 – Communications Coaxial Horizontal Cabling

27 15 33.10 Coaxial Cable and Fittings		Crew	Daily Output	Labor-Hours	Unit	2023 Bare Costs Material	Labor	Equipment	Total	Total Incl O&P
0010	**COAXIAL CABLE & FITTINGS**									
3500	Coaxial connectors, 50 ohm impedance quick disconnect									
3540	BNC plug, for RG A/U #58 cable	1 Elec	42	.190	Ea.	3.25	12.85		16.10	22.50
3550	RG A/U #59 cable		42	.190		3.10	12.85		15.95	22.50
3560	RG A/U #62 cable		42	.190		3.10	12.85		15.95	22.50
3600	BNC jack, for RG A/U #58 cable		42	.190		4.92	12.85		17.77	24.50
3610	RG A/U #59 cable		42	.190		6.10	12.85		18.95	26
3620	RG A/U #62 cable		42	.190		4.38	12.85		17.23	24
3660	BNC panel jack, for RG A/U #58 cable		40	.200		3.88	13.45		17.33	24.50
3670	RG A/U #59 cable		40	.200		7.70	13.45		21.15	28.50
3680	RG A/U #62 cable		40	.200		7.70	13.45		21.15	28.50
3720	BNC bulkhead jack, for RG A/U #58 cable		40	.200		7.75	13.45		21.20	28.50
3730	RG A/U #59 cable		40	.200		7.75	13.45		21.20	28.50
3740	RG A/U #62 cable		40	.200		7.70	13.45		21.15	28.50
3850	Coaxial cable, RG A/U #58, 50 ohm		8	1	C.L.F.	77	67.50		144.50	185
3860	RG A/U #59, 75 ohm		8	1		32	67.50		99.50	136
3870	RG A/U #62, 93 ohm		8	1		58	67.50		125.50	164
3875	RG 6/U, 75 ohm		8	1		31	67.50		98.50	134
3950	Fire rated, RG A/U #58, 50 ohm		8	1		121	67.50		188.50	233
3960	RG A/U #59, 75 ohm		8	1		158	67.50		225.50	274
3970	RG A/U #62, 93 ohm		8	1		139	67.50		206.50	253

27 15 43 – Communications Faceplates and Connectors

27 15 43.13 Communication Outlets		Crew	Daily Output	Labor-Hours	Unit	Material	Labor	Equipment	Total	Total Incl O&P
0010	**COMMUNICATION OUTLETS**									
0100	Voice/data devices not included									
0120	Voice/data outlets, single opening	1 Elec	48	.167	Ea.	7.60	11.25		18.85	25
0140	Two jack openings		48	.167		2.84	11.25		14.09	19.80
0160	One jack & one 3/4" round opening		48	.167		8.25	11.25		19.50	26
0180	One jack & one twinaxial opening		48	.167		8.25	11.25		19.50	26
0200	One jack & one connector cabling opening		48	.167		8.25	11.25		19.50	26
0220	Two 3/8" coaxial openings		48	.167		8.25	11.25		19.50	26
0300	Data outlets, single opening		48	.167		8.25	11.25		19.50	26
0320	One 25-pin subminiature opening		48	.167		8.25	11.25		19.50	26
1000	Voice/data wall plate, plastic, 1 gang, 1-port		72	.111		2.16	7.50		9.66	13.50
1020	2-port		72	.111		2.64	7.50		10.14	14
1040	3-port		72	.111		2.28	7.50		9.78	13.60
1060	4-port		72	.111		2.28	7.50		9.78	13.60
1080	6-port		72	.111		2.16	7.50		9.66	13.50
1100	2 gang, 6-port		48	.167		4.61	11.25		15.86	22
1120	Voice/data wall plate, stainless steel, 1 gang, 1-port		72	.111		11.40	7.50		18.90	23.50
1140	2-port		72	.111		10.70	7.50		18.20	23
1160	3-port		72	.111		9.45	7.50		16.95	21.50
1180	4-port		72	.111		10.65	7.50		18.15	23
1200	2 gang, 6-port		48	.167		18.10	11.25		29.35	36.50

27 21 Data Communications Network Equipment

27 21 29 – Data Communications Switches and Hubs

27 21 29.10 Switching and Routing Equipment		Crew	Daily Output	Labor-Hours	Unit	2023 Bare Costs Material	Labor	Equipment	Total	Total Incl O&P
0010	**SWITCHING AND ROUTING EQUIPMENT**									
1100	Network hub, dual speed, 24 ports, includes cabinet	3 Elec	.66	36.364	Ea.	1,300	2,450		3,750	5,075
1300	Network switch, 50/60 HZ, 8 port, multi-platform, analog KVM	1 Elec	6.85	1.168		1,575	78.50		1,653.50	1,850
1310	16 port, multi-platform, analog KVM		6	1.333		1,825	90		1,915	2,125
1320	Network switch, 0x2x16,CAT5, analog KVM		6	1.333		1,575	90		1,665	1,875
1330	2x1x16, digital KVM, w/VM		16	.500		5,000	33.50		5,033.50	5,550
1340	2x1x32, digital KVM, w/VM		16	.500		5,950	33.50		5,983.50	6,600
1350	8x1x32, digital KVM, w/VM		16	.500		6,375	33.50		6,408.50	7,050
1500	KVM,1 RMU 16 port, no keyboard		16	.500		1,450	33.50		1,483.50	1,650
1510	KVM,1 RMU, 17" LCD, 16 port, US keyboard		15.15	.528		2,800	35.50		2,835.50	3,125
1520	KVM,1 RMU, 17" LCD, 16 port, UK keyboard		15.15	.528		2,800	35.50		2,835.50	3,125
2000	10/100/1000 Mbps, 24 ports		14	.571		2,475	38.50		2,513.50	2,775
2040	10/100/1000 Mbps, 48 ports		12	.667		775	45		820	915
2050	10/100/1000 Mbps, 5 port, industrial ethernet type		32	.250		425	16.85		441.85	490
2060	10/100/1000 Mbps, 6 port, industrial ethernet type		32	.250		1,700	16.85		1,716.85	1,900
2070	10/100/1000 Mbps, 10 port, X307-3		28	.286		3,050	19.25		3,069.25	3,400
2080	10/100/1000 Mbps, 10 port, X308-2		28	.286		6,275	19.25		6,294.25	6,925
3000	10/100/1000 Mbps, 20 port, front ports		20	.400		4,950	27		4,977	5,475
3010	10/100/1000 Mbps, 20 port, rear ports		20	.400		4,950	27		4,977	5,475
3040	KVM, 10/100/1000/10000 Mbps, 28 port, rear ports		16	.500		8,125	33.50		8,158.50	9,000
3050	KVM, 10/100/1000/10000 Mbps, 28 port, front ports		16	.500		9,550	33.50		9,583.50	10,600
3070	KVM, 10/100/1000/10000 Mbps, 52 port, front ports	2 Elec	12	1.333		10,000	90		10,090	11,100
3080	KVM, 10/100/1000/10000 Mbps, 52 port, rear ports	"	12	1.333		10,000	90		10,090	11,100

27 32 Voice Communications Terminal Equipment

27 32 26 – Ring-Down Emergency Telephones

27 32 26.10 Emergency Phone Stations

		Crew	Daily Output	Labor-Hours	Unit	Material	Labor	Equipment	Total	Total Incl O&P
0010	**EMERGENCY PHONE STATIONS**									
0100	Hands free emergency speaker phone w/LED strobe	1 Elec	7.22	1.108	Ea.	885	74.50		959.50	1,075
0110	Wall/pole mounted emergency phone station w/LED strobe	"	4.60	1.739		1,550	117		1,667	1,900
2000	Call station, 30", pole mounted emergency phone, 120V/ VoIP, blue beacon	2 Elec	5	3.200		1,400	216		1,616	1,875
2010	Call station, 36"		5	3.200		1,600	216		1,816	2,100
2020	Call station, 5′-8"		4.80	3.333		2,725	225		2,950	3,325
2030	Call station, 9′		4.80	3.333		2,750	225		2,975	3,350

27 32 36 – TTY Equipment

27 32 36.10 TTY Telephone Equipment

		Crew	Daily Output	Labor-Hours	Unit	Material	Labor	Equipment	Total	Total Incl O&P
0010	**TTY TELEPHONE EQUIPMENT**									
1620	Telephone, TTY, compact, pocket type				Ea.	400			400	440
1630	Advanced, desk type	2 Elec	20	.800		565	54		619	705
1640	Full-featured public, wall type	"	4	4		925	269		1,194	1,425

27 41 Audio-Video Systems

27 41 33 – Master Antenna Television Systems

27 41 33.10 TV Systems		Crew	Daily Output	Labor-Hours	Unit	Material	Labor	Equipment	Total	Total Incl O&P
						2023 Bare Costs				
0010	**TV SYSTEMS,** not including rough-in wires, cables & conduits									
0100	Master TV antenna system									
0200	VHF reception & distribution, 12 outlets	1 Elec	6	1.333	Outlet	137	90		227	284
0400	30 outlets		10	.800		262	54		316	370
0600	100 outlets		13	.615		305	41.50		346.50	395
0800	VHF & UHF reception & distribution, 12 outlets		6	1.333		250	90		340	410
1000	30 outlets		10	.800		169	54		223	266
1200	100 outlets		13	.615		174	41.50		215.50	254
1400	School and deluxe systems, 12 outlets		2.40	3.333		330	225		555	700
1600	30 outlets		4	2		289	135		424	520
1800	80 outlets		5.30	1.509		278	102		380	455
1900	Amplifier		4	2	Ea.	830	135		965	1,100
5000	Antenna, small		6	1.333		55.50	90		145.50	194
5100	Large		4	2		232	135		367	455
5110	Rotor unit		8	1		58	67.50		125.50	164
5120	Single booster		8	1		28	67.50		95.50	131
5130	Antenna pole, 10′		3.20	2.500		21.50	168		189.50	274
6100	Satellite TV system	2 Elec	1	16		2,075	1,075		3,150	3,875
6110	Dish, mesh, 10′ diam.	"	2.40	6.667		1,600	450		2,050	2,450
6111	Two way RF/IF tapeoff	1 Elec	36	.222		3.60	14.95		18.55	26
6112	Two way RF/IF splitter		24	.333		13.85	22.50		36.35	49
6113	Line amplifier		24	.333		12.55	22.50		35.05	47.50
6114	Line splitters		36	.222		4.62	14.95		19.57	27
6115	Line multi switches		8	1		665	67.50		732.50	830
6120	Motor unit		2.40	3.333		235	225		460	595
7000	Home theater, widescreen, 42", high definition, TV		10.24	.781		455	52.50		507.50	585
7050	Flat wall mount bracket		10.24	.781		33	52.50		85.50	115
7100	7 channel home theater receiver		10.24	.781		420	52.50		472.50	545
7200	Home theater speakers		10.24	.781	Set	217	52.50		269.50	315
7300	Home theater programmable remote		10.24	.781	Ea.	278	52.50		330.50	385
8000	Main video splitter		4	2		3,275	135		3,410	3,800
8010	Video distribution units		4	2		142	135		277	355

27 42 Electronic Digital Systems

27 42 13 – Point of Sale Systems

27 42 13.10 Bar Code Scanner		Crew	Daily Output	Labor-Hours	Unit	Material	Labor	Equipment	Total	Total Incl O&P
0010	**BAR CODE SCANNER**									
0100	CR3600, w/B4 battery, handle	1 Elec	6	1.333	Outlet	1,475	90		1,565	1,750
0110	Palm		12	.667		865	45		910	1,025
0120	Batch, B4 batt, handle, chgstn, 3′ USB		9	.889		1,400	60		1,460	1,650
0130	Palm, chgstn, 3′ USB		12	.667		1,350	45		1,395	1,575
0140	CR2500, w/H2 handle, no cable		10	.800		635	54		689	780
0150	Core unit, palm, no cable		16	.500		795	33.50		828.50	920

27 51 Distributed Audio-Video Communications Systems

27 51 16 – Public Address Systems

27 51 16.10 Public Address System		Crew	Daily Output	Labor-Hours	Unit	2023 Bare Costs Material	Labor	Equipment	Total	Total Incl O&P
0010	**PUBLIC ADDRESS SYSTEM**									
0100	Conventional, office	1 Elec	5.33	1.501	Speaker	1,125	101		1,226	1,375
0200	Industrial	"	2.70	2.963	"	1,000	200		1,200	1,400

27 51 19 – Sound Masking Systems

27 51 19.10 Sound System

Line	Description	Crew	Daily Output	Labor-Hours	Unit	Material	Labor	Equipment	Total	Total Incl O&P
0010	**SOUND SYSTEM**, not including rough-in wires, cables & conduits									
0100	Components, projector outlet	1 Elec	8	1	Ea.	96.50	67.50		164	206
0200	Microphone		4	2		99	135		234	310
0400	Speakers, ceiling or wall		8	1		199	67.50		266.50	320
0600	Trumpets		4	2		345	135		480	580
0800	Privacy switch		8	1		58.50	67.50		126	165
1000	Monitor panel		4	2		865	135		1,000	1,150
1200	Antenna, AM/FM		4	2		25	135		160	228
1400	Volume control		8	1		78.50	67.50		146	187
1600	Amplifier, 250 W		1	8		1,475	540		2,015	2,425
1800	Cabinets		1	8		1,175	540		1,715	2,075
2000	Intercom, 30 station capacity, master station	2 Elec	2	8		2,175	540		2,715	3,175
2020	10 station capacity	"	4	4		2,175	269		2,444	2,800
2200	Remote station	1 Elec	8	1		495	67.50		562.50	645
2400	Intercom outlets		8	1		117	67.50		184.50	228
2600	Handset		4	2		181	135		316	400
2800	Emergency call system, 12 zones, annunciator		1.30	6.154		1,075	415		1,490	1,800
3000	Bell		5.30	1.509		108	102		210	270
3200	Light or relay		8	1		149	67.50		216.50	264
3400	Transformer		4	2		305	135		440	535
3600	House telephone, talking station		1.60	5		650	335		985	1,225
3800	Press to talk, release to listen		5.30	1.509		246	102		348	420
4000	System-on button					90.50			90.50	99.50
4200	Door release	1 Elec	4	2		162	135		297	380
4400	Combination speaker and microphone		8	1		345	67.50		412.50	480
4600	Termination box		3.20	2.500		87	168		255	345
4800	Amplifier or power supply		5.30	1.509		995	102		1,097	1,250
5000	Vestibule door unit		16	.500	Name	191	33.50		224.50	260
5200	Strip cabinet		27	.296	Ea.	345	19.95		364.95	410
5400	Directory		16	.500		185	33.50		218.50	254
6000	Master door, button buzzer type, 100 unit	2 Elec	.54	29.630		1,650	2,000		3,650	4,800
6020	200 unit		.30	53.333		3,125	3,600		6,725	8,775
6040	300 unit		.20	80		4,775	5,400		10,175	13,300
6060	Transformer	1 Elec	8	1		48	67.50		115.50	153
6080	Door opener		5.30	1.509		60.50	102		162.50	218
6100	Buzzer with door release and plate		4	2		175	135		310	395
6200	Intercom type, 100 unit	2 Elec	.54	29.630		1,450	2,000		3,450	4,575
6220	200 unit		.30	53.333		1,475	3,600		5,075	6,975
6240	300 unit		.20	80		2,475	5,400		7,875	10,700
6260	Amplifier	1 Elec	2	4		154	269		423	570
6280	Speaker with door release	"	4	2		90.50	135		225.50	300

27 52 Healthcare Communications and Monitoring Systems

27 52 23 – Nurse Call/Code Blue Systems

27 52 23.10 Nurse Call Systems		Crew	Daily Output	Labor-Hours	Unit	2023 Bare Costs Material	Labor	Equipment	Total	Total Incl O&P
0010	**NURSE CALL SYSTEMS**									
0100	Single bedside call station	1 Elec	8	1	Ea.	560	67.50		627.50	715
0200	Ceiling speaker station		8	1		151	67.50		218.50	266
0400	Emergency call station		8	1		112	67.50		179.50	223
0600	Pillow speaker		8	1		211	67.50		278.50	330
0800	Double bedside call station		4	2		248	135		383	475
1000	Duty station		4	2		415	135		550	655
1200	Standard call button		8	1		206	67.50		273.50	325
1400	Lights, corridor, dome or zone indicator		8	1		92	67.50		159.50	201
1600	Master control station for 20 stations	2 Elec	.65	24.615	Total	3,025	1,650		4,675	5,800

27 53 Distributed Systems

27 53 13 – Clock Systems

27 53 13.50 Clock Equipments		Crew	Daily Output	Labor-Hours	Unit	Material	Labor	Equipment	Total	Total Incl O&P
0010	**CLOCK EQUIPMENTS**, not including wires & conduits									
0100	Time system components, master controller	1 Elec	.33	24.242	Ea.	1,525	1,625		3,150	4,100
0200	Program bell		8	1		95	67.50		162.50	205
0400	Combination clock & speaker		3.20	2.500		202	168		370	475
0600	Frequency generator		2	4		3,125	269		3,394	3,825
0800	Job time automatic stamp recorder		4	2		560	135		695	815
1600	Master time clock system, clocks & bells, 20 room	4 Elec	.20	160		6,375	10,800		17,175	23,000
1800	50 room	"	.08	400		13,600	26,900		40,500	55,000
1900	Time clock	1 Elec	3.20	2.500		395	168		563	685
2000	100 cards in & out, 1 color					9.80			9.80	10.80
2200	2 colors					9.80			9.80	10.80
2800	Metal rack for 25 cards	1 Elec	7	1.143		38	77		115	156
4000	Wireless time systems component, master controller	"	2	4		625	269		894	1,100
4010	For transceiver and antenna, see Section 28 47 12.10									
4100	Wireless analog clock w/battery operated	1 Elec	8	1	Ea.	110	67.50		177.50	221
4200	Wireless digital clock w/battery operated	"	8	1	"	420	67.50		487.50	560

Division Notes

		CREW	DAILY OUTPUT	LABOR-HOURS	UNIT	BARE COSTS MAT.	LABOR	EQUIP.	TOTAL	TOTAL INCL O&P

Division 28

Electronic Safety & Security

Estimating Tips

- When estimating material costs for electronic safety and security systems, it is always prudent to obtain manufacturers' quotations for equipment prices and special installation requirements that may affect the total cost.
- Fire alarm systems consist of control panels, annunciator panels, batteries with rack, charger, and fire alarm actuating and indicating devices. Some fire alarm systems include speakers, telephone lines, door closer controls, and other components. Be careful not to overlook the costs related to installation for these items. Also be aware of costs for integrated automation instrumentation and terminal devices, control equipment, control wiring, and programming. Insurance underwriters may have specific requirements for the type of materials to be installed or design requirements based on the hazard to be protected. Local jurisdictions may have requirements not covered by code. It is advisable to be aware of any special conditions.
- Security equipment includes items such as CCTV, access control, and other detection and identification systems to perform alert and alarm functions. Be sure to consider the costs related to installation for this security equipment, such as for integrated automation instrumentation and terminal devices, control equipment, control wiring, and programming.

Reference Numbers

Reference numbers are shown at the beginning of some major classifications. These numbers refer to related items in the Reference Section. The reference information may be an estimating procedure, an alternate pricing method, or technical information.

Note: Trade Service, in part, has been used as a reference source for some of the material prices used in Division 28.

28 01 Operation and Maint. of Electronic Safety and Security

28 01 80 – Operation and Maintenance of Fire Detection and Alarm

28 01 80.51 Maintenance & Admin. of Fire Detection & Alarm		Crew	Daily Output	Labor-Hours	Unit	Material	2023 Bare Costs Labor	Equipment	Total	Total Incl O&P
0010	MAINTENANCE AND ADMINISTRATION OF FIRE DETECTION AND ALARM									
3300	Remove and replace (reinstall), fire alarm device	1 Elec	5.33	1.501	Ea.		101		101	150

28 05 Common Work Results for Electronic Safety and Security

28 05 05 – Selective Demolition for Electronic Safety and Security

28 05 05.10 Safety and Security Demolition

		Crew	Daily Output	Labor-Hours	Unit	Material	Labor	Equipment	Total	Total Incl O&P
0010	SAFETY AND SECURITY DEMOLITION									
1050	Finger print/card reader	1 Elec	8	1	Ea.		67.50		67.50	100
1051	Electrical dml, CA 3000 card reader sys w/25 users		.31	25.600			1,725		1,725	2,575
1060	Video camera		8	1			67.50		67.50	100
1070	Motion detector, multi-channel		7	1.143			77		77	114
1090	Infrared detector		7	1.143			77		77	114
1130	Video monitor, 19″		8	1			67.50		67.50	100
1210	Fire alarm horn and strobe light		16	.500			33.50		33.50	50
1215	Remote fire alarm indicator light		23	.348			23.50		23.50	35
1220	Flame detector		23	.348			23.50		23.50	35
1230	Duct detector		10	.800			54		54	80
1240	Smoke detector		23	.348			23.50		23.50	35
1241	Fire alarm duct smoke remote test station		21.60	.370			25		25	37
1250	Fire alarm pull station		23	.348			23.50		23.50	35
1260	Fire alarm control panel, 4 to 8 zone	2 Elec	4	4			269		269	400
1270	12 to 16 zone	″	2.67	5.993			405		405	600
1280	Fire alarm annunciation panel, 4 to 8 zone	1 Elec	6	1.333			90		90	133
1290	12 to 16 zone	2 Elec	6	2.667			180		180	267
1300	Electrical dml, tamper switch	1 Elec	38	.211			14.20		14.20	21
1310	Electrical dml, flow switch	″	38	.211			14.20		14.20	21

28 05 19 – Storage Appliances for Electronic Safety and Security

28 05 19.11 Digital Video Recorder (DVR)

		Crew	Daily Output	Labor-Hours	Unit	Material	Labor	Equipment	Total	Total Incl O&P
0010	DIGITAL VIDEO RECORDERS									
0100	Pentaplex hybrid, internet protocol, and hard drive									
0200	4 channel	1 Elec	1.33	6.015	Ea.	2,150	405		2,555	2,950
0300	8 channel		1	8		4,900	540		5,440	6,200
0400	16 channel		1	8		7,250	540		7,790	8,750

28 15 Access Control Hardware Devices

28 15 11 – Integrated Credential Readers and Field Entry Management

28 15 11.11 Standard Card Readers

		Crew	Daily Output	Labor-Hours	Unit	Material	Labor	Equipment	Total	Total Incl O&P
0010	STANDARD CARD READERS									
0015	Card key access									
0020	Computerized system, processor, proximity reader and cards									
0030	Does not include door hardware, lockset or wiring									
0040	Card key system for 1 door				Ea.	920			920	1,025
0060	Card key system for 2 doors					1,475			1,475	1,625
0080	Card key system for 4 doors					1,450			1,450	1,600
0100	Processor for card key access system					915			915	1,000
0160	Magnetic lock for electric access, 600 pound holding force					165			165	181
0170	Magnetic lock for electric access, 1200 pound holding force					165			165	181
0200	Proximity card reader					195			195	215
0210	Entrance card systems									

28 15 11 – Integrated Credential Readers and Field Entry Management

28 15 11.11 Standard Card Readers		Crew	Daily Output	Labor-Hours	Unit	2023 Bare Costs Material	Labor	Equipment	Total	Total Incl O&P
0300	Entrance card, barium ferrite				Ea.	7.45			7.45	8.20
0320	Credential					2.48			2.48	2.73
0340	Proximity					2.48			2.48	2.73
0360	Weigand					6.25			6.25	6.90
0700	Entrance card reader, barium ferrite	R-19	4	5		350	335		685	885
0720	Credential		4	5		305	335		640	835
0740	Proximity		4	5		147	335		482	660
0760	Weigand		4	5		163	335		498	680
0850	Scanner, eye retina		4	5		3,525	335		3,860	4,375
0900	Gate opener, cantilever	R-18	3	8.667		3,050	510		3,560	4,100
0910	Light duty		3	8.667		2,725	510		3,235	3,750
0912	Custom		3	8.667		2,250	510		2,760	3,225
0950	Switch, tamper	R-19	6	3.333		119	225		344	465
1100	Accessories, electric door strike/bolt		5	4		300	270		570	730
1120	Electromagnetic lock		5	4		182	270		452	600
1140	Keypad for card reader		4	5		125	335		460	640

28 15 11.13 Keypads		Crew	Daily Output	Labor-Hours	Unit	Material	Labor	Equipment	Total	Total Incl O&P
0010	**KEYPADS**									
0340	Digital keypad, int./ext., basic, excl. striker/power/wiring	1 Elec	3	2.667	Ea.	268	180		448	560
0350	Lockset, mechanical push-button type, complete, incl. hardware	1 Carp	4	2	"	405	117		522	620

28 15 11.15 Biometric Identity Devices		Crew	Daily Output	Labor-Hours	Unit	Material	Labor	Equipment	Total	Total Incl O&P
0010	**BIOMETRIC IDENTITY DEVICES**									
0200	Fingerprint scanner unit, excl. striker/power supply	1 Elec	4	2	Ea.	2,125	135		2,260	2,550
0210	Fingerprint scanner unit, for computer keyboard access		8	1		1,850	67.50		1,917.50	2,125
0220	Hand geometry scanner, mem of 512 users, excl. striker/power		3	2.667		3,250	180		3,430	3,850
0230	Memory upgrade for, adds 9,700 user profiles		8	1		580	67.50		647.50	740
0240	Adds 32,500 user profiles		8	1		580	67.50		647.50	740
0250	Prison type, memory of 256 users, excl. striker/power		3	2.667		3,725	180		3,905	4,375
0260	Memory upgrade for, adds 3,300 user profiles		8	1		545	67.50		612.50	700
0270	Adds 9,700 user profiles		8	1		670	67.50		737.50	835
0280	Adds 27,900 user profiles		8	1		1,025	67.50		1,092.50	1,225
0290	All weather, mem of 512 users, excl. striker/power		3	2.667		5,875	180		6,055	6,725
0300	Facial & fingerprint scanner, combination unit, excl. striker/power		3	2.667		1,250	180		1,430	1,650
0310	Access for, for initial setup, excl. striker/power		3	2.667		1,850	180		2,030	2,300

28 15 11.19 Security Access Control Accessories		Crew	Daily Output	Labor-Hours	Unit	Material	Labor	Equipment	Total	Total Incl O&P
0010	**SECURITY ACCESS CONTROL ACCESSORIES**									
0360	Scanner/reader access, power supply/transf, 110V to 12/24V	1 Elec	4	2	Ea.	72.50	135		207.50	280
0370	Elec/mag strikers, 12/24V		4	2		106	135		241	315
0380	1 hour battery backup power supply		4	2		28.50	135		163.50	231
0390	Deadbolt, digital, batt-operated, indoor/outdoor, complete, incl. hardware	1 Carp	4	2		253	117		370	455

28 18 Security Access Detection Equipment

28 18 11 – Security Access Metal Detectors

28 18 11.13 Security Access Metal Detectors		Crew	Daily Output	Labor-Hours	Unit	2023 Bare Costs Material	Labor	Equipment	Total	Total Incl O&P
0010	**SECURITY ACCESS METAL DETECTORS**									
0240	Metal detector, hand-held, wand type, unit only				Ea.	129			129	138
0250	Metal detector, walk through portal type, single zone	1 Elec	2	4		1,275	269		1,544	1,800
0260	Multi-zone	"	2	4		2,475	269		2,744	3,125

28 18 13 – Security Access X-Ray Equipment

28 18 13.16 Security Access X-Ray Equipment		Crew	Daily Output	Labor-Hours	Unit	Material	Labor	Equipment	Total	Total Incl O&P
0010	**SECURITY ACCESS X-RAY EQUIPMENT**									
0290	X-ray machine, desk top, for mail/small packages/letters	1 Elec	4	2	Ea.	3,425	135		3,560	3,975
0300	Conveyor type, incl. monitor		2	4		19,600	269		19,869	21,900
0310	Includes additional features		2	4		34,800	269		35,069	38,700
0320	X-ray machine, large unit, for airports, incl. monitor	2 Elec	1	16		48,900	1,075		49,975	55,500
0330	Full console	"	.50	32		84,000	2,150		86,150	95,000

28 18 15 – Security Access Explosive Detection Equipment

28 18 15.23 Security Access Explosive Detection Equipment		Crew	Daily Output	Labor-Hours	Unit	Material	Labor	Equipment	Total	Total Incl O&P
0010	**SECURITY ACCESS EXPLOSIVE DETECTION EQUIPMENT**									
0270	Explosives detector, walk through portal type	1 Elec	2	4	Ea.	175,000	269		175,269	193,000
0280	Hand-held, battery operated				"				25,500	28,100

28 23 Video Management System

28 23 13 – Video Management System Interfaces

28 23 13.10 Closed Circuit Television System		Crew	Daily Output	Labor-Hours	Unit	Material	Labor	Equipment	Total	Total Incl O&P
0010	**CLOSED CIRCUIT TELEVISION SYSTEM**									
2000	Surveillance, one station (camera & monitor)	2 Elec	2.60	6.154	Total	570	415		985	1,250
2200	For additional camera stations, add	1 Elec	2.70	2.963	Ea.	160	200		360	475
2400	Industrial quality, one station (camera & monitor)	2 Elec	2.60	6.154	Total	1,450	415		1,865	2,225
2600	For additional camera stations, add	1 Elec	2.70	2.963	Ea.	725	200		925	1,100
2610	For low light, add		2.70	2.963		500	200		700	845
2620	For very low light, add		2.70	2.963		2,700	200		2,900	3,250
2800	For weatherproof camera station, add		1.30	6.154		520	415		935	1,175
3000	For pan and tilt, add		1.30	6.154		1,375	415		1,790	2,125
3200	For zoom lens - remote control, add		2	4		1,575	269		1,844	2,150
3400	Extended zoom lens		2	4		4,400	269		4,669	5,250
3410	For automatic iris for low light, add		2	4		895	269		1,164	1,375
3600	Educational TV studio, basic 3 camera system, black & white,									
3800	electrical & electronic equip. only	4 Elec	.80	40	Total	7,250	2,700		9,950	12,000
4000	Full console		.28	114		22,200	7,700		29,900	35,800
4100	As above, but color system		.28	114		44,200	7,700		51,900	60,000
4120	Full console		.12	267		166,500	18,000		184,500	209,500
4200	For film chain, black & white, add	1 Elec	1	8	Ea.	10,900	540		11,440	12,800
4250	Color, add		.25	32		7,825	2,150		9,975	11,800
4400	For video recorders, add		1	8		2,150	540		2,690	3,150
4600	Premium	4 Elec	.40	80		14,100	5,400		19,500	23,500

28 23 23 – Video Surveillance Systems Infrastructure

28 23 23.50 Video Surveillance Equipments		Crew	Daily Output	Labor-Hours	Unit	Material	Labor	Equipment	Total	Total Incl O&P
0010	**VIDEO SURVEILLANCE EQUIPMENTS**									
0200	Video cameras, wireless, hidden in exit signs, clocks, etc., incl. receiver	1 Elec	3	2.667	Ea.	205	180		385	490
0210	Accessories for video recorder, single camera		3	2.667		178	180		358	465
0220	For multiple cameras		3	2.667		1,500	180		1,680	1,925
0230	Video cameras, wireless, for under vehicle searching, complete		2	4		13,300	269		13,569	15,000

28 23 Video Management System

28 23 23 – Video Surveillance Systems Infrastructure

28 23 23.50 Video Surveillance Equipments		Crew	Daily Output	Labor-Hours	Unit	2023 Bare Costs Material	Labor	Equipment	Total	Total Incl O&P
0234	Master monitor station, 3 doors x 5 color monitor with tilt feature	1 Elec	2	4	Ea.	960	269		1,229	1,450
0400	Internet protocol network camera, day/night, color & power supply		2.60	3.077		460	207		667	820
0500	Monitor, color flat screen, liquid crystal display (LCD), 15″		2.70	2.963		204	200		404	520
0520	17″		2.70	2.963		425	200		625	760
0540	19″		2.70	2.963		495	200		695	840

28 31 Intrusion Detection

28 31 16 – Intrusion Detection Systems Infrastructure

28 31 16.50 Intrusion Detection		Crew	Daily Output	Labor-Hours	Unit	Material	Labor	Equipment	Total	Total Incl O&P
0010	**INTRUSION DETECTION**, not including wires & conduits									
0100	Burglar alarm, battery operated, mechanical trigger	1 Elec	4	2	Ea.	283	135		418	510
0200	Electrical trigger		4	2		340	135		475	570
0400	For outside key control, add		8	1		87	67.50		154.50	196
0600	For remote signaling circuitry, add		8	1		144	67.50		211.50	259
0800	Card reader, flush type, standard		2.70	2.963		680	200		880	1,050
1000	Multi-code		2.70	2.963		620	200		820	975
1010	Card reader, proximity type		2.70	2.963		147	200		347	460
1200	Door switches, hinge switch		5.30	1.509		66.50	102		168.50	224
1400	Magnetic switch		5.30	1.509		145	102		247	310
1600	Exit control locks, horn alarm		4	2		237	135		372	460
1800	Flashing light alarm		4	2		269	135		404	495
2000	Indicating panels, 1 channel		2.70	2.963		248	200		448	570
2200	10 channel	2 Elec	3.20	5		1,150	335		1,485	1,775
2400	20 channel		2	8		2,450	540		2,990	3,500
2600	40 channel		1.14	14.035		4,550	945		5,495	6,400
2800	Ultrasonic motion detector, 12 V	1 Elec	2.30	3.478		164	234		398	530
3000	Infrared photoelectric detector		4	2		124	135		259	335
3200	Passive infrared detector		4	2		54	135		189	259
3400	Glass break alarm switch		8	1		71	67.50		138.50	178
3420	Switchmats, 30″ x 5′		5.30	1.509		118	102		220	281
3440	30″ x 25′		4	2		207	135		342	430
3460	Police connect panel		4	2		286	135		421	515
3480	Telephone dialer		5.30	1.509		390	102		492	580
3500	Alarm bell		4	2		98.50	135		233.50	310
3520	Siren		4	2		149	135		284	365
3540	Microwave detector, 10′ to 200′		2	4		540	269		809	995
3560	10′ to 350′		2	4		1,800	269		2,069	2,375

28 33 Security Monitoring and Control

28 33 11 – Electronic Structural Monitoring Systems

28 33 11.10 Load Cell Units		Crew	Daily Output	Labor-Hours	Unit	Material	Labor	Equipment	Total	Total Incl O&P
0010	**LOAD CELL UNITS**									
0100	Load cell, stainless steel, 0.5/1 ton rated, mounting unit	2 Elec	1.33	12.030	Ea.	720	810		1,530	2,000
0110	2/3 to 5/5 ton rated, mounting unit		1.20	13.333		745	900		1,645	2,150
0120	0.5/1/2/3.5/5 ton, self aligning bottom base		1.66	9.639		195	650		845	1,175
0130	Combo mounting unit, 10/25 ton rated		.86	18.605		1,900	1,250		3,150	3,950
0140	40/60 ton rated		.66	24.242		3,225	1,625		4,850	5,975
0150	60kg/3m, rated		1.84	8.696		1,625	585		2,210	2,650
0160	130kg/3m, rated		1.55	10.323		1,525	695		2,220	2,725

28 33 Security Monitoring and Control

28 33 11 – Electronic Structural Monitoring Systems

28 33 11.10 Load Cell Units		Crew	Daily Output	Labor-Hours	Unit	Material	Labor	Equipment	Total	Total Incl O&P
						2023 Bare Costs				
0170	280 kg, rated	2 Elec	1.22	13.115	Ea.	1,525	885		2,410	3,025

28 46 Fire Detection and Alarm

28 46 11 – Fire Sensors and Detectors

28 46 11.21 Carbon-Monoxide Detection Sensors

		Crew	Daily Output	Labor-Hours	Unit	Material	Labor	Equipment	Total	Total Incl O&P
0010	**CARBON-MONOXIDE DETECTION SENSORS**									
8400	Smoke and carbon monoxide alarm battery operated photoelectric low profile	1 Elec	24	.333	Ea.	98	22.50		120.50	142
8410	low profile photoelectric battery powered		24	.333		48	22.50		70.50	86
8420	photoelectric low profile sealed lithium		24	.333		84	22.50		106.50	126
8430	Photoelectric low profile sealed lithium smoke and CO with voice combo		24	.333		58.50	22.50		81	97.50
8500	Carbon monoxide sensor, wall mount 1Mod 1 relay output smoke & heat		24	.333		470	22.50		492.50	550
8510	1Mod, 1relay no display, smoke & heat		24	.333		445	22.50		467.50	525
8530	1Mod 1 relay no HW logo smoke & heat		24	.333		480	22.50		502.50	560
8700	Carbon monoxide detector, battery operated, wall mounted		16	.500		45	33.50		78.50	99.50
8710	Hardwired, wall and ceiling mounted		8	1		80	67.50		147.50	188
8720	Duct mounted		8	1		360	67.50		427.50	500
8730	Continuous air monitoring system, PC based, incl. remote sensors, min.	2 Elec	.25	64		35,500	4,300		39,800	45,400
8740	Maximum	"	.10	160		64,000	10,800		74,800	86,500

28 46 11.27 Other Sensors

		Crew	Daily Output	Labor-Hours	Unit	Material	Labor	Equipment	Total	Total Incl O&P
0010	**OTHER SENSORS**									
5200	Smoke detector, ceiling type	1 Elec	6.20	1.290	Ea.	155	87		242	300
5240	Smoke detector, addressable type		6	1.333		241	90		331	400
5400	Duct type		3.20	2.500		330	168		498	615
5420	Duct addressable type		3.20	2.500		202	168		370	470
8300	Smoke alarm with integrated strobe light 120 V, 16DB 60 fpm flash rate		16	.500		128	33.50		161.50	191
8310	Photoelectric smoke detector with strobe 120 V, 90 DB ceiling mount		12	.667		239	45		284	330
8320	120 V, 90 DB wall mount		12	.667		137	45		182	218
8330	120 V, 9 VDC, 90 DB ceiling mount		12	.667		227	45		272	315
8340	120 V, 9 VDC backup 90 DB wall mount		12	.667		243	45		288	335
8440	Fire alarm beam detector, motorized reflective, infrared optical beam	2 Elec	1.60	10		810	675		1,485	1,900
8450	Fire alarm beam detector, motorized reflective, IR/UV optical beam	"	1.60	10		985	675		1,660	2,075

28 46 11.50 Fire and Heat Detectors

		Crew	Daily Output	Labor-Hours	Unit	Material	Labor	Equipment	Total	Total Incl O&P
0010	**FIRE & HEAT DETECTORS**									
5000	Detector, rate of rise	1 Elec	8	1	Ea.	33	67.50		100.50	137
5010	Heat addressable type		7.25	1.103		125	74.50		199.50	247
5100	Fixed temp fire alarm		7	1.143		44	77		121	162
5200	125 V SRF MT-135F		7.25	1.103		41.50	74.50		116	156
5300	MT-195F		7.25	1.103		42	74.50		116.50	157
5400	104/85 DB, indoor/outdoor, ceiling/wall, red		10.25	.780		43.50	52.50		96	126
5410	Ceiling/wall, white		10.25	.780		42.50	52.50		95	125
5420	102/98 DB, lumin 110cd, indoor/wall, red		10.25	.780		121	52.50		173.50	211
5430	Lumin15/75cd, indoor/wall, red		10.25	.780		144	52.50		196.50	236
5440	HI/LO DB, 24 V, fire marking, red		10.25	.780		99.50	52.50		152	188

28 46 20 – Fire Alarm

28 46 20.50 Alarm Panels and Devices

		Crew	Daily Output	Labor-Hours	Unit	Material	Labor	Equipment	Total	Total Incl O&P
0010	**ALARM PANELS AND DEVICES**, not including wires & conduits									
2200	Intercom remote station	1 Elec	8	1	Ea.	94.50	67.50		162	204
2400	Intercom outlet		8	1		66	67.50		133.50	173
2600	Sound system, intercom handset		8	1		325	67.50		392.50	455
3590	Signal device, beacon		8	1		227	67.50		294.50	350

28 46 Fire Detection and Alarm

28 46 20 – Fire Alarm

28 46 20.50 Alarm Panels and Devices		Crew	Daily Output	Labor-Hours	Unit	2023 Bare Costs Material	Labor	Equipment	Total	Total Incl O&P
3594	2 zone	1 Elec	1.35	5.926	Ea.	400	400		800	1,025
3598	3 zone	2 Elec	2	8		525	540		1,065	1,375
3600	4 zone		2	8		490	540		1,030	1,350
3700	5 zone		1.50	10.667		645	720		1,365	1,775
3800	8 zone		1	16		660	1,075		1,735	2,325
3900	10 zone		1.25	12.800		1,050	860		1,910	2,425
4000	12 zone		.67	23.988		2,875	1,625		4,500	5,550
4020	Alarm device, tamper, flow	1 Elec	8	1		227	67.50		294.50	350
4025	Fire alarm, loop expander card		16	.500		670	33.50		703.50	790
4050	Actuating device		8	1		370	67.50		437.50	505
4160	Alarm control panel, addressable w/o voice, up to 200 points	2 Elec	1.14	13.998		2,200	945		3,145	3,825
4170	addressable w/voice, up to 400 points	"	.73	22.008		11,400	1,475		12,875	14,700
4175	Addressable interface device	1 Elec	7.25	1.103		168	74.50		242.50	294
4200	Battery and rack		4	2		520	135		655	770
4400	Automatic charger		8	1		590	67.50		657.50	750
4600	Signal bell		8	1		56.50	67.50		124	163
4610	Fire alarm signal bell 10" red 20-24 V P		8	1		205	67.50		272.50	325
4800	Trouble buzzer or manual station		8	1		85	67.50		152.50	194
5425	Duct smoke and heat detector 2 wire		8	1		179	67.50		246.50	296
5430	Fire alarm duct detector controller		3	2.667		222	180		402	510
5435	Fire alarm duct detector sensor kit		8	1		86	67.50		153.50	195
5440	Remote test station for smoke detector duct type		5.30	1.509		59	102		161	216
5460	Remote fire alarm indicator light		5.30	1.509		30.50	102		132.50	185
5600	Strobe and horn		5.30	1.509		105	102		207	267
5610	Strobe and horn (ADA type)		5.30	1.509		132	102		234	296
5620	Visual alarm (ADA type)		6.70	1.194		116	80.50		196.50	247
5800	electric bell		6.70	1.194		56.50	80.50		137	182
6000	Door holder, electro-magnetic		4	2		106	135		241	315
6200	Combination holder and closer		3.20	2.500		176	168		344	445
6600	Drill switch		8	1		545	67.50		612.50	700
6800	Master box		2.70	2.963		6,575	200		6,775	7,550
7000	Break glass station		8	1		65	67.50		132.50	172
7010	Break glass station, addressable		7.25	1.103		166	74.50		240.50	293
7800	Remote annunciator, 8 zone lamp		1.80	4.444		345	299		644	825
8000	12 zone lamp	2 Elec	2.60	6.154		455	415		870	1,125
8200	16 zone lamp	"	2.20	7.273		440	490		930	1,225

28 47 Mass Notification

28 47 12 – Notification Systems

28 47 12.10 Mass Notification System

		Crew	Daily Output	Labor-Hours	Unit	Material	Labor	Equipment	Total	Total Incl O&P
0010	MASS NOTIFICATION SYSTEM									
0100	Wireless command center, 10,000 devices	2 Elec	1.33	12.030	Ea.	3,175	810		3,985	4,675
0200	Option, email notification					2,225			2,225	2,450
0210	Remote device supervision & monitor					2,775			2,775	3,075
0300	Antenna VHF or UHF, for medium range	1 Elec	4	2		110	135		245	320
0310	For high-power transmitter		2	4		1,300	269		1,569	1,825
0400	Transmitter, 25 watt		4	2		1,725	135		1,860	2,100
0410	40 watt		2.66	3.008		2,000	203		2,203	2,500
0420	100 watt		1.33	6.015		6,475	405		6,880	7,725
0500	Wireless receiver/control module for speaker		8	1		300	67.50		367.50	430
0600	Desktop paging controller, stand alone		4	2		895	135		1,030	1,175

28 47 Mass Notification

28 47 12 – Notification Systems

28 47 12.10 Mass Notification System		Crew	Daily Output	Labor-Hours	Unit	2023 Bare Costs Material	Labor	Equipment	Total	Total Incl O&P
0700	Auxiliary level inputs	1 Elec	8.36	.957	Ea.	108	64.50		172.50	215

28 52 Detention Security Systems

28 52 11 – Detention Monitoring and Control Systems

28 52 11.10 Detention Control Systems		Crew	Daily Output	Labor-Hours	Unit	Material	Labor	Equipment	Total	Total Incl O&P
0010	**DETENTION CONTROL SYSTEMS**									
1000	Desk top control systems for 10 doors, 10 intercoms, and 10 lights	2 Elec	.30	53.333	Ea.	68,000	3,600		71,600	80,500
1020	Push button control panel systems for 10 doors, 10 intercoms, and 10 lights	"	.32	50	"	61,500	3,375		64,875	72,500

Estimating Tips

31 05 00 Common Work Results for Earthwork

- Estimating the actual cost of performing earthwork requires careful consideration of the variables involved. This includes items such as type of soil, whether water will be encountered, dewatering, whether banks need bracing, disposal of excavated earth, and length of haul to fill or spoil sites, etc. If the project has large quantities of cut or fill, consider raising or lowering the site to reduce costs, while paying close attention to the effect on site drainage and utilities.
- If the project has large quantities of fill, creating a borrow pit on the site can significantly lower the costs.
- It is very important to consider what time of year the project is scheduled for completion. Bad weather can create large cost overruns from dewatering, site repair, and lost productivity from cold weather.

Reference Numbers

Reference numbers are shown at the beginning of some major classifications. These numbers refer to related items in the Reference Section. The reference information may be an estimating procedure, an alternate pricing method, or technical information.

Note: Not all subdivisions listed here necessarily appear. ■

31 23 16.13 Excavating, Trench		Crew	Daily Output	Labor-Hours	Unit	Material	2023 Bare Costs Labor	Equipment	Total	Total Incl O&P
0010	**EXCAVATING, TRENCH**									
0011	Or continuous footing									
0020	Common earth with no sheeting or dewatering included									
0050	1′ to 4′ deep, 3/8 C.Y. excavator	B-11C	150	.107	B.C.Y.		5.90	1.85	7.75	10.80
0060	1/2 C.Y. excavator	B-11M	200	.080			4.41	1.79	6.20	8.50
0062	3/4 C.Y. excavator	B-12F	270	.059			3.36	3.39	6.75	8.75
1400	By hand with pick and shovel 2′ to 6′ deep, light soil	1 Clab	8	1			47.50		47.50	70.50
1500	Heavy soil	"	4	2	↓		94.50		94.50	141
3000	Backfill trench, F.E. loader, wheel mtd., 1 C.Y. bucket									
3020	Minimal haul	B-10R	400	.030	L.C.Y.		1.73	.99	2.72	3.67
5020	Loam & sandy clay with no sheeting or dewatering included									
5050	1′ to 4′ deep, 3/8 C.Y. tractor loader/backhoe	B-11C	162	.099	B.C.Y.		5.45	1.71	7.16	10
5060	1/2 C.Y. excavator	B-11M	216	.074			4.09	1.66	5.75	7.90
5070	3/4 C.Y. excavator	B-12F	292	.055	↓		3.11	3.13	6.24	8.10
6020	Sand & gravel with no sheeting or dewatering included									
6050	1′ to 4′ deep, 3/8 C.Y. excavator	B-11C	165	.097	B.C.Y.		5.35	1.68	7.03	9.80
6060	1/2 C.Y. excavator	B-11M	220	.073			4.01	1.63	5.64	7.75
6070	3/4 C.Y. excavator	B-12F	297	.054	↓		3.06	3.08	6.14	7.95
7020	Dense hard clay with no sheeting or dewatering included									
7050	1′ to 4′ deep, 3/8 C.Y. excavator	B-11C	132	.121	B.C.Y.		6.70	2.10	8.80	12.25
7060	1/2 C.Y. excavator	B-11M	176	.091			5	2.03	7.03	9.70
7070	3/4 C.Y. excavator	B-12F	238	.067	↓		3.82	3.85	7.67	9.95

31 23 16.14 Excavating, Utility Trench		Crew	Daily Output	Labor-Hours	Unit	Material	Labor	Equipment	Total	Total Incl O&P
0010	**EXCAVATING, UTILITY TRENCH**									
0011	Common earth									
0050	Trenching with chain trencher, 12 HP, operator walking									
0100	4″ wide trench, 12″ deep	B-53	800	.010	L.F.		.60	.25	.85	1.17
0150	18″ deep		750	.011			.64	.27	.91	1.25
0200	24″ deep		700	.011			.68	.29	.97	1.34
0300	6″ wide trench, 12″ deep		650	.012			.73	.31	1.04	1.43
0350	18″ deep		600	.013			.80	.34	1.14	1.55
0400	24″ deep		550	.015			.87	.37	1.24	1.69
0450	36″ deep		450	.018			1.06	.45	1.51	2.07
0600	8″ wide trench, 12″ deep		475	.017			1.01	.43	1.44	1.97
0650	18″ deep		400	.020			1.19	.51	1.70	2.34
0700	24″ deep		350	.023			1.36	.58	1.94	2.67
0750	36″ deep	↓	300	.027	↓		1.59	.67	2.26	3.11
1000	Backfill by hand including compaction, add									
1050	4″ wide trench, 12″ deep	A-1G	800	.010	L.F.		.47	.11	.58	.82
1100	18″ deep		530	.015			.71	.17	.88	1.24
1150	24″ deep		400	.020			.95	.22	1.17	1.65
1300	6″ wide trench, 12″ deep		540	.015			.70	.16	.86	1.22
1350	18″ deep		405	.020			.93	.22	1.15	1.63
1400	24″ deep		270	.030			1.40	.33	1.73	2.44
1450	36″ deep		180	.044			2.10	.49	2.59	3.67
1600	8″ wide trench, 12″ deep		400	.020			.95	.22	1.17	1.65
1650	18″ deep		265	.030			1.43	.33	1.76	2.49
1700	24″ deep		200	.040			1.89	.44	2.33	3.29
1750	36″ deep	↓	135	.059	↓		2.80	.65	3.45	4.89
2000	Chain trencher, 40 HP operator riding									
2050	6″ wide trench and backfill, 12″ deep	B-54	1200	.007	L.F.		.40	.32	.72	.94
2100	18″ deep	↓	1000	.008	↓		.48	.39	.87	1.14

31 23 16.14 Excavating, Utility Trench

	31 23 16.14 Excavating, Utility Trench	Crew	Daily Output	Labor-Hours	Unit	Material	2023 Bare Costs Labor	2023 Bare Costs Equipment	Total	Total Incl O&P
2150	24" deep	B-54	975	.008	L.F.		.49	.40	.89	1.17
2200	36" deep		900	.009			.53	.43	.96	1.26
2250	48" deep		750	.011			.64	.52	1.16	1.52
2300	60" deep		650	.012			.73	.59	1.32	1.74
2400	8" wide trench and backfill, 12" deep		1000	.008			.48	.39	.87	1.14
2450	18" deep		950	.008			.50	.41	.91	1.20
2500	24" deep		900	.009			.53	.43	.96	1.26
2550	36" deep		800	.010			.60	.48	1.08	1.42
2600	48" deep		650	.012			.73	.59	1.32	1.74
2700	12" wide trench and backfill, 12" deep		975	.008			.49	.40	.89	1.17
2750	18" deep		860	.009			.56	.45	1.01	1.32
2800	24" deep		800	.010			.60	.48	1.08	1.42
2850	36" deep		725	.011			.66	.53	1.19	1.57
3000	16" wide trench and backfill, 12" deep		835	.010			.57	.46	1.03	1.36
3050	18" deep		750	.011			.64	.52	1.16	1.52
3100	24" deep		700	.011			.68	.55	1.23	1.63
3200	Compaction with vibratory plate, add								35%	35%
5100	Hand excavate and trim for pipe bells after trench excavation									
5200	8" pipe	1 Clab	155	.052	L.F.		2.44		2.44	3.63
5300	18" pipe	"	130	.062	"		2.91		2.91	4.33

31 23 16.15 Excavating, Utility Trench, Plow

	31 23 16.15 Excavating, Utility Trench, Plow	Crew	Daily Output	Labor-Hours	Unit	Material	Labor	Equipment	Total	Total Incl O&P
0010	**EXCAVATING, UTILITY TRENCH, PLOW**									
0100	Single cable, plowed into fine material	B-54C	3800	.004	L.F.		.23	.33	.56	.71
0200	Two cable		3200	.005			.28	.39	.67	.84
0300	Single cable, plowed into coarse material		2000	.008			.44	.62	1.06	1.35

31 23 16.16 Structural Excavation for Minor Structures

	31 23 16.16 Structural Excavation for Minor Structures	Crew	Daily Output	Labor-Hours	Unit	Material	Labor	Equipment	Total	Total Incl O&P
0010	**STRUCTURAL EXCAVATION FOR MINOR STRUCTURES**									
0015	Hand, pits to 6' deep, sandy soil	1 Clab	8	1	B.C.Y.		47.50		47.50	70.50
0100	Heavy soil or clay		4	2			94.50		94.50	141
0300	Pits 6' to 12' deep, sandy soil		5	1.600			75.50		75.50	113
0500	Heavy soil or clay		3	2.667			126		126	188
0700	Pits 12' to 18' deep, sandy soil		4	2			94.50		94.50	141
0900	Heavy soil or clay		2	4			189		189	281
6030	Common earth, hydraulic backhoe, 1/2 C.Y. bucket	B-12E	55	.291			16.50	13.90	30.40	40
6035	3/4 C.Y. bucket	B-12F	90	.178			10.10	10.15	20.25	26
6040	1 C.Y. bucket	B-12A	108	.148			8.40	9.15	17.55	22.50
6050	1-1/2 C.Y. bucket	B-12B	144	.111			6.30	8.25	14.55	18.45
6060	2 C.Y. bucket	B-12C	200	.080			4.54	5.50	10.04	12.80
6070	Sand and gravel, 3/4 C.Y. bucket	B-12F	100	.160			9.10	9.15	18.25	23.50
6080	1 C.Y. bucket	B-12A	120	.133			7.55	8.20	15.75	20.50
6090	1-1/2 C.Y. bucket	B-12B	160	.100			5.70	7.40	13.10	16.60
6100	2 C.Y. bucket	B-12C	220	.073			4.13	4.98	9.11	11.65
6110	Clay, till, or blasted rock, 3/4 C.Y. bucket	B-12F	80	.200			11.35	11.45	22.80	29.50
6120	1 C.Y. bucket	B-12A	95	.168			9.55	10.40	19.95	25.50
6130	1-1/2 C.Y. bucket	B-12B	130	.123			7	9.10	16.10	20.50
6140	2 C.Y. bucket	B-12C	175	.091			5.20	6.25	11.45	14.65
6230	Sandy clay & loam, hydraulic backhoe, 1/2 C.Y. bucket	B-12E	60	.267			15.15	12.75	27.90	36.50
6235	3/4 C.Y. bucket	B-12F	98	.163			9.25	9.35	18.60	24
6240	1 C.Y. bucket	B-12A	116	.138			7.85	8.50	16.35	21
6250	1-1/2 C.Y. bucket	B-12B	156	.103			5.80	7.60	13.40	17

31 23 Excavation and Fill

31 23 19 – Dewatering

31 23 19.20 Dewatering Systems		Crew	Daily Output	Labor-Hours	Unit	Material	2023 Bare Costs Labor	Equipment	Total	Total Incl O&P
0010	**DEWATERING SYSTEMS**									
0020	Excavate drainage trench, 2′ wide, 2′ deep	B-11C	90	.178	C.Y.		9.80	3.08	12.88	18
0100	2′ wide, 3′ deep, with backhoe loader	″	135	.119			6.55	2.05	8.60	12
0200	Excavate sump pits by hand, light soil	1 Clab	7.10	1.127			53		53	79.50
0300	Heavy soil	″	3.50	2.286			108		108	161
0500	Pumping 8 hrs., attended 2 hrs./day, incl. 20 L.F.									
0550	of suction hose & 100 L.F. discharge hose									
0600	2″ diaphragm pump used for 8 hrs.	B-10H	4	3	Day		173	18.65	191.65	279
0650	4″ diaphragm pump used for 8 hrs.	B-10I	4	3			173	49.50	222.50	315
0800	8 hrs. attended, 2″ diaphragm pump	B-10H	1	12			695	74.50	769.50	1,100
0900	3″ centrifugal pump	B-10J	1	12			695	101	796	1,125
1000	4″ diaphragm pump	B-10I	1	12			695	198	893	1,250
1100	6″ centrifugal pump	B-10K	1	12			695	455	1,150	1,525

31 23 23 – Fill

31 23 23.13 Backfill

		Crew	Daily Output	Labor-Hours	Unit	Material	Labor	Equipment	Total	Total Incl O&P
0010	**BACKFILL**									
0015	By hand, no compaction, light soil	1 Clab	14	.571	L.C.Y.		27		27	40
0100	Heavy soil		11	.727	″		34.50		34.50	51
0300	Compaction in 6″ layers, hand tamp, add to above		20.60	.388	B.C.Y.		18.35		18.35	27.50
0400	Roller compaction operator walking, add	B-10A	100	.120			6.95	1.58	8.53	12.05
0500	Air tamp, add	B-9D	190	.211			10.05	1.88	11.93	17
0600	Vibrating plate, add	A-1D	60	.133			6.30	2.40	8.70	12.05
0800	Compaction in 12″ layers, hand tamp, add to above	1 Clab	34	.235			11.10		11.10	16.55
0900	Roller compaction operator walking, add	B-10A	150	.080			4.62	1.05	5.67	8.05
1000	Air tamp, add	B-9	285	.140			6.70	1.10	7.80	11.15
1100	Vibrating plate, add	A-1E	90	.089			4.20	1.62	5.82	8.05
1300	Dozer backfilling, bulk, up to 300′ haul, no compaction	B-10B	1200	.010	L.C.Y.		.58	1.15	1.73	2.13
1400	Air tamped, add	B-11B	80	.200	B.C.Y.		10.70	6.20	16.90	22.50
1600	Compacting backfill, 6″ to 12″ lifts, vibrating roller	B-10C	800	.015			.87	2.58	3.45	4.13
1700	Sheepsfoot roller	B-10D	750	.016			.92	2.44	3.36	4.06
1900	Dozer backfilling, trench, up to 300′ haul, no compaction	B-10B	900	.013	L.C.Y.		.77	1.54	2.31	2.84
2000	Air tamped, add	B-11B	80	.200	B.C.Y.		10.70	6.20	16.90	22.50
2200	Compacting backfill, 6″ to 12″ lifts, vibrating roller	B-10C	700	.017			.99	2.95	3.94	4.71
2300	Sheepsfoot roller	B-10D	650	.018			1.07	2.81	3.88	4.68

31 23 23.16 Fill By Borrow and Utility Bedding

		Crew	Daily Output	Labor-Hours	Unit	Material	Labor	Equipment	Total	Total Incl O&P
0010	**FILL BY BORROW AND UTILITY BEDDING**									
0049	Utility bedding, for pipe & conduit, not incl. compaction									
0050	Crushed or screened bank run gravel	B-6	150	.160	L.C.Y.	51.50	8.20	1.85	61.55	71
0100	Crushed stone 3/4″ to 1/2″		150	.160		38.50	8.20	1.85	48.55	57
0200	Sand, dead or bank		150	.160		13.85	8.20	1.85	23.90	29.50
0500	Compacting bedding in trench	A-1D	90	.089	B.C.Y.		4.20	1.60	5.80	8
0610	See Section 31 23 23.20 for hauling mileage add.									

31 23 23.20 Hauling

		Crew	Daily Output	Labor-Hours	Unit	Material	Labor	Equipment	Total	Total Incl O&P
0010	**HAULING**									
0011	Excavated or borrow, loose cubic yards									
0012	no loading equipment, including hauling, waiting, loading/dumping									
0013	time per cycle (wait, load, travel, unload or dump & return)									
0014	8 C.Y. truck, 15 MPH avg., cycle 0.5 miles, 10 min. wait/ld./uld.	B-34A	320	.025	L.C.Y.		1.39	1.30	2.69	3.51
0016	cycle 1 mile		272	.029			1.63	1.54	3.17	4.13
0018	cycle 2 miles		208	.038			2.13	2.01	4.14	5.40
0020	cycle 4 miles		144	.056			3.08	2.90	5.98	7.80

31 23 23.20 Hauling		Crew	Daily Output	Labor-Hours	Unit	Material	2023 Bare Costs Labor	Equipment	Total	Total Incl O&P
0022	cycle 6 miles	B-34A	112	.071	L.C.Y.		3.96	3.73	7.69	10
0024	cycle 8 miles		88	.091			5.05	4.74	9.79	12.75
0026	20 MPH avg., cycle 0.5 mile		336	.024			1.32	1.24	2.56	3.34
0028	cycle 1 mile		296	.027			1.50	1.41	2.91	3.79
0030	cycle 2 miles		240	.033			1.85	1.74	3.59	4.67
0032	cycle 4 miles		176	.045			2.52	2.37	4.89	6.40
0034	cycle 6 miles		136	.059			3.26	3.07	6.33	8.25
0036	cycle 8 miles		112	.071			3.96	3.73	7.69	10
0044	25 MPH avg., cycle 4 miles		192	.042			2.31	2.17	4.48	5.85
0046	cycle 6 miles		160	.050			2.77	2.61	5.38	7
0048	cycle 8 miles		128	.063			3.47	3.26	6.73	8.80
0050	30 MPH avg., cycle 4 miles		216	.037			2.05	1.93	3.98	5.20
0052	cycle 6 miles		176	.045			2.52	2.37	4.89	6.40
0054	cycle 8 miles		144	.056			3.08	2.90	5.98	7.80
0114	15 MPH avg., cycle 0.5 mile, 15 min. wait/ld./uld.		224	.036			1.98	1.86	3.84	5
0116	cycle 1 mile		200	.040			2.22	2.09	4.31	5.60
0118	cycle 2 miles		168	.048			2.64	2.49	5.13	6.70
0120	cycle 4 miles		120	.067			3.70	3.48	7.18	9.35
0122	cycle 6 miles		96	.083			4.62	4.35	8.97	11.70
0124	cycle 8 miles		80	.100			5.55	5.20	10.75	14.05
0126	20 MPH avg., cycle 0.5 mile		232	.034			1.91	1.80	3.71	4.84
0128	cycle 1 mile		208	.038			2.13	2.01	4.14	5.40
0130	cycle 2 miles		184	.043			2.41	2.27	4.68	6.10
0132	cycle 4 miles		144	.056			3.08	2.90	5.98	7.80
0134	cycle 6 miles		112	.071			3.96	3.73	7.69	10
0136	cycle 8 miles		96	.083			4.62	4.35	8.97	11.70
0144	25 MPH avg., cycle 4 miles		152	.053			2.92	2.75	5.67	7.40
0146	cycle 6 miles		128	.063			3.47	3.26	6.73	8.80
0148	cycle 8 miles		112	.071			3.96	3.73	7.69	10
0150	30 MPH avg., cycle 4 miles		168	.048			2.64	2.49	5.13	6.70
0152	cycle 6 miles		144	.056			3.08	2.90	5.98	7.80
0154	cycle 8 miles		120	.067			3.70	3.48	7.18	9.35
0214	15 MPH avg., cycle 0.5 mile, 20 min. wait/ld./uld.		176	.045			2.52	2.37	4.89	6.40
0216	cycle 1 mile		160	.050			2.77	2.61	5.38	7
0218	cycle 2 miles		136	.059			3.26	3.07	6.33	8.25
0220	cycle 4 miles		104	.077			4.27	4.01	8.28	10.75
0222	cycle 6 miles		88	.091			5.05	4.74	9.79	12.75
0224	cycle 8 miles		72	.111			6.15	5.80	11.95	15.60
0226	20 MPH avg., cycle 0.5 mile		176	.045			2.52	2.37	4.89	6.40
0228	cycle 1 mile		168	.048			2.64	2.49	5.13	6.70
0230	cycle 2 miles		144	.056			3.08	2.90	5.98	7.80
0232	cycle 4 miles		120	.067			3.70	3.48	7.18	9.35
0234	cycle 6 miles		96	.083			4.62	4.35	8.97	11.70
0236	cycle 8 miles		88	.091			5.05	4.74	9.79	12.75
0244	25 MPH avg., cycle 4 miles		128	.063			3.47	3.26	6.73	8.80
0246	cycle 6 miles		112	.071			3.96	3.73	7.69	10
0248	cycle 8 miles		96	.083			4.62	4.35	8.97	11.70
0250	30 MPH avg., cycle 4 miles		136	.059			3.26	3.07	6.33	8.25
0252	cycle 6 miles		120	.067			3.70	3.48	7.18	9.35
0254	cycle 8 miles		104	.077			4.27	4.01	8.28	10.75
0314	15 MPH avg., cycle 0.5 mile, 25 min. wait/ld./uld.		144	.056			3.08	2.90	5.98	7.80
0316	cycle 1 mile		128	.063			3.47	3.26	6.73	8.80
0318	cycle 2 miles		112	.071			3.96	3.73	7.69	10

31 23 23.20 Hauling		Crew	Daily Output	Labor-Hours	Unit	Material	2023 Bare Costs Labor	Equipment	Total	Total Incl O&P
0320	cycle 4 miles	B-34A	96	.083	L.C.Y.		4.62	4.35	8.97	11.70
0322	cycle 6 miles		80	.100			5.55	5.20	10.75	14.05
0324	cycle 8 miles		64	.125			6.95	6.50	13.45	17.55
0326	20 MPH avg., cycle 0.5 mile		144	.056			3.08	2.90	5.98	7.80
0328	cycle 1 mile		136	.059			3.26	3.07	6.33	8.25
0330	cycle 2 miles		120	.067			3.70	3.48	7.18	9.35
0332	cycle 4 miles		104	.077			4.27	4.01	8.28	10.75
0334	cycle 6 miles		88	.091			5.05	4.74	9.79	12.75
0336	cycle 8 miles		80	.100			5.55	5.20	10.75	14.05
0344	25 MPH avg., cycle 4 miles		112	.071			3.96	3.73	7.69	10
0346	cycle 6 miles		96	.083			4.62	4.35	8.97	11.70
0348	cycle 8 miles		88	.091			5.05	4.74	9.79	12.75
0350	30 MPH avg., cycle 4 miles		112	.071			3.96	3.73	7.69	10
0352	cycle 6 miles		104	.077			4.27	4.01	8.28	10.75
0354	cycle 8 miles		96	.083			4.62	4.35	8.97	11.70
0414	15 MPH avg., cycle 0.5 mile, 30 min. wait/ld./uld.		120	.067			3.70	3.48	7.18	9.35
0416	cycle 1 mile		112	.071			3.96	3.73	7.69	10
0418	cycle 2 miles		96	.083			4.62	4.35	8.97	11.70
0420	cycle 4 miles		80	.100			5.55	5.20	10.75	14.05
0422	cycle 6 miles		72	.111			6.15	5.80	11.95	15.60
0424	cycle 8 miles		64	.125			6.95	6.50	13.45	17.55
0426	20 MPH avg., cycle 0.5 mile		120	.067			3.70	3.48	7.18	9.35
0428	cycle 1 mile		112	.071			3.96	3.73	7.69	10
0430	cycle 2 miles		104	.077			4.27	4.01	8.28	10.75
0432	cycle 4 miles		88	.091			5.05	4.74	9.79	12.75
0434	cycle 6 miles		80	.100			5.55	5.20	10.75	14.05
0436	cycle 8 miles		72	.111			6.15	5.80	11.95	15.60
0444	25 MPH avg., cycle 4 miles		96	.083			4.62	4.35	8.97	11.70
0446	cycle 6 miles		88	.091			5.05	4.74	9.79	12.75
0448	cycle 8 miles		80	.100			5.55	5.20	10.75	14.05
0450	30 MPH avg., cycle 4 miles		96	.083			4.62	4.35	8.97	11.70
0452	cycle 6 miles		88	.091			5.05	4.74	9.79	12.75
0454	cycle 8 miles		80	.100			5.55	5.20	10.75	14.05
0514	15 MPH avg., cycle 0.5 mile, 35 min. wait/ld./uld.		104	.077			4.27	4.01	8.28	10.75
0516	cycle 1 mile		96	.083			4.62	4.35	8.97	11.70
0518	cycle 2 miles		88	.091			5.05	4.74	9.79	12.75
0520	cycle 4 miles		72	.111			6.15	5.80	11.95	15.60
0522	cycle 6 miles		64	.125			6.95	6.50	13.45	17.55
0524	cycle 8 miles		56	.143			7.90	7.45	15.35	20
0526	20 MPH avg., cycle 0.5 mile		104	.077			4.27	4.01	8.28	10.75
0528	cycle 1 mile		96	.083			4.62	4.35	8.97	11.70
0530	cycle 2 miles		96	.083			4.62	4.35	8.97	11.70
0532	cycle 4 miles		80	.100			5.55	5.20	10.75	14.05
0534	cycle 6 miles		72	.111			6.15	5.80	11.95	15.60
0536	cycle 8 miles		64	.125			6.95	6.50	13.45	17.55
0544	25 MPH avg., cycle 4 miles		88	.091			5.05	4.74	9.79	12.75
0546	cycle 6 miles		80	.100			5.55	5.20	10.75	14.05
0548	cycle 8 miles		72	.111			6.15	5.80	11.95	15.60
0550	30 MPH avg., cycle 4 miles		88	.091			5.05	4.74	9.79	12.75
0552	cycle 6 miles		80	.100			5.55	5.20	10.75	14.05
0554	cycle 8 miles		72	.111			6.15	5.80	11.95	15.60
1014	12 C.Y. truck, cycle 0.5 mile, 15 MPH avg., 15 min. wait/ld./uld.	B-34B	336	.024			1.32	2.36	3.68	4.56
1016	cycle 1 mile		300	.027			1.48	2.64	4.12	5.10

31 23 23.20 Hauling		Crew	Daily Output	Labor-Hours	Unit	Material	2023 Bare Costs Labor	Equipment	Total	Total Incl O&P
1018	cycle 2 miles	B-34B	252	.032	L.C.Y.		1.76	3.14	4.90	6.10
1020	cycle 4 miles		180	.044			2.46	4.40	6.86	8.50
1022	cycle 6 miles		144	.056			3.08	5.50	8.58	10.65
1024	cycle 8 miles		120	.067			3.70	6.60	10.30	12.75
1025	cycle 10 miles		96	.083			4.62	8.25	12.87	15.95
1026	20 MPH avg., cycle 0.5 mile		348	.023			1.27	2.27	3.54	4.40
1028	cycle 1 mile		312	.026			1.42	2.54	3.96	4.91
1030	cycle 2 miles		276	.029			1.61	2.87	4.48	5.55
1032	cycle 4 miles		216	.037			2.05	3.66	5.71	7.10
1034	cycle 6 miles		168	.048			2.64	4.71	7.35	9.15
1036	cycle 8 miles		144	.056			3.08	5.50	8.58	10.65
1038	cycle 10 miles		120	.067			3.70	6.60	10.30	12.75
1040	25 MPH avg., cycle 4 miles		228	.035			1.95	3.47	5.42	6.75
1042	cycle 6 miles		192	.042			2.31	4.12	6.43	8
1044	cycle 8 miles		168	.048			2.64	4.71	7.35	9.15
1046	cycle 10 miles		144	.056			3.08	5.50	8.58	10.65
1050	30 MPH avg., cycle 4 miles		252	.032			1.76	3.14	4.90	6.10
1052	cycle 6 miles		216	.037			2.05	3.66	5.71	7.10
1054	cycle 8 miles		180	.044			2.46	4.40	6.86	8.50
1056	cycle 10 miles		156	.051			2.84	5.05	7.89	9.85
1060	35 MPH avg., cycle 4 miles		264	.030			1.68	3	4.68	5.80
1062	cycle 6 miles		228	.035			1.95	3.47	5.42	6.75
1064	cycle 8 miles		204	.039			2.17	3.88	6.05	7.50
1066	cycle 10 miles		180	.044			2.46	4.40	6.86	8.50
1068	cycle 20 miles		120	.067			3.70	6.60	10.30	12.75
1069	cycle 30 miles		84	.095			5.30	9.40	14.70	18.25
1070	cycle 40 miles		72	.111			6.15	11	17.15	21.50
1072	40 MPH avg., cycle 6 miles		240	.033			1.85	3.30	5.15	6.40
1074	cycle 8 miles		216	.037			2.05	3.66	5.71	7.10
1076	cycle 10 miles		192	.042			2.31	4.12	6.43	8
1078	cycle 20 miles		120	.067			3.70	6.60	10.30	12.75
1080	cycle 30 miles		96	.083			4.62	8.25	12.87	15.95
1082	cycle 40 miles		72	.111			6.15	11	17.15	21.50
1084	cycle 50 miles		60	.133			7.40	13.20	20.60	25.50
1094	45 MPH avg., cycle 8 miles		216	.037			2.05	3.66	5.71	7.10
1096	cycle 10 miles		204	.039			2.17	3.88	6.05	7.50
1098	cycle 20 miles		132	.061			3.36	6	9.36	11.60
1100	cycle 30 miles		108	.074			4.11	7.35	11.46	14.20
1102	cycle 40 miles		84	.095			5.30	9.40	14.70	18.25
1104	cycle 50 miles		72	.111			6.15	11	17.15	21.50
1106	50 MPH avg., cycle 10 miles		216	.037			2.05	3.66	5.71	7.10
1108	cycle 20 miles		144	.056			3.08	5.50	8.58	10.65
1110	cycle 30 miles		108	.074			4.11	7.35	11.46	14.20
1112	cycle 40 miles		84	.095			5.30	9.40	14.70	18.25
1114	cycle 50 miles		72	.111			6.15	11	17.15	21.50
1214	15 MPH avg., cycle 0.5 mile, 20 min. wait/ld./uld.		264	.030			1.68	3	4.68	5.80
1216	cycle 1 mile		240	.033			1.85	3.30	5.15	6.40
1218	cycle 2 miles		204	.039			2.17	3.88	6.05	7.50
1220	cycle 4 miles		156	.051			2.84	5.05	7.89	9.85
1222	cycle 6 miles		132	.061			3.36	6	9.36	11.60
1224	cycle 8 miles		108	.074			4.11	7.35	11.46	14.20
1225	cycle 10 miles		96	.083			4.62	8.25	12.87	15.95
1226	20 MPH avg., cycle 0.5 mile		264	.030			1.68	3	4.68	5.80

31 23 23.20 Hauling		Crew	Daily Output	Labor-Hours	Unit	Material	2023 Bare Costs Labor	Equipment	Total	Total Incl O&P
1228	cycle 1 mile	B-34B	252	.032	L.C.Y.		1.76	3.14	4.90	6.10
1230	cycle 2 miles		216	.037			2.05	3.66	5.71	7.10
1232	cycle 4 miles		180	.044			2.46	4.40	6.86	8.50
1234	cycle 6 miles		144	.056			3.08	5.50	8.58	10.65
1236	cycle 8 miles		132	.061			3.36	6	9.36	11.60
1238	cycle 10 miles		108	.074			4.11	7.35	11.46	14.20
1240	25 MPH avg., cycle 4 miles		192	.042			2.31	4.12	6.43	8
1242	cycle 6 miles		168	.048			2.64	4.71	7.35	9.15
1244	cycle 8 miles		144	.056			3.08	5.50	8.58	10.65
1246	cycle 10 miles		132	.061			3.36	6	9.36	11.60
1250	30 MPH avg., cycle 4 miles		204	.039			2.17	3.88	6.05	7.50
1252	cycle 6 miles		180	.044			2.46	4.40	6.86	8.50
1254	cycle 8 miles		156	.051			2.84	5.05	7.89	9.85
1256	cycle 10 miles		144	.056			3.08	5.50	8.58	10.65
1260	35 MPH avg., cycle 4 miles		216	.037			2.05	3.66	5.71	7.10
1262	cycle 6 miles		192	.042			2.31	4.12	6.43	8
1264	cycle 8 miles		168	.048			2.64	4.71	7.35	9.15
1266	cycle 10 miles		156	.051			2.84	5.05	7.89	9.85
1268	cycle 20 miles		108	.074			4.11	7.35	11.46	14.20
1269	cycle 30 miles		72	.111			6.15	11	17.15	21.50
1270	cycle 40 miles		60	.133			7.40	13.20	20.60	25.50
1272	40 MPH avg., cycle 6 miles		192	.042			2.31	4.12	6.43	8
1274	cycle 8 miles		180	.044			2.46	4.40	6.86	8.50
1276	cycle 10 miles		156	.051			2.84	5.05	7.89	9.85
1278	cycle 20 miles		108	.074			4.11	7.35	11.46	14.20
1280	cycle 30 miles		84	.095			5.30	9.40	14.70	18.25
1282	cycle 40 miles		72	.111			6.15	11	17.15	21.50
1284	cycle 50 miles		60	.133			7.40	13.20	20.60	25.50
1294	45 MPH avg., cycle 8 miles		180	.044			2.46	4.40	6.86	8.50
1296	cycle 10 miles		168	.048			2.64	4.71	7.35	9.15
1298	cycle 20 miles		120	.067			3.70	6.60	10.30	12.75
1300	cycle 30 miles		96	.083			4.62	8.25	12.87	15.95
1302	cycle 40 miles		72	.111			6.15	11	17.15	21.50
1304	cycle 50 miles		60	.133			7.40	13.20	20.60	25.50
1306	50 MPH avg., cycle 10 miles		180	.044			2.46	4.40	6.86	8.50
1308	cycle 20 miles		132	.061			3.36	6	9.36	11.60
1310	cycle 30 miles		96	.083			4.62	8.25	12.87	15.95
1312	cycle 40 miles		84	.095			5.30	9.40	14.70	18.25
1314	cycle 50 miles		72	.111			6.15	11	17.15	21.50
1414	15 MPH avg., cycle 0.5 mile, 25 min. wait/ld./uld.		204	.039			2.17	3.88	6.05	7.50
1416	cycle 1 mile		192	.042			2.31	4.12	6.43	8
1418	cycle 2 miles		168	.048			2.64	4.71	7.35	9.15
1420	cycle 4 miles		132	.061			3.36	6	9.36	11.60
1422	cycle 6 miles		120	.067			3.70	6.60	10.30	12.75
1424	cycle 8 miles		96	.083			4.62	8.25	12.87	15.95
1425	cycle 10 miles		84	.095			5.30	9.40	14.70	18.25
1426	20 MPH avg., cycle 0.5 mile		216	.037			2.05	3.66	5.71	7.10
1428	cycle 1 mile		204	.039			2.17	3.88	6.05	7.50
1430	cycle 2 miles		180	.044			2.46	4.40	6.86	8.50
1432	cycle 4 miles		156	.051			2.84	5.05	7.89	9.85
1434	cycle 6 miles		132	.061			3.36	6	9.36	11.60
1436	cycle 8 miles		120	.067			3.70	6.60	10.30	12.75
1438	cycle 10 miles		96	.083			4.62	8.25	12.87	15.95

31 23 23.20 Hauling		Crew	Daily Output	Labor-Hours	Unit	Material	2023 Bare Costs Labor	Equipment	Total	Total Incl O&P
1440	25 MPH avg., cycle 4 miles	B-34B	168	.048	L.C.Y.		2.64	4.71	7.35	9.15
1442	cycle 6 miles		144	.056			3.08	5.50	8.58	10.65
1444	cycle 8 miles		132	.061			3.36	6	9.36	11.60
1446	cycle 10 miles		108	.074			4.11	7.35	11.46	14.20
1450	30 MPH avg., cycle 4 miles		168	.048			2.64	4.71	7.35	9.15
1452	cycle 6 miles		156	.051			2.84	5.05	7.89	9.85
1454	cycle 8 miles		132	.061			3.36	6	9.36	11.60
1456	cycle 10 miles		120	.067			3.70	6.60	10.30	12.75
1460	35 MPH avg., cycle 4 miles		180	.044			2.46	4.40	6.86	8.50
1462	cycle 6 miles		156	.051			2.84	5.05	7.89	9.85
1464	cycle 8 miles		144	.056			3.08	5.50	8.58	10.65
1466	cycle 10 miles		132	.061			3.36	6	9.36	11.60
1468	cycle 20 miles		96	.083			4.62	8.25	12.87	15.95
1469	cycle 30 miles		72	.111			6.15	11	17.15	21.50
1470	cycle 40 miles		60	.133			7.40	13.20	20.60	25.50
1472	40 MPH avg., cycle 6 miles		168	.048			2.64	4.71	7.35	9.15
1474	cycle 8 miles		156	.051			2.84	5.05	7.89	9.85
1476	cycle 10 miles		144	.056			3.08	5.50	8.58	10.65
1478	cycle 20 miles		96	.083			4.62	8.25	12.87	15.95
1480	cycle 30 miles		84	.095			5.30	9.40	14.70	18.25
1482	cycle 40 miles		60	.133			7.40	13.20	20.60	25.50
1484	cycle 50 miles		60	.133			7.40	13.20	20.60	25.50
1494	45 MPH avg., cycle 8 miles		156	.051			2.84	5.05	7.89	9.85
1496	cycle 10 miles		144	.056			3.08	5.50	8.58	10.65
1498	cycle 20 miles		108	.074			4.11	7.35	11.46	14.20
1500	cycle 30 miles		84	.095			5.30	9.40	14.70	18.25
1502	cycle 40 miles		72	.111			6.15	11	17.15	21.50
1504	cycle 50 miles		60	.133			7.40	13.20	20.60	25.50
1506	50 MPH avg., cycle 10 miles		156	.051			2.84	5.05	7.89	9.85
1508	cycle 20 miles		120	.067			3.70	6.60	10.30	12.75
1510	cycle 30 miles		96	.083			4.62	8.25	12.87	15.95
1512	cycle 40 miles		72	.111			6.15	11	17.15	21.50
1514	cycle 50 miles		60	.133			7.40	13.20	20.60	25.50
1614	15 MPH avg., cycle 0.5 mile, 30 min. wait/ld./uld.		180	.044			2.46	4.40	6.86	8.50
1616	cycle 1 mile		168	.048			2.64	4.71	7.35	9.15
1618	cycle 2 miles		144	.056			3.08	5.50	8.58	10.65
1620	cycle 4 miles		120	.067			3.70	6.60	10.30	12.75
1622	cycle 6 miles		108	.074			4.11	7.35	11.46	14.20
1624	cycle 8 miles		84	.095			5.30	9.40	14.70	18.25
1625	cycle 10 miles		84	.095			5.30	9.40	14.70	18.25
1626	20 MPH avg., cycle 0.5 mile		180	.044			2.46	4.40	6.86	8.50
1628	cycle 1 mile		168	.048			2.64	4.71	7.35	9.15
1630	cycle 2 miles		156	.051			2.84	5.05	7.89	9.85
1632	cycle 4 miles		132	.061			3.36	6	9.36	11.60
1634	cycle 6 miles		120	.067			3.70	6.60	10.30	12.75
1636	cycle 8 miles		108	.074			4.11	7.35	11.46	14.20
1638	cycle 10 miles		96	.083			4.62	8.25	12.87	15.95
1640	25 MPH avg., cycle 4 miles		144	.056			3.08	5.50	8.58	10.65
1642	cycle 6 miles		132	.061			3.36	6	9.36	11.60
1644	cycle 8 miles		108	.074			4.11	7.35	11.46	14.20
1646	cycle 10 miles		108	.074			4.11	7.35	11.46	14.20
1650	30 MPH avg., cycle 4 miles		144	.056			3.08	5.50	8.58	10.65
1652	cycle 6 miles		132	.061			3.36	6	9.36	11.60

31 23 23.20 Hauling		Crew	Daily Output	Labor-Hours	Unit	Material	2023 Bare Costs Labor	Equipment	Total	Total Incl O&P
1654	cycle 8 miles	B-34B	120	.067	L.C.Y.		3.70	6.60	10.30	12.75
1656	cycle 10 miles		108	.074			4.11	7.35	11.46	14.20
1660	35 MPH avg., cycle 4 miles		156	.051			2.84	5.05	7.89	9.85
1662	cycle 6 miles		144	.056			3.08	5.50	8.58	10.65
1664	cycle 8 miles		132	.061			3.36	6	9.36	11.60
1666	cycle 10 miles		120	.067			3.70	6.60	10.30	12.75
1668	cycle 20 miles		84	.095			5.30	9.40	14.70	18.25
1669	cycle 30 miles		72	.111			6.15	11	17.15	21.50
1670	cycle 40 miles		60	.133			7.40	13.20	20.60	25.50
1672	40 MPH avg., cycle 6 miles		144	.056			3.08	5.50	8.58	10.65
1674	cycle 8 miles		132	.061			3.36	6	9.36	11.60
1676	cycle 10 miles		120	.067			3.70	6.60	10.30	12.75
1678	cycle 20 miles		96	.083			4.62	8.25	12.87	15.95
1680	cycle 30 miles		72	.111			6.15	11	17.15	21.50
1682	cycle 40 miles		60	.133			7.40	13.20	20.60	25.50
1684	cycle 50 miles		48	.167			9.25	16.50	25.75	32
1694	45 MPH avg., cycle 8 miles		144	.056			3.08	5.50	8.58	10.65
1696	cycle 10 miles		132	.061			3.36	6	9.36	11.60
1698	cycle 20 miles		96	.083			4.62	8.25	12.87	15.95
1700	cycle 30 miles		84	.095			5.30	9.40	14.70	18.25
1702	cycle 40 miles		60	.133			7.40	13.20	20.60	25.50
1704	cycle 50 miles		60	.133			7.40	13.20	20.60	25.50
1706	50 MPH avg., cycle 10 miles		132	.061			3.36	6	9.36	11.60
1708	cycle 20 miles		108	.074			4.11	7.35	11.46	14.20
1710	cycle 30 miles		84	.095			5.30	9.40	14.70	18.25
1712	cycle 40 miles		72	.111			6.15	11	17.15	21.50
1714	cycle 50 miles		60	.133			7.40	13.20	20.60	25.50
2000	Hauling, 8 C.Y. truck, small project cost per hour	B-34A	8	1	Hr.		55.50	52	107.50	141
2100	12 C.Y. truck	B-34B	8	1			55.50	99	154.50	192
2150	16.5 C.Y. truck	B-34C	8	1			55.50	87	142.50	179
2175	18 C.Y. 8 wheel truck	B-34I	8	1			55.50	98.50	154	191
2200	20 C.Y. truck	B-34D	8	1			55.50	89.50	145	182
2300	Grading at dump, or embankment if required, by dozer	B-10B	1000	.012	L.C.Y.		.69	1.38	2.07	2.55
2310	Spotter at fill or cut, if required	1 Clab	8	1	Hr.		47.50		47.50	70.50
9014	18 C.Y. truck, 8 wheels,15 min. wait/ld./uld.,15 MPH, cycle 0.5 mi.	B-34I	504	.016	L.C.Y.		.88	1.56	2.44	3.04
9016	cycle 1 mile		450	.018			.99	1.75	2.74	3.40
9018	cycle 2 miles		378	.021			1.17	2.09	3.26	4.04
9020	cycle 4 miles		270	.030			1.64	2.92	4.56	5.65
9022	cycle 6 miles		216	.037			2.05	3.65	5.70	7.10
9024	cycle 8 miles		180	.044			2.46	4.38	6.84	8.50
9025	cycle 10 miles		144	.056			3.08	5.50	8.58	10.60
9026	20 MPH avg., cycle 0.5 mile		522	.015			.85	1.51	2.36	2.93
9028	cycle 1 mile		468	.017			.95	1.68	2.63	3.27
9030	cycle 2 miles		414	.019			1.07	1.90	2.97	3.69
9032	cycle 4 miles		324	.025			1.37	2.43	3.80	4.73
9034	cycle 6 miles		252	.032			1.76	3.13	4.89	6.05
9036	cycle 8 miles		216	.037			2.05	3.65	5.70	7.10
9038	cycle 10 miles		180	.044			2.46	4.38	6.84	8.50
9040	25 MPH avg., cycle 4 miles		342	.023			1.30	2.31	3.61	4.48
9042	cycle 6 miles		288	.028			1.54	2.74	4.28	5.30
9044	cycle 8 miles		252	.032			1.76	3.13	4.89	6.05
9046	cycle 10 miles		216	.037			2.05	3.65	5.70	7.10
9050	30 MPH avg., cycle 4 miles		378	.021			1.17	2.09	3.26	4.04

31 23 23 – Fill

31 23 23.20 Hauling		Crew	Daily Output	Labor-Hours	Unit	Material	2023 Bare Costs Labor	Equipment	Total	Total Incl O&P
9052	cycle 6 miles	B-34I	324	.025	L.C.Y.		1.37	2.43	3.80	4.73
9054	cycle 8 miles		270	.030			1.64	2.92	4.56	5.65
9056	cycle 10 miles		234	.034			1.90	3.37	5.27	6.55
9060	35 MPH avg., cycle 4 miles		396	.020			1.12	1.99	3.11	3.86
9062	cycle 6 miles		342	.023			1.30	2.31	3.61	4.48
9064	cycle 8 miles		288	.028			1.54	2.74	4.28	5.30
9066	cycle 10 miles		270	.030			1.64	2.92	4.56	5.65
9068	cycle 20 miles		162	.049			2.74	4.87	7.61	9.45
9070	cycle 30 miles		126	.063			3.52	6.25	9.77	12.15
9072	cycle 40 miles		90	.089			4.93	8.75	13.68	17
9074	40 MPH avg., cycle 6 miles		360	.022			1.23	2.19	3.42	4.25
9076	cycle 8 miles		324	.025			1.37	2.43	3.80	4.73
9078	cycle 10 miles		288	.028			1.54	2.74	4.28	5.30
9080	cycle 20 miles		180	.044			2.46	4.38	6.84	8.50
9082	cycle 30 miles		144	.056			3.08	5.50	8.58	10.60
9084	cycle 40 miles		108	.074			4.11	7.30	11.41	14.20
9086	cycle 50 miles		90	.089			4.93	8.75	13.68	17
9094	45 MPH avg., cycle 8 miles		324	.025			1.37	2.43	3.80	4.73
9096	cycle 10 miles		306	.026			1.45	2.58	4.03	5
9098	cycle 20 miles		198	.040			2.24	3.98	6.22	7.75
9100	cycle 30 miles		144	.056			3.08	5.50	8.58	10.60
9102	cycle 40 miles		126	.063			3.52	6.25	9.77	12.15
9104	cycle 50 miles		108	.074			4.11	7.30	11.41	14.20
9106	50 MPH avg., cycle 10 miles		324	.025			1.37	2.43	3.80	4.73
9108	cycle 20 miles		216	.037			2.05	3.65	5.70	7.10
9110	cycle 30 miles		162	.049			2.74	4.87	7.61	9.45
9112	cycle 40 miles		126	.063			3.52	6.25	9.77	12.15
9114	cycle 50 miles		108	.074			4.11	7.30	11.41	14.20
9214	20 min. wait/ld./uld.,15 MPH, cycle 0.5 mi.		396	.020			1.12	1.99	3.11	3.86
9216	cycle 1 mile		360	.022			1.23	2.19	3.42	4.25
9218	cycle 2 miles		306	.026			1.45	2.58	4.03	5
9220	cycle 4 miles		234	.034			1.90	3.37	5.27	6.55
9222	cycle 6 miles		198	.040			2.24	3.98	6.22	7.75
9224	cycle 8 miles		162	.049			2.74	4.87	7.61	9.45
9225	cycle 10 miles		144	.056			3.08	5.50	8.58	10.60
9226	20 MPH avg., cycle 0.5 mile		396	.020			1.12	1.99	3.11	3.86
9228	cycle 1 mile		378	.021			1.17	2.09	3.26	4.04
9230	cycle 2 miles		324	.025			1.37	2.43	3.80	4.73
9232	cycle 4 miles		270	.030			1.64	2.92	4.56	5.65
9234	cycle 6 miles		216	.037			2.05	3.65	5.70	7.10
9236	cycle 8 miles		198	.040			2.24	3.98	6.22	7.75
9238	cycle 10 miles		162	.049			2.74	4.87	7.61	9.45
9240	25 MPH avg., cycle 4 miles		288	.028			1.54	2.74	4.28	5.30
9242	cycle 6 miles		252	.032			1.76	3.13	4.89	6.05
9244	cycle 8 miles		216	.037			2.05	3.65	5.70	7.10
9246	cycle 10 miles		198	.040			2.24	3.98	6.22	7.75
9250	30 MPH avg., cycle 4 miles		306	.026			1.45	2.58	4.03	5
9252	cycle 6 miles		270	.030			1.64	2.92	4.56	5.65
9254	cycle 8 miles		234	.034			1.90	3.37	5.27	6.55
9256	cycle 10 miles		216	.037			2.05	3.65	5.70	7.10
9260	35 MPH avg., cycle 4 miles		324	.025			1.37	2.43	3.80	4.73
9262	cycle 6 miles		288	.028			1.54	2.74	4.28	5.30
9264	cycle 8 miles		252	.032			1.76	3.13	4.89	6.05

31 23 23.20 Hauling		Crew	Daily Output	Labor-Hours	Unit	Material	2023 Bare Costs Labor	Equipment	Total	Total Incl O&P
9266	cycle 10 miles	B-34I	234	.034	L.C.Y.		1.90	3.37	5.27	6.55
9268	cycle 20 miles		162	.049			2.74	4.87	7.61	9.45
9270	cycle 30 miles		108	.074			4.11	7.30	11.41	14.20
9272	cycle 40 miles		90	.089			4.93	8.75	13.68	17
9274	40 MPH avg., cycle 6 miles		288	.028			1.54	2.74	4.28	5.30
9276	cycle 8 miles		270	.030			1.64	2.92	4.56	5.65
9278	cycle 10 miles		234	.034			1.90	3.37	5.27	6.55
9280	cycle 20 miles		162	.049			2.74	4.87	7.61	9.45
9282	cycle 30 miles		126	.063			3.52	6.25	9.77	12.15
9284	cycle 40 miles		108	.074			4.11	7.30	11.41	14.20
9286	cycle 50 miles		90	.089			4.93	8.75	13.68	17
9294	45 MPH avg., cycle 8 miles		270	.030			1.64	2.92	4.56	5.65
9296	cycle 10 miles		252	.032			1.76	3.13	4.89	6.05
9298	cycle 20 miles		180	.044			2.46	4.38	6.84	8.50
9300	cycle 30 miles		144	.056			3.08	5.50	8.58	10.60
9302	cycle 40 miles		108	.074			4.11	7.30	11.41	14.20
9304	cycle 50 miles		90	.089			4.93	8.75	13.68	17
9306	50 MPH avg., cycle 10 miles		270	.030			1.64	2.92	4.56	5.65
9308	cycle 20 miles		198	.040			2.24	3.98	6.22	7.75
9310	cycle 30 miles		144	.056			3.08	5.50	8.58	10.60
9312	cycle 40 miles		126	.063			3.52	6.25	9.77	12.15
9314	cycle 50 miles		108	.074			4.11	7.30	11.41	14.20
9414	25 min. wait/ld./uld.,15 MPH, cycle 0.5 mi.		306	.026			1.45	2.58	4.03	5
9416	cycle 1 mile		288	.028			1.54	2.74	4.28	5.30
9418	cycle 2 miles		252	.032			1.76	3.13	4.89	6.05
9420	cycle 4 miles		198	.040			2.24	3.98	6.22	7.75
9422	cycle 6 miles		180	.044			2.46	4.38	6.84	8.50
9424	cycle 8 miles		144	.056			3.08	5.50	8.58	10.60
9425	cycle 10 miles		126	.063			3.52	6.25	9.77	12.15
9426	20 MPH avg., cycle 0.5 mile		324	.025			1.37	2.43	3.80	4.73
9428	cycle 1 mile		306	.026			1.45	2.58	4.03	5
9430	cycle 2 miles		270	.030			1.64	2.92	4.56	5.65
9432	cycle 4 miles		234	.034			1.90	3.37	5.27	6.55
9434	cycle 6 miles		198	.040			2.24	3.98	6.22	7.75
9436	cycle 8 miles		180	.044			2.46	4.38	6.84	8.50
9438	cycle 10 miles		144	.056			3.08	5.50	8.58	10.60
9440	25 MPH avg., cycle 4 miles		252	.032			1.76	3.13	4.89	6.05
9442	cycle 6 miles		216	.037			2.05	3.65	5.70	7.10
9444	cycle 8 miles		198	.040			2.24	3.98	6.22	7.75
9446	cycle 10 miles		180	.044			2.46	4.38	6.84	8.50
9450	30 MPH avg., cycle 4 miles		252	.032			1.76	3.13	4.89	6.05
9452	cycle 6 miles		234	.034			1.90	3.37	5.27	6.55
9454	cycle 8 miles		198	.040			2.24	3.98	6.22	7.75
9456	cycle 10 miles		180	.044			2.46	4.38	6.84	8.50
9460	35 MPH avg., cycle 4 miles		270	.030			1.64	2.92	4.56	5.65
9462	cycle 6 miles		234	.034			1.90	3.37	5.27	6.55
9464	cycle 8 miles		216	.037			2.05	3.65	5.70	7.10
9466	cycle 10 miles		198	.040			2.24	3.98	6.22	7.75
9468	cycle 20 miles		144	.056			3.08	5.50	8.58	10.60
9470	cycle 30 miles		108	.074			4.11	7.30	11.41	14.20
9472	cycle 40 miles		90	.089			4.93	8.75	13.68	17
9474	40 MPH avg., cycle 6 miles		252	.032			1.76	3.13	4.89	6.05
9476	cycle 8 miles	↓	234	.034	↓		1.90	3.37	5.27	6.55

31 23 23.20 Hauling		Crew	Daily Output	Labor-Hours	Unit	Material	2023 Bare Costs Labor	Equipment	Total	Total Incl O&P
9478	cycle 10 miles	B-34I	216	.037	L.C.Y.		2.05	3.65	5.70	7.10
9480	cycle 20 miles		144	.056			3.08	5.50	8.58	10.60
9482	cycle 30 miles		126	.063			3.52	6.25	9.77	12.15
9484	cycle 40 miles		90	.089			4.93	8.75	13.68	17
9486	cycle 50 miles		90	.089			4.93	8.75	13.68	17
9494	45 MPH avg., cycle 8 miles		234	.034			1.90	3.37	5.27	6.55
9496	cycle 10 miles		216	.037			2.05	3.65	5.70	7.10
9498	cycle 20 miles		162	.049			2.74	4.87	7.61	9.45
9500	cycle 30 miles		126	.063			3.52	6.25	9.77	12.15
9502	cycle 40 miles		108	.074			4.11	7.30	11.41	14.20
9504	cycle 50 miles		90	.089			4.93	8.75	13.68	17
9506	50 MPH avg., cycle 10 miles		234	.034			1.90	3.37	5.27	6.55
9508	cycle 20 miles		180	.044			2.46	4.38	6.84	8.50
9510	cycle 30 miles		144	.056			3.08	5.50	8.58	10.60
9512	cycle 40 miles		108	.074			4.11	7.30	11.41	14.20
9514	cycle 50 miles		90	.089			4.93	8.75	13.68	17
9614	30 min. wait/ld./uld.,15 MPH, cycle 0.5 mi.		270	.030			1.64	2.92	4.56	5.65
9616	cycle 1 mile		252	.032			1.76	3.13	4.89	6.05
9618	cycle 2 miles		216	.037			2.05	3.65	5.70	7.10
9620	cycle 4 miles		180	.044			2.46	4.38	6.84	8.50
9622	cycle 6 miles		162	.049			2.74	4.87	7.61	9.45
9624	cycle 8 miles		126	.063			3.52	6.25	9.77	12.15
9625	cycle 10 miles		126	.063			3.52	6.25	9.77	12.15
9626	20 MPH avg., cycle 0.5 mile		270	.030			1.64	2.92	4.56	5.65
9628	cycle 1 mile		252	.032			1.76	3.13	4.89	6.05
9630	cycle 2 miles		234	.034			1.90	3.37	5.27	6.55
9632	cycle 4 miles		198	.040			2.24	3.98	6.22	7.75
9634	cycle 6 miles		180	.044			2.46	4.38	6.84	8.50
9636	cycle 8 miles		162	.049			2.74	4.87	7.61	9.45
9638	cycle 10 miles		144	.056			3.08	5.50	8.58	10.60
9640	25 MPH avg., cycle 4 miles		216	.037			2.05	3.65	5.70	7.10
9642	cycle 6 miles		198	.040			2.24	3.98	6.22	7.75
9644	cycle 8 miles		180	.044			2.46	4.38	6.84	8.50
9646	cycle 10 miles		162	.049			2.74	4.87	7.61	9.45
9650	30 MPH avg., cycle 4 miles		216	.037			2.05	3.65	5.70	7.10
9652	cycle 6 miles		198	.040			2.24	3.98	6.22	7.75
9654	cycle 8 miles		180	.044			2.46	4.38	6.84	8.50
9656	cycle 10 miles		162	.049			2.74	4.87	7.61	9.45
9660	35 MPH avg., cycle 4 miles		234	.034			1.90	3.37	5.27	6.55
9662	cycle 6 miles		216	.037			2.05	3.65	5.70	7.10
9664	cycle 8 miles		198	.040			2.24	3.98	6.22	7.75
9666	cycle 10 miles		180	.044			2.46	4.38	6.84	8.50
9668	cycle 20 miles		126	.063			3.52	6.25	9.77	12.15
9670	cycle 30 miles		108	.074			4.11	7.30	11.41	14.20
9672	cycle 40 miles		90	.089			4.93	8.75	13.68	17
9674	40 MPH avg., cycle 6 miles		216	.037			2.05	3.65	5.70	7.10
9676	cycle 8 miles		198	.040			2.24	3.98	6.22	7.75
9678	cycle 10 miles		180	.044			2.46	4.38	6.84	8.50
9680	cycle 20 miles		144	.056			3.08	5.50	8.58	10.60
9682	cycle 30 miles		108	.074			4.11	7.30	11.41	14.20
9684	cycle 40 miles		90	.089			4.93	8.75	13.68	17
9686	cycle 50 miles		72	.111			6.15	10.95	17.10	21.50
9694	45 MPH avg., cycle 8 miles		216	.037			2.05	3.65	5.70	7.10

31 23 23.20 Hauling		Crew	Daily Output	Labor-Hours	Unit	2023 Bare Costs Material	Labor	Equipment	Total	Total Incl O&P
9696	cycle 10 miles	B-34I	198	.040	L.C.Y.		2.24	3.98	6.22	7.75
9698	cycle 20 miles		144	.056			3.08	5.50	8.58	10.60
9700	cycle 30 miles		126	.063			3.52	6.25	9.77	12.15
9702	cycle 40 miles		108	.074			4.11	7.30	11.41	14.20
9704	cycle 50 miles		90	.089			4.93	8.75	13.68	17
9706	50 MPH avg., cycle 10 miles		198	.040			2.24	3.98	6.22	7.75
9708	cycle 20 miles		162	.049			2.74	4.87	7.61	9.45
9710	cycle 30 miles		126	.063			3.52	6.25	9.77	12.15
9712	cycle 40 miles		108	.074			4.11	7.30	11.41	14.20
9714	cycle 50 miles	↓	90	.089	↓		4.93	8.75	13.68	17

31 23 23.23 Compaction		Crew	Daily Output	Labor-Hours	Unit	Material	Labor	Equipment	Total	Total Incl O&P
0010	**COMPACTION**									
7000	Walk behind, vibrating plate 18" wide, 6" lifts, 2 passes	A-1D	200	.040	B.C.Y.		1.89	.72	2.61	3.60
7020	3 passes		185	.043			2.04	.78	2.82	3.90
7040	4 passes	↓	140	.057	↓		2.70	1.03	3.73	5.15

Estimating Tips

32 01 00 Operations and Maintenance of Exterior Improvements

- Recycling of asphalt pavement is becoming very popular and is an alternative to removal and replacement. It can be a good value engineering proposal if removed pavement can be recycled, either at the project site or at another site that is reasonably close to the project site. Sections on repair of flexible and rigid pavement are included.

32 10 00 Bases, Ballasts, and Paving

- When estimating paving, keep in mind the project schedule. Also note that prices for asphalt and concrete are generally higher in the cold seasons. Lines for pavement markings, including tactile warning systems and fence lines, are included.

32 90 00 Planting

- The timing of planting and guarantee specifications often dictate the costs for establishing tree and shrub growth and a stand of grass or ground cover. Establish the work performance schedule to coincide with the local planting season. Maintenance and growth guarantees can add 20–100% to the total landscaping cost and can be contractually cumbersome. The cost to replace trees and shrubs can be as high as 5% of the total cost, depending on the planting zone, soil conditions, and time of year.

Reference Numbers

Reference numbers are shown at the beginning of some major classifications. These numbers refer to related items in the Reference Section. The reference information may be an estimating procedure, an alternate pricing method, or technical information.

Note: Not all subdivisions listed here necessarily appear. ■

32 31 Fences and Gates

32 31 13 – Chain Link Fences and Gates

32 31 13.30 Fence, Chain Link, Gates and Posts		Crew	Daily Output	Labor-Hours	Unit	Material	2023 Bare Costs Labor	Equipment	Total	Total Incl O&P
0010	**FENCE, CHAIN LINK, GATES & POSTS**									
0011	(1/3 post length in ground)									
0013	For Concrete, See Section 03 31									
6710	Corner post, galv. steel, 4" OD, set in conc., 4'	B-80	65	.492	Ea.	78	25.50	8.40	111.90	134
6715	6'		63	.508		167	26.50	8.65	202.15	232
6720	7'		61	.525		199	27.50	8.95	235.45	270
6725	8'	↓	65	.492		283	25.50	8.40	316.90	360
7900	Auger fence post hole, 3' deep, medium soil, by hand	1 Clab	30	.267			12.60		12.60	18.75
7925	By machine	B-80	175	.183			9.55	3.11	12.66	17.65
7950	Rock, with jackhammer	B-9	32	1.250			59.50	9.75	69.25	99.50
7975	With rock drill	B-47C	65	.246	↓		13.15	30	43.15	52.50

Estimating Tips

33 10 00 Water Utilities
33 30 00 Sanitary Sewerage Utilities
33 40 00 Storm Drainage Utilities

- Never assume that the water, sewer, and drainage lines will go in at the early stages of the project – both site and project specific conditions must be taken into consideration when assessing the cost implications for utility work, with particular attention paid to the scheduling of works. Consider the site access needs before dividing the site in half with open trenches, loose pipe, and machinery obstructions. Always inspect the site to establish that the site drawings are complete. Check off all existing utilities on your drawings as you locate them. Be especially careful with underground utilities because appurtenances are sometimes buried during regrading or repaving operations. If you find any discrepancies, mark up the site plan for further research. Differing site conditions can be very costly if discovered later in the project.
- See also Section 33 01 00 for restoration of pipe where removal/replacement may be undesirable. Use of new types of piping materials can reduce the overall project cost. Owners/design engineers should consider the installing contractor as a valuable source of current information on utility products and local conditions that could lead to significant cost savings.

Reference Numbers

Reference numbers are shown at the beginning of some major classifications. These numbers refer to related items in the Reference Section. The reference information may be an estimating procedure, an alternate pricing method, or technical information.

Note: Not all subdivisions listed here necessarily appear. ■

Note: "Powered in part by CINX™, based on licensed proprietary information of Harrison Publishing House, Inc."

Note: Trade Service, in part, has been used as a reference source for some of the material prices used in Division 33

33 05 07 – Trenchless Installation of Utility Piping

33 05 07.13 Utility Directional Drilling		Crew	Daily Output	Labor-Hours	Unit	Material	2023 Bare Costs Labor	Equipment	Total	Total Incl O&P
0010	**UTILITY DIRECTIONAL DRILLING**									
0011	Excluding access and splice pits (if required) and conduit (required)									
0012	Drilled hole diameters shown should be 50% larger than conduit									
0013	Assume access to H20 & removal of spoil/drilling mud as non-hazard material									
0014	Actual production rates adj. to account for risk factors for each soil type									
0100	Sand, silt, clay, common earth									
0110	Mobilization or demobilization	B-82A	1	32	Ea.		1,700	3,075	4,775	5,925
0120	6″ diameter		180	.178	L.F.		9.50	17.05	26.55	33
0130	12″ diameter		70	.457			24.50	44	68.50	84.50
0140	18″ diameter		50	.640			34	61.50	95.50	119
0150	24″ diameter		35	.914			49	87.50	136.50	170
0210	Mobilization or demobilization	B-82B	1	32	Ea.		1,700	3,125	4,825	5,975
0220	6″ diameter		125	.256	L.F.		13.70	25	38.70	48
0230	12″ diameter		50	.640			34	62.50	96.50	120
0240	18″ diameter		30	1.067			57	104	161	200
0250	24″ diameter		25	1.280			68.50	125	193.50	239
0260	30″ diameter		20	1.600			85.50	156	241.50	299
0270	36″ diameter		15	2.133			114	208	322	400
0300	Hard rock (solid bed, 24,000+ psi)									
0310	Mobilization or demobilization	B-82C	1	32	Ea.		1,700	3,250	4,950	6,125
0320	6″ diameter		30	1.067	L.F.		57	108	165	204
0330	12″ diameter		12	2.667			143	271	414	510
0340	18″ diameter		8	4			214	405	619	765
0344	20″ diameter		7.50	4.267			228	435	663	815
0350	24″ diameter		7	4.571			244	465	709	875
0360	30″ diameter		6	5.333			285	540	825	1,025
0370	36″ diameter		4.50	7.111			380	725	1,105	1,350

33 05 07.23 Utility Boring and Jacking		Crew	Daily Output	Labor-Hours	Unit	Material	Labor	Equipment	Total	Total Incl O&P
0010	**UTILITY BORING AND JACKING**									
0011	Casing only, 100′ minimum,									
0020	not incl. jacking pits or dewatering									
0100	Roadwork, 1/2″ thick wall, 24″ diameter casing	B-42	20	3.200	L.F.	163	170	143	476	590
0200	36″ diameter		16	4		252	213	179	644	795
0300	48″ diameter		15	4.267		350	227	191	768	935
0500	Railroad work, 24″ diameter		15	4.267		163	227	191	581	730
0600	36″ diameter		14	4.571		252	243	204	699	865
0700	48″ diameter		12	5.333		350	284	238	872	1,075
0900	For ledge, add								20%	20%
1000	Small diameter boring, 3″, sandy soil	B-82	900	.018		44.50	.95	.13	45.58	50.50
1040	Rocky soil	″	500	.032		44.50	1.71	.23	46.44	52
1100	Prepare jacking pits, incl. mobilization & demobilization, minimum				Ea.				3,225	3,700
1101	Maximum				″				22,000	25,500

33 05 07.36 Microtunneling		Crew	Daily Output	Labor-Hours	Unit	Material	Labor	Equipment	Total	Total Incl O&P
0010	**MICROTUNNELING**									
0011	Not including excavation, backfill, shoring,									
0020	or dewatering, average 50′/day, slurry method									
0100	24″ to 48″ outside diameter, minimum				L.F.				965	965
0110	Adverse conditions, add				″				500	500
1000	Rent microtunneling machine, average monthly lease				Month				97,500	107,000
1010	Operating technician				Day				630	705
1100	Mobilization and demobilization, minimum				Job				41,200	45,900
1110	Maximum				″				445,500	490,500

33 05 61 – Concrete Manholes

33 05 61.10 Storm Drainage Manholes, Frames and Covers		Crew	Daily Output	Labor-Hours	Unit	2023 Bare Costs Material	Labor	Equipment	Total	Total Incl O&P
0010	**STORM DRAINAGE MANHOLES, FRAMES & COVERS**									
0020	Excludes footing, excavation, backfill (See line items for frame & cover)									
0050	Brick, 4′ inside diameter, 4′ deep	D-1	1	16	Ea.	1,475	835		2,310	2,875
0100	6′ deep		.70	22.857		2,175	1,200		3,375	4,150
0150	8′ deep		.50	32		2,825	1,675		4,500	5,625
0200	Add for 1′ depth increase		4	4	V.L.F.	370	208		578	725
0400	Concrete blocks (radial), 4′ ID, 4′ deep		1.50	10.667	Ea.	480	555		1,035	1,350
0500	6′ deep		1	16		625	835		1,460	1,925
0600	8′ deep		.70	22.857		770	1,200		1,970	2,625
0700	For depths over 8′, add		5.50	2.909	V.L.F.	76	152		228	310
0800	Concrete, cast in place, 4′ x 4′, 8″ thick, 4′ deep	C-14H	2	24	Ea.	785	1,375	14.90	2,174.90	2,925
0900	6′ deep		1.50	32		1,150	1,850	19.85	3,019.85	4,000
1000	8′ deep		1	48		1,625	2,750	30	4,405	5,925
1100	For depths over 8′, add		8	6	V.L.F.	199	345	3.72	547.72	735
1110	Precast, 4′ ID, 4′ deep	B-22	4.10	7.317	Ea.	1,225	405	70.50	1,700.50	2,000
1120	6′ deep		3	10		1,475	555	96.50	2,126.50	2,550
1130	8′ deep		2	15		1,875	830	145	2,850	3,475
1140	For depths over 8′, add		16	1.875	V.L.F.	167	104	18.10	289.10	360
1150	5′ ID, 4′ deep	B-6	3	8	Ea.	2,325	410	92.50	2,827.50	3,250
1160	6′ deep		2	12		2,850	615	139	3,604	4,200
1170	8′ deep		1.50	16		3,375	820	185	4,380	5,150
1180	For depths over 8′, add		12	2	V.L.F.	340	103	23	466	555
1190	6′ ID, 4′ deep		2	12	Ea.	4,100	615	139	4,854	5,600
1200	6′ deep		1.50	16		4,100	820	185	5,105	5,925
1210	8′ deep		1	24		4,800	1,225	277	6,302	7,400
1220	For depths over 8′, add		8	3	V.L.F.	440	154	34.50	628.50	755
1250	Slab tops, precast, 8″ thick									
1300	4′ diameter manhole	B-6	8	3	Ea.	285	154	34.50	473.50	585
1400	5′ diameter manhole		7.50	3.200		540	164	37	741	880
1500	6′ diameter manhole		7	3.429		925	176	39.50	1,140.50	1,325
3800	Steps, heavyweight cast iron, 7″ x 9″	1 Bric	40	.200		21	11.50		32.50	40.50
3900	8″ x 9″		40	.200		25	11.50		36.50	45
3928	12″ x 10-1/2″		40	.200		86	11.50		97.50	112
4000	Standard sizes, galvanized steel		40	.200		29	11.50		40.50	49.50
4100	Aluminum		40	.200		37	11.50		48.50	58.50
4150	Polyethylene		40	.200		36	11.50		47.50	57

33 05 63 – Concrete Vaults and Chambers

33 05 63.13 Precast Concrete Utility Structures		Crew	Daily Output	Labor-Hours	Unit	Material	Labor	Equipment	Total	Total Incl O&P
0010	**PRECAST CONCRETE UTILITY STRUCTURES**, 6″ thick									
0050	5′ x 10′ x 6′ high, ID	B-13	2	28	Ea.	2,100	1,450	1,125	4,675	5,700
0100	6′ x 10′ x 6′ high, ID		2	28		2,175	1,450	1,125	4,750	5,800
0150	5′ x 12′ x 6′ high, ID		2	28		2,300	1,450	1,125	4,875	5,950
0200	6′ x 12′ x 6′ high, ID		1.80	31.111		2,575	1,600	1,275	5,450	6,650
0250	6′ x 13′ x 6′ high, ID		1.50	37.333		3,400	1,925	1,525	6,850	8,275
0300	8′ x 14′ x 7′ high, ID		1	56		3,675	2,875	2,275	8,825	10,800

33 05 97 – Identification and Signage for Utilities

33 05 97.05 Utility Connection		Crew	Daily Output	Labor-Hours	Unit	Material	Labor	Equipment	Total	Total Incl O&P
0010	**UTILITY CONNECTION**									
0020	Water, sanitary, stormwater, gas, single connection	B-14	1	48	Ea.	4,425	2,375	277	7,077	8,700
0030	Telecommunication	″	3	16	″	450	795	92.50	1,337.50	1,775

33 05 Common Work Results for Utilities

33 05 97 – Identification and Signage for Utilities

33 05 97.10 Utility Accessories		Crew	Daily Output	Labor-Hours	Unit	Material	2023 Bare Costs Labor	Equipment	Total	Total Incl O&P
0010	UTILITY ACCESSORIES									
0400	Underground tape, detectable, reinforced, alum. foil core, 2"	1 Clab	150	.053	C.L.F.	2	2.52		4.52	5.95

33 42 Stormwater Conveyance

33 42 33 – Stormwater Curbside Drains and Inlets

33 42 33.13 Catch Basins		Crew	Daily Output	Labor-Hours	Unit	Material	Labor	Equipment	Total	Total Incl O&P
0010	CATCH BASINS									
0011	Not including footing & excavation									
1600	Frames & grates, C.I., 24" square, 500 lb.	B-6	7.80	3.077	Ea.	1,050	158	35.50	1,243.50	1,425
1700	26" D shape, 600 lb.		7	3.429		1,950	176	39.50	2,165.50	2,450
1800	Light traffic, 18" diameter, 100 lb.		10	2.400		895	123	27.50	1,045.50	1,200
1900	24" diameter, 300 lb.		8.70	2.759		1,000	142	32	1,174	1,350
2000	36" diameter, 900 lb.		5.80	4.138		1,425	213	48	1,686	1,950
2100	Heavy traffic, 24" diameter, 400 lb.		7.80	3.077		945	158	35.50	1,138.50	1,325
2200	36" diameter, 1,150 lb.		3	8		2,900	410	92.50	3,402.50	3,875
2300	Mass. State standard, 26" diameter, 475 lb.		7	3.429		1,225	176	39.50	1,440.50	1,650
2400	30" diameter, 620 lb.		7	3.429		455	176	39.50	670.50	805
2500	Watertight, 24" diameter, 350 lb.		7.80	3.077		2,000	158	35.50	2,193.50	2,475
2600	26" diameter, 500 lb.		7	3.429		1,600	176	39.50	1,815.50	2,050
2700	32" diameter, 575 lb.	↓	6	4	↓	1,100	206	46	1,352	1,550
2800	3 piece cover & frame, 10" deep,									
2900	1,200 lb., for heavy equipment	B-6	3	8	Ea.	1,300	410	92.50	1,802.50	2,150
3000	Raised for paving 1-1/4" to 2" high									
3100	4 piece expansion ring									
3200	20" to 26" diameter	1 Clab	3	2.667	Ea.	269	126		395	485
3300	30" to 36" diameter	"	3	2.667	"	430	126		556	665
3320	Frames and covers, existing, raised for paving, 2", including									
3340	row of brick, concrete collar, up to 12" wide frame	B-6	18	1.333	Ea.	63	68.50	15.40	146.90	188
3360	20" to 26" wide frame		11	2.182		95	112	25	232	300
3380	30" to 36" wide frame	↓	9	2.667		118	137	31	286	370
3400	Inverts, single channel brick	D-1	3	5.333		136	278		414	565
3500	Concrete		5	3.200		165	167		332	430
3600	Triple channel, brick		2	8		224	415		639	870
3700	Concrete	↓	3	5.333	↓	187	278		465	620

33 71 Electrical Utility Transmission and Distribution

33 71 13 – Electrical Utility Towers

33 71 13.23 Steel Electrical Utility Towers		Crew	Daily Output	Labor-Hours	Unit	Material	Labor	Equipment	Total	Total Incl O&P
0010	STEEL ELECTRICAL UTILITY TOWERS									
0500	Towers: material handling and spotting	R-7	22.56	2.128	Ton		104	8.15	112.15	165
0540	Steel tower erection	R-5	7.65	11.503		2,625	680	248	3,553	4,200
0550	Lace and box	"	7.10	12.394		2,625	735	267	3,627	4,300
0600	Special towers: material handling and spotting	R-7	12.31	3.899			190	14.95	204.95	300
0640	Special steel structure erection	R-6	6.52	13.497		3,300	800	455	4,555	5,325
0650	Special steel lace and box	"	6.29	13.990	↓	3,300	830	470	4,600	5,400

33 71 13 – Electrical Utility Towers

33 71 13.80 Transmission Line Right of Way		Crew	Daily Output	Labor-Hours	Unit	2023 Bare Costs Material	Labor	Equipment	Total	Total Incl O&P
0010	**TRANSMISSION LINE RIGHT OF WAY**									
0100	Clearing right of way	B-87	6.67	5.997	Acre		360	555	915	1,150
0200	Restoration & seeding	B-10D	4	3	"	425	173	455	1,053	1,225

33 71 16 – Electrical Utility Poles

33 71 16.20 Line Poles and Fixtures

33 71 16.20 Line Poles and Fixtures		Crew	Daily Output	Labor-Hours	Unit	Material	Labor	Equipment	Total	Total Incl O&P
0010	**LINE POLES & FIXTURES**									
0200	Wood poles, material handling and spotting	R-7	6.49	7.396	Ea.		360	28.50	388.50	575
0220	Erect wood poles & backfill holes, in earth	R-5	6.77	12.999	"	1,375	770	280	2,425	2,975
0300	Crossarms for wood pole structure									
0310	Material handling and spotting	R-7	14.55	3.299	Ea.		161	12.65	173.65	256
0320	Install crossarms	R-5	11	8	"	1,375	475	172	2,022	2,425

33 71 16.23 Steel Electrical Utility Poles

33 71 16.23 Steel Electrical Utility Poles		Crew	Daily Output	Labor-Hours	Unit	Material	Labor	Equipment	Total	Total Incl O&P
0010	**STEEL ELECTRICAL UTILITY POLES**									
0100	Steel, square, tapered shaft, 20′	R-15A	6	8	Ea.	515	475	57.50	1,047.50	1,350
0120	25′		5.35	8.972		2,575	535	64.50	3,174.50	3,700
0140	30′		4.80	10		2,750	595	72	3,417	4,000
0160	35′		4.35	11.034		605	655	79.50	1,339.50	1,725
0180	40′		4	12		1,925	715	86.50	2,726.50	3,275
0300	Galvanized, round, tapered shaft, 40′		4	12		2,100	715	86.50	2,901.50	3,475
0320	45′		3.70	12.973		2,325	770	93.50	3,188.50	3,800
0340	50′		3.45	13.913		2,500	825	100	3,425	4,075
0360	55′		3	16		3,725	950	115	4,790	5,650
0380	60′		2.65	18.113		3,925	1,075	130	5,130	6,075
0400	65′	R-13	2.20	19.091		4,150	1,250	276	5,676	6,725
0420	70′		1.90	22.105		4,475	1,450	320	6,245	7,425
0440	75′		1.70	24.706		4,775	1,625	355	6,755	8,050
0460	80′		1.50	28		5,100	1,825	405	7,330	8,800
0480	85′		1.40	30		5,375	1,950	435	7,760	9,300
0500	90′		1.25	33.600		5,725	2,200	485	8,410	10,100
0520	95′		1.15	36.522		5,975	2,375	530	8,880	10,700
0540	100′		1	42		7,300	2,750	605	10,655	12,800
0700	12 sided, tapered shaft, 40′	R-15A	4	12		2,700	715	86.50	3,501.50	4,125
0720	45′		3.70	12.973		3,000	770	93.50	3,863.50	4,550
0740	50′		3.45	13.913		3,275	825	100	4,200	4,925
0760	55′		3	16		3,625	950	115	4,690	5,550
0780	60′		2.65	18.113		4,675	1,075	130	5,880	6,900
0800	65′	R-13	2.20	19.091		4,950	1,250	276	6,476	7,600
0820	70′		1.90	22.105		5,275	1,450	320	7,045	8,300
0840	75′		1.70	24.706		5,625	1,625	355	7,605	8,975
0860	80′		1.50	28		5,975	1,825	405	8,205	9,725
0880	85′		1.40	30		6,350	1,950	435	8,735	10,400
0900	90′		1.25	33.600		6,650	2,200	485	9,335	11,100
0920	95′		1.15	36.522		6,975	2,375	530	9,880	11,800
0940	100′		1	42		7,425	2,750	605	10,780	12,900
0960	105′		.90	46.667		8,025	3,050	675	11,750	14,100
0980	Ladder clips					370			370	410
1000	Galvanized steel, round, tapered, w/one 6′ arm, 20′	R-15A	9.20	5.217		1,450	310	37.50	1,797.50	2,075
1020	25′		7.65	6.275		2,025	375	45	2,445	2,825
1040	30′		6.55	7.328		2,050	435	53	2,538	2,950
1060	35′		5.75	8.348		2,475	495	60	3,030	3,525
1080	40′		5.15	9.320		2,775	555	67	3,397	3,975

33 71 16.23 Steel Electrical Utility Poles

	33 71 16.23 Steel Electrical Utility Poles	Crew	Daily Output	Labor-Hours	Unit	2023 Bare Costs Material	Labor	Equipment	Total	Total Incl O&P
1200	Two 6′ arms, 20′	R-15A	6.55	7.328	Ea.	2,000	435	53	2,488	2,900
1220	25′		5.75	8.348		2,250	495	60	2,805	3,275
1240	30′		5.15	9.320		2,525	555	67	3,147	3,675
1260	35′		4.60	10.435		2,725	620	75	3,420	4,000
1280	40′		4.20	11.429		3,025	680	82.50	3,787.50	4,425
1400	One 12′ truss arm, 25′		7.65	6.275		1,450	375	45	1,870	2,200
1420	30′		6.55	7.328		1,500	435	53	1,988	2,350
1440	35′		5.75	8.348		1,675	495	60	2,230	2,650
1460	40′		5.15	9.320		2,300	555	67	2,922	3,425
1480	45′		4.60	10.435		3,025	620	75	3,720	4,325
1600	Two 12′ truss arms, 25′		5.75	8.348		1,950	495	60	2,505	2,950
1620	30′		5.15	9.320		1,900	555	67	2,522	3,000
1640	35′		4.60	10.435		2,175	620	75	2,870	3,400
1660	40′		4.20	11.429		2,675	680	82.50	3,437.50	4,050
1680	45′		3.85	12.468		2,450	740	90	3,280	3,900
3400	Galvanized steel, tapered, 10′		15.50	3.097		520	184	22.50	726.50	875
3420	12′		11.50	4.174		775	248	30	1,053	1,250
3440	14′		9.20	5.217		460	310	37.50	807.50	1,000
3460	16′		8.45	5.680		475	340	41	856	1,075
3480	18′		7.65	6.275		490	375	45	910	1,150
3500	20′		7.10	6.761		475	400	48.50	923.50	1,175
5200	Galvanized steel, bracket type, 2″, 6′ long		18.50	2.595		204	154	18.70	376.70	475
5220	8′ long		15.50	3.097		252	184	22.50	458.50	575
5240	10′ long		12.50	3.840		420	228	27.50	675.50	835
6000	Digging holes in earth, average	R-5	25.14	3.500			207	75.50	282.50	395
6010	In rock, average	″	4.51	19.512			1,150	420	1,570	2,175
6020	Formed plate pole structure									
6030	Material handling and spotting	R-7	2.40	20	Ea.		975	76.50	1,051.50	1,550
6040	Erect steel plate pole	R-5	1.95	45.128		9,150	2,675	975	12,800	15,200
6050	Guys, anchors and hardware for pole, in earth		7.04	12.500		119	740	269	1,128	1,525
6060	In rock		17.96	4.900		92.50	290	106	488.50	655
6070	Foundations for line poles									
6080	Excavation, in earth	R-5	135.38	.650	C.Y.		38.50	14	52.50	73
6090	In rock		20	4.400			261	95	356	495
6110	Concrete foundations		11	8		201	475	172	848	1,125

33 71 16.33 Wood Electrical Utility Poles

	33 71 16.33 Wood Electrical Utility Poles	Crew	Daily Output	Labor-Hours	Unit	Material	Labor	Equipment	Total	Total Incl O&P
0010	**WOOD ELECTRICAL UTILITY POLES**									
0011	Excludes excavation, backfill and cast-in-place concrete									
1001	Pole, wood, class 2 yellow pine, CCA-treated, 30′	R-15A	7.70	6.234	Ea.	560	370	45	975	1,225
1002	35′		5.80	8.276		670	490	59.50	1,219.50	1,525
1003	40′		5.30	9.057		820	540	65	1,425	1,775
1004	45′		4.70	10.213		940	605	73.50	1,618.50	2,000
1005	50′		4.20	11.429		1,075	680	82.50	1,837.50	2,275
1006	55′		3.80	12.632		1,225	750	91	2,066	2,575
1007	Electrical utility pole, wood pole, parametric, CCA/ACA-treated, 30′, class		3.50	13.714		1,825	815	98.50	2,738.50	3,325
1020	12″ Ponderosa Pine Poles treated 0.40 ACQ, 16′	R-3	3.20	6.250		1,275	420	60.50	1,755.50	2,100
2001	Pole, wood, class 4 yellow pine, CCA-treated, 30′	R-15A	7.70	6.234		450	370	45	865	1,100
2002	35′		5.80	8.276		515	490	59.50	1,064.50	1,375
2003	40′		5.30	9.057		755	540	65	1,360	1,700
2004	45′		4.70	10.213		940	605	73.50	1,618.50	2,000
2005	50′		4.20	11.429		1,075	680	82.50	1,837.50	2,275
3000	Pole, wood, class 5 yellow pine, CCA-treated, 25′		8.60	5.581		268	330	40	638	835

33 71 Electrical Utility Transmission and Distribution

33 71 16 – Electrical Utility Poles

33 71 16.33 Wood Electrical Utility Poles		Crew	Daily Output	Labor-Hours	Unit	Material	Labor (2023 Bare Costs)	Equipment (2023 Bare Costs)	Total (2023 Bare Costs)	Total Incl O&P
3001	30′	R-15A	7.70	6.234	Ea.	350	370	45	765	985
3002	35′		5.80	8.276		445	490	59.50	994.50	1,275
3003	40′		5.30	9.057		615	540	65	1,220	1,550
3004	45′		4.70	10.213		700	605	73.50	1,378.50	1,750
3005	50′		4.20	11.429		1,075	680	82.50	1,837.50	2,275
3101	Pole, wood, class 6 yellow pine, CCA-treated, 30′		7.70	6.234		192	370	45	607	810
3102	35′		5.80	8.276		243	490	59.50	792.50	1,075
3103	40′		5.30	9.057		300	540	65	905	1,200
3104	45′		4.70	10.213		365	605	73.50	1,043.50	1,400
5000	Wood, class 3 yellow pine, penta-treated, 25′		8.60	5.581		294	330	40	664	865
5005	50′		4.20	11.429		1,075	680	82.50	1,837.50	2,275
5020	30′		7.70	6.234		345	370	45	760	980
5040	35′		5.80	8.276		540	490	59.50	1,089.50	1,375
5060	40′		5.30	9.057		660	540	65	1,265	1,600
5080	45′		4.70	10.213		695	605	73.50	1,373.50	1,750
5100	50′		4.20	11.429		900	680	82.50	1,662.50	2,075
5120	55′		3.80	12.632		1,050	750	91	1,891	2,375
5140	60′		3.50	13.714		1,175	815	98.50	2,088.50	2,625
5160	65′		3.20	15		1,625	890	108	2,623	3,225
5180	70′		3	16		2,325	950	115	3,390	4,100
5301	Wood, class 3 yellow pine, CCA-treated, 30′		7.70	6.234		505	370	45	920	1,150
5305	50′		4.20	11.429		1,100	680	82.50	1,862.50	2,325
5306	55′		3.80	12.632		1,100	750	91	1,941	2,450
5307	60′		3.50	13.714		1,775	815	98.50	2,688.50	3,275
6000	Wood, class 1 type C, CCA/ACA-treated, 25′		8.60	5.581		410	330	40	780	990
6020	30′		7.70	6.234		575	370	45	990	1,225
6040	35′		5.80	8.276		740	490	59.50	1,289.50	1,600
6060	40′		5.30	9.057		980	540	65	1,585	1,950
6080	45′		4.70	10.213		855	605	73.50	1,533.50	1,925
6100	50′		4.20	11.429		1,225	680	82.50	1,987.50	2,450
6120	55′	↓	3.80	12.632		1,400	750	91	2,241	2,750
6200	Wood, class 3 Douglas Fir, penta-treated, 20′	R-3	3.10	6.452		267	435	62.50	764.50	1,000
6600	30′		2.60	7.692		345	520	74	939	1,225
7000	40′		2.30	8.696		635	585	84	1,304	1,675
7200	45′	↓	1.70	11.765	↓	925	790	114	1,829	2,325
7400	Cross arms with hardware & insulators									
7600	4′ long	1 Elec	2.50	3.200	Ea.	161	216		377	495
7800	5′ long		2.40	3.333		177	225		402	530
8000	6′ long	↓	2.20	3.636	↓	222	245		467	610
9000	Disposal of pole & hardware surplus material	R-7	20.87	2.300	Mile		112	8.80	120.80	179
9100	Disposal of crossarms & hardware surplus material	"	40	1.200	"		58.50	4.60	63.10	93

33 71 19 – Electrical Underground Ducts and Manholes

33 71 19.15 Underground Ducts and Manholes		Crew	Daily Output	Labor-Hours	Unit	Material	Labor	Equipment	Total	Total Incl O&P
0010	UNDERGROUND DUCTS AND MANHOLES									
0011	Not incl. excavation, backfill, or concrete in slab and duct bank									
1000	Direct burial R337119-30									
1010	PVC, schedule 40, w/coupling, 1/2″ diameter	1 Elec	340	.024	L.F.	1.04	1.58		2.62	3.50
1020	3/4″ diameter		290	.028		1.23	1.86		3.09	4.11
1030	1″ diameter		260	.031		1.83	2.07		3.90	5.10
1040	1-1/2″ diameter		210	.038		3.02	2.57		5.59	7.15
1050	2″ diameter	↓	180	.044		3.74	2.99		6.73	8.55
1060	3″ diameter	2 Elec	240	.067	↓	7.20	4.49		11.69	14.55

33 71 19 – Electrical Underground Ducts and Manholes

33 71 19.15 Underground Ducts and Manholes		Crew	Daily Output	Labor-Hours	Unit	Material	Labor	Equipment	Total	Total Incl O&P
						2023 Bare Costs				
1070	4" diameter	2 Elec	160	.100	L.F.	9.80	6.75		16.55	21
1080	5" diameter		120	.133		13.70	9		22.70	28.50
1090	6" diameter		90	.178		17.95	11.95		29.90	37.50
1110	Elbows, 1/2" diameter	1 Elec	48	.167	Ea.	1.06	11.25		12.31	17.85
1120	3/4" diameter		38	.211		1.14	14.20		15.34	22.50
1130	1" diameter		32	.250		1.75	16.85		18.60	27
1140	1-1/2" diameter		21	.381		3.51	25.50		29.01	42
1150	2" diameter		16	.500		5.80	33.50		39.30	56.50
1160	3" diameter		12	.667		13.55	45		58.55	81.50
1170	4" diameter		9	.889		32.50	60		92.50	125
1180	5" diameter		8	1		42	67.50		109.50	146
1190	6" diameter		5	1.600		76	108		184	244
1210	Adapters, 1/2" diameter		52	.154		.32	10.35		10.67	15.75
1220	3/4" diameter		43	.186		.54	12.55		13.09	19.20
1230	1" diameter		39	.205		.69	13.80		14.49	21.50
1240	1-1/2" diameter		35	.229		1.18	15.40		16.58	24.50
1250	2" diameter		26	.308		1.55	20.50		22.05	32.50
1260	3" diameter		20	.400		3.82	27		30.82	44
1270	4" diameter		14	.571		6.80	38.50		45.30	64.50
1280	5" diameter		12	.667		13.20	45		58.20	81
1290	6" diameter		9	.889		17.95	60		77.95	109
1340	Bell end & cap, 1-1/2" diameter		35	.229		9	15.40		24.40	33
1350	Bell end & plug, 2" diameter		26	.308		11.15	20.50		31.65	43.50
1360	3" diameter		20	.400		13.85	27		40.85	55
1370	4" diameter		14	.571		15.85	38.50		54.35	74.50
1380	5" diameter		12	.667		24.50	45		69.50	93.50
1390	6" diameter		9	.889		26	60		86	118
1450	Base spacer, 2" diameter		56	.143		2.13	9.60		11.73	16.65
1460	3" diameter		46	.174		2.79	11.70		14.49	20.50
1470	4" diameter		41	.195		2.61	13.15		15.76	22.50
1480	5" diameter		37	.216		3.31	14.55		17.86	25
1490	6" diameter		34	.235		5.60	15.85		21.45	29.50
1550	Intermediate spacer, 2" diameter		60	.133		1.86	9		10.86	15.40
1560	3" diameter		46	.174		2.68	11.70		14.38	20.50
1570	4" diameter		41	.195		2.87	13.15		16.02	22.50
1580	5" diameter		37	.216		3.50	14.55		18.05	25.50
1590	6" diameter		34	.235		4.12	15.85		19.97	28
4010	PVC, schedule 80, w/coupling, 1/2" diameter		215	.037	L.F.	1.23	2.51		3.74	5.05
4020	3/4" diameter		180	.044		1.02	2.99		4.01	5.55
4030	1" diameter		145	.055		1.49	3.72		5.21	7.15
4040	1-1/2" diameter		120	.067		2.33	4.49		6.82	9.20
4050	2" diameter		100	.080		3.23	5.40		8.63	11.55
4060	3" diameter	2 Elec	130	.123		6.60	8.30		14.90	19.55
4070	4" diameter		90	.178		12.15	11.95		24.10	31
4080	5" diameter		70	.229		16.70	15.40		32.10	41.50
4090	6" diameter		50	.320		24.50	21.50		46	59
4110	Elbows, 1/2" diameter	1 Elec	29	.276	Ea.	2.02	18.60		20.62	29.50
4120	3/4" diameter		23	.348		5.45	23.50		28.95	41
4130	1" diameter		20	.400		2.30	27		29.30	42.50
4140	1-1/2" diameter		16	.500		3.30	33.50		36.80	53.50
4150	2" diameter		12	.667		4.33	45		49.33	71.50
4160	3" diameter		9	.889		10.95	60		70.95	101
4170	4" diameter		7	1.143		15.95	77		92.95	132

33 71 19 – Electrical Underground Ducts and Manholes

33 71 19.15 Underground Ducts and Manholes		Crew	Daily Output	Labor-Hours	Unit	2023 Bare Costs Material	Labor	Equipment	Total	Total Incl O&P
4180	5" diameter	1 Elec	6	1.333	Ea.	125	90		215	271
4190	6" diameter		4	2		51.50	135		186.50	257
4210	Adapter, 1/2" diameter		39	.205		.32	13.80		14.12	21
4220	3/4" diameter		33	.242		.54	16.35		16.89	25
4230	1" diameter		29	.276		.69	18.60		19.29	28.50
4240	1-1/2" diameter		26	.308		1.18	20.50		21.68	32.50
4250	2" diameter		23	.348		1.55	23.50		25.05	36.50
4260	3" diameter		18	.444		3.82	30		33.82	48.50
4270	4" diameter		13	.615		6.80	41.50		48.30	69
4280	5" diameter		11	.727		13.20	49		62.20	87.50
4290	6" diameter		8	1		17.95	67.50		85.45	120
4310	Bell end & cap, 1-1/2" diameter		26	.308		9	20.50		29.50	41
4320	Bell end & plug, 2" diameter		23	.348		11.15	23.50		34.65	47.50
4330	3" diameter		18	.444		13.85	30		43.85	59.50
4340	4" diameter		13	.615		15.85	41.50		57.35	79
4350	5" diameter		11	.727		24.50	49		73.50	100
4360	6" diameter		8	1		26	67.50		93.50	129
4370	Base spacer, 2" diameter		42	.190		2.13	12.85		14.98	21.50
4380	3" diameter		33	.242		2.79	16.35		19.14	27.50
4390	4" diameter		29	.276		2.61	18.60		21.21	30.50
4400	5" diameter		26	.308		3.31	20.50		23.81	34.50
4410	6" diameter		25	.320		5.60	21.50		27.10	38
4420	Intermediate spacer, 2" diameter		45	.178		1.86	11.95		13.81	19.85
4430	3" diameter		34	.235		2.68	15.85		18.53	26.50
4440	4" diameter		31	.258		2.87	17.40		20.27	29
4450	5" diameter		28	.286		3.50	19.25		22.75	32.50
4460	6" diameter		25	.320		4.12	21.50		25.62	36.50

33 71 19.17 Electric and Telephone Underground

		Crew	Daily Output	Labor-Hours	Unit	Material	Labor	Equipment	Total	Total Incl O&P
0010	**ELECTRIC AND TELEPHONE UNDERGROUND**									
0011	Not including excavation									
0200	backfill and cast in place concrete									
0250	For bedding, see Section 31 23 23.16 R337119-30									
0400	Hand holes, precast concrete, with concrete cover									
0600	2' x 2' x 3' deep	R-3	2.40	8.333	Ea.	655	560	80.50	1,295.50	1,650
0800	3' x 3' x 3' deep		1.90	10.526		850	710	102	1,662	2,100
1000	4' x 4' x 4' deep		1.40	14.286		1,775	960	138	2,873	3,525
1200	Manholes, precast with iron racks & pulling irons, C.I. frame									
1400	and cover, 4' x 6' x 7' deep	B-13	2	28	Ea.	3,400	1,450	1,125	5,975	7,125
1600	6' x 8' x 7' deep		1.90	29.474		3,825	1,525	1,200	6,550	7,775
1800	6' x 10' x 7' deep		1.80	31.111		4,275	1,600	1,275	7,150	8,500
4200	Underground duct, banks ready for concrete fill, min. of 7.5"									
4400	between conduits, center to center									
4580	PVC, type EB, 1 @ 2" diameter	2 Elec	480	.033	L.F.	6.30	2.25		8.55	10.30
4600	2 @ 2" diameter		240	.067		12.65	4.49		17.14	20.50
4800	4 @ 2" diameter		120	.133		25.50	9		34.50	41.50
4900	1 @ 3" diameter		400	.040		1.68	2.69		4.37	5.85
5000	2 @ 3" diameter		200	.080		3.36	5.40		8.76	11.70
5200	4 @ 3" diameter		100	.160		6.70	10.80		17.50	23.50
5300	1 @ 4" diameter		320	.050		41.50	3.37		44.87	51
5400	2 @ 4" diameter		160	.100		83.50	6.75		90.25	102
5600	4 @ 4" diameter		80	.200		167	13.45		180.45	203
5800	6 @ 4" diameter		54	.296		250	19.95		269.95	305

33 71 19.17 Electric and Telephone Underground		Crew	Daily Output	Labor-Hours	Unit	2023 Bare Costs Material	Labor	Equipment	Total	Total Incl O&P
5810	1 @ 5″ diameter	2 Elec	260	.062	L.F.	9.40	4.14		13.54	16.50
5820	2 @ 5″ diameter		130	.123		18.80	8.30		27.10	33
5840	4 @ 5″ diameter		70	.229		37.50	15.40		52.90	64.50
5860	6 @ 5″ diameter		50	.320		56.50	21.50		78	94
5870	1 @ 6″ diameter		200	.080		8.90	5.40		14.30	17.80
5880	2 @ 6″ diameter		100	.160		17.80	10.80		28.60	35.50
5900	4 @ 6″ diameter		50	.320		35.50	21.50		57	71
5920	6 @ 6″ diameter		30	.533		53.50	36		89.50	113
6200	Rigid galvanized steel, 2 @ 2″ diameter		180	.089		27	6		33	38.50
6400	4 @ 2″ diameter		90	.178		54	11.95		65.95	77
6800	2 @ 3″ diameter		100	.160		60.50	10.80		71.30	82.50
7000	4 @ 3″ diameter		50	.320		121	21.50		142.50	165
7200	2 @ 4″ diameter		70	.229		83	15.40		98.40	114
7400	4 @ 4″ diameter		34	.471		166	31.50		197.50	229
7600	6 @ 4″ diameter		22	.727		249	49		298	345
7620	2 @ 5″ diameter		60	.267		166	17.95		183.95	210
7640	4 @ 5″ diameter		30	.533		330	36		366	420
7660	6 @ 5″ diameter		18	.889		500	60		560	640
7680	2 @ 6″ diameter		40	.400		225	27		252	287
7700	4 @ 6″ diameter		20	.800		450	54		504	575
7720	6 @ 6″ diameter		14	1.143		675	77		752	855
7800	For cast-in-place concrete, add									
7810	Under 1 C.Y.	C-6	16	3	C.Y.	247	147	3.72	397.72	495
7820	1 C.Y. to 5 C.Y.		19.20	2.500		224	122	3.10	349.10	430
7830	Over 5 C.Y.		24	2		185	98	2.48	285.48	350
7850	For reinforcing rods, add									
7860	#4 to #7	2 Rodm	1.10	14.545	Ton	1,425	940		2,365	2,975
7870	#8 to #14	"	1.50	10.667	"	1,425	690		2,115	2,600
8000	Fittings, PVC type EB, elbow, 2″ diameter	1 Elec	16	.500	Ea.	33.50	33.50		67	86.50
8200	3″ diameter		14	.571		19	38.50		57.50	78
8400	4″ diameter		12	.667		64	45		109	137
8420	5″ diameter		10	.800		121	54		175	213
8440	6″ diameter		9	.889		232	60		292	345
8500	Coupling, 2″ diameter					1.21			1.21	1.33
8600	3″ diameter					6.85			6.85	7.55
8700	4″ diameter					5.10			5.10	5.65
8720	5″ diameter					24.50			24.50	27
8740	6″ diameter					27			27	30
8800	Adapter, 2″ diameter	1 Elec	26	.308		1.57	20.50		22.07	32.50
9000	3″ diameter		20	.400		10.45	27		37.45	51.50
9200	4″ diameter		16	.500		5.15	33.50		38.65	55.50
9220	5″ diameter		13	.615		33	41.50		74.50	98
9240	6″ diameter		10	.800		9.30	54		63.30	90.50
9400	End bell, 2″ diameter		16	.500		4.67	33.50		38.17	55
9600	3″ diameter		14	.571		5.50	38.50		44	63
9800	4″ diameter		12	.667		5.65	45		50.65	73
9810	5″ diameter		10	.800		11	54		65	92
9820	6″ diameter		8	1		10.80	67.50		78.30	112
9830	5° angle coupling, 2″ diameter		26	.308		7.45	20.50		27.95	39
9840	3″ diameter		20	.400		27	27		54	69.50
9850	4″ diameter		16	.500		22	33.50		55.50	74
9860	5″ diameter		13	.615		19.15	41.50		60.65	82.50
9870	6″ diameter		10	.800		29.50	54		83.50	113

33 71 19 – Electrical Underground Ducts and Manholes

33 71 19.17 Electric and Telephone Underground		Crew	Daily Output	Labor-Hours	Unit	Material	2023 Bare Costs Labor	Equipment	Total	Total Incl O&P
9880	Expansion joint, 2″ diameter	1 Elec	16	.500	Ea.	47.50	33.50		81	103
9890	3″ diameter		18	.444		58	30		88	108
9900	4″ diameter		12	.667		125	45		170	205
9910	5″ diameter		10	.800		194	54		248	293
9920	6″ diameter		8	1		176	67.50		243.50	294
9930	Heat bender, 2″ diameter					550			550	605
9940	6″ diameter					1,700			1,700	1,875
9950	Cement, quart					27.50			27.50	30.50
9960	Nylon polyethylene pull rope, 1/4″	2 Elec	2000	.008	L.F.	.16	.54		.70	.98

33 71 23 – Insulators and Fittings

33 71 23.16 Post Insulators		Crew	Daily Output	Labor-Hours	Unit	Material	Labor	Equipment	Total	Total Incl O&P
0010	**POST INSULATORS**									
7400	Insulators, pedestal type	R-11	112	.500	Ea.		32	21	53	71
7490	See also line 33 71 39.13 1000									

33 71 26 – Transmission and Distribution Equipment

33 71 26.13 Capacitor Banks		Crew	Daily Output	Labor-Hours	Unit	Material	Labor	Equipment	Total	Total Incl O&P
0010	**CAPACITOR BANKS**									
1300	Station capacitors									
1350	Synchronous, 13 to 26 kV	R-11	3.11	18.006	MVAR	7,675	1,150	750	9,575	11,000
1360	46 kV		3.33	16.817		9,775	1,075	700	11,550	13,200
1370	69 kV		3.81	14.698		9,625	945	615	11,185	12,700
1380	161 kV		6.51	8.602		9,000	555	360	9,915	11,100
1390	500 kV		10.37	5.400		7,825	350	225	8,400	9,375
1450	Static, 13 to 26 kV		3.11	18.006		6,500	1,150	750	8,400	9,700
1460	46 kV		3.01	18.605		8,200	1,200	775	10,175	11,700
1470	69 kV		3.81	14.698		7,975	945	615	9,535	10,900
1480	161 kV		6.51	8.602		7,400	555	360	8,315	9,375
1490	500 kV		10.37	5.400		6,750	350	225	7,325	8,200
1600	Voltage regulators, 13 to 26 kV		.75	74.667	Ea.	294,500	4,800	3,125	302,425	334,000

33 71 26.23 Current Transformers		Crew	Daily Output	Labor-Hours	Unit	Material	Labor	Equipment	Total	Total Incl O&P
0010	**CURRENT TRANSFORMERS**									
4050	Current transformers, 13 to 26 kV	R-11	14	4	Ea.	955	258	167	1,380	1,625
4060	46 kV		9.33	6.002		3,875	385	250	4,510	5,100
4070	69 kV		7	8		4,625	515	335	5,475	6,200
4080	161 kV		1.87	29.947		35,500	1,925	1,250	38,675	43,400

33 71 26.26 Potential Transformers		Crew	Daily Output	Labor-Hours	Unit	Material	Labor	Equipment	Total	Total Incl O&P
0010	**POTENTIAL TRANSFORMERS**									
4100	Potential transformers, 13 to 26 kV	R-11	11.20	5	Ea.	1,200	320	208	1,728	2,025
4110	46 kV		8	7		4,025	450	292	4,767	5,425
4120	69 kV		6.22	9.003		4,925	580	375	5,880	6,700
4130	161 kV		2.24	25		24,400	1,600	1,050	27,050	30,400
4140	500 kV		1.40	40		72,500	2,575	1,675	76,750	85,500

33 71 26.28 Overhead Fuse Cutouts		Crew	Daily Output	Labor-Hours	Unit	Material	Labor	Equipment	Total	Total Incl O&P
0010	**OVERHEAD FUSE CUTOUTS**									
1000	Cutout Fuse Assemblies									
1100	15.0 kV, 110 kV BIL, 100 amp, type C, silicone	R-8	6	8	Ea.	122	480	51	653	905
1200	200 amp		6	8		198	480	51	729	990
1300	300 amp		6	8		236	480	51	767	1,025
2000	Cutout Fuse Links									
2100	Removeable button head, type K, 100 amp	R-3	10	2	Ea.	11.60	135	19.30	165.90	234
2140	140 amp	″	10	2	″	26	135	19.30	180.30	250

33 71 26 – Transmission and Distribution Equipment

33 71 26.28 Overhead Fuse Cutouts		Crew	Daily Output	Labor-Hours	Unit	Material	Labor	Equipment	Total	Total Incl O&P
						2023 Bare Costs				
3000	Cutout Fuse Hardware									
3100	Tri-mount bracket, aluminum	R-3	10	2	Ea.	231	135	19.30	385.30	475
3200	Arrester, surge, 12.7 kV		10	2		61.50	135	19.30	215.80	289
3300	Clamp, hot-line tap, bronze, 5"		10	2		23.50	135	19.30	177.80	247
3400	Clamp, stirrup, bronze, 1-13/16"		10	2		16.95	135	19.30	171.25	240
3500	Insulator, dead-end, clevis tongue, 12-1/2"		10	2		29.50	135	19.30	183.80	254

33 71 39 – High-Voltage Wiring

33 71 39.13 Overhead High-Voltage Wiring

		Crew	Daily Output	Labor-Hours	Unit	Material	Labor	Equipment	Total	Total Incl O&P
0010	**OVERHEAD HIGH-VOLTAGE WIRING** R337116-60									
0100	Conductors, primary circuits									
0110	Material handling and spotting	R-5	9.78	8.998	W.Mile		535	194	729	1,000
0120	For river crossing, add		11	8			475	172	647	900
0150	Conductors, per wire, 210 to 636 kcmil		1.96	44.898		21,900	2,650	970	25,520	29,100
0160	795 to 954 kcmil		1.87	47.059		38,600	2,800	1,025	42,425	47,700
0170	1,000 to 1,600 kcmil		1.47	59.864		84,500	3,550	1,300	89,350	99,500
0180	Over 1,600 kcmil		1.35	65.185		109,000	3,850	1,400	114,250	127,500
0200	For river crossing, add, 210 to 636 kcmil		1.24	70.968			4,200	1,525	5,725	7,950
0220	795 to 954 kcmil		1.09	80.734			4,775	1,750	6,525	9,075
0230	1,000 to 1,600 kcmil		.97	90.722			5,375	1,950	7,325	10,200
0240	Over 1,600 kcmil		.87	101			6,000	2,175	8,175	11,400
0300	Joints and dead ends	R-8	6	8	Ea.	2,250	480	51	2,781	3,250
0400	Sagging	R-6	7.33	12.001	W.Mile		710	405	1,115	1,500
0500	Clipping, per structure, 69 kV	R-10	9.60	5	Ea.		320	44	364	525
0510	161 kV		5.33	9.006			575	79	654	940
0520	345 to 500 kV		2.53	18.972			1,200	167	1,367	1,975
0600	Make and install jumpers, per structure, 69 kV	R-8	3.20	15		610	900	95.50	1,605.50	2,125
0620	161 kV		1.20	40		1,225	2,400	255	3,880	5,200
0640	345 to 500 kV		.32	150		2,050	9,000	955	12,005	16,700
0700	Spacers	R-10	68.57	.700		122	44.50	6.15	172.65	207
0720	For river crossings, add	"	60	.800			51	7	58	84
0800	Installing pulling line (500 kV only)	R-9	1.45	44.138	W.Mile	905	2,475	211	3,591	4,950
0810	Disposal of surplus material, high voltage conductors	R-7	6.96	6.897	Mile		335	26.50	361.50	535
0820	With trailer mounted reel stands	"	13.71	3.501	"		171	13.40	184.40	272
0900	Insulators and hardware, primary circuits									
0920	Material handling and spotting, 69 kV	R-7	480	.100	Ea.		4.88	.38	5.26	7.75
0930	161 kV		685.71	.070			3.41	.27	3.68	5.45
0950	345 to 500 kV		960	.050			2.44	.19	2.63	3.88
1000	Disk insulators, 69 kV	R-5	880	.100		124	5.95	2.16	132.11	148
1020	161 kV		977.78	.090		142	5.35	1.94	149.29	166
1040	345 to 500 kV		1100	.080		142	4.74	1.72	148.46	165
1060	See Section 33 71 23.16 for pin or pedestal insulator									
1100	Install disk insulator at river crossing, add									
1110	69 kV	R-5	586.67	.150	Ea.		8.90	3.23	12.13	16.80
1120	161 kV		880	.100			5.95	2.16	8.11	11.20
1140	345 to 500 kV		880	.100			5.95	2.16	8.11	11.20
1150	Disposal of surplus material, high voltage insulators	R-7	41.74	1.150	Mile		56	4.40	60.40	89.50
1300	Overhead ground wire installation									
1320	Material handling and spotting	R-7	5.65	8.496	W.Mile		415	32.50	447.50	660
1340	Overhead ground wire	R-5	1.76	50		4,650	2,975	1,075	8,700	10,700
1350	At river crossing, add		1.17	75.214			4,450	1,625	6,075	8,425
1360	Disposal of surplus material, grounding wire		41.74	2.108	Mile		125	45.50	170.50	237
1400	Installing conductors, underbuilt circuits									

33 71 Electrical Utility Transmission and Distribution

33 71 39 – High-Voltage Wiring

33 71 39.13 Overhead High-Voltage Wiring		Crew	Daily Output	Labor-Hours	Unit	Material	2023 Bare Costs Labor	Equipment	Total	Total Incl O&P
1420	Material handling and spotting	R-7	5.65	8.496	W.Mile		415	32.50	447.50	660
1440	Conductors, per wire, 210 to 636 kcmil	R-5	1.96	44.898		21,900	2,650	970	25,520	29,100
1450	795 to 954 kcmil		1.87	47.059		38,600	2,800	1,025	42,425	47,700
1460	1,000 to 1,600 kcmil		1.47	59.864		84,500	3,550	1,300	89,350	99,500
1470	Over 1,600 kcmil		1.35	65.185		109,000	3,850	1,400	114,250	127,500
1500	Joints and dead ends	R-8	6	8	Ea.	2,250	480	51	2,781	3,250
1550	Sagging	R-6	8.80	10	W.Mile		595	335	930	1,250
1600	Clipping, per structure, 69 kV	R-10	9.60	5	Ea.		320	44	364	525
1620	161 kV		5.33	9.006			575	79	654	940
1640	345 to 500 kV		2.53	18.972			1,200	167	1,367	1,975
1700	Making and installing jumpers, per structure, 69 kV	R-8	5.87	8.177		610	490	52	1,152	1,475
1720	161 kV		.96	50		1,225	3,000	320	4,545	6,175
1740	345 to 500 kV		.32	150		2,050	9,000	955	12,005	16,700
1800	Spacers	R-10	96	.500		122	32	4.39	158.39	186
1810	Disposal of surplus material, conductors & hardware	R-7	6.96	6.897	Mile		335	26.50	361.50	535
2000	Insulators and hardware for underbuilt circuits									
2100	Material handling and spotting	R-7	1200	.040	Ea.		1.95	.15	2.10	3.11
2150	Disk insulators, 69 kV	R-8	600	.080		124	4.80	.51	129.31	145
2160	161 kV		686	.070		142	4.20	.45	146.65	163
2170	345 to 500 kV		800	.060		142	3.60	.38	145.98	162
2180	Disposal of surplus material, insulators & hardware	R-7	41.74	1.150	Mile		56	4.40	60.40	89.50
2300	Sectionalizing switches, 69 kV	R-5	1.26	69.841	Ea.	32,100	4,150	1,500	37,750	43,100
2310	161 kV		.80	110		36,300	6,525	2,375	45,200	52,000
2500	Protective devices		5.50	16		10,500	950	345	11,795	13,300
2600	Clearance poles, 8 poles per mile									
2650	In earth, 69 kV	R-5	1.16	75.862	Mile	8,625	4,500	1,625	14,750	18,000
2660	161 kV	"	.64	138		14,200	8,150	2,975	25,325	31,100
2670	345 to 500 kV	R-6	.48	183		17,000	10,900	6,150	34,050	41,700
2800	In rock, 69 kV	R-5	.69	128		8,625	7,550	2,750	18,925	23,800
2820	161 kV	"	.35	251		14,200	14,900	5,425	34,525	43,800
2840	345 to 500 kV	R-6	.24	367		17,000	21,700	12,300	51,000	64,500

33 72 Utility Substations

33 72 26 – Substation Bus Assemblies

33 72 26.13 Aluminum Substation Bus Assemblies		Crew	Daily Output	Labor-Hours	Unit	Material	Labor	Equipment	Total	Total Incl O&P
0010	ALUMINUM SUBSTATION BUS ASSEMBLIES									
7300	Bus	R-11	590	.095	Lb.	3.58	6.10	3.96	13.64	17.40

33 72 33 – Control House Equipment

33 72 33.43 Substation Backup Batteries		Crew	Daily Output	Labor-Hours	Unit	Material	Labor	Equipment	Total	Total Incl O&P
0010	SUBSTATION BACKUP BATTERIES									
9120	Battery chargers	R-11	11.20	5	Ea.	5,125	320	208	5,653	6,325
9200	Control batteries	"	14	4	K.A.H.	630	258	167	1,055	1,275

33 72 53 – Shunt Reactors

33 72 53.13 Reactors		Crew	Daily Output	Labor-Hours	Unit	Material	Labor	Equipment	Total	Total Incl O&P
0010	REACTORS									
8000	Protective equipment									
8150	Reactors and resistors, 13 to 26 kV	R-11	28	2	Ea.	4,200	129	83.50	4,412.50	4,875
8160	46 kV		4.31	12.993		14,800	835	540	16,175	18,100
8170	69 kV		2.80	20		23,400	1,300	835	25,535	28,500
8180	161 kV		2.24	25		26,000	1,600	1,050	28,650	32,200

33 72 Utility Substations

33 72 53 – Shunt Reactors

33 72 53.13 Reactors		Crew	Daily Output	Labor-Hours	Unit	Material	Labor	Equipment	Total	Total Incl O&P
						2023 Bare Costs				
8190	500 kV	R-11	.08	700	Ea.	100,000	45,100	29,200	174,300	209,000

33 73 Utility Transformers

33 73 23 – Dry-Type Utility Transformers

33 73 23.20 Primary Transformers

		Crew	Daily Output	Labor-Hours	Unit	Material	Labor	Equipment	Total	Total Incl O&P
0010	**PRIMARY TRANSFORMERS**									
1000	Main conversion equipment									
1050	Power transformers, 13 to 26 kV	R-11	1.72	32.558	MVA	29,200	2,100	1,350	32,650	36,700
1060	46 kV		3.50	16		27,300	1,025	665	28,990	32,400
1070	69 kV		3.11	18.006		23,300	1,150	750	25,200	28,200
1080	110 kV		3.29	17.021		22,200	1,100	710	24,010	26,800
1090	161 kV		4.31	12.993		20,600	835	540	21,975	24,400
1100	500 kV		7	8		20,500	515	335	21,350	23,600
1200	Grounding transformers		3.11	18.006	Ea.	130,000	1,150	750	131,900	145,500

33 75 High-Voltage Switchgear and Protection Devices

33 75 13 – Air High-Voltage Circuit Breaker

33 75 13.13 High-Voltage Circuit Breaker, Air

		Crew	Daily Output	Labor-Hours	Unit	Material	Labor	Equipment	Total	Total Incl O&P
0010	**HIGH-VOLTAGE CIRCUIT BREAKER, AIR**									
2100	Air circuit breakers, 13 to 26 kV	R-11	.56	100	Ea.	71,500	6,450	4,175	82,125	93,000
2110	161 kV	"	.24	233	"	307,500	15,000	9,725	332,225	371,000

33 75 16 – Oil High-Voltage Circuit Breaker

33 75 16.13 Oil Circuit Breaker

		Crew	Daily Output	Labor-Hours	Unit	Material	Labor	Equipment	Total	Total Incl O&P
0010	**OIL CIRCUIT BREAKER**									
2000	Power circuit breakers									
2050	Oil circuit breakers, 13 to 26 kV	R-11	1.12	50	Ea.	73,000	3,225	2,075	78,300	87,500
2060	46 kV		.75	74.667		106,000	4,800	3,125	113,925	127,000
2070	69 kV		.45	124		246,000	8,025	5,200	259,225	288,000
2080	161 kV		.16	350		355,000	22,500	14,600	392,100	440,000
2090	500 kV		.06	933		1,325,500	60,000	38,900	1,424,400	1,590,500

33 75 19 – Gas High-Voltage Circuit Breaker

33 75 19.13 Gas Circuit Breaker

		Crew	Daily Output	Labor-Hours	Unit	Material	Labor	Equipment	Total	Total Incl O&P
0010	**GAS CIRCUIT BREAKER**									
2000	Power circuit breakers									
2150	Gas circuit breakers, 13 to 26 kV	R-11	.56	100	Ea.	57,500	6,450	4,175	68,125	77,500
2160	161 kV		.08	700		97,500	45,100	29,200	171,800	206,500
2170	500 kV		.04	1400		452,000	90,000	58,500	600,500	695,500

33 75 23 – Vacuum High-Voltage Circuit Breaker

33 75 23.13 Vacuum Circuit Breaker

		Crew	Daily Output	Labor-Hours	Unit	Material	Labor	Equipment	Total	Total Incl O&P
0010	**VACUUM CIRCUIT BREAKER**									
2000	Power circuit breakers									
2200	Vacuum circuit breakers, 13 to 26 kV	R-11	.56	100	Ea.	28,400	6,450	4,175	39,025	45,400
2300	Vacuum circuit breakers, 46 kV	"	.56	100	"	43,700	6,450	4,175	54,325	62,000

33 75 High-Voltage Switchgear and Protection Devices

33 75 36 – High-Voltage Utility Fuses

33 75 36.13 Fuses		Crew	Daily Output	Labor-Hours	Unit	Material	2023 Bare Costs Labor	Equipment	Total	Total Incl O&P
0010	**FUSES**									
8000	Protective equipment									
8250	Fuses, 13 to 26 kV	R-11	18.67	2.999	Ea.	5,625	193	125	5,943	6,625
8260	46 kV		11.20	5		6,100	320	208	6,628	7,400
8270	69 kV		8	7		2,225	450	292	2,967	3,450
8280	161 kV		4.67	11.991		4,300	770	500	5,570	6,450

33 75 39 – High-Voltage Surge Arresters

33 75 39.13 Surge Arresters		Crew	Daily Output	Labor-Hours	Unit	Material	Labor	Equipment	Total	Total Incl O&P
0010	**SURGE ARRESTERS**									
8000	Protective equipment									
8050	Lightning arresters, 13 to 26 kV	R-11	18.67	2.999	Ea.	199	193	125	517	645
8060	46 kV		14	4		1,650	258	167	2,075	2,400
8070	69 kV		11.20	5		2,500	320	208	3,028	3,450
8080	161 kV		5.60	10		5,350	645	415	6,410	7,300
8090	500 kV		1.40	40		4,350	2,575	1,675	8,600	10,400

33 75 53 – High-Voltage Switches

33 75 53.13 Switches		Crew	Daily Output	Labor-Hours	Unit	Material	Labor	Equipment	Total	Total Incl O&P
0010	**SWITCHES**									
3000	Disconnecting switches									
3050	Gang operated switches									
3060	Manual operation, 13 to 26 kV	R-11	1.65	33.939	Ea.	5,325	2,175	1,425	8,925	10,700
3070	46 kV		1.12	50		7,975	3,225	2,075	13,275	15,900
3080	69 kV		.80	70		10,600	4,500	2,925	18,025	21,600
3090	161 kV		.56	100		16,000	6,450	4,175	26,625	31,800
3100	500 kV		.14	400		34,900	25,800	16,700	77,400	95,000
3110	Motor operation, 161 kV		.51	110		21,300	7,075	4,575	32,950	38,900
3120	500 kV		.28	200		39,900	12,900	8,350	61,150	72,500
3250	Circuit switches, 161 kV		.41	137		111,000	8,800	5,700	125,500	142,000
3300	Single pole switches									
3350	Disconnecting switches, 13 to 26 kV	R-11	28	2	Ea.	4,000	129	83.50	4,212.50	4,675
3360	46 kV		8	7		4,875	450	292	5,617	6,375
3370	69 kV		5.60	10		7,975	645	415	9,035	10,200
3380	161 kV		2.80	20		114,500	1,300	835	116,635	129,000
3390	500 kV		.22	255		325,000	16,400	10,600	352,000	393,500
3450	Grounding switches, 46 kV		5.60	10		43,800	645	415	44,860	49,600
3460	69 kV		3.73	15.013		44,000	965	625	45,590	50,500
3470	161 kV		2.24	25		47,100	1,600	1,050	49,750	55,500
3480	500 kV		.62	90.323		60,000	5,825	3,775	69,600	78,500

33 78 Substation Converter Stations

33 78 33 – Converter Stations

33 78 33.46 Substation Converter Stations		Crew	Daily Output	Labor-Hours	Unit	Material	Labor	Equipment	Total	Total Incl O&P
0010	**SUBSTATION CONVERTER STATIONS**									
9000	Station service equipment									
9100	Conversion equipment									
9110	Station service transformers	R-11	5.60	10	Ea.	123,500	645	415	124,560	137,500

33 79 Site Grounding

33 79 83 – Site Grounding Conductors

33 79 83.13 Grounding Wire, Bar, and Rod		Crew	Daily Output	Labor-Hours	Unit	Material	Labor	Equipment	Total	Total Incl O&P
						2023 Bare Costs				
0010	**GROUNDING WIRE, BAR, AND ROD**									
7500	Grounding systems	R-11	280	.200	Lb.	12.70	12.90	8.35	33.95	42.50

33 81 Communications Structures

33 81 13 – Communications Transmission Towers

33 81 13.10 Radio Towers

		Crew	Daily Output	Labor-Hours	Unit	Material	Labor	Equipment	Total	Total Incl O&P
0010	**RADIO TOWERS**									
0020	Guyed, 50' H, 40 lb. section, 70 MPH basic wind speed	2 Sswk	1	16	Ea.	4,100	1,025		5,125	6,125
0100	Wind load 90 MPH basic wind speed	"	1	16		4,375	1,025		5,400	6,400
0300	190' high, 40 lb. section, wind load 70 MPH basic wind speed	K-2	.33	72.727		15,200	4,450	1,175	20,825	24,800
0400	200' high, 70 lb. section, wind load 90 MPH basic wind speed		.33	72.727		20,500	4,450	1,175	26,125	30,700
0600	300' high, 70 lb. section, wind load 70 MPH basic wind speed		.20	120		24,700	7,350	1,950	34,000	40,500
0700	270' high, 90 lb. section, wind load 90 MPH basic wind speed		.20	120		25,000	7,350	1,950	34,300	40,900
0800	400' high, 100 lb. section, wind load 70 MPH basic wind speed		.14	171		33,500	10,500	2,800	46,800	56,000
0900	Self-supporting, 60' high, wind load 70 MPH basic wind speed		.80	30		6,975	1,850	490	9,315	11,000
0910	60' high, wind load 90 MPH basic wind speed		.45	53.333		7,050	3,275	870	11,195	13,700
1000	120' high, wind load 70 MPH basic wind speed		.40	60		10,800	3,675	975	15,450	18,600
1200	190' high, wind load 90 MPH basic wind speed		.20	120		38,300	7,350	1,950	47,600	55,500
2000	For states west of Rocky Mountains, add for shipping					10%				

Estimating Tips

34 11 00 Rail Tracks

This subdivision includes items that may involve either repair of existing or construction of new railroad tracks. Additional preparation work, such as the roadbed earthwork, would be found in Division 31. Additional new construction siding and turnouts are found in Subdivision 34 72. Maintenance of railroads is found under 34 01 23 Operation and Maintenance of Railways.

34 40 00 Traffic Signals

This subdivision includes traffic signal systems. Other traffic control devices such as traffic signs are found in Subdivision 10 14 53 Traffic Signage.

34 70 00 Vehicle Barriers

This subdivision includes security vehicle barriers, guide and guard rails, crash barriers, and delineators. The actual maintenance and construction of concrete and asphalt pavement are found in Division 32.

Reference Numbers

Reference numbers are shown at the beginning of some major classifications. These numbers refer to related items in the Reference Section. The reference information may be an estimating procedure, an alternate pricing method, or technical information.

Note: Not all subdivisions listed here necessarily appear. ■

34 43 Airfield Signaling and Control Equipment

34 43 13 – Airfield Signals and Lighting

34 43 13.16 Airfield Runway and Taxiway Inset Lighting		Crew	Daily Output	Labor-Hours	Unit	2023 Bare Costs Material	Labor	Equipment	Total	Total Incl O&P
0010	AIRFIELD RUNWAY AND TAXIWAY INSET LIGHTING									
0100	Runway centerline, bidir., semi-flush, 200 W, w/shallow insert base	R-22	12.40	3.006	Ea.	1,600	185		1,785	2,025
0110	for mounting in base housing		18.60	2.004		820	124		944	1,100
0120	Flush, 200 W, w/shallow insert base		12.40	3.006		1,450	185		1,635	1,875
0130	for mounting in base housing		18.64	2		735	123		858	995
0140	45 W, for mounting in base housing		18.64	2		485	123		608	715
0150	Touchdown zone light, unidirectional, 200 W, w/shallow insert base		12.40	3.006		1,175	185		1,360	1,575
0160	115 W		12.40	3.006		1,250	185		1,435	1,650
0170	Bidirectional, 62 W		12.40	3.006		2,300	185		2,485	2,800
0180	Unidirectional, 200 W, for mounting in base housing		18.60	2.004		705	124		829	960
0190	115 W		18.60	2.004		525	124		649	760
0200	Bidirectional, 62 W		18.60	2.004		485	124		609	715
0210	Runway edge & threshold light, bidir., 200 W, for base housing		9.36	3.983		770	246		1,016	1,200
0220	300 W		9.36	3.983		1,075	246		1,321	1,550
0230	499 W		7.44	5.011		1,800	310		2,110	2,425
0240	Threshold & approach light, unidir., 200 W, for base housing		9.36	3.983		470	246		716	880
0250	499 W		7.44	5.011		625	310		935	1,150
0260	Runway edge, bidirectional, 2-115 W, for base housing		12.40	3.006		1,150	185		1,335	1,550
0270	2-185 W		12.40	3.006		1,300	185		1,485	1,700
0280	Runway threshold & end, bidir., 2-115 W, for base housing		12.40	3.006		1,275	185		1,460	1,675
0370	45 W, flush, for mounting in base housing		18.64	2		625	123		748	875
0380	115 W		18.64	2		640	123		763	890
0400	Transformer, 45 W		37.20	1.002		127	62		189	232
0410	65 W		37.20	1.002		129	62		191	234
0420	100 W		37.20	1.002		206	62		268	320
0430	200 W, 6.6/6.6 A		37.20	1.002		209	62		271	320
0440	20/6.6 A		24.80	1.503		239	92.50		331.50	400
0450	500 W		24.80	1.503		315	92.50		407.50	485
0460	Base housing, 24" deep, 12" diameter		18.64	2		365	123		488	585
0470	15" diameter		18.64	2		510	123		633	750
0480	Connection kit for 1 conductor cable		24.80	1.503		32	92.50		124.50	173
0500	Elevated runway marker, high intensity quartz, edge, 115 W		14.88	2.505		555	154		709	840
0510	175 W		14.88	2.505		298	154		452	560
0520	Threshold, 115 W		14.88	2.505		325	154		479	585
0530	Edge, 200 W, w/base and transformer		11.85	3.146		855	194		1,049	1,225
0540	Elevated runway light, quartz, runway edge, 45 W		14.88	2.505		213	154		367	465
0550	Threshold, 115 W		14.88	2.505		305	154		459	565
0560	Taxiway, 30 W		14.88	2.505		169	154		323	415
0570	Fixture, 200 W, w/base and transformer		11.85	3.146		865	194		1,059	1,250
0580	Elevated threshold marker, quartz, 115 W		14.88	2.505		380	154		534	650
0590	175 W	↓	14.88	2.505	↓	380	154		534	650

34 43 23 – Weather Observation Equipment

34 43 23.16 Airfield Wind Cones		Crew	Daily Output	Labor-Hours	Unit	Material	Labor	Equipment	Total	Total Incl O&P
0010	AIRFIELD WIND CONES									
1200	Wind cone, 12' lighted assembly, rigid, w/obstruction light	R-21	1.36	24.118	Ea.	5,225	1,625	68.50	6,918.50	8,250
1210	Without obstruction light		1.52	21.579		4,825	1,450	61	6,336	7,525
1220	Unlighted assembly, w/obstruction light		1.68	19.524		7,575	1,325	55.50	8,955.50	10,300
1230	Without obstruction light		1.84	17.826		6,950	1,200	50.50	8,200.50	9,450
1240	Wind cone slip fitter, 2-1/2" pipe		21.84	1.502		92.50	101	4.25	197.75	257
1250	Wind cone sock, 12' x 3', cotton		6.56	5		189	335	14.15	538.15	725
1260	Nylon	↓	6.56	5	↓	287	335	14.15	636.15	830

Estimating Tips

- When estimating costs for the installation of electrical power generation equipment, factors to review include access to the job site, access and setting up at the installation site, required connections, uncrating pads, anchors, leveling, final assembly of the components, and temporary protection from physical damage, such as environmental exposure.
- Be aware of the costs of equipment supports, concrete pads, and vibration isolators. Cross-reference them against other trades' specifications. Also, review site and structural drawings for items that must be included in the estimates.
- It is important to include items that are not documented in the plans and specifications but must be priced. These items include, but are not limited to, testing, dust protection, roof penetration, core drilling concrete floors and walls, patching, cleanup, and final adjustments. Add a contingency or allowance for utility company fees for power hookups, if needed.
- The project size and scope of electrical power generation equipment will have a significant impact on cost. The intent of RSMeans cost data is to provide a benchmark cost so that owners, engineers, and electrical contractors will have a comfortable number with which to start a project. Additionally, there are many websites available to use for research and to obtain a vendor's quote to finalize costs.

Reference Numbers

Reference numbers are shown at the beginning of some major classifications. These numbers refer to related items in the Reference Section. The reference information may be an estimating procedure, an alternate pricing method, or technical information.

Note: Trade Service, in part, has been used as a reference source for some of the material prices used in Division 48.

48 13 Hydroelectric Plant Electrical Power Generation Equipment

48 13 13 – Hydroelectric Power Plant Water Turbines

48 13 13.10 Water Turbines and Components		Crew	Daily Output	Labor-Hours	Unit	Material	2023 Bare Costs Labor	Equipment	Total	Total Incl O&P
0010	**WATER TURBINES & COMPONENTS**									
0500	Water turbine, 100-500 watt, 3P, 48VDC, 54″W x 24″H, 260LBS	2 Elec	2	8	Ea.	11,900	540		12,440	13,900
0600	Water turbine, 1500-2000 watt, 3P, 130-200VAC to DC, 95LBS	″	3	5.333	″	4,500	360		4,860	5,475

48 15 Wind Energy Electrical Power Generation Equipment

48 15 13 – Wind Turbines

48 15 13.50 Wind Turbines and Components		Crew	Daily Output	Labor-Hours	Unit	Material	Labor	Equipment	Total	Total Incl O&P
0010	**WIND TURBINES & COMPONENTS**									
0500	Complete system, grid connected									
0501	Wind turbine marine rated, 160 W, 12 V, DC	2 Elec	2.20	7.273	Ea.	1,250	490		1,740	2,100
0510	160 W, 24 V, DC		2.20	7.273		1,275	490		1,765	2,125
0520	160 W, 48 V, DC		2.20	7.273		1,275	490		1,765	2,125
1000	20 kW, 31′ diam., incl. labor & material G				System				49,900	49,900
1001	Wind turbine, 300 W, 12 V, DC	2 Elec	2.20	7.273	Ea.	950	490		1,440	1,775
1011	300 W, 24 V, DC		2.20	7.273		950	490		1,440	1,775
1020	300 W, 48 V, DC		2.20	7.273		950	490		1,440	1,775
1030	Wind turbine, 400 W, 12 V, DC		2.20	7.273		1,000	490		1,490	1,825
1040	400 W, 24 V, DC		2.20	7.273		1,000	490		1,490	1,825
1050	400 W, 48 V, DC		2.20	7.273		1,000	490		1,490	1,825
2000	2.4 kW, 12′ diam., incl. labor & material G				System				18,000	18,000
2900	Component system									
3200	1,000 W, 9′ diam. G	1 Elec	2.05	3.902	Ea.	1,500	263		1,763	2,050
3300	Wind turbine/charge control, 2,900-7,900 W, 5.5″ H x 11′ W, 180 lb.	2 Elec	2	8		17,700	540		18,240	20,300
3320	Wind turbine/charge control, 4,000-10,800 W, 5.5″ H x 13′ W, 240 lb.	″	2	8		29,400	540		29,940	33,100
3400	Mounting hardware									
3401	Wind turbine tower, 2 stage steel, 8′ H x 6′ W	2 Elec	2	8	Ea.	2,225	540		2,765	3,250
3500	30′ guyed tower kit G	2 Clab	5.12	3.125		440	148		588	705
3505	3′ galvanized helical earth screw G	1 Clab	8	1		62	47.50		109.50	139
3510	Attic mount kit G	1 Rofc	2.56	3.125		248	162		410	535
3520	Roof mount kit G	1 Clab	3.41	2.346		263	111		374	455
4000	Anemometer, standard AC or 9V, 2-digit LCD, wood case, +/-2% of Input	2 Elec	2	8		190	540		730	1,000
8900	Equipment									
9100	DC to AC inverter for, 48 V, 4,000 W G	1 Elec	2	4	Ea.	2,275	269		2,544	2,900

48 18 Fuel Cell Electrical Power Generation Equipment

48 18 13 – Electrical Power Generation Fuel Cells

48 18 13.10 Fuel Cells		Crew	Daily Output	Labor-Hours	Unit	Material	Labor	Equipment	Total	Total Incl O&P
0010	**FUEL CELLS**									
2001	Complete system, natural gas, installed, 200 kW G				System				1,150,000	1,150,000
2002	400 kW G								2,168,000	2,168,000
2003	600 kW G								3,060,000	3,060,000
2004	800 kW G								4,000,000	4,000,000
2005	1,000 kW G								5,005,000	5,005,000
2010	Comm type, for battery charging, uses hydrogen, 100 W, 12 V G				Ea.	1,575			1,575	1,725
2020	500 W, 12 V G					9,475			9,475	10,400
2030	1,000 W, 48 V G					12,300			12,300	13,500
2040	Small, for demonstration or battery charging units, 12 V G					600			600	660
2050	Spare anode set for unit G					55			55	60.50
2060	3 W, uses hydrogen gas G					315			315	345

48 18 Fuel Cell Electrical Power Generation Equipment

48 18 13 – Electrical Power Generation Fuel Cells

48 18 13.10 Fuel Cells		Crew	Daily Output	Labor-Hours	Unit	2023 Bare Costs Material	Labor	Equipment	Total	Total Incl O&P
2070	6 W, uses hydrogen gas G				Ea.	595			595	655
2080	10 W, uses hydrogen gas G				↓	725			725	800

Assemblies Section

Table of Contents

RSMeans data: Assemblies— How They Work

Assemblies estimating provides a fast and reasonably accurate way to develop construction costs. An assembly is the grouping of individual work items – with appropriate quantities – to provide a cost for a major construction component in a convenient unit of measure.

An assemblies estimate is often used during early stages of design development to compare the cost impact of various design alternatives on total building cost.

Assemblies estimates are also used as an efficient tool to verify construction estimates.

Assemblies estimates do not require a completed design or detailed drawings. Instead, they are based on the general size of the structure and other known parameters of the project. The degree of accuracy of an assemblies estimate is generally within +/- 15%.

Most assemblies consist of three major elements: a graphic, the system components, and the cost data itself. The **graphic** is a visual representation showing the typical appearance of the assembly

1 Unique 12-Character Identifier

Our assemblies are identified by a **unique 12-character identifier**. The assemblies are numbered using UNIFORMAT II, ASTM Standard E1557. The first five characters represent this system to level three. The last seven characters represent further breakdown in order to arrange items in understandable groups of similar tasks. Line numbers are consistent across all of our publications, so a line number in any assemblies data set will always refer to the same item.

2 Reference Box

Information is available in the Reference Section to assist the estimator with estimating procedures, alternate pricing methods, and additional technical information.

The **Reference Box** indicates the exact location of this information in the Reference Section. The "R" stands for "reference," and the remaining characters are the line numbers.

3 Narrative Descriptions

Our assemblies descriptions appear in two formats: narrative and table. **Narrative descriptions** are shown in a hierarchical structure to make them readable. In order to read a complete description, read up through the indents to the top of the section. Include everything that is above and to the left that is not contradicted by information below.

D20 Plumbing

D2020 Domestic Water Distribution

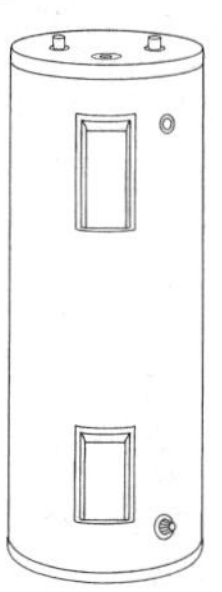

Installation includes piping and fittings within 10′ of heater. Electric water heaters do not require venting.

1 Kilowatt hour will raise:			
Gallons of Water	Degrees F	Gallons of Water	Degrees F
4.1	100°	6.8	60°
4.5	90°	8.2	50°
5.1	80°	10.0	40°
5.9	70°		

System Components	QUANTITY	UNIT	COST EACH MAT.	COST EACH INST.	COST EACH TOTAL
1 SYSTEM D2020 210 1780					
ELECTRIC WATER HEATER, RESIDENTIAL, 100°F RISE					
10 GALLON TANK, 7 GPH					
Water heater, residential electric, glass lined tank, 10 gal.	1.000	Ea.	485	375	860
Copper tubing, type L, solder joint, hanger 10′ OC 1/2″ diam.	30.000	L.F.	162	318	480
Wrought copper 90° elbow for solder joints 1/2″ diam.	4.000	Ea.	13	172	185
Wrought copper Tee for solder joints, 1/2″ diam.	2.000	Ea.	4.16	132	136.16
Union, wrought copper, 1/2″ diam.	2.000	Ea.	142	90	232
Valve, gate, bronze, 125 lb, NRS, soldered 1/2″ diam.	2.000	Ea.	254	72	326
Relief valve, bronze, press & temp, self-close, 3/4″ IPS	1.000	Ea.	335	30.50	365.50
Wrought copper adapter, CTS to MPT 3/4″ IPS	1.000	Ea.	18.15	50.50	68.65
Copper tubing, type L, solder joints, 3/4″ diam.	1.000	L.F.	7.05	11.30	18.35
Wrought copper 90° elbow for solder joints 3/4″ diam.	1.000	Ea.	7.15	45	52.15
TOTAL			1,427.51	1,296.30	2,723.81

D2020 210	Electric Water Heaters - Residential Systems	COST EACH MAT.	COST EACH INST.	COST EACH TOTAL
1760	Electric water heater, residential, 100°F rise			
1780	10 gallon tank, 7 GPH	1,425	1,300	2,725
1820	20 gallon tank, 7 GPH (2) R224000-20	1,625	1,375	3,000
1860	30 gallon tank, 7 GPH	2,225	1,450	3,675
1900	(3) 40 gallon tank, 8 GPH	2,525	1,600	4,125
1940	52 gallon tank, 10 GPH	3,225	1,600	4,825
1980	66 gallon tank, 13 GPH	4,850	1,850	6,700
2020	80 gallon tank, 16 GPH	5,175	1,925	7,100
2060	120 gallon tank, 23 GPH	7,375	2,250	9,625

For supplemental customizable square foot estimating forms, visit: **RSMeans.com/2023books** in question. It is frequently accompanied by additional explanatory technical information describing the class of items. The **System Components** is a listing of the individual tasks that make up the assembly, including the quantity and unit of measure for each item, along with the cost of material and installation. The **Assemblies data** below lists prices for other similar systems with dimensional and/or size variations.

All of our assemblies costs represent the cost for the installing contractor. An allowance for profit has been added to all material, labor, and equipment rental costs. A markup for labor burdens, including workers' compensation, fixed overhead, and business overhead, is included with installation costs.

The information in RSMeans cost data represents a "national average" cost. This data should be modified to the project location using the **City Cost Indexes** or **Location Factors** tables found in the Reference Section.

D20 Plumbing

D2020 Domestic Water Distribution

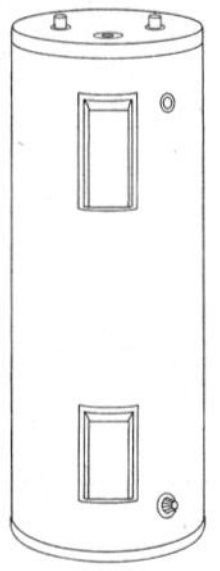

Installation includes piping and fittings within 10′ of heater. Electric water heaters do not require venting.

1 Kilowatt hour will raise:			
Gallons of Water	Degrees F	Gallons of Water	Degrees F
4.1	100°	6.8	60°
4.5	90°	8.2	50°
5.1	80°	10.0	40°
5.9	70°		

System Components (5)	QUANTITY	UNIT	COST EACH (4) MAT.	INST.	TOTAL
SYSTEM D2020 210 1780					
ELECTRIC WATER HEATER, RESIDENTIAL, 100°F RISE					
10 GALLON TANK, 7 GPH					
Water heater, residential electric, glass lined tank, 10 gal.	1.000	Ea.	485	375	860
Copper tubing, type L, solder joint, hanger 10′ OC 1/2″ diam.	30.000	L.F.	162	318	480
Wrought copper 90° elbow for solder joints 1/2″ diam.	4.000	Ea.	13	172	185
Wrought copper Tee for solder joints, 1/2″ diam.	2.000	Ea.	4.16	132	136.16
Union, wrought copper, 1/2″ diam.	2.000	Ea.	142	90	232
Valve, gate, bronze, 125 lb, NRS, soldered 1/2″ diam.	2.000	Ea.	254	72	326
Relief valve, bronze, press & temp, self-close, 3/4″ IPS	1.000	Ea.	335	30.50	365.50
Wrought copper adapter, CTS to MPT 3/4″ IPS	1.000	Ea.	18.15	50.50	68.65
Copper tubing, type L, solder joints, 3/4″ diam.	1.000	L.F.	7.05	11.30	18.35
Wrought copper 90° elbow for solder joints 3/4″ diam.	1.000	Ea.	7.15	45	52.15
TOTAL			1,427.51	1,296.30	2,723.81

D2020 210	Electric Water Heaters - Residential Systems	COST EACH MAT.	INST.	TOTAL
1760	Electric water heater, residential, 100°F rise			
1780	10 gallon tank, 7 GPH	1,425	1,300	2,725
1820	20 gallon tank, 7 GPH (R224000 -20)	1,625	1,375	3,000
1860	30 gallon tank, 7 GPH	2,225	1,450	3,675
1900	40 gallon tank, 8 GPH	2,525	1,600	4,125
1940	52 gallon tank, 10 GPH	3,225	1,600	4,825
1980	66 gallon tank, 13 GPH	4,850	1,850	6,700
2020	80 gallon tank, 16 GPH	5,175	1,925	7,100
2060	120 gallon tank, 23 GPH	7,375	2,250	9,625

4 Unit of Measure

All RSMeans data: Assemblies include a typical **Unit of Measure** used for estimating that item. For instance, for continuous footings or foundation walls the unit is linear feet (L.F.). For spread footings the unit is each (Ea.). The estimator needs to take special care that the unit in the data matches the unit in the takeoff. Abbreviations and unit conversions can be found in the Reference Section.

5 System Components

System Components are listed separately to detail what is included in the development of the total system price.

RSMeans data: Assemblies—How They Work (Continued)

Sample Estimate

This sample demonstrates the elements of an estimate, including a tally of the RSMeans data lines. Published assemblies costs include all markups for labor burden and profit for the installing contractor. This estimate adds a summary of the markups applied by a general contractor on the installing contractor's work. These figures represent the total cost to the owner. The location factor with RSMeans data is applied at the bottom of the estimate to adjust the cost of the work to a specific location.

Project Name:	Interior Fit-out, ABC Office			
Location:	Anywhere, USA	Date: 1/1/2023		STD
Assembly Number	Description	Qty.	Unit	Subtotal
1 C1010 124 1200	Wood partition, 2 x 4 @ 16" OC w/5/8" FR gypsum board	560	S.F.	$3,656.80
C1020 114 1800	Metal door & frame, flush hollow core, 3'-0" x 7'-0"	2	Ea.	$2,370.00
C3010 230 0080	Painting, brushwork, primer & 2 coats	1,120	S.F.	$1,556.80
C3020 410 0140	Carpet, tufted, nylon, roll goods, 12' wide, 26 oz	240	S.F.	$703.20
C3030 210 6000	Acoustic ceilings, 24" x 48" tile, tee grid suspension	200	S.F.	$1,896.00
D5020 125 0560	Receptacles incl plate, box, conduit, wire, 20 A duplex	8	Ea.	$2,844.00
D5020 125 0720	Light switch incl plate, box, conduit, wire, 20 A single pole	2	Ea.	$692.00
D5020 210 0560	Fluorescent fixtures, recess mounted, 20 per 1000 SF	200	S.F.	$3,310.00
	Assembly Subtotal			**$17,028.80**
	Sales Tax @ 2	**5 %**		**$ 425.72**
	General Requirements @ 3	**7 %**		**$ 1,192.02**
	Subtotal A			**$18,646.54**
	GC Overhead @ 4	**5 %**		**$ 932.33**
	Subtotal B			**$19,578.86**
	GC Profit @ 5	**5 %**		**$ 978.94**
	Subtotal C			**$20,557.81**
	Adjusted by Location Factor 6	**112.5**		**$ 23,127.53**
	Architects Fee @ 7	**8 %**		**$ 1,850.20**
	Contingency @ 8	**15 %**		**$ 3,469.13**
	Project Total Cost			**$ 28,446.86**

This estimate is based on an interactive spreadsheet. You are free to download it and adjust it to your methodology.
A copy of this spreadsheet is available at **RSMeans.com/2023books.**

1 Work Performed

The body of the estimate shows the RSMeans data selected, including line numbers, a brief description of each item, its takeoff quantity and unit, and the total installed cost, including the installing contractor's overhead and profit.

2 Sales Tax

If the work is subject to state or local sales taxes, the amount must be added to the estimate. In a conceptual estimate, it can be assumed that one half of the total represents material costs. Therefore, apply the sales tax rate to 50% of the assembly subtotal.

3 General Requirements

This item covers project-wide needs provided by the general contractor. These items vary by project but may include temporary facilities and utilities, security, testing, project cleanup, etc. In assemblies estimates a percentage is used—typically between 5% and 15% of project cost.

4 General Contractor Overhead

This entry represents the general contractor's markup on all work to cover project administration costs.

5 General Contractor Profit

This entry represents the General Contractor's profit on all work performed. The value included here can vary widely by project and is influenced by the General Contractor's perception of the project's financial risk and market conditions.

6 Location Factor

RSMeans published data are based on national average costs. If necessary, adjust the total cost of the project using a location factor from the "Location Factor" table or the "City Cost Indexes" table found in the Reference Section. Use location factors if the work is general, covering the work of multiple trades. If the work is by a single trade (e.g., masonry), use the more specific data found in the City Cost Indexes.

To adjust costs by location factors, multiply the base cost by the factor and divide by 100.

7 Architect's Fee

If appropriate, add the design cost to the project estimate. These fees vary based on project complexity and size. Typical design and engineering fees can be found in the Reference Section.

8 Contingency

A factor for contingency may be added to any estimate to represent the cost of unknowns that may occur between the time that the estimate is performed and the time the project is constructed. The amount of the allowance will depend on the stage of design at which the estimate is done, as well as the contractor's assessment of the risk involved.

D2020 Domestic Water Distribution

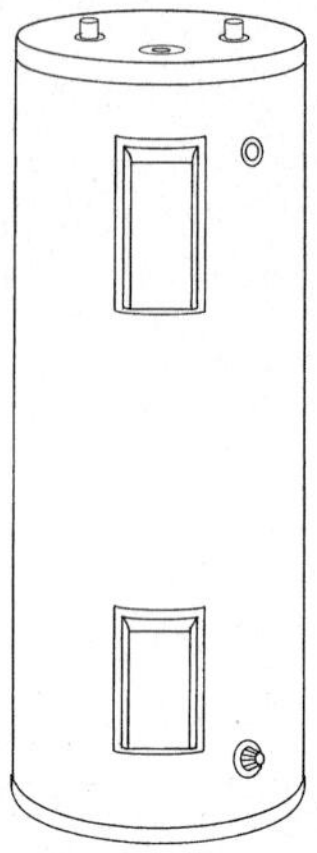

Installation includes piping and fittings within 10′ of heater. Electric water heaters do not require venting.

1 Kilowatt hour will raise:			
Gallons of Water	Degrees F	Gallons of Water	Degrees F
4.1	100°	6.8	60°
4.5	90°	8.2	50°
5.1	80°	10.0	40°
5.9	70°		

System Components	QUANTITY	UNIT	COST EACH MAT.	COST EACH INST.	COST EACH TOTAL
SYSTEM D2020 210 1780					
ELECTRIC WATER HEATER, RESIDENTIAL, 100°F RISE					
10 GALLON TANK, 7 GPH					
Water heater, residential electric, glass lined tank, 10 gal.	1.000	Ea.	485	375	860
Copper tubing, type L, solder joint, hanger 10′ OC 1/2″ diam.	30.000	L.F.	162	318	480
Wrought copper 90° elbow for solder joints 1/2″ diam.	4.000	Ea.	13	172	185
Wrought copper Tee for solder joints, 1/2″ diam.	2.000	Ea.	4.16	132	136.16
Union, wrought copper, 1/2″ diam.	2.000	Ea.	142	90	232
Valve, gate, bronze, 125 lb, NRS, soldered 1/2″ diam.	2.000	Ea.	254	72	326
Relief valve, bronze, press & temp, self-close, 3/4″ IPS	1.000	Ea.	335	30.50	365.50
Wrought copper adapter, CTS to MPT 3/4″ IPS	1.000	Ea.	18.15	50.50	68.65
Copper tubing, type L, solder joints, 3/4″ diam.	1.000	L.F.	7.05	11.30	18.35
Wrought copper 90° elbow for solder joints 3/4″ diam.	1.000	Ea.	7.15	45	52.15
TOTAL			1,427.51	1,296.30	2,723.81

D2020 210	Electric Water Heaters - Residential Systems	COST EACH MAT.	COST EACH INST.	COST EACH TOTAL
1760	Electric water heater, residential, 100°F rise			
1780	10 gallon tank, 7 GPH	1,425	1,300	2,725
1820	20 gallon tank, 7 GPH R224000-20	1,625	1,375	3,000
1860	30 gallon tank, 7 GPH	2,225	1,450	3,675
1900	40 gallon tank, 8 GPH	2,525	1,600	4,125
1940	52 gallon tank, 10 GPH	3,225	1,600	4,825
1980	66 gallon tank, 13 GPH	4,850	1,850	6,700
2020	80 gallon tank, 16 GPH	5,175	1,925	7,100
2060	120 gallon tank, 23 GPH	7,375	2,250	9,625

D2020 Domestic Water Distribution

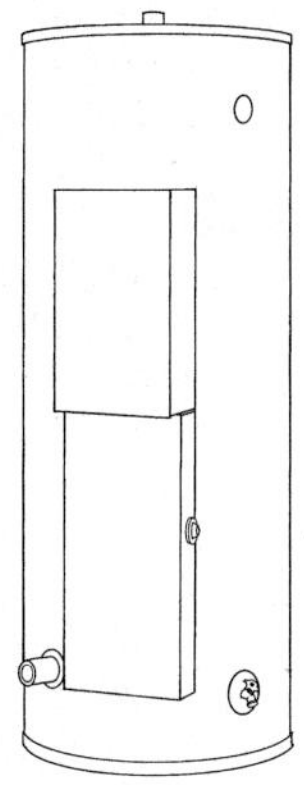

Systems below include piping and fittings within 10′ of heater. Electric water heaters do not require venting.

System Components	QUANTITY	UNIT	COST EACH MAT.	COST EACH INST.	COST EACH TOTAL
SYSTEM D2020 240 1820					
ELECTRIC WATER HEATER, COMMERCIAL, 100°F RISE					
50 GALLON TANK, 9 KW, 37 GPH					
Water heater, commercial, electric, 50 Gal, 9 KW, 37 GPH	1.000	Ea.	7,150	480	7,630
Copper tubing, type L, solder joint, hanger 10′ OC, 3/4″ diam	34.000	L.F.	239.70	384.20	623.90
Wrought copper 90° elbow for solder joints 3/4″ diam	5.000	Ea.	35.75	225	260.75
Wrought copper Tee for solder joints, 3/4″ diam	2.000	Ea.	26.30	143	169.30
Wrought copper union for soldered joints, 3/4″ diam.	2.000	Ea.	178	96	274
Valve, gate, bronze, 125 lb, NRS, soldered 3/4″ diam	2.000	Ea.	278	86	364
Relief valve, bronze, press & temp, self-close, 3/4″ IPS	1.000	Ea.	335	30.50	365.50
Wrought copper adapter, copper tubing to male, 3/4″ IPS	1.000	Ea.	18.15	50.50	68.65
TOTAL			8,260.90	1,495.20	9,756.10

D2020 240	Electric Water Heaters - Commercial Systems		COST EACH MAT.	COST EACH INST.	COST EACH TOTAL
1800	Electric water heater, commercial, 100°F rise				
1820	50 gallon tank, 9 KW 37 GPH		8,250	1,500	9,750
1860	80 gal, 12 KW 49 GPH	R224000 -10	10,800	1,850	12,650
1900	36 KW 147 GPH		16,100	2,000	18,100
1940	120 gal, 36 KW 147 GPH	R224000 -20	17,700	2,150	19,850
1980	150 gal, 120 KW 490 GPH		56,500	2,300	58,800
2020	200 gal, 120 KW 490 GPH		59,000	2,375	61,375
2060	250 gal, 150 KW 615 GPH		57,000	2,750	59,750
2100	300 gal, 180 KW 738 GPH		86,500	2,925	89,425
2140	350 gal, 30 KW 123 GPH		46,300	3,125	49,425
2180	180 KW 738 GPH		64,000	3,125	67,125
2220	500 gal, 30 KW 123 GPH		72,000	3,675	75,675
2260	240 KW 984 GPH		117,000	3,675	120,675
2300	700 gal, 30 KW 123 GPH		72,000	4,225	76,225
2340	300 KW 1230 GPH		106,000	4,225	110,225
2380	1000 gal, 60 KW 245 GPH		88,500	5,900	94,400
2420	480 KW 1970 GPH		141,000	5,900	146,900
2460	1500 gal, 60 KW 245 GPH		127,500	7,275	134,775
2500	480 KW 1970 GPH		173,500	7,275	180,775

D3020 Heat Generating Systems

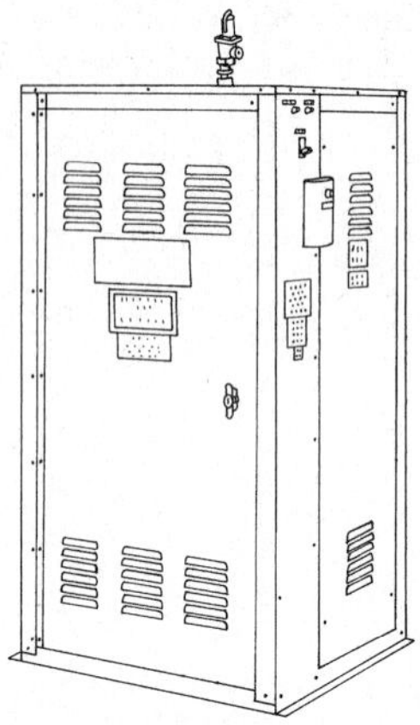

Boiler

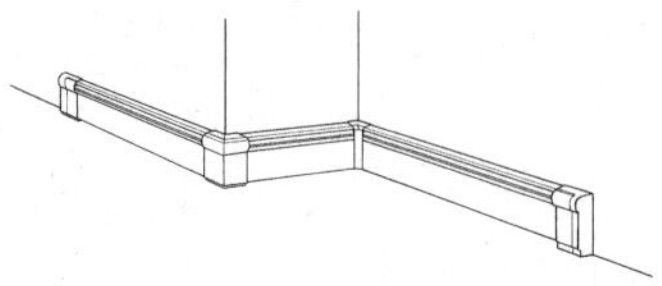

Baseboard Radiation

Small Electric Boiler System Considerations:

1. Terminal units are fin tube baseboard radiation rated at 720 BTU/hr with 200° water temperature or 820 BTU/hr steam.
2. Primary use being for residential or smaller supplementary areas, the floor levels are based on 7-1/2′ ceiling heights.
3. All distribution piping is copper for boilers through 205 MBH. All piping for larger systems is steel pipe.

System Components	QUANTITY	UNIT	COST EACH MAT.	COST EACH INST.	COST EACH TOTAL
SYSTEM D3020 102 1120					
SMALL HEATING SYSTEM, HYDRONIC, ELECTRIC BOILER					
1,480 S.F., 61 MBH, STEAM, 1 FLOOR					
Boiler, electric steam, std cntrls, trim, ftngs and valves, 18 KW, 61.4 MBH	1.000	Ea.	5,417.50	2,172.50	7,590
Copper tubing type L, solder joint, hanger 10′OC, 1-1/4″ diam	160.000	L.F.	1,560	2,368	3,928
Radiation, 3/4″ copper tube w/alum fin baseboard pkg 7″ high	60.000	L.F.	519	1,620	2,139
Rough in baseboard panel or fin tube with valves & traps	10.000	Set	4,900	8,150	13,050
Pipe covering, calcium silicate w/cover, 1″ wall 1-1/4″ diam	160.000	L.F.	1,080	1,392	2,472
Low water cut-off, quick hookup, in gage glass tappings	1.000	Ea.	595	54	649
TOTAL			14,071.50	15,756.50	29,828
COST PER S.F.			9.85	11.03	20.88

D3020 102	Small Heating Systems, Hydronic, Electric Boilers	COST PER S.F. MAT.	COST PER S.F. INST.	COST PER S.F. TOTAL
1100	Small heating systems, hydronic, electric boilers			
1120	Steam, 1 floor, 1480 S.F., 61 M.B.H.	9.87	11.06	20.93
1160	3,000 S.F., 123 M.B.H.	7.55	9.35	16.90
1200	5,000 S.F., 205 M.B.H.	6.65	8.60	15.25
1240	2 floors, 12,400 S.F., 512 M.B.H.	6.25	8.55	14.80
1280	3 floors, 24,800 S.F., 1023 M.B.H.	6.50	8.45	14.95
1320	34,750 S.F., 1,433 M.B.H.	6.05	8.20	14.25
1360	Hot water, 1 floor, 1,000 S.F., 41 M.B.H.	14.50	5.95	20.45
1400	2,500 S.F., 103 M.B.H.	11.15	10.65	21.80
1440	2 floors, 4,850 S.F., 205 M.B.H.	11.05	12.75	23.80
1480	3 floors, 9,700 S.F., 410 M.B.H.	11.95	13.25	25.20

D3020 Heat Generating Systems

Boiler

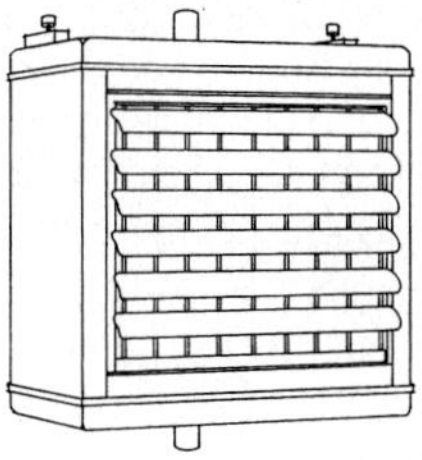

Unit Heater

Large Electric Boiler System Considerations:

1. Terminal units are all unit heaters of the same size. Quantities are varied to accommodate total requirements.
2. All air is circulated through the heaters a minimum of three times per hour.
3. As the capacities are adequate for commercial use, floor levels are based on 10′ ceiling heights.
4. All distribution piping is black steel pipe.

System Components	QUANTITY	UNIT	COST EACH MAT.	COST EACH INST.	COST EACH TOTAL
SYSTEM D3020 104 1240					
LARGE HEATING SYSTEM, HYDRONIC, ELECTRIC BOILER					
9,280 S.F., 135 KW, 461 MBH, 1 FLOOR					
Boiler, electric hot water, std ctrls, trim, ftngs, valves, 135 KW, 461 MBH	1.000	Ea.	12,487.50	4,725	17,212.50
Expansion tank, painted steel, 60 Gal capacity ASME	1.000	Ea.	6,525	260	6,785
Circulating pump, CI, close cpld, 50 GPM, 2 HP, 2″ pipe conn	1.000	Ea.	3,725	515	4,240
Unit heater, 1 speed propeller, horizontal, 200° EWT, 72.7 MBH	7.000	Ea.	11,900	1,981	13,881
Unit heater piping hookup with controls	7.000	Set	9,800	12,950	22,750
Pipe, steel, black, schedule 40, welded, 2-1/2″ diam	380.000	L.F.	13,680	13,110	26,790
Pipe covering, calcium silicate w/cover, 1″ wall, 2-1/2″ diam	380.000	L.F.	1,561.80	3,420	4,981.80
TOTAL			59,679.30	36,961	96,640.30
COST PER S.F.			5.97	3.70	9.67

D3020 104	Large Heating Systems, Hydronic, Electric Boilers	COST PER S.F. MAT.	COST PER S.F. INST.	COST PER S.F. TOTAL
1230	Large heating systems, hydronic, electric boilers			
1240	9,280 S.F., 135 K.W., 461 M.B.H., 1 floor	5.95	3.70	9.65
1280	14,900 S.F., 240 K.W., 820 M.B.H., 2 floors	8.90	6.45	15.35
1320	18,600 S.F., 296 K.W., 1,010 M.B.H., 3 floors	9.10	7	16.10
1360	26,100 S.F., 420 K.W., 1,432 M.B.H., 4 floors	8.95	6.85	15.80
1400	39,100 S.F., 666 K.W., 2,273 M.B.H., 4 floors	7.65	5.75	13.40
1440	57,700 S.F., 900 K.W., 3,071 M.B.H., 5 floors	8	5.65	13.65
1480	111,700 S.F., 1,800 K.W., 6,148 M.B.H., 6 floors	7.15	4.86	12.01
1520	149,000 S.F., 2,400 K.W., 8,191 M.B.H., 8 floors	7.10	4.85	11.95
1560	223,300 S.F., 3,600 K.W., 12,283 M.B.H., 14 floors	7.75	5.50	13.25

D4090 Other Fire Protection Systems

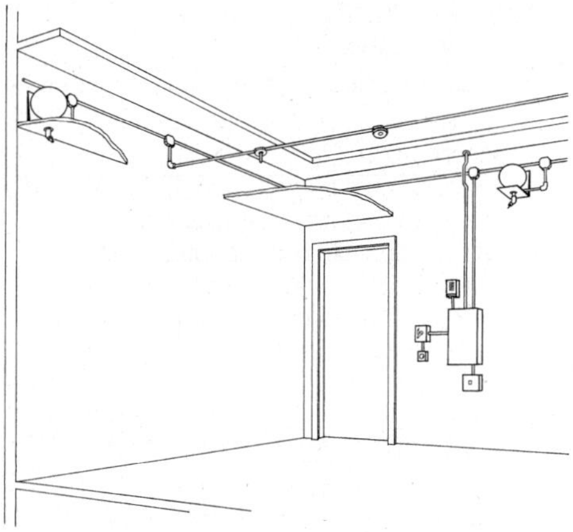

General: Automatic fire protection (suppression) systems other than water sprinklers may be desired for special environments, high risk areas, isolated locations or unusual hazards. Some typical applications would include:

- Paint dip tanks
- Securities vaults
- Electronic data processing
- Tape and data storage
- Transformer rooms
- Spray booths
- Petroleum storage
- High rack storage

Piping and wiring costs are dependent on the individual application and must be added to the component costs shown below.

All areas are assumed to be open.

D4090 910	Fire Suppression Unit Components	COST EACH		
		MAT.	INST.	TOTAL
0020	Detectors with brackets			
0040	Fixed temperature heat detector	48	114	162
0060	Rate of temperature rise detector	36.50	100	136.50
0080	Ion detector (smoke) detector	171	129	300
0200	Extinguisher agent			
0240	200 lb FM200, container	8,550	385	8,935
0280	75 lb carbon dioxide cylinder	1,725	258	1,983
0320	Dispersion nozzle			
0340	FM200 1-1/2" dispersion nozzle	310	61.50	371.50
0380	Carbon dioxide 3" x 5" dispersion nozzle	193	48	241
0420	Control station			
0440	Single zone control station with batteries	1,550	800	2,350
0470	Multizone (4) control station with batteries	3,750	1,600	5,350
0490				
0500	Electric mechanical release	1,275	415	1,690
0520				
0550	Manual pull station	112	143	255
0570				
0640	Battery standby power 10" x 10" x 17"	570	200	770
0700				
0740	Bell signalling device	62.50	100	162.50

D4090 920	FM200 Systems	COST PER C.F.		
		MAT.	INST.	TOTAL
0820	Average FM200 system, minimum	2.32		2.32
0840	Maximum	4.62		4.62

D5010 Electrical Service/Distribution

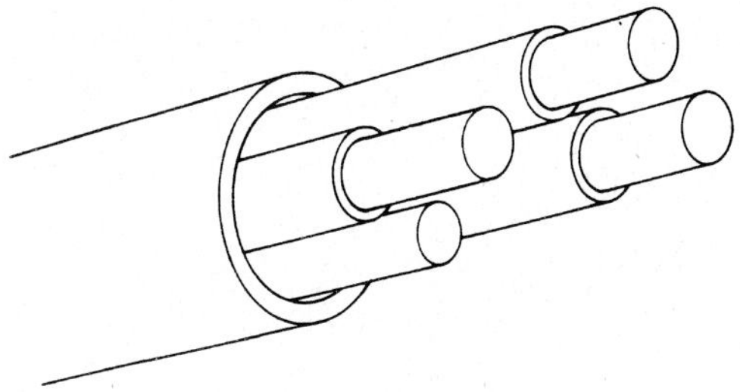

System Components	QUANTITY	UNIT	COST PER L.F. MAT.	INST.	TOTAL
SYSTEM D5010 110 0200					
HIGH VOLTAGE CABLE, NEUTRAL AND CONDUIT INCLUDED, COPPER #2, 5 kV					
Shielded cable, no splice/termn, copper, XLP shielding, 5 kV, #2	.030	C.L.F.	8.28	12	20.28
Wire, 600 volt, type THW, copper, stranded, #8	.010	C.L.F.	.58	1	1.58
Rigid galv steel conduit to 15′ H, 2″ diam, w/term, ftng & support	1.000	L.F.	17	17.80	34.80
TOTAL			25.86	30.80	56.66

D5010 110	High Voltage Shielded Conductors	COST PER L.F. MAT.	INST.	TOTAL
0200	High voltage cable, neutral & conduit included, copper #2, 5 kV	26	31	57
0240	Copper #1, 5 kV	46	36	82
0280	15 kV	47	36	83
0320	Copper 1/0, 5 kV	51	46	97
0360	15 kV	53	46	99
0400	25 kV	59	46.50	105.50
0440	35 kV	59.50	47.50	107
0480	Copper 2/0, 5 kV	53	47	100
0520	15 kV	56	47	103
0560	25 kV	62	47.50	109.50
0600	35 kV	75.50	53	128.50
0640	Copper 4/0, 5 kV	71.50	53.50	125
0680	15 kV	73	53.50	126.50
0720	25 kV	79.50	54.50	134
0760	35 kV	83	55.50	138.50
0800	Copper 250 kcmil, 5 kV	76	54.50	130.50
0840	15 kV	75.50	54.50	130
0880	25 kV	86.50	55.50	142
0920	35 kV	92	60	152
0960	Copper 350 kcmil, 5 kV	86.50	60	146.50
1000	15 kV	85	60	145
1040	25 kV	95.50	61.50	157
1080	35 kV	100	63.50	163.50
1120	Copper 500 kcmil, 5 kV	136	76	212
1160	15 kV	137	76	213
1200	25 kV	151	78	229
1240	35 kV	156	80	236

D5010 Electrical Service/Distribution

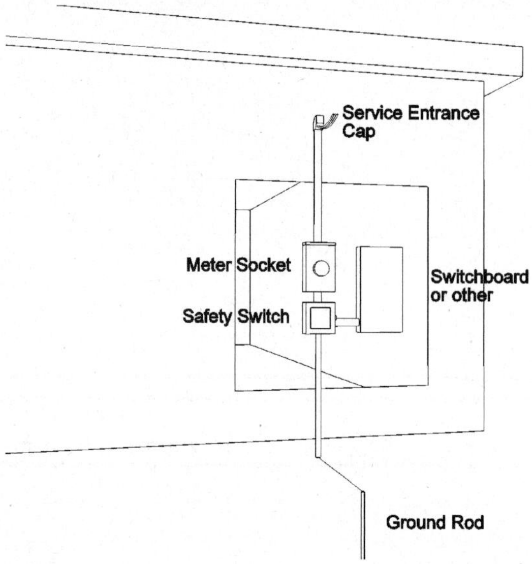

System Components	QUANTITY	UNIT	COST EACH MAT.	COST EACH INST.	COST EACH TOTAL
SYSTEM D5010 120 0220					
SERVICE INSTALLATION, INCLUDES BREAKERS, METERING, 20′ CONDUIT & WIRE					
3 PHASE, 4 WIRE, 60 A					
Wire, 600 volt, copper type XHHW, stranded #6	.600	C.L.F.	81.60	73.80	155.40
Rigid galvanized steel conduit, 3/4″ including fittings	20.000	L.F.	106	200	306
Service entrance cap, 3/4″ diameter	1.000	Ea.	10.85	61.50	72.35
Conduit LB fitting with cover, 3/4″ diameter	1.000	Ea.	14.30	61.50	75.80
Meter socket, three phase, 100 A	1.000	Ea.	201	286	487
Safety switches, heavy duty, 240 volt, 3 pole NEMA 1 fusible, 60 amp	1.000	Ea.	250	350	600
Grounding, wire ground bare armored, #8-1 conductor	.200	C.L.F.	17.10	80	97.10
Grounding, clamp, bronze, 3/4″ diameter	1.000	Ea.	4.70	25	29.70
Grounding, rod, copper clad, 8′ long, 3/4″ diameter	1.000	Ea.	55	151	206
Wireway w/fittings, 2-1/2″ x 2-1/2″	1.000	L.F.	18.60	17.80	36.40
TOTAL			759.15	1,306.60	2,065.75

D5010 120	Overhead Electric Service, 3 Phase - 4 Wire	COST EACH MAT.	COST EACH INST.	COST EACH TOTAL
0200	Service installation, includes breakers, metering, 20′ conduit & wire			
0220	3 phase, 4 wire, 120/208 volts, 60 A	760	1,300	2,060
0240	100 A	1,025	1,475	2,500
0245	100 A w/circuit breaker	1,750	1,825	3,575
0280	200 A	1,925	2,025	3,950
0285	200 A w/circuit breaker	3,200	2,575	5,775
0320	400 A	3,825	4,050	7,875
0325	400 A w/circuit breaker	8,800	5,050	13,850
0360	600 A	7,050	6,000	13,050
0365	600 A, w/switchboard	12,500	7,600	20,100
0400	800 A	13,900	7,175	21,075
0405	800 A, w/switchboard	19,400	9,000	28,400
0440	1000 A	16,200	8,825	25,025
0445	1000 A, w/switchboard	22,800	10,800	33,600
0480	1200 A	23,000	10,100	33,100
0485	1200 A, w/groundfault switchboard	51,500	12,500	64,000
0520	1600 A	28,400	13,200	41,600
0525	1600 A, w/groundfault switchboard	59,500	15,800	75,300

D5010 Electrical Service/Distribution

D5010 120	Overhead Electric Service, 3 Phase - 4 Wire	COST EACH		
		MAT.	INST.	TOTAL
0560	2000 A	38,100	16,000	54,100
0565	2000 A, w/groundfault switchboard	73,500	19,700	93,200
0610	1 phase, 3 wire, 120/240 volts, 100 A (no safety switch)	310	720	1,030
0615	100 A w/load center	685	1,375	2,060
0620	200 A	900	990	1,890
0625	200 A w/load center	1,725	2,100	3,825

D5010 Electrical Service/Distribution

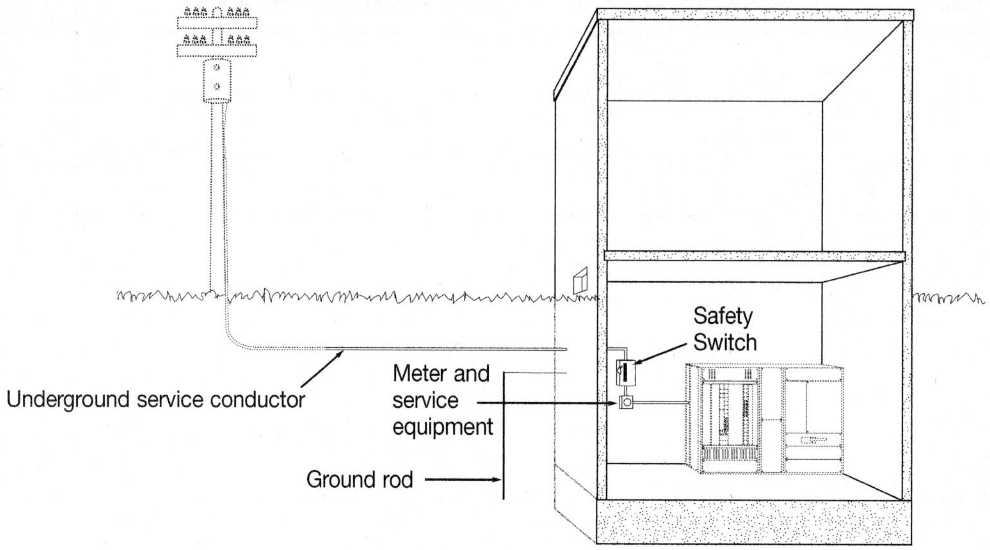

System Components	QUANTITY	UNIT	COST EACH MAT.	COST EACH INST.	COST EACH TOTAL
SYSTEM D5010 130 1000					
2000 AMP UNDERGROUND ELECTRIC SERVICE WITH SAFETY SWITCH					
INCLUDING EXCAVATION, BACKFILL AND COMPACTION					
Excavate Trench	44.440	C.Y.		387.96	387.96
4 inch conduit bank	108.000	L.F.	29,700	3,186	32,886
4 inch fitting	8.000	Ea.	564	532	1,096
4 inch bells	4.000	Ea.	25	266	291
Concrete material	16.580	C.Y.	2,818.60		2,818.60
Concrete placement	16.580	C.Y.		489.77	489.77
Backfill trench	33.710	L.C.Y.		123.71	123.71
Compact fill material in trench	25.930	C.Y.		148.84	148.84
Dispose of excess fill material on-site	24.070	L.C.Y.		352.38	352.38
500 kcmil power cable	18.000	C.L.F.	31,050	9,000	40,050
Wire, 600 volt, type THW, copper, stranded, 1/0	6.000	C.L.F.	1,980	1,458	3,438
Saw cutting, concrete walls, plain, per inch of depth	64.000	L.F.	2.56	672	674.56
Meter centers and sockets, single pos, 4 terminal, 400 amp	5.000	Ea.	18,125	2,350	20,475
Safety switch, 400 amp	5.000	Ea.	7,500	4,450	11,950
Ground rod clamp	6.000	Ea.	28.20	150	178.20
Wireway	1.000	L.F.	18.60	17.80	36.40
600 volt stranded copper wire, 1/0	1.200	C.L.F.	396	291.60	687.60
Flexible metallic conduit	120.000	L.F.	112.80	600	712.80
Ground rod	6.000	Ea.	672	1,200	1,872
TOTAL			92,992.76	25,676.06	118,668.82

D5010 130	Underground Electric Service	COST EACH MAT.	COST EACH INST.	COST EACH TOTAL
0950	Underground electric service including excavation, backfill and compaction			
1000	3 phase, 4 wire, 277/480 volts, 2000 A	93,000	25,700	118,700
1050	2000 A w/groundfault switchboard	127,000	28,500	155,500
1100	1600 A	70,500	20,700	91,200
1150	1600 A w/groundfault switchboard	101,500	23,300	124,800
1200	1200 A	58,000	16,500	74,500
1250	1200 A w/groundfault switchboard	86,500	18,900	105,400
1400	800 A	27,500	13,700	41,200

D5010 Electrical Service/Distribution

D5010 130	Underground Electric Service	COST EACH MAT.	COST EACH INST.	COST EACH TOTAL
1450	800 A w/switchboard	33,000	15,500	48,500
1500	600 A	17,200	12,600	29,800
1550	600 A w/switchboard	22,700	14,200	36,900
1600	1 phase, 3 wire, 120/240 volts, 200 A	5,150	4,375	9,525
1650	200 A w/load center	5,950	5,475	11,425
1700	100 A	3,800	3,575	7,375
1750	100 A w/load center	4,625	4,675	9,300

D5010 Electrical Service/Distribution

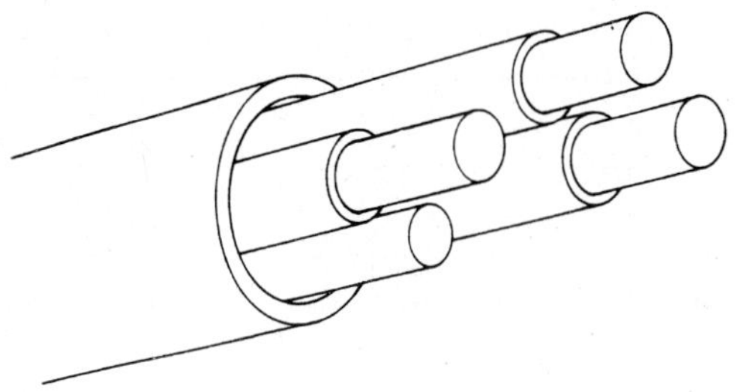

System Components	QUANTITY	UNIT	COST PER L.F.		
			MAT.	INST.	TOTAL
SYSTEM D5010 230 0200					
FEEDERS, INCLUDING STEEL CONDUIT & WIRE, 60 A					
Rigid galvanized steel conduit, 3/4", including fittings	1.000	L.F.	5.30	10	15.30
Wire 600 volt, type XHHW copper stranded #6	.030	C.L.F.	4.08	3.69	7.77
Wire 600 volt, type XHHW copper stranded #8	.010	C.L.F.	.87	1	1.87
TOTAL			10.25	14.69	24.94

D5010 230	Feeder Installation	COST PER L.F.		
		MAT.	INST.	TOTAL
0200	Feeder installation 600 V, including RGS conduit and XHHW wire, 60 A	10.25	14.70	24.95
0240	100 A	20	19.15	39.15
0280	200 A	39	29	68
0320	400 A	78	58	136
0360	600 A	158	94.50	252.50
0400	800 A	211	112	323
0440	1000 A	261	147	408
0480	1200 A	315	189	504
0520	1600 A	420	224	644
0560	2000 A	520	294	814
1200	Branch installation 600 V, including EMT conduit and THW wire, 15 A	2.10	7.15	9.25
1240	20 A	2.39	7.65	10.04
1280	30 A	2.89	7.90	10.79
1320	50 A	5.95	10.95	16.90
1360	65 A	6.70	11.65	18.35
1400	85 A	11.20	13.55	24.75
1440	100 A	12.15	13.80	25.95
1480	130 A	16.45	16.15	32.60
1520	150 A	19.85	18.50	38.35
1560	200 A	27	21	48

D5010 Electrical Service/Distribution

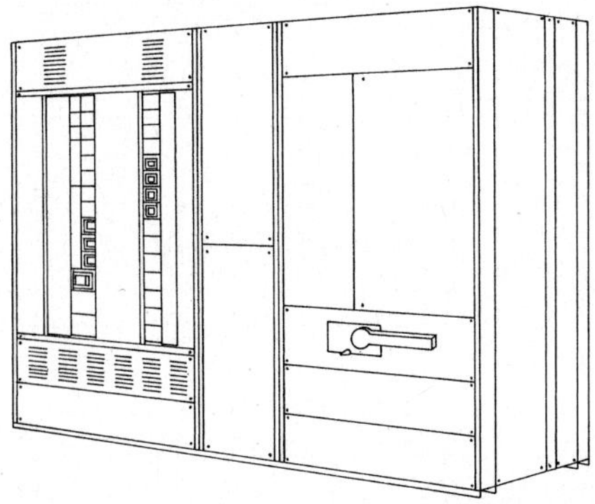

System Components	QUANTITY	UNIT	COST EACH MAT.	INST.	TOTAL
SYSTEM D5010 240 0240					
SWITCHGEAR INSTALLATION, INCL SWBD, PANELS & CIRC BREAKERS, 600 A					
Switchboards, 120/208 V, 600 amp	1.000	Ea.	5,475	1,600	7,075
Aluminum bus bars, 120/208 V, 600 amp	1.000	Ea.	1,750	1,600	3,350
Feeder section, circuit breakers, KA frame, 70 to 225 amp	1.000	Ea.	1,600	250	1,850
Feeder section, circuit breakers, LA frame, 125 to 400 amp	1.000	Ea.	4,800	350	5,150
TOTAL			13,625	3,800	17,425

D5010 240	Switchgear	COST PER EACH MAT.	INST.	TOTAL
0190	Switchgear installation, including switchboard, panels, & circuit breaker			
0200	120/208 V, 3 phase, 400 A	9,975	3,400	13,375
0240	600 A	13,600	3,800	17,400
0280	800 A	15,900	4,400	20,300
0300	1000 A	17,700	4,875	22,575
0320	1200 A	20,400	5,500	25,900
0360	1600 A	33,100	6,350	39,450
0400	2000 A	40,100	6,900	47,000
0500	277/480 V, 3 phase, 400 A	13,700	6,300	20,000
0520	600 A	18,700	7,250	25,950
0540	800 A	20,400	8,050	28,450
0560	1000 A	23,700	8,875	32,575
0580	1200 A	27,500	9,950	37,450
0600	1600 A	42,300	11,000	53,300
0620	2000 A	53,500	12,100	65,600

D5010 Electrical Service/Distribution

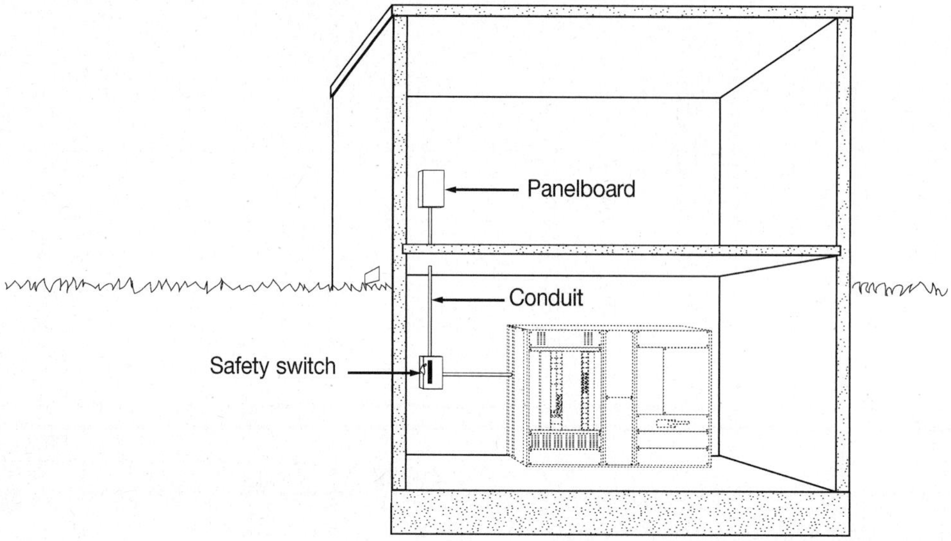

System Components	QUANTITY	UNIT	COST EACH MAT.	COST EACH INST.	COST EACH TOTAL
SYSTEM D5010 250 1020					
PANELBOARD INSTALLATION, INCLUDES PANELBOARD, CONDUCTOR, & CONDUIT					
Conduit, galvanized steel, 1-1/4"dia.	37.000	L.F.	436.60	493.95	930.55
Panelboards, NQOD, 4 wire, 120/208 volts, 100 amp main, 24 circuits	1.000	Ea.	2,700	1,700	4,400
Wire, 600 volt, type THW, copper, stranded, #3	1.480	C.L.F.	278.24	236.80	515.04
TOTAL			3,414.84	2,430.75	5,845.59

D5010 250	Panelboard	COST EACH MAT.	COST EACH INST.	COST EACH TOTAL
0900	Panelboards, NQOD, 4 wire, 120/208 volts w/conductor & conduit			
1000	100 A, 0 stories, 0′ horizontal	2,525	4,275	6,800
1020	1 story, 25′ horizontal	3,425	2,425	5,850
1040	5 stories, 50′ horizontal	4,825	3,875	8,700
1060	10 stories, 75′ horizontal	6,475	5,550	12,025
1080	225A, 0 stories, 0′ horizontal	3,050	2,225	5,275
2000	1 story, 25′ horizontal	5,075	3,550	8,625
2020	5 stories, 50′ horizontal	9,050	6,150	15,200
2040	10 stories, 75′ horizontal	13,700	9,200	22,900
2060	400A, 0 stories, 0′ horizontal	7,375	3,325	10,700
2080	1 story, 25′ horizontal	9,950	5,475	15,425
3000	5 stories, 50′ horizontal	15,100	9,675	24,775
3020	10 stories, 75′ horizontal	28,000	18,900	46,900
3040	600 A, 0 stories, 0′ horizontal	10,800	4,000	14,800
3060	1 story, 25′ horizontal	16,400	7,500	23,900
3080	5 stories, 50′ horizontal	27,400	14,400	41,800
4000	10 stories, 75′ horizontal	55,500	28,300	83,800
4010	Panelboards, NEHB, 4 wire, 277/480 volts w/conductor, conduit, & safety switch			
4020	100 A, 0 stories, 0′ horizontal, includes safety switch	6,400	2,325	8,725
4040	1 story, 25′ horizontal	7,125	3,050	10,175
4060	5 stories, 50′ horizontal	8,525	4,500	13,025
4080	10 stories, 75′ horizontal	10,200	6,175	16,375
5000	225 A, 0 stories, 0′ horizontal	8,100	2,850	10,950
5020	1 story, 25′ horizontal	10,100	4,150	14,250
5040	5 stories, 50′ horizontal	14,100	6,775	20,875
5060	10 stories, 75′ horizontal	18,700	9,800	28,500

D5010 Electrical Service/Distribution

D5010 250	Panelboard	COST EACH		
		MAT.	INST.	TOTAL
5080	400 A, 0 stories, 0′ horizontal	14,400	4,375	18,775
6000	1 story, 25′ horizontal	17,000	6,500	23,500
6020	5 stories, 50′ horizontal	22,100	10,700	32,800
6040	10 stories, 75′ horizontal	35,000	20,000	55,000
6060	600 A, 0 stories, 0′ horizontal	19,100	5,550	24,650
6080	1 story, 25′ horizontal	24,700	9,050	33,750
7000	5 stories, 50′ horizontal	35,700	15,900	51,600
7020	10 stories, 75′ horizontal	63,500	29,800	93,300

D5020 Lighting and Branch Wiring

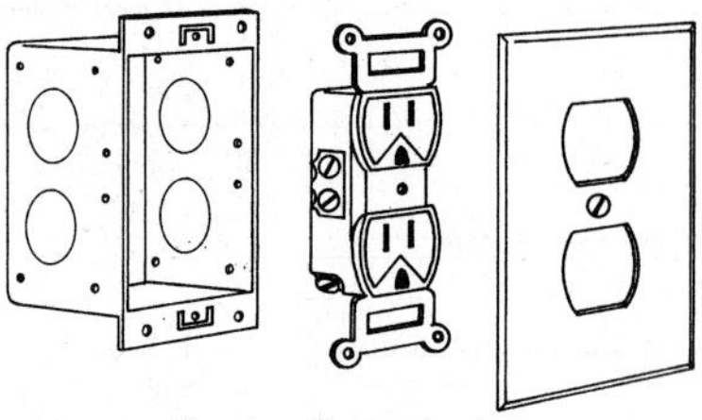

Duplex Receptacle

System Components	QUANTITY	UNIT	COST PER S.F. MAT.	COST PER S.F. INST.	COST PER S.F. TOTAL
SYSTEM D5020 110 0200					
RECEPTACLES INCL. PLATE, BOX, CONDUIT, WIRE & TRANS. WHEN REQUIRED					
2.5 PER 1000 S.F., .3 WATTS PER S.F.					
Steel intermediate conduit, (IMC) 1/2" diam	167.000	L.F.	.58	1.34	1.92
Wire 600V type THWN-THHN, copper solid #12	3.340	C.L.F.	.08	.24	.32
Wiring device, receptacle, duplex, 120V grounded, 15 amp	2.500	Ea.		.05	.05
Wall plate, 1 gang, brown plastic	2.500	Ea.		.03	.03
Steel outlet box 4" square	2.500	Ea.	.01	.10	.11
Steel outlet box 4" plaster rings	2.500	Ea.	.01	.03	.04
TOTAL			.68	1.79	2.47

D5020 110	Receptacle (by Wattage)	COST PER S.F. MAT.	COST PER S.F. INST.	COST PER S.F. TOTAL
0190	Receptacles include plate, box, conduit, wire & transformer when required			
0200	2.5 per 1000 S.F., .3 watts per S.F.	.68	1.79	2.47
0240	With transformer	.84	1.87	2.71
0280	4 per 1000 S.F., .5 watts per S.F.	.76	2.08	2.84
0320	With transformer	1.03	2.22	3.25
0360	5 per 1000 S.F., .6 watts per S.F.	.21	.82	1.03
0400	With transformer	1.22	2.63	3.85
0440	8 per 1000 S.F., .9 watts per S.F.	.92	2.72	3.64
0480	With transformer	1.46	3.01	4.47
0520	10 per 1000 S.F., 1.2 watts per S.F.	.97	2.95	3.92
0560	With transformer	1.64	3.31	4.95
0600	16.5 per 1000 S.F., 2.0 watts per S.F.	1.11	3.69	4.80
0640	With transformer	2.21	4.27	6.48
0680	20 per 1000 S.F., 2.4 watts per S.F.	1.15	4.02	5.17
0720	With transformer	2.50	4.73	7.23

D5020 Lighting and Branch Wiring

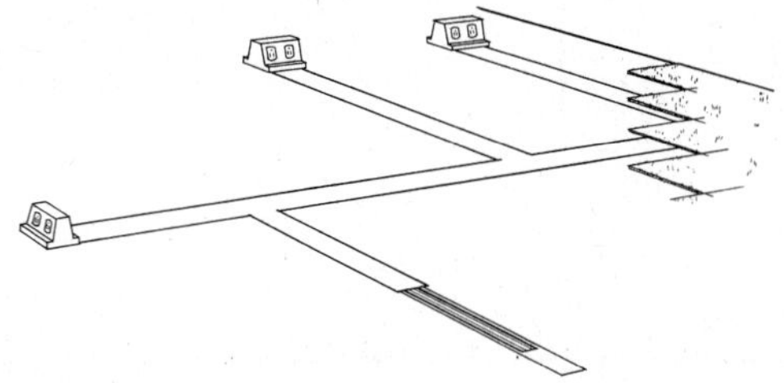

Underfloor Receptacle System

Description: Table D5020 115 includes installed costs of raceways and copper wire from panel to and including receptacle.

National Electrical Code prohibits use of undercarpet system in residential, school or hospital buildings. Can only be used with carpet squares.

Low density = (1) Outlet per 259 S.F. of floor area.

High density = (1) Outlet per 127 S.F. of floor area.

System Components	QUANTITY	UNIT	COST PER S.F. MAT.	COST PER S.F. INST.	COST PER S.F. TOTAL
SYSTEM D5020 115 0200					
RECEPTACLE SYSTEMS, UNDERFLOOR DUCT, 5′ ON CENTER, LOW DENSITY					
Underfloor duct 3-1/8″ x 7/8″ w/insert 24″ on center	.190	L.F.	4.56	2.18	6.74
Underfloor duct junction box, single duct, 3-1/8″	.003	Ea.	1.61	.60	2.21
Underfloor junction box carpet pan	.003	Ea.	1.34	.03	1.37
Underfloor duct outlet, high tension receptacle	.004	Ea.	.51	.40	.91
Wire 600V type THWN-THHN copper solid #12	.010	C.L.F.	.23	.73	.96
Vertical elbow for underfloor duct, 3-1/8″, included					
Underfloor duct conduit adapter, 2″ x 1-1/4″, included					
TOTAL			8.25	3.94	12.19

D5020 115	Receptacles, Floor	COST PER S.F. MAT.	COST PER S.F. INST.	COST PER S.F. TOTAL
0200	Receptacle systems, underfloor duct, 5′ on center, low density	8.25	3.94	12.19
0240	High density	9	5.05	14.05
0280	7′ on center, low density	6.55	3.38	9.93
0320	High density	7.30	4.51	11.81
0400	Poke thru fittings, low density	2	1.92	3.92
0440	High density	4	3.83	7.83
0520	Telepoles, using Romex, low density	2.07	1.18	3.25
0560	High density	4.14	2.37	6.51
0600	Using EMT, low density	2.16	1.57	3.73
0640	High density	4.32	3.13	7.45
0720	Conduit system with floor boxes, low density	2.22	1.34	3.56
0760	High density	4.44	2.69	7.13
0840	Undercarpet power system, 3 conductor with 5 conductor feeder, low density	1.75	.49	2.24
0880	High density	3.49	.98	4.47

D5020 Lighting and Branch Wiring

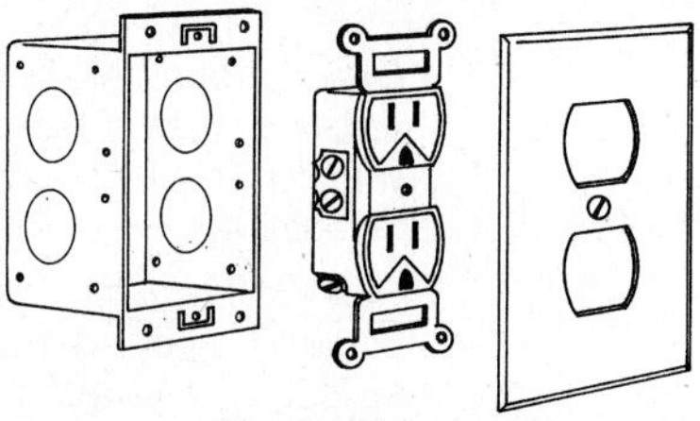
Duplex Receptacle

Wall Switch

System Components	QUANTITY	UNIT	COST PER S.F. MAT.	COST PER S.F. INST.	COST PER S.F. TOTAL
SYSTEM D5020 120 0520					
RECEPTACLES AND WALL SWITCHES					
4 RECEPTACLES PER 400 S.F.					
Steel intermediate conduit, (IMC), 1/2" diam	.220	L.F.	.76	1.76	2.52
Wire, 600 volt, type THWN-THHN, copper, solid #12	.005	C.L.F.	.12	.37	.49
Steel outlet box 4" square	.010	Ea.	.04	.40	.44
Steel outlet box, 4" square, plaster rings	.010	Ea.	.03	.13	.16
Receptacle, duplex, 120 volt grounded, 15 amp	.010	Ea.	.02	.20	.22
Wall plate, 1 gang, brown plastic	.010	Ea.		.10	.10
TOTAL			.97	2.96	3.93

D5020 120	Receptacles & Wall Switches	COST PER S.F. MAT.	COST PER S.F. INST.	COST PER S.F. TOTAL
0520	Receptacles and wall switches, 400 S.F., 4 receptacles	.96	2.95	3.91
0560	6 receptacles	1.04	3.44	4.48
0600	8 receptacles	1.13	4	5.13
0640	1 switch	.20	.66	.86
0680	600 S.F., 6 receptacles	.96	2.95	3.91
0720	8 receptacles	1.04	3.34	4.38
0760	10 receptacles	1.11	3.75	4.86
0800	2 switches	.28	.87	1.15
0840	1000 S.F., 10 receptacles	.95	2.94	3.89
0880	12 receptacles	.96	3.10	4.06
0920	14 receptacles	1.02	3.35	4.37
0960	2 switches	.15	.48	.63
1000	1600 S.F., 12 receptacles	.86	2.62	3.48
1040	14 receptacles	.93	2.85	3.78
1080	16 receptacles	.95	2.94	3.89
1120	4 switches	.18	.56	.74
1160	2000 S.F., 14 receptacles	.91	2.69	3.60
1200	16 receptacles	.90	2.70	3.60
1240	18 receptacles	.93	2.85	3.78
1280	4 switches	.15	.48	.63
1320	3000 S.F., 12 receptacles	.74	2.06	2.80
1360	18 receptacles	.88	2.53	3.41
1400	24 receptacles	.90	2.70	3.60
1440	6 switches	.15	.48	.63
1480	3600 S.F., 20 receptacles	.85	2.45	3.30
1520	24 receptacles	.86	2.54	3.40
1560	28 receptacles	.89	2.62	3.51
1600	8 switches	.17	.55	.72
1640	4000 S.F., 16 receptacles	.74	2.06	2.80
1680	24 receptacles	.88	2.53	3.41
1720	30 receptacles	.86	2.62	3.48
1760	8 switches	.15	.48	.63
1800	5000 S.F., 20 receptacles	.74	2.06	2.80
1840	26 receptacles	.87	2.45	3.32
1880	30 receptacles	.88	2.53	3.41
1920	10 switches	.15	.48	.63

D5020 Lighting and Branch Wiring

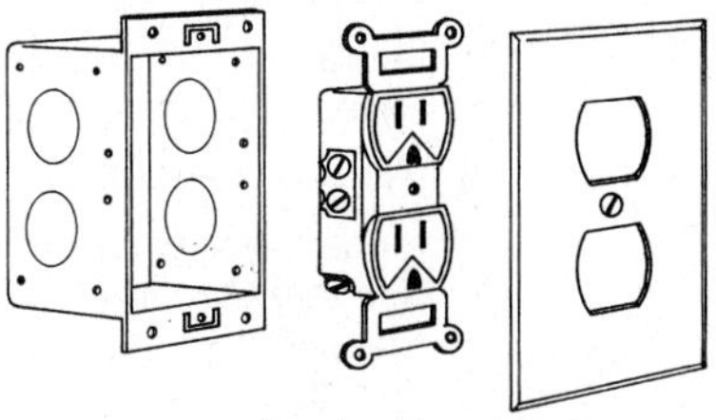

Duplex Receptacle

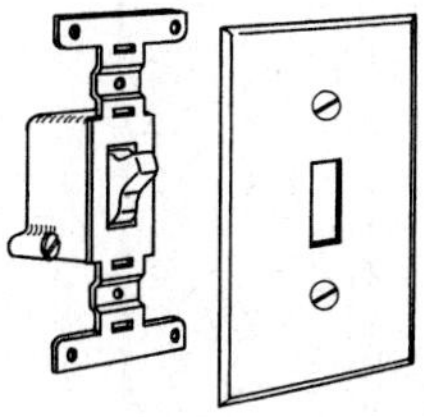

Wall Switch

System Components	QUANTITY	UNIT	COST PER EACH MAT.	COST PER EACH INST.	COST PER EACH TOTAL
SYSTEM D5020 125 0520					
RECEPTACLES AND WALL SWITCHES, RECEPTICLE DUPLEX 120 V GROUNDED, 15 A					
Electric metallic tubing conduit, (EMT), 3/4″ diam	22.000	L.F.	46.86	135.30	182.16
Wire, 600 volt, type THWN-THHN, copper, solid #12	.630	C.L.F.	14.49	45.99	60.48
Steel outlet box 4″ square	1.000	Ea.	3.59	40	43.59
Steel outlet box, 4″ square, plaster rings	1.000	Ea.	3.16	12.50	15.66
Receptacle, duplex, 120 volt grounded, 15 amp	1.000	Ea.	1.69	20	21.69
Wall plate, 1 gang, brown plastic	1.000	Ea.	.43	10	10.43
TOTAL			70.22	263.79	334.01

D5020 125	Receptacles & Switches by Each	COST PER EACH MAT.	COST PER EACH INST.	COST PER EACH TOTAL
0460	Receptacles & Switches, with box, plate, 3/4″ EMT conduit & wire			
0520	Receptacle duplex 120 V grounded, 15 A	70	264	334
0560	20 A	82.50	273	355.50
0600	Receptacle duplex ground fault interrupting, 15 A	91.50	273	364.50
0640	20 A	111	273	384
0680	Toggle switch single, 15 A	71.50	264	335.50
0720	20 A	73	273	346
0760	3 way switch, 15 A	70.50	279	349.50
0800	20 A	75.50	288	363.50
0840	4 way switch, 15 A	79.50	297	376.50
0880	20 A	139	315	454

D5020 Lighting and Branch Wiring

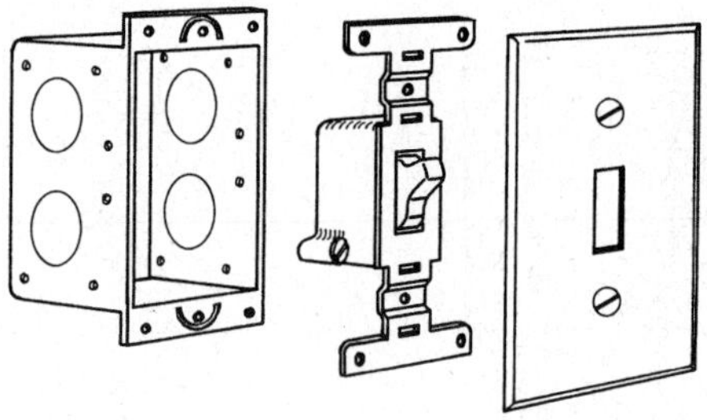

Description: Table D5020 130 includes the cost for switch, plate, box, conduit in slab or EMT exposed and copper wire. Add 20% for exposed conduit.

No power required for switches.

Federal energy guidelines recommend the maximum lighting area controlled per switch shall not exceed 1000 S.F. and that areas over 500 S.F. shall be so controlled that total illumination can be reduced by at least 50%.

System Components	QUANTITY	UNIT	COST PER S.F. MAT.	COST PER S.F. INST.	COST PER S.F. TOTAL
SYSTEM D5020 130 0360					
WALL SWITCHES, 5.0 PER 1000 S.F.					
Steel, intermediate conduit (IMC), 1/2" diameter	88.000	L.F.	.30	.70	1
Wire, 600V type THWN-THHN, copper solid #12	1.710	C.L.F.	.04	.12	.16
Toggle switch, single pole, 15 amp	5.000	Ea.	.01	.10	.11
Wall plate, 1 gang, brown plastic	5.000	Ea.		.05	.05
Steel outlet box 4" plaster rings	5.000	Ea.	.02	.20	.22
Plaster rings	5.000	Ea.	.02	.06	.08
TOTAL			.39	1.23	1.62

D5020 130	Wall Switch by Sq. Ft.	COST PER S.F. MAT.	COST PER S.F. INST.	COST PER S.F. TOTAL
0200	Wall switches, 1.0 per 1000 S.F.	.10	.29	.39
0240	1.2 per 1000 S.F.	.10	.32	.42
0280	2.0 per 1000 S.F.	.14	.46	.60
0320	2.5 per 1000 S.F.	.18	.58	.76
0360	5.0 per 1000 S.F.	.39	1.24	1.63
0400	10.0 per 1000 S.F.	.80	2.51	3.31

D5020 Lighting and Branch Wiring

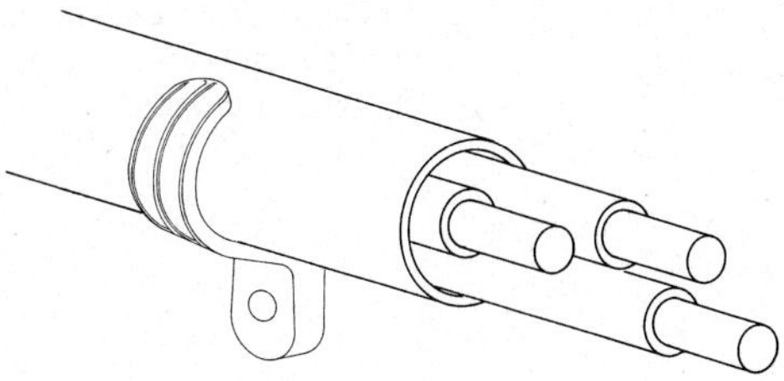

System D5020 135 includes all wiring and connections.

System Components	QUANTITY	UNIT	COST PER S.F. MAT.	INST.	TOTAL
SYSTEM D5020 135 0200					
MISCELLANEOUS POWER, TO .5 WATTS					
Steel intermediate conduit, (IMC) 1/2" diam	15.000	L.F.	.05	.12	.17
Wire 600V type THWN-THHN, copper solid #12	.325	C.L.F.	.01	.02	.03
TOTAL			.06	.14	.20

D5020 135	Miscellaneous Power	COST PER S.F. MAT.	INST.	TOTAL
0200	Miscellaneous power, to .5 watts	.06	.14	.20
0240	.8 watts	.08	.20	.28
0280	1 watt	.11	.27	.38
0320	1.2 watts	.13	.32	.45
0360	1.5 watts	.16	.37	.53
0400	1.8 watts	.18	.43	.61
0440	2 watts	.21	.52	.73
0480	2.5 watts	.26	.63	.89
0520	3 watts	.31	.75	1.06

D5020 Lighting and Branch Wiring

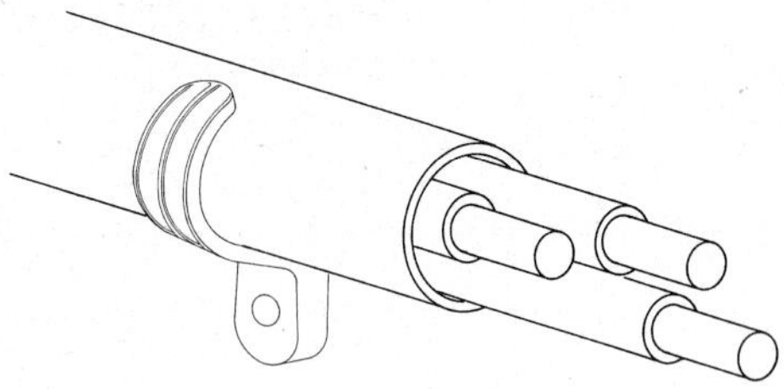

System D5020 140 includes all wiring and connections for central air conditioning units.

System Components	QUANTITY	UNIT	COST PER S.F. MAT.	COST PER S.F. INST.	COST PER S.F. TOTAL
SYSTEM D5020 140 0200					
CENTRAL AIR CONDITIONING POWER, 1 WATT					
Steel intermediate conduit, 1/2" diam.	.030	L.F.	.10	.24	.34
Wire 600V type THWN-THHN, copper solid #12	.001	C.L.F.	.02	.07	.09
TOTAL			.12	.31	.43

D5020 140	Central A. C. Power (by Wattage)	COST PER S.F. MAT.	COST PER S.F. INST.	COST PER S.F. TOTAL
0200	Central air conditioning power, 1 watt	.13	.31	.44
0220	2 watts	.15	.36	.51
0240	3 watts	.30	.54	.84
0280	4 watts	.28	.54	.82
0320	6 watts	.55	.72	1.27
0360	8 watts	.69	.78	1.47
0400	10 watts	.97	.90	1.87

D5020 Lighting and Branch Wiring

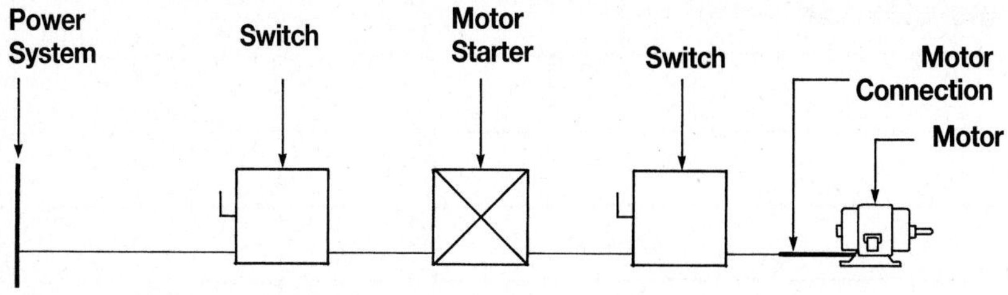

System D5020 145 installed cost of motor wiring using 50′ of rigid conduit and copper wire. **Cost and setting of motor not included.**

System Components	QUANTITY	UNIT	COST EACH MAT.	COST EACH INST.	COST EACH TOTAL
SYSTEM D5020 145 0200					
MOTOR INST., SINGLE PHASE, 115V, TO AND INCLUDING 1/3 HP MOTOR SIZE					
Wire 600V type THWN-THHN, copper solid #12	1.250	C.L.F.	28.75	91.25	120
Steel intermediate conduit, (IMC) 1/2″ diam.	50.000	L.F.	172.50	400	572.50
Magnetic FVNR, 115V, 1/3 HP, size 00 starter	1.000	Ea.	196	200	396
Safety switch, fused, heavy duty, 240V 2P 30 amp	1.000	Ea.	115	229	344
Safety switch, non fused, heavy duty, 600V, 3 phase, 30 A	1.000	Ea.	134	250	384
Flexible metallic conduit, Greenfield 1/2″ diam.	1.500	L.F.	1.02	6	7.02
Connectors for flexible metallic conduit Greenfield 1/2″ diam.	1.000	Ea.	2.05	10	12.05
Coupling for Greenfield to conduit 1/2″ diam. flexible metallic conduit	1.000	Ea.	1.33	16	17.33
Fuse cartridge nonrenewable, 250V 30 amp	1.000	Ea.	3.01	16	19.01
TOTAL			653.66	1,218.25	1,871.91

D5020 145	Motor Installation	COST EACH MAT.	COST EACH INST.	COST EACH TOTAL
0200	Motor installation, single phase, 115V, 1/3 HP motor size	655	1,225	1,880
0240	1 HP motor size	675	1,225	1,900
0280	2 HP motor size	750	1,300	2,050
0320	3 HP motor size	850	1,325	2,175
0360	230V, 1 HP motor size	655	1,225	1,880
0400	2 HP motor size	730	1,225	1,955
0440	3 HP motor size	800	1,325	2,125
0520	Three phase, 200V, 1-1/2 HP motor size	700	1,350	2,050
0560	3 HP motor size	1,050	1,475	2,525
0600	5 HP motor size	870	1,650	2,520
0640	7-1/2 HP motor size	930	1,675	2,605
0680	10 HP motor size	1,300	2,100	3,400
0720	15 HP motor size	1,775	2,350	4,125
0760	20 HP motor size	2,325	2,700	5,025
0800	25 HP motor size	2,375	2,700	5,075
0840	30 HP motor size	3,550	3,175	6,725
0880	40 HP motor size	4,600	3,750	8,350
0920	50 HP motor size	7,400	4,375	11,775
0960	60 HP motor size	7,850	4,625	12,475
1000	75 HP motor size	10,500	5,300	15,800
1040	100 HP motor size	20,400	6,225	26,625
1080	125 HP motor size	21,300	6,850	28,150
1120	150 HP motor size	25,400	8,050	33,450
1160	200 HP motor size	28,200	9,500	37,700
1240	230V, 1-1/2 HP motor size	680	1,350	2,030
1280	3 HP motor size	1,025	1,450	2,475
1320	5 HP motor size	855	1,625	2,480
1360	7-1/2 HP motor size	855	1,625	2,480
1400	10 HP motor size	1,250	2,000	3,250
1440	15 HP motor size	1,475	2,175	3,650
1480	20 HP motor size	2,200	2,625	4,825
1520	25 HP motor size	2,325	2,700	5,025

D5020 Lighting and Branch Wiring

D5020 145	Motor Installation	COST EACH		
		MAT.	INST.	TOTAL
1560	30 HP motor size	2,425	2,700	5,125
1600	40 HP motor size	4,325	3,650	7,975
1640	50 HP motor size	4,775	3,875	8,650
1680	60 HP motor size	7,425	4,400	11,825
1720	75 HP motor size	9,525	4,975	14,500
1760	100 HP motor size	11,400	5,550	16,950
1800	125 HP motor size	21,200	6,450	27,650
1840	150 HP motor size	22,600	7,300	29,900
1880	200 HP motor size	24,800	8,125	32,925
1960	460V, 2 HP motor size	915	1,350	2,265
2000	5 HP motor size	1,250	1,475	2,725
2040	10 HP motor size	985	1,625	2,610
2080	15 HP motor size	1,250	1,875	3,125
2120	20 HP motor size	1,425	2,000	3,425
2160	25 HP motor size	1,525	2,100	3,625
2200	30 HP motor size	1,850	2,250	4,100
2240	40 HP motor size	2,475	2,425	4,900
2280	50 HP motor size	2,800	2,700	5,500
2320	60 HP motor size	3,850	3,150	7,000
2360	75 HP motor size	4,775	3,475	8,250
2400	100 HP motor size	5,425	3,875	9,300
2440	125 HP motor size	8,100	4,400	12,500
2480	150 HP motor size	10,700	4,950	15,650
2520	200 HP motor size	13,100	5,575	18,675
2600	575V, 2 HP motor size	915	1,350	2,265
2640	5 HP motor size	1,250	1,475	2,725
2680	10 HP motor size	985	1,625	2,610
2720	20 HP motor size	1,250	1,875	3,125
2760	25 HP motor size	1,425	2,000	3,425
2800	30 HP motor size	1,850	2,250	4,100
2840	50 HP motor size	2,025	2,350	4,375
2880	60 HP motor size	3,775	3,125	6,900
2920	75 HP motor size	3,850	3,150	7,000
2960	100 HP motor size	4,775	3,475	8,250
3000	125 HP motor size	7,700	4,325	12,025
3040	150 HP motor size	8,100	4,400	12,500
3080	200 HP motor size	11,300	5,000	16,300

D5020 Lighting and Branch Wiring

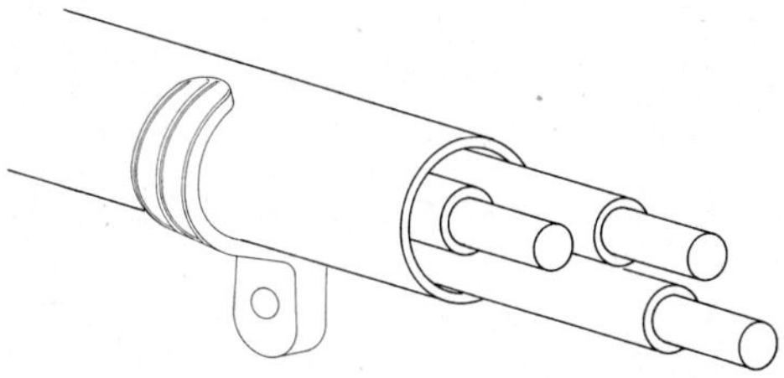

System Components	QUANTITY	UNIT	COST PER L.F. MAT.	INST.	TOTAL
SYSTEM D5020 155 0200					
MOTOR FEEDER SYSTEMS, SINGLE PHASE, UP TO 115V, 1HP OR 230V, 2HP					
Steel intermediate conduit, (IMC) 1/2" diam	1.000	L.F.	3.45	8	11.45
Wire 600V type THWN-THHN, copper solid #12	.020	C.L.F.	.46	1.46	1.92
TOTAL			3.91	9.46	13.37

D5020 155	Motor Feeder	COST PER L.F. MAT.	INST.	TOTAL
0200	Motor feeder systems, single phase, feed up to 115V 1HP or 230V 2HP	3.91	9.45	13.36
0240	115V 2HP, 230V 3HP	4.19	9.60	13.79
0280	115V 3HP	4.84	10	14.84
0360	Three phase, feed to 200V 3HP, 230V 5HP, 460V 10HP, 575V 10HP	4.14	10.20	14.34
0440	200V 5HP, 230V 7.5HP, 460V 15HP, 575V 20HP	4.56	10.40	14.96
0520	200V 10HP, 230V 10HP, 460V 30HP, 575V 30HP	5.55	11	16.55
0600	200V 15HP, 230V 15HP, 460V 40HP, 575V 50HP	7.50	12.60	20.10
0680	200V 20HP, 230V 25HP, 460V 50HP, 575V 60HP	11.50	16	27.50
0760	200V 25HP, 230V 30HP, 460V 60HP, 575V 75HP	12.65	16.25	28.90
0840	200V 30HP	14.20	16.80	31
0920	230V 40HP, 460V 75HP, 575V 100HP	17.55	18.30	35.85
1000	200V 40HP	19.30	19.60	38.90
1080	230V 50HP, 460V 100HP, 575V 125HP	24.50	21.50	46
1160	200V 50HP, 230V 60HP, 460V 125HP, 575V 150HP	27.50	23	50.50
1240	200V 60HP, 460V 150HP	34.50	27	61.50
1320	230V 75HP, 575V 200HP	37.50	28	65.50
1400	200V 75HP	42	28.50	70.50
1480	230V 100HP, 460V 200HP	60.50	33.50	94
1560	200V 100HP	83.50	41.50	125
1640	230V 125HP	83.50	41.50	125
1720	200V 125HP, 230V 150HP	91	51.50	142.50
1800	200V 150HP	110	56	166
1880	200V 200HP	140	59.50	199.50
1960	230V 200HP	144	62	206

D5020 Lighting and Branch Wiring

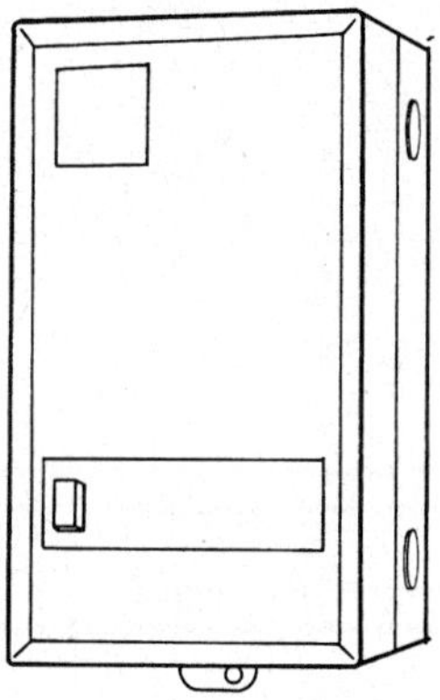

Starters are full voltage, type NEMA 1 for general purpose indoor application with motor overload protection and include mounting and wire connections.

System Components	QUANTITY	UNIT	COST EACH MAT.	COST EACH INST.	COST EACH TOTAL
SYSTEM D5020 160 0200 MAGNETIC STARTER, SIZE 00 TO 1/3 HP, 1 PHASE 115V OR 1 HP 230V					
Magnetic starter, size 00, to 1/3 HP, 1 phase, 115V or 1 HP 230V	1.000	Ea.	196	200	396
TOTAL			196	200	396

D5020 160	Magnetic Starter	COST EACH MAT.	COST EACH INST.	COST EACH TOTAL
0200	Magnetic starter, size 00, to 1/3 HP, 1 phase, 115V or 1 HP 230V	196	200	396
0280	Size 00, to 1-1/2 HP, 3 phase, 200-230V or 2 HP 460-575V	167	229	396
0360	Size 0, to 1 HP, 1 phase, 115V or 2 HP 230V	218	200	418
0440	Size 0, to 3 HP, 3 phase, 200-230V or 5 HP 460-575V	505	350	855
0520	Size 1, to 2 HP, 1 phase, 115V or 3 HP 230V	250	267	517
0600	Size 1, to 7-1/2 HP, 3 phase, 200-230V or 10 HP 460-575V	235	500	735
0680	Size 2, to 10 HP, 3 phase, 200V, 15 HP-230V or 25 HP 460-575V	465	730	1,195
0760	Size 3, to 25 HP, 3 phase, 200V, 30 HP-230V or 50 HP 460-575V	775	890	1,665
0840	Size 4, to 40 HP, 3 phase, 200V, 50 HP-230V or 100 HP 460-575V	1,750	1,325	3,075
0920	Size 5, to 75 HP, 3 phase, 200V, 100 HP-230V or 200 HP 460-575V	4,025	1,775	5,800
1000	Size 6, to 150 HP, 3 phase, 200V, 200 HP-230V or 400 HP 460-575V	11,600	2,000	13,600

D5020 Lighting and Branch Wiring

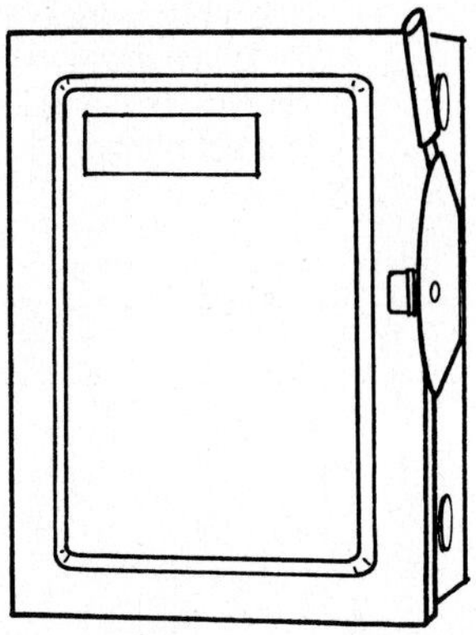

Safety switches are type NEMA 1 for general purpose indoor application, and include time delay fuses, insulation and wire terminations.

System Components	QUANTITY	UNIT	COST EACH MAT.	COST EACH INST.	COST EACH TOTAL
SYSTEM D5020 165 0200					
SAFETY SWITCH, 30A FUSED, 1 PHASE, 115V OR 230V					
Safety switch fused, hvy duty, 240V 2p 30 amp	1.000	Ea.	115	229	344
Fuse, dual element time delay 250V, 30 amp	2.000	Ea.	58	32	90
TOTAL			173	261	434

D5020 165	Safety Switches	COST EACH MAT.	COST EACH INST.	COST EACH TOTAL
0200	Safety switch, 30 A fused, 1 phase, 2 HP 115 V or 3 HP, 230 V	173	261	434
0280	3 phase, 5 HP, 200 V or 7 1/2 HP, 230 V	240	298	538
0360	15 HP, 460 V or 20 HP, 575 V	395	310	705
0440	60 A fused, 3 phase, 15 HP 200 V or 15 HP 230 V	355	400	755
0520	30 HP 460 V or 40 HP 575 V	580	410	990
0600	100 A fused, 3 phase, 20 HP 200 V or 25 HP 230 V	565	480	1,045
0680	50 HP 460 V or 60 HP 575 V	1,025	485	1,510
0760	200 A fused, 3 phase, 50 HP 200 V or 60 HP 230 V	1,050	680	1,730
0840	125 HP 460 V or 150 HP 575 V	1,700	695	2,395
0920	400 A fused, 3 phase, 100 HP 200 V or 125 HP 230 V	2,450	970	3,420
1000	250 HP 460 V or 350 HP 575 V	4,200	990	5,190
1020	600 A fused, 3 phase, 150 HP 200 V or 200 HP 230 V	3,700	1,425	5,125
1040	400 HP 460 V	6,325	1,450	7,775

D5020 Lighting and Branch Wiring

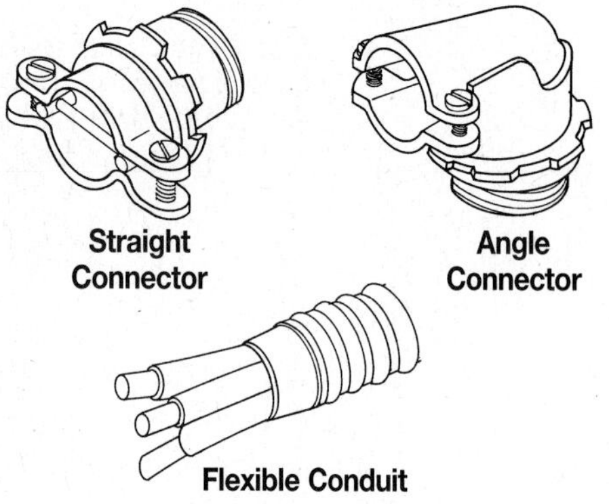

Table below includes costs for the flexible conduit. Not included are wire terminations and testing motor for correct rotation.

System Components	QUANTITY	UNIT	COST EACH MAT.	COST EACH INST.	COST EACH TOTAL
SYSTEM D5020 170 0200					
MOTOR CONNECTIONS, SINGLE PHASE, 115V/230V UP TO 1 HP					
Motor connection, flexible conduit & fittings, 1 HP motor 115V	1.000	Ea.	7.25	100	107.25
TOTAL			7.25	100	107.25

D5020 170	Motor Connections	COST EACH MAT.	COST EACH INST.	COST EACH TOTAL
0200	Motor connections, single phase, 115/230V, up to 1 HP	7.25	100	107.25
0240	Up to 3 HP	15.25	123	138.25
0280	Three phase, 200/230/460/575V, up to 3 HP	8.80	118	126.80
0320	Up to 5 HP	7.55	146	153.55
0360	Up to 7-1/2 HP	13.25	174	187.25
0400	Up to 10 HP	23.50	191	214.50
0440	Up to 15 HP	23.50	243	266.50
0480	Up to 25 HP	35	297	332
0520	Up to 50 HP	73.50	365	438.50
0560	Up to 100 HP	166	535	701

D5020 Lighting and Branch Wiring

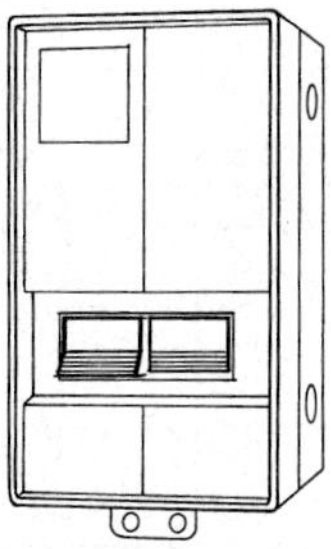

Manual Starter

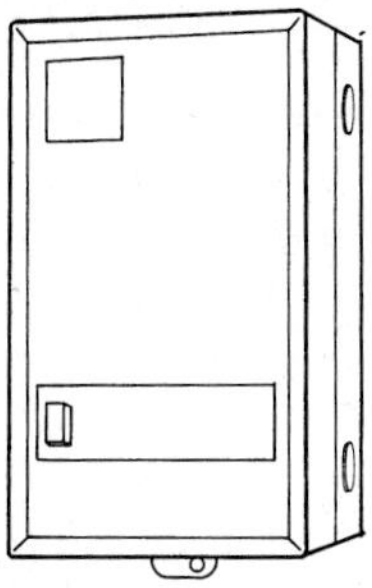

Magnetic Starter

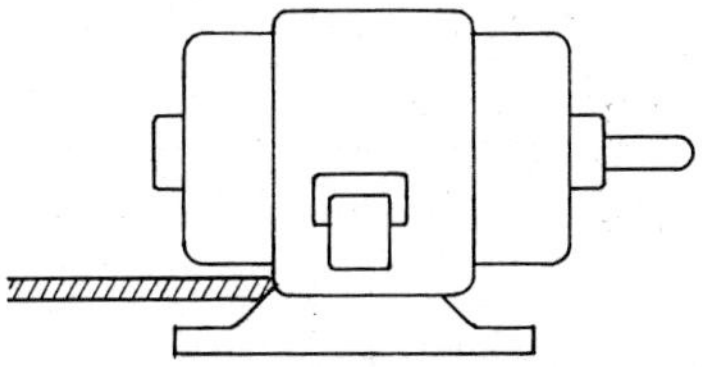

Induction Motor

For 230/460 Volt A.C., 3 phase, 60 cycle ball bearing squirrel cage induction motors, NEMA Class B standard line. Installation included.

No conduit, wire, or terminations included.

System Components	QUANTITY	UNIT	COST EACH MAT.	COST EACH INST.	COST EACH TOTAL
SYSTEM D5020 175 0220					
MOTOR, DRIPPROOF CLASS B INSULATION, 1.15 SERVICE FACTOR, WITH STARTER					
1 H.P., 1200 RPM WITH MANUAL STARTER					
Motor, dripproof, class B insul, 1.15 serv fact, 1,200 RPM, 1 HP	1.000	Ea.	855	178	1,033
Motor starter, manual, 3 phase, 1 HP motor	1.000	Ea.	279	229	508
TOTAL			1,134	407	1,541

D5020 175	Motor & Starter	COST EACH MAT.	COST EACH INST.	COST EACH TOTAL
0190	Motor, dripproof, premium efficient, 1.15 service factor			
0200	1 HP, 1200 RPM, motor only	855	178	1,033
0220	With manual starter	1,125	405	1,530
0240	With magnetic starter	1,025	405	1,430
0260	1800 RPM, motor only	375	178	553
0280	With manual starter	655	405	1,060
0300	With magnetic starter	540	405	945
0320	2 HP, 1200 RPM, motor only	1,025	178	1,203
0340	With manual starter	1,300	405	1,705
0360	With magnetic starter	1,525	530	2,055
0380	1800 RPM, motor only	335	178	513
0400	With manual starter	615	405	1,020
0420	With magnetic starter	840	530	1,370
0440	3600 RPM, motor only	845	178	1,023
0460	With manual starter	1,125	405	1,530
0480	With magnetic starter	1,350	530	1,880
0500	3 HP, 1200 RPM, motor only	1,300	178	1,478
0520	With manual starter	1,575	405	1,980
0540	With magnetic starter	1,800	530	2,330
0560	1800 RPM, motor only	775	178	953
0580	With manual starter	1,050	405	1,455
0600	With magnetic starter	1,275	530	1,805
0620	3600 RPM, motor only	955	178	1,133
0640	With manual starter	1,225	405	1,630
0660	With magnetic starter	1,450	530	1,980
0680	5 HP, 1200 RPM, motor only	1,700	178	1,878
0700	With manual starter	2,025	580	2,605
0720	With magnetic starter	1,925	680	2,605
0740	1800 RPM, motor only	1,025	178	1,203
0760	With manual starter	1,350	580	1,930
0780	With magnetic starter	1,250	680	1,930
0800	3600 RPM, motor only	1,025	178	1,203

D5020 Lighting and Branch Wiring

D5020 175	Motor & Starter	COST EACH		
		MAT.	INST.	TOTAL
0820	With manual starter	1,350	580	1,930
0840	With magnetic starter	1,250	680	1,930
0860	7.5 HP, 1800 RPM, motor only	1,450	191	1,641
0880	With manual starter	1,775	590	2,365
0900	With magnetic starter	1,925	920	2,845
0920	10 HP, 1800 RPM, motor only	1,875	200	2,075
0940	With manual starter	2,200	600	2,800
0960	With magnetic starter	2,350	930	3,280
0980	15 HP, 1800 RPM, motor only	2,650	250	2,900
1000	With magnetic starter	3,125	980	4,105
1040	20 HP, 1800 RPM, motor only	3,300	310	3,610
1060	With magnetic starter	4,075	1,200	5,275
1100	25 HP, 1800 RPM, motor only	4,025	320	4,345
1120	With magnetic starter	4,800	1,200	6,000
1160	30 HP, 1800 RPM, motor only	4,400	335	4,735
1180	With magnetic starter	5,175	1,225	6,400
1220	40 HP, 1800 RPM, motor only	5,900	400	6,300
1240	With magnetic starter	7,650	1,725	9,375
1280	50 HP, 1800 RPM, motor only	6,325	500	6,825
1300	With magnetic starter	8,075	1,825	9,900
1340	60 HP, 1800 RPM, motor only	7,975	570	8,545
1360	With magnetic starter	12,000	2,350	14,350
1400	75 HP, 1800 RPM, motor only	10,000	665	10,665
1420	With magnetic starter	14,000	2,450	16,450
1460	100 HP, 1800 RPM, motor only	10,900	890	11,790
1480	With magnetic starter	14,900	2,675	17,575
1520	125 HP, 1800 RPM, motor only	9,550	1,150	10,700
1540	With magnetic starter	21,200	3,150	24,350
1580	150 HP, 1800 RPM, motor only	15,900	1,325	17,225
1600	With magnetic starter	27,500	3,325	30,825
1640	200 HP, 1800 RPM, motor only	17,500	1,600	19,100
1660	With magnetic starter	29,100	3,600	32,700
1680	Totally encl, premium efficient, 1.0 ser. fac., 1 HP, 1200 RPM, motor only	560	178	738
1700	With manual starter	840	405	1,245
1720	With magnetic starter	725	405	1,130
1740	1800 RPM, motor only	975	178	1,153
1760	With manual starter	1,250	405	1,655
1780	With magnetic starter	1,150	405	1,555
1800	2 HP, 1200 RPM, motor only	710	178	888
1820	With manual starter	990	405	1,395
1840	With magnetic starter	1,225	530	1,755
1860	1800 RPM, motor only	1,125	178	1,303
1880	With manual starter	1,400	405	1,805
1900	With magnetic starter	1,625	530	2,155
1920	3600 RPM, motor only	945	178	1,123
1940	With manual starter	1,225	405	1,630
1960	With magnetic starter	1,450	530	1,980
1980	3 HP, 1200 RPM, motor only	950	178	1,128
2000	With manual starter	1,225	405	1,630
2020	With magnetic starter	1,450	530	1,980
2040	1800 RPM, motor only	1,350	178	1,528
2060	With manual starter	1,625	405	2,030
2080	With magnetic starter	1,850	530	2,380
2100	3600 RPM, motor only	620	178	798
2120	With manual starter	900	405	1,305
2140	With magnetic starter	1,125	530	1,655
2160	5 HP, 1200 RPM, motor only	1,125	178	1,303
2180	With manual starter	1,450	580	2,030

D5020 Lighting and Branch Wiring

D5020 175	Motor & Starter	COST EACH		
		MAT.	INST.	TOTAL
2200	With magnetic starter	1,350	680	2,030
2220	1800 RPM, motor only	1,575	178	1,753
2240	With manual starter	1,900	580	2,480
2260	With magnetic starter	1,800	680	2,480
2280	3600 RPM, motor only	890	178	1,068
2300	With manual starter	1,225	580	1,805
2320	With magnetic starter	1,125	680	1,805
2340	7.5 HP, 1800 RPM, motor only	1,900	191	2,091
2360	With manual starter	2,225	590	2,815
2380	With magnetic starter	2,375	920	3,295
2400	10 HP, 1800 RPM, motor only	2,375	200	2,575
2420	With manual starter	2,700	600	3,300
2440	With magnetic starter	2,850	930	3,780
2460	15 HP, 1800 RPM, motor only	3,300	250	3,550
2480	With magnetic starter	3,775	980	4,755
2500	20 HP, 1800 RPM, motor only	4,550	310	4,860
2520	With magnetic starter	5,325	1,200	6,525
2540	25 HP, 1800 RPM, motor only	5,150	320	5,470
2560	With magnetic starter	5,925	1,200	7,125
2580	30 HP, 1800 RPM, motor only	6,825	335	7,160
2600	With magnetic starter	7,600	1,225	8,825
2620	40 HP, 1800 RPM, motor only	7,250	400	7,650
2640	With magnetic starter	9,000	1,725	10,725
2660	50 HP, 1800 RPM, motor only	8,800	500	9,300
2680	With magnetic starter	10,600	1,825	12,425
2700	60 HP, 1800 RPM, motor only	5,350	570	5,920
2720	With magnetic starter	9,375	2,350	11,725
2740	75 HP, 1800 RPM, motor only	9,600	665	10,265
2760	With magnetic starter	13,600	2,450	16,050
2780	100 HP, 1800 RPM, motor only	11,700	890	12,590
2800	With magnetic starter	15,700	2,675	18,375
2820	125 HP, 1800 RPM, motor only	16,200	1,150	17,350
2840	With magnetic starter	27,800	3,150	30,950
2860	150 HP, 1800 RPM, motor only	17,400	1,325	18,725
2880	With magnetic starter	29,000	3,325	32,325
2900	200 HP, 1800 RPM, motor only	23,200	1,600	24,800
2920	With magnetic starter	34,800	3,600	38,400

D5020 Lighting and Branch Wiring

General: The cost of the lighting portion of the electrical costs is dependent upon:
1. The footcandle requirement of the proposed building.
2. The type of fixtures required.
3. The ceiling heights of the building.
4. Reflectance value of ceilings, walls and floors.
5. Fixture efficiencies and spacing vs. mounting height ratios.

Footcandle Requirements: See Table D5020-204 for Footcandle and Watts per S.F. determination.

Table D5020-201 IESNA* Recommended Illumination Levels in Footcandles

Commercial Buildings			Industrial Buildings		
Type	**Description**	**Footcandles**	**Type**	**Description**	**Footcandles**
Bank	Lobby	50	Assembly Areas	Rough bench & machine work	50
	Customer Areas	70		Medium bench & machine work	100
	Teller Stations	150		Fine bench & machine work	500
	Accounting Areas	150	Inspection Areas	Ordinary	50
Offices	Routine Work	100		Difficult	100
	Accounting	150		Highly Difficult	200
	Drafting	200	Material Handling	Loading	20
	Corridors, Halls, Washrooms	30		Stock Picking	30
Schools	Reading or Writing	70		Packing, Wrapping	50
	Drafting, Labs, Shops	100	Stairways	Service Areas	20
	Libraries	70	Washrooms	Service Areas	20
	Auditoriums, Assembly	15	Storage Areas	Inactive	5
	Auditoriums, Exhibition	30		Active, Rough, Bulky	10
Stores	Circulation Areas	30		Active, Medium	20
	Stock Rooms	30		Active, Fine	50
	Merchandise Areas, Service	100	Garages	Active Traffic Areas	20
	Self-Service Areas	200		Service & Repair	100

*IESNA - Illuminating Engineering Society of North America

Table D5020-202 General Lighting Loads by Occupancies

Type of Occupancy	Unit Load per S.F. (Watts)
Armories and Auditoriums	1
Banks	5
Barber Shops and Beauty Parlors	3
Churches	1
Clubs	2
Court Rooms	2
*Dwelling Units	3
Garages — Commercial (storage)	½
Hospitals	2
*Hotels and Motels, including apartment houses without provisions for cooking by tenants	2
Industrial Commercial (Loft) Buildings	2
Lodge Rooms	1½
Office Buildings	5
Restaurants	2
Schools	3
Stores	3
Warehouses (storage)	¼
*In any of the above occupancies except one-family dwellings and individual dwelling units of multi-family dwellings:	
Assembly Halls and Auditoriums	1
Halls, Corridors, Closets	½
Storage Spaces	¼

Table D5020-203 Lighting Limit (Connected Load) for Listed Occupancies: New Building Proposed Energy Conservation Guideline

Type of Use	Maximum Watts per S.F.
Interior	
Category A: Classrooms, office areas, automotive mechanical areas, museums, conference rooms, drafting rooms, clerical areas, laboratories, merchandising areas, kitchens, examining rooms, book stacks, athletic facilities.	3.00
Category B: Auditoriums, waiting areas, spectator areas, restrooms, dining areas, transportation terminals, working corridors in prisons and hospitals, book storage areas, active inventory storage, hospital bedrooms, hotel and motel bedrooms, enclosed shopping mall concourse areas, stairways.	1.00
Category C: Corridors, lobbies, elevators, inactive storage areas.	0.50
Category D: Indoor parking.	0.25
Exterior	
Category E: Building perimeter: wall-wash, facade, canopy.	5.00 (per linear foot)
Category F: Outdoor parking.	0.10

Table D5020-204 Procedure for Calculating Footcandles and Watts Per Square Foot

1. Initial footcandles = No. of fixtures × lamps per fixture × lumens per lamp × coefficient of utilization ÷ square feet
2. Maintained footcandles = initial footcandles × maintenance factor
3. Watts per square foot = No. of fixtures × lamps × (lamp watts + ballast watts) ÷ square feet

Example: To find footcandles and watts per S.F. for an office 20′ x 20′ with 11 fluorescent fixtures each having 4–40 watt C.W. lamps.

Based on good reflectance and clean conditions:

Lumens per lamp = 40 watt cool white at 3150 lumens per lamp RD5020-250, Table RD5020-251

Coefficient of utilization = .42 (varies from .62 for light colored areas to .27 for dark)

Maintenance factor = .75 (varies from .80 for clean areas with good maintenance to .50 for poor)

Ballast loss = 8 watts per lamp. (Varies with manufacturer. See manufacturers' catalog.)

1. Initial footcandles:

$$\frac{11 \times 4 \times 3150 \times .42}{400} = \frac{58{,}212}{400} = 145 \text{ footcandles}$$

2. Maintained footcandles:

145 × .75 = 109 footcandles

3. Watts per S.F.

$$\frac{11 \times 4\ (40 + 8)}{400} = \frac{2{,}112}{400} = 5.3 \text{ watts per S.F.}$$

Table D5020-205 Approximate Watts Per Square Foot for Popular Fixture Types

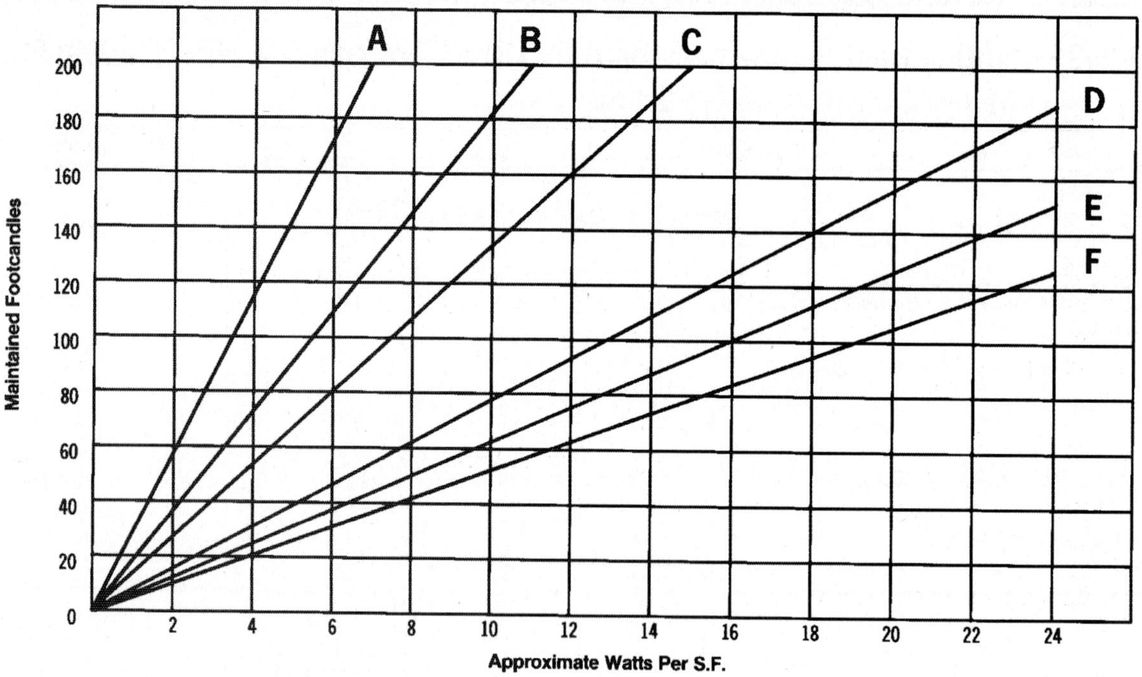

Due to the many variables involved, use for preliminary estimating only:

a. Fluorescent – industrial System D5020 208
b. Fluorescent – lens unit System D5020 208 Fixture types B & C
c. Fluorescent – louvered unit
d. Incandescent – open reflector System D5020 214, Type D
e. Incandescent – lens unit System D5020 214, Type A
f. Incandescent – down light System D5020 214, Type B

D5020 Lighting and Branch Wiring

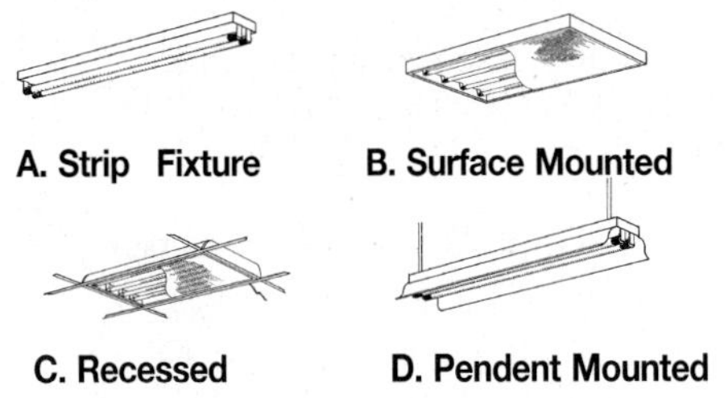

Design Assumptions:

1. A 100 footcandle average maintained level of illumination.
2. Ceiling heights range from 9′ to 11′.
3. Average reflectance values are assumed for ceilings, walls and floors.
4. Cool white (CW) fluorescent lamps with 3150 lumens for 40 watt lamps and 6300 lumens for 8′ slimline lamps.
5. Four 40 watt lamps per 4′ fixture and two 8′ lamps per 8′ fixture.
6. Average fixture efficiency values and spacing to mounting height ratios.
7. Installation labor is average U.S. rate as of January 1.

System Components	QUANTITY	UNIT	COST PER S.F. MAT.	COST PER S.F. INST.	COST PER S.F. TOTAL
SYSTEM D5020 208 0520					
FLUORESCENT FIXTURES MOUNTED 9′-11″ ABOVE FLOOR, 100 FC					
TYPE A, 8 FIXTURES PER 400 S.F.					
Conduit, steel intermediate, 1/2″ diam.	.185	L.F.	.64	1.48	2.12
Wire, 600V, type THWN-THHN, copper, solid, #12	.004	C.L.F.	.09	.27	.36
Fluorescent strip fixture 8′ long, surface mounted, two 75W SL	.020	Ea.	2.66	2.58	5.24
Steel outlet box 4″ concrete	.020	Ea.	.55	.80	1.35
Steel outlet box plate with stud, 4″ concrete	.020	Ea.	.26	.20	.46
Fixture hangers, flexible, 1/2″ diameter, 4″ long	.040	Ea.	.74	2.66	3.40
Fixture whip, THHN wire, three #12, 3/8″ Greenfield	.040	Ea.	.54	1	1.54
TOTAL			5.48	8.99	14.47

D5020 208	Fluorescent Fixtures (by Type)	COST PER S.F. MAT.	COST PER S.F. INST.	COST PER S.F. TOTAL
0520	Fluorescent fixtures, type A, 8 fixtures per 400 S.F.	5.50	9	14.50
0560	11 fixtures per 600 S.F.	4.97	8.20	13.17
0600	17 fixtures per 1000 S.F.	4.65	7.65	12.30
0640	23 fixtures per 1600 S.F.	3.88	6.40	10.28
0680	28 fixtures per 2000 S.F.	3.84	6.30	10.14
0720	41 fixtures per 3000 S.F.	3.79	6.15	9.94
0800	53 fixtures per 4000 S.F.	3.60	5.95	9.55
0840	64 fixtures per 5000 S.F.	3.55	5.85	9.40
0880	Type B, 11 fixtures per 400 S.F.	10.65	12.80	23.45
0920	15 fixtures per 600 S.F.	9.55	11.55	21.10
0960	24 fixtures per 1000 S.F.	9.20	11.15	20.35
1000	35 fixtures per 1600 S.F.	8.40	10.15	18.55
1040	42 fixtures per 2000 S.F.	8.05	9.70	17.75
1080	61 fixtures per 3000 S.F.	7.70	9.35	17.05
1160	80 fixtures per 4000 S.F.	6.50	5.95	12.45
1200	98 fixtures per 5000 S.F.	7.60	9.10	16.70
1240	Type C, 11 fixtures per 400 S.F.	7.35	13.30	20.65
1280	14 fixtures per 600 S.F.	6.15	11.15	17.30
1320	23 fixtures per 1000 S.F.	6.10	11.05	17.15
1360	34 fixtures per 1600 S.F.	5.60	10.20	15.80
1400	43 fixtures per 2000 S.F.	5.75	10.45	16.20
1440	63 fixtures per 3000 S.F.	5.55	10.10	15.65
1520	81 fixtures per 4000 S.F.	5.35	9.70	15.05
1560	101 fixtures per 5000 S.F.	5.30	9.60	14.90
1600	Type D, 8 fixtures per 400 S.F.	5.10	10.05	15.15
1640	12 fixtures per 600 S.F.	5.10	10.05	15.15
1680	19 fixtures per 1000 S.F.	4.86	9.55	14.41
1720	27 fixtures per 1600 S.F.	4.34	8.55	12.89
1760	34 fixtures per 2000 S.F.	4.35	8.55	12.90
1800	48 fixtures per 3000 S.F.	4.09	8.05	12.14
1880	64 fixtures per 4000 S.F.	4.09	8.05	12.14
1920	79 fixtures per 5000 S.F.	4.08	8	12.08

D5020 Lighting and Branch Wiring

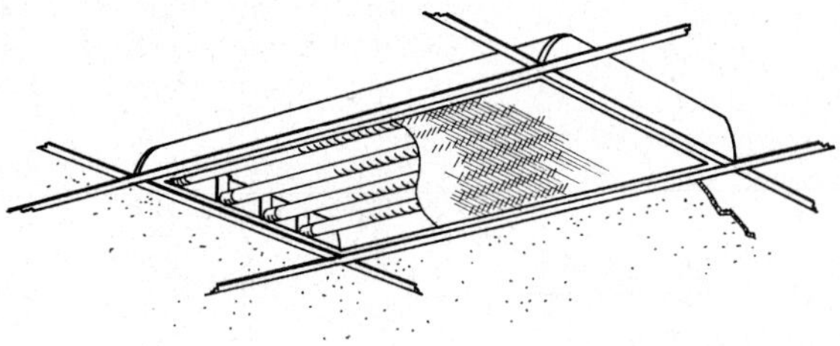

Type C. Recessed, mounted on grid ceiling suspension system, 2′ x 4′, four 40 watt lamps, acrylic prismatic diffusers.

5.3 watts per S.F. for 100 footcandles.

3 watts per S.F. for 57 footcandles.

System Components	QUANTITY	UNIT	COST PER S.F. MAT.	INST.	TOTAL
SYSTEM D5020 210 0200					
FLUORESCENT FIXTURES RECESS MOUNTED IN CEILING					
1 WATT PER S.F., 20 FC, 5 FIXTURES PER 1000 S.F.					
Steel intermediate conduit, (IMC) 1/2″ diam.	.128	L.F.	.44	1.02	1.46
Wire, 600 volt, type THW, copper, solid, #12	.003	C.L.F.	.06	.22	.28
Fluorescent fixture, recessed, 2′x 4′, four 40W, w/lens, for grid ceiling	.005	Ea.	.64	.85	1.49
Steel outlet box 4″ square	.005	Ea.	.14	.20	.34
Fixture whip, Greenfield w/#12 THHN wire	.005	Ea.	.07	.05	.12
TOTAL			1.35	2.34	3.69

D5020 210	Fluorescent Fixtures (by Wattage)	COST PER S.F. MAT.	INST.	TOTAL
0190	Fluorescent fixtures recess mounted in ceiling			
0195	T8, standard 40 watt lamps			
0200	1 watt per S.F., 20 FC, 5 fixtures @40 watts per 1000 S.F.	1.34	2.34	3.68
0240	2 watt per S.F., 40 FC, 10 fixtures @40 watt per 1000 S.F.	2.66	4.61	7.27
0280	3 watt per S.F., 60 FC, 15 fixtures @40 watt per 1000 S.F	4	6.95	10.95
0320	4 watt per S.F., 80 FC, 20 fixtures @40 watt per 1000 S.F.	5.35	9.25	14.60
0400	5 watt per S.F., 100 FC, 25 fixtures @40 watt per 1000 S.F.	6.70	11.55	18.25
0450	T8, energy saver 32 watt lamps			
0500	0.8 watt per S.F., 20 FC, 5 fixtures @32 watt per 1000 S.F.	1.84	2.34	4.18
0520	1.6 watt per S.F., 40 FC, 10 fixtures @32 watt per 1000 S.F.	3.65	4.61	8.26
0540	2.4 watt per S.F., 60 FC, 15 fixtures @ 32 watt per 1000 S.F	5.50	6.95	12.45
0560	3.2 watt per S.F., 80 FC, 20 fixtures @32 watt per 1000 S.F.	7.30	9.25	16.55
0580	4 watt per S.F., 100 FC, 25 fixtures @32 watt per 1000 S.F.	9.15	11.55	20.70

D5020 Lighting and Branch Wiring

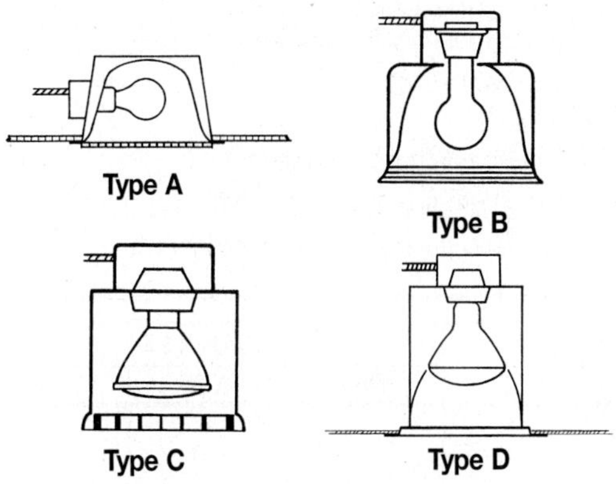

Type A. Recessed wide distribution reflector with flat glass lens 150 W.

Maximum spacing = 1.2 x mounting height.

13 watts per S.F. for 100 footcandles.

Type B. Recessed reflector down light with baffles 150 W.

Maximum spacing = 0.8 x mounting height.

18 watts per S.F. for 100 footcandles.

Type C. Recessed PAR–38 flood lamp with concentric louver 150 W.

Maximum spacing = 0.5 x mounting height.

19 watts per S.F. for 100 footcandles.

Type D. Recessed R–40 flood lamp with reflector skirt.

Maximum spacing = 0.7 x mounting height.

15 watts per S.F. for 100 footcandles.

System Components	QUANTITY	UNIT	COST PER S.F. MAT.	COST PER S.F. INST.	COST PER S.F. TOTAL
SYSTEM D5020 214 0400					
INCANDESCENT FIXTURE RECESS MOUNTED, 100 FC					
TYPE A, 34 FIXTURES PER 400 S.F.					
Steel intermediate conduit, (IMC) 1/2" diam	1.060	L.F.	3.66	8.48	12.14
Wire, 600V, type THWN-THHN, copper, solid, #12	.033	C.L.F.	.76	2.41	3.17
Steel outlet box 4" square	.085	Ea.	2.34	3.40	5.74
Fixture whip, Greenfield w/#12 THHN wire	.085	Ea.	1.12	.85	1.97
Incandescent fixture, recessed, w/lens, prewired, square trim, 200W	.085	Ea.	9.44	10.20	19.64
TOTAL			17.32	25.34	42.66

D5020 214	Incandescent Fixture (by Type)	COST PER S.F. MAT.	COST PER S.F. INST.	COST PER S.F. TOTAL
0380	Incandescent fixture recess mounted, 100 FC			
0400	Type A, 34 fixtures per 400 S.F.	17.30	25.50	42.80
0440	49 fixtures per 600 S.F.	16.90	25	41.90
0480	63 fixtures per 800 S.F.	16.55	24.50	41.05
0520	90 fixtures per 1200 S.F.	16	24	40
0560	116 fixtures per 1600 S.F.	15.75	24	39.75
0600	143 fixtures per 2000 S.F.	15.60	24	39.60
0640	Type B, 47 fixtures per 400 S.F.	17.80	32	49.80
0680	66 fixtures per 600 S.F.	17.15	31	48.15
0720	88 fixtures per 800 S.F.	17.15	31	48.15
0760	127 fixtures per 1200 S.F.	16.85	31	47.85
0800	160 fixtures per 1600 S.F.	16.65	30.50	47.15
0840	206 fixtures per 2000 S.F.	16.60	30.50	47.10
0880	Type C, 51 fixtures per 400 S.F.	22.50	33.50	56
0920	74 fixtures per 600 S.F.	22	33	55
0960	97 fixtures per 800 S.F.	21.50	32.50	54
1000	142 fixtures per 1200 S.F.	21.50	32.50	54
1040	186 fixtures per 1600 S.F.	21	32	53
1080	230 fixtures per 2000 S.F.	21	32	53
1120	Type D, 39 fixtures per 400 S.F.	20.50	26.50	47
1160	57 fixtures per 600 S.F.	19.80	26	45.80
1200	75 fixtures per 800 S.F.	19.70	26	45.70
1240	109 fixtures per 1200 S.F.	19.30	25.50	44.80
1280	143 fixtures per 1600 S.F.	19	25.50	44.50
1320	176 fixtures per 2000 S.F.	18.85	25.50	44.35

D5020 Lighting and Branch Wiring

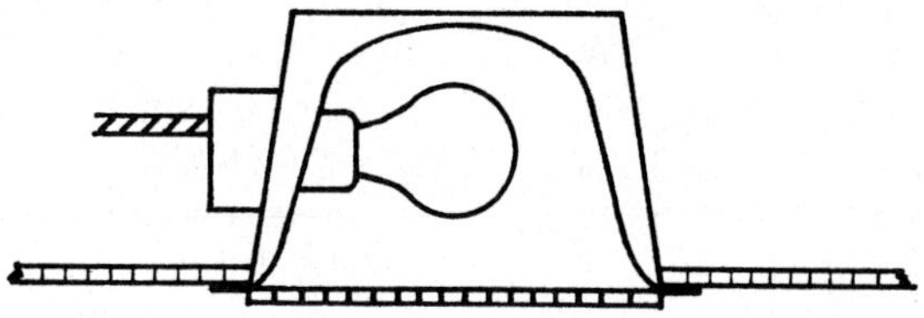

Type A. Recessed, wide distribution reflector with flat glass lens.

150 watt inside frost—2500 lumens per lamp.

PS-25 extended service lamp.

Maximum spacing = 1.2 x mounting height.

13 watts per S.F. for 100 footcandles.

System Components	QUANTITY	UNIT	COST PER S.F. MAT.	INST.	TOTAL
SYSTEM D5020 216 0200					
INCANDESCENT FIXTURE RECESS MOUNTED, TYPE A					
1 WATT PER S.F., 8 FC, 6 FIXT PER 1000 S.F.					
Steel intermediate conduit, (IMC) 1/2" diam	.091	L.F.	.31	.73	1.04
Wire, 600V, type THWN-THHN, copper, solid, #12	.002	C.L.F.	.05	.15	.20
Incandescent fixture, recessed, w/lens, prewired, square trim, 200W	.006	Ea.	.67	.72	1.39
Steel outlet box 4" square	.006	Ea.	.17	.24	.41
Fixture whip, Greenfield w/#12 THHN wire	.006	Ea.	.08	.06	.14
TOTAL			1.28	1.90	3.18

D5020 216	Incandescent Fixture (by Wattage)	COST PER S.F. MAT.	INST.	TOTAL
0190	Incandescent fixture recess mounted, type A			
0200	1 watt per S.F., 8 FC, 6 fixtures per 1000 S.F.	1.27	1.89	3.16
0240	2 watt per S.F., 16 FC, 12 fixtures per 1000 S.F.	2.54	3.79	6.33
0280	3 watt per S.F., 24 FC, 18 fixtures, per 1000 S.F.	3.79	5.60	9.39
0320	4 watt per S.F., 32 FC, 24 fixtures per 1000 S.F.	5.05	7.50	12.55
0400	5 watt per S.F., 40 FC, 30 fixtures per 1000 S.F.	6.35	9.40	15.75

D5020 Lighting and Branch Wiring

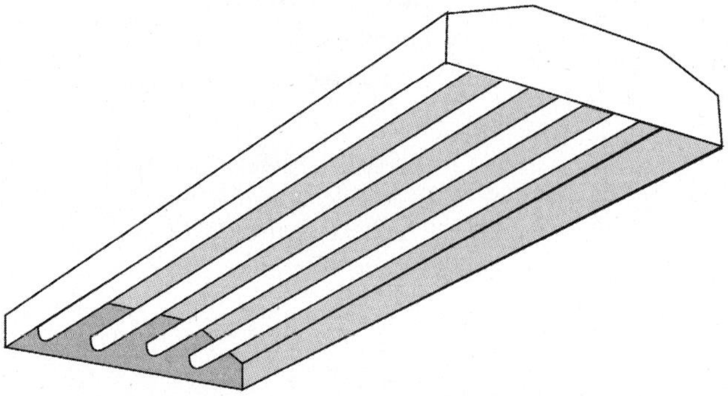

High Bay Fluorescent Fixtures
Four T5 HO/54 watt lamps

System Components	QUANTITY	UNIT	COST PER S.F. MAT.	COST PER S.F. INST.	COST PER S.F. TOTAL
SYSTEM D5020 218 0200					
FLUORESCENT HIGH BAY FIXTURE, 4 LAMP, 8′-10′ ABOVE WORK PLANE					
0.5 WATT/S.F., 29 FC, 2 FIXTURES/1000 S.F.					
Steel intermediate conduit, (IMC) 1/2″ diam	.100	L.F.	.35	.80	1.15
Wire, 600V, type THWN-THHN, copper, solid, #10	.002	C.L.F.	.07	.16	.23
Steel outlet box 4″ concrete	.002	Ea.	.06	.08	.14
Steel outlet box plate with stud, 4″ concrete	.002	Ea.	.03	.02	.05
Flourescent , hi bay, 4 lamp, T-5 fixture	.002	Ea.	.64	.36	1
TOTAL			1.15	1.42	2.57

D5020 218	Fluorescent Fixture, High Bay, 8′-10′ (by Wattage)	COST PER S.F. MAT.	COST PER S.F. INST.	COST PER S.F. TOTAL
0190	Fluorescent high bay-4 lamp fixture, 8′-10′ above work plane			
0200	.5 watt/SF, 29 FC, 2 fixtures per 1000 S.F.	1.14	1.42	2.56
0400	1 watt/SF, 59 FC, 4 fixtures per 1000 S.F.	2.23	2.73	4.96
0600	1.5 watt/SF, 103 FC, 7 fixtures per 1000 S.F.	3.68	4.25	7.93
0800	2 watt/SF, 133 FC, 9 fixtures per 1000 S.F.	4.79	5.60	10.39
1000	2.5 watt/SF, 162 FC, 11 fixtures per 1000 S.F.	5.90	6.95	12.85

D5020 Lighting and Branch Wiring

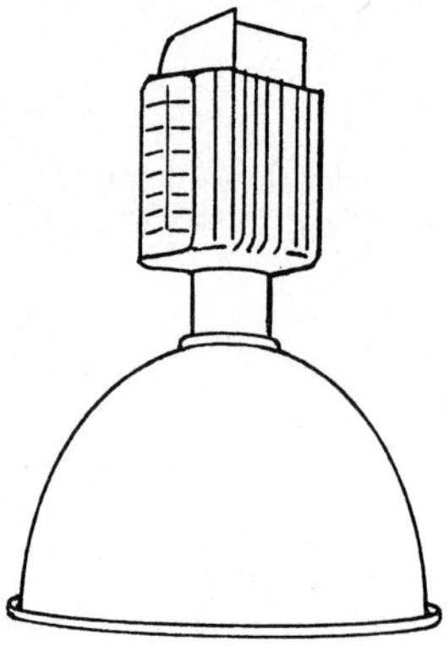

HIGH BAY FIXTURES

B. Metal halide 400 watt
C. High pressure sodium 400 watt
E. Metal halide 1000 watt
F. High pressure sodium 1000 watt
G. Metal halide 1000 watt
125,000 lumen lamp

System Components	QUANTITY	UNIT	COST PER S.F. MAT.	COST PER S.F. INST.	COST PER S.F. TOTAL
SYSTEM D5020 220 0880					
HIGH INTENSITY DISCHARGE FIXTURE, 8′-10′ ABOVE WORK PLANE, 100 FC					
TYPE B, 8 FIXTURES PER 900 S.F.					
Steel intermediate conduit, (IMC) 1/2″ diam	.460	L.F.	1.59	3.68	5.27
Wire, 600V, type THWN-THHN, copper, solid, #10	.009	C.L.F.	.33	.72	1.05
Steel outlet box 4″ concrete	.009	Ea.	.25	.36	.61
Steel outlet box plate with stud 4″ concrete	.009	Ea.	.12	.09	.21
Metal halide, hi bay, aluminum reflector, 400 W lamp	.009	Ea.	3.74	3.15	6.89
TOTAL			6.03	8	14.03

D5020 220	H.I.D. Fixture, High Bay, 8′-10′ (by Type)	COST PER S.F. MAT.	COST PER S.F. INST.	COST PER S.F. TOTAL
0500	High intensity discharge fixture, 8′-10′ above work plane, 100 FC			
0880	Type B, 8 fixtures per 900 S.F.	6	8	14
0920	15 fixtures per 1800 S.F.	5.60	7.70	13.30
0960	24 fixtures per 3000 S.F.	5.60	7.70	13.30
1000	31 fixtures per 4000 S.F.	5.60	7.70	13.30
1040	38 fixtures per 5000 S.F.	5.60	7.70	13.30
1080	60 fixtures per 8000 S.F.	5.60	7.70	13.30
1120	72 fixtures per 10000 S.F.	5.10	7.10	12.20
1160	115 fixtures per 16000 S.F.	5.10	7.10	12.20
1200	230 fixtures per 32000 S.F.	5.10	7.10	12.20
1240	Type C, 4 fixtures per 900 S.F.	3.38	4.88	8.26
1280	8 fixtures per 1800 S.F.	3.40	4.91	8.31
1320	13 fixtures per 3000 S.F.	3.38	4.88	8.26
1360	17 fixtures per 4000 S.F.	3.38	4.88	8.26
1400	21 fixtures per 5000 S.F.	3.20	4.48	7.68
1440	33 fixtures per 8000 S.F.	3.16	4.40	7.56
1480	40 fixtures per 10000 S.F.	3.06	4.16	7.22
1520	63 fixtures per 16000 S.F.	3.06	4.16	7.22
1560	126 fixtures per 32000 S.F.	3.06	4.16	7.22

D5020 Lighting and Branch Wiring

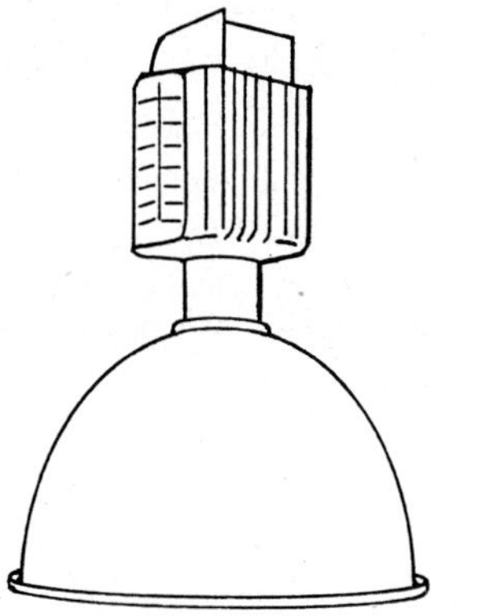

HIGH BAY FIXTURES

B. Metal halide 400 watt
C. High pressure sodium 400 watt
E. Metal halide 1000 watt
F. High pressure sodium 1000 watt
G. Metal halide 1000 watt
125,000 lumen lamp

System Components	QUANTITY	UNIT	COST PER S.F. MAT.	COST PER S.F. INST.	COST PER S.F. TOTAL
SYSTEM D5020 222 0240					
HIGH INTENSITY DISCHARGE FIXTURE, 8′-10′ ABOVE WORK PLANE					
1 WATT/S.F., TYPE B, 29 FC, 2 FIXTURES/1000 S.F.					
Steel intermediate conduit, (IMC) 1/2″ diam	.100	L.F.	.35	.80	1.15
Wire, 600V, type THWN-THHN, copper, solid, #10	.002	C.L.F.	.07	.16	.23
Steel outlet box 4″ concrete	.002	Ea.	.06	.08	.14
Steel outlet box plate with stud, 4″ concrete	.002	Ea.	.03	.02	.05
Metal halide, hi bay, aluminum reflector, 400 W lamp	.002	Ea.	.83	.70	1.53
TOTAL			1.34	1.76	3.10

D5020 222	H.I.D. Fixture, High Bay, 8′-10′ (by Wattage)	COST PER S.F. MAT.	COST PER S.F. INST.	COST PER S.F. TOTAL
0190	High intensity discharge fixture, 8′-10′ above work plane			
0240	1 watt/S.F., type B, 29 FC, 2 fixtures/1000 S.F.	1.33	1.76	3.09
0280	Type C, 54 FC, 2 fixtures/1000 S.F.	1.21	1.34	2.55
0400	2 watt/S.F., type B, 59 FC, 4 fixtures/1000 S.F.	2.61	3.41	6.02
0440	Type C, 108 FC, 4 fixtures/1000 S.F.	2.38	2.60	4.98
0560	3 watt/S.F., type B, 103 FC, 7 fixtures/1000 S.F.	4.34	5.45	9.79
0600	Type C, 189 FC, 6 fixtures/1000 S.F.	3.65	3.36	7.01
0720	4 watt/S.F., type B, 133 FC, 9 fixtures/1000 S.F.	5.65	7.15	12.80
0760	Type C, 243 FC, 9 fixtures/1000 S.F.	5.35	5.80	11.15
0880	5 watt/S.F., type B, 162 FC, 11 fixtures/1000 S.F.	6.95	8.85	15.80
0920	Type C, 297 FC, 11 fixtures/1000 S.F.	6.55	7.20	13.75

D5020 Lighting and Branch Wiring

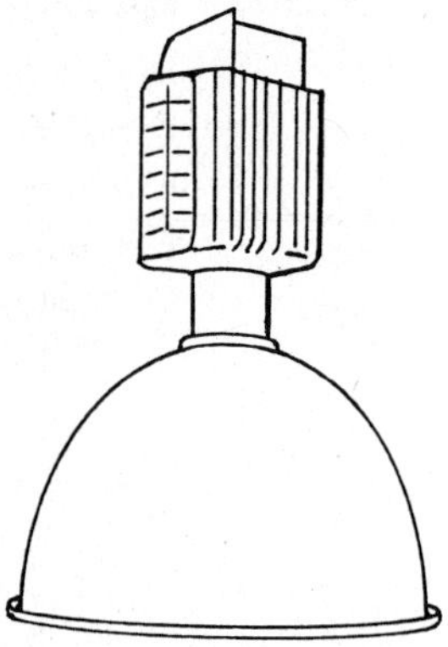

HIGH BAY FIXTURES
B. Metal halide 400 watt
C. High pressure sodium 400 watt
E. Metal halide 1000 watt
F. High pressure sodium 1000 watt
G. Metal halide 1000 watt
125,000 lumen lamp

System Components	QUANTITY	UNIT	COST PER S.F. MAT.	INST.	TOTAL
SYSTEM D5020 224 1240					
HIGH INTENSITY DISCHARGE FIXTURE, 16′ ABOVE WORK PLANE, 100 FC					
TYPE C, 5 FIXTURES PER 900 S.F.					
Steel intermediate conduit, (IMC) 1/2″ diam	.260	L.F.	.90	2.08	2.98
Wire, 600V, type THWN-THHN, copper, solid, #10	.007	C.L.F.	.26	.56	.82
Steel outlet box 4″ concrete	.006	Ea.	.17	.24	.41
Steel outlet box plate with stud, 4″ concrete	.006	Ea.	.08	.06	.14
High pressure sodium, hi bay, aluminum reflector, 400 W lamp	.006	Ea.	2.67	2.10	4.77
TOTAL			4.08	5.04	9.12

D5020 224	H.I.D. Fixture, High Bay, 16′ (by Type)	COST PER S.F. MAT.	INST.	TOTAL
0510	High intensity discharge fixture, 16′ above work plane, 100 FC			
1240	Type C, 5 fixtures per 900 S.F.	4.07	5.05	9.12
1280	9 fixtures per 1800 S.F.	3.86	5.30	9.16
1320	15 fixtures per 3000 S.F.	3.86	5.30	9.16
1360	18 fixtures per 4000 S.F.	3.62	4.72	8.34
1400	22 fixtures per 5000 S.F.	3.62	4.72	8.34
1440	36 fixtures per 8000 S.F.	3.62	4.72	8.34
1480	42 fixtures per 10,000 S.F.	3.38	4.88	8.26
1520	65 fixtures per 16,000 S.F.	3.38	4.88	8.26
1600	Type G, 4 fixtures per 900 S.F.	6.55	7.95	14.50
1640	6 fixtures per 1800 S.F.	5.55	7.45	13
1720	9 fixtures per 4000 S.F.	4.68	7.20	11.88
1760	11 fixtures per 5000 S.F.	4.68	7.20	11.88
1840	21 fixtures per 10,000 S.F.	4.37	6.50	10.87
1880	33 fixtures per 16,000 S.F.	4.37	6.50	10.87

D5020 Lighting and Branch Wiring

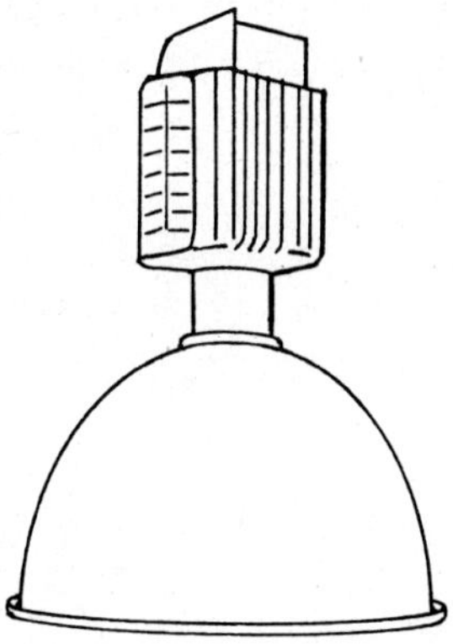

HIGH BAY FIXTURES
B. Metal halide 400 watt
C. High pressure sodium 400 watt
E. Metal halide 1000 watt
F. High pressure sodium 1000 watt
G. Metal halide 1000 watt
125,000 lumen lamp

System Components	QUANTITY	UNIT	COST PER S.F. MAT.	COST PER S.F. INST.	COST PER S.F. TOTAL
SYSTEM D5020 226 0240					
HIGH INTENSITY DISCHARGE FIXTURE, 16′ ABOVE WORK PLANE					
1 WATT/S.F., TYPE E, 42 FC, 1 FIXTURE/1000 S.F.					
Steel intermediate conduit, (IMC) 1/2″ diam	.160	L.F.	.55	1.28	1.83
Wire, 600V, type THWN-THHN, copper, solid, #10	.003	C.L.F.	.11	.24	.35
Steel outlet box 4″ concrete	.001	Ea.	.03	.04	.07
Steel outlet box plate with stud, 4″ concrete	.001	Ea.	.01	.01	.02
Metal halide, hi bay, aluminum reflector, 1000 W lamp	.001	Ea.	.92	.40	1.32
TOTAL			1.62	1.97	3.59

D5020 226	H.I.D. Fixture, High Bay, 16′ (by Wattage)	COST PER S.F. MAT.	COST PER S.F. INST.	COST PER S.F. TOTAL
0190	High intensity discharge fixture, 16′ above work plane			
0240	1 watt/S.F., type E, 42 FC, 1 fixture/1000 S.F.	1.62	1.97	3.59
0280	Type G, 52 FC, 1 fixture/1000 S.F.	1.62	1.97	3.59
0320	Type C, 54 FC, 2 fixture/1000 S.F.	1.59	2.21	3.80
0440	2 watt/S.F., type E, 84 FC, 2 fixture/1000 S.F.	3.28	4.02	7.30
0480	Type G, 105 FC, 2 fixture/1000 S.F.	3.28	4.02	7.30
0520	Type C, 108 FC, 4 fixture/1000 S.F.	3.17	4.42	7.59
0640	3 watt/S.F., type E, 126 FC, 3 fixture/1000 S.F.	4.91	6	10.91
0680	Type G, 157 FC, 3 fixture/1000 S.F.	4.91	6	10.91
0720	Type C, 162 FC, 6 fixture/1000 S.F.	4.76	6.60	11.36
0840	4 watt/S.F., type E, 168 FC, 4 fixture/1000 S.F.	6.55	8.05	14.60
0880	Type G, 210 FC, 4 fixture/1000 S.F.	6.55	8.05	14.60
0920	Type C, 243 FC, 9 fixture/1000 S.F.	6.85	9.25	16.10
1040	5 watt/S.F., type E, 210 FC, 5 fixture/1000 S.F.	8.20	10	18.20
1080	Type G, 262 FC, 5 fixture/1000 S.F.	8.20	10	18.20
1120	Type C, 297 FC, 11 fixture/1000 S.F.	8.40	11.45	19.85

D5020 Lighting and Branch Wiring

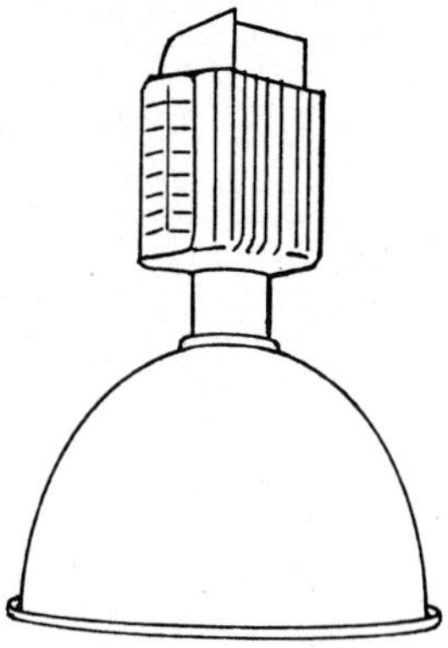

HIGH BAY FIXTURES

B. Metal halide 400 watt
C. High pressure sodium 400 watt
E. Metal halide 1000 watt
F. High pressure sodium 1000 watt
G. Metal halide 1000 watt
125,000 lumen lamp

System Components	QUANTITY	UNIT	COST PER S.F. MAT.	COST PER S.F. INST.	COST PER S.F. TOTAL
SYSTEM D5020 228 1240					
HIGH INTENSITY DISCHARGE FIXTURE, 20′ ABOVE WORK PLANE, 100 FC					
TYPE C, 6 FIXTURES PER 900 S.F.					
Steel intermediate conduit, (IMC) 1/2″ diam	.350	L.F.	1.21	2.80	4.01
Wire, 600V, type THWN-THHN, copper, solid, #10.	.011	C.L.F.	.41	.88	1.29
Steel outlet box 4″ concrete	.007	Ea.	.19	.28	.47
Steel outlet box plate with stud, 4″ concrete	.007	Ea.	.09	.07	.16
High pressure sodium, hi bay, aluminum reflector, 400 W lamp	.007	Ea.	3.12	2.45	5.57
TOTAL			5.02	6.48	11.50

D5020 228	H.I.D. Fixture, High Bay, 20′ (by Type)	COST PER S.F. MAT.	COST PER S.F. INST.	COST PER S.F. TOTAL
0510	High intensity discharge fixture 20′ above work plane, 100 FC			
1240	Type C, 6 fixtures per 900 S.F.	5	6.50	11.50
1280	10 fixtures per 1800 S.F.	4.53	6.10	10.63
1320	16 fixtures per 3000 S.F.	4.11	5.85	9.96
1360	20 fixtures per 4000 S.F.	4.11	5.85	9.96
1400	24 fixtures per 5000 S.F.	4.11	5.85	9.96
1440	38 fixtures per 8000 S.F.	4.01	5.60	9.61
1520	68 fixtures per 16000 S.F.	3.94	6.15	10.09
1560	132 fixtures per 32000 S.F.	3.94	6.15	10.09
1600	Type G, 4 fixtures per 900 S.F.	6.45	7.80	14.25
1640	6 fixtures per 1800 S.F.	5.55	7.45	13
1680	7 fixtures per 3000 S.F.	5.45	7.20	12.65
1720	10 fixtures per 4000 S.F.	5.40	7.10	12.50
1760	11 fixtures per 5000 S.F.	4.86	7.60	12.46
1800	18 fixtures per 8000 S.F.	4.86	7.60	12.46
1840	22 fixtures per 10000 S.F.	4.86	7.60	12.46
1880	34 fixtures per 16000 S.F.	4.76	7.40	12.16
1920	66 fixtures per 32000 S.F.	4.48	6.75	11.23

D5020 Lighting and Branch Wiring

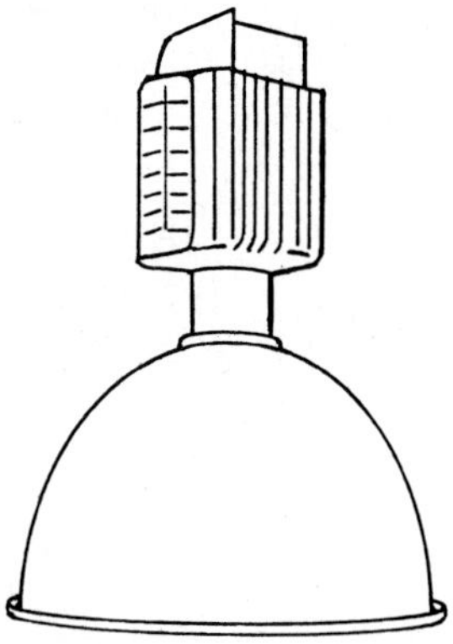

HIGH BAY FIXTURES
B. Metal halide 400 watt
C. High pressure sodium 400 watt
E. Metal halide 1000 watt
F. High pressure sodium 1000 watt
G. Metal halide 1000 watt
125,000 lumen lamp

System Components	QUANTITY	UNIT	COST PER S.F. MAT.	COST PER S.F. INST.	COST PER S.F. TOTAL
SYSTEM D5020 230 0240					
HIGH INTENSITY DISCHARGE FIXTURE, 20′ ABOVE WORK PLANE					
1 WATT/S.F., TYPE E, 40 FC, 1 FIXTURE 1000 S.F.					
Steel intermediate conduit, (IMC) 1/2″ diam	.160	L.F.	.55	1.28	1.83
Wire, 600V, type THWN-THHN, copper, solid, #10	.005	C.L.F.	.19	.40	.59
Steel outlet box 4″ concrete	.001	Ea.	.03	.04	.07
Steel outlet box plate with stud, 4″ concrete	.001	Ea.	.01	.01	.02
Metal halide, hi bay, aluminum reflector, 1000 W lamp	.001	Ea.	.92	.40	1.32
TOTAL			1.70	2.13	3.83

D5020 230	H.I.D. Fixture, High Bay, 20′ (by Wattage)	COST PER S.F. MAT.	COST PER S.F. INST.	COST PER S.F. TOTAL
0190	High intensity discharge fixture, 20′ above work plane			
0240	1 watt/S.F., type E, 40 FC, 1 fixture/1000 S.F.	1.70	2.13	3.83
0280	Type G, 50 FC, 1 fixture/1000 S.F.	1.70	2.13	3.83
0320	Type C, 52 FC, 2 fixtures/1000 S.F.	1.70	2.46	4.16
0440	2 watt/S.F., type E, 81 FC, 2 fixtures/1000 S.F.	3.40	4.26	7.66
0480	Type G, 101 FC, 2 fixtures/1000 S.F.	3.40	4.26	7.66
0520	Type C, 104 FC, 4 fixtures/1000 S.F.	3.37	4.85	8.22
0640	3 watt/S.F., type E, 121 FC, 3 fixtures/1000 S.F.	5.10	6.40	11.50
0680	Type G, 151 FC, 3 fixtures/1000 S.F.	5.10	6.40	11.50
0720	Type C, 155 FC, 6 fixtures/1000 S.F.	5.05	7.30	12.35
0840	4 watt/S.F., type E, 161 FC, 4 fixtures/1000 S.F.	6.80	8.50	15.30
0880	Type G, 202 FC, 4 fixtures/1000 S.F.	6.80	8.50	15.30
0920	Type C, 233 FC, 9 fixtures/1000 S.F.	7.20	10.10	17.30
1040	5 watt/S.F., type E, 202 FC, 5 fixtures/1000 S.F.	8.50	10.65	19.15
1080	Type G, 252 FC, 5 fixtures/1000 S.F.	8.50	10.65	19.15
1120	Type C, 285 FC, 11 fixtures/1000 S.F.	8.90	12.55	21.45

D5020 Lighting and Branch Wiring

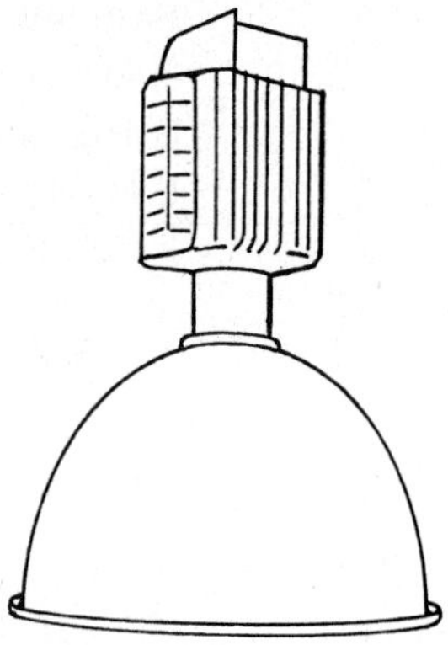

HIGH BAY FIXTURES
B. Metal halide 400 watt
C. High pressure sodium 400 watt
E. Metal halide 1000 watt
F. High pressure sodium 1000 watt
G. Metal halide 1000 watt
125,000 lumen lamp

System Components	QUANTITY	UNIT	COST PER S.F. MAT.	INST.	TOTAL
SYSTEM D5020 232 1240					
HIGH INTENSITY DISCHARGE FIXTURE, 30′ ABOVE WORK PLANE, 100 FC					
TYPE F, 4 FIXTURES PER 900 S.F.					
Steel intermediate conduit, (IMC) 1/2″ diam	.580	L.F.	2	4.64	6.64
Wire, 600V, type THWN-THHN, copper, solid, #10	.018	C.L.F.	.67	1.44	2.11
Steel outlet box 4″ concrete	.004	Ea.	.11	.16	.27
Steel outlet box plate with stud, 4″ concrete	.004	Ea.	.05	.04	.09
High pressure sodium, hi bay, aluminum, 1000 W lamp	.004	Ea.	2.48	1.60	4.08
TOTAL			5.31	7.88	13.19

D5020 232	H.I.D. Fixture, High Bay, 30′ (by Type)	COST PER S.F. MAT.	INST.	TOTAL
0510	High intensity discharge fixture, 30′ above work plane, 100 FC			
1240	Type F, 4 fixtures per 900 S.F.	5.30	7.90	13.20
1280	6 fixtures per 1800 S.F.	4.68	7.50	12.18
1320	8 fixtures per 3000 S.F.	4.68	7.50	12.18
1360	9 fixtures per 4000 S.F.	4.06	7.15	11.21
1400	10 fixtures per 5000 S.F.	4.06	7.15	11.21
1440	17 fixtures per 8000 S.F.	4.06	7.15	11.21
1480	18 fixtures per 10,000 S.F.	3.82	6.60	10.42
1520	27 fixtures per 16,000 S.F.	3.82	6.60	10.42
1560	52 fixtures per 32000 S.F.	3.78	6.50	10.28
1600	Type G, 4 fixtures per 900 S.F.	6.70	8.35	15.05
1640	6 fixtures per 1800 S.F.	5.60	7.60	13.20
1680	9 fixtures per 3000 S.F.	5.50	7.35	12.85
1720	11 fixtures per 4000 S.F.	5.40	7.10	12.50
1760	13 fixtures per 5000 S.F.	5.40	7.10	12.50
1800	21 fixtures per 8000 S.F.	5.40	7.10	12.50
1840	23 fixtures per 10,000 S.F.	4.85	7.55	12.40
1880	36 fixtures per 16,000 S.F.	4.85	7.55	12.40
1920	70 fixtures per 32,000 S.F.	4.85	7.55	12.40

D5020 Lighting and Branch Wiring

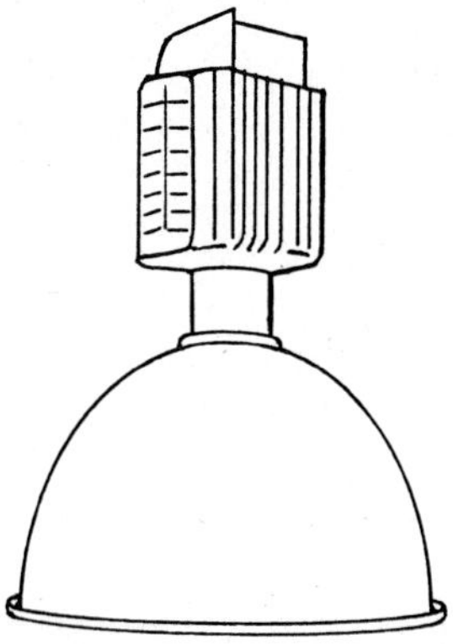

HIGH BAY FIXTURES
B. Metal halide 400 watt
C. High pressure sodium 400 watt
E. Metal halide 1000 watt
F. High pressure sodium 1000 watt
G. Metal halide 1000 watt
125,000 lumen lamp

System Components	QUANTITY	UNIT	COST PER S.F. MAT.	COST PER S.F. INST.	COST PER S.F. TOTAL
SYSTEM D5020 234 0240					
HIGH INTENSITY DISCHARGE FIXTURE, 30′ ABOVE WORK PLANE					
1 WATT/S.F., TYPE E, 37 FC, 1 FIXTURE/1000 S.F.					
Steel intermediate conduit, (IMC) 1/2″ diam	.196	L.F.	.68	1.57	2.25
Wire, 600V type THWN-THHN, copper, solid, #10	.006	C.L.F.	.22	.48	.70
Steel outlet box 4″ concrete	.001	Ea.	.03	.04	.07
Steel outlet box plate with stud, 4″ concrete	.001	Ea.	.01	.01	.02
Metal halide, hi bay, aluminum reflector, 1000 W lamp	.001	Ea.	.92	.40	1.32
TOTAL			1.86	2.50	4.36

D5020 234	H.I.D. Fixture, High Bay, 30′ (by Wattage)	COST PER S.F. MAT.	COST PER S.F. INST.	COST PER S.F. TOTAL
0190	High intensity discharge fixture, 30′ above work plane			
0240	1 watt/S.F., type E, 37 FC, 1 fixture/1000 S.F.	1.86	2.50	4.36
0280	Type G, 45 FC., 1 fixture/1000 S.F.	1.86	2.50	4.36
0320	Type F, 50 FC, 1 fixture/1000 S.F.	1.32	1.95	3.27
0440	2 watt/S.F., type E, 74 FC, 2 fixtures/1000 S.F.	3.72	5	8.72
0480	Type G, 92 FC, 2 fixtures/1000 S.F.	3.72	5	8.72
0520	Type F, 100 FC, 2 fixtures/1000 S.F.	2.68	3.99	6.67
0640	3 watt/S.F., type E, 110 FC, 3 fixtures/1000 S.F.	5.60	7.55	13.15
0680	Type G, 138 FC, 3 fixtures/1000 S.F.	5.60	7.55	13.15
0720	Type F, 150 FC, 3 fixtures/1000 S.F.	3.99	5.95	9.94
0840	4 watt/S.F., type E, 148 FC, 4 fixtures/1000 S.F.	7.45	10.05	17.50
0880	Type G, 185 FC, 4 fixtures/1000 S.F.	7.45	10.05	17.50
0920	Type F, 200 FC, 4 fixtures/1000 S.F.	5.35	8	13.35
1040	5 watt/S.F., type E, 185 FC, 5 fixtures/1000 S.F.	9.35	12.55	21.90
1080	Type G, 230 FC, 5 fixtures/1000 S.F.	9.35	12.55	21.90
1120	Type F, 250 FC, 5 fixtures/1000 S.F.	6.65	9.95	16.60

D5020 Lighting and Branch Wiring

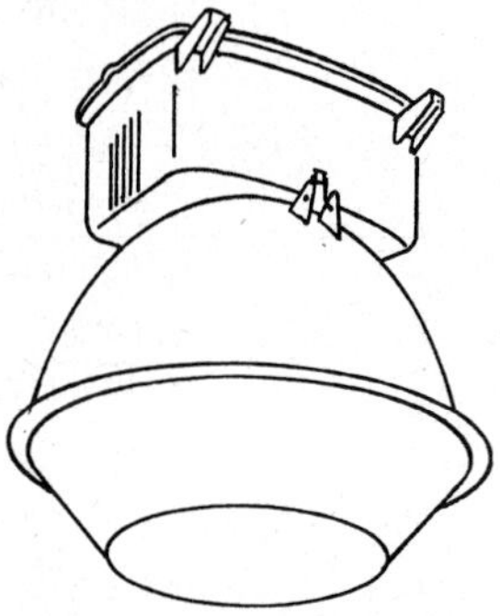

LOW BAY FIXTURES

J. Metal halide 250 watt

K. High pressure sodium 150 watt

System Components	QUANTITY	UNIT	COST PER S.F. MAT.	COST PER S.F. INST.	COST PER S.F. TOTAL
SYSTEM D5020 236 0920					
HIGH INTENSITY DISCHARGE FIXTURE, 8′-10′ ABOVE WORK PLANE, 50 FC					
TYPE J, 13 FIXTURES PER 1800 S.F.					
Steel intermediate conduit, (IMC) 1/2″ diam	.550	L.F.	1.90	4.40	6.30
Wire, 600V, type THWN-THHN, copper, solid, #10	.012	C.L.F.	.44	.96	1.40
Steel outlet box 4″ concrete	.007	Ea.	.19	.28	.47
Steel outlet box plate with stud, 4″ concrete	.007	Ea.	.09	.07	.16
Metal halide, lo bay, aluminum reflector, 250 W DX lamp	.007	Ea.	2.91	1.75	4.66
TOTAL			5.53	7.46	12.99

D5020 236	H.I.D. Fixture, Low Bay, 8′-10′ (by Type)	COST PER S.F. MAT.	COST PER S.F. INST.	COST PER S.F. TOTAL
0510	High intensity discharge fixture, 8′-10′ above work plane, 50 FC			
0880	Type J, 7 fixtures per 900 S.F.	5.90	7.50	13.40
0920	13 fixtures per 1800 S.F.	5.55	7.45	13
0960	21 fixtures per 3000 S.F.	5.55	7.45	13
1000	28 fixtures per 4000 S.F.	5.55	7.45	13
1040	35 fixtures per 5000 S.F.	5.55	7.45	13
1120	62 fixtures per 10,000 S.F.	5.10	7.15	12.25
1160	99 fixtures per 16,000 S.F.	5.10	7.15	12.25
1200	199 fixtures per 32,000 S.F.	5.10	7.15	12.25
1240	Type K, 9 fixtures per 900 S.F.	5.75	6.45	12.20
1280	16 fixtures per 1800 S.F.	5.35	6.20	11.55
1320	26 fixtures per 3000 S.F.	5.35	6.15	11.50
1360	31 fixtures per 4000 S.F.	4.98	6	10.98
1400	39 fixtures per 5000 S.F.	4.98	6	10.98
1440	62 fixtures per 8000 S.F.	4.98	6	10.98
1480	78 fixtures per 10,000 S.F.	4.98	6	10.98
1520	124 fixtures per 16,000 S.F.	4.91	5.85	10.76
1560	248 fixtures per 32,000 S.F.	4.90	6.50	11.40

D5020 Lighting and Branch Wiring

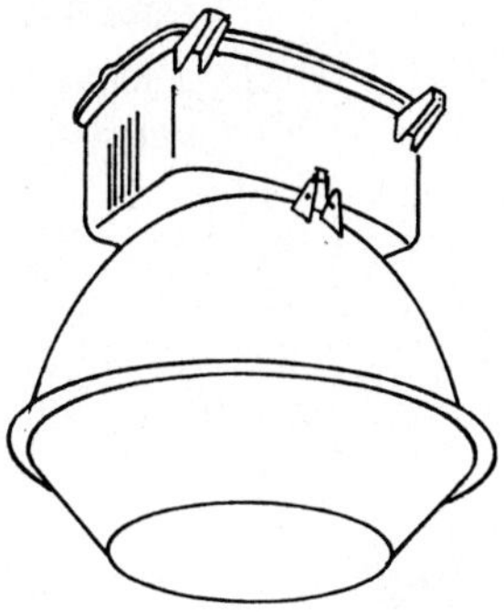

LOW BAY FIXTURES

J. Metal halide 250 watt

K. High pressure sodium 150 watt

System Components	QUANTITY	UNIT	COST PER S.F. MAT.	INST.	TOTAL
SYSTEM D5020 238 0240					
HIGH INTENSITY DISCHARGE FIXTURE, 8'-10' ABOVE WORK PLANE					
1 WATT/S.F., TYPE J, 30 FC, 4 FIXTURES/1000 S.F.					
Steel intermediate conduit, (IMC) 1/2" diam	.280	L.F.	.97	2.24	3.21
Wire, 600V, type THWN-THHN, copper, solid, #10	.008	C.L.F.	.30	.64	.94
Steel outlet box 4" concrete	.004	Ea.	.11	.16	.27
Steel outlet box plate with stud, 4" concrete	.004	Ea.	.05	.04	.09
Metal halide, lo bay, aluminum reflector, 250 W DX lamp	.004	Ea.	1.66	1	2.66
TOTAL			3.09	4.08	7.17

D5020 238	H.I.D. Fixture, Low Bay, 8'-10' (by Wattage)	COST PER S.F. MAT.	INST.	TOTAL
0190	High intensity discharge fixture, 8'-10' above work plane			
0240	1 watt/S.F., type J, 30 FC, 4 fixtures/1000 S.F.	3.08	4.08	7.16
0280	Type K, 29 FC, 5 fixtures/1000 S.F.	3.07	3.66	6.73
0400	2 watt/S.F., type J, 52 FC, 7 fixtures/1000 S.F.	5.55	7.50	13.05
0440	Type K, 63 FC, 11 fixtures/1000 S.F.	6.60	7.70	14.30
0560	3 watt/S.F., type J, 81 FC, 11 fixtures/1000 S.F.	8.50	11.30	19.80
0600	Type K, 92 FC, 16 fixtures/1000 S.F.	9.70	11.35	21.05
0720	4 watt/S.F., type J, 103 FC, 14 fixtures/1000 S.F.	11.05	14.85	25.90
0760	Type K, 127 FC, 22 fixtures/1000 S.F.	13.20	15.40	28.60
0880	5 watt/S.F., type J, 133 FC, 18 fixtures/1000 S.F.	14.05	18.75	32.80
0920	Type K, 155 FC, 27 fixtures/1000 S.F.	16.30	19.05	35.35

D5020 Lighting and Branch Wiring

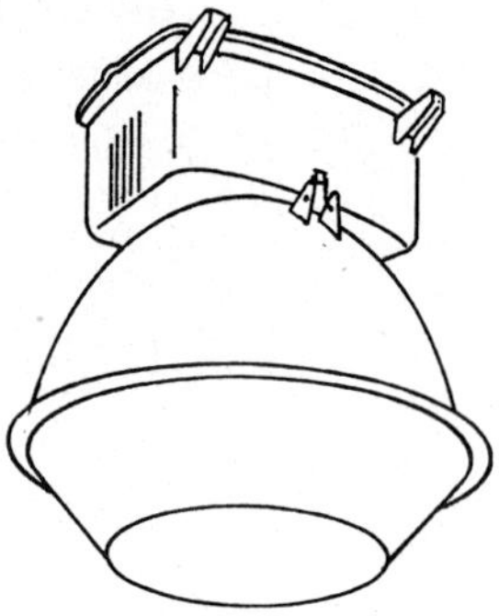

LOW BAY FIXTURES

J. Metal halide 250 watt

K. High pressure sodium 150 watt

System Components	QUANTITY	UNIT	COST PER S.F. MAT.	COST PER S.F. INST.	COST PER S.F. TOTAL
SYSTEM D5020 240 0880					
HIGH INTENSITY DISCHARGE FIXTURE, 16′ ABOVE WORK PLANE, 50 FC					
TYPE J, 9 FIXTURES PER 900 S.F.					
Steel intermediate conduit, (IMC) 1/2″ diam	.630	L.F.	2.17	5.04	7.21
Wire, 600V type, THWN-THHN, copper, solid, #10	.012	C.L.F.	.44	.96	1.40
Steel outlet box 4″ concrete	.010	Ea.	.28	.40	.68
Steel outlet box plate with stud, 4″ concrete	.010	Ea.	.13	.10	.23
Metal halide, lo bay, aluminum reflector, 250 W DX lamp	.010	Ea.	4.15	2.50	6.65
TOTAL			7.17	9	16.17

D5020 240	H.I.D. Fixture, Low Bay, 16′ (by Type)	COST PER S.F. MAT.	COST PER S.F. INST.	COST PER S.F. TOTAL
0510	High intensity discharge fixture, 16′ above work plane, 50 FC			
0880	Type J, 9 fixtures per 900 S.F.	7.15	9	16.15
0920	14 fixtures per 1800 S.F.	6.30	8.50	14.80
0960	24 fixtures per 3000 S.F.	6.35	8.65	15
1000	32 fixtures per 4000 S.F.	6.35	8.65	15
1040	35 fixtures per 5000 S.F.	5.95	8.40	14.35
1080	56 fixtures per 8000 S.F.	5.95	8.40	14.35
1120	70 fixtures per 10,000 S.F.	5.95	8.40	14.35
1160	111 fixtures per 16,000 S.F.	5.95	8.40	14.35
1200	222 fixtures per 32,000 S.F.	5.95	8.40	14.35
1240	Type K, 11 fixtures per 900 S.F.	7.20	8.40	15.60
1280	20 fixtures per 1800 S.F.	6.65	7.80	14.45
1320	29 fixtures per 3000 S.F.	6.30	7.65	13.95
1360	39 fixtures per 4000 S.F.	6.25	7.55	13.80
1400	44 fixtures per 5000 S.F.	5.90	7.40	13.30
1440	62 fixtures per 8000 S.F.	5.90	7.40	13.30
1480	87 fixtures per 10,000 S.F.	5.90	7.40	13.30
1520	138 fixtures per 16,000 S.F.	5.90	7.40	13.30

D5020 Lighting and Branch Wiring

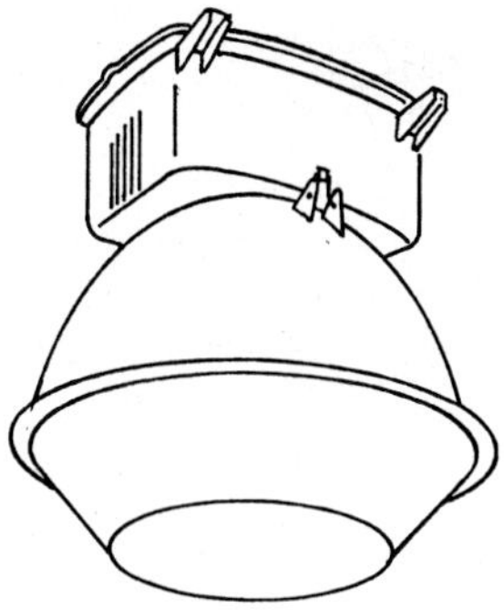

LOW BAY FIXTURES

J. Metal halide 250 watt

K. High pressure sodium 150 watt

System Components	QUANTITY	UNIT	COST PER S.F. MAT.	COST PER S.F. INST.	COST PER S.F. TOTAL
SYSTEM D5020 242 0240					
HIGH INTENSITY DISCHARGE FIXTURE, 16′ ABOVE WORK PLANE					
1 WATT/S.F., TYPE J, 28 FC, 4 FIXTURES/1000 S.F.					
Steel intermediate conduit, (IMC) 1/2″ diam	.328	L.F.	1.13	2.62	3.75
Wire, 600V, type THWN-THHN, copper, solid, #10	.010	C.L.F.	.37	.80	1.17
Steel outlet box 4″ concrete	.004	Ea.	.11	.16	.27
Steel outlet box plate with stud, 4″ concrete	.004	Ea.	.05	.04	.09
Metal halide, lo bay, aluminum reflector, 250 W DX lamp	.004	Ea.	1.66	1	2.66
TOTAL			3.32	4.62	7.94

D5020 242	H.I.D. Fixture, Low Bay, 16′ (by Wattage)	COST PER S.F. MAT.	COST PER S.F. INST.	COST PER S.F. TOTAL
0190	High intensity discharge fixture, mounted 16′ above work plane			
0240	1 watt/S.F., type J, 28 FC, 4 fixt./1000 S.F.	3.32	4.62	7.94
0280	Type K, 27 FC, 5 fixt./1000 S.F.	3.74	5.20	8.94
0400	2 watt/S.F., type J, 48 FC, 7 fixt/1000 S.F.	6.20	8.95	15.15
0440	Type K, 58 FC, 11 fixt/1000 S.F.	7.85	10.60	18.45
0560	3 watt/S.F., type J, 75 FC, 11 fixt/1000 S.F.	9.50	13.55	23.05
0600	Type K, 85 FC, 16 fixt/1000 S.F.	11.60	15.75	27.35
0720	4 watt/S.F., type J, 95 FC, 14 fixt/1000 S.F.	12.40	17.90	30.30
0760	Type K, 117 FC, 22 fixt/1000 S.F.	15.75	21	36.75
0880	5 watt/S.F., type J, 122 FC, 18 fixt/1000 S.F.	15.70	22.50	38.20
0920	Type K, 143 FC, 27 fixt/1000 S.F.	19.50	26.50	46

D5020 Lighting and Branch Wiring

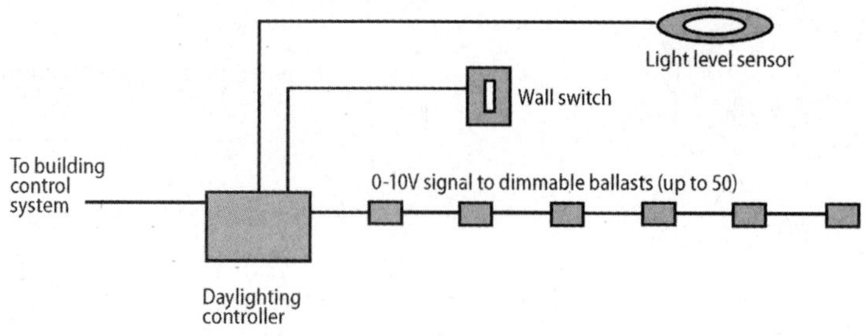

Daylight Dimming System

System Components	QUANTITY	UNIT	COST PER S.F. MAT.	INST.	TOTAL
SYSTEM D5020 290 0800					
DAYLIGHT DIMMING CONTROL SYSTEM					
5 FIXTURES PER 1000 S.F.					
Tray cable, type TC, copper #16-4 conductor	.300	C.L.F.	.02	.03	.05
Wire, 600 volt, type THWN-THHN, copper, solid, #12	.320	C.L.F.	.01	.02	.03
Conduit (EMT) to 10′ H, incl 2 termn,2 elb&11 bm clp per 100′, 3/4″	10.000	L.F.	.02	.06	.08
Cabinet, hinged, steel, NEMA 1, 12″W x 12″H x 4″D	.200	Ea.	.01	.03	.04
Lighting control module	.200	Ea.	.09	.08	.17
Dimmable ballast three-lamp	5.000	Ea.	.72	.58	1.30
Daylight level sensor, wall mounted, on/off or dimming	.200	Ea.	.03	.02	.05
Automatic wall switches	.200	Ea.	.02	.01	.03
Remote power pack	.100	Ea.	.01	.01	.02
TOTAL			.93	.84	1.77

D5020 290	Daylight Dimming System	COST PER S.F. MAT.	INST.	TOTAL
0500	Daylight Dimming System (no fixtures or fixture power)			
0800	5 fixtures per 1000 S.F.	.92	.84	1.76
1000	10 fixtures per 1000 S.F.	1.80	1.59	3.39
2000	12 fixtures per 1000 S.F.	2.16	1.90	4.06
3000	15 fixtures per 1000 S.F.	2.69	2.35	5.04
4000	20 fixtures per 1000 S.F.	3.58	3.10	6.68
5000	25 fixtures per 1000 S.F.	4.47	3.86	8.33
6000	50 fixtures per 1000 S.F.	8.90	7.65	16.55

D5020 Lighting and Branch Wiring

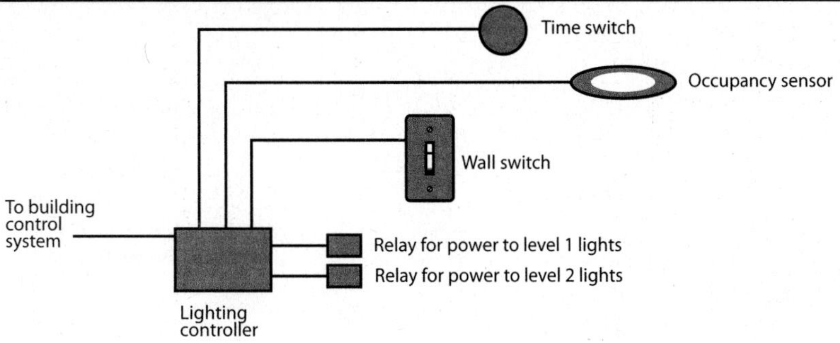

Lighting AC Control System

System Components	QUANTITY	UNIT	COST PER S.F. MAT.	COST PER S.F. INST.	COST PER S.F. TOTAL
SYSTEM D5020 295 0800					
LIGHTING ON/OFF CONTROL SYSTEM					
5 FIXTURES PER 1000 S.F.					
Tray cable, type TC, copper #16-4 conductor	.600	C.L.F.	.05	.07	.12
Wire, 600 volt, type THWN-THHN, copper, solid, #12	.320	C.L.F.	.01	.02	.03
Conduit (EMT) to 10′ H, incl 2 termn,2 elb&11 bm clp per 100′, 3/4″	10.000	L.F.	.02	.06	.08
Cabinet, hinged, steel, NEMA 1, 12″W x 12″H x 4″D	.400	Ea.	.02	.05	.07
Relays, 120 V or 277 V standard	.800	Ea.	.04	.05	.09
24 hour dial with reserve power	.400	Ea.	.41	.09	.50
Lighting control module	.200	Ea.	.09	.08	.17
Occupancy sensors, passive infrared ceiling mounted	.400	Ea.	.03	.05	.08
Automatic wall switches	.400	Ea.	.04	.01	.05
Remote power pack	.200	Ea.	.01	.02	.03
TOTAL			.72	.50	1.22

D5020 295	Lighting On/Off Control System	COST PER S.F. MAT.	COST PER S.F. INST.	COST PER S.F. TOTAL
0500	Includes occupancy and time switching (no fixtures or fixture power)			
0800	5 fixtures per 1000 SF	.70	.50	1.20
1000	10 fixtures per 1000 S.F.	.79	.58	1.37
2000	12 fixtures per 1000 S.F.	.94	.68	1.62
3000	15 fixtures per 1000 S.F.	1.17	.83	2
4000	20 fixtures per 1000 S.F.	1.55	1.08	2.63
5000	25 fixtures per 1000 S.F.	1.93	1.33	3.26
6000	50 fixtures per 1000 S.F.	3.83	2.57	6.40

D5030 Communications and Security

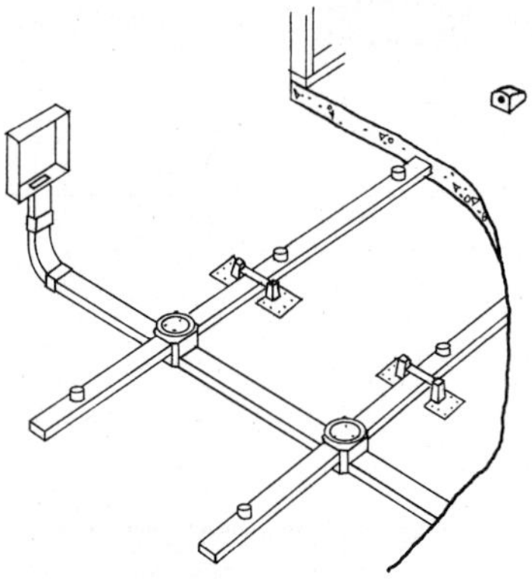

Description: System below includes telephone fitting installed. Does not include cable.

When poke thru fittings and telepoles are used for power, they can also be used for telephones at a negligible additional cost.

System Components	QUANTITY	UNIT	COST PER S.F. MAT.	COST PER S.F. INST.	COST PER S.F. TOTAL
SYSTEM D5030 310 0200					
TELEPHONE SYSTEMS, UNDERFLOOR DUCT, 5′ ON CENTER, LOW DENSITY					
Underfloor duct 7-1/4″ w/insert 2′ O.C. 1-3/8″ x 7-1/4″ super duct	.190	L.F.	8.08	3.04	11.12
Vertical elbow for underfloor superduct, 7-1/4″, included					
Underfloor duct conduit adapter, 2″ x 1-1/4″, included					
Underfloor duct junction box, single duct, 7-1/4″ x 3 1/8″	.003	Ea.	2.09	.60	2.69
Underfloor junction box carpet pan	.003	Ea.	1.34	.03	1.37
Underfloor duct outlet, low tension	.004	Ea.	.50	.40	.90
TOTAL			12.01	4.07	16.08

D5030 310	Telephone Systems	COST PER S.F. MAT.	COST PER S.F. INST.	COST PER S.F. TOTAL
0200	Telephone systems, underfloor duct, 5′ on center, low density	12	4.07	16.07
0240	5′ on center, high density	12.50	4.47	16.97
0280	7′ on center, low density	9.60	3.38	12.98
0320	7′ on center, high density	10.10	3.78	13.88
0400	Poke thru fittings, low density	1.87	1.44	3.31
0440	High density	3.75	2.88	6.63
0520	Telepoles, low density	2	.86	2.86
0560	High density	4	1.73	5.73
0640	Conduit system with floor boxes, low density	2.34	1.42	3.76
0680	High density	4.65	2.81	7.46
1020	Telephone wiring for offices & laboratories, 8 jacks/M.S.F.	.58	2.19	2.77

D5030 810	Security & Detection Systems	COST EACH MAT.	COST EACH INST.	COST EACH TOTAL
0200	Security system, head end equipment	30,100	5,350	35,450
0240	Security system, door/window contact biased, box, conduit & cable	234	600	834
0280	Security system, door/window contact balanced, box, conduit & cable	180	600	780
0440	Security system, proximity card reader, box, conduit & cable	345	800	1,145
1600	Card control entrance system, to 6 zone, including hardware for 100 doors	44,400	37,100	81,500

D5030 Communications and Security

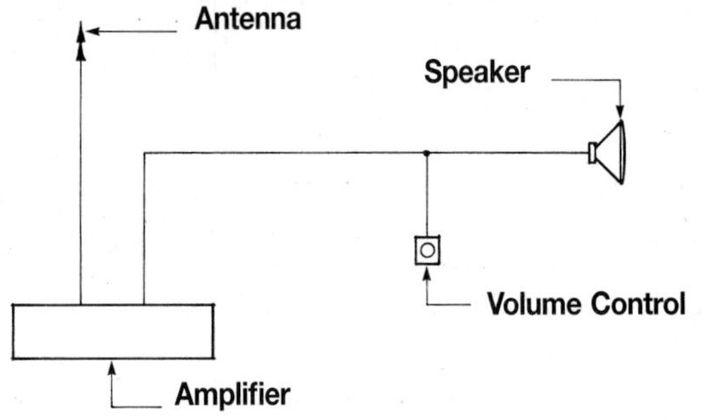

Sound System Includes AM–FM antenna, outlets, rigid conduit, and copper wire.
Fire Detection System Includes pull stations, signals, smoke and heat detectors, rigid conduit, and copper wire.
Intercom System Includes master and remote stations, rigid conduit, and copper wire.
Master Clock System Includes clocks, bells, rigid conduit, and copper wire.
Master TV Antenna Includes antenna, VHF–UHF reception and distribution, rigid conduit, and copper wire.

System Components	QUANTITY	UNIT	COST EACH MAT.	COST EACH INST.	COST EACH TOTAL
SYSTEM D5030 910 0220					
SOUND SYSTEM, INCLUDES OUTLETS, BOXES, CONDUIT & WIRE					
Steel intermediate conduit, (IMC) 1/2″ diam	1200.000	L.F.	4,140	9,600	13,740
Wire sound shielded w/drain, #22-2 conductor	15.500	C.L.F.	225.53	1,550	1,775.53
Sound system speakers ceiling or wall	12.000	Ea.	2,628	1,200	3,828
Sound system volume control	12.000	Ea.	1,038	1,200	2,238
Sound system amplifier, 250 W	1.000	Ea.	1,625	800	2,425
Sound system antenna, AM FM	1.000	Ea.	27.50	200	227.50
Sound system monitor panel	1.000	Ea.	955	200	1,155
Sound system cabinet	1.000	Ea.	1,275	800	2,075
Steel outlet box 4″ square	12.000	Ea.	43.08	480	523.08
Steel outlet box 4″ plaster rings	12.000	Ea.	37.92	150	187.92
TOTAL			11,995.03	16,180	28,175.03

D5030 910	Communication & Alarm Systems	COST EACH MAT.	COST EACH INST.	COST EACH TOTAL
0200	Communication & alarm systems, includes outlets, boxes, conduit & wire			
0210	Sound system, 6 outlets	8,100	10,100	18,200
0220	12 outlets	12,000	16,200	28,200
0240	30 outlets	21,600	30,600	52,200
0280	100 outlets	66,000	102,500	168,500
0320	Fire detection systems, non-addressable, 12 detectors	4,875	8,400	13,275
0360	25 detectors	8,725	14,200	22,925
0400	50 detectors	17,300	28,100	45,400
0440	100 detectors	32,300	51,000	83,300
0450	Addressable type, 12 detectors	6,300	8,450	14,750
0452	25 detectors	11,400	14,300	25,700
0454	50 detectors	22,100	28,100	50,200
0456	100 detectors	42,200	51,500	93,700
0458	Fire alarm control panel, 8 zone, excluding wire and conduit	725	1,600	2,325
0459	12 zone	3,150	2,400	5,550
0460	Fire alarm command center, addressable without voice, excl. wire & conduit	2,425	1,400	3,825
0462	Addressable with voice	12,500	2,200	14,700
0480	Intercom systems, 6 stations	8,150	6,925	15,075
0520	12 stations	13,900	13,800	27,700
0560	25 stations	25,700	26,500	52,200
0600	50 stations	50,000	49,800	99,800
0640	100 stations	99,000	97,500	196,500
0680	Master clock systems, 6 rooms	6,250	11,300	17,550
0720	12 rooms	10,400	19,200	29,600
0760	20 rooms	14,700	27,200	41,900
0800	30 rooms	25,600	50,000	75,600

D5030 Communications and Security

D5030 910	Communication & Alarm Systems	COST EACH		
		MAT.	INST.	TOTAL
0840	50 rooms	42,500	84,500	127,000
0880	100 rooms	83,500	168,000	251,500
0920	Master TV antenna systems, 6 outlets	3,250	7,150	10,400
0960	12 outlets	6,175	13,300	19,475
1000	30 outlets	19,400	30,800	50,200
1040	100 outlets	69,500	100,500	170,000

D5030 920	Data Communication	COST PER M.S.F.		
		MAT.	INST.	TOTAL
0100	Data communication system, incl data/voice outlets, boxes, conduit & cable			
0102	Data and voice system, 2 data/voice outlets per 1000 S.F.	193	590	783
0104	4 data/voice outlets per 1000 S.F.	365	1,175	1,540
0106	6 data/voice outlets per 1000 S.F.	520	1,725	2,245
0110	8 data/voice outlets per 1000 S.F.	670	2,275	2,945

D5090 Other Electrical Systems

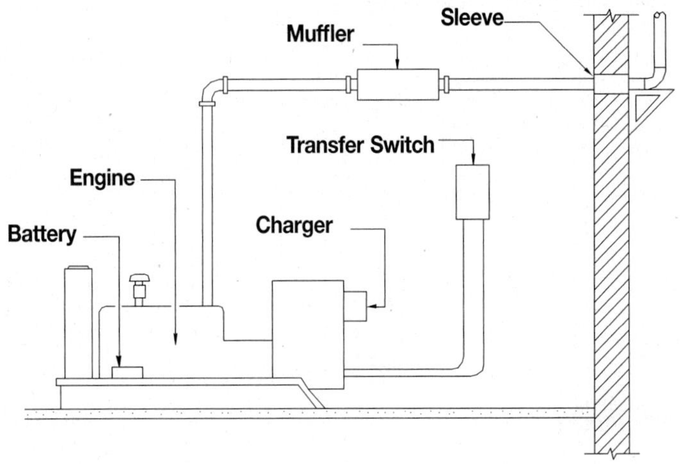

Description: System below tabulates the installed cost for generators by kW. Included in costs are battery, charger, muffler, and transfer switch.

No conduit, wire, or terminations included.

System Components	QUANTITY	UNIT	COST PER kW MAT.	COST PER kW INST.	COST PER kW TOTAL
SYSTEM D5090 210 0200 GENERATOR SET, INCL. BATTERY, CHARGER, MUFFLER & TRANSFER SWITCH GAS/GASOLINE OPER., 3 PHASE, 4 WIRE, 277/480V, 7.5 kW					
Generator set, gas or gasoline operated, 3 ph 4 W, 277/480 V, 7.5 kW	.133	Ea.	1,200	354.13	1,554.13
TOTAL			1,200	354.13	1,554.13

D5090 210	Generators (by kW)	COST PER kW MAT.	COST PER kW INST.	COST PER kW TOTAL
0190	Generator sets, include battery, charger, muffler & transfer switch			
0200	Gas/gasoline operated, 3 phase, 4 wire, 277/480 volt, 7.5 kW	1,200	355	1,555
0240	11.5 kW	1,125	272	1,397
0280	20 kW	650	176	826
0320	35 kW	525	115	640
0360	80 kW	365	148	513
0400	100 kW	320	144	464
0440	125 kW	279	136	415
0480	185 kW	470	103	573
0560	Diesel engine with fuel tank, 30 kW	595	135	730
0600	50 kW	410	106	516
0640	75 kW	450	84.50	534.50
0680	100 kW	395	71.50	466.50
0720	125 kW	284	61	345
0760	150 kW	178	57	235
0800	175 kW	265	50.50	315.50
0840	200 kW	390	46	436
0880	250 kW	252	38.50	290.50
0920	300 kW	235	33.50	268.50
0960	350 kW	249	31.50	280.50
1000	400 kW	209	29	238
1040	500 kW	189	24.50	213.50
1200	750 kW	330	16.60	346.60
1400	1000 kW	282	17.60	299.60

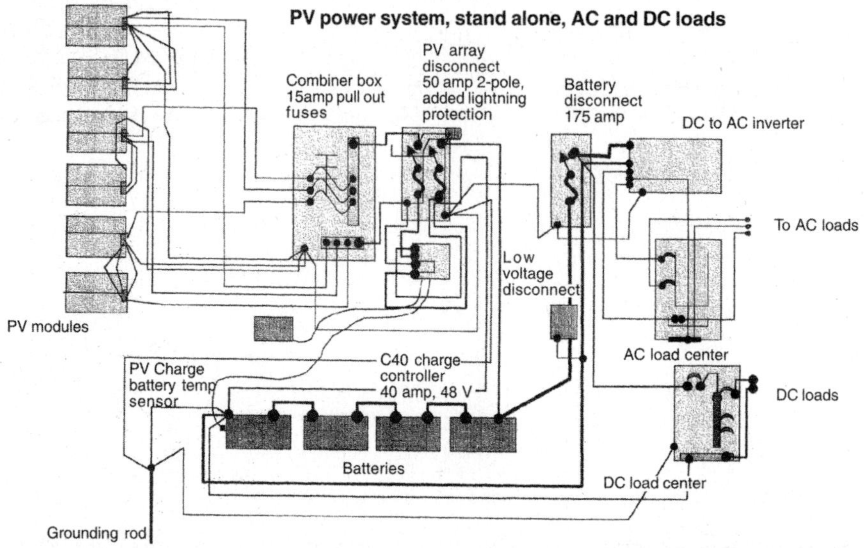

System Components	QUANTITY	UNIT	COST EACH MAT.	COST EACH INST.	COST EACH TOTAL
SYSTEM D5090 420 0100					
PHOTOVOLTAIC POWER SYSTEM, STAND ALONE					
Photovoltaic module, 400 watt, 37 V	3.000	Ea.	915	300	1,215
On wood framing, 1 panel	3.000	Ea.	106.50	393	499.50
DC to AC inverter for, 24 V, 2,500 watt	1.000	Ea.	1,925	200	2,125
PV components, combiner box, 10 lug, NEMA 3R enclosure	1.000	Ea.	345	200	545
Alternative energy sources, PV components, fuse, 15 A for combiner box	10.000	Ea.	475	200	675
Battery charger controller w/temperature sensor	1.000	Ea.	510	200	710
Digital readout panel, displays hours, volts, amps, etc.	1.000	Ea.	182	200	382
Deep cycle solar battery, 6 V, 180 Ah (C/20)	4.000	Ea.	1,600	400	2,000
Battery interconnection, 15″ AWG #2/0, sealed w/copper ring lugs	3.000	Ea.	79.50	150	229.50
Battery interconn, 24″ AWG #2/0, sealed w/copper ring lugs	2.000	Ea.	61	100	161
Battery interconn, 60″ AWG #2/0, sealed w/copper ring lugs	2.000	Ea.	113	100	213
Batt temp computer probe, RJ11 jack, 15′ cord	1.000	Ea.	25.50	50	75.50
System disconnect, DC 175 amp circuit breaker	1.000	Ea.	136	100	236
Conduit box for inverter	1.000	Ea.	65	100	165
Low voltage disconnect	1.000	Ea.	375	100	475
Vented battery enclosure, wood	1.000	Ea.	330	350	680
Grounding, rod, copper clad, 8′ long, 5/8″ diameter	1.000	Ea.	24.50	146	170.50
Grounding, clamp, bronze, 5/8″ dia	1.000	Ea.	2.83	25	27.83
Bare copper wire, stranded, #8	1.000	C.L.F.	39.50	73	112.50
Wire, 600 volt, type THW, copper, stranded, #12	3.600	C.L.F.	91.80	262.80	354.60
Wire, 600 volt, type THW, copper, stranded, #10	1.050	C.L.F.	39.90	84	123.90
Cond to 10′ H,incl 2 termn,2 elb&11 bm CLP per 100′,galv stl,1/2″ dia	120.000	L.F.	590.40	1,068	1,658.40
Conduit,to 10′ H,incl 2 termn,2 elb&11 bm clp per 100′ (EMT), 1″ dia	30.000	L.F.	108.30	208.50	316.80
Lightning surge suppressor	1.000	Ea.	103	25	128
General duty 240 volt, 2 pole, nonfusible, NEMA 3R, 60 amp	1.000	Ea.	168	350	518
Load centers, 3 wire, 120/240V, 100 amp main lugs, indoor, 8 circuits	2.000	Ea.	452	1,140	1,592
Circuit breaker, plug-in, 120/240 volt, to 60 amp, 1 pole	5.000	Ea.	95.50	332.50	428
Fuses, dual element, time delay, 250 volt, 50 amp	2.000	Ea.	35.90	32	67.90
TOTAL			8,995.13	6,889.80	15,884.93

D5090 Other Electrical Systems

D5090 420	Photovoltaic Power System, Stand Alone	COST EACH		
		MAT.	INST.	TOTAL
0050	24 V capacity, 900 W (~102 SF)			
0100	Roof mounted, on wood framing	9,000	6,900	15,900
0150	with standoff	9,000	6,900	15,900
0200	Ground placement, ballast, fixed	10,700	8,650	19,350
0250	Adjustable	11,700	8,650	20,350
0300	Top of pole, passive tracking	11,000	8,650	19,650
0350	1.8 kW (~204 SF)			
0400	Roof mounted, on wood framing	11,700	9,850	21,550
0450	with standoff	11,700	9,850	21,550
0500	Ground placement, ballast, fixed	15,300	11,400	26,700
0550	Adjustable	15,400	11,400	26,800
0600	Top of pole, passive tracking	14,900	11,400	26,300
0650	3.2 kW (~408 SF)			
0700	Roof mounted, on wood framing	16,200	15,200	31,400
0750	with standoff	16,300	15,200	31,500
0800	Ground placement, ballast, fixed	21,000	16,500	37,500
0850	Adjustable	21,300	16,500	37,800
0900	Top of pole, passive tracking	20,100	16,500	36,600

D5090 Other Electrical Systems

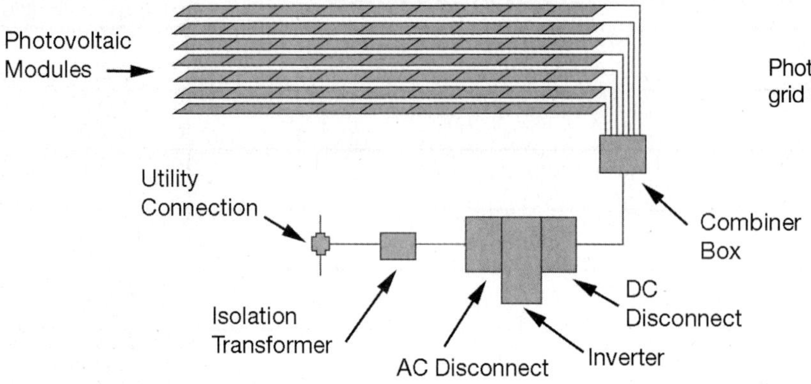

Photovoltaic power system, grid connected 10 kW

System Components	QUANTITY	UNIT	COST EACH MAT.	COST EACH INST.	COST EACH TOTAL
SYSTEM D5090 430 0100					
PHOTOVOLTAIC POWER SYSTEM, GRID CONNECTED 10 kW					
Photovoltaic module, 400 watt, 37 V	25.000	Ea.	7,625	2,500	10,125
PV rack system, roof, non-penetrating ballast, 1 panel	25.000	Ea.	1,225	1,187.50	2,412.50
DC to AC inverter for, 24 V, 4,000 watt	3.000	Ea.	4,875	1,200	6,075
Combiner box 10 lug, NEMA 3R	1.000	Ea.	345	200	545
15 amp fuses	10.000	Ea.	475	200	675
Safety switch, 60 amp	1.000	Ea.	415	365	780
Safety switch, 100 amp	1.000	Ea.	750	445	1,195
Utility connection, 3 pole breaker	1.000	Ea.	670	129	799
Fuse, 60 A	3.000	Ea.	103.50	48	151.50
Fuse, 100 A	3.000	Ea.	178.50	60	238.50
10 kVA isolation tranformer	1.000	Ea.	4,400	1,000	5,400
EMT Conduit w/fittings & support	180.000	L.F.	649.80	1,251	1,900.80
RGS Conduit w/fittings & support	267.000	L.F.	2,149.35	3,284.10	5,433.45
Enclosure 24" x 24" x 10", NEMA 4	1.000	Ea.	10,200	1,600	11,800
Wire, 600 volt, type THWN-THHN, copper, stranded, #6	8.000	C.L.F.	864	984	1,848
Wire, 600 volt, copper type XLPE-USE(RHW), stranded, #12	18.000	C.L.F.	945	1,314	2,259
Grounding, bare copper wire stranded, 4/0	2.000	C.L.F.	1,440	562	2,002
Grounding, exothermic weld, 4/0 wire to building steel	4.000	Ea.	20.20	456	476.20
Grounding, brazed connections, #6 wire	2.000	Ea.	41	133	174
Insulated ground wire, copper, #6	.400	C.L.F.	43.20	49.20	92.40
TOTAL			37,414.55	16,967.80	54,382.35

D5090 430	Photovoltaic Power System, Grid Connected	COST EACH MAT.	COST EACH INST.	COST EACH TOTAL
0050	10 kW			
0100	Roof mounted, non-penetrating ballast	37,400	17,000	54,400
0200	Penetrating surface mount, on steel framing	37,000	22,800	59,800
0300	on wood framing	37,100	19,100	56,200
0400	with standoff	36,400	18,100	54,500
0500	Ground placement, ballast, fixed	51,000	18,200	69,200
0600	adjustable	51,500	18,200	69,700
0700	Top of pole, passive tracking	50,500	18,700	69,200
1050	20 kW			
1100	Roof mounted, non-penetrating ballast	65,500	26,700	92,200
1200	Penetrating surface mount, on steel framing	64,500	38,400	102,900
1300	on wood framing	64,500	30,900	95,400
1400	with standoff	65,000	30,900	95,900
1500	Ground placement, ballast, fixed	89,500	27,900	117,400
1600	adjustable	91,000	27,900	118,900
1700	Top of pole, passive tracking	89,500	28,900	118,400

D5090 Other Electrical Systems

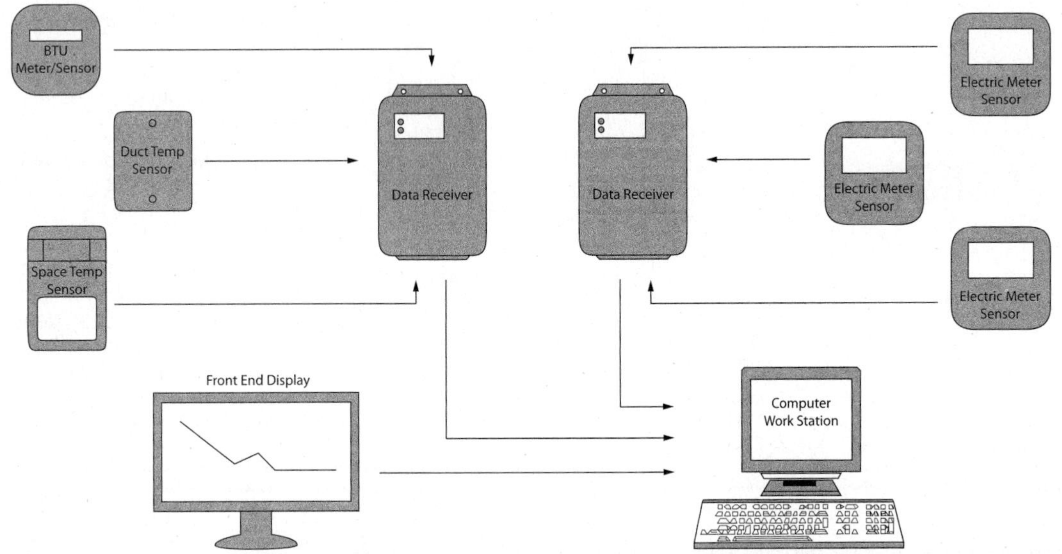

System Components	QUANTITY	UNIT	COST EACH MAT.	COST EACH INST.	COST EACH TOTAL
SYSTEM D5090 480 1100					
ELECTRICAL, SINGLE PHASE, 1 METER					
#18 twisted shielded pair in 1/2" EMT conduit	.050	C.L.F.	11.40	13.30	24.70
Wire, 600 volt, type THW, copper, solid, #12	.150	C.L.F.	2.81	10.95	13.76
Conduit (EMT) to 10' H, incl 2 termn,2 elb&11 bm clp per 100', 3/4"	5.000	L.F.	10.65	30.75	41.40
Outlet boxes, pressed steel, handy box	1.000	Ea.	4.37	29.50	33.87
Outlet boxes, pressed steel, handy box, covers, device	1.000	Ea.	1.07	12.50	13.57
Wiring devices, receptacle, duplex, 120 volt, ground, 20 amp	1.000	Ea.	14.20	29.50	43.70
Single phase, 277 volt, 200 amp	1.000	Ea.	530	91	621
Data recorder, 8 meters	1.000	Ea.	2,600	73	2,673
Software package, per meter, premium	1.000	Ea.	585		585
TOTAL			3,759.50	290.50	4,050

D5090 480	Energy Monitoring Systems	COST EACH MAT.	COST EACH INST.	COST EACH TOTAL
1000	Electrical			
1100	Single phase, 1 meter	3,750	291	4,041
1110	4 meters	8,225	2,200	10,425
1120	8 meters	16,600	4,525	21,125
1200	Three phase, 1 meter	4,400	370	4,770
1210	5 meters	12,800	3,450	16,250
1220	10 meters	26,200	7,050	33,250
1230	25 meters	55,500	13,900	69,400
2000	Mechanical			
2100	BTU, 1 meter	4,300	1,050	5,350
2110	w/1 duct sensor	4,575	1,300	5,875
2120	& 1 space sensor	5,275	1,475	6,750
2130	& 5 space sensors	8,000	2,200	10,200
2140	& 10 space sensors	12,600	3,100	15,700
2200	BTU, 3 meters	7,675	3,000	10,675
2210	w/3 duct sensors	8,550	3,775	12,325
2220	& 3 space sensors	10,600	4,300	14,900
2230	& 15 space sensors	18,800	6,450	25,250
2240	& 30 space sensors	30,300	9,125	39,425
9000	Front end display	540	156	696
9100	Computer workstation	2,675	2,075	4,750

D5090 Other Electrical Systems

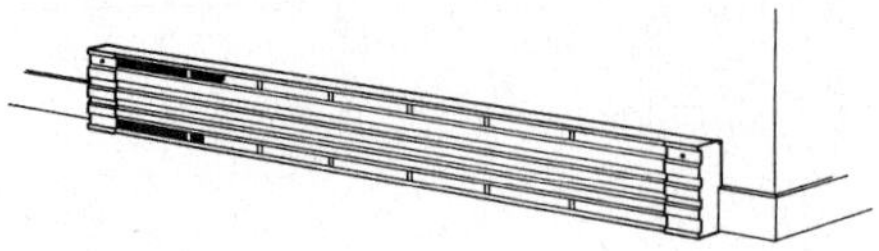

Low Density and Medium Density Baseboard Radiation
The costs shown in Table below are based on the following system considerations:

1. The heat loss per square foot is based on approximately 34 BTU/hr. per S.F. of floor or 10 watts per S.F. of floor.
2. Baseboard radiation is based on the low watt density type rated 187 watts per L.F. and the medium density type rated 250 watts per L.F.
3. Thermostat is not included.
4. Wiring costs include branch circuit wiring.

System Components	QUANTITY	UNIT	COST PER S.F. MAT.	COST PER S.F. INST.	COST PER S.F. TOTAL
SYSTEM D5090 510 1000					
ELECTRIC BASEBOARD RADIATION, LOW DENSITY, 900 S.F., 31 MBH, 9 kW					
Electric baseboard radiator, 5′ long 935 watt	.011	Ea.	.78	1.54	2.32
Steel intermediate conduit, (IMC) 1/2″ diam	.170	L.F.	.59	1.36	1.95
Wire 600 volt, type THW, copper, solid, #12	.005	C.L.F.	.09	.37	.46
TOTAL			1.46	3.27	4.73

D5090 510	Electric Baseboard Radiation (Low Density)	COST PER S.F. MAT.	COST PER S.F. INST.	COST PER S.F. TOTAL
1000	Electric baseboard radiation, low density, 900 S.F., 31 MBH, 9 kW	1.46	3.27	4.73
1200	1500 S.F., 51 MBH, 15 kW	1.43	3.19	4.62
1400	2100 S.F., 72 MBH, 21 kW	1.29	2.85	4.14
1600	3000 S.F., 102 MBH, 30 kW	1.17	2.60	3.77
2000	Medium density, 900 S.F., 31 MBH, 9 kW	1.32	2.99	4.31
2200	1500 S.F., 51 MBH, 15 kW	1.28	2.91	4.19
2400	2100 S.F., 72 MBH, 21 kW	1.21	2.71	3.92
2600	3000 S.F., 102 MBH, 30 kW	1.10	2.46	3.56

D5090 Other Electrical Systems

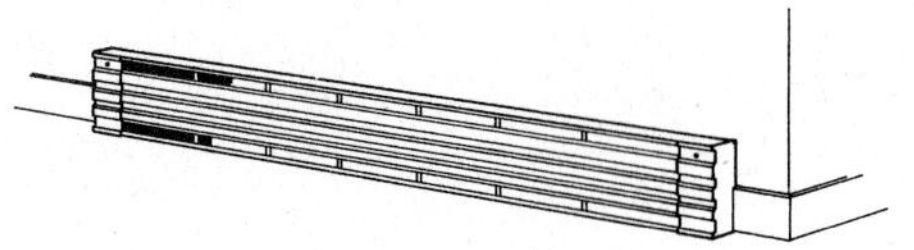

Commercial Duty Baseboard Radiation
The costs shown in Table below are based on the following system considerations:

1. The heat loss per square foot is based on approximately 41 BTU/hr. per S.F. of floor or 12 watts per S.F.
2. The baseboard radiation is of the commercial duty type rated 250 watts per L.F. served by 277 volt, single phase power.
3. Thermostat is not included.
4. Wiring costs include branch circuit wiring.

System Components	QUANTITY	UNIT	COST PER S.F. MAT.	COST PER S.F. INST.	COST PER S.F. TOTAL
SYSTEM D5090 520 1000					
ELECTRIC BASEBOARD RADIATION, MEDIUM DENSITY, 1230 S.F., 51 MBH, 15 kW					
Electric baseboard radiator, 5′ long	.013	Ea.	.92	1.82	2.74
Steel intermediate conduit, (IMC) 1/2″ diam	.154	L.F.	.53	1.23	1.76
Wire 600 volt, type THW, copper, solid, #12	.004	C.L.F.	.08	.29	.37
TOTAL			1.53	3.34	4.87

D5090 520	Electric Baseboard Radiation (Medium Density)	COST PER S.F. MAT.	COST PER S.F. INST.	COST PER S.F. TOTAL
1000	Electric baseboard radiation, medium density, 1230 SF, 51 MBH, 15 kW	1.53	3.34	4.87
1200	2500 S.F. floor area, 106 MBH, 31 kW	1.43	3.13	4.56
1400	3700 S.F. floor area, 157 MBH, 46 kW	1.39	3.04	4.43
1600	4800 S.F. floor area, 201 MBH, 59 kW	1.28	2.82	4.10
1800	11,300 S.F. floor area, 464 MBH, 136 kW	1.19	2.58	3.77
2000	30,000 S.F. floor area, 1229 MBH, 360 kW	1.17	2.52	3.69

G1030 Site Earthwork

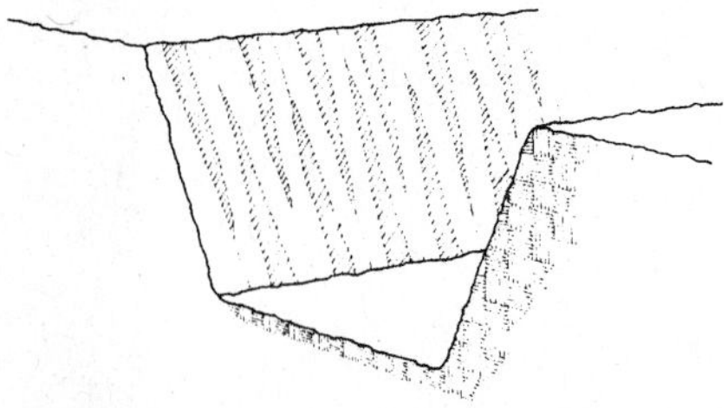

Trenching Systems are shown on a cost per linear foot basis. The systems include: excavation; backfill and removal of spoil; and compaction for various depths and trench bottom widths. The backfill has been reduced to accommodate a pipe of suitable diameter and bedding.

The slope for trench sides varies from none to 1:1.

The Expanded System Listing shows Trenching Systems that range from 2′ to 12′ in width. Depths range from 2′ to 25′.

System Components	QUANTITY	UNIT	COST PER L.F. EQUIP.	COST PER L.F. LABOR	COST PER L.F. TOTAL
SYSTEM G1030 805 1310					
TRENCHING, COMMON EARTH, NO SLOPE, 2′ WIDE, 2′ DP, 3/8 C.Y. BUCKET					
Excavation, trench, hyd. backhoe, track mtd., 3/8 C.Y. bucket	.148	C.Y.	.30	1.30	1.60
Backfill and load spoil, from stockpile	.153	L.C.Y.	.17	.39	.56
Compaction by vibrating plate, 6″ lifts, 4 passes	.118	C.Y.	.13	.47	.60
Remove excess spoil, 8 C.Y. dump truck, 2 mile roundtrip	.040	L.C.Y.	.15	.22	.37
TOTAL			.75	2.38	3.13

G1030 805	Trenching Common Earth	COST PER L.F. EQUIP.	COST PER L.F. LABOR	COST PER L.F. TOTAL
1310	Trenching, common earth, no slope, 2′ wide, 2′ deep, 3/8 C.Y. bucket	.75	2.38	3.14
1320	3′ deep, 3/8 C.Y. bucket	1.09	3.58	4.67
1330	4′ deep, 3/8 C.Y. bucket	1.43	4.77	6.20
1340	6′ deep, 3/8 C.Y. bucket	2.08	6.20	8.25
1350	8′ deep, 1/2 C.Y. bucket	2.80	8.20	11
1360	10′ deep, 1 C.Y. bucket	5.25	9.80	15.05
1400	4′ wide, 2′ deep, 3/8 C.Y. bucket	1.64	4.75	6.40
1410	3′ deep, 3/8 C.Y. bucket	2.31	7.15	9.45
1420	4′ deep, 1/2 C.Y. bucket	3.11	7.95	11.05
1430	6′ deep, 1/2 C.Y. bucket	4.22	12.80	17
1440	8′ deep, 1/2 C.Y. bucket	8.50	16.60	25
1450	10′ deep, 1 C.Y. bucket	10.15	20.50	30.50
1460	12′ deep, 1 C.Y. bucket	13.20	26	39.50
1470	15′ deep, 1-1/2 C.Y. bucket	10.55	23.50	34
1480	18′ deep, 2-1/2 C.Y. bucket	15.20	32.50	48
1520	6′ wide, 6′ deep, 5/8 C.Y. bucket w/trench box	10.95	19.20	30
1530	8′ deep, 3/4 C.Y. bucket	14.75	25	40
1540	10′ deep, 1 C.Y. bucket	13.55	26	39.50
1550	12′ deep, 1-1/2 C.Y. bucket	14.10	28	42
1560	16′ deep, 2-1/2 C.Y. bucket	18.35	35	53
1570	20′ deep, 3-1/2 C.Y. bucket	23	41.50	64.50
1580	24′ deep, 3-1/2 C.Y. bucket	27.50	50	77.50
1640	8′ wide, 12′ deep, 1-1/2 C.Y. bucket w/trench box	19.45	35.50	55
1650	15′ deep, 1-1/2 C.Y. bucket	25.50	46.50	72
1660	18′ deep, 2-1/2 C.Y. bucket	26	46.50	72.50
1680	24′ deep, 3-1/2 C.Y. bucket	37	64.50	101
1730	10′ wide, 20′ deep, 3-1/2 C.Y. bucket w/trench box	30	61.50	91.50
1740	24′ deep, 3-1/2 C.Y. bucket	43.50	74	118
1780	12′ wide, 20′ deep, 3-1/2 C.Y. bucket w/trench box	46.50	78	125
1790	25′ deep, bucket	58	99.50	157
1800	1/2 to 1 slope, 2′ wide, 2′ deep, 3/8 C.Y. bucket	1.09	3.58	4.67
1810	3′ deep, 3/8 C.Y. bucket	1.86	6.25	8.15
1820	4′ deep, 3/8 C.Y. bucket	2.79	9.55	12.35
1840	6′ deep, 3/8 C.Y. bucket	5.10	15.45	20.50

G1030 Site Earthwork

G1030 805	Trenching Common Earth	COST PER L.F.		
		EQUIP.	LABOR	TOTAL
1860	8' deep, 1/2 C.Y. bucket	8.15	24.50	33
1880	10' deep, 1 C.Y. bucket	18.25	34.50	53
2300	4' wide, 2' deep, 3/8 C.Y. bucket	1.98	5.95	7.90
2310	3' deep, 3/8 C.Y. bucket	3.08	9.85	12.90
2320	4' deep, 1/2 C.Y. bucket	4.46	12.10	16.55
2340	6' deep, 1/2 C.Y. bucket	7.05	22.50	29.50
2360	8' deep, 1/2 C.Y. bucket	16.40	33.50	50
2380	10' deep, 1 C.Y. bucket	22.50	47	69.50
2400	12' deep, 1 C.Y. bucket	28.50	63.50	92
2430	15' deep, 1-1/2 C.Y. bucket	30	68	98
2460	18' deep, 2-1/2 C.Y. bucket	50	106	156
2840	6' wide, 6' deep, 5/8 C.Y. bucket w/trench box	16.45	28.50	45
2860	8' deep, 3/4 C.Y. bucket	24	42.50	66.50
2880	10' deep, 1 C.Y. bucket	21	43	64.50
2900	12' deep, 1-1/2 C.Y. bucket	27	56.50	83.50
2940	16' deep, 2-1/2 C.Y. bucket	42	83	125
2980	20' deep, 3-1/2 C.Y. bucket	57.50	112	169
3020	24' deep, 3-1/2 C.Y. bucket	81.50	153	234
3100	8' wide, 12' deep, 1-1/2 C.Y. bucket w/trench box	33	64.50	97.50
3120	15' deep, 1-1/2 C.Y. bucket	48.50	93.50	142
3140	18' deep, 2-1/2 C.Y. bucket	57.50	111	169
3180	24' deep, 3-1/2 C.Y. bucket	91	167	258
3270	10' wide, 20' deep, 3-1/2 C.Y. bucket w/trench box	59	129	187
3280	24' deep, 3-1/2 C.Y. bucket	100	183	283
3370	12' wide, 20' deep, 3-1/2 C.Y. bucket w/trench box	84	149	234
3380	25' deep, 3-1/2 C.Y. bucket	117	213	330
3500	1 to 1 slope, 2' wide, 2' deep, 3/8 C.Y. bucket	1.43	4.78	6.20
3520	3' deep, 3/8 C.Y. bucket	4	10.95	14.95
3540	4' deep, 3/8 C.Y. bucket	4.15	14.35	18.50
3560	6' deep, 1/2 C.Y. bucket	5.10	15.45	20.50
3580	8' deep, 1/2 C.Y. bucket	10.15	31	41
3600	10' deep, 1 C.Y. bucket	31.50	59.50	90.50
3800	4' wide, 2' deep, 3/8 C.Y. bucket	2.32	7.15	9.45
3820	3' deep, 3/8 C.Y. bucket	3.84	12.50	16.35
3840	4' deep, 1/2 C.Y. bucket	5.80	16.20	22
3860	6' deep, 1/2 C.Y. bucket	9.85	32.50	42.50
3880	8' deep, 1/2 C.Y. bucket	24.50	50.50	75
3900	10' deep, 1 C.Y. bucket	35	73.50	109
3920	12' deep, 1 C.Y. bucket	52	106	158
3940	15' deep, 1-1/2 C.Y. bucket	49.50	113	162
3960	18' deep, 2-1/2 C.Y. bucket	68.50	147	215
4030	6' wide, 6' deep, 5/8 C.Y. bucket w/trench box	21.50	38.50	60
4040	8' deep, 3/4 C.Y. bucket	32	52.50	84.50
4050	10' deep, 1 C.Y. bucket	30.50	63.50	94
4060	12' deep, 1-1/2 C.Y. bucket	41.50	86	127
4070	16' deep, 2-1/2 C.Y. bucket	66	131	197
4080	20' deep, 3-1/2 C.Y. bucket	93	182	275
4090	24' deep, 3-1/2 C.Y. bucket	136	256	390
4500	8' wide, 12' deep, 1-1/2 C.Y. bucket w/trench box	46.50	93.50	140
4550	15' deep, 1-1/2 C.Y. bucket	71	140	211
4600	18' deep, 2-1/2 C.Y. bucket	88	172	260
4650	24' deep, 3-1/2 C.Y. bucket	145	270	415
4800	10' wide, 20' deep, 3-1/2 C.Y. bucket w/trench box	87.50	196	283
4850	24' deep, 3-1/2 C.Y. bucket	154	286	440
4950	12' wide, 20' deep, 3-1/2 C.Y. bucket w/trench box	122	220	340
4980	25' deep, 3-1/2 C.Y. bucket	175	325	500

G1030 Site Earthwork

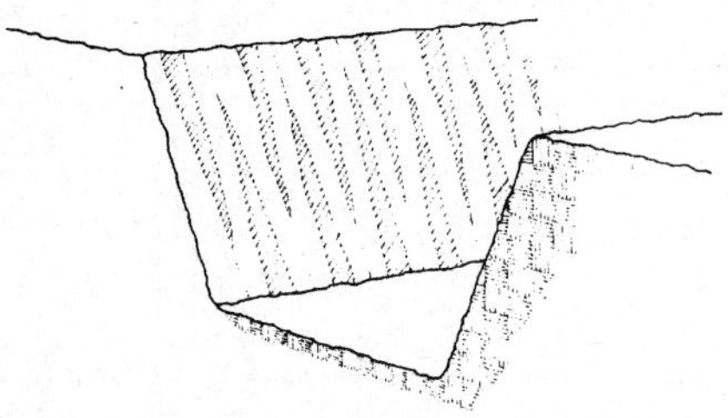

Trenching Systems are shown on a cost per linear foot basis. The systems include: excavation; backfill and removal of spoil; and compaction for various depths and trench bottom widths. The backfill has been reduced to accommodate a pipe of suitable diameter and bedding.

The slope for trench sides varies from none to 1:1.

The Expanded System Listing shows Trenching Systems that range from 2′ to 12′ in width. Depths range from 2′ to 25′.

System Components	QUANTITY	UNIT	COST PER L.F. EQUIP.	LABOR	TOTAL
SYSTEM G1030 806 1310					
TRENCHING, LOAM & SANDY CLAY, NO SLOPE, 2′ WIDE, 2′ DP, 3/8 C.Y. BUCKET					
Excavation, trench, hyd. backhoe, track mtd., 3/8 C.Y. bucket	.148	C.Y.	.28	1.20	1.48
Backfill and load spoil, from stockpile	.165	L.C.Y.	.18	.43	.61
Compaction by vibrating plate 18″ wide, 6″ lifts, 4 passes	.118	C.Y.	.13	.47	.60
Remove excess spoil, 8 C.Y. dump truck, 2 mile roundtrip	.042	L.C.Y.	.16	.23	.39
TOTAL			.75	2.33	3.08

G1030 806	Trenching Loam & Sandy Clay	COST PER L.F. EQUIP.	LABOR	TOTAL
1310	Trenching, loam & sandy clay, no slope, 2′ wide, 2′ deep, 3/8 C.Y. bucket	.75	2.33	3.08
1320	3′ deep, 3/8 C.Y. bucket	1.16	3.83	4.98
1330	4′ deep, 3/8 C.Y. bucket	1.42	4.66	6.10
1340	6′ deep, 3/8 C.Y. bucket	2.70	5.55	8.25
1350	8′ deep, 1/2 C.Y. bucket	3.62	7.35	10.95
1360	10′ deep, 1 C.Y. bucket	3.88	7.85	11.75
1400	4′ wide, 2′ deep, 3/8 C.Y. bucket	1.66	4.66	6.30
1410	3′ deep, 3/8 C.Y. bucket	2.33	7	9.30
1420	4′ deep, 1/2 C.Y. bucket	3.13	7.85	11
1430	6′ deep, 1/2 C.Y. bucket	5.50	11.55	17
1440	8′ deep, 1/2 C.Y. bucket	8.25	16.35	24.50
1450	10′ deep, 1 C.Y. bucket	7.45	16.70	24
1460	12′ deep, 1 C.Y. bucket	9.40	21	30
1470	15′ deep, 1-1/2 C.Y. bucket	11.05	24	35
1480	18′ deep, 2-1/2 C.Y. bucket	12.40	26.50	39
1520	6′ wide, 6′ deep, 5/8 C.Y. bucket w/trench box	10.50	18.85	29.50
1530	8′ deep, 3/4 C.Y. bucket	14.15	24.50	39
1540	10′ deep, 1 C.Y. bucket	12.40	25	37.50
1550	12′ deep, 1-1/2 C.Y. bucket	13.75	28	41.50
1560	16′ deep, 2-1/2 C.Y. bucket	18	35	53
1570	20′ deep, 3-1/2 C.Y. bucket	21.50	41.50	63
1580	24′ deep, 3-1/2 C.Y. bucket	26.50	50.50	77.50
1640	8′ wide, 12′ deep, 1-1/4 C.Y. bucket w/trench box	19.10	35.50	54.50
1650	15′ deep, 1-1/2 C.Y. bucket	23.50	45	68.50
1660	18′ deep, 2-1/2 C.Y. bucket	27	50.50	78
1680	24′ deep, 3-1/2 C.Y. bucket	36	65.50	102
1730	10′ wide, 20′ deep, 3-1/2 C.Y. bucket w/trench box	36	66	102
1740	24′ deep, 3-1/2 C.Y. bucket	45.50	81.50	127
1780	12′ wide, 20′ deep, 3-1/2 C.Y. bucket w/trench box	43.50	78.50	122
1790	25′ deep, 3-1/2 C.Y. bucket	56.50	101	158
1800	1/2:1 slope, 2′ wide, 2′ deep, 3/8 C.Y. bucket	1.09	3.50	4.58
1810	3′ deep, 3/8 C.Y. bucket	1.85	6.10	7.95
1820	4′ deep, 3/8 C.Y. bucket	2.77	9.30	12.10
1840	6′ deep, 3/8 C.Y. bucket	6.65	13.90	20.50

G1030 Site Earthwork

G1030 806	Trenching Loam & Sandy Clay	COST PER L.F.		
		EQUIP.	LABOR	TOTAL
1860	8' deep, 1/2 C.Y. bucket	10.60	22	33
1880	10' deep, 1 C.Y. bucket	13.45	28	41
2300	4' wide, 2' deep, 3/8 C.Y. bucket	1.99	5.85	7.85
2310	3' deep, 3/8 C.Y. bucket	3.08	9.60	12.70
2320	4' deep, 1/2 C.Y. bucket	4.45	11.90	16.35
2340	6' deep, 1/2 C.Y. bucket	9.20	20.50	29.50
2360	8' deep, 1/2 C.Y. bucket	15.90	33	49
2380	10' deep, 1 C.Y. bucket	16.45	38.50	54.50
2400	12' deep, 1 C.Y. bucket	27.50	63.50	91
2430	15' deep, 1-1/2 C.Y. bucket	31.50	70.50	102
2460	18' deep, 2-1/2 C.Y. bucket	49	108	157
2840	6' wide, 6' deep, 5/8 C.Y. bucket w/trench box	15.40	28.50	44
2860	8' deep, 3/4 C.Y. bucket	23	41.50	64.50
2880	10' deep, 1 C.Y. bucket	22.50	47	69
2900	12' deep, 1-1/2 C.Y. bucket	27	57	84
2940	16' deep, 2-1/2 C.Y. bucket	41.50	84	125
2980	20' deep, 3-1/2 C.Y. bucket	56	113	169
3020	24' deep, 3-1/2 C.Y. bucket	79.50	155	234
3100	8' wide, 12' deep, 1-1/2 C.Y. bucket w/trench box	32.50	64.50	97
3120	15' deep, 1-1/2 C.Y. bucket	44	91	135
3140	18' deep, 2-1/2 C.Y. bucket	56.50	112	169
3180	24' deep, 3-1/2 C.Y. bucket	88.50	170	259
3270	10' wide, 20' deep, 3-1/2 C.Y. bucket w/trench box	71	138	209
3280	24' deep, 3-1/2 C.Y. bucket	98	186	284
3320	12' wide, 20' deep, 3-1/2 C.Y. bucket w/trench box	78.50	150	228
3380	25' deep, 3-1/2 C.Y. bucket w/trench box	107	201	310
3500	1:1 slope, 2' wide, 2' deep, 3/8 C.Y. bucket	1.43	4.66	6.10
3520	3' deep, 3/8 C.Y. bucket	2.60	8.75	11.35
3540	4' deep, 3/8 C.Y. bucket	4.11	14	18.10
3560	6' deep, 1/2 C.Y. bucket	6.65	13.90	20.50
3580	8' deep, 1/2 C.Y. bucket	17.60	37	54.50
3600	10' deep, 1 C.Y. bucket	23	47.50	70.50
3800	4' wide, 2' deep, 3/8 C.Y. bucket	2.33	7	9.35
3820	3' deep, 1/2 C.Y. bucket	3.84	12.25	16.10
3840	4' deep, 1/2 C.Y. bucket	5.80	16	22
3860	6' deep, 1/2 C.Y. bucket	12.95	29.50	42.50
3880	8' deep, 1/2 C.Y. bucket	23.50	49.50	73.50
3900	10' deep, 1 C.Y. bucket	25.50	60	85.50
3920	12' deep, 1 C.Y. bucket	37	85	122
3940	15' deep, 1-1/2 C.Y. bucket	51.50	117	169
3960	18' deep, 2-1/2 C.Y. bucket	67.50	148	216
4030	6' wide, 6' deep, 5/8 C.Y. bucket w/trench box	20.50	38	58.50
4040	8' deep, 3/4 C.Y. bucket	31.50	58.50	90
4050	10' deep, 1 C.Y. bucket	32	69	101
4060	12' deep, 1-1/2 C.Y. bucket	40	86.50	127
4070	16' deep, 2-1/2 C.Y. bucket	64.50	132	197
4080	20' deep, 3-1/2 C.Y. bucket	91	185	276
4090	24' deep, 3-1/2 C.Y. bucket	132	259	390
4500	8' wide, 12' deep, 1-1/4 C.Y. bucket w/trench box	45.50	94	140
4550	15' deep, 1-1/2 C.Y. bucket	65	137	202
4600	18' deep, 2-1/2 C.Y. bucket	86	174	260
4650	24' deep, 3-1/2 C.Y. bucket	141	274	415
4800	10' wide, 20' deep, 3-1/2 C.Y. bucket w/trench box	106	209	315
4850	24' deep, 3-1/2 C.Y. bucket	151	290	440
4950	12' wide, 20' deep, 3-1/2 C.Y. bucket w/trench box	113	222	335
4980	25' deep, 3-1/2 C.Y. bucket	171	325	500

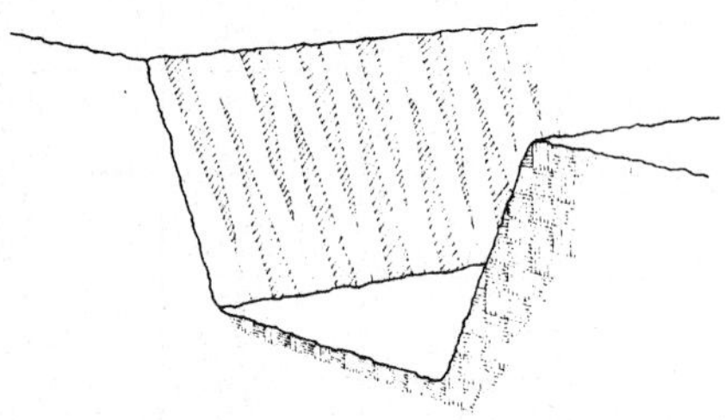

Trenching Systems are shown on a cost per linear foot basis. The systems include: excavation; backfill and removal of spoil; and compaction for various depths and trench bottom widths. The backfill has been reduced to accommodate a pipe of suitable diameter and bedding.

The slope for trench sides varies from none to 1:1.

The Expanded System Listing shows Trenching Systems that range from 2′ to 12′ in width. Depths range from 2′ to 25′.

System Components	QUANTITY	UNIT	COST PER L.F.		
			EQUIP.	LABOR	TOTAL
SYSTEM G1030 807 1310					
TRENCHING, SAND & GRAVEL, NO SLOPE, 2′ WIDE, 2′ DEEP, 3/8 C.Y. BUCKET					
Excavation, trench, hyd. backhoe, track mtd., 3/8 C.Y. bucket	.148	C.Y.	.27	1.18	1.45
Backfill and load spoil, from stockpile	.140	L.C.Y.	.15	.36	.51
Compaction by vibrating plate 18″ wide, 6″ lifts, 4 passes	.118	C.Y.	.13	.47	.60
Remove excess spoil, 8 C.Y. dump truck, 2 mile roundtrip	.035	L.C.Y.	.14	.19	.33
TOTAL			.69	2.20	2.89

G1030 807	Trenching Sand & Gravel	COST PER L.F.		
		EQUIP.	LABOR	TOTAL
1310	Trenching, sand & gravel, no slope, 2′ wide, 2′ deep, 3/8 C.Y. bucket	.70	2.21	2.90
1320	3′ deep, 3/8 C.Y. bucket	1.09	3.68	4.77
1330	4′ deep, 3/8 C.Y. bucket	1.33	4.43	5.75
1340	6′ deep, 3/8 C.Y. bucket	2.58	5.30	7.90
1350	8′ deep, 1/2 C.Y. bucket	3.46	7	10.50
1360	10′ deep, 1 C.Y. bucket	3.66	7.40	11.05
1400	4′ wide, 2′ deep, 3/8 C.Y. bucket	1.51	4.38	5.90
1410	3′ deep, 3/8 C.Y. bucket	2.14	6.60	8.75
1420	4′ deep, 1/2 C.Y. bucket	2.88	7.40	10.30
1430	6′ deep, 1/2 C.Y. bucket	5.20	11.05	16.20
1440	8′ deep, 1/2 C.Y. bucket	7.75	15.50	23.50
1450	10′ deep, 1 C.Y. bucket	6.95	15.75	22.50
1460	12′ deep, 1 C.Y. bucket	8.80	19.65	28.50
1470	15′ deep, 1-1/2 C.Y. bucket	10.35	23	33
1480	18′ deep, 2-1/2 C.Y. bucket	11.65	25	36.50
1520	6′ wide, 6′ deep, 5/8 C.Y. bucket w/trench box	9.95	17.85	28
1530	8′ deep, 3/4 C.Y. bucket	13.40	23.50	37
1540	10′ deep, 1 C.Y. bucket	11.65	23.50	35
1550	12′ deep, 1-1/2 C.Y. bucket	12.90	26.50	39.50
1560	16′ deep, 2 C.Y. bucket	17.05	33	50.50
1570	20′ deep, 3-1/2 C.Y. bucket	19.95	39	59
1580	24′ deep, 3-1/2 C.Y. bucket	25	47.50	72.50
1640	8′ wide, 12′ deep, 1-1/2 C.Y. bucket w/trench box	17.95	33.50	51.50
1650	15′ deep, 1-1/2 C.Y. bucket	22	42.50	64.50
1660	18′ deep, 2-1/2 C.Y. bucket	25.50	47.50	73
1680	24′ deep, 3-1/2 C.Y. bucket	33.50	61.50	95
1730	10′ wide, 20′ deep, 3-1/2 C.Y. bucket w/trench box	34	61.50	95.50
1740	24′ deep, 3-1/2 C.Y. bucket	42.50	76	118
1780	12′ wide, 20′ deep, 3-1/2 C.Y. bucket w/trench box	40.50	73	114
1790	25′ deep, 3-1/2 C.Y. bucket	53	94.50	147
1800	1/2:1 slope, 2′ wide, 2′ deep, 3/8 C.Y. bucket	1.01	3.32	4.33
1810	3′ deep, 3/8 C.Y. bucket	1.72	5.80	7.55
1820	4′ deep, 3/8 C.Y. bucket	2.59	8.90	11.45
1840	6′ deep, 3/8 C.Y. bucket	6.35	13.30	19.65

G1030 Site Earthwork

G1030 807	Trenching Sand & Gravel	COST PER L.F.		
		EQUIP.	LABOR	TOTAL
1860	8′ deep, 1/2 C.Y. bucket	10.15	21	31.50
1880	10′ deep, 1 C.Y. bucket	12.70	26	39
2300	4′ wide, 2′ deep, 3/8 C.Y. bucket	1.82	5.50	7.30
2310	3′ deep, 3/8 C.Y. bucket	2.85	9.10	11.95
2320	4′ deep, 1/2 C.Y. bucket	4.12	11.25	15.35
2340	6′ deep, 1/2 C.Y. bucket	8.75	19.60	28.50
2360	8′ deep, 1/2 C.Y. bucket	15.05	31.50	46.50
2380	10′ deep, 1 C.Y. bucket	15.45	36	51.50
2400	12′ deep, 1 C.Y. bucket	26	60	86
2430	15′ deep, 1-1/2 C.Y. bucket	29.50	66.50	96
2460	18′ deep, 2-1/2 C.Y. bucket	46	101	148
2840	6′ wide, 6′ deep, 5/8 C.Y. bucket w/trench box	14.60	27	41.50
2860	8′ deep, 3/4 C.Y. bucket	21.50	39.50	61.50
2880	10′ deep, 1 C.Y. bucket	21	44.50	65.50
2900	12′ deep, 1-1/2 C.Y. bucket	25.50	54	79.50
2940	16′ deep, 2 C.Y. bucket	39	79	118
2980	20′ deep, 3-1/2 C.Y. bucket	52.50	106	159
3020	24′ deep, 3-1/2 C.Y. bucket	74.50	146	220
3100	8′ wide, 12′ deep, 1-1/4 C.Y. bucket w/trench box	30.50	61	91.50
3120	15′ deep, 1-1/2 C.Y. bucket	41.50	85.50	127
3140	18′ deep, 2-1/2 C.Y. bucket	53.50	106	159
3180	24′ deep, 3-1/2 C.Y. bucket	83.50	159	243
3270	10′ wide, 20′ deep, 3-1/2 C.Y. bucket w/trench box	66.50	129	195
3280	24′ deep, 3-1/2 C.Y. bucket	92	174	266
3370	12′ wide, 20′ deep, 3-1/2 C.Y. bucket w/trench box	74.50	143	218
3380	25′ deep, 3-1/2 C.Y. bucket	107	201	310
3500	1:1 slope, 2′ wide, 2′ deep, 3/8 C.Y. bucket	2.23	5.60	7.80
3520	3′ deep, 3/8 C.Y. bucket	2.43	8.30	10.75
3540	4′ deep, 3/8 C.Y. bucket	3.86	13.35	17.20
3560	6′ deep, 3/8 C.Y. bucket	6.35	13.30	19.65
3580	8′ deep, 1/2 C.Y. bucket	16.90	35.50	52.50
3600	10′ deep, 1 C.Y. bucket	22	45	66.50
3800	4′ wide, 2′ deep, 3/8 C.Y. bucket	2.14	6.60	8.75
3820	3′ deep, 3/8 C.Y. bucket	3.56	11.60	15.15
3840	4′ deep, 1/2 C.Y. bucket	5.35	15.10	20.50
3860	6′ deep, 1/2 C.Y. bucket	12.35	28	40.50
3880	8′ deep, 1/2 C.Y. bucket	22.50	47.50	69.50
3900	10′ deep, 1 C.Y. bucket	24	56.50	80.50
3920	12′ deep, 1 C.Y. bucket	34.50	80.50	115
3940	15′ deep, 1-1/2 C.Y. bucket	48.50	110	159
3960	18′ deep, 2-1/2 C.Y. bucket	63.50	140	203
4030	6′ wide, 6′ deep, 5/8 C.Y. bucket w/trench box	19.30	36	55.50
4040	8′ deep, 3/4 C.Y. bucket	30	56	86
4050	10′ deep, 1 C.Y. bucket	30.50	65	95.50
4060	12′ deep, 1-1/2 C.Y. bucket	38	81.50	119
4070	16′ deep, 2 C.Y. bucket	61.50	125	186
4080	20′ deep, 3-1/2 C.Y. bucket	85.50	173	259
4090	24′ deep, 3-1/2 C.Y. bucket	124	244	370
4500	8′ wide, 12′ deep, 1-1/2 C.Y. bucket w/trench box	43	89	132
4550	15′ deep, 1-1/2 C.Y. bucket	61	129	190
4600	18′ deep, 2-1/2 C.Y. bucket	81	164	245
4650	24′ deep, 3-1/2 C.Y. bucket	133	257	390
4800	10′ wide, 20′ deep, 3-1/2 C.Y. bucket w/trench box	99.50	196	295
4850	24′ deep, 3-1/2 C.Y. bucket	141	272	415
4950	12′ wide, 20′ deep, 3-1/2 C.Y. bucket w/trench box	106	207	315
4980	25′ deep, 3-1/2 C.Y. bucket	161	305	470

G4010 Electrical Distribution

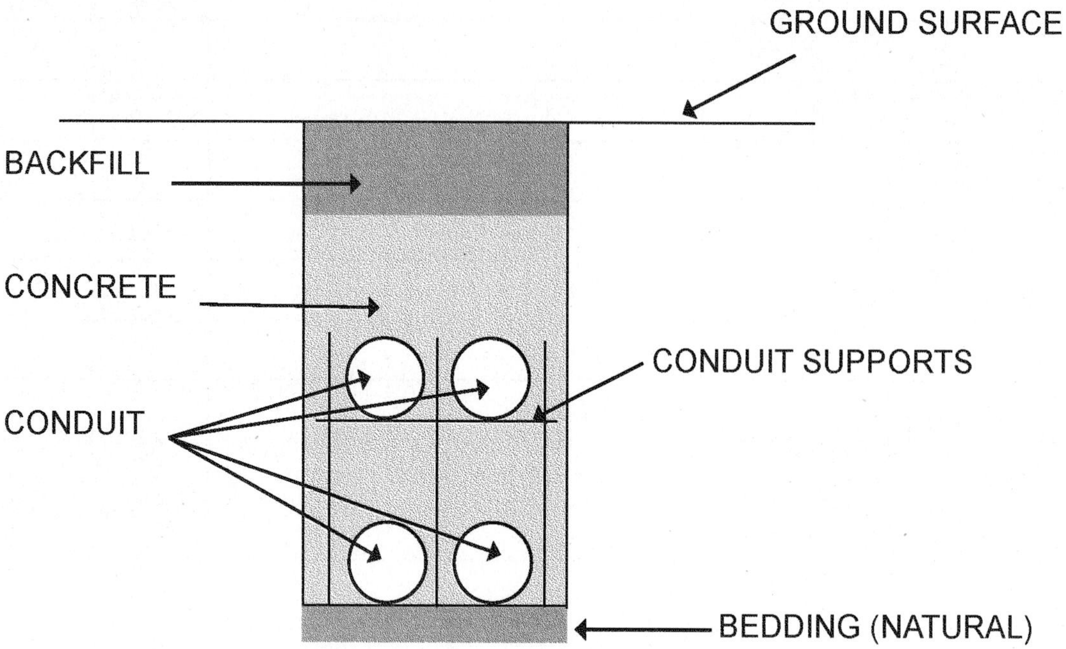

UNDERGROUND ELECTRICAL CONDUIT

System Components	QUANTITY	UNIT	COST EACH MAT.	COST EACH INST.	COST EACH TOTAL
SYSTEM G4010 312 1000					
2000 AMP UNDERGROUND SERVICE INCLUDING COMMON EARTH EXCAVATION, CONCRETE, BACKFILL AND COMPACTION					
Excavate Trench	44.440	C.Y.		387.96	387.96
4 inch conduit bank	108.000	L.F.	29,700	3,186	32,886
4 inch fitting	8.000	Ea.	564	532	1,096
4 inch bells	4.000	Ea.	25	266	291
Concrete material	16.580	C.Y.	2,818.60		2,818.60
Concrete placement	16.580	C.Y.		489.77	489.77
Backfill trench	33.710	L.C.Y.		123.71	123.71
Compact fill material in trench	25.930	C.Y.		148.84	148.84
Dispose of excess fill material on-site	24.070	L.C.Y.		352.38	352.38
500 kcmil power cable	18.000	C.L.F.	31,050	9,000	40,050
Wire, 600 volt stranded copper wire, type THW, 1/0	6.000	C.L.F.	1,980	1,458	3,438
TOTAL			66,137.60	15,944.66	82,082.26

G4010 312	Underground Power Feed	COST EACH MAT.	COST EACH INST.	COST EACH TOTAL
0900	Underground electrical			
0950	Including common earth excavation, concrete, backfill and compaction			
1000	2000 Amp service, 100′ length, 4′ depth	66,000	15,900	81,900
1100	1600 Amp service	48,500	12,300	60,800
1200	1200 Amp service	41,900	10,200	52,100
1300	1000 Amp service	18,600	9,350	27,950
1400	800 Amp service	16,500	8,775	25,275
1500	600 Amp service	13,600	8,150	21,750

G4010 Electrical Distribution

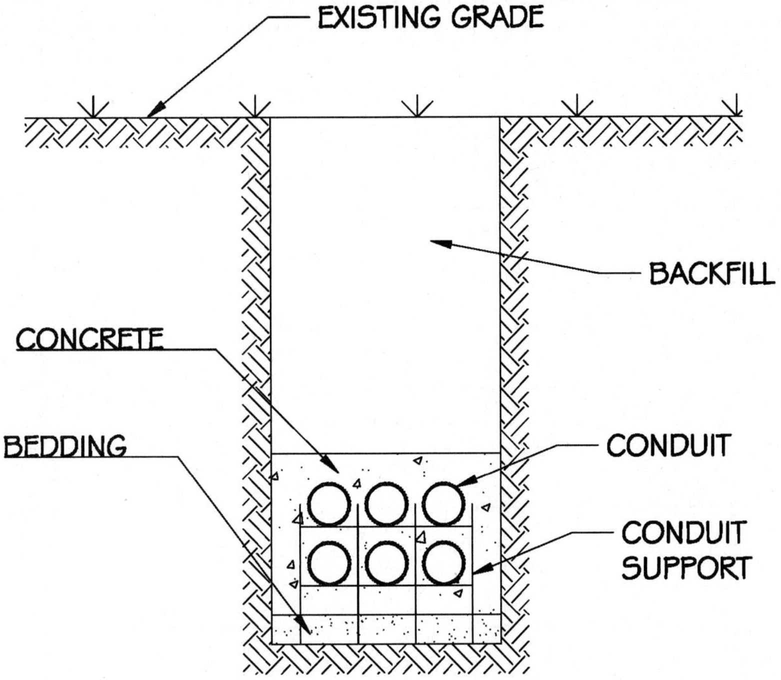

System Components	QUANTITY	UNIT	COST L.F. MAT.	COST L.F. INST.	COST L.F. TOTAL
SYSTEM G4010 320 1012					
UNDERGROUND ELECTRICAL CONDUIT, 2″ DIAMETER, INCLUDING EXCAVATION, CONCRETE, BEDDING, BACKFILL AND COMPACTION					
Excavate Trench	.150	C.Y.		1.31	1.31
Base spacer	.200	Ea.	.47	2.86	3.33
Conduit	1.000	L.F.	4.11	4.45	8.56
Concrete material	.050	C.Y.	8.50		8.50
Concrete placement	.050	C.Y.		1.48	1.48
Backfill trench	.120	L.C.Y.		.44	.44
Compact fill material in trench	.100	C.Y.		.57	.57
Dispose of excess fill material on-site	.120	L.C.Y.		1.76	1.76
Marking tape	.010	C.L.F.	.08	.04	.12
TOTAL			13.16	12.91	26.07

G4010 320	Underground Electrical Conduit	COST L.F. MAT.	COST L.F. INST.	COST L.F. TOTAL
0950	Underground electrical conduit, including common earth excavation,			
0952	Concrete, bedding, backfill and compaction			
1012	2″ dia. Schedule 40 PVC, 2′ deep	13.15	12.90	26.05
1014	4′ deep	13.15	18.50	31.65
1016	6′ deep	13.15	24	37.15
1022	2 @ 2″ dia. Schedule 40 PVC, 2′ deep	17.75	20	37.75
1024	4′ deep	17.75	26	43.75
1026	6′ deep	17.75	31	48.75
1032	3 @ 2″ dia. Schedule 40 PVC, 2′ deep	22.50	27.50	50
1034	4′ deep	22.50	33	55.50
1036	6′ deep	22.50	38.50	61
1042	4 @ 2″ dia. Schedule 40 PVC, 2′ deep	30	34.50	64.50
1044	4′ deep	30	40	70
1046	6′ deep	30	45.50	75.50

G4010 Electrical Distribution

G4010 320	Underground Electrical Conduit	COST L.F. MAT.	INST.	TOTAL
1062	6 @ 2″ dia. Schedule 40 PVC, 2′ deep	39.50	49	88.50
1064	4′ deep	39.50	54.50	94
1066	6′ deep	39.50	60	99.50
1082	8 @ 2″ dia. Schedule 40 PVC, 2′ deep	48.50	63	111.50
1084	4′ deep	48.50	69	117.50
1086	6′ deep	48.50	74	122.50
1092	9 @ 2″ dia. Schedule 40 PVC, 2′ deep	53	70	123
1094	4′ deep	56	75.50	131.50
1096	6′ deep	56	81	137
1212	3″ dia. Schedule 40 PVC, 2′ deep	18.80	15.80	34.60
1214	4′ deep	18.80	21.50	40.30
1216	6′ deep	18.80	27	45.80
1222	2 @ 3″ dia. Schedule 40 PVC, 2′ deep	25.50	25.50	51
1224	4′ deep	25.50	31.50	57
1226	6′ deep	25.50	36.50	62
1232	3 @ 3″ dia. Schedule 40 PVC, 2′ deep	34	36	70
1234	4′ deep	34	41.50	75.50
1236	6′ deep	34	47	81
1242	4 @ 3″ dia. Schedule 40 PVC, 2′ deep	47.50	46	93.50
1244	4′ deep	47.50	51.50	99
1246	6′ deep	47.50	57	104.50
1262	6 @ 3″ dia. Schedule 40 PVC, 2′ deep	63	66	129
1264	4′ deep	63	71.50	134.50
1266	6′ deep	63	77	140
1282	8 @ 3″ dia. Schedule 40 PVC, 2′ deep	80	86.50	166.50
1284	4′ deep	80	92	172
1286	6′ deep	80	98	178
1292	9 @ 3″ dia. Schedule 40 PVC, 2′ deep	92	97.50	189.50
1294	4′ deep	93.50	102	195.50
1296	6′ deep	93.50	107	200.50
1312	4″ dia. Schedule 40 PVC, 2′ deep	21.50	19.30	40.80
1314	4′ deep	21.50	25	46.50
1316	6′ deep	21.50	30.50	52
1322	2 @ 4″ dia. Schedule 40 PVC, 2′ deep	33	33	66
1324	4′ deep	33	39	72
1326	6′ deep	33	44.50	77.50
1332	3 @ 4″ dia. Schedule 40 PVC, 2′ deep	42.50	47	89.50
1334	4′ deep	42.50	52.50	95
1336	6′ deep	42.50	58	100.50
1342	4 @ 4″ dia. Schedule 40 PVC, 2′ deep	61	61	122
1344	4′ deep	61	66.50	127.50
1346	6′ deep	61	72	133
1362	6 @ 4″ dia. Schedule 40 PVC, 2′ deep	82	88.50	170.50
1364	4′ deep	82	94	176
1366	6′ deep	82	99.50	181.50
1382	8 @ 4″ dia. Schedule 40 PVC, 2′ deep	106	117	223
1384	4′ deep	106	124	230
1386	6′ deep	106	130	236
1392	9 @ 4″ dia. Schedule 40 PVC, 2′ deep	119	132	251
1394	4′ deep	119	135	254
1396	6′ deep	119	141	260
1412	5″ dia. Schedule 40 PVC, 2′ deep	26	23	49
1414	4′ deep	26	28.50	54.50
1416	6′ deep	26	34	60
1422	2 @ 5″ dia. Schedule 40 PVC, 2′ deep	42	40.50	82.50
1424	4′ deep	42	46	88
1426	6′ deep	42	51.50	93.50
1432	3 @ 5″ dia. Schedule 40 PVC, 2′ deep	57.50	58.50	116

G4010 Electrical Distribution

G4010 320	Underground Electrical Conduit	COST L.F.		
		MAT.	INST.	TOTAL
1434	4′ deep	57.50	64.50	122
1436	6′ deep	57.50	70.50	128
1442	4 @ 5″ dia. Schedule 40 PVC, 2′ deep	78.50	75.50	154
1444	4′ deep	78.50	81	159.50
1446	6′ deep	78.50	86.50	165
1462	6 @ 5″ dia. Schedule 40 PVC, 2′ deep	108	111	219
1464	4′ deep	108	117	225
1466	6′ deep	108	122	230
1482	8 @ 5″ dia. Schedule 40 PVC, 2′ deep	143	147	290
1484	4′ deep	143	155	298
1486	6′ deep	143	162	305
1492	9 @ 5″ dia. Schedule 40 PVC, 2′ deep	161	166	327
1494	4′ deep	161	169	330
1496	6′ deep	161	175	336
1512	6″ dia. Schedule 40 PVC, 2′ deep	33	28	61
1514	4′ deep	33	33.50	66.50
1516	6′ deep	33	39	72
1522	2 @ 6″ dia. Schedule 40 PVC, 2′ deep	52	50	102
1524	4′ deep	52	55.50	107.50
1526	6′ deep	52	61	113
1532	3 @ 6″ dia. Schedule 40 PVC, 2′ deep	75	73.50	148.50
1534	4′ deep	75	80.50	155.50
1536	6′ deep	75	87	162
1542	4 @ 6″ dia. Schedule 40 PVC, 2′ deep	98.50	94.50	193
1544	4′ deep	98.50	100	198.50
1546	6′ deep	98.50	105	203.50
1562	6 @ 6″ dia. Schedule 40 PVC, 2′ deep	142	140	282
1564	4′ deep	142	147	289
1566	6′ deep	142	154	296
1582	8 @ 6″ dia. Schedule 40 PVC, 2′ deep	189	187	376
1584	4′ deep	189	195	384
1586	6′ deep	189	204	393
1592	9 @ 6″ dia. Schedule 40 PVC, 2′ deep	211	210	421
1594	4′ deep	211	214	425
1596	6′ deep	211	221	432

G4020 Site Lighting

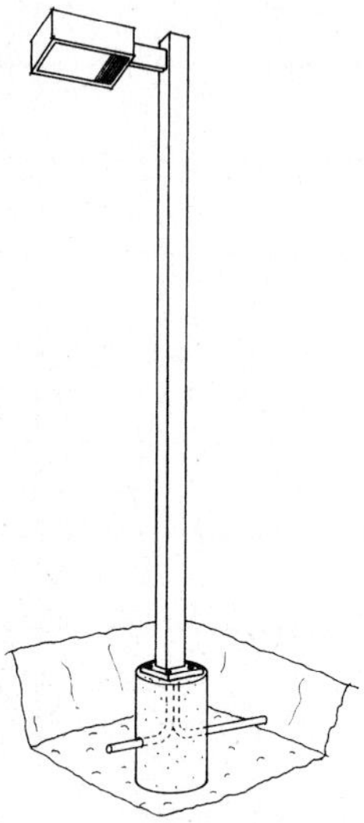

The Site Lighting System includes the complete unit from foundation to electrical fixtures. Each system includes: excavation; concrete base; backfill by hand; compaction with a plate compacter; pole of specified material; all fixtures; and lamps.

The Expanded System Listing shows Site Lighting Systems that use the following types of lamps: high pressure sodium, metal halide, and LED. Systems are listed for 400-watt and 1000-watt lamps. Pole height varies from 20′ to 40′. There are four types of poles possibly listed: aluminum, fiberglass, steel and wood.

System Components	QUANTITY	UNIT	COST EACH MAT.	COST EACH INST.	COST EACH TOTAL
SYSTEM G4020 110 5820					
SITE LIGHTING, METAL HALIDE, 400 WATT, ALUMINUM POLE, 20′ HIGH					
Excavating, by hand, pits to 6′ deep, heavy soil	2.368	C.Y.		333.89	333.89
Concrete in place incl. forms and reinf. stl. spread footings under 1 CY	.465	C.Y.	131.60	156.32	287.92
Backfill	1.903	C.Y.		97.05	97.05
Compact, vibrating plate	1.903	C.Y.		15.30	15.30
Aluminum light pole, 20′, no concrete base	1.000	Ea.	820	763	1,583
Road area luminaire wire	.300	C.L.F.	20.85	30	50.85
Roadway area luminaire, metal halide 400 W	1.000	Ea.	885	365	1,250
TOTAL			1,857.45	1,760.56	3,618.01

G4020 110	Site Lighting	COST EACH MAT.	COST EACH INST.	COST EACH TOTAL
2320	Site lighting, high pressure sodium, 400 watt, aluminum pole, 20′ high	1,450	1,750	3,200
2340	30′ high	2,500	2,150	4,650
2360	40′ high	3,650	2,775	6,425
2520	Fiberglass pole, 20′ high	1,850	1,550	3,400
2540	30′ high	2,175	1,925	4,100
2560	40′ high	4,125	2,475	6,600
2720	Steel pole, 20′ high	2,075	1,850	3,925
2740	30′ high	2,625	2,275	4,900
2760	40′ high	3,425	2,975	6,400
2920	Wood pole, 20′ high	920	1,700	2,620
2940	30′ high	1,050	2,150	3,200
2960	40′ high	1,400	2,625	4,025
3120	1000 watt, aluminum pole, 20′ high	2,200	1,800	4,000
3140	30′ high	3,250	2,200	5,450
3160	40′ high	4,400	2,825	7,225
3320	Fiberglass pole, 20′ high	2,600	1,575	4,175
3340	30′ high	2,925	1,950	4,875
3360	40′ high	4,875	2,500	7,375
3420	Steel pole, 20′ high	2,825	1,875	4,700
3440	30′ high	3,375	2,300	5,675

G4020 Site Lighting

G4020 110	Site Lighting	COST EACH MAT.	COST EACH INST.	COST EACH TOTAL
3460	40′ high	4,175	3,000	7,175
3520	Wood pole, 20′ high	1,675	1,750	3,425
3540	30′ high	1,800	2,200	4,000
3560	40′ high	2,150	2,675	4,825
5820	Metal halide, 400 watt, aluminum pole, 20′ high	1,850	1,750	3,600
5840	30′ high	2,900	2,150	5,050
5860	40′ high	4,075	2,775	6,850
6120	Fiberglass pole, 20′ high	2,250	1,550	3,800
6140	30′ high	2,575	1,925	4,500
6160	40′ high	4,550	2,475	7,025
6320	Steel pole, 20′ high	2,475	1,850	4,325
6340	30′ high	3,025	2,275	5,300
6360	40′ high	3,850	2,975	6,825
7620	1000 watt, aluminum pole, 20′ high	2,225	1,800	4,025
7640	30′ high	3,275	2,200	5,475
7660	40′ high	4,425	2,825	7,250
7900	Fiberglass pole, 20′ high	2,625	1,575	4,200
7920	30′ high	2,950	1,950	4,900
7940	40′ high	4,900	2,500	7,400
8120	Steel pole, 20′ high	2,850	1,875	4,725
8140	30′ high	3,400	2,300	5,700
8160	40′ high	4,200	3,000	7,200
8220	LED (~HPS 175 watt), aluminum pole, 20′ high	1,475	1,700	3,175
8240	30′ high	2,525	2,100	4,625
8260	40′ high	3,675	2,700	6,375
8320	Fiberglass pole, 20′ high	1,875	1,475	3,350
8340	30′ high	2,200	1,850	4,050
8360	40′ high	4,150	2,400	6,550
8420	Steel pole, 20′ high	2,975	2,150	5,125
8440	30′ high	2,650	2,200	4,850
8460	40′ high	3,450	2,900	6,350
8520	LED (~HPS 320 watt), Aluminum pole, 20′ high	1,775	1,750	3,525
8540	30′ high	2,825	2,150	4,975
8560	40′ high	3,975	2,775	6,750
8620	Fiberglass pole, 20′ high	2,175	1,550	3,725
8640	30′ high	2,500	1,925	4,425
8660	40′ high	4,450	2,475	6,925
8720	Steel pole, 20′ high	2,400	1,850	4,250
8740	30′ high	2,950	2,275	5,225
8760	40′ high	3,750	2,975	6,725
9010	LED Parking lighting, Solar, 30′ pole mount, 20W, 2000 Lumens, 5 Hrs	2,475	2,275	4,750
9020	40W, 4000 Lumens	2,625	2,275	4,900
9030	60W, 6000 Lumens	2,850	2,275	5,125
9040	80W, 8000 Lumens	3,075	2,275	5,350
9050	100W,10000 Lumens	3,225	2,275	5,500
9060	120W, 12000 Lumens	3,375	2,275	5,650
9110	Roadway lighting with pole, LED solar powered, 10 Watt 900 Lm 10 Hrs	2,450	2,175	4,625
9120	20 Watt, 2200 Lumens	2,650	2,175	4,825
9130	30 Watt, 3300 Lumens	2,875	2,175	5,050
9140	Roadway lighting pole, LED solar pwr, Hvy Duty 20 Watt 2000 Lm 10 Hrs	2,875	2,175	5,050
9150	30 Watt 6000 Lm	3,675	2,175	5,850
9160	50 Watt 9000 Lm	3,675	2,175	5,850

G4020 Site Lighting

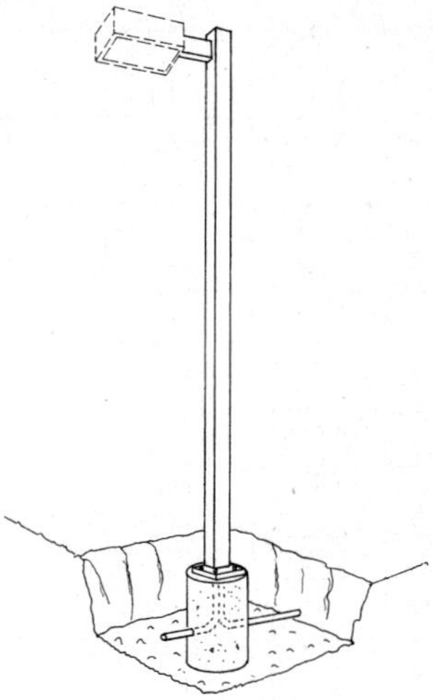

Table G4020 210 Procedure for Calculating Floodlights Required for Various Footcandles
Poles should not be spaced more than 4 times the fixture mounting height for good light distribution.

To maintain 1 footcandle over a large area use these watts per square foot:

Incandescent	0.15
Metal Halide	0.032
Mercury Vapor	0.05
High Pressure Sodium	0.024

Estimating Chart
Select Lamp type.

Determine total square feet.

Chart will show quantity of fixtures to provide 1 footcandle initial, at intersection of lines. Multiply fixture quantity by desired footcandle level.

Chart based on use of wide beam luminaires in an area whose dimensions are large compared to mounting height and is approximate only.

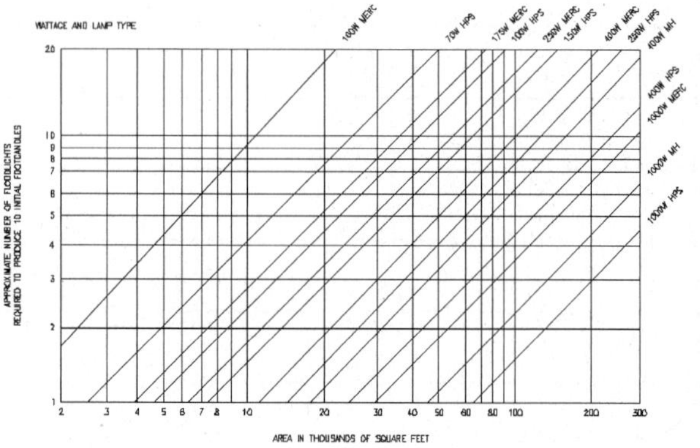

System Components	QUANTITY	UNIT	COST EACH MAT.	COST EACH INST.	COST EACH TOTAL
SYSTEM G4020 210 0200					
LIGHT POLES, ALUMINUM, 20′ HIGH, 1 ARM BRACKET					
Aluminum light pole, 20′, no concrete base	1.000	Ea.	820	763	1,583
Bracket arm for aluminum light pole	1.000	Ea.	640	100	740
Excavation by hand, pits to 6′ deep, heavy soil or clay	2.368	C.Y.		333.89	333.89
Footing, concrete incl forms, reinforcing, spread, under 1 C.Y.	.465	C.Y.	131.60	156.32	287.92
Backfill by hand	1.903	C.Y.		97.05	97.05
Compaction vibrating plate	1.903	C.Y.		15.30	15.30
TOTAL			1,591.60	1,465.56	3,057.16

G4020 210	Light Pole (Installed)	COST EACH MAT.	COST EACH INST.	COST EACH TOTAL
0200	Light pole, aluminum, 20′ high, 1 arm bracket	1,600	1,475	3,075
0240	2 arm brackets	2,225	1,475	3,700
0280	3 arm brackets	1,450	1,525	2,975
0320	4 arm brackets	1,600	1,525	3,125
0360	30′ high, 1 arm bracket	2,625	1,850	4,475
0400	2 arm brackets	3,275	1,850	5,125
0440	3 arm brackets	2,500	1,900	4,400
0480	4 arm brackets	2,650	1,925	4,575
0680	40′ high, 1 arm bracket	3,800	2,475	6,275
0720	2 arm brackets	4,425	2,475	6,900
0760	3 arm brackets	3,650	2,525	6,175
0800	4 arm brackets	3,800	2,525	6,325
0840	Steel, 20′ high, 1 arm bracket	2,075	1,550	3,625
0880	2 arm brackets	2,475	1,550	4,025
0920	3 arm brackets	2,575	1,600	4,175
0960	4 arm brackets	2,800	1,600	4,400
1000	30′ high, 1 arm bracket	2,600	1,975	4,575
1040	2 arm brackets	3,000	1,975	4,975
1080	3 arm brackets	3,125	2,025	5,150
1120	4 arm brackets	3,350	2,025	5,375
1320	40′ high, 1 arm bracket	3,400	2,650	6,050
1360	2 arm brackets	3,825	2,650	6,475
1400	3 arm brackets	3,925	2,700	6,625
1440	4 arm brackets	4,150	2,700	6,850

Reference Section

All the reference information is in one section, making it easy to find what you need to know and easy to use the data set on a daily basis. This section is visually identified by a vertical black bar on the page edges.

In this Reference Section, we've included Equipment Rental Costs, a listing of rental and operating costs; Crew Listings, a full listing of all crews, equipment, and their costs; Historical Cost Indexes for cost comparisons over time; City Cost Indexes and Location Factors for adjusting costs to the region you are in; Reference Tables, where you will find explanations, estimating information and procedures, and technical data; and an explanation of all the Abbreviations in the data set.

Table of Contents

Estimating Tips

- This section contains the average costs to rent and operate hundreds of pieces of construction equipment. This is useful information when one is estimating the time and material requirements of any particular operation in order to establish a unit or total cost. Bare equipment costs shown on a unit cost line include, not only rental, but also operating costs for equipment under normal use.

Rental Costs

- Equipment rental rates are obtained from the following industry sources throughout North America: contractors, suppliers, dealers, manufacturers, and distributors.
- Rental rates vary throughout the country, with larger cities generally having lower rates. Lease plans for new equipment are available for periods in excess of six months, with a percentage of payments applying toward purchase.
- Monthly rental rates vary from 2% to 5% of the purchase price of the equipment depending on the anticipated life of the equipment and its wearing parts.
- Rental rates can also be treated as reimbursement costs for contractor-owned equipment. Owned equipment costs include depreciation, loan payments, interest, taxes, insurance, storage, and major repairs.

Operating Costs

- The operating costs include parts and labor for routine servicing, such as the repair and replacement of pumps, filters, and worn lines. Normal operating expendables, such as fuel, lubricants, tires, and electricity (where applicable), are also included.
- Extraordinary operating expendables with highly variable wear patterns, such as diamond bits and blades, are excluded. These costs can be found as material costs in the Unit Price section.
- The hourly operating costs listed do not include the operator's wages.

Equipment Cost/Day

- Any power equipment required by a crew is shown in the Crew Listings with a daily cost.
- This daily cost of equipment needed by a crew includes both the rental cost and the operating cost and is based on dividing the weekly rental rate by 5 (the number of working days in the week), then adding the hourly operating cost multiplied by 8 (the number of hours in a day). This "Equipment Cost/Day" is shown in the far right column of the Equipment Rental section.
- If equipment is needed for only one or two days, it is best to develop your own cost by including components for daily rent and hourly operating costs. This is important when the listed Crew for a task does not contain the equipment needed, such as a crane for lifting mechanical heating/cooling equipment up onto a roof.
- If the quantity of work is less than the crew's Daily Output shown for a Unit Price line item that includes a bare unit equipment cost, the recommendation is to estimate one day's rental cost and operating cost for equipment shown in the Crew Listing for that line item.
- Please note, in some cases the equipment description in the crew is followed by a time period in parenthesis. For example: (daily) or (monthly). In these cases the equipment cost/day is calculated by adding the rental cost per time period to the hourly operating cost multiplied by 8.

Mobilization, Demobilization Costs

- The cost to move construction equipment from an equipment yard or rental company to the job site and back again is not included in equipment rental costs listed in the Reference Section. It is also not included in the bare equipment cost of any Unit Price line item or in any equipment costs shown in the Crew Listings.
- Mobilization (to the site) and demobilization (from the site) costs can be found in the Unit Price section.
- If a piece of equipment is already at the job site, it is not appropriate to utilize mobilization or demobilization costs again in an estimate. ■

01 54 33 | Equipment Rental

		01 54 33 Equipment Rental	UNIT	HOURLY OPER. COST	RENT PER DAY	RENT PER WEEK	RENT PER MONTH	EQUIPMENT COST/DAY	
10	0010	**CONCRETE EQUIPMENT RENTAL** without operators R015433-10							10
	0200	Bucket, concrete lightweight, 1/2 C.Y.	Ea.	.83	58.58	175.73	527.18	41.75	
	0300	1 C.Y.		1.08	70.61	211.82	635.46	50.97	
	0400	1-1/2 C.Y.		1.40	92.10	276.31	828.93	66.47	
	0500	2 C.Y.		1.52	107.25	321.76	965.28	76.52	
	0580	8 C.Y.		7.61	134.90	404.70	1,214.10	141.86	
	0600	Cart, concrete, self-propelled, operator walking, 10 C.F.		3.13	208.12	624.35	1,873.05	149.92	
	0700	Operator riding, 18 C.F.		5.27	145	402.71	965.71	122.73	
	0800	Conveyer for concrete, portable, gas, 16″ wide, 26′ long		11.64	114	342	1,026	161.50	
	0900	46′ long		12.05	155	465	1,395	189.41	
	1000	56′ long		12.23	161.53	484.58	1,453.73	194.76	
	1100	Core drill, electric, 2-1/2 H.P., 1″ to 8″ bit diameter		1.72	75	238.33	568.33	61.41	
	1150	11 H.P., 8″ to 18″ cores		5.92	131.80	354	895	118.14	
	1200	Finisher, concrete floor, gas, riding trowel, 96″ wide		10.59	241	703	1,843.10	225.34	
	1300	Gas, walk-behind, 3 blade, 36″ trowel		2.23	107.57	334.08	969.15	84.69	
	1400	4 blade, 48″ trowel		3.37	110	293.33	710	85.62	
	1500	Float, hand-operated (Bull float), 48″ wide		.09	13.85	43.07	124.61	9.33	
	1570	Curb builder, 14 H.P., gas, single screw		15.36	160	480	1,440	218.85	
	1590	Double screw		13.58	350	1,050	3,150	318.63	
	1600	Floor grinder, concrete and terrazzo, electric, 22″ path		3.33	140.63	416.25	1,013.13	109.91	
	1700	Edger, concrete, electric, 7″ path		1.30	77	211.25	513.13	52.63	
	1750	Vacuum pick-up system for floor grinders, wet/dry		1.78	98.78	296.67	832.78	73.53	
	1800	Mixer, powered, mortar and concrete, gas, 6 C.F., 18 H.P.		8.13	84.29	255.71	707.14	116.18	
	1900	10 C.F., 25 H.P.		9.86	122.17	354.29	859.35	149.77	
	2000	16 C.F.		10.26	112.50	310	812.50	144.05	
	2100	Concrete, stationary, tilt drum, 2 C.Y.		8.67	84	249.38	686.25	119.22	
	2120	Pump, concrete, truck mounted, 4″ line, 80′ boom		33.94	926.67	2,780	8,340	827.49	
	2140	5″ line, 110′ boom		43.44	1,203.33	3,610	10,830	1,069.53	
	2160	Mud jack, 50 C.F. per hr.		7.06	170	510	1,530	158.45	
	2180	225 C.F. per hr.		9.35	201.67	605	1,815	195.81	
	2190	Shotcrete pump rig, 12 C.Y./hr.		18.17	843	2,529	7,587	651.19	
	2200	35 C.Y./hr.		17.28	1,098.33	3,295	9,885	797.28	
	2600	Saw, concrete, manual, gas, 18 H.P.		6.07	107.67	320.83	832.50	112.72	
	2650	Self-propelled, gas, 30 H.P.		8.65	193.33	533.89	1,411.11	176	
	2675	V-groove crack chaser, manual, gas, 6 H.P.		1.80	138.92	361.15	1,022.75	86.61	
	2700	Vibrators, concrete, electric, 60 cycle, 2 H.P.		.51	41	144	425	32.92	
	2800	3 H.P.		.62	73.33	198.67	461.67	44.66	
	2900	Gas engine, 5 H.P.		1.69	18.16	56.56	164.01	24.85	
	3000	8 H.P.		2.28	18.37	57.14	165.08	29.68	
	3050	Vibrating screed, gas engine, 8 H.P.		3.08	128.75	330.13	781.25	90.64	
	3120	Concrete transit mixer, 6 x 4, 250 H.P., 8 C.Y., rear discharge		55.49	167	501	1,503	544.13	
	3200	Front discharge		64.42	102.55	307.64	922.92	576.87	
	3300	6 x 6, 285 H.P., 12 C.Y., rear discharge		63.61	333.33	1,000	3,000	708.92	
	3400	Front discharge		66.28	283.33	850	2,550	700.26	
20	0010	**EARTHWORK EQUIPMENT RENTAL** without operators R015433-10							20
	0040	Aggregate spreader, push type, 8′ to 12′ wide	Ea.	2.84	74.55	223.65	670.95	67.49	
	0045	Tailgate type, 8′ wide		2.79	56.09	168.27	504.81	55.94	
	0055	Earth auger, truck mounted, for fence & sign posts, utility poles		15.16	66.30	163.60	464.30	153.97	
	0060	For borings and monitoring wells		46.66	122.70	368.09	1,104.27	446.91	
	0070	Portable, trailer mounted		2.52	119.75	314.25	746.25	83.02	
	0075	Truck mounted, for caissons, water wells		93.42	181.47	544.40	1,633.20	856.23	
	0080	Horizontal boring machine, 12″ to 36″ diameter, 45 H.P.		24.91	231.67	695	2,085	338.28	
	0090	12″ to 48″ diameter, 65 H.P.		34.19	273.33	820	2,460	437.50	
	0095	Auger, for fence posts, gas engine, hand held		.49	77.79	241.44	578.16	52.21	
	0100	Excavator, diesel hydraulic, crawler mounted, 1/2 C.Y. cap.		23.81	977.86	2,872.14	5,938.57	764.88	
	0120	5/8 C.Y. capacity		31.83	1,052.44	2,792.78	6,226.11	813.17	
	0140	3/4 C.Y. capacity		35.80	1,195.25	3,144.88	7,524.38	915.34	
	0150	1 C.Y. capacity		45.17	1,160.22	3,126	7,463.89	986.56	

01 54 33 | Equipment Rental

			UNIT	HOURLY OPER. COST	RENT PER DAY	RENT PER WEEK	RENT PER MONTH	EQUIPMENT COST/DAY
20	0200	1-1/2 C.Y. capacity	Ea.	53.25	1,479	3,796	9,465	1,185.24
	0300	2 C.Y. capacity		62.02	1,000	3,000	9,000	1,096.14
	0320	2-1/2 C.Y. capacity		90.57	1,868.60	4,795.50	12,022.50	1,683.69
	0325	3-1/2 C.Y. capacity		131.66	2,156.63	6,705.94	19,383	2,394.44
	0330	4-1/2 C.Y. capacity		166.19	3,940.50	12,294.23	35,571	3,788.37
	0335	6 C.Y. capacity		210.86	3,461.25	10,785.39	31,204.50	3,843.97
	0340	7 C.Y. capacity		192.03	4,450	13,350	40,050	4,206.21
	0342	Excavator attachments, bucket thumbs		3.73	277.97	865.74	2,502.75	202.95
	0345	Grapples		3.44	239.63	744.53	2,156.63	176.44
	0346	Hydraulic hammer for boom mounting, 4000 ft lb.		14.77	958.50	2,984.15	8,626.50	715.03
	0347	5000 ft lb.		17.48	1,022.40	3,185.33	9,212.25	776.94
	0348	8000 ft lb.		25.80	1,304.63	4,023.57	11,608.50	1,011.13
	0349	12,000 ft lb.		29.67	1,500.32	4,627.11	13,349.78	1,162.80
	0350	Gradall type, truck mounted, 3 ton @ 15′ radius, 5/8 C.Y.		47.61	833.33	2,500	7,500	880.91
	0370	1 C.Y. capacity		65.11	1,666.67	5,000	15,000	1,520.84
	0400	Backhoe-loader, 40 to 45 H.P., 5/8 C.Y. capacity		13.04	211.38	589.63	1,520.13	222.27
	0450	45 H.P. to 60 H.P., 3/4 C.Y. capacity		19.75	214.56	595.78	1,565.67	277.19
	0460	80 H.P., 1-1/4 C.Y. capacity		22.31	325	896	2,266.44	357.71
	0470	112 H.P., 1-1/2 C.Y. capacity		36.15	660.30	2,048.91	5,937.38	699
	0482	Backhoe-loader attachment, compactor, 20,000 lb.		7.06	397	1,009	2,993	258.25
	0485	Hydraulic hammer, 750 ft lb.		4.03	115.02	357.84	1,033.05	103.85
	0486	Hydraulic hammer, 1200 ft lb.		7.18	220.46	686.82	1,996.88	194.78
	0500	Brush chipper, gas engine, 6″ cutter head, 35 H.P.		10.05	276.50	920.13	2,218.13	264.41
	0550	Diesel engine, 12″ cutter head, 130 H.P.		25.95	512.33	1,552.78	4,121	518.12
	0600	15″ cutter head, 165 H.P.		29.14	548.48	1,706.31	4,925.63	574.37
	0750	Bucket, clamshell, general purpose, 3/8 C.Y.		1.53	40	120	360	36.25
	0800	1/2 C.Y.		1.66	40	120	360	37.28
	0850	3/4 C.Y.		1.80	43.67	131	393	40.58
	0900	1 C.Y.		1.86	53.33	160	480	46.89
	0950	1-1/2 C.Y.		3.05	49.17	147.50	442.50	53.92
	1000	2 C.Y.		3.20	168.33	505	1,515	126.58
	1010	Bucket, dragline, medium duty, 1/2 C.Y.		.90	35	105	315	28.17
	1020	3/4 C.Y.		.85	37.83	113.50	340.50	29.54
	1030	1 C.Y.		.87	43.17	129.50	388.50	32.89
	1040	1-1/2 C.Y.		1.38	43.83	131.50	394.50	37.32
	1050	2 C.Y.		1.70	43.20	129.60	388.80	39.49
	1070	3 C.Y.		2.28	55.83	167.50	502.50	51.71
	1200	Compactor, manually guided 2-drum vibratory smooth roller, 7.5 H.P.		7.91	182.38	471	1,302.56	157.50
	1250	Rammer/tamper, gas, 8″		2.42	108.50	272.50	807.50	73.84
	1260	15″		2.88	104.37	324.83	755.09	88.02
	1300	Vibratory plate, gas, 18″ plate, 3000 lb. blow		2.33	213.97	625.83	1,586.50	143.82
	1350	21″ plate, 5000 lb. blow		2.87	244.63	615.88	1,715.88	146.12
	1370	Curb builder/extruder, 14 H.P., gas, single screw		13.58	1,065	3,195	9,585	747.63
	1390	Double screw		16.29	1,278	3,834	11,502	897.16
	1500	Disc harrow attachment, for tractor		.52	372.75	1,171.50	3,514.50	238.45
	1810	Feller buncher, shearing & accumulating trees, 100 H.P.		47.53	1,236.67	3,710	11,130	1,122.21
	1860	Grader, self-propelled, 25,000 lb.		36.55	1,058.33	3,175	9,525	927.41
	1910	30,000 lb.		46.71	1,195.83	3,587.50	10,762.50	1,091.19
	1920	40,000 lb.		56.87	1,333.33	4,000	12,000	1,254.97
	1930	55,000 lb.		73.36	1,666.67	5,000	15,000	1,586.87
	1950	Hammer, pavement breaker, self-propelled, diesel, 1000 to 1250 lb.		31.13	600	1,800	5,400	609.02
	2000	1300 to 1500 lb.		46.91	600	1,800	5,400	735.29
	2050	Pile driving hammer, steam or air, 4150 ft lb. @ 225 bpm		13.32	537.83	1,676.49	4,845.75	441.85
	2100	8750 ft lb. @ 145 bpm		15.72	756.15	2,347.08	6,789.38	595.21
	2150	15,000 ft lb. @ 60 bpm		16.08	899.93	2,794.14	8,094	687.50
	2200	24,450 ft lb. @ 111 bpm		17.19	1,043.70	3,241.21	9,372	785.80
	2250	Leads, 60′ high for pile driving hammers up to 20,000 ft lb.		4.02	324.83	1,005.89	2,902.13	233.36
	2300	90′ high for hammers over 20,000 ft lb.	↓	5.97	580.43	1,810.61	5,245.13	409.90

01 54 33 | Equipment Rental

			UNIT	HOURLY OPER. COST	RENT PER DAY	RENT PER WEEK	RENT PER MONTH	EQUIPMENT COST/DAY	
20	2350	Diesel type hammer, 22,400 ft lb.	Ea.	19.53	527.18	1,644.90	4,765.88	485.21	20
	2400	41,300 ft lb.		28.15	665.63	2,077.77	6,017.25	640.74	
	2450	141,000 ft lb.		45.30	1,059.68	3,289.81	9,505.13	1,020.34	
	2500	Vib. elec. hammer/extractor, 200 kW diesel generator, 34 H.P.		45.34	772.13	2,395.21	6,922.50	841.80	
	2550	80 H.P.		80.04	1,118.25	3,462.95	10,011	1,332.90	
	2600	150 H.P.		148.12	2,130	6,666.18	19,276.50	2,518.21	
	2700	Hydro Excavator w/EXT boom 12 C.Y., 1200 gallons		41.44	1,730.63	5,364.76	15,549	1,404.51	
	2800	Log chipper, up to 22″ diameter, 600 H.P.		48.88	492.50	1,477.50	4,432.50	686.57	
	2850	Logger, for skidding & stacking logs, 150 H.P.		47.62	141.67	425	1,275	465.97	
	2860	Mulcher, diesel powered, trailer mounted		21.79	765.50	2,296.50	6,889.50	633.63	
	2900	Rake, spring tooth, with tractor		16.13	58.20	162.50	410.60	161.55	
	3000	Roller, vibratory, tandem, smooth drum, 20 H.P.		8.56	380.83	1,095	2,632.50	287.45	
	3050	35 H.P.		11.11	496.88	1,451.88	3,263.13	379.22	
	3100	Towed type vibratory compactor, smooth drum, 50 H.P.		27.70	766.67	2,300	6,900	681.59	
	3150	Sheepsfoot, 50 H.P.		28.10	366.67	1,100	3,300	444.83	
	3170	Landfill compactor, 220 H.P.		76.59	1,798.33	5,395	16,185	1,691.72	
	3200	Pneumatic tire roller, 80 H.P.		14.16	436.65	1,356.32	3,913.88	384.55	
	3250	120 H.P.		21.25	566.67	1,700	5,100	510	
	3300	Sheepsfoot vibratory roller, 240 H.P.		68.18	366.67	1,100	3,300	765.47	
	3320	340 H.P.		91.87	1,500	4,500	13,500	1,635	
	3350	Smooth drum vibratory roller, 75 H.P.		25.58	268.33	711.67	2,012.22	346.96	
	3400	125 H.P.		30.27	479.25	1,437.75	4,206.75	529.68	
	3410	Rotary mower, brush, 60″, with tractor		20.59	133	370.50	944	238.84	
	3420	Rototiller, walk-behind, gas, 5 H.P.		2.34	125	260	645	70.72	
	3422	8 H.P.		3.08	130	325	706	89.64	
	3440	Scrapers, towed type, 7 C.Y. capacity		7.06	137.39	427.10	1,224.75	141.88	
	3450	10 C.Y. capacity		7.90	183.18	571.38	1,650.75	177.45	
	3500	15 C.Y. capacity		8.11	211.94	657.96	1,890.38	196.46	
	3525	Self-propelled, single engine, 14 C.Y. capacity		146.09	1,666.67	5,000	15,000	2,168.71	
	3550	Dual engine, 21 C.Y. capacity		154.95	1,666.67	5,000	15,000	2,239.60	
	3600	31 C.Y. capacity		205.89	2,208.33	6,625	19,875	2,972.09	
	3640	44 C.Y. capacity		255.02	2,333.33	7,000	21,000	3,440.19	
	3650	Elevating type, single engine, 11 C.Y. capacity		67.81	800	2,400	7,200	1,022.46	
	3700	22 C.Y. capacity		125.63	1,666.67	5,000	15,000	2,005.03	
	3710	Screening plant, 110 H.P. w/5′ x 10′ screen		23.16	692.25	2,156.42	6,230.25	616.57	
	3720	5′ x 16′ screen		29.24	1,222.22	3,666.67	11,000	967.25	
	3850	Shovel, crawler-mounted, front-loading, 7 C.Y. capacity		239.65	4,233.38	13,159.21	38,020.50	4,549.05	
	3855	12 C.Y. capacity		369.25	5,857.50	18,238.21	52,717.50	6,601.66	
	3860	Shovel/backhoe bucket, 1/2 C.Y.		2.95	78.81	244.72	708.23	72.55	
	3870	3/4 C.Y.		2.92	88.40	274.73	793.43	78.31	
	3880	1 C.Y.		3.02	59.13	175	488.75	59.18	
	3890	1-1/2 C.Y.		3.24	115.02	357.84	1,033.05	97.47	
	3910	3 C.Y.		3.77	155.49	484.81	1,411.13	127.10	
	3950	Stump chipper, 18″ deep, 30 H.P.		7.55	329.43	1,017.29	2,480.14	263.85	
	4110	Dozer, crawler, torque converter, diesel 80 H.P.		27.68	692.50	1,852	4,464	591.82	
	4150	105 H.P.		37.63	644.33	2,008.05	5,804.25	702.68	
	4200	140 H.P.		45.24	660	1,980	5,940	757.89	
	4260	200 H.P.		69.22	1,381	4,143	12,429	1,382.36	
	4310	300 H.P.		88.48	1,611.11	4,833.33	14,500	1,674.53	
	4360	410 H.P.		117.00	2,666.67	8,000	24,000	2,535.96	
	4370	500 H.P.		146.19	2,333.33	7,000	21,000	2,569.55	
	4380	700 H.P.		252.27	3,466.67	10,400	31,200	4,098.16	
	4400	Loader, crawler, torque conv., diesel, 1-1/2 C.Y., 80 H.P.		32.38	591.08	1,841.82	5,325	627.38	
	4450	1-1/2 to 1-3/4 C.Y., 95 H.P.		33.18	750.83	2,341.34	6,762.75	733.70	
	4510	1-3/4 to 2-1/4 C.Y., 130 H.P.		52.34	900	2,700	8,100	958.76	
	4530	2-1/2 to 3-1/4 C.Y., 190 H.P.		63.34	1,198.13	3,754.98	10,863	1,257.68	
	4560	3-1/2 to 5 C.Y., 275 H.P.		78.26	1,466.67	4,400	13,200	1,506.11	
	4610	Front end loader, 4WD, articulated frame, diesel, 1 to 1-1/4 C.Y., 70 H.P.	↓	18.22	495.20	1,245.10	3,126	394.79	

	01 54 33 | Equipment Rental		UNIT	HOURLY OPER. COST	RENT PER DAY	RENT PER WEEK	RENT PER MONTH	EQUIPMENT COST/DAY	
20	4620	1-1/2 to 1-3/4 C.Y., 95 H.P.	Ea.	21.92	466.67	1,400	4,200	455.32	20
	4650	1-3/4 to 2 C.Y., 130 H.P.		23.09	497.14	1,455.50	4,235.40	475.82	
	4710	2-1/2 to 3-1/2 C.Y., 145 H.P.		32.36	666.67	2,000	6,000	658.89	
	4730	3 to 4-1/2 C.Y., 185 H.P.		35.17	879.10	2,543	5,789.50	789.98	
	4760	5-1/4 to 5-3/4 C.Y., 270 H.P.		58.30	1,200	3,600	10,800	1,186.42	
	4810	7 to 9 C.Y., 475 H.P.		99.93	2,000	6,000	18,000	1,999.44	
	4870	9 to 11 C.Y., 620 H.P.		144.59	3,470	8,530	21,500	2,862.71	
	4880	Skid-steer loader, wheeled, 10 C.F., 30 H.P. gas		10.49	295	885.40	1,880.40	260.99	
	4890	1 C.Y., 78 H.P., diesel		20.21	438.75	1,341.25	3,095	429.91	
	4892	Skid-steer attachment, auger		.82	135.67	341.11	875	74.76	
	4893	Backhoe		.81	100.29	262.86	759.29	59.06	
	4894	Broom		.78	184.60	429.20	969.60	92.04	
	4895	Forks		.17	44.63	117.75	310	24.90	
	4896	Grapple		.79	86.53	235.63	652.85	53.47	
	4897	Concrete hammer		1.15	209.29	588.57	1,515	126.94	
	4898	Tree spade		.66	335.48	1,006.43	2,415.42	206.55	
	4899	Trencher		.72	152.78	415.56	1,068.89	88.83	
	4900	Trencher, chain, boom type, gas, operator walking, 12 H.P.		4.58	277.13	829.25	2,053.88	202.47	
	4910	Operator riding, 40 H.P.		18.29	453	1,201	2,779	386.50	
	5000	Wheel type, diesel, 4′ deep, 12″ wide		75.31	1,038.38	3,232.08	9,345.38	1,248.89	
	5100	6′ deep, 20″ wide		95.99	1,268.75	2,852.50	6,592.50	1,338.44	
	5150	Chain type, diesel, 5′ deep, 8″ wide		17.87	388.73	1,212.03	3,514.50	385.33	
	5200	Diesel, 8′ deep, 16″ wide		98.27	2,076.75	6,464.18	18,744	2,079.03	
	5202	Rock trencher, wheel type, 6″ wide x 18″ deep		51.55	1,268.75	2,900	6,592.50	992.44	
	5206	Chain type, 18″ wide x 7′ deep		114.54	271.67	815	2,445	1,079.31	
	5210	Tree spade, self-propelled		14.98	415	1,245	3,735	368.85	
	5250	Truck, dump, 2-axle, 12 ton, 8 C.Y. payload, 220 H.P.		26.25	366.85	1,037.44	2,773.47	417.49	
	5300	Three axle dump, 16 ton, 12 C.Y. payload, 400 H.P.		48.92	666.67	2,000	6,000	791.36	
	5310	Four axle dump, 25 ton, 18 C.Y. payload, 450 H.P.		54.80	583.33	1,750	5,250	788.42	
	5350	Dump trailer only, rear dump, 16-1/2 C.Y.		6.30	162.95	507.90	1,464.38	151.94	
	5400	20 C.Y.		6.80	183.18	571.38	1,650.75	168.66	
	5450	Flatbed, single axle, 1-1/2 ton rating		20.88	271.58	974.48	2,556	361.95	
	5500	3 ton rating		28.19	275.83	827.50	2,482.50	391.02	
	5550	Off highway rear dump, 25 ton capacity		68.89	1,533.33	4,600	13,800	1,471.16	
	5600	35 ton capacity		73.55	1,533.33	4,600	13,800	1,508.36	
	5610	50 ton capacity		92.20	2,166.67	6,500	19,500	2,037.60	
	5620	65 ton capacity		98.46	2,156.63	6,695.04	19,383	2,126.70	
	5630	100 ton capacity		133.29	3,168.38	9,869.41	28,542	3,040.18	
	6000	Vibratory plow, 25 H.P., walking	▼	7.43	344.35	1,033.05	3,099.15	266.08	
40	0010	**GENERAL EQUIPMENT RENTAL** without operators	R015433 -10						40
	0020	Aerial lift, scissor type, to 20′ high, 1200 lb. capacity, electric	Ea.	3.83	195.84	399.97	744.90	110.61	
	0030	To 30′ high, 1200 lb. capacity		4.15	350	815	1,975	196.19	
	0040	Over 30′ high, 1500 lb. capacity		5.64	410	861.25	1,817.50	217.41	
	0070	Articulating boom, to 45′ high, 500 lb. capacity, diesel	R015433 -15	13.51	561.06	1,309.50	2,950.56	369.98	
	0075	To 60′ high, 500 lb. capacity		15.02	623.40	1,455	3,278.40	411.13	
	0080	To 80′ high, 500 lb. capacity		17.65	918.44	2,459.44	6,057	633.06	
	0085	To 125′ high, 500 lb. capacity		20.17	1,986.67	4,695	11,533.89	1,100.34	
	0100	Telescoping boom to 40′ high, 500 lb. capacity, diesel		12.35	540	1,233.75	2,615	345.57	
	0105	To 45′ high, 500 lb. capacity		13.75	520	1,209	2,582	351.80	
	0110	To 60′ high, 500 lb. capacity		17.98	520	1,209	2,582	385.68	
	0115	To 80′ high, 500 lb. capacity		23.38	1,112	2,615	5,357	710.06	
	0120	To 100′ high, 500 lb. capacity		31.57	918.44	2,459.44	6,057	744.42	
	0125	To 120′ high, 500 lb. capacity		32.06	1,818.33	4,756.11	11,001.67	1,207.69	
	0195	Air compressor, portable, 6.5 CFM, electric		.99	46.05	121.75	353	32.29	
	0196	Gasoline		.72	50.74	144	387.43	34.53	
	0200	Towed type, gas engine, 60 CFM		10.37	150.25	451.25	984.38	173.21	
	0300	160 CFM	▼	11.51	250	760	1,810	244.12	

01 54 33 | Equipment Rental

			UNIT	HOURLY OPER. COST	RENT PER DAY	RENT PER WEEK	RENT PER MONTH	EQUIPMENT COST/DAY	
40	0400	Diesel engine, rotary screw, 250 CFM	Ea.	13.29	137.50	450	1,155	196.28	40
	0500	365 CFM		17.59	474.29	1,246.43	3,123.57	389.99	
	0550	450 CFM		21.93	357.78	966.67	2,764.44	368.76	
	0600	600 CFM		37.49	267.32	831.10	2,396.25	466.11	
	0700	750 CFM		38.06	690	1,757	4,224	655.87	
	0915	Air purifier		.77	10.53	24.89	69.11	11.12	
	0917	Air scrubber, 500 - 700 CFM, 110 V		.76	86.80	270.58	782.78	60.20	
	0919	200 - 1200 CFM, 110 V		.76	102.77	320.28	926.55	70.14	
	0930	Air tools, breaker, pavement, 60 lb.		.62	52	147.50	381.67	34.47	
	0940	80 lb.		.62	49.80	154	389	35.75	
	0950	Drills, hand (jackhammer), 65 lb.		.74	66	184.29	465	42.75	
	0960	Track or wagon, swing boom, 4″ drifter		67.89	1,080	3,240	9,720	1,191.15	
	0970	5″ drifter		67.89	1,080	3,240	9,720	1,191.15	
	0975	Track mounted quarry drill, 6″ diameter drill		111.83	798.33	2,395	7,185	1,373.61	
	0980	Dust control per drill		1.14	10.67	32	96	15.54	
	0990	Hammer, chipping, 12 lb.		.66	39	109.50	270	27.16	
	1000	Hose, air with couplings, 50′ long, 3/4″ diameter		.07	14.40	37.83	95.83	8.16	
	1100	1″ diameter		.09	17.18	43.13	127.25	9.31	
	1200	1-1/2″ diameter		.24	43.87	108.33	304.44	23.60	
	1300	2″ diameter		.26	61.50	151.25	419.38	32.35	
	1400	2-1/2″ diameter		.39	65.78	183.56	534.56	39.86	
	1410	3″ diameter		.46	83	215.50	636	46.76	
	1450	Drill, steel, 7/8″ x 2′		.09	14.47	35	104.22	7.74	
	1460	7/8″ x 6′		.13	21.14	65.80	190.64	14.17	
	1520	Moil points		.03	8.98	20.88	61.13	4.42	
	1525	Pneumatic nailer w/accessories		.52	25	75	150	19.20	
	1530	Sheeting driver for 60 lb. breaker		.05	8.36	25.98	75.08	5.58	
	1540	For 90 lb. breaker		.14	11.34	35.21	101.71	8.19	
	1550	Spade, 25 lb.		.55	7.99	24.81	71.89	9.37	
	1560	Tamper, single, 35 lb.		.65	96	259.20	701.70	57.02	
	1570	Triple, 140 lb.		.97	56.43	155	402.86	38.79	
	1580	Wrenches, impact, air powered, up to 3/4″ bolt		.47	41.82	110.22	305.89	25.78	
	1590	Up to 1-1/4″ bolt		.63	79.33	206.11	581.11	46.28	
	1600	Barricades, barrels, reflectorized, 1 to 99 barrels		.04	4.70	11.80	35	2.64	
	1610	100 to 200 barrels		.03	5.33	12.67	40.11	2.75	
	1620	Barrels with flashers, 1 to 99 barrels		.04	5.33	12.67	40.11	2.84	
	1630	100 to 200 barrels		.03	5.33	12.67	40.11	2.78	
	1640	Barrels with steady burn type C lights		.05	5.33	12.67	40.11	2.94	
	1650	Illuminated board, trailer mounted, with generator		3.60	91	288.57	734.14	86.53	
	1670	Portable barricade, stock, with flashers, 1 to 6 units		.04	4.29	12.14	39	2.73	
	1680	25 to 50 units		.04	4.29	12.14	39	2.72	
	1685	Butt fusion machine, wheeled, 1.5 HP electric, 2″ - 8″ diameter pipe		2.89	429	1,287	3,861	280.48	
	1690	Tracked, 20 HP diesel, 4″-12″ diameter pipe		10.91	408.33	1,225	3,675	332.25	
	1695	83 HP diesel, 8″ - 24″ diameter pipe		56.31	561.67	1,685	5,055	787.50	
	1700	Carts, brick, gas engine, 1000 lb. capacity		3.23	32.22	84.52	215.66	42.77	
	1800	1500 lb., 7-1/2′ lift		3.21	74.55	232.47	670.95	72.14	
	1822	Dehumidifier, medium, 6 lb./hr., 150 CFM		1.31	45.86	159.86	487.43	42.42	
	1824	Large, 18 lb./hr., 600 CFM		2.41	257.50	1,795	5,382.50	378.29	
	1830	Distributor, asphalt, trailer mounted, 2000 gal., 38 H.P. diesel		12.09	378.08	1,183.17	3,434.63	333.32	
	1840	3000 gal., 38 H.P. diesel		14.14	410.03	1,269.75	3,674.25	367.10	
	1850	Drill, rotary hammer, electric		1.22	36	126	378	34.98	
	1860	Carbide bit, 1-1/2″ diameter, add to electric rotary hammer		.03	51.98	131.70	385.50	26.61	
	1865	Rotary, crawler, 250 H.P.		149.26	2,458.33	7,375	22,125	2,669.07	
	1870	Emulsion sprayer, 65 gal., 5 H.P. gas engine		3.04	115.02	357.84	1,033.05	95.90	
	1880	200 gal., 5 H.P. engine		7.94	192.77	600.24	1,730.63	183.58	
	1900	Floor auto-scrubbing machine, walk-behind, 28″ path		6.18	222.67	728.67	1,475	195.20	
	1930	Floodlight, mercury vapor, or quartz, on tripod, 1000 watt		.50	43.10	108.70	293.30	25.76	
	1940	2000 watt	↓	.65	45.60	124.50	343	30.09	

01 54 33 | Equipment Rental

			UNIT	HOURLY OPER. COST	RENT PER DAY	RENT PER WEEK	RENT PER MONTH	EQUIPMENT COST/DAY	
40	1950	Floodlights, trailer mounted with generator, 1 - 300 watt light	Ea.	3.90	185	413.33	916.67	113.84	40
	1960	2 - 1000 watt lights		4.93	185	413.33	916.67	122.12	
	2000	4 - 300 watt lights		4.67	185	413.33	916.67	119.99	
	2005	Foam spray rig, incl. box trailer, compressor, generator, proportioner		27.99	575.10	1,789.19	5,165.25	581.75	
	2015	Forklift, pneumatic tire, rough terr, straight mast, 5000 lb, 12′ lift, gas		20.44	535.67	1,292.78	2,935.11	422.09	
	2025	8000 lb, 12′ lift		24.93	687.78	1,678.33	3,556.11	535.15	
	2030	5000 lb, 12′ lift, diesel		16.94	427.33	1,069	2,580.17	349.30	
	2035	8000 lb, 12′ lift, diesel		18.36	687.78	1,678.33	3,556.11	482.54	
	2045	All terrain, telescoping boom, diesel, 5000 lb, 10′ reach, 19′ lift		18.91	535.67	1,292.78	2,935.11	409.81	
	2055	6600 lb, 29′ reach, 42′ lift		23.13	593.75	1,432.50	3,192.50	471.51	
	2065	10,000 lb, 31′ reach, 45′ lift		25.31	957.50	2,353.75	4,978.75	673.26	
	2070	Cushion tire, smooth floor, gas, 5000 lb capacity		9.04	381.11	938.89	2,223.33	260.12	
	2075	8000 lb capacity		12.46	435	1,057	2,638	311.06	
	2085	Diesel, 5000 lb capacity		8.49	327.50	823	2,002.50	232.55	
	2090	12,000 lb capacity		13.21	680.63	1,817.64	4,240.39	469.19	
	2095	20,000 lb capacity		18.91	866.79	2,460.30	6,396.21	643.35	
	2100	Generator, electric, gas engine, 1.5 kW to 3 kW		2.82	59.25	167.50	408.75	56.08	
	2200	5 kW		3.53	84.83	238.33	585.83	75.88	
	2300	10 kW		6.50	129.17	340.83	949.17	120.15	
	2400	25 kW		8.12	370.50	958.50	2,186.50	256.64	
	2500	Diesel engine, 20 kW		10.09	288.50	733.50	1,665	227.44	
	2600	50 kW		17.48	388.33	1,125	2,645	364.82	
	2700	100 kW		31.34	626	1,586.50	3,968	568.06	
	2800	250 kW		59.57	1,019.50	2,677.50	6,297.50	1,012.10	
	2850	Hammer, hydraulic, for mounting on boom, to 500 ft lb.		3.18	100.64	312.82	905.25	88	
	2860	1000 ft lb.		5.05	150.17	467.50	1,357.88	133.88	
	2900	Heaters, space, oil or electric, 50 MBH		1.60	93.20	284	750	69.63	
	3000	100 MBH		2.98	135.63	352.50	861.25	94.34	
	3100	300 MBH		8.69	678.50	1,928	5,358	455.08	
	3150	500 MBH		14.42	267.06	609.69	1,686.25	237.32	
	3200	Hose, water, suction with coupling, 20′ long, 2″ diameter		.02	8.33	21	60	4.37	
	3210	3″ diameter		.03	15.88	43.50	124.38	8.96	
	3220	4″ diameter		.03	30.35	93.88	271.58	19.04	
	3230	6″ diameter		.12	43.67	135.80	394.05	28.12	
	3240	8″ diameter		.30	57.51	178.82	516.53	38.13	
	3250	Discharge hose with coupling, 50′ long, 2″ diameter		.01	7.20	20	55.60	4.09	
	3260	3″ diameter		.01	9.10	23.95	74.55	4.88	
	3270	4″ diameter		.02	22.37	69.85	202.35	14.15	
	3280	6″ diameter		.07	31.42	97.23	281.16	19.99	
	3290	8″ diameter		.26	40.47	125.73	362.10	27.24	
	3295	Insulation blower		.91	125.67	390.45	1,118.25	85.38	
	3300	Ladders, extension type, 16′ to 36′ long		.20	44.05	122	347.25	25.99	
	3400	40′ to 60′ long		.70	119.03	333.67	989.67	72.33	
	3405	Lance for cutting concrete		2.42	103.33	310	930	81.33	
	3407	Lawn mower, rotary, 22″, 5 H.P.		1.16	25	140	400	37.25	
	3408	48″ self-propelled		3.18	161.20	429	1,186	111.21	
	3410	Level, electronic, automatic, with tripod and leveling rod		1.15	47.37	121.83	344.50	33.60	
	3430	Laser type, for pipe and sewer line and grade		2.38	144.37	365.14	1,111.86	92.11	
	3440	Rotating beam for interior control		.99	83.28	214	622.80	50.71	
	3460	Builder's optical transit, with tripod and rod		.11	47.37	121.83	344.50	25.23	
	3500	Light towers, towable, with diesel generator, 2000 watt		4.68	185	413.33	916.67	120.08	
	3600	4000 watt		4.95	185	413.33	916.67	122.23	
	3700	Mixer, powered, plaster and mortar, 6 C.F., 7 H.P.		2.26	89.29	257.86	648.57	69.62	
	3800	10 C.F., 9 H.P.		2.46	111	328	956	85.26	
	3850	Nailer, pneumatic		.53	25	75	150	19.21	
	3900	Paint sprayers complete, 8 CFM		.96	93.16	222.09	619.25	52.14	
	4000	17 CFM		1.75	169.38	403.80	1,125.90	94.79	
	4020	Pavers, bituminous, rubber tires, 8′ wide, 50 H.P., diesel	↓	35.10	612.38	1,904.62	5,511.38	661.71	

01 54 33 | Equipment Rental

			UNIT	HOURLY OPER. COST	RENT PER DAY	RENT PER WEEK	RENT PER MONTH	EQUIPMENT COST/DAY	
40	4030	10′ wide, 150 H.P.	Ea.	105.12	2,103.38	6,521.89	18,850.50	2,145.33	40
	4050	Crawler, 8′ wide, 100 H.P., diesel		96.29	1,200	3,560	9,240	1,482.34	
	4060	10′ wide, 150 H.P.		114.29	1,425	4,225	10,975	1,759.34	
	4070	Concrete paver, 12′ to 24′ wide, 250 H.P.		96.32	1,810.50	5,656.15	16,401	1,901.82	
	4080	Placer-spreader-trimmer, 24′ wide, 300 H.P.		129.19	2,742.38	8,570.80	24,814.50	2,747.64	
	4100	Pump, centrifugal gas pump, 1-1/2″ diam., 65 GPM		4.31	58.04	181.23	521.85	70.74	
	4200	2″ diameter, 130 GPM		5.47	44.44	140	368.80	71.79	
	4300	3″ diameter, 250 GPM		5.62	62.94	187	521	82.39	
	4400	6″ diameter, 1500 GPM		24.40	366.90	956.30	2,400.30	386.48	
	4500	Submersible electric pump, 1-1/4″ diameter, 55 GPM		.44	47.70	125.17	331.50	28.54	
	4600	1-1/2″ diameter, 83 GPM		.49	59.23	160.43	428.57	35.99	
	4700	2″ diameter, 120 GPM		1.81	58.58	182.23	527.18	50.89	
	4800	3″ diameter, 300 GPM		3.33	132.11	347.80	976.83	96.23	
	4900	4″ diameter, 560 GPM		16.19	80.76	242.29	726.86	177.96	
	5000	6″ diameter, 1590 GPM		24.22	225.43	676.28	2,028.83	329.05	
	5100	Diaphragm pump, gas, single, 1-1/2″ diameter		1.24	40	120	360	33.88	
	5200	2″ diameter		4.37	45	135	405	61.92	
	5300	3″ diameter		4.44	79.40	243.40	614.20	84.23	
	5400	Double, 4″ diameter		6.62	218.19	488.77	1,246.91	150.72	
	5450	Pressure washer 5 GPM, 3000 psi		4.25	109.50	351	838	104.23	
	5460	7 GPM, 3000 psi		5.43	112	350	847	113.42	
	5470	High Pressure Water Jet 10 KSI		43.48	777.45	2,414.14	6,975.75	830.66	
	5480	40 KSI		30.65	1,054.35	3,285.92	9,505.13	902.38	
	5500	Trash pump, self-priming, gas, 2″ diameter		4.19	82.50	247.50	742.50	83	
	5600	Diesel, 4″ diameter		7.33	275	717.22	1,955.56	202.06	
	5650	Diesel, 6″ diameter		18.49	366.90	956.30	2,400.30	339.17	
	5655	Grout Pump		20.55	302.46	940.77	2,715.75	352.58	
	5700	Salamanders, L.P. gas fired, 100,000 Btu		3.17	60.10	169.40	451.90	59.23	
	5705	50,000 Btu		1.83	28.20	72.30	192	29.07	
	5720	Sandblaster, portable, open top, 3 C.F. capacity		.66	131.67	395	1,185	84.26	
	5730	6 C.F. capacity		1.10	263.33	790	2,370	166.82	
	5740	Accessories for above		.15	25.56	79.65	230.04	17.14	
	5750	Sander, floor		.84	75.68	215	521.49	49.75	
	5760	Edger		.57	33	109	319	26.35	
	5800	Saw, chain, gas engine, 18″ long		1.93	46.25	160.88	426.25	47.58	
	5900	Hydraulic powered, 36″ long		.86	77.92	233.77	701.30	53.61	
	5950	60″ long		.86	86.98	260.93	782.78	59.04	
	6000	Masonry, table mounted, 14″ diameter, 5 H.P.		1.45	86.87	297.65	723.88	71.14	
	6050	Portable cut-off, 8 H.P.		1.99	81.25	262.50	590	68.42	
	6100	Circular, hand held, electric, 7-1/4″ diameter		.25	23	50	125	11.99	
	6200	12″ diameter		.26	48.14	126.43	331.43	27.37	
	6250	Wall saw, w/hydraulic power, 10 H.P.		3.61	137.74	413.22	1,239.66	111.53	
	6275	Shot blaster, walk-behind, 20″ wide		5.20	302.46	940.77	2,715.75	229.79	
	6280	Sidewalk broom, walk-behind		2.46	88.93	277.04	804.08	75.10	
	6300	Steam cleaner, 100 gallons per hour		3.67	88.93	277.04	804.08	84.77	
	6310	200 gallons per hour		4.76	107.57	334.75	969.15	105.05	
	6340	Tar Kettle/Pot, 400 gallons		18.08	126.67	380	1,140	220.65	
	6350	Torch, cutting, acetylene-oxygen, 150′ hose, excludes gases		.50	16.51	51.36	149.10	14.24	
	6360	Hourly operating cost includes tips and gas		23.00	7.56	23.45	67.63	188.67	
	6410	Toilet, portable chemical		.14	25.03	77.34	223.65	16.63	
	6420	Recycle flush type		.18	30.89	95.81	276.90	20.58	
	6430	Toilet, fresh water flush, garden hose,		.21	36.74	114.27	330.15	24.56	
	6440	Hoisted, non-flush, for high rise		.17	29.82	93.50	270.51	20.08	
	6465	Tractor, farm with attachment		19.09	342.50	984	2,422	349.52	
	6480	Trailers, platform, flush deck, 2 axle, 3 ton capacity		1.86	102.24	317.41	915.90	78.34	
	6500	25 ton capacity		6.85	154.43	479.04	1,384.50	150.61	
	6600	40 ton capacity		8.84	219.39	681.05	1,970.25	206.92	
	6700	3 axle, 50 ton capacity	↓	9.59	433.33	1,300	3,900	336.69	

01 54 33 | Equipment Rental

			UNIT	HOURLY OPER. COST	RENT PER DAY	RENT PER WEEK	RENT PER MONTH	EQUIPMENT COST/DAY
40	6800	75 ton capacity	Ea.	12.18	324.83	1,002.39	2,902.13	297.90
	6810	Trailer mounted cable reel for high voltage line work		6.46	252.67	758	2,274	203.26
	6820	Trailer mounted cable tensioning rig		12.81	83.33	250	750	152.47
	6830	Cable pulling rig		80.95	156.67	470	1,410	741.56
	6850	Portable cable/wire puller, 8000 lb max pulling capacity		4.06	170.69	428.86	1,132.86	118.26
	6900	Water tank trailer, engine driven discharge, 5000 gallons		7.87	170.40	530.99	1,544.25	169.14
	6925	10,000 gallons		10.72	232.17	721.45	2,076.75	230.04
	6950	Water truck, off highway, 6000 gallons		78.88	1,333.33	4,000	12,000	1,431.03
	7010	Tram car for high voltage line work, powered, 2 conductor		7.55	31.33	94	282	79.21
	7020	Transit (builder's level) with tripod		.11	47.37	121.83	344.50	25.23
	7030	Trench box, 3000 lb., 6′ x 8′		.61	103.84	323.76	937.20	69.67
	7040	7200 lb., 6′ x 20′		.79	201.29	625.89	1,810.50	131.49
	7050	8000 lb., 8′ x 16′		1.18	218.33	679.21	1,970.25	145.31
	7060	9500 lb., 8′ x 20′		1.32	250.28	779.16	2,263.13	166.41
	7065	11,000 lb., 8′ x 24′		1.39	235.37	732.99	2,130	157.70
	7070	12,000 lb., 10′ x 20′		1.64	284.36	883.06	2,556	189.71
	7100	Truck, pickup, 3/4 ton, 2 wheel drive		10.15	66.56	206.62	596.40	122.56
	7200	4 wheel drive		10.42	185.73	541.70	1,602.98	191.73
	7250	Crew carrier, 9 passenger		13.91	116.09	362.57	1,049.03	183.83
	7290	Flat bed truck, 20,000 lb. GVW		16.78	142.71	444.41	1,278	223.10
	7300	Tractor, 4 x 2, 220 H.P.		24.46	232.17	721.45	2,076.75	339.98
	7410	330 H.P.		35.54	317.37	986.95	2,848.88	481.71
	7500	6 x 4, 380 H.P.		39.68	367.43	1,142.78	3,301.50	545.98
	7600	450 H.P.		48.63	447.30	1,385.18	4,020.38	666.04
	7610	Tractor, with A frame, boom and winch, 225 H.P.		27.20	315.24	979.34	2,822.25	413.43
	7620	Vacuum truck, hazardous material, 2500 gallons		14.06	335.48	1,038.89	3,008.63	320.26
	7625	5,000 gallons		14.32	473.93	1,471.76	4,260	408.90
	7650	Vacuum, HEPA, 16 gallon, wet/dry		.93	126	362	959.50	79.88
	7655	55 gallon, wet/dry		.93	126	362	959	79.84
	7660	Water tank, portable		.80	156.99	453.41	1,153.82	97.09
	7690	Sewer/catch basin vacuum, 14 C.Y., 1500 gallons		19.03	713.55	2,222.06	6,416.63	596.69
	7700	Welder, electric, 200 amp		4.19	35.40	81.80	236.50	49.91
	7800	300 amp		6.10	29.96	76.90	198.50	64.17
	7900	Gas engine, 200 amp		9.83	107.10	290.20	681.10	136.72
	8000	300 amp		11.13	107.10	290.20	681.10	147.09
	8100	Wheelbarrow, any size		.07	12	32	93	6.97
	8200	Wrecking ball, 4000 lb.	↓	2.75	68.33	205	615	62.98
50	0010	**HIGHWAY EQUIPMENT RENTAL** without operators R015433-10						
	0050	Asphalt batch plant, portable drum mixer, 100 ton/hr.	Ea.	97.19	1,650.75	5,165.57	14,910	1,810.63
	0060	200 ton/hr.		112.12	1,783.88	5,511.86	15,975	1,999.31
	0070	300 ton/hr.		131.76	2,076.75	6,464.18	18,744	2,346.93
	0100	Backhoe attachment, long stick, up to 185 H.P., 10.5′ long		.41	27.69	85.42	247.08	20.33
	0140	Up to 250 H.P., 12′ long		.45	30.89	95.81	276.90	22.78
	0180	Over 250 H.P., 15′ long		.62	42.07	130.44	378.08	31.05
	0200	Special dipper arm, up to 100 H.P., 32′ long		1.27	85.73	266.64	772.13	63.50
	0240	Over 100 H.P., 33′ long		1.59	107.57	334.75	969.15	79.65
	0280	Catch basin/sewer cleaning truck, 3 ton, 9 C.Y., 1000 gal.		38.90	452.63	1,414.04	4,100.25	594.04
	0300	Concrete batch plant, portable, electric, 200 C.Y./hr.		26.59	601.73	1,875.76	5,431.50	587.85
	0520	Grader/dozer attachment, ripper/scarifier, rear mounted, up to 135 H.P.		3.46	68.16	212.39	612.38	70.18
	0540	Up to 180 H.P.		4.55	103.31	320.90	926.55	100.54
	0580	Up to 250 H.P.		6.43	165.08	513.67	1,491	154.19
	0700	Pvmt. removal bucket, for hyd. excavator, up to 90 H.P.		2.37	62.84	195.08	564.45	58
	0740	Up to 200 H.P.		2.53	80.41	249.33	718.88	70.14
	0780	Over 200 H.P.		2.77	98.51	305.89	883.95	83.32
	0900	Aggregate spreader, self-propelled, 187 H.P.		55.63	798.75	2,481.78	7,188.75	941.36
	1000	Chemical spreader, 3 C.Y.		3.48	99.67	299	897	87.61
	1900	Hammermill, traveling, 250 H.P.	↓	73.90	358.67	1,076	3,228	806.43

01 54 33 | Equipment Rental

		01 54 33 Equipment Rental	UNIT	HOURLY OPER. COST	RENT PER DAY	RENT PER WEEK	RENT PER MONTH	EQUIPMENT COST/DAY	
50	2000	Horizontal borer, 3" diameter, 13 H.P. gas driven	Ea.	5.94	111.67	335	1,005	114.54	50
	2150	Horizontal directional drill, 20,000 lb. thrust, 78 H.P. diesel		30.26	738.67	2,216	6,648	685.30	
	2160	30,000 lb. thrust, 115 H.P.		37.20	738.67	2,216	6,648	740.76	
	2170	50,000 lb. thrust, 170 H.P.		53.33	738.67	2,216	6,648	869.81	
	2190	Mud trailer for HDD, 1500 gallons, 175 H.P., gas		27.98	787.17	2,361.50	7,084.50	696.17	
	2200	Hydromulcher, diesel, 3000 gallon, for truck mounting		19.13	986.90	2,960.70	8,882.10	745.16	
	2300	Gas, 600 gallon		8.22	281.67	845	2,535	234.78	
	2400	Joint & crack cleaner, walk behind, 25 H.P.		3.47	232.67	698	2,094	167.33	
	2500	Filler, trailer mounted, 400 gallons, 20 H.P.		9.16	213.33	640	1,920	201.26	
	3000	Paint striper, self-propelled, 40 gallon, 22 H.P.		7.42	24	72	216	73.74	
	3100	120 gallon, 120 H.P.		19.36	155	465	1,395	247.91	
	3200	Post drivers, 6" I-Beam frame, for truck mounting		13.62	125	375	1,125	183.96	
	3400	Road sweeper, self-propelled, 8' wide, 90 H.P.		39.47	397.01	1,111.15	2,832.90	538.01	
	3450	Road sweeper, vacuum assisted, 4 C.Y., 220 gallons		64.07	3,232.28	6,938.48	13,360.43	1,900.22	
	4000	Road mixer, self-propelled, 130 H.P.		50.83	889.28	2,770.36	8,014.13	960.69	
	4100	310 H.P.		82.46	2,316.38	7,243.34	20,980.50	2,108.32	
	4220	Cold mix paver, incl. pug mill and bitumen tank, 165 H.P.		104.40	716.67	2,150	6,450	1,265.22	
	4240	Pavement brush, towed		3.77	107.57	334.75	969.15	97.08	
	4250	Paver, asphalt, wheel or crawler, 130 H.P., diesel		103.60	2,449.50	7,618.49	22,045.50	2,352.46	
	4300	Paver, road widener, gas, 1' to 6', 67 H.P.		51.29	1,049.03	3,260.94	9,425.25	1,062.55	
	4400	Diesel, 2' to 14', 88 H.P.		61.98	1,251.38	3,866.96	11,182.50	1,269.25	
	4600	Slipform pavers, curb and gutter, 2 track, 75 H.P.		63.58	910.58	2,828.08	8,173.88	1,074.23	
	4700	4 track, 165 H.P.		39.23	1,357.88	4,213.26	12,141	1,156.49	
	4800	Median barrier, 215 H.P.		64.23	1,437.75	4,501.84	12,993	1,414.24	
	4901	Trailer, low bed, 75 ton capacity		11.77	304.59	946.54	2,742.38	283.47	
	5000	Road planer, walk behind, 10" cutting width, 10 H.P.		2.69	421	1,089	2,635	239.34	
	5100	Self-propelled, 12" cutting width, 64 H.P.		9.06	347.31	934.84	2,587.95	259.43	
	5120	Traffic line remover, metal ball blaster, truck mounted, 115 H.P.		51.09	2,066.67	6,200	18,600	1,648.72	
	5140	Grinder, truck mounted, 115 H.P.		55.84	2,066.67	6,200	18,600	1,686.74	
	5160	Walk-behind, 11 H.P.		3.90	305.30	915.90	2,747.70	214.39	
	5200	Pavement profiler, 4' to 6' wide, 450 H.P.		237.65	1,125	3,375	10,125	2,576.21	
	5300	8' to 10' wide, 750 H.P.		363.84	1,283.33	3,850	11,550	3,680.74	
	5400	Roadway plate, steel, 1" x 8' x 20'		.09	65.50	203.97	591.08	41.55	
	5600	Stabilizer, self-propelled, 150 H.P.		45.14	251.67	755	2,265	512.10	
	5700	310 H.P.		83.59	313.33	940	2,820	856.73	
	5800	Striper, truck mounted, 120 gallon paint, 460 H.P.		53.49	410	1,230	3,690	673.88	
	5900	Thermal paint heating kettle, 115 gallons		8.46	170	510	1,530	169.64	
	6000	Tar kettle, 330 gallon, trailer mounted		13.47	153	459	1,377	199.54	
	7000	Tunnel locomotive, diesel, 8 to 12 ton		32.71	665.63	2,077.77	6,017.25	677.26	
	7005	Electric, 10 ton		32.15	761.48	2,366.34	6,842.63	730.48	
	7010	Muck cars, 1/2 C.Y. capacity		2.53	28.76	89.46	258.80	38.10	
	7020	1 C.Y. capacity		2.76	37.28	116.59	335.48	45.41	
	7030	2 C.Y. capacity		2.92	42.07	130.44	378.08	49.44	
	7040	Side dump, 2 C.Y. capacity		3.16	52.19	161.60	468.60	57.56	
	7050	3 C.Y. capacity		4.24	56.98	177.77	516.53	69.44	
	7060	5 C.Y. capacity		6.18	74.02	229.71	665.63	95.40	
	7100	Ventilating blower for tunnel, 7-1/2 H.P.		2.35	56.98	176.61	511.20	54.12	
	7110	10 H.P.		2.66	59.11	184.69	532.50	58.22	
	7120	20 H.P.		3.89	77.21	240.09	692.25	79.16	
	7140	40 H.P.		6.75	102.24	317.43	915.90	117.47	
	7160	60 H.P.		9.55	109.70	340.52	985.13	144.52	
	7175	75 H.P.		11.40	170.40	530.99	1,544.25	197.38	
	7180	200 H.P.		22.85	335.48	1,044.66	3,035.25	391.71	
	7800	Windrow loader, elevating		59.19	1,666.67	5,000	15,000	1,473.50	
60	0010	**LIFTING AND HOISTING EQUIPMENT RENTAL** without operators R015433 -10							60
	0150	Crane, flatbed mounted, 3 ton capacity	Ea.	15.84	815	2,348.50	5,692	596.44	
	0200	Crane, climbing, 106' jib, 6000 lb. capacity, 410 fpm R312316 -45		43.59	3,006.59	9,019.77	27,059.32	2,152.66	
	0300	101' jib, 10,250 lb. capacity, 270 fpm		50.95	3,165.64	9,496.92	28,490.76	2,306.99	

01 54 33 | Equipment Rental

		01 54 33 Equipment Rental	UNIT	HOURLY OPER. COST	RENT PER DAY	RENT PER WEEK	RENT PER MONTH	EQUIPMENT COST/DAY	
60	0500	Tower, static, 130′ high, 106′ jib, 6200 lb. capacity at 400 fpm	Ea.	49.55	2,588.20	7,764.59	23,293.78	1,949.33	60
	0520	Mini crawler spider crane, up to 24″ wide, 1990 lb. lifting capacity		13.74	591.08	1,846.91	5,351.63	479.34	
	0525	Up to 30″ wide, 6450 lb. lifting capacity		15.97	702.90	2,193.20	6,336.75	566.37	
	0530	Up to 52″ wide, 6680 lb. lifting capacity		25.40	862.65	2,683.79	7,774.50	739.94	
	0535	Up to 55″ wide, 8920 lb. lifting capacity		28.36	953.18	2,972.36	8,599.88	821.33	
	0540	Up to 66″ wide, 13,350 lb. lifting capacity		38.39	1,491	4,617.26	13,312.50	1,230.57	
	0600	Crawler mounted, lattice boom, 1/2 C.Y., 15 tons at 12′ radius		40.56	957.29	2,871.87	8,615.60	898.84	
	0700	3/4 C.Y., 20 tons at 12′ radius		59.44	1,075.55	3,226.64	9,679.92	1,120.87	
	0800	1 C.Y., 25 tons at 12′ radius		73.98	1,136.92	3,410.76	10,232.29	1,274	
	0900	1-1/2 C.Y., 40 tons at 12′ radius		72.77	1,300.84	3,902.51	11,707.52	1,362.63	
	1000	2 C.Y., 50 tons at 12′ radius		97.40	1,541.84	4,625.52	13,876.57	1,704.33	
	1100	3 C.Y., 75 tons at 12′ radius		71.32	2,698.22	8,094.67	24,284	2,189.46	
	1200	100 ton capacity, 60′ boom		94.27	1,330	3,990	11,970	1,552.12	
	1300	165 ton capacity, 60′ boom		116.43	1,593.33	4,780	14,340	1,887.41	
	1400	200 ton capacity, 70′ boom		151.66	1,775	5,325	15,975	2,278.25	
	1500	350 ton capacity, 80′ boom		199.92	3,725	11,175	33,525	3,834.39	
	1600	Truck mounted, lattice boom, 6 x 4, 20 tons at 10′ radius		43.62	1,026.25	2,595.54	7,663.02	868.10	
	1700	25 tons at 10′ radius		46.88	2,698.11	8,094.34	24,283.02	1,993.94	
	1800	8 x 4, 30 tons at 10′ radius		59.43	2,891.04	8,673.13	26,019.39	2,210.08	
	1900	40 tons at 12′ radius		59.43	3,160.64	9,481.91	28,445.73	2,371.83	
	2000	60 tons at 15′ radius		58.91	3,315.05	9,945.16	29,835.48	2,460.30	
	2050	82 tons at 15′ radius		65.21	3,411.34	10,234.01	30,702.03	2,568.46	
	2100	90 tons at 15′ radius		72.85	3,511.25	10,533.76	31,601.28	2,689.54	
	2200	115 tons at 15′ radius		82.18	3,615.53	10,846.59	32,539.77	2,826.79	
	2300	150 tons at 18′ radius		88.98	3,122.12	9,366.37	28,099.11	2,585.11	
	2350	165 tons at 18′ radius		95.50	3,180.26	9,540.77	28,622.31	2,672.17	
	2400	Truck mounted, hydraulic, 12 ton capacity		32.37	3,152.78	9,458.34	28,375.03	2,150.65	
	2500	25 ton capacity		39.89	3,256.95	9,770.86	29,312.57	2,273.31	
	2550	33 ton capacity		59.43	3,256.95	9,770.86	29,312.57	2,429.62	
	2560	40 ton capacity		59.43	3,285.77	9,857.31	29,571.92	2,446.91	
	2600	55 ton capacity		59.01	3,314.96	9,944.88	29,834.63	2,461.06	
	2700	80 ton capacity		77.27	3,372.59	10,117.77	30,353.32	2,641.70	
	2720	100 ton capacity		82.25	3,517.04	10,551.13	31,653.40	2,768.24	
	2740	120 ton capacity		115.52	3,565.70	10,697.09	32,091.26	3,063.55	
	2760	150 ton capacity		123.62	3,791.37	11,374.11	34,122.32	3,263.79	
	2800	Self-propelled, 4 x 4, with telescoping boom, 5 ton		16.61	421.67	1,265	3,795	385.89	
	2900	12-1/2 ton capacity		23.50	750	2,250	6,750	637.99	
	3000	15 ton capacity		37.77	855	2,565	7,695	815.14	
	3050	20 ton capacity		24.50	941.67	2,825	8,475	760.97	
	3100	25 ton capacity		40.26	1,008.33	3,025	9,075	927.07	
	3150	40 ton capacity		49.27	1,241.67	3,725	11,175	1,139.14	
	3200	Derricks, guy, 20 ton capacity, 60′ boom, 75′ mast		24.96	1,638.39	4,915.18	14,745.54	1,182.69	
	3300	100′ boom, 115′ mast		39.55	2,312.76	6,938.29	20,814.86	1,704.04	
	3400	Stiffleg, 20 ton capacity, 70′ boom, 37′ mast		27.88	713.29	2,139.87	6,419.60	650.99	
	3500	100′ boom, 47′ mast		43.14	770.92	2,312.76	6,938.29	807.69	
	3550	Helicopter, small, lift to 1250 lb. maximum, w/pilot		108.79	8,233.33	24,700	74,100	5,810.29	
	3600	Hoists, chain type, overhead, manual, 3/4 ton		.16	15.98	40.47	79.88	9.37	
	3900	10 ton		.86	124	310	620	68.92	
	4000	Hoist and tower, 5000 lb. cap., portable electric, 40′ high		5.24	163.91	491.74	1,475.23	140.24	
	4100	For each added 10′ section, add		.13	36.67	110.02	330.07	23.02	
	4200	Hoist and single tubular tower, 5000 lb. electric, 100′ high		7.63	121.63	364.88	1,094.63	134.03	
	4300	For each added 6′-6″ section, add		.23	44.16	132.48	397.44	28.31	
	4400	Hoist and double tubular tower, 5000 lb., 100′ high		8.31	139.88	419.65	1,258.95	150.40	
	4500	For each added 6′-6″ section, add		.25	44.33	132.98	398.94	28.58	
	4550	Hoist and tower, mast type, 6000 lb., 100′ high		10.12	519.22	1,557.67	4,673.01	392.53	
	4570	For each added 10′ section, add		.14	36.67	110.02	330.07	23.16	
	4600	Hoist and tower, personnel, electric, 2000 lb., 100′ @ 125 fpm		19.20	576.32	1,728.96	5,186.87	499.39	
	4700	3000 lb., 100′ @ 200 fpm	↓	21.97	605.14	1,815.41	5,446.22	538.83	

01 54 33 | Equipment Rental

			UNIT	HOURLY OPER. COST	RENT PER DAY	RENT PER WEEK	RENT PER MONTH	EQUIPMENT COST/DAY	
60	4800	3000 lb., 150′ @ 300 fpm	Ea.	24.38	817.33	2,451.98	7,355.93	685.43	60
	4900	4000 lb., 100′ @ 300 fpm		25.22	845.77	2,537.30	7,611.91	709.22	
	5000	6000 lb., 100′ @ 275 fpm		27.10	874.96	2,624.87	7,874.62	741.81	
	5100	For added heights up to 500′, add	L.F.	.01	3.74	11.23	33.68	2.33	
	5200	Jacks, hydraulic, 20 ton	Ea.	.05	35	80	175	16.44	
	5500	100 ton		.44	27.75	68.91	142.16	17.29	
	6100	Jacks, hydraulic, climbing w/50′ jackrods, control console, 30 ton cap.		2.38	35.93	107.78	323.34	40.57	
	6150	For each added 10′ jackrod section, add		.05	5.61	16.84	50.52	3.81	
	6300	50 ton capacity		3.82	38.55	115.64	346.91	53.69	
	6350	For each added 10′ jackrod section, add		.07	5.61	16.84	50.52	3.89	
	6500	125 ton capacity		9.99	38.55	115.64	346.91	103.05	
	6550	For each added 10′ jackrod section, add		.68	5.61	16.84	50.52	8.77	
	6600	Cable jack, 10 ton capacity with 200′ cable		1.74	41.17	123.50	370.49	38.60	
	6650	For each added 50′ of cable, add	↓	.24	17.21	51.64	154.93	12.27	
70	0010	**WELLPOINT EQUIPMENT RENTAL** without operators R015433-10							70
	0020	Based on 2 months rental							
	0100	Combination jetting & wellpoint pump, 60 H.P. diesel	Ea.	17.20	345.04	1,035.13	3,105.39	344.59	
	0200	High pressure gas jet pump, 200 H.P., 300 psi	"	37.12	192	576	1,728	412.18	
	0300	Discharge pipe, 8″ diameter	L.F.	.01	53.25	159.75	479.25	32.03	
	0350	12″ diameter		.01	56.80	170.40	511.20	34.19	
	0400	Header pipe, flows up to 150 GPM, 4″ diameter		.01	31.33	94	282	18.87	
	0500	400 GPM, 6″ diameter		.01	41.33	124	372	24.88	
	0600	800 GPM, 8″ diameter		.01	45.67	137	411	27.51	
	0700	1500 GPM, 10″ diameter		.01	57.51	172.53	517.59	34.62	
	0800	2500 GPM, 12″ diameter		.03	65.32	195.96	587.88	39.41	
	0900	4500 GPM, 16″ diameter		.04	55.67	167	501	33.68	
	0950	For quick coupling aluminum and plastic pipe, add	↓	.04	10.55	31.64	94.91	6.62	
	1100	Wellpoint, 25′ long, with fittings & riser pipe, 1-1/2″ or 2″ diameter	Ea.	.07	82.27	246.81	740.44	49.95	
	1200	Wellpoint pump, diesel powered, 4″ suction, 20 H.P.		7.68	161.67	485	1,455	158.46	
	1300	6″ suction, 30 H.P.		10.31	296.67	890	2,670	260.45	
	1400	8″ suction, 40 H.P.		13.96	258.33	775	2,325	266.71	
	1500	10″ suction, 75 H.P.		20.37	290.67	872	2,616	337.35	
	1600	12″ suction, 100 H.P.		29.89	298.33	895	2,685	418.09	
	1700	12″ suction, 175 H.P.	↓	42.77	306.67	920	2,760	526.15	
80	0010	**MARINE EQUIPMENT RENTAL** without operators R015433-10							80
	0200	Barge, 400 Ton, 30′ wide x 90′ long	Ea.	19.38	1,278	4,011.25	11,608.50	957.33	
	0240	800 Ton, 45′ wide x 90′ long		24.34	1,597.50	4,934.71	14,271	1,181.66	
	2000	Tugboat, diesel, 100 H.P.		32.51	255.60	796.48	2,316.38	419.35	
	2040	250 H.P.		63.11	463.28	1,442.89	4,180.13	793.50	
	2080	380 H.P.		137.40	1,384.50	4,328.69	12,567	1,964.96	
	3000	Small work boat, gas, 16-foot, 50 H.P.		12.47	51.65	160.15	463.28	131.82	
	4000	Large, diesel, 48-foot, 200 H.P.	↓	82.09	1,464.38	4,588.41	13,312.50	1,574.43	

Crew No.	Bare Costs		Incl. Subs O&P		Cost Per Labor-Hour	

Crew A-1	Hr.	Daily	Hr.	Daily	Bare Costs	Incl. O&P
1 Building Laborer	$47.25	$378.00	$70.35	$562.80	$47.25	$70.35
1 Concrete Saw, Gas Manual		112.72		123.99	14.09	15.50
8 L.H., Daily Totals		$490.72		$686.79	$61.34	$85.85

Crew A-1A	Hr.	Daily	Hr.	Daily	Bare Costs	Incl. O&P
1 Skilled Worker	$61.25	$490.00	$92.00	$736.00	$61.25	$92.00
1 Shot Blaster, 20"		229.79		252.77	28.72	31.60
8 L.H., Daily Totals		$719.79		$988.77	$89.97	$123.60

Crew A-1B	Hr.	Daily	Hr.	Daily	Bare Costs	Incl. O&P
1 Building Laborer	$47.25	$378.00	$70.35	$562.80	$47.25	$70.35
1 Concrete Saw		176.00		193.60	22.00	24.20
8 L.H., Daily Totals		$554.00		$756.40	$69.25	$94.55

Crew A-1C	Hr.	Daily	Hr.	Daily	Bare Costs	Incl. O&P
1 Building Laborer	$47.25	$378.00	$70.35	$562.80	$47.25	$70.35
1 Chain Saw, Gas, 18"		47.58		52.34	5.95	6.54
8 L.H., Daily Totals		$425.58		$615.14	$53.20	$76.89

Crew A-1D	Hr.	Daily	Hr.	Daily	Bare Costs	Incl. O&P
1 Building Laborer	$47.25	$378.00	$70.35	$562.80	$47.25	$70.35
1 Vibrating Plate, Gas, 18"		143.82		158.20	17.98	19.78
8 L.H., Daily Totals		$521.82		$721.00	$65.23	$90.13

Crew A-1E	Hr.	Daily	Hr.	Daily	Bare Costs	Incl. O&P
1 Building Laborer	$47.25	$378.00	$70.35	$562.80	$47.25	$70.35
1 Vibrating Plate, Gas, 21"		146.12		160.73	18.27	20.09
8 L.H., Daily Totals		$524.12		$723.53	$65.52	$90.44

Crew A-1F	Hr.	Daily	Hr.	Daily	Bare Costs	Incl. O&P
1 Building Laborer	$47.25	$378.00	$70.35	$562.80	$47.25	$70.35
1 Rammer/Tamper, Gas, 8"		73.84		81.22	9.23	10.15
8 L.H., Daily Totals		$451.84		$644.02	$56.48	$80.50

Crew A-1G	Hr.	Daily	Hr.	Daily	Bare Costs	Incl. O&P
1 Building Laborer	$47.25	$378.00	$70.35	$562.80	$47.25	$70.35
1 Rammer/Tamper, Gas, 15"		88.02		96.82	11.00	12.10
8 L.H., Daily Totals		$466.02		$659.62	$58.25	$82.45

Crew A-1H	Hr.	Daily	Hr.	Daily	Bare Costs	Incl. O&P
1 Building Laborer	$47.25	$378.00	$70.35	$562.80	$47.25	$70.35
1 Exterior Steam Cleaner		84.77		93.25	10.60	11.66
8 L.H., Daily Totals		$462.77		$656.05	$57.85	$82.01

Crew A-1J	Hr.	Daily	Hr.	Daily	Bare Costs	Incl. O&P
1 Building Laborer	$47.25	$378.00	$70.35	$562.80	$47.25	$70.35
1 Cultivator, Walk-Behind, 5 H.P.		70.72		77.79	8.84	9.72
8 L.H., Daily Totals		$448.72		$640.59	$56.09	$80.07

Crew A-1K	Hr.	Daily	Hr.	Daily	Bare Costs	Incl. O&P
1 Building Laborer	$47.25	$378.00	$70.35	$562.80	$47.25	$70.35
1 Cultivator, Walk-Behind, 8 H.P.		89.64		98.60	11.21	12.33
8 L.H., Daily Totals		$467.64		$661.40	$58.45	$82.68

Crew A-1M	Hr.	Daily	Hr.	Daily	Bare Costs	Incl. O&P
1 Building Laborer	$47.25	$378.00	$70.35	$562.80	$47.25	$70.35
1 Snow Blower, Walk-Behind		75.10		82.61	9.39	10.33
8 L.H., Daily Totals		$453.10		$645.41	$56.64	$80.68

Crew A-2	Hr.	Daily	Hr.	Daily	Bare Costs	Incl. O&P
2 Laborers	$47.25	$756.00	$70.35	$1125.60	$49.13	$73.23
1 Truck Driver (light)	52.90	423.20	79.00	632.00		
1 Flatbed Truck, Gas, 1.5 Ton		361.95		398.14	15.08	16.59
24 L.H., Daily Totals		$1541.15		$2155.74	$64.21	$89.82

Crew A-2A	Hr.	Daily	Hr.	Daily	Bare Costs	Incl. O&P
2 Laborers	$47.25	$756.00	$70.35	$1125.60	$49.13	$73.23
1 Truck Driver (light)	52.90	423.20	79.00	632.00		
1 Flatbed Truck, Gas, 1.5 Ton		361.95		398.14		
1 Concrete Saw		176.00		193.60	22.41	24.66
24 L.H., Daily Totals		$1717.15		$2349.34	$71.55	$97.89

Crew A-2B	Hr.	Daily	Hr.	Daily	Bare Costs	Incl. O&P
1 Truck Driver (light)	$52.90	$423.20	$79.00	$632.00	$52.90	$79.00
1 Flatbed Truck, Gas, 1.5 Ton		361.95		398.14	45.24	49.77
8 L.H., Daily Totals		$785.15		$1030.15	$98.14	$128.77

Crew A-3A	Hr.	Daily	Hr.	Daily	Bare Costs	Incl. O&P
1 Equip. Oper. (light)	$59.70	$477.60	$88.85	$710.80	$59.70	$88.85
1 Pickup Truck, 4x4, 3/4 Ton		191.73		210.90	23.97	26.36
8 L.H., Daily Totals		$669.33		$921.70	$83.67	$115.21

Crew A-3B	Hr.	Daily	Hr.	Daily	Bare Costs	Incl. O&P
1 Equip. Oper. (medium)	$63.05	$504.40	$93.80	$750.40	$59.25	$88.33
1 Truck Driver (heavy)	55.45	443.60	82.85	662.80		
1 Dump Truck, 12 C.Y., 400 H.P.		791.36		870.50		
1 F.E. Loader, W.M., 2.5 C.Y.		658.89		724.78	90.64	99.70
16 L.H., Daily Totals		$2398.25		$3008.47	$149.89	$188.03

Crew A-3C	Hr.	Daily	Hr.	Daily	Bare Costs	Incl. O&P
1 Equip. Oper. (light)	$59.70	$477.60	$88.85	$710.80	$59.70	$88.85
1 Loader, Skid Steer, 78 H.P.		429.91		472.90	53.74	59.11
8 L.H., Daily Totals		$907.51		$1183.70	$113.44	$147.96

Crew A-3D	Hr.	Daily	Hr.	Daily	Bare Costs	Incl. O&P
1 Truck Driver (light)	$52.90	$423.20	$79.00	$632.00	$52.90	$79.00
1 Pickup Truck, 4x4, 3/4 Ton		191.73		210.90		
1 Flatbed Trailer, 25 Ton		150.61		165.67	42.79	47.07
8 L.H., Daily Totals		$765.54		$1008.57	$95.69	$126.07

Crew A-3E	Hr.	Daily	Hr.	Daily	Bare Costs	Incl. O&P
1 Equip. Oper. (crane)	$66.30	$530.40	$98.65	$789.20	$60.88	$90.75
1 Truck Driver (heavy)	55.45	443.60	82.85	662.80		
1 Pickup Truck, 4x4, 3/4 Ton		191.73		210.90	11.98	13.18
16 L.H., Daily Totals		$1165.73		$1662.90	$72.86	$103.93

Crew A-3F	Hr.	Daily	Hr.	Daily	Bare Costs	Incl. O&P
1 Equip. Oper. (crane)	$66.30	$530.40	$98.65	$789.20	$60.88	$90.75
1 Truck Driver (heavy)	55.45	443.60	82.85	662.80		
1 Pickup Truck, 4x4, 3/4 Ton		191.73		210.90		
1 Truck Tractor, 6x4, 380 H.P.		545.98		600.58		
1 Lowbed Trailer, 75 Ton		283.47		311.82	63.82	70.21
16 L.H., Daily Totals		$1995.18		$2575.30	$124.70	$160.96

Crew No.	Bare Costs		Incl. Subs O&P		Cost Per Labor-Hour	
Crew A-3G	**Hr.**	**Daily**	**Hr.**	**Daily**	**Bare Costs**	**Incl. O&P**
1 Equip. Oper. (crane)	$66.30	$530.40	$98.65	$789.20	$60.88	$90.75
1 Truck Driver (heavy)	55.45	443.60	82.85	662.80		
1 Pickup Truck, 4x4, 3/4 Ton		191.73		210.90		
1 Truck Tractor, 6x4, 450 H.P.		666.04		732.64		
1 Lowbed Trailer, 75 Ton		283.47		311.82	71.33	78.46
16 L.H., Daily Totals		$2115.24		$2707.36	$132.20	$169.21

Crew A-3H	Hr.	Daily	Hr.	Daily	Bare Costs	Incl. O&P
1 Equip. Oper. (crane)	$66.30	$530.40	$98.65	$789.20	$66.30	$98.65
1 Hyd. Crane, 12 Ton (Daily)		2150.65		2365.72	268.83	295.71
8 L.H., Daily Totals		$2681.05		$3154.92	$335.13	$394.36

Crew A-3I	Hr.	Daily	Hr.	Daily	Bare Costs	Incl. O&P
1 Equip. Oper. (crane)	$66.30	$530.40	$98.65	$789.20	$66.30	$98.65
1 Hyd. Crane, 25 Ton (Daily)		2273.31		2500.64	284.16	312.58
8 L.H., Daily Totals		$2803.71		$3289.84	$350.46	$411.23

Crew A-3J	Hr.	Daily	Hr.	Daily	Bare Costs	Incl. O&P
1 Equip. Oper. (crane)	$66.30	$530.40	$98.65	$789.20	$66.30	$98.65
1 Hyd. Crane, 40 Ton (Daily)		2446.91		2691.60	305.86	336.45
8 L.H., Daily Totals		$2977.31		$3480.80	$372.16	$435.10

Crew A-3K	Hr.	Daily	Hr.	Daily	Bare Costs	Incl. O&P
1 Equip. Oper. (crane)	$66.30	$530.40	$98.65	$789.20	$61.35	$91.28
1 Equip. Oper. (oiler)	56.40	451.20	83.90	671.20		
1 Hyd. Crane, 55 Ton (Daily)		2461.06		2707.17		
1 P/U Truck, 3/4 Ton (Daily)		157.41		173.15	163.65	180.02
16 L.H., Daily Totals		$3600.07		$4340.72	$225.00	$271.29

Crew A-3L	Hr.	Daily	Hr.	Daily	Bare Costs	Incl. O&P
1 Equip. Oper. (crane)	$66.30	$530.40	$98.65	$789.20	$61.35	$91.28
1 Equip. Oper. (oiler)	56.40	451.20	83.90	671.20		
1 Hyd. Crane, 80 Ton (Daily)		2641.70		2905.87		
1 P/U Truck, 3/4 Ton (Daily)		157.41		173.15	174.94	192.44
16 L.H., Daily Totals		$3780.71		$4539.42	$236.29	$283.71

Crew A-3M	Hr.	Daily	Hr.	Daily	Bare Costs	Incl. O&P
1 Equip. Oper. (crane)	$66.30	$530.40	$98.65	$789.20	$61.35	$91.28
1 Equip. Oper. (oiler)	56.40	451.20	83.90	671.20		
1 Hyd. Crane, 100 Ton (Daily)		2768.24		3045.06		
1 P/U Truck, 3/4 Ton (Daily)		157.41		173.15	182.85	201.14
16 L.H., Daily Totals		$3907.25		$4678.61	$244.20	$292.41

Crew A-3N	Hr.	Daily	Hr.	Daily	Bare Costs	Incl. O&P
1 Equip. Oper. (crane)	$66.30	$530.40	$98.65	$789.20	$66.30	$98.65
1 Tower Crane (monthly)		1891.47		2080.62	236.43	260.08
8 L.H., Daily Totals		$2421.87		$2869.82	$302.73	$358.73

Crew A-3P	Hr.	Daily	Hr.	Daily	Bare Costs	Incl. O&P
1 Equip. Oper. (light)	$59.70	$477.60	$88.85	$710.80	$59.70	$88.85
1 A.T. Forklift, 31' reach, 45' lift		673.26		740.59	84.16	92.57
8 L.H., Daily Totals		$1150.86		$1451.39	$143.86	$181.42

Crew A-3Q	Hr.	Daily	Hr.	Daily	Bare Costs	Incl. O&P
1 Equip. Oper. (light)	$59.70	$477.60	$88.85	$710.80	$59.70	$88.85
1 Pickup Truck, 4x4, 3/4 Ton		191.73		210.90		
1 Flatbed Trailer, 3 Ton		78.34		86.17	33.76	37.13
8 L.H., Daily Totals		$747.67		$1007.88	$93.46	$125.98

Crew A-3R	Hr.	Daily	Hr.	Daily	Bare Costs	Incl. O&P
1 Equip. Oper. (light)	$59.70	$477.60	$88.85	$710.80	$59.70	$88.85
1 Forklift, Smooth Floor, 8,000 Lb.		311.06		342.17	38.88	42.77
8 L.H., Daily Totals		$788.66		$1052.97	$98.58	$131.62

Crew A-4	Hr.	Daily	Hr.	Daily	Bare Costs	Incl. O&P
2 Carpenters	$58.60	$937.60	$87.25	$1396.00	$55.62	$82.68
1 Painter, Ordinary	49.65	397.20	73.55	588.40		
24 L.H., Daily Totals		$1334.80		$1984.40	$55.62	$82.68

Crew A-5	Hr.	Daily	Hr.	Daily	Bare Costs	Incl. O&P
2 Laborers	$47.25	$756.00	$70.35	$1125.60	$47.88	$71.31
.25 Truck Driver (light)	52.90	105.80	79.00	158.00		
.25 Flatbed Truck, Gas, 1.5 Ton		90.49		99.54	5.03	5.53
18 L.H., Daily Totals		$952.29		$1383.14	$52.90	$76.84

Crew A-6	Hr.	Daily	Hr.	Daily	Bare Costs	Incl. O&P
1 Instrument Man	$61.25	$490.00	$92.00	$736.00	$58.65	$87.65
1 Rodman/Chainman	56.05	448.40	83.30	666.40		
1 Level, Electronic		33.60		36.96	2.10	2.31
16 L.H., Daily Totals		$972.00		$1439.36	$60.75	$89.96

Crew A-7	Hr.	Daily	Hr.	Daily	Bare Costs	Incl. O&P
1 Chief of Party	$71.80	$574.40	$107.20	$857.60	$63.03	$94.17
1 Instrument Man	61.25	490.00	92.00	736.00		
1 Rodman/Chainman	56.05	448.40	83.30	666.40		
1 Level, Electronic		33.60		36.96	1.40	1.54
24 L.H., Daily Totals		$1546.40		$2296.96	$64.43	$95.71

Crew A-8	Hr.	Daily	Hr.	Daily	Bare Costs	Incl. O&P
1 Chief of Party	$71.80	$574.40	$107.20	$857.60	$61.29	$91.45
1 Instrument Man	61.25	490.00	92.00	736.00		
2 Rodmen/Chainmen	56.05	896.80	83.30	1332.80		
1 Level, Electronic		33.60		36.96	1.05	1.16
32 L.H., Daily Totals		$1994.80		$2963.36	$62.34	$92.61

Crew A-9	Hr.	Daily	Hr.	Daily	Bare Costs	Incl. O&P
1 Asbestos Foreman	$65.75	$526.00	$100.60	$804.80	$65.31	$99.90
7 Asbestos Workers	65.25	3654.00	99.80	5588.80		
64 L.H., Daily Totals		$4180.00		$6393.60	$65.31	$99.90

Crew A-10A	Hr.	Daily	Hr.	Daily	Bare Costs	Incl. O&P
1 Asbestos Foreman	$65.75	$526.00	$100.60	$804.80	$65.42	$100.07
2 Asbestos Workers	65.25	1044.00	99.80	1596.80		
24 L.H., Daily Totals		$1570.00		$2401.60	$65.42	$100.07

Crew A-10B	Hr.	Daily	Hr.	Daily	Bare Costs	Incl. O&P
1 Asbestos Foreman	$65.75	$526.00	$100.60	$804.80	$65.38	$100.00
3 Asbestos Workers	65.25	1566.00	99.80	2395.20		
32 L.H., Daily Totals		$2092.00		$3200.00	$65.38	$100.00

Crew A-10C	Hr.	Daily	Hr.	Daily	Bare Costs	Incl. O&P
3 Asbestos Workers	$65.25	$1566.00	$99.80	$2395.20	$65.25	$99.80
1 Flatbed Truck, Gas, 1.5 Ton		361.95		398.14	15.08	16.59
24 L.H., Daily Totals		$1927.95		$2793.34	$80.33	$116.39

Crew No.	Bare Costs		Incl. Subs O&P		Cost Per Labor-Hour	
Crew A-10D	**Hr.**	**Daily**	**Hr.**	**Daily**	**Bare Costs**	**Incl. O&P**
2 Asbestos Workers	$65.25	$1044.00	$99.80	$1596.80	$63.30	$95.54
1 Equip. Oper. (crane)	66.30	530.40	98.65	789.20		
1 Equip. Oper. (oiler)	56.40	451.20	83.90	671.20		
1 Hydraulic Crane, 33 Ton		2429.62		2672.58	75.93	83.52
32 L.H., Daily Totals		$4455.22		$5729.78	$139.23	$179.06

Crew A-11	Hr.	Daily	Hr.	Daily	Bare Costs	Incl. O&P
1 Asbestos Foreman	$65.75	$526.00	$100.60	$804.80	$65.31	$99.90
7 Asbestos Workers	65.25	3654.00	99.80	5588.80		
2 Chip. Hammers, 12 Lb., Elec.		54.32		59.75	.85	.93
64 L.H., Daily Totals		$4234.32		$6453.35	$66.16	$100.83

Crew A-12	Hr.	Daily	Hr.	Daily	Bare Costs	Incl. O&P
1 Asbestos Foreman	$65.75	$526.00	$100.60	$804.80	$65.31	$99.90
7 Asbestos Workers	65.25	3654.00	99.80	5588.80		
1 Trk-Mtd Vac, 14 CY, 1500 Gal.		596.69		656.36		
1 Flatbed Truck, 20,000 GVW		223.10		245.41	12.81	14.09
64 L.H., Daily Totals		$4999.79		$7295.37	$78.12	$113.99

Crew A-13	Hr.	Daily	Hr.	Daily	Bare Costs	Incl. O&P
1 Equip. Oper. (light)	$59.70	$477.60	$88.85	$710.80	$59.70	$88.85
1 Trk-Mtd Vac, 14 CY, 1500 Gal.		596.69		656.36		
1 Flatbed Truck, 20,000 GVW		223.10		245.41	102.47	112.72
8 L.H., Daily Totals		$1297.39		$1612.57	$162.17	$201.57

Crew B-1	Hr.	Daily	Hr.	Daily	Bare Costs	Incl. O&P
1 Labor Foreman (outside)	$49.25	$394.00	$73.30	$586.40	$47.92	$71.33
2 Laborers	47.25	756.00	70.35	1125.60		
24 L.H., Daily Totals		$1150.00		$1712.00	$47.92	$71.33

Crew B-1A	Hr.	Daily	Hr.	Daily	Bare Costs	Incl. O&P
1 Labor Foreman (outside)	$49.25	$394.00	$73.30	$586.40	$47.92	$71.33
2 Laborers	47.25	756.00	70.35	1125.60		
2 Cutting Torches		28.48		31.33		
2 Sets of Gases		377.34		415.07	16.91	18.60
24 L.H., Daily Totals		$1555.82		$2158.40	$64.83	$89.93

Crew B-1B	Hr.	Daily	Hr.	Daily	Bare Costs	Incl. O&P
1 Labor Foreman (outside)	$49.25	$394.00	$73.30	$586.40	$52.51	$78.16
2 Laborers	47.25	756.00	70.35	1125.60		
1 Equip. Oper. (crane)	66.30	530.40	98.65	789.20		
2 Cutting Torches		28.48		31.33		
2 Sets of Gases		377.34		415.07		
1 Hyd. Crane, 12 Ton		2150.65		2365.72	79.89	87.88
32 L.H., Daily Totals		$4236.87		$5313.32	$132.40	$166.04

Crew B-1C	Hr.	Daily	Hr.	Daily	Bare Costs	Incl. O&P
1 Labor Foreman (outside)	$49.25	$394.00	$73.30	$586.40	$47.92	$71.33
2 Laborers	47.25	756.00	70.35	1125.60		
1 Telescoping Boom Lift, to 60'		385.68		424.25	16.07	17.68
24 L.H., Daily Totals		$1535.68		$2136.25	$63.99	$89.01

Crew B-1D	Hr.	Daily	Hr.	Daily	Bare Costs	Incl. O&P
2 Laborers	$47.25	$756.00	$70.35	$1125.60	$47.25	$70.35
1 Small Work Boat, Gas, 50 H.P.		131.82		145.00		
1 Pressure Washer, 7 GPM		113.42		124.76	15.33	16.86
16 L.H., Daily Totals		$1001.24		$1395.36	$62.58	$87.21

Crew B-1E	Hr.	Daily	Hr.	Daily	Bare Costs	Incl. O&P
1 Labor Foreman (outside)	$49.25	$394.00	$73.30	$586.40	$47.75	$71.09
3 Laborers	47.25	1134.00	70.35	1688.40		
1 Work Boat, Diesel, 200 H.P.		1574.43		1731.87		
2 Pressure Washers, 7 GPM		226.84		249.52	56.29	61.92
32 L.H., Daily Totals		$3329.27		$4256.20	$104.04	$133.01

Crew B-1F	Hr.	Daily	Hr.	Daily	Bare Costs	Incl. O&P
2 Skilled Workers	$61.25	$980.00	$92.00	$1472.00	$56.58	$84.78
1 Laborer	47.25	378.00	70.35	562.80		
1 Small Work Boat, Gas, 50 H.P.		131.82		145.00		
1 Pressure Washer, 7 GPM		113.42		124.76	10.22	11.24
24 L.H., Daily Totals		$1603.24		$2304.56	$66.80	$96.02

Crew B-1G	Hr.	Daily	Hr.	Daily	Bare Costs	Incl. O&P
2 Laborers	$47.25	$756.00	$70.35	$1125.60	$47.25	$70.35
1 Small Work Boat, Gas, 50 H.P.		131.82		145.00	8.24	9.06
16 L.H., Daily Totals		$887.82		$1270.60	$55.49	$79.41

Crew B-1H	Hr.	Daily	Hr.	Daily	Bare Costs	Incl. O&P
2 Skilled Workers	$61.25	$980.00	$92.00	$1472.00	$56.58	$84.78
1 Laborer	47.25	378.00	70.35	562.80		
1 Small Work Boat, Gas, 50 H.P.		131.82		145.00	5.49	6.04
24 L.H., Daily Totals		$1489.82		$2179.80	$62.08	$90.83

Crew B-1J	Hr.	Daily	Hr.	Daily	Bare Costs	Incl. O&P
1 Labor Foreman (inside)	$47.75	$382.00	$71.10	$568.80	$47.50	$70.72
1 Laborer	47.25	378.00	70.35	562.80		
16 L.H., Daily Totals		$760.00		$1131.60	$47.50	$70.72

Crew B-1K	Hr.	Daily	Hr.	Daily	Bare Costs	Incl. O&P
1 Carpenter Foreman (inside)	$59.10	$472.80	$88.00	$704.00	$58.85	$87.63
1 Carpenter	58.60	468.80	87.25	698.00		
16 L.H., Daily Totals		$941.60		$1402.00	$58.85	$87.63

Crew B-2	Hr.	Daily	Hr.	Daily	Bare Costs	Incl. O&P
1 Labor Foreman (outside)	$49.25	$394.00	$73.30	$586.40	$47.65	$70.94
4 Laborers	47.25	1512.00	70.35	2251.20		
40 L.H., Daily Totals		$1906.00		$2837.60	$47.65	$70.94

Crew B-2A	Hr.	Daily	Hr.	Daily	Bare Costs	Incl. O&P
1 Labor Foreman (outside)	$49.25	$394.00	$73.30	$586.40	$47.92	$71.33
2 Laborers	47.25	756.00	70.35	1125.60		
1 Telescoping Boom Lift, to 60'		385.68		424.25	16.07	17.68
24 L.H., Daily Totals		$1535.68		$2136.25	$63.99	$89.01

Crew B-3	Hr.	Daily	Hr.	Daily	Bare Costs	Incl. O&P
1 Labor Foreman (outside)	$49.25	$394.00	$73.30	$586.40	$52.95	$78.92
2 Laborers	47.25	756.00	70.35	1125.60		
1 Equip. Oper. (medium)	63.05	504.40	93.80	750.40		
2 Truck Drivers (heavy)	55.45	887.20	82.85	1325.60		
1 Crawler Loader, 3 C.Y.		1257.68		1383.45		
2 Dump Trucks, 12 C.Y., 400 H.P.		1582.72		1740.99	59.17	65.09
48 L.H., Daily Totals		$5382.00		$6912.44	$112.13	$144.01

Crew B-3A	Hr.	Daily	Hr.	Daily	Bare Costs	Incl. O&P
4 Laborers	$47.25	$1512.00	$70.35	$2251.20	$50.41	$75.04
1 Equip. Oper. (medium)	63.05	504.40	93.80	750.40		
1 Hyd. Excavator, 1.5 C.Y.		1185.24		1303.76	29.63	32.59
40 L.H., Daily Totals		$3201.64		$4305.36	$80.04	$107.63

Crew B-3B	Bare Costs Hr.	Bare Costs Daily	Incl. Subs O&P Hr.	Incl. Subs O&P Daily	Cost Per Labor-Hour Bare Costs	Cost Per Labor-Hour Incl. O&P
2 Laborers	$47.25	$756.00	$70.35	$1125.60	$53.25	$79.34
1 Equip. Oper. (medium)	63.05	504.40	93.80	750.40		
1 Truck Driver (heavy)	55.45	443.60	82.85	662.80		
1 Backhoe Loader, 80 H.P.		357.71		393.48		
1 Dump Truck, 12 C.Y., 400 H.P.		791.36		870.50	35.91	39.50
32 L.H., Daily Totals		$2853.07		$3802.78	$89.16	$118.84

Crew B-3C	Hr.	Daily	Hr.	Daily	Bare Costs	Incl. O&P
3 Laborers	$47.25	$1134.00	$70.35	$1688.40	$51.20	$76.21
1 Equip. Oper. (medium)	63.05	504.40	93.80	750.40		
1 Crawler Loader, 4 C.Y.		1506.11		1656.72	47.07	51.77
32 L.H., Daily Totals		$3144.51		$4095.52	$98.27	$127.99

Crew B-4	Hr.	Daily	Hr.	Daily	Bare Costs	Incl. O&P
1 Labor Foreman (outside)	$49.25	$394.00	$73.30	$586.40	$48.95	$72.92
4 Laborers	47.25	1512.00	70.35	2251.20		
1 Truck Driver (heavy)	55.45	443.60	82.85	662.80		
1 Truck Tractor, 220 H.P.		339.98		373.98		
1 Flatbed Trailer, 40 Ton		206.92		227.61	11.39	12.53
48 L.H., Daily Totals		$2896.50		$4101.99	$60.34	$85.46

Crew B-5	Hr.	Daily	Hr.	Daily	Bare Costs	Incl. O&P
1 Labor Foreman (outside)	$49.25	$394.00	$73.30	$586.40	$52.05	$77.47
4 Laborers	47.25	1512.00	70.35	2251.20		
2 Equip. Oper. (medium)	63.05	1008.80	93.80	1500.80		
1 Air Compressor, 250 cfm		196.28		215.91		
2 Breakers, Pavement, 60 lb.		68.94		75.83		
2 -50' Air Hoses, 1.5"		47.20		51.92		
1 Crawler Loader, 3 C.Y.		1257.68		1383.45	28.04	30.84
56 L.H., Daily Totals		$4484.90		$6065.51	$80.09	$108.31

Crew B-5A	Hr.	Daily	Hr.	Daily	Bare Costs	Incl. O&P
1 Labor Foreman (outside)	$49.25	$394.00	$73.30	$586.40	$52.45	$78.13
6 Laborers	47.25	2268.00	70.35	3376.80		
2 Equip. Oper. (medium)	63.05	1008.80	93.80	1500.80		
1 Equip. Oper. (light)	59.70	477.60	88.85	710.80		
2 Truck Drivers (heavy)	55.45	887.20	82.85	1325.60		
1 Air Compressor, 365 cfm		389.99		428.99		
2 Breakers, Pavement, 60 lb.		68.94		75.83		
8 -50' Air Hoses, 1"		74.48		81.93		
2 Dump Trucks, 8 C.Y., 220 H.P.		834.98		918.48	14.25	15.68
96 L.H., Daily Totals		$6403.99		$9005.63	$66.71	$93.81

Crew B-5B	Hr.	Daily	Hr.	Daily	Bare Costs	Incl. O&P
1 Powderman	$61.25	$490.00	$92.00	$736.00	$58.95	$88.03
2 Equip. Oper. (medium)	63.05	1008.80	93.80	1500.80		
3 Truck Drivers (heavy)	55.45	1330.80	82.85	1988.40		
1 F.E. Loader, W.M., 2.5 C.Y.		658.89		724.78		
3 Dump Trucks, 12 C.Y., 400 H.P.		2374.08		2611.49		
1 Air Compressor, 365 cfm		389.99		428.99	71.31	78.44
48 L.H., Daily Totals		$6252.56		$7990.46	$130.26	$166.47

Crew B-5C	Hr.	Daily	Hr.	Daily	Bare Costs	Incl. O&P
3 Laborers	$47.25	$1134.00	$70.35	$1688.40	$54.80	$81.64
1 Equip. Oper. (medium)	63.05	504.40	93.80	750.40		
2 Truck Drivers (heavy)	55.45	887.20	82.85	1325.60		
1 Equip. Oper. (crane)	66.30	530.40	98.65	789.20		
1 Equip. Oper. (oiler)	56.40	451.20	83.90	671.20		
2 Dump Trucks, 12 C.Y., 400 H.P.		1582.72		1740.99		
1 Crawler Loader, 4 C.Y.		1506.11		1656.72		
1 S.P. Crane, 4x4, 25 Ton		927.07		1019.78	62.75	69.02
64 L.H., Daily Totals		$7523.10		$9642.29	$117.55	$150.66

Crew B-5D	Hr.	Daily	Hr.	Daily	Bare Costs	Incl. O&P
1 Labor Foreman (outside)	$49.25	$394.00	$73.30	$586.40	$52.48	$78.14
4 Laborers	47.25	1512.00	70.35	2251.20		
2 Equip. Oper. (medium)	63.05	1008.80	93.80	1500.80		
1 Truck Driver (heavy)	55.45	443.60	82.85	662.80		
1 Air Compressor, 250 cfm		196.28		215.91		
2 Breakers, Pavement, 60 lb.		68.94		75.83		
2 -50' Air Hoses, 1.5"		47.20		51.92		
1 Crawler Loader, 3 C.Y.		1257.68		1383.45		
1 Dump Truck, 12 C.Y., 400 H.P.		791.36		870.50	36.90	40.59
64 L.H., Daily Totals		$5719.86		$7598.81	$89.37	$118.73

Crew B-5E	Hr.	Daily	Hr.	Daily	Bare Costs	Incl. O&P
1 Labor Foreman (outside)	$49.25	$394.00	$73.30	$586.40	$52.48	$78.14
4 Laborers	47.25	1512.00	70.35	2251.20		
2 Equip. Oper. (medium)	63.05	1008.80	93.80	1500.80		
1 Truck Driver (heavy)	55.45	443.60	82.85	662.80		
1 Water Tank Trailer, 5000 Gal.		169.14		186.05		
1 High Pressure Water Jet 40 KSI		902.38		992.62		
2 -50' Air Hoses, 1.5"		47.20		51.92		
1 Crawler Loader, 3 C.Y.		1257.68		1383.45		
1 Dump Truck, 12 C.Y., 400 H.P.		791.36		870.50	49.50	54.45
64 L.H., Daily Totals		$6526.16		$8485.74	$101.97	$132.59

Crew B-6	Hr.	Daily	Hr.	Daily	Bare Costs	Incl. O&P
2 Laborers	$47.25	$756.00	$70.35	$1125.60	$51.40	$76.52
1 Equip. Oper. (light)	59.70	477.60	88.85	710.80		
1 Backhoe Loader, 48 H.P.		277.19		304.91	11.55	12.70
24 L.H., Daily Totals		$1510.79		$2141.31	$62.95	$89.22

Crew B-6A	Hr.	Daily	Hr.	Daily	Bare Costs	Incl. O&P
.5 Labor Foreman (outside)	$49.25	$197.00	$73.30	$293.20	$53.97	$80.32
1 Laborer	47.25	378.00	70.35	562.80		
1 Equip. Oper. (medium)	63.05	504.40	93.80	750.40		
1 Vacuum Truck, 5000 Gal.		408.90		449.79	20.45	22.49
20 L.H., Daily Totals		$1488.30		$2056.19	$74.42	$102.81

Crew B-6B	Hr.	Daily	Hr.	Daily	Bare Costs	Incl. O&P
2 Labor Foremen (outside)	$49.25	$788.00	$73.30	$1172.80	$47.92	$71.33
4 Laborers	47.25	1512.00	70.35	2251.20		
1 S.P. Crane, 4x4, 5 Ton		385.89		424.48		
1 Flatbed Truck, Gas, 1.5 Ton		361.95		398.14		
1 Butt Fusion Mach., 4"-12" diam.		332.25		365.48	22.50	24.75
48 L.H., Daily Totals		$3380.09		$4612.10	$70.42	$96.09

Crew B-6C	Bare Costs Hr.	Bare Costs Daily	Incl. Subs O&P Hr.	Incl. Subs O&P Daily	Cost Per Labor-Hour Bare Costs	Cost Per Labor-Hour Incl. O&P
2 Labor Foremen (outside)	$49.25	$788.00	$73.30	$1172.80	$47.92	$71.33
4 Laborers	47.25	1512.00	70.35	2251.20		
1 S.P. Crane, 4x4, 12 Ton		637.99		701.79		
1 Flatbed Truck, Gas, 3 Ton		391.02		430.12		
1 Butt Fusion Mach., 8"-24" diam.		787.50		866.25	37.84	41.63
48 L.H., Daily Totals		$4116.51		$5422.16	$85.76	$112.96

Crew B-6D	Hr.	Daily	Hr.	Daily	Bare Costs	Incl. O&P
.5 Labor Foreman (outside)	$49.25	$197.00	$73.30	$293.20	$53.97	$80.32
1 Laborer	47.25	378.00	70.35	562.80		
1 Equip. Oper. (medium)	63.05	504.40	93.80	750.40		
1 Hydro Excavator, 12 C.Y.		1404.51		1544.96	70.23	77.25
20 L.H., Daily Totals		$2483.91		$3151.36	$124.20	$157.57

Crew B-7	Hr.	Daily	Hr.	Daily	Bare Costs	Incl. O&P
1 Labor Foreman (outside)	$49.25	$394.00	$73.30	$586.40	$50.22	$74.75
4 Laborers	47.25	1512.00	70.35	2251.20		
1 Equip. Oper. (medium)	63.05	504.40	93.80	750.40		
1 Brush Chipper, 12", 130 H.P.		518.12		569.93		
1 Crawler Loader, 3 C.Y.		1257.68		1383.45		
2 Chain Saws, Gas, 36" Long		107.22		117.94	39.23	43.15
48 L.H., Daily Totals		$4293.42		$5659.32	$89.45	$117.90

Crew B-7A	Hr.	Daily	Hr.	Daily	Bare Costs	Incl. O&P
2 Laborers	$47.25	$756.00	$70.35	$1125.60	$51.40	$76.52
1 Equip. Oper. (light)	59.70	477.60	88.85	710.80		
1 Rake w/Tractor		161.55		177.71		
2 Chain Saws, Gas, 18"		95.16		104.68	10.70	11.77
24 L.H., Daily Totals		$1490.31		$2118.78	$62.10	$88.28

Crew B-7B	Hr.	Daily	Hr.	Daily	Bare Costs	Incl. O&P
1 Labor Foreman (outside)	$49.25	$394.00	$73.30	$586.40	$50.96	$75.91
4 Laborers	47.25	1512.00	70.35	2251.20		
1 Equip. Oper. (medium)	63.05	504.40	93.80	750.40		
1 Truck Driver (heavy)	55.45	443.60	82.85	662.80		
1 Brush Chipper, 12", 130 H.P.		518.12		569.93		
1 Crawler Loader, 3 C.Y.		1257.68		1383.45		
2 Chain Saws, Gas, 36" Long		107.22		117.94		
1 Dump Truck, 8 C.Y., 220 H.P.		417.49		459.24	41.08	45.19
56 L.H., Daily Totals		$5154.51		$6781.36	$92.04	$121.10

Crew B-7C	Hr.	Daily	Hr.	Daily	Bare Costs	Incl. O&P
1 Labor Foreman (outside)	$49.25	$394.00	$73.30	$586.40	$50.96	$75.91
4 Laborers	47.25	1512.00	70.35	2251.20		
1 Equip. Oper. (medium)	63.05	504.40	93.80	750.40		
1 Truck Driver (heavy)	55.45	443.60	82.85	662.80		
1 Brush Chipper, 12", 130 H.P.		518.12		569.93		
1 Crawler Loader, 3 C.Y.		1257.68		1383.45		
2 Chain Saws, Gas, 36" Long		107.22		117.94		
1 Dump Truck, 12 C.Y., 400 H.P.		791.36		870.50	47.76	52.53
56 L.H., Daily Totals		$5528.38		$7192.62	$98.72	$128.44

Crew B-8	Hr.	Daily	Hr.	Daily	Bare Costs	Incl. O&P
1 Labor Foreman (outside)	$49.25	$394.00	$73.30	$586.40	$54.64	$81.40
2 Laborers	47.25	756.00	70.35	1125.60		
2 Equip. Oper. (medium)	63.05	1008.80	93.80	1500.80		
1 Equip. Oper. (oiler)	56.40	451.20	83.90	671.20		
2 Truck Drivers (heavy)	55.45	887.20	82.85	1325.60		
1 Hyd. Crane, 25 Ton		2273.31		2500.64		
1 Crawler Loader, 3 C.Y.		1257.68		1383.45		
2 Dump Trucks, 12 C.Y., 400 H.P.		1582.72		1740.99	79.90	87.89
64 L.H., Daily Totals		$8610.91		$10834.68	$134.55	$169.29

Crew B-9	Hr.	Daily	Hr.	Daily	Bare Costs	Incl. O&P
1 Labor Foreman (outside)	$49.25	$394.00	$73.30	$586.40	$47.65	$70.94
4 Laborers	47.25	1512.00	70.35	2251.20		
1 Air Compressor, 250 cfm		196.28		215.91		
2 Breakers, Pavement, 60 lb.		68.94		75.83		
2 -50' Air Hoses, 1.5"		47.20		51.92	7.81	8.59
40 L.H., Daily Totals		$2218.42		$3181.26	$55.46	$79.53

Crew B-9A	Hr.	Daily	Hr.	Daily	Bare Costs	Incl. O&P
2 Laborers	$47.25	$756.00	$70.35	$1125.60	$49.98	$74.52
1 Truck Driver (heavy)	55.45	443.60	82.85	662.80		
1 Water Tank Trailer, 5000 Gal.		169.14		186.05		
1 Truck Tractor, 220 H.P.		339.98		373.98		
2 -50' Discharge Hoses, 3"		9.76		10.74	21.62	23.78
24 L.H., Daily Totals		$1718.48		$2359.17	$71.60	$98.30

Crew B-9B	Hr.	Daily	Hr.	Daily	Bare Costs	Incl. O&P
2 Laborers	$47.25	$756.00	$70.35	$1125.60	$49.98	$74.52
1 Truck Driver (heavy)	55.45	443.60	82.85	662.80		
2 -50' Discharge Hoses, 3"		9.76		10.74		
1 Water Tank Trailer, 5000 Gal.		169.14		186.05		
1 Truck Tractor, 220 H.P.		339.98		373.98		
1 Pressure Washer		104.23		114.65	25.96	28.56
24 L.H., Daily Totals		$1822.71		$2473.82	$75.95	$103.08

Crew B-9D	Hr.	Daily	Hr.	Daily	Bare Costs	Incl. O&P
1 Labor Foreman (outside)	$49.25	$394.00	$73.30	$586.40	$47.65	$70.94
4 Common Laborers	47.25	1512.00	70.35	2251.20		
1 Air Compressor, 250 cfm		196.28		215.91		
2 -50' Air Hoses, 1.5"		47.20		51.92		
2 Air Powered Tampers		114.04		125.44	8.94	9.83
40 L.H., Daily Totals		$2263.52		$3230.87	$56.59	$80.77

Crew B-9E	Hr.	Daily	Hr.	Daily	Bare Costs	Incl. O&P
1 Cement Finisher	$55.00	$440.00	$80.45	$643.60	$51.13	$75.40
1 Laborer	47.25	378.00	70.35	562.80		
1 Chip. Hammers, 12 Lb., Elec.		27.16		29.88	1.70	1.87
16 L.H., Daily Totals		$845.16		$1236.28	$52.82	$77.27

Crew B-10	Hr.	Daily	Hr.	Daily	Bare Costs	Incl. O&P
1 Equip. Oper. (medium)	$63.05	$504.40	$93.80	$750.40	$57.78	$85.98
.5 Laborer	47.25	189.00	70.35	281.40		
12 L.H., Daily Totals		$693.40		$1031.80	$57.78	$85.98

Crew B-10A	Hr.	Daily	Hr.	Daily	Bare Costs	Incl. O&P
1 Equip. Oper. (medium)	$63.05	$504.40	$93.80	$750.40	$57.78	$85.98
.5 Laborer	47.25	189.00	70.35	281.40		
1 Roller, 2-Drum, W.B., 7.5 H.P.		157.50		173.25	13.13	14.44
12 L.H., Daily Totals		$850.90		$1205.05	$70.91	$100.42

Crew No.	Bare Costs		Incl. Subs O&P		Cost Per Labor-Hour	

Crew B-10B	Hr.	Daily	Hr.	Daily	Bare Costs	Incl. O&P
1 Equip. Oper. (medium)	$63.05	$504.40	$93.80	$750.40	$57.78	$85.98
.5 Laborer	47.25	189.00	70.35	281.40		
1 Dozer, 200 H.P.		1382.36		1520.60	115.20	126.72
12 L.H., Daily Totals		$2075.76		$2552.40	$172.98	$212.70

Crew B-10C	Hr.	Daily	Hr.	Daily	Bare Costs	Incl. O&P
1 Equip. Oper. (medium)	$63.05	$504.40	$93.80	$750.40	$57.78	$85.98
.5 Laborer	47.25	189.00	70.35	281.40		
1 Dozer, 200 H.P.		1382.36		1520.60		
1 Vibratory Roller, Towed, 23 Ton		681.59		749.75	172.00	189.20
12 L.H., Daily Totals		$2757.35		$3302.15	$229.78	$275.18

Crew B-10D	Hr.	Daily	Hr.	Daily	Bare Costs	Incl. O&P
1 Equip. Oper. (medium)	$63.05	$504.40	$93.80	$750.40	$57.78	$85.98
.5 Laborer	47.25	189.00	70.35	281.40		
1 Dozer, 200 H.P.		1382.36		1520.60		
1 Sheepsft. Roller, Towed		444.83		489.31	152.27	167.49
12 L.H., Daily Totals		$2520.59		$3041.71	$210.05	$253.48

Crew B-10E	Hr.	Daily	Hr.	Daily	Bare Costs	Incl. O&P
1 Equip. Oper. (medium)	$63.05	$504.40	$93.80	$750.40	$57.78	$85.98
.5 Laborer	47.25	189.00	70.35	281.40		
1 Tandem Roller, 5 Ton		287.45		316.19	23.95	26.35
12 L.H., Daily Totals		$980.85		$1347.99	$81.74	$112.33

Crew B-10F	Hr.	Daily	Hr.	Daily	Bare Costs	Incl. O&P
1 Equip. Oper. (medium)	$63.05	$504.40	$93.80	$750.40	$57.78	$85.98
.5 Laborer	47.25	189.00	70.35	281.40		
1 Tandem Roller, 10 Ton		379.22		417.14	31.60	34.76
12 L.H., Daily Totals		$1072.62		$1448.94	$89.39	$120.75

Crew B-10G	Hr.	Daily	Hr.	Daily	Bare Costs	Incl. O&P
1 Equip. Oper. (medium)	$63.05	$504.40	$93.80	$750.40	$57.78	$85.98
.5 Laborer	47.25	189.00	70.35	281.40		
1 Sheepsfoot Roller, 240 H.P.		765.47		842.02	63.79	70.17
12 L.H., Daily Totals		$1458.87		$1873.82	$121.57	$156.15

Crew B-10H	Hr.	Daily	Hr.	Daily	Bare Costs	Incl. O&P
1 Equip. Oper. (medium)	$63.05	$504.40	$93.80	$750.40	$57.78	$85.98
.5 Laborer	47.25	189.00	70.35	281.40		
1 Diaphragm Water Pump, 2"		61.92		68.11		
1 -20' Suction Hose, 2"		4.37		4.81		
2 -50' Discharge Hoses, 2"		8.18		9.00	6.21	6.83
12 L.H., Daily Totals		$767.87		$1113.72	$63.99	$92.81

Crew B-10I	Hr.	Daily	Hr.	Daily	Bare Costs	Incl. O&P
1 Equip. Oper. (medium)	$63.05	$504.40	$93.80	$750.40	$57.78	$85.98
.5 Laborer	47.25	189.00	70.35	281.40		
1 Diaphragm Water Pump, 4"		150.72		165.79		
1 -20' Suction Hose, 4"		19.04		20.94		
2 -50' Discharge Hoses, 4"		28.30		31.13	16.50	18.16
12 L.H., Daily Totals		$891.46		$1249.67	$74.29	$104.14

Crew B-10J	Hr.	Daily	Hr.	Daily	Bare Costs	Incl. O&P
1 Equip. Oper. (medium)	$63.05	$504.40	$93.80	$750.40	$57.78	$85.98
.5 Laborer	47.25	189.00	70.35	281.40		
1 Centrifugal Water Pump, 3"		82.39		90.63		
1 -20' Suction Hose, 3"		8.96		9.86		
2 -50' Discharge Hoses, 3"		9.76		10.74	8.43	9.27
12 L.H., Daily Totals		$794.51		$1143.02	$66.21	$95.25

Crew No.	Bare Costs		Incl. Subs O&P		Cost Per Labor-Hour	

Crew B-10K	Hr.	Daily	Hr.	Daily	Bare Costs	Incl. O&P
1 Equip. Oper. (medium)	$63.05	$504.40	$93.80	$750.40	$57.78	$85.98
.5 Laborer	47.25	189.00	70.35	281.40		
1 Centr. Water Pump, 6"		386.48		425.13		
1 -20' Suction Hose, 6"		28.12		30.93		
2 -50' Discharge Hoses, 6"		39.98		43.98	37.88	41.67
12 L.H., Daily Totals		$1147.98		$1531.84	$95.67	$127.65

Crew B-10L	Hr.	Daily	Hr.	Daily	Bare Costs	Incl. O&P
1 Equip. Oper. (medium)	$63.05	$504.40	$93.80	$750.40	$57.78	$85.98
.5 Laborer	47.25	189.00	70.35	281.40		
1 Dozer, 80 H.P.		591.82		651.00	49.32	54.25
12 L.H., Daily Totals		$1285.22		$1682.80	$107.10	$140.23

Crew B-10M	Hr.	Daily	Hr.	Daily	Bare Costs	Incl. O&P
1 Equip. Oper. (medium)	$63.05	$504.40	$93.80	$750.40	$57.78	$85.98
.5 Laborer	47.25	189.00	70.35	281.40		
1 Dozer, 300 H.P.		1674.53		1841.98	139.54	153.50
12 L.H., Daily Totals		$2367.93		$2873.78	$197.33	$239.48

Crew B-10N	Hr.	Daily	Hr.	Daily	Bare Costs	Incl. O&P
1 Equip. Oper. (medium)	$63.05	$504.40	$93.80	$750.40	$57.78	$85.98
.5 Laborer	47.25	189.00	70.35	281.40		
1 F.E. Loader, T.M., 1.5 C.Y.		627.38		690.12	52.28	57.51
12 L.H., Daily Totals		$1320.78		$1721.92	$110.07	$143.49

Crew B-10O	Hr.	Daily	Hr.	Daily	Bare Costs	Incl. O&P
1 Equip. Oper. (medium)	$63.05	$504.40	$93.80	$750.40	$57.78	$85.98
.5 Laborer	47.25	189.00	70.35	281.40		
1 F.E. Loader, T.M., 2.25 C.Y.		958.76		1054.64	79.90	87.89
12 L.H., Daily Totals		$1652.16		$2086.44	$137.68	$173.87

Crew B-10P	Hr.	Daily	Hr.	Daily	Bare Costs	Incl. O&P
1 Equip. Oper. (medium)	$63.05	$504.40	$93.80	$750.40	$57.78	$85.98
.5 Laborer	47.25	189.00	70.35	281.40		
1 Crawler Loader, 3 C.Y.		1257.68		1383.45	104.81	115.29
12 L.H., Daily Totals		$1951.08		$2415.25	$162.59	$201.27

Crew B-10Q	Hr.	Daily	Hr.	Daily	Bare Costs	Incl. O&P
1 Equip. Oper. (medium)	$63.05	$504.40	$93.80	$750.40	$57.78	$85.98
.5 Laborer	47.25	189.00	70.35	281.40		
1 Crawler Loader, 4 C.Y.		1506.11		1656.72	125.51	138.06
12 L.H., Daily Totals		$2199.51		$2688.52	$183.29	$224.04

Crew B-10R	Hr.	Daily	Hr.	Daily	Bare Costs	Incl. O&P
1 Equip. Oper. (medium)	$63.05	$504.40	$93.80	$750.40	$57.78	$85.98
.5 Laborer	47.25	189.00	70.35	281.40		
1 F.E. Loader, W.M., 1 C.Y.		394.79		434.27	32.90	36.19
12 L.H., Daily Totals		$1088.19		$1466.07	$90.68	$122.17

Crew B-10S	Hr.	Daily	Hr.	Daily	Bare Costs	Incl. O&P
1 Equip. Oper. (medium)	$63.05	$504.40	$93.80	$750.40	$57.78	$85.98
.5 Laborer	47.25	189.00	70.35	281.40		
1 F.E. Loader, W.M., 1.5 C.Y.		455.32		500.85	37.94	41.74
12 L.H., Daily Totals		$1148.72		$1532.65	$95.73	$127.72

Crew B-10T	Hr.	Daily	Hr.	Daily	Bare Costs	Incl. O&P
1 Equip. Oper. (medium)	$63.05	$504.40	$93.80	$750.40	$57.78	$85.98
.5 Laborer	47.25	189.00	70.35	281.40		
1 F.E. Loader, W.M., 2.5 C.Y.		658.89		724.78	54.91	60.40
12 L.H., Daily Totals		$1352.29		$1756.58	$112.69	$146.38

Crew No.	Bare Costs		Incl. Subs O&P		Cost Per Labor-Hour	

Crew B-10U	Hr.	Daily	Hr.	Daily	Bare Costs	Incl. O&P
1 Equip. Oper. (medium)	$63.05	$504.40	$93.80	$750.40	$57.78	$85.98
.5 Laborer	47.25	189.00	70.35	281.40		
1 F.E. Loader, W.M., 5.5 C.Y.		1186.42		1305.06	98.87	108.76
12 L.H., Daily Totals		$1879.82		$2336.86	$156.65	$194.74

Crew B-10V	Hr.	Daily	Hr.	Daily	Bare Costs	Incl. O&P
1 Equip. Oper. (medium)	$63.05	$504.40	$93.80	$750.40	$57.78	$85.98
.5 Laborer	47.25	189.00	70.35	281.40		
1 Dozer, 700 H.P.		4098.16		4507.98	341.51	375.66
12 L.H., Daily Totals		$4791.56		$5539.78	$399.30	$461.65

Crew B-10W	Hr.	Daily	Hr.	Daily	Bare Costs	Incl. O&P
1 Equip. Oper. (medium)	$63.05	$504.40	$93.80	$750.40	$57.78	$85.98
.5 Laborer	47.25	189.00	70.35	281.40		
1 Dozer, 105 H.P.		702.68		772.95	58.56	64.41
12 L.H., Daily Totals		$1396.08		$1804.75	$116.34	$150.40

Crew B-10X	Hr.	Daily	Hr.	Daily	Bare Costs	Incl. O&P
1 Equip. Oper. (medium)	$63.05	$504.40	$93.80	$750.40	$57.78	$85.98
.5 Laborer	47.25	189.00	70.35	281.40		
1 Dozer, 410 H.P.		2535.96		2789.56	211.33	232.46
12 L.H., Daily Totals		$3229.36		$3821.36	$269.11	$318.45

Crew B-10Y	Hr.	Daily	Hr.	Daily	Bare Costs	Incl. O&P
1 Equip. Oper. (medium)	$63.05	$504.40	$93.80	$750.40	$57.78	$85.98
.5 Laborer	47.25	189.00	70.35	281.40		
1 Vibr. Roller, Towed, 12 Ton		346.96		381.66	28.91	31.80
12 L.H., Daily Totals		$1040.36		$1413.46	$86.70	$117.79

Crew B-11A	Hr.	Daily	Hr.	Daily	Bare Costs	Incl. O&P
1 Equipment Oper. (med.)	$63.05	$504.40	$93.80	$750.40	$55.15	$82.08
1 Laborer	47.25	378.00	70.35	562.80		
1 Dozer, 200 H.P.		1382.36		1520.60	86.40	95.04
16 L.H., Daily Totals		$2264.76		$2833.80	$141.55	$177.11

Crew B-11B	Hr.	Daily	Hr.	Daily	Bare Costs	Incl. O&P
1 Equipment Oper. (light)	$59.70	$477.60	$88.85	$710.80	$53.48	$79.60
1 Laborer	47.25	378.00	70.35	562.80		
1 Air Powered Tamper		57.02		62.72		
1 Air Compressor, 365 cfm		389.99		428.99		
2 -50' Air Hoses, 1.5"		47.20		51.92	30.89	33.98
16 L.H., Daily Totals		$1349.81		$1817.23	$84.36	$113.58

Crew B-11C	Hr.	Daily	Hr.	Daily	Bare Costs	Incl. O&P
1 Equipment Oper. (med.)	$63.05	$504.40	$93.80	$750.40	$55.15	$82.08
1 Laborer	47.25	378.00	70.35	562.80		
1 Backhoe Loader, 48 H.P.		277.19		304.91	17.32	19.06
16 L.H., Daily Totals		$1159.59		$1618.11	$72.47	$101.13

Crew B-11J	Hr.	Daily	Hr.	Daily	Bare Costs	Incl. O&P
1 Equipment Oper. (med.)	$63.05	$504.40	$93.80	$750.40	$55.15	$82.08
1 Laborer	47.25	378.00	70.35	562.80		
1 Grader, 30,000 Lbs.		1091.19		1200.31		
1 Ripper, Beam & 1 Shank		100.54		110.59	74.48	81.93
16 L.H., Daily Totals		$2074.13		$2624.10	$129.63	$164.01

Crew B-11K	Hr.	Daily	Hr.	Daily	Bare Costs	Incl. O&P
1 Equipment Oper. (med.)	$63.05	$504.40	$93.80	$750.40	$55.15	$82.08
1 Laborer	47.25	378.00	70.35	562.80		
1 Trencher, Chain Type, 8' D		2079.03		2286.93	129.94	142.93
16 L.H., Daily Totals		$2961.43		$3600.13	$185.09	$225.01

Crew B-11L	Hr.	Daily	Hr.	Daily	Bare Costs	Incl. O&P
1 Equipment Oper. (med.)	$63.05	$504.40	$93.80	$750.40	$55.15	$82.08
1 Laborer	47.25	378.00	70.35	562.80		
1 Grader, 30,000 Lbs.		1091.19		1200.31	68.20	75.02
16 L.H., Daily Totals		$1973.59		$2513.51	$123.35	$157.09

Crew B-11M	Hr.	Daily	Hr.	Daily	Bare Costs	Incl. O&P
1 Equipment Oper. (med.)	$63.05	$504.40	$93.80	$750.40	$55.15	$82.08
1 Laborer	47.25	378.00	70.35	562.80		
1 Backhoe Loader, 80 H.P.		357.71		393.48	22.36	24.59
16 L.H., Daily Totals		$1240.11		$1706.68	$77.51	$106.67

Crew B-11N	Hr.	Daily	Hr.	Daily	Bare Costs	Incl. O&P
1 Labor Foreman (outside)	$49.25	$394.00	$73.30	$586.40	$56.45	$84.22
2 Equipment Operators (med.)	63.05	1008.80	93.80	1500.80		
6 Truck Drivers (heavy)	55.45	2661.60	82.85	3976.80		
1 F.E. Loader, W.M., 5.5 C.Y.		1186.42		1305.06		
1 Dozer, 410 H.P.		2535.96		2789.56		
6 Dump Trucks, Off Hwy., 50 Ton		12225.60		13448.16	221.50	243.65
72 L.H., Daily Totals		$20012.38		$23606.78	$277.95	$327.87

Crew B-11Q	Hr.	Daily	Hr.	Daily	Bare Costs	Incl. O&P
1 Equipment Operator (med.)	$63.05	$504.40	$93.80	$750.40	$57.78	$85.98
.5 Laborer	47.25	189.00	70.35	281.40		
1 Dozer, 140 H.P.		757.89		833.68	63.16	69.47
12 L.H., Daily Totals		$1451.29		$1865.48	$120.94	$155.46

Crew B-11R	Hr.	Daily	Hr.	Daily	Bare Costs	Incl. O&P
1 Equipment Operator (med.)	$63.05	$504.40	$93.80	$750.40	$57.78	$85.98
.5 Laborer	47.25	189.00	70.35	281.40		
1 Dozer, 200 H.P.		1382.36		1520.60	115.20	126.72
12 L.H., Daily Totals		$2075.76		$2552.40	$172.98	$212.70

Crew B-11S	Hr.	Daily	Hr.	Daily	Bare Costs	Incl. O&P
1 Equipment Operator (med.)	$63.05	$504.40	$93.80	$750.40	$57.78	$85.98
.5 Laborer	47.25	189.00	70.35	281.40		
1 Dozer, 300 H.P.		1674.53		1841.98		
1 Ripper, Beam & 1 Shank		100.54		110.59	147.92	162.71
12 L.H., Daily Totals		$2468.47		$2984.38	$205.71	$248.70

Crew B-11T	Hr.	Daily	Hr.	Daily	Bare Costs	Incl. O&P
1 Equipment Operator (med.)	$63.05	$504.40	$93.80	$750.40	$57.78	$85.98
.5 Laborer	47.25	189.00	70.35	281.40		
1 Dozer, 410 H.P.		2535.96		2789.56		
1 Ripper, Beam & 2 Shanks		154.19		169.61	224.18	246.60
12 L.H., Daily Totals		$3383.55		$3990.97	$281.96	$332.58

Crew B-11U	Hr.	Daily	Hr.	Daily	Bare Costs	Incl. O&P
1 Equipment Operator (med.)	$63.05	$504.40	$93.80	$750.40	$57.78	$85.98
.5 Laborer	47.25	189.00	70.35	281.40		
1 Dozer, 520 H.P.		2569.55		2826.51	214.13	235.54
12 L.H., Daily Totals		$3262.95		$3858.30	$271.91	$321.53

Crew No.	Bare Costs		Incl. Subs O&P		Cost Per Labor-Hour	

Crew B-11V	Hr.	Daily	Hr.	Daily	Bare Costs	Incl. O&P
3 Laborers	$47.25	$1134.00	$70.35	$1688.40	$47.25	$70.35
1 Roller, 2-Drum, W.B., 7.5 H.P.		157.50		173.25	6.56	7.22
24 L.H., Daily Totals		$1291.50		$1861.65	$53.81	$77.57

Crew B-11W	Hr.	Daily	Hr.	Daily	Bare Costs	Incl. O&P
1 Equipment Operator (med.)	$63.05	$504.40	$93.80	$750.40	$55.40	$82.72
1 Common Laborer	47.25	378.00	70.35	562.80		
10 Truck Drivers (heavy)	55.45	4436.00	82.85	6628.00		
1 Dozer, 200 H.P.		1382.36		1520.60		
1 Vibratory Roller, Towed, 23 Ton		681.59		749.75		
10 Dump Trucks, 8 C.Y., 220 H.P.		4174.90		4592.39	64.99	71.49
96 L.H., Daily Totals		$11557.25		$14803.93	$120.39	$154.21

Crew B-11Y	Hr.	Daily	Hr.	Daily	Bare Costs	Incl. O&P
1 Labor Foreman (outside)	$49.25	$394.00	$73.30	$586.40	$52.74	$78.49
5 Common Laborers	47.25	1890.00	70.35	2814.00		
3 Equipment Operators (med.)	63.05	1513.20	93.80	2251.20		
1 Dozer, 80 H.P.		591.82		651.00		
2 Rollers, 2-Drum, W.B., 7.5 H.P.		315.00		346.50		
4 Vibrating Plates, Gas, 21"		584.48		642.93	20.71	22.78
72 L.H., Daily Totals		$5288.50		$7292.03	$73.45	$101.28

Crew B-12A	Hr.	Daily	Hr.	Daily	Bare Costs	Incl. O&P
1 Equip. Oper. (crane)	$66.30	$530.40	$98.65	$789.20	$56.77	$84.50
1 Laborer	47.25	378.00	70.35	562.80		
1 Hyd. Excavator, 1 C.Y.		986.56		1085.22	61.66	67.83
16 L.H., Daily Totals		$1894.96		$2437.22	$118.44	$152.33

Crew B-12B	Hr.	Daily	Hr.	Daily	Bare Costs	Incl. O&P
1 Equip. Oper. (crane)	$66.30	$530.40	$98.65	$789.20	$56.77	$84.50
1 Laborer	47.25	378.00	70.35	562.80		
1 Hyd. Excavator, 1.5 C.Y.		1185.24		1303.76	74.08	81.49
16 L.H., Daily Totals		$2093.64		$2655.76	$130.85	$165.99

Crew B-12C	Hr.	Daily	Hr.	Daily	Bare Costs	Incl. O&P
1 Equip. Oper. (crane)	$66.30	$530.40	$98.65	$789.20	$56.77	$84.50
1 Laborer	47.25	378.00	70.35	562.80		
1 Hyd. Excavator, 2 C.Y.		1096.14		1205.75	68.51	75.36
16 L.H., Daily Totals		$2004.54		$2557.75	$125.28	$159.86

Crew B-12D	Hr.	Daily	Hr.	Daily	Bare Costs	Incl. O&P
1 Equip. Oper. (crane)	$66.30	$530.40	$98.65	$789.20	$56.77	$84.50
1 Laborer	47.25	378.00	70.35	562.80		
1 Hyd. Excavator, 3.5 C.Y.		2394.44		2633.88	149.65	164.62
16 L.H., Daily Totals		$3302.84		$3985.88	$206.43	$249.12

Crew B-12E	Hr.	Daily	Hr.	Daily	Bare Costs	Incl. O&P
1 Equip. Oper. (crane)	$66.30	$530.40	$98.65	$789.20	$56.77	$84.50
1 Laborer	47.25	378.00	70.35	562.80		
1 Hyd. Excavator, .5 C.Y.		764.88		841.37	47.81	52.59
16 L.H., Daily Totals		$1673.28		$2193.37	$104.58	$137.09

Crew B-12F	Hr.	Daily	Hr.	Daily	Bare Costs	Incl. O&P
1 Equip. Oper. (crane)	$66.30	$530.40	$98.65	$789.20	$56.77	$84.50
1 Laborer	47.25	378.00	70.35	562.80		
1 Hyd. Excavator, .75 C.Y.		915.34		1006.87	57.21	62.93
16 L.H., Daily Totals		$1823.74		$2358.87	$113.98	$147.43

Crew B-12G	Hr.	Daily	Hr.	Daily	Bare Costs	Incl. O&P
1 Equip. Oper. (crane)	$66.30	$530.40	$98.65	$789.20	$56.77	$84.50
1 Laborer	47.25	378.00	70.35	562.80		
1 Crawler Crane, 15 Ton		898.84		988.72		
1 Clamshell Bucket, .5 C.Y.		37.28		41.01	58.51	64.36
16 L.H., Daily Totals		$1844.52		$2381.73	$115.28	$148.86

Crew B-12H	Hr.	Daily	Hr.	Daily	Bare Costs	Incl. O&P
1 Equip. Oper. (crane)	$66.30	$530.40	$98.65	$789.20	$56.77	$84.50
1 Laborer	47.25	378.00	70.35	562.80		
1 Crawler Crane, 25 Ton		1274.00		1401.40		
1 Clamshell Bucket, 1 C.Y.		46.89		51.58	82.56	90.81
16 L.H., Daily Totals		$2229.29		$2804.98	$139.33	$175.31

Crew B-12I	Hr.	Daily	Hr.	Daily	Bare Costs	Incl. O&P
1 Equip. Oper. (crane)	$66.30	$530.40	$98.65	$789.20	$56.77	$84.50
1 Laborer	47.25	378.00	70.35	562.80		
1 Crawler Crane, 20 Ton		1120.87		1232.96		
1 Dragline Bucket, .75 C.Y.		29.54		32.49	71.90	79.09
16 L.H., Daily Totals		$2058.81		$2617.45	$128.68	$163.59

Crew B-12J	Hr.	Daily	Hr.	Daily	Bare Costs	Incl. O&P
1 Equip. Oper. (crane)	$66.30	$530.40	$98.65	$789.20	$56.77	$84.50
1 Laborer	47.25	378.00	70.35	562.80		
1 Gradall, 5/8 C.Y.		880.91		969.00	55.06	60.56
16 L.H., Daily Totals		$1789.31		$2321.00	$111.83	$145.06

Crew B-12K	Hr.	Daily	Hr.	Daily	Bare Costs	Incl. O&P
1 Equip. Oper. (crane)	$66.30	$530.40	$98.65	$789.20	$56.77	$84.50
1 Laborer	47.25	378.00	70.35	562.80		
1 Gradall, 3 Ton, 1 C.Y.		1520.84		1672.92	95.05	104.56
16 L.H., Daily Totals		$2429.24		$3024.92	$151.83	$189.06

Crew B-12L	Hr.	Daily	Hr.	Daily	Bare Costs	Incl. O&P
1 Equip. Oper. (crane)	$66.30	$530.40	$98.65	$789.20	$56.77	$84.50
1 Laborer	47.25	378.00	70.35	562.80		
1 Crawler Crane, 15 Ton		898.84		988.72		
1 F.E. Attachment, .5 C.Y.		72.55		79.81	60.71	66.78
16 L.H., Daily Totals		$1879.79		$2420.53	$117.49	$151.28

Crew B-12M	Hr.	Daily	Hr.	Daily	Bare Costs	Incl. O&P
1 Equip. Oper. (crane)	$66.30	$530.40	$98.65	$789.20	$56.77	$84.50
1 Laborer	47.25	378.00	70.35	562.80		
1 Crawler Crane, 20 Ton		1120.87		1232.96		
1 F.E. Attachment, .75 C.Y.		78.31		86.14	74.95	82.44
16 L.H., Daily Totals		$2107.58		$2671.10	$131.72	$166.94

Crew B-12N	Hr.	Daily	Hr.	Daily	Bare Costs	Incl. O&P
1 Equip. Oper. (crane)	$66.30	$530.40	$98.65	$789.20	$56.77	$84.50
1 Laborer	47.25	378.00	70.35	562.80		
1 Crawler Crane, 25 Ton		1274.00		1401.40		
1 F.E. Attachment, 1 C.Y.		59.18		65.10	83.32	91.66
16 L.H., Daily Totals		$2241.58		$2818.50	$140.10	$176.16

Crew B-12O	Hr.	Daily	Hr.	Daily	Bare Costs	Incl. O&P
1 Equip. Oper. (crane)	$66.30	$530.40	$98.65	$789.20	$56.77	$84.50
1 Laborer	47.25	378.00	70.35	562.80		
1 Crawler Crane, 40 Ton		1362.63		1498.89		
1 F.E. Attachment, 1.5 C.Y.		97.47		107.22	91.26	100.38
16 L.H., Daily Totals		$2368.50		$2958.11	$148.03	$184.88

Crew No.	Bare Costs		Incl. Subs O&P		Cost Per Labor-Hour	
Crew B-12P	**Hr.**	**Daily**	**Hr.**	**Daily**	**Bare Costs**	**Incl. O&P**
1 Equip. Oper. (crane)	$66.30	$530.40	$98.65	$789.20	$56.77	$84.50
1 Laborer	47.25	378.00	70.35	562.80		
1 Crawler Crane, 40 Ton		1362.63		1498.89		
1 Dragline Bucket, 1.5 C.Y.		37.32		41.05	87.50	96.25
16 L.H., Daily Totals		$2308.35		$2891.95	$144.27	$180.75

Crew B-12Q	Hr.	Daily	Hr.	Daily	Bare Costs	Incl. O&P
1 Equip. Oper. (crane)	$66.30	$530.40	$98.65	$789.20	$56.77	$84.50
1 Laborer	47.25	378.00	70.35	562.80		
1 Hyd. Excavator, 5/8 C.Y.		813.17		894.49	50.82	55.91
16 L.H., Daily Totals		$1721.57		$2246.49	$107.60	$140.41

Crew B-12S	Hr.	Daily	Hr.	Daily	Bare Costs	Incl. O&P
1 Equip. Oper. (crane)	$66.30	$530.40	$98.65	$789.20	$56.77	$84.50
1 Laborer	47.25	378.00	70.35	562.80		
1 Hyd. Excavator, 2.5 C.Y.		1683.69		1852.06	105.23	115.75
16 L.H., Daily Totals		$2592.09		$3204.06	$162.01	$200.25

Crew B-12T	Hr.	Daily	Hr.	Daily	Bare Costs	Incl. O&P
1 Equip. Oper. (crane)	$66.30	$530.40	$98.65	$789.20	$56.77	$84.50
1 Laborer	47.25	378.00	70.35	562.80		
1 Crawler Crane, 75 Ton		2189.46		2408.41		
1 F.E. Attachment, 3 C.Y.		127.10		139.81	144.79	159.26
16 L.H., Daily Totals		$3224.96		$3900.22	$201.56	$243.76

Crew B-12V	Hr.	Daily	Hr.	Daily	Bare Costs	Incl. O&P
1 Equip. Oper. (crane)	$66.30	$530.40	$98.65	$789.20	$56.77	$84.50
1 Laborer	47.25	378.00	70.35	562.80		
1 Crawler Crane, 75 Ton		2189.46		2408.41		
1 Dragline Bucket, 3 C.Y.		51.71		56.88	140.07	154.08
16 L.H., Daily Totals		$3149.57		$3817.29	$196.85	$238.58

Crew B-12Y	Hr.	Daily	Hr.	Daily	Bare Costs	Incl. O&P
1 Equip. Oper. (crane)	$66.30	$530.40	$98.65	$789.20	$53.60	$79.78
2 Laborers	47.25	756.00	70.35	1125.60		
1 Hyd. Excavator, 3.5 C.Y.		2394.44		2633.88	99.77	109.75
24 L.H., Daily Totals		$3680.84		$4548.68	$153.37	$189.53

Crew B-12Z	Hr.	Daily	Hr.	Daily	Bare Costs	Incl. O&P
1 Equip. Oper. (crane)	$66.30	$530.40	$98.65	$789.20	$53.60	$79.78
2 Laborers	47.25	756.00	70.35	1125.60		
1 Hyd. Excavator, 2.5 C.Y.		1683.69		1852.06	70.15	77.17
24 L.H., Daily Totals		$2970.09		$3766.86	$123.75	$156.95

Crew B-13	Hr.	Daily	Hr.	Daily	Bare Costs	Incl. O&P
1 Labor Foreman (outside)	$49.25	$394.00	$73.30	$586.40	$51.56	$76.75
4 Laborers	47.25	1512.00	70.35	2251.20		
1 Equip. Oper. (crane)	66.30	530.40	98.65	789.20		
1 Equip. Oper. (oiler)	56.40	451.20	83.90	671.20		
1 Hyd. Crane, 25 Ton		2273.31		2500.64	40.59	44.65
56 L.H., Daily Totals		$5160.91		$6798.64	$92.16	$121.40

Crew B-13A	Hr.	Daily	Hr.	Daily	Bare Costs	Incl. O&P
1 Labor Foreman (outside)	$49.25	$394.00	$73.30	$586.40	$54.39	$81.04
2 Laborers	47.25	756.00	70.35	1125.60		
2 Equipment Operators (med.)	63.05	1008.80	93.80	1500.80		
2 Truck Drivers (heavy)	55.45	887.20	82.85	1325.60		
1 Crawler Crane, 75 Ton		2189.46		2408.41		
1 Crawler Loader, 4 C.Y.		1506.11		1656.72		
2 Dump Trucks, 8 C.Y., 220 H.P.		834.98		918.48	80.90	88.99
56 L.H., Daily Totals		$7576.55		$9522.00	$135.30	$170.04

Crew B-13B	Hr.	Daily	Hr.	Daily	Bare Costs	Incl. O&P
1 Labor Foreman (outside)	$49.25	$394.00	$73.30	$586.40	$51.56	$76.75
4 Laborers	47.25	1512.00	70.35	2251.20		
1 Equip. Oper. (crane)	66.30	530.40	98.65	789.20		
1 Equip. Oper. (oiler)	56.40	451.20	83.90	671.20		
1 Hyd. Crane, 55 Ton		2461.06		2707.17	43.95	48.34
56 L.H., Daily Totals		$5348.66		$7005.17	$95.51	$125.09

Crew B-13C	Hr.	Daily	Hr.	Daily	Bare Costs	Incl. O&P
1 Labor Foreman (outside)	$49.25	$394.00	$73.30	$586.40	$51.56	$76.75
4 Laborers	47.25	1512.00	70.35	2251.20		
1 Equip. Oper. (crane)	66.30	530.40	98.65	789.20		
1 Equip. Oper. (oiler)	56.40	451.20	83.90	671.20		
1 Crawler Crane, 100 Ton		1552.12		1707.33	27.72	30.49
56 L.H., Daily Totals		$4439.72		$6005.33	$79.28	$107.24

Crew B-13D	Hr.	Daily	Hr.	Daily	Bare Costs	Incl. O&P
1 Laborer	$47.25	$378.00	$70.35	$562.80	$56.77	$84.50
1 Equip. Oper. (crane)	66.30	530.40	98.65	789.20		
1 Hyd. Excavator, 1 C.Y.		986.56		1085.22		
1 Trench Box		131.49		144.64	69.88	76.87
16 L.H., Daily Totals		$2026.45		$2581.86	$126.65	$161.37

Crew B-13E	Hr.	Daily	Hr.	Daily	Bare Costs	Incl. O&P
1 Laborer	$47.25	$378.00	$70.35	$562.80	$56.77	$84.50
1 Equip. Oper. (crane)	66.30	530.40	98.65	789.20		
1 Hyd. Excavator, 1.5 C.Y.		1185.24		1303.76		
1 Trench Box		131.49		144.64	82.30	90.53
16 L.H., Daily Totals		$2225.13		$2800.40	$139.07	$175.03

Crew B-13F	Hr.	Daily	Hr.	Daily	Bare Costs	Incl. O&P
1 Laborer	$47.25	$378.00	$70.35	$562.80	$56.77	$84.50
1 Equip. Oper. (crane)	66.30	530.40	98.65	789.20		
1 Hyd. Excavator, 3.5 C.Y.		2394.44		2633.88		
1 Trench Box		131.49		144.64	157.87	173.66
16 L.H., Daily Totals		$3434.33		$4130.52	$214.65	$258.16

Crew B-13G	Hr.	Daily	Hr.	Daily	Bare Costs	Incl. O&P
1 Laborer	$47.25	$378.00	$70.35	$562.80	$56.77	$84.50
1 Equip. Oper. (crane)	66.30	530.40	98.65	789.20		
1 Hyd. Excavator, .75 C.Y.		915.34		1006.87		
1 Trench Box		131.49		144.64	65.43	71.97
16 L.H., Daily Totals		$1955.23		$2503.51	$122.20	$156.47

Crew B-13H	Hr.	Daily	Hr.	Daily	Bare Costs	Incl. O&P
1 Laborer	$47.25	$378.00	$70.35	$562.80	$56.77	$84.50
1 Equip. Oper. (crane)	66.30	530.40	98.65	789.20		
1 Gradall, 5/8 C.Y.		880.91		969.00		
1 Trench Box		131.49		144.64	63.27	69.60
16 L.H., Daily Totals		$1920.80		$2465.64	$120.05	$154.10

Crew No.	Bare Costs		Incl. Subs O&P		Cost Per Labor-Hour	
Crew B-13I	**Hr.**	**Daily**	**Hr.**	**Daily**	**Bare Costs**	**Incl. O&P**
1 Laborer	$47.25	$378.00	$70.35	$562.80	$56.77	$84.50
1 Equip. Oper. (crane)	66.30	530.40	98.65	789.20		
1 Gradall, 3 Ton, 1 C.Y.		1520.84		1672.92		
1 Trench Box		131.49		144.64	103.27	113.60
16 L.H., Daily Totals		$2560.73		$3169.56	$160.05	$198.10
Crew B-13J	**Hr.**	**Daily**	**Hr.**	**Daily**	**Bare Costs**	**Incl. O&P**
1 Laborer	$47.25	$378.00	$70.35	$562.80	$56.77	$84.50
1 Equip. Oper. (crane)	66.30	530.40	98.65	789.20		
1 Hyd. Excavator, 2.5 C.Y.		1683.69		1852.06		
1 Trench Box		131.49		144.64	113.45	124.79
16 L.H., Daily Totals		$2723.58		$3348.70	$170.22	$209.29
Crew B-13K	**Hr.**	**Daily**	**Hr.**	**Daily**	**Bare Costs**	**Incl. O&P**
2 Equip. Opers. (crane)	$66.30	$1060.80	$98.65	$1578.40	$66.30	$98.65
1 Hyd. Excavator, .75 C.Y.		915.34		1006.87		
1 Hyd. Hammer, 4000 ft-lb		715.03		786.53		
1 Hyd. Excavator, .75 C.Y.		915.34		1006.87	159.11	175.02
16 L.H., Daily Totals		$3606.51		$4378.68	$225.41	$273.67
Crew B-13L	**Hr.**	**Daily**	**Hr.**	**Daily**	**Bare Costs**	**Incl. O&P**
2 Equip. Opers. (crane)	$66.30	$1060.80	$98.65	$1578.40	$66.30	$98.65
1 Hyd. Excavator, 1.5 C.Y.		1185.24		1303.76		
1 Hyd. Hammer, 5000 ft-lb		776.94		854.63		
1 Hyd. Excavator, .75 C.Y.		915.34		1006.87	179.85	197.83
16 L.H., Daily Totals		$3938.32		$4743.67	$246.15	$296.48
Crew B-13M	**Hr.**	**Daily**	**Hr.**	**Daily**	**Bare Costs**	**Incl. O&P**
2 Equip. Opers. (crane)	$66.30	$1060.80	$98.65	$1578.40	$66.30	$98.65
1 Hyd. Excavator, 2.5 C.Y.		1683.69		1852.06		
1 Hyd. Hammer, 8000 ft-lb		1011.13		1112.24		
1 Hyd. Excavator, 1.5 C.Y.		1185.24		1303.76	242.50	266.75
16 L.H., Daily Totals		$4940.86		$5846.47	$308.80	$365.40
Crew B-13N	**Hr.**	**Daily**	**Hr.**	**Daily**	**Bare Costs**	**Incl. O&P**
2 Equip. Opers. (crane)	$66.30	$1060.80	$98.65	$1578.40	$66.30	$98.65
1 Hyd. Excavator, 3.5 C.Y.		2394.44		2633.88		
1 Hyd. Hammer, 12,000 ft-lb		1162.80		1279.08		
1 Hyd. Excavator, 1.5 C.Y.		1185.24		1303.76	296.40	326.05
16 L.H., Daily Totals		$5803.28		$6795.13	$362.70	$424.70
Crew B-14	**Hr.**	**Daily**	**Hr.**	**Daily**	**Bare Costs**	**Incl. O&P**
1 Labor Foreman (outside)	$49.25	$394.00	$73.30	$586.40	$49.66	$73.92
4 Laborers	47.25	1512.00	70.35	2251.20		
1 Equip. Oper. (light)	59.70	477.60	88.85	710.80		
1 Backhoe Loader, 48 H.P.		277.19		304.91	5.77	6.35
48 L.H., Daily Totals		$2660.79		$3853.31	$55.43	$80.28
Crew B-14A	**Hr.**	**Daily**	**Hr.**	**Daily**	**Bare Costs**	**Incl. O&P**
1 Equip. Oper. (crane)	$66.30	$530.40	$98.65	$789.20	$59.95	$89.22
.5 Laborer	47.25	189.00	70.35	281.40		
1 Hyd. Excavator, 4.5 C.Y.		3788.37		4167.21	315.70	347.27
12 L.H., Daily Totals		$4507.77		$5237.81	$375.65	$436.48
Crew B-14B	**Hr.**	**Daily**	**Hr.**	**Daily**	**Bare Costs**	**Incl. O&P**
1 Equip. Oper. (crane)	$66.30	$530.40	$98.65	$789.20	$59.95	$89.22
.5 Laborer	47.25	189.00	70.35	281.40		
1 Hyd. Excavator, 6 C.Y.		3843.97		4228.37	320.33	352.36
12 L.H., Daily Totals		$4563.37		$5298.97	$380.28	$441.58

Crew No.	Bare Costs		Incl. Subs O&P		Cost Per Labor-Hour	
Crew B-14C	**Hr.**	**Daily**	**Hr.**	**Daily**	**Bare Costs**	**Incl. O&P**
1 Equip. Oper. (crane)	$66.30	$530.40	$98.65	$789.20	$59.95	$89.22
.5 Laborer	47.25	189.00	70.35	281.40		
1 Hyd. Excavator, 7 C.Y.		4206.21		4626.83	350.52	385.57
12 L.H., Daily Totals		$4925.61		$5697.43	$410.47	$474.79
Crew B-14F	**Hr.**	**Daily**	**Hr.**	**Daily**	**Bare Costs**	**Incl. O&P**
1 Equip. Oper. (crane)	$66.30	$530.40	$98.65	$789.20	$59.95	$89.22
.5 Laborer	47.25	189.00	70.35	281.40		
1 Hyd. Shovel, 7 C.Y.		4549.05		5003.95	379.09	417.00
12 L.H., Daily Totals		$5268.45		$6074.56	$439.04	$506.21
Crew B-14G	**Hr.**	**Daily**	**Hr.**	**Daily**	**Bare Costs**	**Incl. O&P**
1 Equip. Oper. (crane)	$66.30	$530.40	$98.65	$789.20	$59.95	$89.22
.5 Laborer	47.25	189.00	70.35	281.40		
1 Hyd. Shovel, 12 C.Y.		6601.66		7261.83	550.14	605.15
12 L.H., Daily Totals		$7321.06		$8332.43	$610.09	$694.37
Crew B-14J	**Hr.**	**Daily**	**Hr.**	**Daily**	**Bare Costs**	**Incl. O&P**
1 Equip. Oper. (medium)	$63.05	$504.40	$93.80	$750.40	$57.78	$85.98
.5 Laborer	47.25	189.00	70.35	281.40		
1 F.E. Loader, 8 C.Y.		1999.44		2199.38	166.62	183.28
12 L.H., Daily Totals		$2692.84		$3231.18	$224.40	$269.27
Crew B-14K	**Hr.**	**Daily**	**Hr.**	**Daily**	**Bare Costs**	**Incl. O&P**
1 Equip. Oper. (medium)	$63.05	$504.40	$93.80	$750.40	$57.78	$85.98
.5 Laborer	47.25	189.00	70.35	281.40		
1 F.E. Loader, 10 C.Y.		2862.71		3148.98	238.56	262.42
12 L.H., Daily Totals		$3556.11		$4180.78	$296.34	$348.40
Crew B-15	**Hr.**	**Daily**	**Hr.**	**Daily**	**Bare Costs**	**Incl. O&P**
1 Equipment Oper. (med.)	$63.05	$504.40	$93.80	$750.40	$56.45	$84.19
.5 Laborer	47.25	189.00	70.35	281.40		
2 Truck Drivers (heavy)	55.45	887.20	82.85	1325.60		
2 Dump Trucks, 12 C.Y., 400 H.P.		1582.72		1740.99		
1 Dozer, 200 H.P.		1382.36		1520.60	105.90	116.49
28 L.H., Daily Totals		$4545.68		$5618.99	$162.35	$200.68
Crew B-16	**Hr.**	**Daily**	**Hr.**	**Daily**	**Bare Costs**	**Incl. O&P**
1 Labor Foreman (outside)	$49.25	$394.00	$73.30	$586.40	$49.80	$74.21
2 Laborers	47.25	756.00	70.35	1125.60		
1 Truck Driver (heavy)	55.45	443.60	82.85	662.80		
1 Dump Truck, 12 C.Y., 400 H.P.		791.36		870.50	24.73	27.20
32 L.H., Daily Totals		$2384.96		$3245.30	$74.53	$101.42
Crew B-17	**Hr.**	**Daily**	**Hr.**	**Daily**	**Bare Costs**	**Incl. O&P**
2 Laborers	$47.25	$756.00	$70.35	$1125.60	$52.41	$78.10
1 Equip. Oper. (light)	59.70	477.60	88.85	710.80		
1 Truck Driver (heavy)	55.45	443.60	82.85	662.80		
1 Backhoe Loader, 48 H.P.		277.19		304.91		
1 Dump Truck, 8 C.Y., 220 H.P.		417.49		459.24	21.71	23.88
32 L.H., Daily Totals		$2371.88		$3263.35	$74.12	$101.98
Crew B-17A	**Hr.**	**Daily**	**Hr.**	**Daily**	**Bare Costs**	**Incl. O&P**
2 Labor Foremen (outside)	$49.25	$788.00	$73.30	$1172.80	$50.65	$75.57
6 Laborers	47.25	2268.00	70.35	3376.80		
1 Skilled Worker Foreman (out)	63.25	506.00	95.00	760.00		
1 Skilled Worker	61.25	490.00	92.00	736.00		
80 L.H., Daily Totals		$4052.00		$6045.60	$50.65	$75.57

Crew No.	Bare Costs		Incl. Subs O&P		Cost Per Labor-Hour	
Crew B-17B	**Hr.**	**Daily**	**Hr.**	**Daily**	**Bare Costs**	**Incl. O&P**
2 Laborers	$47.25	$756.00	$70.35	$1125.60	$52.41	$78.10
1 Equip. Oper. (light)	59.70	477.60	88.85	710.80		
1 Truck Driver (heavy)	55.45	443.60	82.85	662.80		
1 Backhoe Loader, 48 H.P.		277.19		304.91		
1 Dump Truck, 12 C.Y., 400 H.P.		791.36		870.50	33.39	36.73
32 L.H., Daily Totals		$2745.75		$3674.61	$85.80	$114.83
Crew B-17C	**Hr.**	**Daily**	**Hr.**	**Daily**	**Bare Costs**	**Incl. O&P**
1 Labor Foreman (outside)	$49.25	$394.00	$73.30	$586.40	$52.13	$77.64
3 Laborers	47.25	1134.00	70.35	1688.40		
1 Equip. Oper. (heavy)	66.30	530.40	98.65	789.20		
1 Truck Driver (heavy)	55.45	443.60	82.85	662.80		
1 Hyd. Excavator, 2 C.Y.		1096.14		1205.75		
1 Dump Truck, 12 C.Y., 400 H.P.		791.36		870.50		
1 P/U, 3/4 ton, Tool Truck		157.41		173.15	42.60	46.86
48 L.H., Daily Totals		$4546.91		$5976.20	$94.73	$124.50
Crew B-18	**Hr.**	**Daily**	**Hr.**	**Daily**	**Bare Costs**	**Incl. O&P**
1 Labor Foreman (outside)	$49.25	$394.00	$73.30	$586.40	$47.92	$71.33
2 Laborers	47.25	756.00	70.35	1125.60		
1 Vibrating Plate, Gas, 21"		146.12		160.73	6.09	6.70
24 L.H., Daily Totals		$1296.12		$1872.73	$54.01	$78.03
Crew B-19	**Hr.**	**Daily**	**Hr.**	**Daily**	**Bare Costs**	**Incl. O&P**
1 Pile Driver Foreman (outside)	$62.50	$500.00	$96.70	$773.60	$61.69	$94.04
4 Pile Drivers	60.50	1936.00	93.60	2995.20		
2 Equip. Oper. (crane)	66.30	1060.80	98.65	1578.40		
1 Equip. Oper. (oiler)	56.40	451.20	83.90	671.20		
1 Crawler Crane, 40 Ton		1362.63		1498.89		
1 Lead, 90' High		409.90		450.89		
1 Hammer, Diesel, 22k ft-lb		485.21		533.73	35.28	38.80
64 L.H., Daily Totals		$6205.74		$8501.91	$96.96	$132.84
Crew B-19A	**Hr.**	**Daily**	**Hr.**	**Daily**	**Bare Costs**	**Incl. O&P**
1 Pile Driver Foreman (outside)	$62.50	$500.00	$96.70	$773.60	$61.69	$94.04
4 Pile Drivers	60.50	1936.00	93.60	2995.20		
2 Equip. Oper. (crane)	66.30	1060.80	98.65	1578.40		
1 Equip. Oper. (oiler)	56.40	451.20	83.90	671.20		
1 Crawler Crane, 75 Ton		2189.46		2408.41		
1 Lead, 90' High		409.90		450.89		
1 Hammer, Diesel, 41k ft-lb		640.74		704.81	50.63	55.69
64 L.H., Daily Totals		$7188.10		$9582.51	$112.31	$149.73
Crew B-19B	**Hr.**	**Daily**	**Hr.**	**Daily**	**Bare Costs**	**Incl. O&P**
1 Pile Driver Foreman (outside)	$62.50	$500.00	$96.70	$773.60	$61.69	$94.04
4 Pile Drivers	60.50	1936.00	93.60	2995.20		
2 Equip. Oper. (crane)	66.30	1060.80	98.65	1578.40		
1 Equip. Oper. (oiler)	56.40	451.20	83.90	671.20		
1 Crawler Crane, 40 Ton		1362.63		1498.89		
1 Lead, 90' High		409.90		450.89		
1 Hammer, Diesel, 22k ft-lb		485.21		533.73		
1 Barge, 400 Ton		957.33		1053.06	50.24	55.26
64 L.H., Daily Totals		$7163.07		$9554.98	$111.92	$149.30

Crew No.	Bare Costs		Incl. Subs O&P		Cost Per Labor-Hour	
Crew B-19C	**Hr.**	**Daily**	**Hr.**	**Daily**	**Bare Costs**	**Incl. O&P**
1 Pile Driver Foreman (outside)	$62.50	$500.00	$96.70	$773.60	$61.69	$94.04
4 Pile Drivers	60.50	1936.00	93.60	2995.20		
2 Equip. Oper. (crane)	66.30	1060.80	98.65	1578.40		
1 Equip. Oper. (oiler)	56.40	451.20	83.90	671.20		
1 Crawler Crane, 75 Ton		2189.46		2408.41		
1 Lead, 90' High		409.90		450.89		
1 Hammer, Diesel, 41k ft-lb		640.74		704.81		
1 Barge, 400 Ton		957.33		1053.06	65.58	72.14
64 L.H., Daily Totals		$8145.43		$10635.57	$127.27	$166.18
Crew B-20	**Hr.**	**Daily**	**Hr.**	**Daily**	**Bare Costs**	**Incl. O&P**
1 Labor Foreman (outside)	$49.25	$394.00	$73.30	$586.40	$52.58	$78.55
1 Skilled Worker	61.25	490.00	92.00	736.00		
1 Laborer	47.25	378.00	70.35	562.80		
24 L.H., Daily Totals		$1262.00		$1885.20	$52.58	$78.55
Crew B-20A	**Hr.**	**Daily**	**Hr.**	**Daily**	**Bare Costs**	**Incl. O&P**
1 Labor Foreman (outside)	$49.25	$394.00	$73.30	$586.40	$56.55	$84.26
1 Laborer	47.25	378.00	70.35	562.80		
1 Plumber	72.05	576.40	107.45	859.60		
1 Plumber Apprentice	57.65	461.20	85.95	687.60		
32 L.H., Daily Totals		$1809.60		$2696.40	$56.55	$84.26
Crew B-21	**Hr.**	**Daily**	**Hr.**	**Daily**	**Bare Costs**	**Incl. O&P**
1 Labor Foreman (outside)	$49.25	$394.00	$73.30	$586.40	$54.54	$81.42
1 Skilled Worker	61.25	490.00	92.00	736.00		
1 Laborer	47.25	378.00	70.35	562.80		
.5 Equip. Oper. (crane)	66.30	265.20	98.65	394.60		
.5 S.P. Crane, 4x4, 5 Ton		192.94		212.24	6.89	7.58
28 L.H., Daily Totals		$1720.15		$2492.04	$61.43	$89.00
Crew B-21A	**Hr.**	**Daily**	**Hr.**	**Daily**	**Bare Costs**	**Incl. O&P**
1 Labor Foreman (outside)	$49.25	$394.00	$73.30	$586.40	$58.50	$87.14
1 Laborer	47.25	378.00	70.35	562.80		
1 Plumber	72.05	576.40	107.45	859.60		
1 Plumber Apprentice	57.65	461.20	85.95	687.60		
1 Equip. Oper. (crane)	66.30	530.40	98.65	789.20		
1 S.P. Crane, 4x4, 12 Ton		637.99		701.79	15.95	17.54
40 L.H., Daily Totals		$2977.99		$4187.39	$74.45	$104.68
Crew B-21B	**Hr.**	**Daily**	**Hr.**	**Daily**	**Bare Costs**	**Incl. O&P**
1 Labor Foreman (outside)	$49.25	$394.00	$73.30	$586.40	$51.46	$76.60
3 Laborers	47.25	1134.00	70.35	1688.40		
1 Equip. Oper. (crane)	66.30	530.40	98.65	789.20		
1 Hyd. Crane, 12 Ton		2150.65		2365.72	53.77	59.14
40 L.H., Daily Totals		$4209.05		$5429.72	$105.23	$135.74
Crew B-21C	**Hr.**	**Daily**	**Hr.**	**Daily**	**Bare Costs**	**Incl. O&P**
1 Labor Foreman (outside)	$49.25	$394.00	$73.30	$586.40	$51.56	$76.75
4 Laborers	47.25	1512.00	70.35	2251.20		
1 Equip. Oper. (crane)	66.30	530.40	98.65	789.20		
1 Equip. Oper. (oiler)	56.40	451.20	83.90	671.20		
2 Cutting Torches		28.48		31.33		
2 Sets of Gases		377.34		415.07		
1 Lattice Boom Crane, 90 Ton		2689.54		2958.49	55.27	60.80
56 L.H., Daily Totals		$5982.96		$7702.90	$106.84	$137.55

Crew B-22	Bare Costs Hr.	Bare Costs Daily	Incl. Subs O&P Hr.	Incl. Subs O&P Daily	Cost Per Labor-Hour Bare Costs	Cost Per Labor-Hour Incl. O&P
1 Labor Foreman (outside)	$49.25	$394.00	$73.30	$586.40	$55.33	$82.57
1 Skilled Worker	61.25	490.00	92.00	736.00		
1 Laborer	47.25	378.00	70.35	562.80		
.75 Equip. Oper. (crane)	66.30	397.80	98.65	591.90		
.75 S.P. Crane, 4x4, 5 Ton		289.42		318.36	9.65	10.61
30 L.H., Daily Totals		$1949.22		$2795.46	$64.97	$93.18

Crew B-22A	Bare Costs Hr.	Bare Costs Daily	Incl. Subs O&P Hr.	Incl. Subs O&P Daily	Cost Per Labor-Hour Bare Costs	Cost Per Labor-Hour Incl. O&P
1 Labor Foreman (outside)	$49.25	$394.00	$73.30	$586.40	$54.26	$80.93
1 Skilled Worker	61.25	490.00	92.00	736.00		
2 Laborers	47.25	756.00	70.35	1125.60		
1 Equipment Operator, Crane	66.30	530.40	98.65	789.20		
1 S.P. Crane, 4x4, 5 Ton		385.89		424.48		
1 Butt Fusion Mach., 4"-12" diam.		332.25		365.48	17.95	19.75
40 L.H., Daily Totals		$2888.54		$4027.15	$72.21	$100.68

Crew B-22B	Bare Costs Hr.	Bare Costs Daily	Incl. Subs O&P Hr.	Incl. Subs O&P Daily	Cost Per Labor-Hour Bare Costs	Cost Per Labor-Hour Incl. O&P
1 Labor Foreman (outside)	$49.25	$394.00	$73.30	$586.40	$54.26	$80.93
1 Skilled Worker	61.25	490.00	92.00	736.00		
2 Laborers	47.25	756.00	70.35	1125.60		
1 Equip. Oper. (crane)	66.30	530.40	98.65	789.20		
1 S.P. Crane, 4x4, 5 Ton		385.89		424.48		
1 Butt Fusion Mach., 8"-24" diam.		787.50		866.25	29.33	32.27
40 L.H., Daily Totals		$3343.79		$4527.93	$83.59	$113.20

Crew B-22C	Bare Costs Hr.	Bare Costs Daily	Incl. Subs O&P Hr.	Incl. Subs O&P Daily	Cost Per Labor-Hour Bare Costs	Cost Per Labor-Hour Incl. O&P
1 Skilled Worker	$61.25	$490.00	$92.00	$736.00	$54.25	$81.17
1 Laborer	47.25	378.00	70.35	562.80		
1 Butt Fusion Mach., 2"-8" diam.		280.48		308.53	17.53	19.28
16 L.H., Daily Totals		$1148.48		$1607.33	$71.78	$100.46

Crew B-23	Bare Costs Hr.	Bare Costs Daily	Incl. Subs O&P Hr.	Incl. Subs O&P Daily	Cost Per Labor-Hour Bare Costs	Cost Per Labor-Hour Incl. O&P
1 Labor Foreman (outside)	$49.25	$394.00	$73.30	$586.40	$47.65	$70.94
4 Laborers	47.25	1512.00	70.35	2251.20		
1 Drill Rig, Truck-Mounted		856.23		941.85		
1 Flatbed Truck, Gas, 3 Ton		391.02		430.12	31.18	34.30
40 L.H., Daily Totals		$3153.25		$4209.57	$78.83	$105.24

Crew B-23A	Bare Costs Hr.	Bare Costs Daily	Incl. Subs O&P Hr.	Incl. Subs O&P Daily	Cost Per Labor-Hour Bare Costs	Cost Per Labor-Hour Incl. O&P
1 Labor Foreman (outside)	$49.25	$394.00	$73.30	$586.40	$53.18	$79.15
1 Laborer	47.25	378.00	70.35	562.80		
1 Equip. Oper. (medium)	63.05	504.40	93.80	750.40		
1 Drill Rig, Truck-Mounted		856.23		941.85		
1 Pickup Truck, 3/4 Ton		122.56		134.82	40.78	44.86
24 L.H., Daily Totals		$2255.19		$2976.27	$93.97	$124.01

Crew B-23B	Bare Costs Hr.	Bare Costs Daily	Incl. Subs O&P Hr.	Incl. Subs O&P Daily	Cost Per Labor-Hour Bare Costs	Cost Per Labor-Hour Incl. O&P
1 Labor Foreman (outside)	$49.25	$394.00	$73.30	$586.40	$53.18	$79.15
1 Laborer	47.25	378.00	70.35	562.80		
1 Equip. Oper. (medium)	63.05	504.40	93.80	750.40		
1 Drill Rig, Truck-Mounted		856.23		941.85		
1 Pickup Truck, 3/4 Ton		122.56		134.82		
1 Centr. Water Pump, 6"		386.48		425.13	56.89	62.57
24 L.H., Daily Totals		$2641.67		$3401.40	$110.07	$141.72

Crew B-24	Bare Costs Hr.	Bare Costs Daily	Incl. Subs O&P Hr.	Incl. Subs O&P Daily	Cost Per Labor-Hour Bare Costs	Cost Per Labor-Hour Incl. O&P
1 Cement Finisher	$55.00	$440.00	$80.45	$643.60	$53.62	$79.35
1 Laborer	47.25	378.00	70.35	562.80		
1 Carpenter	58.60	468.80	87.25	698.00		
24 L.H., Daily Totals		$1286.80		$1904.40	$53.62	$79.35

Crew B-25	Bare Costs Hr.	Bare Costs Daily	Incl. Subs O&P Hr.	Incl. Subs O&P Daily	Cost Per Labor-Hour Bare Costs	Cost Per Labor-Hour Incl. O&P
1 Labor Foreman (outside)	$49.25	$394.00	$73.30	$586.40	$51.74	$77.01
7 Laborers	47.25	2646.00	70.35	3939.60		
3 Equip. Oper. (medium)	63.05	1513.20	93.80	2251.20		
1 Asphalt Paver, 130 H.P.		2352.46		2587.71		
1 Tandem Roller, 10 Ton		379.22		417.14		
1 Roller, Pneum. Whl., 12 Ton		384.55		423.01	35.41	38.95
88 L.H., Daily Totals		$7669.43		$10205.05	$87.15	$115.97

Crew B-25B	Bare Costs Hr.	Bare Costs Daily	Incl. Subs O&P Hr.	Incl. Subs O&P Daily	Cost Per Labor-Hour Bare Costs	Cost Per Labor-Hour Incl. O&P
1 Labor Foreman (outside)	$49.25	$394.00	$73.30	$586.40	$52.68	$78.41
7 Laborers	47.25	2646.00	70.35	3939.60		
4 Equip. Oper. (medium)	63.05	2017.60	93.80	3001.60		
1 Asphalt Paver, 130 H.P.		2352.46		2587.71		
2 Tandem Rollers, 10 Ton		758.44		834.28		
1 Roller, Pneum. Whl., 12 Ton		384.55		423.01	36.41	40.05
96 L.H., Daily Totals		$8553.05		$11372.59	$89.09	$118.46

Crew B-25C	Bare Costs Hr.	Bare Costs Daily	Incl. Subs O&P Hr.	Incl. Subs O&P Daily	Cost Per Labor-Hour Bare Costs	Cost Per Labor-Hour Incl. O&P
1 Labor Foreman (outside)	$49.25	$394.00	$73.30	$586.40	$52.85	$78.66
3 Laborers	47.25	1134.00	70.35	1688.40		
2 Equip. Oper. (medium)	63.05	1008.80	93.80	1500.80		
1 Asphalt Paver, 130 H.P.		2352.46		2587.71		
1 Tandem Roller, 10 Ton		379.22		417.14	56.91	62.60
48 L.H., Daily Totals		$5268.48		$6780.45	$109.76	$141.26

Crew B-25D	Bare Costs Hr.	Bare Costs Daily	Incl. Subs O&P Hr.	Incl. Subs O&P Daily	Cost Per Labor-Hour Bare Costs	Cost Per Labor-Hour Incl. O&P
1 Labor Foreman (outside)	$49.25	$394.00	$73.30	$586.40	$53.12	$79.06
3 Laborers	47.25	1134.00	70.35	1688.40		
2.130 Equip. Oper. (medium)	63.05	1074.37	93.80	1598.35		
.13 Truck Driver (heavy)	55.45	57.67	82.85	86.16		
.13 Truck Tractor, 6x4, 380 H.P.		70.98		78.08		
.13 Dist. Tanker, 3000 Gallon		47.72		52.50		
1 Asphalt Paver, 130 H.P.		2352.46		2587.71		
1 Tandem Roller, 10 Ton		379.22		417.14	56.92	62.61
50.08 L.H., Daily Totals		$5510.42		$7094.73	$110.03	$141.67

Crew B-25E	Bare Costs Hr.	Bare Costs Daily	Incl. Subs O&P Hr.	Incl. Subs O&P Daily	Cost Per Labor-Hour Bare Costs	Cost Per Labor-Hour Incl. O&P
1 Labor Foreman (outside)	$49.25	$394.00	$73.30	$586.40	$53.34	$79.40
3 Laborers	47.25	1134.00	70.35	1688.40		
2.250 Equip. Oper. (medium)	63.05	1134.90	93.80	1688.40		
.25 Truck Driver (heavy)	55.45	110.90	82.85	165.70		
.25 Truck Tractor, 6x4, 380 H.P.		136.50		150.14		
.25 Dist. Tanker, 3000 Gallon		91.78		100.95		
1 Asphalt Paver, 130 H.P.		2352.46		2587.71		
1 Tandem Roller, 10 Ton		379.22		417.14	56.92	62.61
52 L.H., Daily Totals		$5733.75		$7384.85	$110.26	$142.02

Crew B-26	Bare Costs Hr.	Bare Costs Daily	Incl. Subs O&P Hr.	Incl. Subs O&P Daily	Cost Per Labor-Hour Bare Costs	Cost Per Labor-Hour Incl. O&P
1 Labor Foreman (outside)	$49.25	$394.00	$73.30	$586.40	$52.58	$78.17
6 Laborers	47.25	2268.00	70.35	3376.80		
2 Equip. Oper. (medium)	63.05	1008.80	93.80	1500.80		
1 Rodman (reinf.)	64.55	516.40	96.40	771.20		
1 Cement Finisher	55.00	440.00	80.45	643.60		
1 Grader, 30,000 Lbs.		1091.19		1200.31		
1 Paving Mach. & Equip.		2747.64		3022.40	43.62	47.99
88 L.H., Daily Totals		$8466.03		$11101.51	$96.20	$126.15

Crew B-26A	Bare Costs Hr.	Bare Costs Daily	Incl. Subs O&P Hr.	Incl. Subs O&P Daily	Cost Per Labor-Hour Bare Costs	Cost Per Labor-Hour Incl. O&P
1 Labor Foreman (outside)	$49.25	$394.00	$73.30	$586.40	$52.58	$78.17
6 Laborers	47.25	2268.00	70.35	3376.80		
2 Equip. Oper. (medium)	63.05	1008.80	93.80	1500.80		
1 Rodman (reinf.)	64.55	516.40	96.40	771.20		
1 Cement Finisher	55.00	440.00	80.45	643.60		
1 Grader, 30,000 Lbs.		1091.19		1200.31		
1 Paving Mach. & Equip.		2747.64		3022.40		
1 Concrete Saw		176.00		193.60	45.62	50.19
88 L.H., Daily Totals		$8642.03		$11295.11	$98.20	$128.35

Crew B-26B	Hr.	Daily	Hr.	Daily	Bare Costs	Incl. O&P
1 Labor Foreman (outside)	$49.25	$394.00	$73.30	$586.40	$53.45	$79.47
6 Laborers	47.25	2268.00	70.35	3376.80		
3 Equip. Oper. (medium)	63.05	1513.20	93.80	2251.20		
1 Rodman (reinf.)	64.55	516.40	96.40	771.20		
1 Cement Finisher	55.00	440.00	80.45	643.60		
1 Grader, 30,000 Lbs.		1091.19		1200.31		
1 Paving Mach. & Equip.		2747.64		3022.40		
1 Concrete Pump, 110' Boom		1069.53		1176.48	51.13	56.24
96 L.H., Daily Totals		$10039.96		$13028.40	$104.58	$135.71

Crew B-26C	Hr.	Daily	Hr.	Daily	Bare Costs	Incl. O&P
1 Labor Foreman (outside)	$49.25	$394.00	$73.30	$586.40	$51.53	$76.61
6 Laborers	47.25	2268.00	70.35	3376.80		
1 Equip. Oper. (medium)	63.05	504.40	93.80	750.40		
1 Rodman (reinf.)	64.55	516.40	96.40	771.20		
1 Cement Finisher	55.00	440.00	80.45	643.60		
1 Paving Mach. & Equip.		2747.64		3022.40		
1 Concrete Saw		176.00		193.60	36.55	40.20
80 L.H., Daily Totals		$7046.44		$9344.40	$88.08	$116.81

Crew B-27	Hr.	Daily	Hr.	Daily	Bare Costs	Incl. O&P
1 Labor Foreman (outside)	$49.25	$394.00	$73.30	$586.40	$47.75	$71.09
3 Laborers	47.25	1134.00	70.35	1688.40		
1 Berm Machine		897.16		986.88	28.04	30.84
32 L.H., Daily Totals		$2425.16		$3261.68	$75.79	$101.93

Crew B-28	Hr.	Daily	Hr.	Daily	Bare Costs	Incl. O&P
2 Carpenters	$58.60	$937.60	$87.25	$1396.00	$54.82	$81.62
1 Laborer	47.25	378.00	70.35	562.80		
24 L.H., Daily Totals		$1315.60		$1958.80	$54.82	$81.62

Crew B-29	Hr.	Daily	Hr.	Daily	Bare Costs	Incl. O&P
1 Labor Foreman (outside)	$49.25	$394.00	$73.30	$586.40	$51.56	$76.75
4 Laborers	47.25	1512.00	70.35	2251.20		
1 Equip. Oper. (crane)	66.30	530.40	98.65	789.20		
1 Equip. Oper. (oiler)	56.40	451.20	83.90	671.20		
1 Gradall, 5/8 C.Y.		880.91		969.00	15.73	17.30
56 L.H., Daily Totals		$3768.51		$5267.00	$67.29	$94.05

Crew B-30	Hr.	Daily	Hr.	Daily	Bare Costs	Incl. O&P
1 Equip. Oper. (medium)	$63.05	$504.40	$93.80	$750.40	$57.98	$86.50
2 Truck Drivers (heavy)	55.45	887.20	82.85	1325.60		
1 Hyd. Excavator, 1.5 C.Y.		1185.24		1303.76		
2 Dump Trucks, 12 C.Y., 400 H.P.		1582.72		1740.99	115.33	126.86
24 L.H., Daily Totals		$4159.56		$5120.76	$173.32	$213.36

Crew B-31	Hr.	Daily	Hr.	Daily	Bare Costs	Incl. O&P
1 Labor Foreman (outside)	$49.25	$394.00	$73.30	$586.40	$49.92	$74.32
3 Laborers	47.25	1134.00	70.35	1688.40		
1 Carpenter	58.60	468.80	87.25	698.00		
1 Air Compressor, 250 cfm		196.28		215.91		
1 Sheeting Driver		8.19		9.01		
2 -50' Air Hoses, 1.5"		47.20		51.92	6.29	6.92
40 L.H., Daily Totals		$2248.47		$3249.64	$56.21	$81.24

Crew B-32	Hr.	Daily	Hr.	Daily	Bare Costs	Incl. O&P
1 Laborer	$47.25	$378.00	$70.35	$562.80	$59.10	$87.94
3 Equip. Oper. (medium)	63.05	1513.20	93.80	2251.20		
1 Grader, 30,000 Lbs.		1091.19		1200.31		
1 Tandem Roller, 10 Ton		379.22		417.14		
1 Dozer, 200 H.P.		1382.36		1520.60	89.15	98.06
32 L.H., Daily Totals		$4743.97		$5952.05	$148.25	$186.00

Crew B-32A	Hr.	Daily	Hr.	Daily	Bare Costs	Incl. O&P
1 Laborer	$47.25	$378.00	$70.35	$562.80	$57.78	$85.98
2 Equip. Oper. (medium)	63.05	1008.80	93.80	1500.80		
1 Grader, 30,000 Lbs.		1091.19		1200.31		
1 Roller, Vibratory, 25 Ton		529.68		582.65	67.54	74.29
24 L.H., Daily Totals		$3007.67		$3846.56	$125.32	$160.27

Crew B-32B	Hr.	Daily	Hr.	Daily	Bare Costs	Incl. O&P
1 Laborer	$47.25	$378.00	$70.35	$562.80	$57.78	$85.98
2 Equip. Oper. (medium)	63.05	1008.80	93.80	1500.80		
1 Dozer, 200 H.P.		1382.36		1520.60		
1 Roller, Vibratory, 25 Ton		529.68		582.65	79.67	87.64
24 L.H., Daily Totals		$3298.84		$4166.84	$137.45	$173.62

Crew B-32C	Hr.	Daily	Hr.	Daily	Bare Costs	Incl. O&P
1 Labor Foreman (outside)	$49.25	$394.00	$73.30	$586.40	$55.48	$82.57
2 Laborers	47.25	756.00	70.35	1125.60		
3 Equip. Oper. (medium)	63.05	1513.20	93.80	2251.20		
1 Grader, 30,000 Lbs.		1091.19		1200.31		
1 Tandem Roller, 10 Ton		379.22		417.14		
1 Dozer, 200 H.P.		1382.36		1520.60	59.43	65.38
48 L.H., Daily Totals		$5515.97		$7101.25	$114.92	$147.94

Crew B-33A	Hr.	Daily	Hr.	Daily	Bare Costs	Incl. O&P
1 Equip. Oper. (medium)	$63.05	$504.40	$93.80	$750.40	$58.54	$87.10
.5 Laborer	47.25	189.00	70.35	281.40		
.25 Equip. Oper. (medium)	63.05	126.10	93.80	187.60		
1 Scraper, Towed, 7 C.Y.		141.88		156.07		
1.25 Dozers, 300 H.P.		2093.16		2302.48	159.65	175.61
14 L.H., Daily Totals		$3054.54		$3677.95	$218.18	$262.71

Crew B-33B	Hr.	Daily	Hr.	Daily	Bare Costs	Incl. O&P
1 Equip. Oper. (medium)	$63.05	$504.40	$93.80	$750.40	$58.54	$87.10
.5 Laborer	47.25	189.00	70.35	281.40		
.25 Equip. Oper. (medium)	63.05	126.10	93.80	187.60		
1 Scraper, Towed, 10 C.Y.		177.45		195.19		
1.25 Dozers, 300 H.P.		2093.16		2302.48	162.19	178.41
14 L.H., Daily Totals		$3090.11		$3717.07	$220.72	$265.51

Crew No.	Bare Costs		Incl. Subs O&P		Cost Per Labor-Hour	
Crew B-33C	**Hr.**	**Daily**	**Hr.**	**Daily**	**Bare Costs**	**Incl. O&P**
1 Equip. Oper. (medium)	$63.05	$504.40	$93.80	$750.40	$58.54	$87.10
.5 Laborer	47.25	189.00	70.35	281.40		
.25 Equip. Oper. (medium)	63.05	126.10	93.80	187.60		
1 Scraper, Towed, 15 C.Y.		196.46		216.11		
1.25 Dozers, 300 H.P.		2093.16		2302.48	163.54	179.90
14 L.H., Daily Totals		$3109.12		$3737.98	$222.08	$267.00

Crew B-33D	Hr.	Daily	Hr.	Daily	Bare Costs	Incl. O&P
1 Equip. Oper. (medium)	$63.05	$504.40	$93.80	$750.40	$58.54	$87.10
.5 Laborer	47.25	189.00	70.35	281.40		
.25 Equip. Oper. (medium)	63.05	126.10	93.80	187.60		
1 S.P. Scraper, 14 C.Y.		2168.71		2385.58		
.25 Dozer, 300 H.P.		418.63		460.50	184.81	203.29
14 L.H., Daily Totals		$3406.84		$4065.48	$243.35	$290.39

Crew B-33E	Hr.	Daily	Hr.	Daily	Bare Costs	Incl. O&P
1 Equip. Oper. (medium)	$63.05	$504.40	$93.80	$750.40	$58.54	$87.10
.5 Laborer	47.25	189.00	70.35	281.40		
.25 Equip. Oper. (medium)	63.05	126.10	93.80	187.60		
1 S.P. Scraper, 21 C.Y.		2239.60		2463.56		
.25 Dozer, 300 H.P.		418.63		460.50	189.87	208.86
14 L.H., Daily Totals		$3477.73		$4143.46	$248.41	$295.96

Crew B-33F	Hr.	Daily	Hr.	Daily	Bare Costs	Incl. O&P
1 Equip. Oper. (medium)	$63.05	$504.40	$93.80	$750.40	$58.54	$87.10
.5 Laborer	47.25	189.00	70.35	281.40		
.25 Equip. Oper. (medium)	63.05	126.10	93.80	187.60		
1 Elev. Scraper, 11 C.Y.		1022.46		1124.71		
.25 Dozer, 300 H.P.		418.63		460.50	102.94	113.23
14 L.H., Daily Totals		$2260.59		$2804.60	$161.47	$200.33

Crew B-33G	Hr.	Daily	Hr.	Daily	Bare Costs	Incl. O&P
1 Equip. Oper. (medium)	$63.05	$504.40	$93.80	$750.40	$58.54	$87.10
.5 Laborer	47.25	189.00	70.35	281.40		
.25 Equip. Oper. (medium)	63.05	126.10	93.80	187.60		
1 Elev. Scraper, 22 C.Y.		2005.03		2205.53		
.25 Dozer, 300 H.P.		418.63		460.50	173.12	190.43
14 L.H., Daily Totals		$3243.16		$3885.43	$231.65	$277.53

Crew B-33H	Hr.	Daily	Hr.	Daily	Bare Costs	Incl. O&P
.5 Laborer	$47.25	$189.00	$70.35	$281.40	$58.54	$87.10
1 Equipment Operator (med.)	63.05	504.40	93.80	750.40		
.25 Equipment Operator (med.)	63.05	126.10	93.80	187.60		
1 S.P. Scraper, 44 C.Y.		3440.19		3784.21		
.25 Dozer, 410 H.P.		633.99		697.39	291.01	320.11
14 L.H., Daily Totals		$4893.68		$5701.00	$349.55	$407.21

Crew B-33J	Hr.	Daily	Hr.	Daily	Bare Costs	Incl. O&P
1 Equipment Operator (med.)	$63.05	$504.40	$93.80	$750.40	$63.05	$93.80
1 S.P. Scraper, 14 C.Y.		2168.71		2385.58	271.09	298.20
8 L.H., Daily Totals		$2673.11		$3135.98	$334.14	$392.00

Crew B-33K	Hr.	Daily	Hr.	Daily	Bare Costs	Incl. O&P
1 Equipment Operator (med.)	$63.05	$504.40	$93.80	$750.40	$58.54	$87.10
.25 Equipment Operator (med.)	63.05	126.10	93.80	187.60		
.5 Laborer	47.25	189.00	70.35	281.40		
1 S.P. Scraper, 31 C.Y.		2972.09		3269.30		
.25 Dozer, 410 H.P.		633.99		697.39	257.58	283.33
14 L.H., Daily Totals		$4425.58		$5186.09	$316.11	$370.43

Crew No.	Bare Costs		Incl. Subs O&P		Cost Per Labor-Hour	
Crew B-34A	**Hr.**	**Daily**	**Hr.**	**Daily**	**Bare Costs**	**Incl. O&P**
1 Truck Driver (heavy)	$55.45	$443.60	$82.85	$662.80	$55.45	$82.85
1 Dump Truck, 8 C.Y., 220 H.P.		417.49		459.24	52.19	57.40
8 L.H., Daily Totals		$861.09		$1122.04	$107.64	$140.25

Crew B-34B	Hr.	Daily	Hr.	Daily	Bare Costs	Incl. O&P
1 Truck Driver (heavy)	$55.45	$443.60	$82.85	$662.80	$55.45	$82.85
1 Dump Truck, 12 C.Y., 400 H.P.		791.36		870.50	98.92	108.81
8 L.H., Daily Totals		$1234.96		$1533.30	$154.37	$191.66

Crew B-34C	Hr.	Daily	Hr.	Daily	Bare Costs	Incl. O&P
1 Truck Driver (heavy)	$55.45	$443.60	$82.85	$662.80	$55.45	$82.85
1 Truck Tractor, 6x4, 380 H.P.		545.98		600.58		
1 Dump Trailer, 16.5 C.Y.		151.94		167.13	87.24	95.96
8 L.H., Daily Totals		$1141.52		$1430.51	$142.69	$178.81

Crew B-34D	Hr.	Daily	Hr.	Daily	Bare Costs	Incl. O&P
1 Truck Driver (heavy)	$55.45	$443.60	$82.85	$662.80	$55.45	$82.85
1 Truck Tractor, 6x4, 380 H.P.		545.98		600.58		
1 Dump Trailer, 20 C.Y.		168.66		185.53	89.33	98.26
8 L.H., Daily Totals		$1158.24		$1448.90	$144.78	$181.11

Crew B-34E	Hr.	Daily	Hr.	Daily	Bare Costs	Incl. O&P
1 Truck Driver (heavy)	$55.45	$443.60	$82.85	$662.80	$55.45	$82.85
1 Dump Truck, Off Hwy., 25 Ton		1471.16		1618.28	183.90	202.28
8 L.H., Daily Totals		$1914.76		$2281.08	$239.35	$285.13

Crew B-34F	Hr.	Daily	Hr.	Daily	Bare Costs	Incl. O&P
1 Truck Driver (heavy)	$55.45	$443.60	$82.85	$662.80	$55.45	$82.85
1 Dump Truck, Off Hwy., 35 Ton		1508.36		1659.20	188.54	207.40
8 L.H., Daily Totals		$1951.96		$2322.00	$244.00	$290.25

Crew B-34G	Hr.	Daily	Hr.	Daily	Bare Costs	Incl. O&P
1 Truck Driver (heavy)	$55.45	$443.60	$82.85	$662.80	$55.45	$82.85
1 Dump Truck, Off Hwy., 50 Ton		2037.60		2241.36	254.70	280.17
8 L.H., Daily Totals		$2481.20		$2904.16	$310.15	$363.02

Crew B-34H	Hr.	Daily	Hr.	Daily	Bare Costs	Incl. O&P
1 Truck Driver (heavy)	$55.45	$443.60	$82.85	$662.80	$55.45	$82.85
1 Dump Truck, Off Hwy., 65 Ton		2126.70		2339.37	265.84	292.42
8 L.H., Daily Totals		$2570.30		$3002.17	$321.29	$375.27

Crew B-34I	Hr.	Daily	Hr.	Daily	Bare Costs	Incl. O&P
1 Truck Driver (heavy)	$55.45	$443.60	$82.85	$662.80	$55.45	$82.85
1 Dump Truck, 18 C.Y., 450 H.P.		788.42		867.26	98.55	108.41
8 L.H., Daily Totals		$1232.02		$1530.06	$154.00	$191.26

Crew B-34J	Hr.	Daily	Hr.	Daily	Bare Costs	Incl. O&P
1 Truck Driver (heavy)	$55.45	$443.60	$82.85	$662.80	$55.45	$82.85
1 Dump Truck, Off Hwy., 100 Ton		3040.18		3344.20	380.02	418.02
8 L.H., Daily Totals		$3483.78		$4007.00	$435.47	$500.87

Crew B-34K	Hr.	Daily	Hr.	Daily	Bare Costs	Incl. O&P
1 Truck Driver (heavy)	$55.45	$443.60	$82.85	$662.80	$55.45	$82.85
1 Truck Tractor, 6x4, 450 H.P.		666.04		732.64		
1 Lowbed Trailer, 75 Ton		283.47		311.82	118.69	130.56
8 L.H., Daily Totals		$1393.11		$1707.26	$174.14	$213.41

Crew No.	Bare Costs		Incl. Subs O&P		Cost Per Labor-Hour	
Crew B-34L	**Hr.**	**Daily**	**Hr.**	**Daily**	**Bare Costs**	**Incl. O&P**
1 Equip. Oper. (light)	$59.70	$477.60	$88.85	$710.80	$59.70	$88.85
1 Flatbed Truck, Gas, 1.5 Ton		361.95		398.14	45.24	49.77
8 L.H., Daily Totals		$839.55		$1108.94	$104.94	$138.62

Crew B-34M	Hr.	Daily	Hr.	Daily	Bare Costs	Incl. O&P
1 Equip. Oper. (light)	$59.70	$477.60	$88.85	$710.80	$59.70	$88.85
1 Flatbed Truck, Gas, 3 Ton		391.02		430.12	48.88	53.77
8 L.H., Daily Totals		$868.62		$1140.92	$108.58	$142.62

Crew B-34N	Hr.	Daily	Hr.	Daily	Bare Costs	Incl. O&P
1 Truck Driver (heavy)	$55.45	$443.60	$82.85	$662.80	$59.25	$88.33
1 Equip. Oper. (medium)	63.05	504.40	93.80	750.40		
1 Truck Tractor, 6x4, 380 H.P.		545.98		600.58		
1 Flatbed Trailer, 40 Ton		206.92		227.61	47.06	51.76
16 L.H., Daily Totals		$1700.90		$2241.39	$106.31	$140.09

Crew B-34P	Hr.	Daily	Hr.	Daily	Bare Costs	Incl. O&P
1 Pipe Fitter	$72.55	$580.40	$108.20	$865.60	$62.83	$93.67
1 Truck Driver (light)	52.90	423.20	79.00	632.00		
1 Equip. Oper. (medium)	63.05	504.40	93.80	750.40		
1 Flatbed Truck, Gas, 3 Ton		391.02		430.12		
1 Backhoe Loader, 48 H.P.		277.19		304.91	27.84	30.63
24 L.H., Daily Totals		$2176.21		$2983.03	$90.68	$124.29

Crew B-34Q	Hr.	Daily	Hr.	Daily	Bare Costs	Incl. O&P
1 Pipe Fitter	$72.55	$580.40	$108.20	$865.60	$63.92	$95.28
1 Truck Driver (light)	52.90	423.20	79.00	632.00		
1 Equip. Oper. (crane)	66.30	530.40	98.65	789.20		
1 Flatbed Trailer, 25 Ton		150.61		165.67		
1 Dump Truck, 8 C.Y., 220 H.P.		417.49		459.24		
1 Hyd. Crane, 25 Ton		2273.31		2500.64	118.39	130.23
24 L.H., Daily Totals		$4375.41		$5412.35	$182.31	$225.51

Crew B-34R	Hr.	Daily	Hr.	Daily	Bare Costs	Incl. O&P
1 Pipe Fitter	$72.55	$580.40	$108.20	$865.60	$63.92	$95.28
1 Truck Driver (light)	52.90	423.20	79.00	632.00		
1 Equip. Oper. (crane)	66.30	530.40	98.65	789.20		
1 Flatbed Trailer, 25 Ton		150.61		165.67		
1 Dump Truck, 8 C.Y., 220 H.P.		417.49		459.24		
1 Hyd. Crane, 25 Ton		2273.31		2500.64		
1 Hyd. Excavator, 1 C.Y.		986.56		1085.22	159.50	175.45
24 L.H., Daily Totals		$5361.97		$6497.57	$223.42	$270.73

Crew B-34S	Hr.	Daily	Hr.	Daily	Bare Costs	Incl. O&P
2 Pipe Fitters	$72.55	$1160.80	$108.20	$1731.20	$66.71	$99.47
1 Truck Driver (heavy)	55.45	443.60	82.85	662.80		
1 Equip. Oper. (crane)	66.30	530.40	98.65	789.20		
1 Flatbed Trailer, 40 Ton		206.92		227.61		
1 Truck Tractor, 6x4, 380 H.P.		545.98		600.58		
1 Hyd. Crane, 80 Ton		2641.70		2905.87		
1 Hyd. Excavator, 2 C.Y.		1096.14		1205.75	140.34	154.37
32 L.H., Daily Totals		$6625.54		$8123.01	$207.05	$253.84

Crew B-34T	Hr.	Daily	Hr.	Daily	Bare Costs	Incl. O&P
2 Pipe Fitters	$72.55	$1160.80	$108.20	$1731.20	$66.71	$99.47
1 Truck Driver (heavy)	55.45	443.60	82.85	662.80		
1 Equip. Oper. (crane)	66.30	530.40	98.65	789.20		
1 Flatbed Trailer, 40 Ton		206.92		227.61		
1 Truck Tractor, 6x4, 380 H.P.		545.98		600.58		
1 Hyd. Crane, 80 Ton		2641.70		2905.87	106.08	116.69
32 L.H., Daily Totals		$5529.40		$6917.26	$172.79	$216.16

Crew B-34U	Hr.	Daily	Hr.	Daily	Bare Costs	Incl. O&P
1 Truck Driver (heavy)	$55.45	$443.60	$82.85	$662.80	$57.58	$85.85
1 Equip. Oper. (light)	59.70	477.60	88.85	710.80		
1 Truck Tractor, 220 H.P.		339.98		373.98		
1 Flatbed Trailer, 25 Ton		150.61		165.67	30.66	33.73
16 L.H., Daily Totals		$1411.79		$1913.25	$88.24	$119.58

Crew B-34V	Hr.	Daily	Hr.	Daily	Bare Costs	Incl. O&P
1 Truck Driver (heavy)	$55.45	$443.60	$82.85	$662.80	$60.48	$90.12
1 Equip. Oper. (crane)	66.30	530.40	98.65	789.20		
1 Equip. Oper. (light)	59.70	477.60	88.85	710.80		
1 Truck Tractor, 6x4, 450 H.P.		666.04		732.64		
1 Equipment Trailer, 50 Ton		336.69		370.36		
1 Pickup Truck, 4x4, 3/4 Ton		191.73		210.90	49.77	54.75
24 L.H., Daily Totals		$2646.06		$3476.71	$110.25	$144.86

Crew B-34W	Hr.	Daily	Hr.	Daily	Bare Costs	Incl. O&P
5 Truck Drivers (heavy)	$55.45	$2218.00	$82.85	$3314.00	$58.17	$86.74
2 Equip. Opers. (crane)	66.30	1060.80	98.65	1578.40		
1 Equip. Oper. (mechanic)	66.40	531.20	98.80	790.40		
1 Laborer	47.25	378.00	70.35	562.80		
4 Truck Tractors, 6x4, 380 H.P.		2183.92		2402.31		
2 Equipment Trailers, 50 Ton		673.38		740.72		
2 Flatbed Trailers, 40 Ton		413.84		455.22		
1 Pickup Truck, 4x4, 3/4 Ton		191.73		210.90		
1 S.P. Crane, 4x4, 20 Ton		760.97		837.07	58.66	64.53
72 L.H., Daily Totals		$8411.84		$10891.82	$116.83	$151.28

Crew B-35	Hr.	Daily	Hr.	Daily	Bare Costs	Incl. O&P
1 Labor Foreman (outside)	$49.25	$394.00	$73.30	$586.40	$60.65	$90.44
1 Skilled Worker	61.25	490.00	92.00	736.00		
2 Welders	72.05	1152.80	107.45	1719.20		
1 Laborer	47.25	378.00	70.35	562.80		
1 Equip. Oper. (crane)	66.30	530.40	98.65	789.20		
1 Equip. Oper. (oiler)	56.40	451.20	83.90	671.20		
2 Welder, Electric, 300 amp		128.34		141.17		
1 Hyd. Excavator, .75 C.Y.		915.34		1006.87	18.64	20.50
56 L.H., Daily Totals		$4440.08		$6212.85	$79.29	$110.94

Crew B-35A	Hr.	Daily	Hr.	Daily	Bare Costs	Incl. O&P
1 Labor Foreman (outside)	$49.25	$394.00	$73.30	$586.40	$57.11	$85.14
2 Laborers	47.25	756.00	70.35	1125.60		
1 Skilled Worker	61.25	490.00	92.00	736.00		
1 Welder (plumber)	72.05	576.40	107.45	859.60		
1 Equip. Oper. (crane)	66.30	530.40	98.65	789.20		
1 Equip. Oper. (oiler)	56.40	451.20	83.90	671.20		
1 Welder, Gas Engine, 300 amp		147.09		161.80		
1 Crawler Crane, 75 Ton		2189.46		2408.41	41.72	45.90
56 L.H., Daily Totals		$5534.55		$7338.20	$98.83	$131.04

Crew B-36	Hr.	Daily	Hr.	Daily	Bare Costs	Incl. O&P
1 Labor Foreman (outside)	$49.25	$394.00	$73.30	$586.40	$53.97	$80.32
2 Laborers	47.25	756.00	70.35	1125.60		
2 Equip. Oper. (medium)	63.05	1008.80	93.80	1500.80		
1 Dozer, 200 H.P.		1382.36		1520.60		
1 Aggregate Spreader		67.49		74.24		
1 Tandem Roller, 10 Ton		379.22		417.14	45.73	50.30
40 L.H., Daily Totals		$3987.87		$5224.78	$99.70	$130.62

Crew B-36A	Bare Costs Hr.	Bare Costs Daily	Incl. Subs O&P Hr.	Incl. Subs O&P Daily	Cost Per Labor-Hour Bare Costs	Cost Per Labor-Hour Incl. O&P
1 Labor Foreman (outside)	$49.25	$394.00	$73.30	$586.40	$56.56	$84.17
2 Laborers	47.25	756.00	70.35	1125.60		
4 Equip. Oper. (medium)	63.05	2017.60	93.80	3001.60		
1 Dozer, 200 H.P.		1382.36		1520.60		
1 Aggregate Spreader		67.49		74.24		
1 Tandem Roller, 10 Ton		379.22		417.14		
1 Roller, Pneum. Whl., 12 Ton		384.55		423.01	39.53	43.48
56 L.H., Daily Totals		$5381.22		$7148.58	$96.09	$127.65

Crew B-36B	Hr.	Daily	Hr.	Daily	Bare Costs	Incl. O&P
1 Labor Foreman (outside)	$49.25	$394.00	$73.30	$586.40	$56.42	$84.01
2 Laborers	47.25	756.00	70.35	1125.60		
4 Equip. Oper. (medium)	63.05	2017.60	93.80	3001.60		
1 Truck Driver (heavy)	55.45	443.60	82.85	662.80		
1 Grader, 30,000 Lbs.		1091.19		1200.31		
1 F.E. Loader, Crl, 1.5 C.Y.		733.70		807.07		
1 Dozer, 300 H.P.		1674.53		1841.98		
1 Roller, Vibratory, 25 Ton		529.68		582.65		
1 Truck Tractor, 6x4, 450 H.P.		666.04		732.64		
1 Water Tank Trailer, 5000 Gal.		169.14		186.05	76.00	83.60
64 L.H., Daily Totals		$8475.48		$10727.11	$132.43	$167.61

Crew B-36C	Hr.	Daily	Hr.	Daily	Bare Costs	Incl. O&P
1 Labor Foreman (outside)	$49.25	$394.00	$73.30	$586.40	$58.77	$87.51
3 Equip. Oper. (medium)	63.05	1513.20	93.80	2251.20		
1 Truck Driver (heavy)	55.45	443.60	82.85	662.80		
1 Grader, 30,000 Lbs.		1091.19		1200.31		
1 Dozer, 300 H.P.		1674.53		1841.98		
1 Roller, Vibratory, 25 Ton		529.68		582.65		
1 Truck Tractor, 6x4, 450 H.P.		666.04		732.64		
1 Water Tank Trailer, 5000 Gal.		169.14		186.05	103.26	113.59
40 L.H., Daily Totals		$6481.38		$8044.04	$162.03	$201.10

Crew B-36D	Hr.	Daily	Hr.	Daily	Bare Costs	Incl. O&P
1 Labor Foreman (outside)	$49.25	$394.00	$73.30	$586.40	$59.60	$88.67
3 Equip. Oper. (medium)	63.05	1513.20	93.80	2251.20		
1 Grader, 30,000 Lbs.		1091.19		1200.31		
1 Dozer, 300 H.P.		1674.53		1841.98		
1 Roller, Vibratory, 25 Ton		529.68		582.65	102.98	113.28
32 L.H., Daily Totals		$5202.60		$6462.54	$162.58	$201.95

Crew B-37	Hr.	Daily	Hr.	Daily	Bare Costs	Incl. O&P
1 Labor Foreman (outside)	$49.25	$394.00	$73.30	$586.40	$49.66	$73.92
4 Laborers	47.25	1512.00	70.35	2251.20		
1 Equip. Oper. (light)	59.70	477.60	88.85	710.80		
1 Tandem Roller, 5 Ton		287.45		316.19	5.99	6.59
48 L.H., Daily Totals		$2671.05		$3864.59	$55.65	$80.51

Crew B-37A	Hr.	Daily	Hr.	Daily	Bare Costs	Incl. O&P
2 Laborers	$47.25	$756.00	$70.35	$1125.60	$49.13	$73.23
1 Truck Driver (light)	52.90	423.20	79.00	632.00		
1 Flatbed Truck, Gas, 1.5 Ton		361.95		398.14		
1 Tar Kettle, T.M.		199.54		219.49	23.40	25.73
24 L.H., Daily Totals		$1740.69		$2375.24	$72.53	$98.97

Crew B-37B	Hr.	Daily	Hr.	Daily	Bare Costs	Incl. O&P
3 Laborers	$47.25	$1134.00	$70.35	$1688.40	$48.66	$72.51
1 Truck Driver (light)	52.90	423.20	79.00	632.00		
1 Flatbed Truck, Gas, 1.5 Ton		361.95		398.14		
1 Tar Kettle, T.M.		199.54		219.49	17.55	19.30
32 L.H., Daily Totals		$2118.69		$2938.04	$66.21	$91.81

Crew B-37C	Hr.	Daily	Hr.	Daily	Bare Costs	Incl. O&P
2 Laborers	$47.25	$756.00	$70.35	$1125.60	$50.08	$74.67
2 Truck Drivers (light)	52.90	846.40	79.00	1264.00		
2 Flatbed Trucks, Gas, 1.5 Ton		723.90		796.29		
1 Tar Kettle, T.M.		199.54		219.49	28.86	31.74
32 L.H., Daily Totals		$2525.84		$3405.38	$78.93	$106.42

Crew B-37D	Hr.	Daily	Hr.	Daily	Bare Costs	Incl. O&P
1 Laborer	$47.25	$378.00	$70.35	$562.80	$50.08	$74.67
1 Truck Driver (light)	52.90	423.20	79.00	632.00		
1 Pickup Truck, 3/4 Ton		122.56		134.82	7.66	8.43
16 L.H., Daily Totals		$923.76		$1329.62	$57.73	$83.10

Crew B-37E	Hr.	Daily	Hr.	Daily	Bare Costs	Incl. O&P
3 Laborers	$47.25	$1134.00	$70.35	$1688.40	$52.90	$78.81
1 Equip. Oper. (light)	59.70	477.60	88.85	710.80		
1 Equip. Oper. (medium)	63.05	504.40	93.80	750.40		
2 Truck Drivers (light)	52.90	846.40	79.00	1264.00		
4 Barrels w/ Flasher		11.36		12.50		
1 Concrete Saw		176.00		193.60		
1 Rotary Hammer Drill		34.98		38.48		
1 Hammer Drill Bit		26.61		29.27		
1 Loader, Skid Steer, 30 H.P.		260.99		287.09		
1 Conc. Hammer Attach.		126.94		139.63		
1 Vibrating Plate, Gas, 18"		143.82		158.20		
2 Flatbed Trucks, Gas, 1.5 Ton		723.90		796.29	26.87	29.55
56 L.H., Daily Totals		$4467.00		$6068.66	$79.77	$108.37

Crew B-37F	Hr.	Daily	Hr.	Daily	Bare Costs	Incl. O&P
3 Laborers	$47.25	$1134.00	$70.35	$1688.40	$48.66	$72.51
1 Truck Driver (light)	52.90	423.20	79.00	632.00		
4 Barrels w/ Flasher		11.36		12.50		
1 Concrete Mixer, 10 C.F.		149.77		164.75		
1 Air Compressor, 60 cfm		173.21		190.53		
1 -50' Air Hose, 3/4"		8.16		8.98		
1 Spade (Chipper)		9.37		10.31		
1 Flatbed Truck, Gas, 1.5 Ton		361.95		398.14	22.31	24.54
32 L.H., Daily Totals		$2271.02		$3105.60	$70.97	$97.05

Crew B-37G	Hr.	Daily	Hr.	Daily	Bare Costs	Incl. O&P
1 Labor Foreman (outside)	$49.25	$394.00	$73.30	$586.40	$49.66	$73.92
4 Laborers	47.25	1512.00	70.35	2251.20		
1 Equip. Oper. (light)	59.70	477.60	88.85	710.80		
1 Berm Machine		897.16		986.88		
1 Tandem Roller, 5 Ton		287.45		316.19	24.68	27.15
48 L.H., Daily Totals		$3568.21		$4851.47	$74.34	$101.07

Crew B-37H	Hr.	Daily	Hr.	Daily	Bare Costs	Incl. O&P
1 Labor Foreman (outside)	$49.25	$394.00	$73.30	$586.40	$49.66	$73.92
4 Laborers	47.25	1512.00	70.35	2251.20		
1 Equip. Oper. (light)	59.70	477.60	88.85	710.80		
1 Tandem Roller, 5 Ton		287.45		316.19		
1 Flatbed Truck, Gas, 1.5 Ton		361.95		398.14		
1 Tar Kettle, T.M.		199.54		219.49	17.69	19.45
48 L.H., Daily Totals		$3232.54		$4482.23	$67.34	$93.38

Crew No.	Bare Costs		Incl. Subs O&P		Cost Per Labor-Hour	
Crew B-37I	**Hr.**	**Daily**	**Hr.**	**Daily**	**Bare Costs**	**Incl. O&P**
3 Laborers	$47.25	$1134.00	$70.35	$1688.40	$52.90	$78.81
1 Equip. Oper. (light)	59.70	477.60	88.85	710.80		
1 Equip. Oper. (medium)	63.05	504.40	93.80	750.40		
2 Truck Drivers (light)	52.90	846.40	79.00	1264.00		
4 Barrels w/ Flasher		11.36		12.50		
1 Concrete Saw		176.00		193.60		
1 Rotary Hammer Drill		34.98		38.48		
1 Hammer Drill Bit		26.61		29.27		
1 Air Compressor, 60 cfm		173.21		190.53		
1 -50' Air Hose, 3/4"		8.16		8.98		
1 Spade (Chipper)		9.37		10.31		
1 Loader, Skid Steer, 30 H.P.		260.99		287.09		
1 Conc. Hammer Attach.		126.94		139.63		
1 Concrete Mixer, 10 C.F.		149.77		164.75		
1 Vibrating Plate, Gas, 18"		143.82		158.20		
2 Flatbed Trucks, Gas, 1.5 Ton		723.90		796.29	32.95	36.24
56 L.H., Daily Totals		$4807.51		$6443.22	$85.85	$115.06

Crew B-37J	Hr.	Daily	Hr.	Daily	Bare Costs	Incl. O&P
1 Labor Foreman (outside)	$49.25	$394.00	$73.30	$586.40	$49.66	$73.92
4 Laborers	47.25	1512.00	70.35	2251.20		
1 Equip. Oper. (light)	59.70	477.60	88.85	710.80		
1 Air Compressor, 60 cfm		173.21		190.53		
1 -50' Air Hose, 3/4"		8.16		8.98		
2 Concrete Mixers, 10 C.F.		299.54		329.49		
2 Flatbed Trucks, Gas, 1.5 Ton		723.90		796.29		
1 Shot Blaster, 20"		229.79		252.77	29.89	32.88
48 L.H., Daily Totals		$3818.20		$5126.46	$79.55	$106.80

Crew B-37K	Hr.	Daily	Hr.	Daily	Bare Costs	Incl. O&P
1 Labor Foreman (outside)	$49.25	$394.00	$73.30	$586.40	$49.66	$73.92
4 Laborers	47.25	1512.00	70.35	2251.20		
1 Equip. Oper. (light)	59.70	477.60	88.85	710.80		
1 Air Compressor, 60 cfm		173.21		190.53		
1 -50' Air Hose, 3/4"		8.16		8.98		
2 Flatbed Trucks, Gas, 1.5 Ton		723.90		796.29		
1 Shot Blaster, 20"		229.79		252.77	23.65	26.01
48 L.H., Daily Totals		$3518.66		$4796.97	$73.31	$99.94

Crew B-38	Hr.	Daily	Hr.	Daily	Bare Costs	Incl. O&P
1 Labor Foreman (outside)	$49.25	$394.00	$73.30	$586.40	$53.30	$79.33
2 Laborers	47.25	756.00	70.35	1125.60		
1 Equip. Oper. (light)	59.70	477.60	88.85	710.80		
1 Equip. Oper. (medium)	63.05	504.40	93.80	750.40		
1 Backhoe Loader, 48 H.P.		277.19		304.91		
1 Hyd. Hammer (1200 lb.)		194.78		214.26		
1 F.E. Loader, W.M., 4 C.Y.		789.98		868.98		
1 Pvmt. Rem. Bucket		70.14		77.15	33.30	36.63
40 L.H., Daily Totals		$3464.09		$4638.50	$86.60	$115.96

Crew B-39	Hr.	Daily	Hr.	Daily	Bare Costs	Incl. O&P
1 Labor Foreman (outside)	$49.25	$394.00	$73.30	$586.40	$49.66	$73.92
4 Laborers	47.25	1512.00	70.35	2251.20		
1 Equip. Oper. (light)	59.70	477.60	88.85	710.80		
1 Air Compressor, 250 cfm		196.28		215.91		
2 Breakers, Pavement, 60 lb.		68.94		75.83		
2 -50' Air Hoses, 1.5"		47.20		51.92	6.51	7.16
48 L.H., Daily Totals		$2696.02		$3892.06	$56.17	$81.08

Crew No.	Bare Costs		Incl. Subs O&P		Cost Per Labor-Hour	
Crew B-40	**Hr.**	**Daily**	**Hr.**	**Daily**	**Bare Costs**	**Incl. O&P**
1 Pile Driver Foreman (outside)	$62.50	$500.00	$96.70	$773.60	$61.69	$94.04
4 Pile Drivers	60.50	1936.00	93.60	2995.20		
2 Equip. Oper. (crane)	66.30	1060.80	98.65	1578.40		
1 Equip. Oper. (oiler)	56.40	451.20	83.90	671.20		
1 Crawler Crane, 40 Ton		1362.63		1498.89		
1 Vibratory Hammer & Gen.		2518.21		2770.03	60.64	66.70
64 L.H., Daily Totals		$7828.84		$10287.32	$122.33	$160.74

Crew B-40B	Hr.	Daily	Hr.	Daily	Bare Costs	Incl. O&P
1 Labor Foreman (outside)	$49.25	$394.00	$73.30	$586.40	$52.28	$77.82
3 Laborers	47.25	1134.00	70.35	1688.40		
1 Equip. Oper. (crane)	66.30	530.40	98.65	789.20		
1 Equip. Oper. (oiler)	56.40	451.20	83.90	671.20		
1 Lattice Boom Crane, 40 Ton		2371.83		2609.01	49.41	54.35
48 L.H., Daily Totals		$4881.43		$6344.21	$101.70	$132.17

Crew B-41	Hr.	Daily	Hr.	Daily	Bare Costs	Incl. O&P
1 Labor Foreman (outside)	$49.25	$394.00	$73.30	$586.40	$48.90	$72.79
4 Laborers	47.25	1512.00	70.35	2251.20		
.25 Equip. Oper. (crane)	66.30	132.60	98.65	197.30		
.25 Equip. Oper. (oiler)	56.40	112.80	83.90	167.80		
.25 Crawler Crane, 40 Ton		340.66		374.72	7.74	8.52
44 L.H., Daily Totals		$2492.06		$3577.42	$56.64	$81.31

Crew B-42	Hr.	Daily	Hr.	Daily	Bare Costs	Incl. O&P
1 Labor Foreman (outside)	$49.25	$394.00	$73.30	$586.40	$53.19	$79.58
4 Laborers	47.25	1512.00	70.35	2251.20		
1 Equip. Oper. (crane)	66.30	530.40	98.65	789.20		
1 Equip. Oper. (oiler)	56.40	451.20	83.90	671.20		
1 Welder	64.55	516.40	99.40	795.20		
1 Hyd. Crane, 25 Ton		2273.31		2500.64		
1 Welder, Gas Engine, 300 amp		147.09		161.80		
1 Horz. Boring Csg. Mch.		437.50		481.25	44.65	49.12
64 L.H., Daily Totals		$6261.90		$8236.89	$97.84	$128.70

Crew B-43	Hr.	Daily	Hr.	Daily	Bare Costs	Incl. O&P
1 Labor Foreman (outside)	$49.25	$394.00	$73.30	$586.40	$52.28	$77.82
3 Laborers	47.25	1134.00	70.35	1688.40		
1 Equip. Oper. (crane)	66.30	530.40	98.65	789.20		
1 Equip. Oper. (oiler)	56.40	451.20	83.90	671.20		
1 Drill Rig, Truck-Mounted		856.23		941.85	17.84	19.62
48 L.H., Daily Totals		$3365.83		$4677.05	$70.12	$97.44

Crew B-44	Hr.	Daily	Hr.	Daily	Bare Costs	Incl. O&P
1 Pile Driver Foreman (outside)	$62.50	$500.00	$96.70	$773.60	$60.54	$92.34
4 Pile Drivers	60.50	1936.00	93.60	2995.20		
2 Equip. Oper. (crane)	66.30	1060.80	98.65	1578.40		
1 Laborer	47.25	378.00	70.35	562.80		
1 Crawler Crane, 40 Ton		1362.63		1498.89		
1 Lead, 60' High		233.36		256.70		
1 Hammer, Diesel, 15K ft.-lbs.		687.50		756.25	35.68	39.25
64 L.H., Daily Totals		$6158.29		$8421.84	$96.22	$131.59

Crew B-45	Hr.	Daily	Hr.	Daily	Bare Costs	Incl. O&P
1 Equip. Oper. (medium)	$63.05	$504.40	$93.80	$750.40	$59.25	$88.33
1 Truck Driver (heavy)	55.45	443.60	82.85	662.80		
1 Dist. Tanker, 3000 Gallon		367.10		403.81		
1 Truck Tractor, 6x4, 380 H.P.		545.98		600.58	57.07	62.77
16 L.H., Daily Totals		$1861.08		$2417.59	$116.32	$151.10

Crew No.	Bare Costs		Incl. Subs O&P		Cost Per Labor-Hour	
Crew B-46	**Hr.**	**Daily**	**Hr.**	**Daily**	**Bare Costs**	**Incl. O&P**
1 Pile Driver Foreman (outside)	$62.50	$500.00	$96.70	$773.60	$54.21	$82.49
2 Pile Drivers	60.50	968.00	93.60	1497.60		
3 Laborers	47.25	1134.00	70.35	1688.40		
1 Chain Saw, Gas, 36" Long		53.61		58.97	1.12	1.23
48 L.H., Daily Totals		$2655.61		$4018.57	$55.33	$83.72
Crew B-47	**Hr.**	**Daily**	**Hr.**	**Daily**	**Bare Costs**	**Incl. O&P**
1 Blast Foreman (outside)	$49.25	$394.00	$73.30	$586.40	$52.07	$77.50
1 Driller	47.25	378.00	70.35	562.80		
1 Equip. Oper. (light)	59.70	477.60	88.85	710.80		
1 Air Track Drill, 4"		1191.15		1310.27		
1 Air Compressor, 600 cfm		466.11		512.72		
2 -50' Air Hoses, 3"		93.52		102.87	72.95	80.24
24 L.H., Daily Totals		$3000.38		$3785.86	$125.02	$157.74
Crew B-47A	**Hr.**	**Daily**	**Hr.**	**Daily**	**Bare Costs**	**Incl. O&P**
1 Drilling Foreman (outside)	$49.25	$394.00	$73.30	$586.40	$57.32	$85.28
1 Equip. Oper. (heavy)	66.30	530.40	98.65	789.20		
1 Equip. Oper. (oiler)	56.40	451.20	83.90	671.20		
1 Air Track Drill, 5"		1191.15		1310.27	49.63	54.59
24 L.H., Daily Totals		$2566.75		$3357.07	$106.95	$139.88
Crew B-47C	**Hr.**	**Daily**	**Hr.**	**Daily**	**Bare Costs**	**Incl. O&P**
1 Laborer	$47.25	$378.00	$70.35	$562.80	$53.48	$79.60
1 Equip. Oper. (light)	59.70	477.60	88.85	710.80		
1 Air Compressor, 750 C.F.M.		655.87		721.46		
2 -50' Air Hoses, 3"		93.52		102.87		
1 Air Track Drill, 4"		1191.15		1310.27	121.28	133.41
16 L.H., Daily Totals		$2796.14		$3408.19	$174.76	$213.01
Crew B-47E	**Hr.**	**Daily**	**Hr.**	**Daily**	**Bare Costs**	**Incl. O&P**
1 Labor Foreman (outside)	$49.25	$394.00	$73.30	$586.40	$47.75	$71.09
3 Laborers	47.25	1134.00	70.35	1688.40		
1 Flatbed Truck, Gas, 3 Ton		391.02		430.12	12.22	13.44
32 L.H., Daily Totals		$1919.02		$2704.92	$59.97	$84.53
Crew B-47G	**Hr.**	**Daily**	**Hr.**	**Daily**	**Bare Costs**	**Incl. O&P**
1 Labor Foreman (outside)	$49.25	$394.00	$73.30	$586.40	$50.86	$75.71
2 Laborers	47.25	756.00	70.35	1125.60		
1 Equip. Oper. (light)	59.70	477.60	88.85	710.80		
1 Air Track Drill, 4"		1191.15		1310.27		
1 Air Compressor, 600 cfm		466.11		512.72		
2 -50' Air Hoses, 3"		93.52		102.87		
1 Gunite Pump Rig		352.58		387.84	65.73	72.30
32 L.H., Daily Totals		$3730.96		$4736.50	$116.59	$148.02
Crew B-47H	**Hr.**	**Daily**	**Hr.**	**Daily**	**Bare Costs**	**Incl. O&P**
1 Skilled Worker Foreman (out)	$63.25	$506.00	$95.00	$760.00	$61.75	$92.75
3 Skilled Workers	61.25	1470.00	92.00	2208.00		
1 Flatbed Truck, Gas, 3 Ton		391.02		430.12	12.22	13.44
32 L.H., Daily Totals		$2367.02		$3398.12	$73.97	$106.19

Crew No.	Bare Costs		Incl. Subs O&P		Cost Per Labor-Hour	
Crew B-48	**Hr.**	**Daily**	**Hr.**	**Daily**	**Bare Costs**	**Incl. O&P**
1 Labor Foreman (outside)	$49.25	$394.00	$73.30	$586.40	$53.34	$79.39
3 Laborers	47.25	1134.00	70.35	1688.40		
1 Equip. Oper. (crane)	66.30	530.40	98.65	789.20		
1 Equip. Oper. (oiler)	56.40	451.20	83.90	671.20		
1 Equip. Oper. (light)	59.70	477.60	88.85	710.80		
1 Centr. Water Pump, 6"		386.48		425.13		
1 -20' Suction Hose, 6"		28.12		30.93		
1 -50' Discharge Hose, 6"		19.99		21.99		
1 Drill Rig, Truck-Mounted		856.23		941.85	23.05	25.36
56 L.H., Daily Totals		$4278.02		$5865.90	$76.39	$104.75
Crew B-49	**Hr.**	**Daily**	**Hr.**	**Daily**	**Bare Costs**	**Incl. O&P**
1 Labor Foreman (outside)	$49.25	$394.00	$73.30	$586.40	$56.10	$84.14
3 Laborers	47.25	1134.00	70.35	1688.40		
2 Equip. Oper. (crane)	66.30	1060.80	98.65	1578.40		
2 Equip. Oper. (oilers)	56.40	902.40	83.90	1342.40		
1 Equip. Oper. (light)	59.70	477.60	88.85	710.80		
2 Pile Drivers	60.50	968.00	93.60	1497.60		
1 Hyd. Crane, 25 Ton		2273.31		2500.64		
1 Centr. Water Pump, 6"		386.48		425.13		
1 -20' Suction Hose, 6"		28.12		30.93		
1 -50' Discharge Hose, 6"		19.99		21.99		
1 Drill Rig, Truck-Mounted		856.23		941.85	40.50	44.55
88 L.H., Daily Totals		$8500.93		$11324.54	$96.60	$128.69
Crew B-50	**Hr.**	**Daily**	**Hr.**	**Daily**	**Bare Costs**	**Incl. O&P**
2 Pile Driver Foremen (outside)	$62.50	$1000.00	$96.70	$1547.20	$58.48	$89.09
6 Pile Drivers	60.50	2904.00	93.60	4492.80		
2 Equip. Oper. (crane)	66.30	1060.80	98.65	1578.40		
1 Equip. Oper. (oiler)	56.40	451.20	83.90	671.20		
3 Laborers	47.25	1134.00	70.35	1688.40		
1 Crawler Crane, 40 Ton		1362.63		1498.89		
1 Lead, 60' High		233.36		256.70		
1 Hammer, Diesel, 15K ft.-lbs.		687.50		756.25		
1 Air Compressor, 600 cfm		466.11		512.72		
2 -50' Air Hoses, 3"		93.52		102.87		
1 Chain Saw, Gas, 36" Long		53.61		58.97	25.86	28.45
112 L.H., Daily Totals		$9446.73		$13164.40	$84.35	$117.54
Crew B-51	**Hr.**	**Daily**	**Hr.**	**Daily**	**Bare Costs**	**Incl. O&P**
1 Labor Foreman (outside)	$49.25	$394.00	$73.30	$586.40	$48.52	$72.28
4 Laborers	47.25	1512.00	70.35	2251.20		
1 Truck Driver (light)	52.90	423.20	79.00	632.00		
1 Flatbed Truck, Gas, 1.5 Ton		361.95		398.14	7.54	8.29
48 L.H., Daily Totals		$2691.15		$3867.74	$56.07	$80.58
Crew B-52	**Hr.**	**Daily**	**Hr.**	**Daily**	**Bare Costs**	**Incl. O&P**
1 Carpenter Foreman (outside)	$60.60	$484.80	$90.20	$721.60	$54.25	$80.58
1 Carpenter	58.60	468.80	87.25	698.00		
3 Laborers	47.25	1134.00	70.35	1688.40		
1 Cement Finisher	55.00	440.00	80.45	643.60		
.5 Rodman (reinf.)	64.55	258.20	96.40	385.60		
.5 Equip. Oper. (medium)	63.05	252.20	93.80	375.20		
.5 Crawler Loader, 3 C.Y.		628.84		691.72	11.23	12.35
56 L.H., Daily Totals		$3666.84		$5204.12	$65.48	$92.93
Crew B-53	**Hr.**	**Daily**	**Hr.**	**Daily**	**Bare Costs**	**Incl. O&P**
1 Equip. Oper. (light)	$59.70	$477.60	$88.85	$710.80	$59.70	$88.85
1 Trencher, Chain, 12 H.P.		202.47		222.72	25.31	27.84
8 L.H., Daily Totals		$680.07		$933.52	$85.01	$116.69

Crew No.	Bare Costs		Incl. Subs O&P		Cost Per Labor-Hour	
Crew B-54	**Hr.**	**Daily**	**Hr.**	**Daily**	**Bare Costs**	**Incl. O&P**
1 Equip. Oper. (light)	$59.70	$477.60	$88.85	$710.80	$59.70	$88.85
1 Trencher, Chain, 40 H.P.		386.50		425.15	48.31	53.14
8 L.H., Daily Totals		$864.10		$1135.95	$108.01	$141.99

Crew B-54A	Hr.	Daily	Hr.	Daily	Bare Costs	Incl. O&P
.17 Labor Foreman (outside)	$49.25	$66.98	$73.30	$99.69	$61.04	$90.82
1 Equipment Operator (med.)	63.05	504.40	93.80	750.40		
1 Wheel Trencher, 67 H.P.		1248.89		1373.78	133.43	146.77
9.36 L.H., Daily Totals		$1820.27		$2223.87	$194.47	$237.59

Crew B-54B	Hr.	Daily	Hr.	Daily	Bare Costs	Incl. O&P
.25 Labor Foreman (outside)	$49.25	$98.50	$73.30	$146.60	$60.29	$89.70
1 Equipment Operator (med.)	63.05	504.40	93.80	750.40		
1 Wheel Trencher, 150 H.P.		1338.44		1472.28	133.84	147.23
10 L.H., Daily Totals		$1941.34		$2369.28	$194.13	$236.93

Crew B-54C	Hr.	Daily	Hr.	Daily	Bare Costs	Incl. O&P
1 Laborer	$47.25	$378.00	$70.35	$562.80	$55.15	$82.08
1 Equipment Operator (med.)	63.05	504.40	93.80	750.40		
1 Wheel Trencher, 67 H.P.		1248.89		1373.78	78.06	85.86
16 L.H., Daily Totals		$2131.29		$2686.98	$133.21	$167.94

Crew B-54D	Hr.	Daily	Hr.	Daily	Bare Costs	Incl. O&P
1 Laborer	$47.25	$378.00	$70.35	$562.80	$55.15	$82.08
1 Equipment Operator (med.)	63.05	504.40	93.80	750.40		
1 Rock Trencher, 6" Width		992.44		1091.68	62.03	68.23
16 L.H., Daily Totals		$1874.84		$2404.88	$117.18	$150.31

Crew B-54E	Hr.	Daily	Hr.	Daily	Bare Costs	Incl. O&P
1 Laborer	$47.25	$378.00	$70.35	$562.80	$55.15	$82.08
1 Equipment Operator (med.)	63.05	504.40	93.80	750.40		
1 Rock Trencher, 18" Width		1079.31		1187.24	67.46	74.20
16 L.H., Daily Totals		$1961.71		$2500.44	$122.61	$156.28

Crew B-55	Hr.	Daily	Hr.	Daily	Bare Costs	Incl. O&P
2 Laborers	$47.25	$756.00	$70.35	$1125.60	$49.13	$73.23
1 Truck Driver (light)	52.90	423.20	79.00	632.00		
1 Truck-Mounted Earth Auger		446.91		491.60		
1 Flatbed Truck, Gas, 3 Ton		391.02		430.12	34.91	38.41
24 L.H., Daily Totals		$2017.13		$2679.32	$84.05	$111.64

Crew B-56	Hr.	Daily	Hr.	Daily	Bare Costs	Incl. O&P
1 Laborer	$47.25	$378.00	$70.35	$562.80	$53.48	$79.60
1 Equip. Oper. (light)	59.70	477.60	88.85	710.80		
1 Air Track Drill, 4"		1191.15		1310.27		
1 Air Compressor, 600 cfm		466.11		512.72		
1 -50' Air Hose, 3"		46.76		51.44	106.50	117.15
16 L.H., Daily Totals		$2559.62		$3148.02	$159.98	$196.75

Crew B-57	Hr.	Daily	Hr.	Daily	Bare Costs	Incl. O&P
1 Labor Foreman (outside)	$49.25	$394.00	$73.30	$586.40	$54.36	$80.90
2 Laborers	47.25	756.00	70.35	1125.60		
1 Equip. Oper. (crane)	66.30	530.40	98.65	789.20		
1 Equip. Oper. (light)	59.70	477.60	88.85	710.80		
1 Equip. Oper. (oiler)	56.40	451.20	83.90	671.20		
1 Crawler Crane, 25 Ton		1274.00		1401.40		
1 Clamshell Bucket, 1 C.Y.		46.89		51.58		
1 Centr. Water Pump, 6"		386.48		425.13		
1 -20' Suction Hose, 6"		28.12		30.93		
20 -50' Discharge Hoses, 6"		399.80		439.78	44.49	48.93
48 L.H., Daily Totals		$4744.49		$6232.02	$98.84	$129.83

Crew B-58	Hr.	Daily	Hr.	Daily	Bare Costs	Incl. O&P
2 Laborers	$47.25	$756.00	$70.35	$1125.60	$51.40	$76.52
1 Equip. Oper. (light)	59.70	477.60	88.85	710.80		
1 Backhoe Loader, 48 H.P.		277.19		304.91		
1 Small Helicopter, w/ Pilot		5810.29		6391.32	253.65	279.01
24 L.H., Daily Totals		$7321.08		$8532.63	$305.05	$355.53

Crew B-59	Hr.	Daily	Hr.	Daily	Bare Costs	Incl. O&P
1 Truck Driver (heavy)	$55.45	$443.60	$82.85	$662.80	$55.45	$82.85
1 Truck Tractor, 220 H.P.		339.98		373.98		
1 Water Tank Trailer, 5000 Gal.		169.14		186.05	63.64	70.00
8 L.H., Daily Totals		$952.72		$1222.83	$119.09	$152.85

Crew B-59A	Hr.	Daily	Hr.	Daily	Bare Costs	Incl. O&P
2 Laborers	$47.25	$756.00	$70.35	$1125.60	$49.98	$74.52
1 Truck Driver (heavy)	55.45	443.60	82.85	662.80		
1 Water Tank Trailer, 5000 Gal.		169.14		186.05		
1 Truck Tractor, 220 H.P.		339.98		373.98	21.21	23.33
24 L.H., Daily Totals		$1708.72		$2348.43	$71.20	$97.85

Crew B-60	Hr.	Daily	Hr.	Daily	Bare Costs	Incl. O&P
1 Labor Foreman (outside)	$49.25	$394.00	$73.30	$586.40	$55.12	$82.04
2 Laborers	47.25	756.00	70.35	1125.60		
1 Equip. Oper. (crane)	66.30	530.40	98.65	789.20		
2 Equip. Oper. (light)	59.70	955.20	88.85	1421.60		
1 Equip. Oper. (oiler)	56.40	451.20	83.90	671.20		
1 Crawler Crane, 40 Ton		1362.63		1498.89		
1 Lead, 60' High		233.36		256.70		
1 Hammer, Diesel, 15K ft.-lbs.		687.50		756.25		
1 Backhoe Loader, 48 H.P.		277.19		304.91	45.73	50.30
56 L.H., Daily Totals		$5647.48		$7410.75	$100.85	$132.33

Crew B-61	Hr.	Daily	Hr.	Daily	Bare Costs	Incl. O&P
1 Labor Foreman (outside)	$49.25	$394.00	$73.30	$586.40	$50.14	$74.64
3 Laborers	47.25	1134.00	70.35	1688.40		
1 Equip. Oper. (light)	59.70	477.60	88.85	710.80		
1 Cement Mixer, 2 C.Y.		119.22		131.14		
1 Air Compressor, 160 cfm		244.12		268.53	9.08	9.99
40 L.H., Daily Totals		$2368.94		$3385.27	$59.22	$84.63

Crew B-62	Hr.	Daily	Hr.	Daily	Bare Costs	Incl. O&P
2 Laborers	$47.25	$756.00	$70.35	$1125.60	$51.40	$76.52
1 Equip. Oper. (light)	59.70	477.60	88.85	710.80		
1 Loader, Skid Steer, 30 H.P.		260.99		287.09	10.87	11.96
24 L.H., Daily Totals		$1494.59		$2123.49	$62.27	$88.48

Crew No.	Bare Costs		Incl. Subs O&P		Cost Per Labor-Hour	
Crew B-62A	**Hr.**	**Daily**	**Hr.**	**Daily**	**Bare Costs**	**Incl. O&P**
2 Laborers	$47.25	$756.00	$70.35	$1125.60	$51.40	$76.52
1 Equip. Oper. (light)	59.70	477.60	88.85	710.80		
1 Loader, Skid Steer, 30 H.P.		260.99		287.09		
1 Trencher Attachment		88.83		97.71	14.58	16.03
24 L.H., Daily Totals		$1583.42		$2221.20	$65.98	$92.55

Crew B-63	Hr.	Daily	Hr.	Daily	Bare Costs	Incl. O&P
4 Laborers	$47.25	$1512.00	$70.35	$2251.20	$49.74	$74.05
1 Equip. Oper. (light)	59.70	477.60	88.85	710.80		
1 Loader, Skid Steer, 30 H.P.		260.99		287.09	6.52	7.18
40 L.H., Daily Totals		$2250.59		$3249.09	$56.26	$81.23

Crew B-63B	Hr.	Daily	Hr.	Daily	Bare Costs	Incl. O&P
1 Labor Foreman (inside)	$47.75	$382.00	$71.10	$568.80	$50.49	$75.16
2 Laborers	47.25	756.00	70.35	1125.60		
1 Equip. Oper. (light)	59.70	477.60	88.85	710.80		
1 Loader, Skid Steer, 78 H.P.		429.91		472.90	13.43	14.78
32 L.H., Daily Totals		$2045.51		$2878.10	$63.92	$89.94

Crew B-64	Hr.	Daily	Hr.	Daily	Bare Costs	Incl. O&P
1 Laborer	$47.25	$378.00	$70.35	$562.80	$50.08	$74.67
1 Truck Driver (light)	52.90	423.20	79.00	632.00		
1 Power Mulcher (small)		264.41		290.85		
1 Flatbed Truck, Gas, 1.5 Ton		361.95		398.14	39.15	43.06
16 L.H., Daily Totals		$1427.56		$1883.80	$89.22	$117.74

Crew B-65	Hr.	Daily	Hr.	Daily	Bare Costs	Incl. O&P
1 Laborer	$47.25	$378.00	$70.35	$562.80	$50.08	$74.67
1 Truck Driver (light)	52.90	423.20	79.00	632.00		
1 Power Mulcher (Large)		633.63		696.99		
1 Flatbed Truck, Gas, 1.5 Ton		361.95		398.14	62.22	68.45
16 L.H., Daily Totals		$1796.78		$2289.94	$112.30	$143.12

Crew B-66	Hr.	Daily	Hr.	Daily	Bare Costs	Incl. O&P
1 Equip. Oper. (light)	$59.70	$477.60	$88.85	$710.80	$59.70	$88.85
1 Loader-Backhoe, 40 H.P.		222.27		244.50	27.78	30.56
8 L.H., Daily Totals		$699.87		$955.30	$87.48	$119.41

Crew B-67	Hr.	Daily	Hr.	Daily	Bare Costs	Incl. O&P
1 Millwright	$62.85	$502.80	$90.80	$726.40	$61.27	$89.83
1 Equip. Oper. (light)	59.70	477.60	88.85	710.80		
1 R.T. Forklift, 5,000 Lb., diesel		349.30		384.23	21.83	24.01
16 L.H., Daily Totals		$1329.70		$1821.43	$83.11	$113.84

Crew B-67B	Hr.	Daily	Hr.	Daily	Bare Costs	Incl. O&P
1 Millwright Foreman (inside)	$63.35	$506.80	$91.55	$732.40	$63.10	$91.17
1 Millwright	62.85	502.80	90.80	726.40		
16 L.H., Daily Totals		$1009.60		$1458.80	$63.10	$91.17

Crew B-68	Hr.	Daily	Hr.	Daily	Bare Costs	Incl. O&P
2 Millwrights	$62.85	$1005.60	$90.80	$1452.80	$61.80	$90.15
1 Equip. Oper. (light)	59.70	477.60	88.85	710.80		
1 R.T. Forklift, 5,000 Lb., diesel		349.30		384.23	14.55	16.01
24 L.H., Daily Totals		$1832.50		$2547.83	$76.35	$106.16

Crew B-68A	Hr.	Daily	Hr.	Daily	Bare Costs	Incl. O&P
1 Millwright Foreman (inside)	$63.35	$506.80	$91.55	$732.40	$63.02	$91.05
2 Millwrights	62.85	1005.60	90.80	1452.80		
1 Forklift, Smooth Floor, 8,000 Lb.		311.06		342.17	12.96	14.26
24 L.H., Daily Totals		$1823.46		$2527.37	$75.98	$105.31

Crew B-68B	Hr.	Daily	Hr.	Daily	Bare Costs	Incl. O&P
1 Millwright Foreman (inside)	$63.35	$506.80	$91.55	$732.40	$66.84	$98.32
2 Millwrights	62.85	1005.60	90.80	1452.80		
2 Electricians	67.35	1077.60	100.10	1601.60		
2 Plumbers	72.05	1152.80	107.45	1719.20		
1 R.T. Forklift, 5,000 Lb., gas		422.09		464.30	7.54	8.29
56 L.H., Daily Totals		$4164.89		$5970.30	$74.37	$106.61

Crew B-68C	Hr.	Daily	Hr.	Daily	Bare Costs	Incl. O&P
1 Millwright Foreman (inside)	$63.35	$506.80	$91.55	$732.40	$66.40	$97.47
1 Millwright	62.85	502.80	90.80	726.40		
1 Electrician	67.35	538.80	100.10	800.80		
1 Plumber	72.05	576.40	107.45	859.60		
1 R.T. Forklift, 5,000 Lb., gas		422.09		464.30	13.19	14.51
32 L.H., Daily Totals		$2546.89		$3583.50	$79.59	$111.98

Crew B-68D	Hr.	Daily	Hr.	Daily	Bare Costs	Incl. O&P
1 Labor Foreman (inside)	$47.75	$382.00	$71.10	$568.80	$51.57	$76.77
1 Laborer	47.25	378.00	70.35	562.80		
1 Equip. Oper. (light)	59.70	477.60	88.85	710.80		
1 R.T. Forklift, 5,000 Lb., gas		422.09		464.30	17.59	19.35
24 L.H., Daily Totals		$1659.69		$2306.70	$69.15	$96.11

Crew B-68E	Hr.	Daily	Hr.	Daily	Bare Costs	Incl. O&P
1 Struc. Steel Foreman (inside)	$65.05	$520.40	$100.20	$801.60	$64.65	$99.56
3 Struc. Steel Workers	64.55	1549.20	99.40	2385.60		
1 Welder	64.55	516.40	99.40	795.20		
1 Forklift, Smooth Floor, 8,000 Lb.		311.06		342.17	7.78	8.55
40 L.H., Daily Totals		$2897.06		$4324.57	$72.43	$108.11

Crew B-68F	Hr.	Daily	Hr.	Daily	Bare Costs	Incl. O&P
1 Skilled Worker Foreman (out)	$63.25	$506.00	$95.00	$760.00	$61.92	$93.00
2 Skilled Workers	61.25	980.00	92.00	1472.00		
1 R.T. Forklift, 5,000 Lb., gas		422.09		464.30	17.59	19.35
24 L.H., Daily Totals		$1908.09		$2696.30	$79.50	$112.35

Crew B-68G	Hr.	Daily	Hr.	Daily	Bare Costs	Incl. O&P
2 Structural Steel Workers	$64.55	$1032.80	$99.40	$1590.40	$64.55	$99.40
1 R.T. Forklift, 5,000 Lb., gas		422.09		464.30	26.38	29.02
16 L.H., Daily Totals		$1454.89		$2054.70	$90.93	$128.42

Crew B-69	Hr.	Daily	Hr.	Daily	Bare Costs	Incl. O&P
1 Labor Foreman (outside)	$49.25	$394.00	$73.30	$586.40	$52.28	$77.82
3 Laborers	47.25	1134.00	70.35	1688.40		
1 Equip. Oper. (crane)	66.30	530.40	98.65	789.20		
1 Equip. Oper. (oiler)	56.40	451.20	83.90	671.20		
1 Hyd. Crane, 80 Ton		2641.70		2905.87	55.04	60.54
48 L.H., Daily Totals		$5151.30		$6641.07	$107.32	$138.36

Crew B-69A	Hr.	Daily	Hr.	Daily	Bare Costs	Incl. O&P
1 Labor Foreman (outside)	$49.25	$394.00	$73.30	$586.40	$51.51	$76.43
3 Laborers	47.25	1134.00	70.35	1688.40		
1 Equip. Oper. (medium)	63.05	504.40	93.80	750.40		
1 Concrete Finisher	55.00	440.00	80.45	643.60		
1 Curb/Gutter Paver, 2-Track		1074.23		1181.65	22.38	24.62
48 L.H., Daily Totals		$3546.63		$4850.45	$73.89	$101.05

Crew No.	Bare Costs		Incl. Subs O&P		Cost Per Labor-Hour	
Crew B-69B	**Hr.**	**Daily**	**Hr.**	**Daily**	**Bare Costs**	**Incl. O&P**
1 Labor Foreman (outside)	$49.25	$394.00	$73.30	$586.40	$51.51	$76.43
3 Laborers	47.25	1134.00	70.35	1688.40		
1 Equip. Oper. (medium)	63.05	504.40	93.80	750.40		
1 Cement Finisher	55.00	440.00	80.45	643.60		
1 Curb/Gutter Paver, 4-Track		1156.49		1272.14	24.09	26.50
48 L.H., Daily Totals		$3628.89		$4940.94	$75.60	$102.94
Crew B-70	**Hr.**	**Daily**	**Hr.**	**Daily**	**Bare Costs**	**Incl. O&P**
1 Labor Foreman (outside)	$49.25	$394.00	$73.30	$586.40	$54.31	$80.82
3 Laborers	47.25	1134.00	70.35	1688.40		
3 Equip. Oper. (medium)	63.05	1513.20	93.80	2251.20		
1 Grader, 30,000 Lbs.		1091.19		1200.31		
1 Ripper, Beam & 1 Shank		100.54		110.59		
1 Road Sweeper, S.P., 8' wide		538.01		591.81		
1 F.E. Loader, W.M., 1.5 C.Y.		455.32		500.85	39.02	42.92
56 L.H., Daily Totals		$5226.26		$6929.57	$93.33	$123.74
Crew B-70A	**Hr.**	**Daily**	**Hr.**	**Daily**	**Bare Costs**	**Incl. O&P**
1 Laborer	$47.25	$378.00	$70.35	$562.80	$59.89	$89.11
4 Equip. Oper. (medium)	63.05	2017.60	93.80	3001.60		
1 Grader, 40,000 Lbs.		1254.97		1380.47		
1 F.E. Loader, W.M., 2.5 C.Y.		658.89		724.78		
1 Dozer, 80 H.P.		591.82		651.00		
1 Roller, Pneum. Whl., 12 Ton		384.55		423.01	72.26	79.48
40 L.H., Daily Totals		$5285.83		$6743.65	$132.15	$168.59
Crew B-71	**Hr.**	**Daily**	**Hr.**	**Daily**	**Bare Costs**	**Incl. O&P**
1 Labor Foreman (outside)	$49.25	$394.00	$73.30	$586.40	$54.31	$80.82
3 Laborers	47.25	1134.00	70.35	1688.40		
3 Equip. Oper. (medium)	63.05	1513.20	93.80	2251.20		
1 Pvmt. Profiler, 750 H.P.		3680.74		4048.81		
1 Road Sweeper, S.P., 8' wide		538.01		591.81		
1 F.E. Loader, W.M., 1.5 C.Y.		455.32		500.85	83.47	91.81
56 L.H., Daily Totals		$7715.27		$9667.48	$137.77	$172.63
Crew B-72	**Hr.**	**Daily**	**Hr.**	**Daily**	**Bare Costs**	**Incl. O&P**
1 Labor Foreman (outside)	$49.25	$394.00	$73.30	$586.40	$55.40	$82.44
3 Laborers	47.25	1134.00	70.35	1688.40		
4 Equip. Oper. (medium)	63.05	2017.60	93.80	3001.60		
1 Pvmt. Profiler, 750 H.P.		3680.74		4048.81		
1 Hammermill, 250 H.P.		806.43		887.07		
1 Windrow Loader		1473.50		1620.85		
1 Mix Paver, 165 H.P.		1265.22		1391.74		
1 Roller, Pneum. Whl., 12 Ton		384.55		423.01	118.91	130.80
64 L.H., Daily Totals		$11156.04		$13647.88	$174.31	$213.25
Crew B-73	**Hr.**	**Daily**	**Hr.**	**Daily**	**Bare Costs**	**Incl. O&P**
1 Labor Foreman (outside)	$49.25	$394.00	$73.30	$586.40	$57.38	$85.38
2 Laborers	47.25	756.00	70.35	1125.60		
5 Equip. Oper. (medium)	63.05	2522.00	93.80	3752.00		
1 Road Mixer, 310 H.P.		2108.32		2319.15		
1 Tandem Roller, 10 Ton		379.22		417.14		
1 Hammermill, 250 H.P.		806.43		887.07		
1 Grader, 30,000 Lbs.		1091.19		1200.31		
.5 F.E. Loader, W.M., 1.5 C.Y.		227.66		250.43		
.5 Truck Tractor, 220 H.P.		169.99		186.99		
.5 Water Tank Trailer, 5000 Gal.		84.57		93.03	76.05	83.66
64 L.H., Daily Totals		$8539.38		$10818.12	$133.43	$169.03

Crew No.	Bare Costs		Incl. Subs O&P		Cost Per Labor-Hour	
Crew B-74	**Hr.**	**Daily**	**Hr.**	**Daily**	**Bare Costs**	**Incl. O&P**
1 Labor Foreman (outside)	$49.25	$394.00	$73.30	$586.40	$57.45	$85.57
1 Laborer	47.25	378.00	70.35	562.80		
4 Equip. Oper. (medium)	63.05	2017.60	93.80	3001.60		
2 Truck Drivers (heavy)	55.45	887.20	82.85	1325.60		
1 Grader, 30,000 Lbs.		1091.19		1200.31		
1 Ripper, Beam & 1 Shank		100.54		110.59		
2 Stabilizers, 310 H.P.		1713.46		1884.81		
1 Flatbed Truck, Gas, 3 Ton		391.02		430.12		
1 Chem. Spreader, Towed		87.61		96.37		
1 Roller, Vibratory, 25 Ton		529.68		582.65		
1 Water Tank Trailer, 5000 Gal.		169.14		186.05		
1 Truck Tractor, 220 H.P.		339.98		373.98	69.10	76.01
64 L.H., Daily Totals		$8099.42		$10341.28	$126.55	$161.58
Crew B-75	**Hr.**	**Daily**	**Hr.**	**Daily**	**Bare Costs**	**Incl. O&P**
1 Labor Foreman (outside)	$49.25	$394.00	$73.30	$586.40	$57.74	$85.96
1 Laborer	47.25	378.00	70.35	562.80		
4 Equip. Oper. (medium)	63.05	2017.60	93.80	3001.60		
1 Truck Driver (heavy)	55.45	443.60	82.85	662.80		
1 Grader, 30,000 Lbs.		1091.19		1200.31		
1 Ripper, Beam & 1 Shank		100.54		110.59		
2 Stabilizers, 310 H.P.		1713.46		1884.81		
1 Dist. Tanker, 3000 Gallon		367.10		403.81		
1 Truck Tractor, 6x4, 380 H.P.		545.98		600.58		
1 Roller, Vibratory, 25 Ton		529.68		582.65	77.64	85.41
56 L.H., Daily Totals		$7581.15		$9596.34	$135.38	$171.36
Crew B-76	**Hr.**	**Daily**	**Hr.**	**Daily**	**Bare Costs**	**Incl. O&P**
1 Dock Builder Foreman (outside)	$62.50	$500.00	$96.70	$773.60	$61.56	$93.99
5 Dock Builders	60.50	2420.00	93.60	3744.00		
2 Equip. Oper. (crane)	66.30	1060.80	98.65	1578.40		
1 Equip. Oper. (oiler)	56.40	451.20	83.90	671.20		
1 Crawler Crane, 50 Ton		1704.33		1874.76		
1 Barge, 400 Ton		957.33		1053.06		
1 Hammer, Diesel, 15K ft.-lbs.		687.50		756.25		
1 Lead, 60' High		233.36		256.70		
1 Air Compressor, 600 cfm		466.11		512.72		
2 -50' Air Hoses, 3"		93.52		102.87	57.53	63.28
72 L.H., Daily Totals		$8574.15		$11323.57	$119.09	$157.27
Crew B-76A	**Hr.**	**Daily**	**Hr.**	**Daily**	**Bare Costs**	**Incl. O&P**
1 Labor Foreman (outside)	$49.25	$394.00	$73.30	$586.40	$51.02	$75.95
5 Laborers	47.25	1890.00	70.35	2814.00		
1 Equip. Oper. (crane)	66.30	530.40	98.65	789.20		
1 Equip. Oper. (oiler)	56.40	451.20	83.90	671.20		
1 Crawler Crane, 50 Ton		1704.33		1874.76		
1 Barge, 400 Ton		957.33		1053.06	41.59	45.75
64 L.H., Daily Totals		$5927.26		$7788.63	$92.61	$121.70
Crew B-77	**Hr.**	**Daily**	**Hr.**	**Daily**	**Bare Costs**	**Incl. O&P**
1 Labor Foreman (outside)	$49.25	$394.00	$73.30	$586.40	$48.78	$72.67
3 Laborers	47.25	1134.00	70.35	1688.40		
1 Truck Driver (light)	52.90	423.20	79.00	632.00		
1 Crack Cleaner, 25 H.P.		167.33		184.06		
1 Crack Filler, Trailer Mtd.		201.26		221.39		
1 Flatbed Truck, Gas, 3 Ton		391.02		430.12	18.99	20.89
40 L.H., Daily Totals		$2710.81		$3742.37	$67.77	$93.56

Crew No.	Bare Costs		Incl. Subs O&P		Cost Per Labor-Hour	
Crew B-78	**Hr.**	**Daily**	**Hr.**	**Daily**	**Bare Costs**	**Incl. O&P**
1 Labor Foreman (outside)	$49.25	$394.00	$73.30	$586.40	$48.52	$72.28
4 Laborers	47.25	1512.00	70.35	2251.20		
1 Truck Driver (light)	52.90	423.20	79.00	632.00		
1 Paint Striper, S.P., 40 Gallon		73.74		81.11		
1 Flatbed Truck, Gas, 3 Ton		391.02		430.12		
1 Pickup Truck, 3/4 Ton		122.56		134.82	12.24	13.46
48 L.H., Daily Totals		$2916.52		$4115.65	$60.76	$85.74
Crew B-78A	**Hr.**	**Daily**	**Hr.**	**Daily**	**Bare Costs**	**Incl. O&P**
1 Equip. Oper. (light)	$59.70	$477.60	$88.85	$710.80	$59.70	$88.85
1 Line Rem. (Metal Balls) 115 H.P.		1648.72		1813.59	206.09	226.70
8 L.H., Daily Totals		$2126.32		$2524.39	$265.79	$315.55
Crew B-78B	**Hr.**	**Daily**	**Hr.**	**Daily**	**Bare Costs**	**Incl. O&P**
2 Laborers	$47.25	$756.00	$70.35	$1125.60	$48.63	$72.41
.25 Equip. Oper. (light)	59.70	119.40	88.85	177.70		
1 Pickup Truck, 3/4 Ton		122.56		134.82		
1 Line Rem.,11 H.P.,Walk Behind		214.39		235.83		
.25 Road Sweeper, S.P., 8' wide		134.50		147.95	26.19	28.81
18 L.H., Daily Totals		$1346.85		$1821.90	$74.83	$101.22
Crew B-78C	**Hr.**	**Daily**	**Hr.**	**Daily**	**Bare Costs**	**Incl. O&P**
1 Labor Foreman (outside)	$49.25	$394.00	$73.30	$586.40	$48.52	$72.28
4 Laborers	47.25	1512.00	70.35	2251.20		
1 Truck Driver (light)	52.90	423.20	79.00	632.00		
1 Paint Striper, T.M., 120 Gal.		673.88		741.27		
1 Flatbed Truck, Gas, 3 Ton		391.02		430.12		
1 Pickup Truck, 3/4 Ton		122.56		134.82	24.74	27.21
48 L.H., Daily Totals		$3516.66		$4775.81	$73.26	$99.50
Crew B-78D	**Hr.**	**Daily**	**Hr.**	**Daily**	**Bare Costs**	**Incl. O&P**
2 Labor Foremen (outside)	$49.25	$788.00	$73.30	$1172.80	$48.22	$71.81
7 Laborers	47.25	2646.00	70.35	3939.60		
1 Truck Driver (light)	52.90	423.20	79.00	632.00		
1 Paint Striper, T.M., 120 Gal.		673.88		741.27		
1 Flatbed Truck, Gas, 3 Ton		391.02		430.12		
3 Pickup Trucks, 3/4 Ton		367.68		404.45		
1 Air Compressor, 60 cfm		173.21		190.53		
1 -50' Air Hose, 3/4"		8.16		8.98		
1 Breaker, Pavement, 60 lb.		34.47		37.92	20.61	22.67
80 L.H., Daily Totals		$5505.62		$7557.66	$68.82	$94.47
Crew B-78E	**Hr.**	**Daily**	**Hr.**	**Daily**	**Bare Costs**	**Incl. O&P**
2 Labor Foremen (outside)	$49.25	$788.00	$73.30	$1172.80	$48.05	$71.56
9 Laborers	47.25	3402.00	70.35	5065.20		
1 Truck Driver (light)	52.90	423.20	79.00	632.00		
1 Paint Striper, T.M., 120 Gal.		673.88		741.27		
1 Flatbed Truck, Gas, 3 Ton		391.02		430.12		
4 Pickup Trucks, 3/4 Ton		490.24		539.26		
2 Air Compressors, 60 cfm		346.42		381.06		
2 -50' Air Hoses, 3/4"		16.32		17.95		
2 Breakers, Pavement, 60 lb.		68.94		75.83	20.70	22.77
96 L.H., Daily Totals		$6600.02		$9055.50	$68.75	$94.33

Crew No.	Bare Costs		Incl. Subs O&P		Cost Per Labor-Hour	
Crew B-78F	**Hr.**	**Daily**	**Hr.**	**Daily**	**Bare Costs**	**Incl. O&P**
2 Labor Foremen (outside)	$49.25	$788.00	$73.30	$1172.80	$47.94	$71.39
11 Laborers	47.25	4158.00	70.35	6190.80		
1 Truck Driver (light)	52.90	423.20	79.00	632.00		
1 Paint Striper, T.M., 120 Gal.		673.88		741.27		
1 Flatbed Truck, Gas, 3 Ton		391.02		430.12		
7 Pickup Trucks, 3/4 Ton		857.92		943.71		
3 Air Compressors, 60 cfm		519.63		571.59		
3 -50' Air Hoses, 3/4"		24.48		26.93		
3 Breakers, Pavement, 60 lb.		103.41		113.75	22.95	25.24
112 L.H., Daily Totals		$7939.54		$10822.97	$70.89	$96.63
Crew B-79	**Hr.**	**Daily**	**Hr.**	**Daily**	**Bare Costs**	**Incl. O&P**
1 Labor Foreman (outside)	$49.25	$394.00	$73.30	$586.40	$48.78	$72.67
3 Laborers	47.25	1134.00	70.35	1688.40		
1 Truck Driver (light)	52.90	423.20	79.00	632.00		
1 Paint Striper, T.M., 120 Gal.		673.88		741.27		
1 Heating Kettle, 115 Gallon		169.64		186.60		
1 Flatbed Truck, Gas, 3 Ton		391.02		430.12		
2 Pickup Trucks, 3/4 Ton		245.12		269.63	36.99	40.69
40 L.H., Daily Totals		$3430.86		$4534.43	$85.77	$113.36
Crew B-79A	**Hr.**	**Daily**	**Hr.**	**Daily**	**Bare Costs**	**Incl. O&P**
1.5 Equip. Oper. (light)	$59.70	$716.40	$88.85	$1066.20	$59.70	$88.85
.5 Line Remov. (Grinder) 115 H.P.		843.37		927.71		
1 Line Rem. (Metal Balls) 115 H.P.		1648.72		1813.59	207.67	228.44
12 L.H., Daily Totals		$3208.49		$3807.50	$267.37	$317.29
Crew B-79B	**Hr.**	**Daily**	**Hr.**	**Daily**	**Bare Costs**	**Incl. O&P**
1 Laborer	$47.25	$378.00	$70.35	$562.80	$47.25	$70.35
1 Set of Gases		188.67		207.54	23.58	25.94
8 L.H., Daily Totals		$566.67		$770.34	$70.83	$96.29
Crew B-79C	**Hr.**	**Daily**	**Hr.**	**Daily**	**Bare Costs**	**Incl. O&P**
1 Labor Foreman (outside)	$49.25	$394.00	$73.30	$586.40	$48.34	$72.01
5 Laborers	47.25	1890.00	70.35	2814.00		
1 Truck Driver (light)	52.90	423.20	79.00	632.00		
1 Paint Striper, T.M., 120 Gal.		673.88		741.27		
1 Heating Kettle, 115 Gallon		169.64		186.60		
1 Flatbed Truck, Gas, 3 Ton		391.02		430.12		
3 Pickup Trucks, 3/4 Ton		367.68		404.45		
1 Air Compressor, 60 cfm		173.21		190.53		
1 -50' Air Hose, 3/4"		8.16		8.98		
1 Breaker, Pavement, 60 lb.		34.47		37.92	32.47	35.71
56 L.H., Daily Totals		$4525.26		$6032.27	$80.81	$107.72
Crew B-79D	**Hr.**	**Daily**	**Hr.**	**Daily**	**Bare Costs**	**Incl. O&P**
2 Labor Foremen (outside)	$49.25	$788.00	$73.30	$1172.80	$48.46	$72.17
5 Laborers	47.25	1890.00	70.35	2814.00		
1 Truck Driver (light)	52.90	423.20	79.00	632.00		
1 Paint Striper, T.M., 120 Gal.		673.88		741.27		
1 Heating Kettle, 115 Gallon		169.64		186.60		
1 Flatbed Truck, Gas, 3 Ton		391.02		430.12		
4 Pickup Trucks, 3/4 Ton		490.24		539.26		
1 Air Compressor, 60 cfm		173.21		190.53		
1 -50' Air Hose, 3/4"		8.16		8.98		
1 Breaker, Pavement, 60 lb.		34.47		37.92	30.32	33.35
64 L.H., Daily Totals		$5041.82		$6753.48	$78.78	$105.52

Crew No.	Bare Costs		Incl. Subs O&P		Cost Per Labor-Hour	

Crew B-79E	Hr.	Daily	Hr.	Daily	Bare Costs	Incl. O&P
2 Labor Foremen (outside)	$49.25	$788.00	$73.30	$1172.80	$48.22	$71.81
7 Laborers	47.25	2646.00	70.35	3939.60		
1 Truck Driver (light)	52.90	423.20	79.00	632.00		
1 Paint Striper, T.M., 120 Gal.		673.88		741.27		
1 Heating Kettle, 115 Gallon		169.64		186.60		
1 Flatbed Truck, Gas, 3 Ton		391.02		430.12		
5 Pickup Trucks, 3/4 Ton		612.80		674.08		
2 Air Compressors, 60 cfm		346.42		381.06		
2 -50' Air Hoses, 3/4"		16.32		17.95		
2 Breakers, Pavement, 60 lb.		68.94		75.83	28.49	31.34
80 L.H., Daily Totals		$6136.22		$8251.32	$76.70	$103.14

Crew B-80	Hr.	Daily	Hr.	Daily	Bare Costs	Incl. O&P
1 Labor Foreman (outside)	$49.25	$394.00	$73.30	$586.40	$52.27	$77.88
1 Laborer	47.25	378.00	70.35	562.80		
1 Truck Driver (light)	52.90	423.20	79.00	632.00		
1 Equip. Oper. (light)	59.70	477.60	88.85	710.80		
1 Flatbed Truck, Gas, 3 Ton		391.02		430.12		
1 Earth Auger, Truck-Mtd.		153.97		169.37	17.03	18.73
32 L.H., Daily Totals		$2217.79		$3091.49	$69.31	$96.61

Crew B-80A	Hr.	Daily	Hr.	Daily	Bare Costs	Incl. O&P
3 Laborers	$47.25	$1134.00	$70.35	$1688.40	$47.25	$70.35
1 Flatbed Truck, Gas, 3 Ton		391.02		430.12	16.29	17.92
24 L.H., Daily Totals		$1525.02		$2118.52	$63.54	$88.27

Crew B-80B	Hr.	Daily	Hr.	Daily	Bare Costs	Incl. O&P
3 Laborers	$47.25	$1134.00	$70.35	$1688.40	$50.36	$74.97
1 Equip. Oper. (light)	59.70	477.60	88.85	710.80		
1 Crane, Flatbed Mounted, 3 Ton		596.44		656.08	18.64	20.50
32 L.H., Daily Totals		$2208.04		$3055.28	$69.00	$95.48

Crew B-80C	Hr.	Daily	Hr.	Daily	Bare Costs	Incl. O&P
2 Laborers	$47.25	$756.00	$70.35	$1125.60	$49.13	$73.23
1 Truck Driver (light)	52.90	423.20	79.00	632.00		
1 Flatbed Truck, Gas, 1.5 Ton		361.95		398.14		
1 Manual Fence Post Auger, Gas		52.21		57.43	17.26	18.98
24 L.H., Daily Totals		$1593.36		$2213.18	$66.39	$92.22

Crew B-81	Hr.	Daily	Hr.	Daily	Bare Costs	Incl. O&P
1 Laborer	$47.25	$378.00	$70.35	$562.80	$55.25	$82.33
1 Equip. Oper. (medium)	63.05	504.40	93.80	750.40		
1 Truck Driver (heavy)	55.45	443.60	82.85	662.80		
1 Hydromulcher, T.M., 3000 Gal.		745.16		819.68		
1 Truck Tractor, 220 H.P.		339.98		373.98	45.21	49.74
24 L.H., Daily Totals		$2411.14		$3169.65	$100.46	$132.07

Crew B-81A	Hr.	Daily	Hr.	Daily	Bare Costs	Incl. O&P
1 Laborer	$47.25	$378.00	$70.35	$562.80	$50.08	$74.67
1 Truck Driver (light)	52.90	423.20	79.00	632.00		
1 Hydromulcher, T.M., 600 Gal.		234.78		258.26		
1 Flatbed Truck, Gas, 3 Ton		391.02		430.12	39.11	43.02
16 L.H., Daily Totals		$1427.00		$1883.18	$89.19	$117.70

Crew B-82	Hr.	Daily	Hr.	Daily	Bare Costs	Incl. O&P
1 Laborer	$47.25	$378.00	$70.35	$562.80	$53.48	$79.60
1 Equip. Oper. (light)	59.70	477.60	88.85	710.80		
1 Horiz. Borer, 6 H.P.		114.54		125.99	7.16	7.87
16 L.H., Daily Totals		$970.14		$1399.59	$60.63	$87.47

Crew B-82A	Hr.	Daily	Hr.	Daily	Bare Costs	Incl. O&P
2 Laborers	$47.25	$756.00	$70.35	$1125.60	$53.48	$79.60
2 Equip. Opers. (light)	59.70	955.20	88.85	1421.60		
2 Dump Truck, 8 C.Y., 220 H.P.		834.98		918.48		
1 Flatbed Trailer, 25 Ton		150.61		165.67		
1 Horiz. Dir. Drill, 20k lb. Thrust		685.30		753.83		
1 Mud Trailer for HDD, 1500 Gal.		696.17		765.79		
1 Pickup Truck, 4x4, 3/4 Ton		191.73		210.90		
1 Flatbed Trailer, 3 Ton		78.34		86.17		
1 Loader, Skid Steer, 78 H.P.		429.91		472.90	95.84	105.43
32 L.H., Daily Totals		$4778.24		$5920.94	$149.32	$185.03

Crew B-82B	Hr.	Daily	Hr.	Daily	Bare Costs	Incl. O&P
2 Laborers	$47.25	$756.00	$70.35	$1125.60	$53.48	$79.60
2 Equip. Opers. (light)	59.70	955.20	88.85	1421.60		
2 Dump Truck, 8 C.Y., 220 H.P.		834.98		918.48		
1 Flatbed Trailer, 25 Ton		150.61		165.67		
1 Horiz. Dir. Drill, 30k lb. Thrust		740.76		814.84		
1 Mud Trailer for HDD, 1500 Gal.		696.17		765.79		
1 Pickup Truck, 4x4, 3/4 Ton		191.73		210.90		
1 Flatbed Trailer, 3 Ton		78.34		86.17		
1 Loader, Skid Steer, 78 H.P.		429.91		472.90	97.58	107.34
32 L.H., Daily Totals		$4833.70		$5981.95	$151.05	$186.94

Crew B-82C	Hr.	Daily	Hr.	Daily	Bare Costs	Incl. O&P
2 Laborers	$47.25	$756.00	$70.35	$1125.60	$53.48	$79.60
2 Equip. Opers. (light)	59.70	955.20	88.85	1421.60		
2 Dump Truck, 8 C.Y., 220 H.P.		834.98		918.48		
1 Flatbed Trailer, 25 Ton		150.61		165.67		
1 Horiz. Dir. Drill, 50k lb. Thrust		869.81		956.79		
1 Mud Trailer for HDD, 1500 Gal.		696.17		765.79		
1 Pickup Truck, 4x4, 3/4 Ton		191.73		210.90		
1 Flatbed Trailer, 3 Ton		78.34		86.17		
1 Loader, Skid Steer, 78 H.P.		429.91		472.90	101.61	111.77
32 L.H., Daily Totals		$4962.75		$6123.90	$155.09	$191.37

Crew B-82D	Hr.	Daily	Hr.	Daily	Bare Costs	Incl. O&P
1 Equip. Oper. (light)	$59.70	$477.60	$88.85	$710.80	$59.70	$88.85
1 Mud Trailer for HDD, 1500 Gal.		696.17		765.79	87.02	95.72
8 L.H., Daily Totals		$1173.77		$1476.59	$146.72	$184.57

Crew B-83	Hr.	Daily	Hr.	Daily	Bare Costs	Incl. O&P
1 Tugboat Captain	$63.05	$504.40	$93.80	$750.40	$55.15	$82.08
1 Tugboat Hand	47.25	378.00	70.35	562.80		
1 Tugboat, 250 H.P.		793.50		872.85	49.59	54.55
16 L.H., Daily Totals		$1675.90		$2186.05	$104.74	$136.63

Crew B-84	Hr.	Daily	Hr.	Daily	Bare Costs	Incl. O&P
1 Equip. Oper. (medium)	$63.05	$504.40	$93.80	$750.40	$63.05	$93.80
1 Rotary Mower/Tractor		238.84		262.72	29.86	32.84
8 L.H., Daily Totals		$743.24		$1013.12	$92.91	$126.64

Crew B-85	Hr.	Daily	Hr.	Daily	Bare Costs	Incl. O&P
3 Laborers	$47.25	$1134.00	$70.35	$1688.40	$52.05	$77.54
1 Equip. Oper. (medium)	63.05	504.40	93.80	750.40		
1 Truck Driver (heavy)	55.45	443.60	82.85	662.80		
1 Telescoping Boom Lift, to 80'		710.06		781.07		
1 Brush Chipper, 12", 130 H.P.		518.12		569.93		
1 Pruning Saw, Rotary		27.37		30.11	31.39	34.53
40 L.H., Daily Totals		$3337.55		$4482.70	$83.44	$112.07

Crew No.	Bare Costs		Incl. Subs O&P		Cost Per Labor-Hour	
Crew B-86	**Hr.**	**Daily**	**Hr.**	**Daily**	**Bare Costs**	**Incl. O&P**
1 Equip. Oper. (medium)	$63.05	$504.40	$93.80	$750.40	$63.05	$93.80
1 Stump Chipper, S.P.		263.85		290.24	32.98	36.28
8 L.H., Daily Totals		$768.25		$1040.64	$96.03	$130.08
Crew B-86A	**Hr.**	**Daily**	**Hr.**	**Daily**	**Bare Costs**	**Incl. O&P**
1 Equip. Oper. (medium)	$63.05	$504.40	$93.80	$750.40	$63.05	$93.80
1 Grader, 30,000 Lbs.		1091.19		1200.31	136.40	150.04
8 L.H., Daily Totals		$1595.59		$1950.71	$199.45	$243.84
Crew B-86B	**Hr.**	**Daily**	**Hr.**	**Daily**	**Bare Costs**	**Incl. O&P**
1 Equip. Oper. (medium)	$63.05	$504.40	$93.80	$750.40	$63.05	$93.80
1 Dozer, 200 H.P.		1382.36		1520.60	172.79	190.07
8 L.H., Daily Totals		$1886.76		$2271.00	$235.85	$283.87
Crew B-87	**Hr.**	**Daily**	**Hr.**	**Daily**	**Bare Costs**	**Incl. O&P**
1 Laborer	$47.25	$378.00	$70.35	$562.80	$59.89	$89.11
4 Equip. Oper. (medium)	63.05	2017.60	93.80	3001.60		
2 Feller Bunchers, 100 H.P.		2244.42		2468.86		
1 Log Chipper, 22" Tree		686.57		755.23		
1 Dozer, 105 H.P.		702.68		772.95		
1 Chain Saw, Gas, 36" Long		53.61		58.97	92.18	101.40
40 L.H., Daily Totals		$6082.88		$7620.41	$152.07	$190.51
Crew B-88	**Hr.**	**Daily**	**Hr.**	**Daily**	**Bare Costs**	**Incl. O&P**
1 Laborer	$47.25	$378.00	$70.35	$562.80	$60.79	$90.45
6 Equip. Oper. (medium)	63.05	3026.40	93.80	4502.40		
2 Feller Bunchers, 100 H.P.		2244.42		2468.86		
1 Log Chipper, 22" Tree		686.57		755.23		
2 Log Skidders, 50 H.P.		931.94		1025.13		
1 Dozer, 105 H.P.		702.68		772.95		
1 Chain Saw, Gas, 36" Long		53.61		58.97	82.49	90.73
56 L.H., Daily Totals		$8023.62		$10146.34	$143.28	$181.18
Crew B-89	**Hr.**	**Daily**	**Hr.**	**Daily**	**Bare Costs**	**Incl. O&P**
1 Equip. Oper. (light)	$59.70	$477.60	$88.85	$710.80	$56.30	$83.92
1 Truck Driver (light)	52.90	423.20	79.00	632.00		
1 Flatbed Truck, Gas, 3 Ton		391.02		430.12		
1 Concrete Saw		176.00		193.60		
1 Water Tank, 65 Gal.		97.09		106.80	41.51	45.66
16 L.H., Daily Totals		$1564.91		$2073.32	$97.81	$129.58
Crew B-89A	**Hr.**	**Daily**	**Hr.**	**Daily**	**Bare Costs**	**Incl. O&P**
1 Skilled Worker	$61.25	$490.00	$92.00	$736.00	$54.25	$81.17
1 Laborer	47.25	378.00	70.35	562.80		
1 Core Drill (Large)		118.14		129.95	7.38	8.12
16 L.H., Daily Totals		$986.14		$1428.75	$61.63	$89.30
Crew B-89B	**Hr.**	**Daily**	**Hr.**	**Daily**	**Bare Costs**	**Incl. O&P**
1 Equip. Oper. (light)	$59.70	$477.60	$88.85	$710.80	$56.30	$83.92
1 Truck Driver (light)	52.90	423.20	79.00	632.00		
1 Wall Saw, Hydraulic, 10 H.P.		111.53		122.68		
1 Generator, Diesel, 100 kW		568.06		624.87		
1 Water Tank, 65 Gal.		97.09		106.80		
1 Flatbed Truck, Gas, 3 Ton		391.02		430.12	72.98	80.28
16 L.H., Daily Totals		$2068.50		$2627.27	$129.28	$164.20
Crew B-89C	**Hr.**	**Daily**	**Hr.**	**Daily**	**Bare Costs**	**Incl. O&P**
1 Cement Finisher	$55.00	$440.00	$80.45	$643.60	$55.00	$80.45
1 Masonry cut-off saw, gas		68.42		75.26	8.55	9.41
8 L.H., Daily Totals		$508.42		$718.86	$63.55	$89.86

Crew No.	Bare Costs		Incl. Subs O&P		Cost Per Labor-Hour	
Crew B-90	**Hr.**	**Daily**	**Hr.**	**Daily**	**Bare Costs**	**Incl. O&P**
1 Labor Foreman (outside)	$49.25	$394.00	$73.30	$586.40	$52.66	$78.47
3 Laborers	47.25	1134.00	70.35	1688.40		
2 Equip. Oper. (light)	59.70	955.20	88.85	1421.60		
2 Truck Drivers (heavy)	55.45	887.20	82.85	1325.60		
1 Road Mixer, 310 H.P.		2108.32		2319.15		
1 Dist. Truck, 2000 Gal.		333.32		366.65	38.15	41.97
64 L.H., Daily Totals		$5812.04		$7707.80	$90.81	$120.43
Crew B-90A	**Hr.**	**Daily**	**Hr.**	**Daily**	**Bare Costs**	**Incl. O&P**
1 Labor Foreman (outside)	$49.25	$394.00	$73.30	$586.40	$56.56	$84.17
2 Laborers	47.25	756.00	70.35	1125.60		
4 Equip. Oper. (medium)	63.05	2017.60	93.80	3001.60		
2 Graders, 30,000 Lbs.		2182.38		2400.62		
1 Tandem Roller, 10 Ton		379.22		417.14		
1 Roller, Pneum. Whl., 12 Ton		384.55		423.01	52.61	57.87
56 L.H., Daily Totals		$6113.75		$7954.36	$109.17	$142.04
Crew B-90B	**Hr.**	**Daily**	**Hr.**	**Daily**	**Bare Costs**	**Incl. O&P**
1 Labor Foreman (outside)	$49.25	$394.00	$73.30	$586.40	$55.48	$82.57
2 Laborers	47.25	756.00	70.35	1125.60		
3 Equip. Oper. (medium)	63.05	1513.20	93.80	2251.20		
1 Roller, Pneum. Whl., 12 Ton		384.55		423.01		
1 Road Mixer, 310 H.P.		2108.32		2319.15	51.93	57.13
48 L.H., Daily Totals		$5156.07		$6705.36	$107.42	$139.69
Crew B-90C	**Hr.**	**Daily**	**Hr.**	**Daily**	**Bare Costs**	**Incl. O&P**
1 Labor Foreman (outside)	$49.25	$394.00	$73.30	$586.40	$53.98	$80.42
4 Laborers	47.25	1512.00	70.35	2251.20		
3 Equip. Oper. (medium)	63.05	1513.20	93.80	2251.20		
3 Truck Drivers (heavy)	55.45	1330.80	82.85	1988.40		
3 Road Mixers, 310 H.P.		6324.96		6957.46	71.87	79.06
88 L.H., Daily Totals		$11074.96		$14034.66	$125.85	$159.48
Crew B-90D	**Hr.**	**Daily**	**Hr.**	**Daily**	**Bare Costs**	**Incl. O&P**
1 Labor Foreman (outside)	$49.25	$394.00	$73.30	$586.40	$52.94	$78.87
6 Laborers	47.25	2268.00	70.35	3376.80		
3 Equip. Oper. (medium)	63.05	1513.20	93.80	2251.20		
3 Truck Drivers (heavy)	55.45	1330.80	82.85	1988.40		
3 Road Mixers, 310 H.P.		6324.96		6957.46	60.82	66.90
104 L.H., Daily Totals		$11830.96		$15160.26	$113.76	$145.77
Crew B-90E	**Hr.**	**Daily**	**Hr.**	**Daily**	**Bare Costs**	**Incl. O&P**
1 Labor Foreman (outside)	$49.25	$394.00	$73.30	$586.40	$53.65	$79.88
4 Laborers	47.25	1512.00	70.35	2251.20		
3 Equip. Oper. (medium)	63.05	1513.20	93.80	2251.20		
1 Truck Driver (heavy)	55.45	443.60	82.85	662.80		
1 Road Mixer, 310 H.P.		2108.32		2319.15	29.28	32.21
72 L.H., Daily Totals		$5971.12		$8070.75	$82.93	$112.09
Crew B-91	**Hr.**	**Daily**	**Hr.**	**Daily**	**Bare Costs**	**Incl. O&P**
1 Labor Foreman (outside)	$49.25	$394.00	$73.30	$586.40	$56.42	$84.01
2 Laborers	47.25	756.00	70.35	1125.60		
4 Equip. Oper. (medium)	63.05	2017.60	93.80	3001.60		
1 Truck Driver (heavy)	55.45	443.60	82.85	662.80		
1 Dist. Tanker, 3000 Gallon		367.10		403.81		
1 Truck Tractor, 6x4, 380 H.P.		545.98		600.58		
1 Aggreg. Spreader, S.P.		941.36		1035.50		
1 Roller, Pneum. Whl., 12 Ton		384.55		423.01		
1 Tandem Roller, 10 Ton		379.22		417.14	40.91	45.00
64 L.H., Daily Totals		$6229.41		$8256.43	$97.33	$129.01

Crew No.	Bare Costs		Incl. Subs O&P		Cost Per Labor-Hour	
Crew B-91B	**Hr.**	**Daily**	**Hr.**	**Daily**	**Bare Costs**	**Incl. O&P**
1 Laborer	$47.25	$378.00	$70.35	$562.80	$55.15	$82.08
1 Equipment Oper. (med.)	63.05	504.40	93.80	750.40		
1 Road Sweeper, Vac. Assist.		1900.22		2090.24	118.76	130.64
16 L.H., Daily Totals		$2782.62		$3403.44	$173.91	$212.72
Crew B-91C	**Hr.**	**Daily**	**Hr.**	**Daily**	**Bare Costs**	**Incl. O&P**
1 Laborer	$47.25	$378.00	$70.35	$562.80	$50.08	$74.67
1 Truck Driver (light)	52.90	423.20	79.00	632.00		
1 Catch Basin Cleaning Truck		594.04		653.44	37.13	40.84
16 L.H., Daily Totals		$1395.24		$1848.24	$87.20	$115.52
Crew B-91D	**Hr.**	**Daily**	**Hr.**	**Daily**	**Bare Costs**	**Incl. O&P**
1 Labor Foreman (outside)	$49.25	$394.00	$73.30	$586.40	$54.74	$81.52
5 Laborers	47.25	1890.00	70.35	2814.00		
5 Equip. Oper. (medium)	63.05	2522.00	93.80	3752.00		
2 Truck Drivers (heavy)	55.45	887.20	82.85	1325.60		
1 Aggreg. Spreader, S.P.		941.36		1035.50		
2 Truck Tractors, 6x4, 380 H.P.		1091.96		1201.16		
2 Dist. Tankers, 3000 Gallon		734.20		807.62		
2 Pavement Brushes, Towed		194.16		213.58		
2 Rollers Pneum. Whl., 12 Ton		769.10		846.01	35.87	39.46
104 L.H., Daily Totals		$9423.98		$12581.86	$90.62	$120.98
Crew B-92	**Hr.**	**Daily**	**Hr.**	**Daily**	**Bare Costs**	**Incl. O&P**
1 Labor Foreman (outside)	$49.25	$394.00	$73.30	$586.40	$47.75	$71.09
3 Laborers	47.25	1134.00	70.35	1688.40		
1 Crack Cleaner, 25 H.P.		167.33		184.06		
1 Air Compressor, 60 cfm		173.21		190.53		
1 Tar Kettle, T.M.		199.54		219.49		
1 Flatbed Truck, Gas, 3 Ton		391.02		430.12	29.10	32.01
32 L.H., Daily Totals		$2459.10		$3299.01	$76.85	$103.09
Crew B-93	**Hr.**	**Daily**	**Hr.**	**Daily**	**Bare Costs**	**Incl. O&P**
1 Equip. Oper. (medium)	$63.05	$504.40	$93.80	$750.40	$63.05	$93.80
1 Feller Buncher, 100 H.P.		1122.21		1234.43	140.28	154.30
8 L.H., Daily Totals		$1626.61		$1984.83	$203.33	$248.10
Crew B-94A	**Hr.**	**Daily**	**Hr.**	**Daily**	**Bare Costs**	**Incl. O&P**
1 Laborer	$47.25	$378.00	$70.35	$562.80	$47.25	$70.35
1 Diaphragm Water Pump, 2"		61.92		68.11		
1 -20' Suction Hose, 2"		4.37		4.81		
2 -50' Discharge Hoses, 2"		8.18		9.00	9.31	10.24
8 L.H., Daily Totals		$452.47		$644.72	$56.56	$80.59
Crew B-94B	**Hr.**	**Daily**	**Hr.**	**Daily**	**Bare Costs**	**Incl. O&P**
1 Laborer	$47.25	$378.00	$70.35	$562.80	$47.25	$70.35
1 Diaphragm Water Pump, 4"		150.72		165.79		
1 -20' Suction Hose, 4"		19.04		20.94		
2 -50' Discharge Hoses, 4"		28.30		31.13	24.76	27.23
8 L.H., Daily Totals		$576.06		$780.67	$72.01	$97.58
Crew B-94C	**Hr.**	**Daily**	**Hr.**	**Daily**	**Bare Costs**	**Incl. O&P**
1 Laborer	$47.25	$378.00	$70.35	$562.80	$47.25	$70.35
1 Centrifugal Water Pump, 3"		82.39		90.63		
1 -20' Suction Hose, 3"		8.96		9.86		
2 -50' Discharge Hoses, 3"		9.76		10.74	12.64	13.90
8 L.H., Daily Totals		$479.11		$674.02	$59.89	$84.25

Crew No.	Bare Costs		Incl. Subs O&P		Cost Per Labor-Hour	
Crew B-94D	**Hr.**	**Daily**	**Hr.**	**Daily**	**Bare Costs**	**Incl. O&P**
1 Laborer	$47.25	$378.00	$70.35	$562.80	$47.25	$70.35
1 Centr. Water Pump, 6"		386.48		425.13		
1 -20' Suction Hose, 6"		28.12		30.93		
2 -50' Discharge Hoses, 6"		39.98		43.98	56.82	62.50
8 L.H., Daily Totals		$832.58		$1062.84	$104.07	$132.85
Crew C-1	**Hr.**	**Daily**	**Hr.**	**Daily**	**Bare Costs**	**Incl. O&P**
3 Carpenters	$58.60	$1406.40	$87.25	$2094.00	$55.76	$83.03
1 Laborer	47.25	378.00	70.35	562.80		
32 L.H., Daily Totals		$1784.40		$2656.80	$55.76	$83.03
Crew C-2	**Hr.**	**Daily**	**Hr.**	**Daily**	**Bare Costs**	**Incl. O&P**
1 Carpenter Foreman (outside)	$60.60	$484.80	$90.20	$721.60	$57.04	$84.92
4 Carpenters	58.60	1875.20	87.25	2792.00		
1 Laborer	47.25	378.00	70.35	562.80		
48 L.H., Daily Totals		$2738.00		$4076.40	$57.04	$84.92
Crew C-2A	**Hr.**	**Daily**	**Hr.**	**Daily**	**Bare Costs**	**Incl. O&P**
1 Carpenter Foreman (outside)	$60.60	$484.80	$90.20	$721.60	$56.44	$83.79
3 Carpenters	58.60	1406.40	87.25	2094.00		
1 Cement Finisher	55.00	440.00	80.45	643.60		
1 Laborer	47.25	378.00	70.35	562.80		
48 L.H., Daily Totals		$2709.20		$4022.00	$56.44	$83.79
Crew C-3	**Hr.**	**Daily**	**Hr.**	**Daily**	**Bare Costs**	**Incl. O&P**
1 Rodman Foreman (outside)	$66.55	$532.40	$99.40	$795.20	$59.87	$89.32
4 Rodmen (reinf.)	64.55	2065.60	96.40	3084.80		
1 Equip. Oper. (light)	59.70	477.60	88.85	710.80		
2 Laborers	47.25	756.00	70.35	1125.60		
3 Stressing Equipment		51.87		57.06		
.5 Grouting Equipment		97.91		107.70	2.34	2.57
64 L.H., Daily Totals		$3981.38		$5881.15	$62.21	$91.89
Crew C-4	**Hr.**	**Daily**	**Hr.**	**Daily**	**Bare Costs**	**Incl. O&P**
1 Rodman Foreman (outside)	$66.55	$532.40	$99.40	$795.20	$65.05	$97.15
3 Rodmen (reinf.)	64.55	1549.20	96.40	2313.60		
3 Stressing Equipment		51.87		57.06	1.62	1.78
32 L.H., Daily Totals		$2133.47		$3165.86	$66.67	$98.93
Crew C-4A	**Hr.**	**Daily**	**Hr.**	**Daily**	**Bare Costs**	**Incl. O&P**
2 Rodmen (reinf.)	$64.55	$1032.80	$96.40	$1542.40	$64.55	$96.40
4 Stressing Equipment		69.16		76.08	4.32	4.75
16 L.H., Daily Totals		$1101.96		$1618.48	$68.87	$101.15
Crew C-5	**Hr.**	**Daily**	**Hr.**	**Daily**	**Bare Costs**	**Incl. O&P**
1 Rodman Foreman (outside)	$66.55	$532.40	$99.40	$795.20	$63.92	$95.36
4 Rodmen (reinf.)	64.55	2065.60	96.40	3084.80		
1 Equip. Oper. (crane)	66.30	530.40	98.65	789.20		
1 Equip. Oper. (oiler)	56.40	451.20	83.90	671.20		
1 Hyd. Crane, 25 Ton		2273.31		2500.64	40.59	44.65
56 L.H., Daily Totals		$5852.91		$7841.04	$104.52	$140.02
Crew C-6	**Hr.**	**Daily**	**Hr.**	**Daily**	**Bare Costs**	**Incl. O&P**
1 Labor Foreman (outside)	$49.25	$394.00	$73.30	$586.40	$48.88	$72.53
4 Laborers	47.25	1512.00	70.35	2251.20		
1 Cement Finisher	55.00	440.00	80.45	643.60		
2 Gas Engine Vibrators		59.36		65.30	1.24	1.36
48 L.H., Daily Totals		$2405.36		$3546.50	$50.11	$73.89

Crew C-6A	Bare Costs Hr.	Bare Costs Daily	Incl. Subs O&P Hr.	Incl. Subs O&P Daily	Cost Per Labor-Hour Bare Costs	Cost Per Labor-Hour Incl. O&P
2 Cement Finishers	$55.00	$880.00	$80.45	$1287.20	$55.00	$80.45
1 Concrete Vibrator, Elec, 2 HP		32.92		36.21	2.06	2.26
16 L.H., Daily Totals		$912.92		$1323.41	$57.06	$82.71

Crew C-7	Hr.	Daily	Hr.	Daily	Bare Costs	Incl. O&P
1 Labor Foreman (outside)	$49.25	$394.00	$73.30	$586.40	$51.11	$75.91
5 Laborers	47.25	1890.00	70.35	2814.00		
1 Cement Finisher	55.00	440.00	80.45	643.60		
1 Equip. Oper. (medium)	63.05	504.40	93.80	750.40		
1 Equip. Oper. (oiler)	56.40	451.20	83.90	671.20		
2 Gas Engine Vibrators		59.36		65.30		
1 Concrete Bucket, 1 C.Y.		50.97		56.07		
1 Hyd. Crane, 55 Ton		2461.06		2707.17	35.71	39.29
72 L.H., Daily Totals		$6250.99		$8294.13	$86.82	$115.20

Crew C-7A	Hr.	Daily	Hr.	Daily	Bare Costs	Incl. O&P
1 Labor Foreman (outside)	$49.25	$394.00	$73.30	$586.40	$49.55	$73.84
5 Laborers	47.25	1890.00	70.35	2814.00		
2 Truck Drivers (heavy)	55.45	887.20	82.85	1325.60		
2 Conc. Transit Mixers		1400.52		1540.57	21.88	24.07
64 L.H., Daily Totals		$4571.72		$6266.57	$71.43	$97.92

Crew C-7B	Hr.	Daily	Hr.	Daily	Bare Costs	Incl. O&P
1 Labor Foreman (outside)	$49.25	$394.00	$73.30	$586.40	$51.02	$75.95
5 Laborers	47.25	1890.00	70.35	2814.00		
1 Equipment Operator, Crane	66.30	530.40	98.65	789.20		
1 Equipment Oiler	56.40	451.20	83.90	671.20		
1 Conc. Bucket, 2 C.Y.		76.52		84.17		
1 Lattice Boom Crane, 165 Ton		2672.17		2939.39	42.95	47.24
64 L.H., Daily Totals		$6014.29		$7884.36	$93.97	$123.19

Crew C-7C	Hr.	Daily	Hr.	Daily	Bare Costs	Incl. O&P
1 Labor Foreman (outside)	$49.25	$394.00	$73.30	$586.40	$51.45	$76.58
5 Laborers	47.25	1890.00	70.35	2814.00		
2 Equipment Operators (med.)	63.05	1008.80	93.80	1500.80		
2 F.E. Loaders, W.M., 4 C.Y.		1579.96		1737.96	24.69	27.16
64 L.H., Daily Totals		$4872.76		$6639.16	$76.14	$103.74

Crew C-7D	Hr.	Daily	Hr.	Daily	Bare Costs	Incl. O&P
1 Labor Foreman (outside)	$49.25	$394.00	$73.30	$586.40	$49.79	$74.12
5 Laborers	47.25	1890.00	70.35	2814.00		
1 Equip. Oper. (medium)	63.05	504.40	93.80	750.40		
1 Concrete Conveyer		194.76		214.24	3.48	3.83
56 L.H., Daily Totals		$2983.16		$4365.04	$53.27	$77.95

Crew C-8	Hr.	Daily	Hr.	Daily	Bare Costs	Incl. O&P
1 Labor Foreman (outside)	$49.25	$394.00	$73.30	$586.40	$52.01	$77.01
3 Laborers	47.25	1134.00	70.35	1688.40		
2 Cement Finishers	55.00	880.00	80.45	1287.20		
1 Equip. Oper. (medium)	63.05	504.40	93.80	750.40		
1 Concrete Pump (Small)		827.49		910.24	14.78	16.25
56 L.H., Daily Totals		$3739.89		$5222.64	$66.78	$93.26

Crew C-8A	Hr.	Daily	Hr.	Daily	Bare Costs	Incl. O&P
1 Labor Foreman (outside)	$49.25	$394.00	$73.30	$586.40	$50.17	$74.21
3 Laborers	47.25	1134.00	70.35	1688.40		
2 Cement Finishers	55.00	880.00	80.45	1287.20		
48 L.H., Daily Totals		$2408.00		$3562.00	$50.17	$74.21

Crew C-8B	Hr.	Daily	Hr.	Daily	Bare Costs	Incl. O&P
1 Labor Foreman (outside)	$49.25	$394.00	$73.30	$586.40	$50.81	$75.63
3 Laborers	47.25	1134.00	70.35	1688.40		
1 Equip. Oper. (medium)	63.05	504.40	93.80	750.40		
1 Vibrating Power Screed		90.64		99.70		
1 Roller, Vibratory, 25 Ton		529.68		582.65		
1 Dozer, 200 H.P.		1382.36		1520.60	50.07	55.07
40 L.H., Daily Totals		$4035.08		$5228.15	$100.88	$130.70

Crew C-8C	Hr.	Daily	Hr.	Daily	Bare Costs	Incl. O&P
1 Labor Foreman (outside)	$49.25	$394.00	$73.30	$586.40	$51.51	$76.43
3 Laborers	47.25	1134.00	70.35	1688.40		
1 Cement Finisher	55.00	440.00	80.45	643.60		
1 Equip. Oper. (medium)	63.05	504.40	93.80	750.40		
1 Shotcrete Pump Rig, 12 C.Y./hr		651.19		716.31		
1 Air Compressor, 160 cfm		244.12		268.53		
4 -50' Air Hoses, 1"		37.24		40.96		
4 -50' Air Hoses, 2"		129.40		142.34	22.12	24.34
48 L.H., Daily Totals		$3534.35		$4836.94	$73.63	$100.77

Crew C-8D	Hr.	Daily	Hr.	Daily	Bare Costs	Incl. O&P
1 Labor Foreman (outside)	$49.25	$394.00	$73.30	$586.40	$52.80	$78.24
1 Laborer	47.25	378.00	70.35	562.80		
1 Cement Finisher	55.00	440.00	80.45	643.60		
1 Equipment Oper. (light)	59.70	477.60	88.85	710.80		
1 Air Compressor, 250 cfm		196.28		215.91		
2 -50' Air Hoses, 1"		18.62		20.48	6.72	7.39
32 L.H., Daily Totals		$1904.50		$2739.99	$59.52	$85.62

Crew C-8E	Hr.	Daily	Hr.	Daily	Bare Costs	Incl. O&P
1 Labor Foreman (outside)	$49.25	$394.00	$73.30	$586.40	$50.95	$75.61
3 Laborers	47.25	1134.00	70.35	1688.40		
1 Cement Finisher	55.00	440.00	80.45	643.60		
1 Equipment Oper. (light)	59.70	477.60	88.85	710.80		
1 Shotcrete Rig, 35 C.Y./hr		797.28		877.01		
1 Air Compressor, 250 cfm		196.28		215.91		
4 -50' Air Hoses, 1"		37.24		40.96		
4 -50' Air Hoses, 2"		129.40		142.34	24.17	26.59
48 L.H., Daily Totals		$3605.80		$4905.42	$75.12	$102.20

Crew C-9	Hr.	Daily	Hr.	Daily	Bare Costs	Incl. O&P
1 Cement Finisher	$55.00	$440.00	$80.45	$643.60	$52.30	$77.50
2 Laborers	47.25	756.00	70.35	1125.60		
1 Equipment Oper. (light)	59.70	477.60	88.85	710.80		
1 Grout Pump, 50 C.F./hr.		158.45		174.29		
1 Air Compressor, 160 cfm		244.12		268.53		
2 -50' Air Hoses, 1"		18.62		20.48		
2 -50' Air Hoses, 2"		64.70		71.17	15.18	16.70
32 L.H., Daily Totals		$2159.49		$3014.48	$67.48	$94.20

Crew C-10	Hr.	Daily	Hr.	Daily	Bare Costs	Incl. O&P
1 Laborer	$47.25	$378.00	$70.35	$562.80	$52.42	$77.08
2 Cement Finishers	55.00	880.00	80.45	1287.20		
24 L.H., Daily Totals		$1258.00		$1850.00	$52.42	$77.08

Crew C-10B	Hr.	Daily	Hr.	Daily	Bare Costs	Incl. O&P
3 Laborers	$47.25	$1134.00	$70.35	$1688.40	$50.35	$74.39
2 Cement Finishers	55.00	880.00	80.45	1287.20		
1 Concrete Mixer, 10 C.F.		149.77		164.75		
2 Trowels, 48" Walk-Behind		171.24		188.36	8.03	8.83
40 L.H., Daily Totals		$2335.01		$3328.71	$58.38	$83.22

Crew No.	Bare Costs		Incl. Subs O&P		Cost Per Labor-Hour	
Crew C-10C	**Hr.**	**Daily**	**Hr.**	**Daily**	**Bare Costs**	**Incl. O&P**
1 Laborer	$47.25	$378.00	$70.35	$562.80	$52.42	$77.08
2 Cement Finishers	55.00	880.00	80.45	1287.20		
1 Trowel, 48" Walk-Behind		85.62		94.18	3.57	3.92
24 L.H., Daily Totals		$1343.62		$1944.18	$55.98	$81.01

Crew C-10D	Hr.	Daily	Hr.	Daily	Bare Costs	Incl. O&P
1 Laborer	$47.25	$378.00	$70.35	$562.80	$52.42	$77.08
2 Cement Finishers	55.00	880.00	80.45	1287.20		
1 Vibrating Power Screed		90.64		99.70		
1 Trowel, 48" Walk-Behind		85.62		94.18	7.34	8.08
24 L.H., Daily Totals		$1434.26		$2043.89	$59.76	$85.16

Crew C-10E	Hr.	Daily	Hr.	Daily	Bare Costs	Incl. O&P
1 Laborer	$47.25	$378.00	$70.35	$562.80	$52.42	$77.08
2 Cement Finishers	55.00	880.00	80.45	1287.20		
1 Vibrating Power Screed		90.64		99.70		
1 Cement Trowel, 96" Ride-On		225.34		247.87	13.17	14.48
24 L.H., Daily Totals		$1573.98		$2197.58	$65.58	$91.57

Crew C-10F	Hr.	Daily	Hr.	Daily	Bare Costs	Incl. O&P
1 Laborer	$47.25	$378.00	$70.35	$562.80	$52.42	$77.08
2 Cement Finishers	55.00	880.00	80.45	1287.20		
1 Telescoping Boom Lift, to 60'		385.68		424.25	16.07	17.68
24 L.H., Daily Totals		$1643.68		$2274.25	$68.49	$94.76

Crew C-11	Hr.	Daily	Hr.	Daily	Bare Costs	Incl. O&P
1 Struc. Steel Foreman (outside)	$66.55	$532.40	$102.50	$820.00	$64.06	$97.94
6 Struc. Steel Workers	64.55	3098.40	99.40	4771.20		
1 Equip. Oper. (crane)	66.30	530.40	98.65	789.20		
1 Equip. Oper. (oiler)	56.40	451.20	83.90	671.20		
1 Lattice Boom Crane, 150 Ton		2585.11		2843.62	35.90	39.49
72 L.H., Daily Totals		$7197.51		$9895.22	$99.97	$137.43

Crew C-12	Hr.	Daily	Hr.	Daily	Bare Costs	Incl. O&P
1 Carpenter Foreman (outside)	$60.60	$484.80	$90.20	$721.60	$58.33	$86.83
3 Carpenters	58.60	1406.40	87.25	2094.00		
1 Laborer	47.25	378.00	70.35	562.80		
1 Equip. Oper. (crane)	66.30	530.40	98.65	789.20		
1 Hyd. Crane, 12 Ton		2150.65		2365.72	44.81	49.29
48 L.H., Daily Totals		$4950.25		$6533.31	$103.13	$136.11

Crew C-13	Hr.	Daily	Hr.	Daily	Bare Costs	Incl. O&P
1 Struc. Steel Worker	$64.55	$516.40	$99.40	$795.20	$62.57	$95.35
1 Welder	64.55	516.40	99.40	795.20		
1 Carpenter	58.60	468.80	87.25	698.00		
1 Welder, Gas Engine, 300 amp		147.09		161.80	6.13	6.74
24 L.H., Daily Totals		$1648.69		$2450.20	$68.70	$102.09

Crew C-14	Hr.	Daily	Hr.	Daily	Bare Costs	Incl. O&P
1 Carpenter Foreman (outside)	$60.60	$484.80	$90.20	$721.60	$57.42	$85.38
5 Carpenters	58.60	2344.00	87.25	3490.00		
4 Laborers	47.25	1512.00	70.35	2251.20		
4 Rodmen (reinf.)	64.55	2065.60	96.40	3084.80		
2 Cement Finishers	55.00	880.00	80.45	1287.20		
1 Equip. Oper. (crane)	66.30	530.40	98.65	789.20		
1 Equip. Oper. (oiler)	56.40	451.20	83.90	671.20		
1 Hyd. Crane, 80 Ton		2641.70		2905.87	18.35	20.18
144 L.H., Daily Totals		$10909.70		$15201.07	$75.76	$105.56

Crew C-14A	Hr.	Daily	Hr.	Daily	Bare Costs	Incl. O&P
1 Carpenter Foreman (outside)	$60.60	$484.80	$90.20	$721.60	$58.76	$87.47
16 Carpenters	58.60	7500.80	87.25	11168.00		
4 Rodmen (reinf.)	64.55	2065.60	96.40	3084.80		
2 Laborers	47.25	756.00	70.35	1125.60		
1 Cement Finisher	55.00	440.00	80.45	643.60		
1 Equip. Oper. (medium)	63.05	504.40	93.80	750.40		
1 Gas Engine Vibrator		29.68		32.65		
1 Concrete Pump (Small)		827.49		910.24	4.29	4.71
200 L.H., Daily Totals		$12608.77		$18436.89	$63.04	$92.18

Crew C-14B	Hr.	Daily	Hr.	Daily	Bare Costs	Incl. O&P
1 Carpenter Foreman (outside)	$60.60	$484.80	$90.20	$721.60	$58.61	$87.20
16 Carpenters	58.60	7500.80	87.25	11168.00		
4 Rodmen (reinf.)	64.55	2065.60	96.40	3084.80		
2 Laborers	47.25	756.00	70.35	1125.60		
2 Cement Finishers	55.00	880.00	80.45	1287.20		
1 Equip. Oper. (medium)	63.05	504.40	93.80	750.40		
1 Gas Engine Vibrator		29.68		32.65		
1 Concrete Pump (Small)		827.49		910.24	4.12	4.53
208 L.H., Daily Totals		$13048.77		$19080.49	$62.73	$91.73

Crew C-14C	Hr.	Daily	Hr.	Daily	Bare Costs	Incl. O&P
1 Carpenter Foreman (outside)	$60.60	$484.80	$90.20	$721.60	$56.09	$83.45
6 Carpenters	58.60	2812.80	87.25	4188.00		
2 Rodmen (reinf.)	64.55	1032.80	96.40	1542.40		
4 Laborers	47.25	1512.00	70.35	2251.20		
1 Cement Finisher	55.00	440.00	80.45	643.60		
1 Gas Engine Vibrator		29.68		32.65	.27	.29
112 L.H., Daily Totals		$6312.08		$9379.45	$56.36	$83.75

Crew C-14D	Hr.	Daily	Hr.	Daily	Bare Costs	Incl. O&P
1 Carpenter Foreman (outside)	$60.60	$484.80	$90.20	$721.60	$58.28	$86.74
18 Carpenters	58.60	8438.40	87.25	12564.00		
2 Rodmen (reinf.)	64.55	1032.80	96.40	1542.40		
2 Laborers	47.25	756.00	70.35	1125.60		
1 Cement Finisher	55.00	440.00	80.45	643.60		
1 Equip. Oper. (medium)	63.05	504.40	93.80	750.40		
1 Gas Engine Vibrator		29.68		32.65		
1 Concrete Pump (Small)		827.49		910.24	4.29	4.71
200 L.H., Daily Totals		$12513.57		$18290.49	$62.57	$91.45

Crew C-14E	Hr.	Daily	Hr.	Daily	Bare Costs	Incl. O&P
1 Carpenter Foreman (outside)	$60.60	$484.80	$90.20	$721.60	$57.52	$85.62
2 Carpenters	58.60	937.60	87.25	1396.00		
4 Rodmen (reinf.)	64.55	2065.60	96.40	3084.80		
3 Laborers	47.25	1134.00	70.35	1688.40		
1 Cement Finisher	55.00	440.00	80.45	643.60		
1 Gas Engine Vibrator		29.68		32.65	.34	.37
88 L.H., Daily Totals		$5091.68		$7567.05	$57.86	$85.99

Crew C-14F	Hr.	Daily	Hr.	Daily	Bare Costs	Incl. O&P
1 Labor Foreman (outside)	$49.25	$394.00	$73.30	$586.40	$52.64	$77.41
2 Laborers	47.25	756.00	70.35	1125.60		
6 Cement Finishers	55.00	2640.00	80.45	3861.60		
1 Gas Engine Vibrator		29.68		32.65	.41	.45
72 L.H., Daily Totals		$3819.68		$5606.25	$53.05	$77.86

Crew C-14G	Bare Costs Hr.	Bare Costs Daily	Incl. Subs O&P Hr.	Incl. Subs O&P Daily	Cost Per Labor-Hour Bare Costs	Cost Per Labor-Hour Incl. O&P
1 Labor Foreman (outside)	$49.25	$394.00	$73.30	$586.40	$51.96	$76.54
2 Laborers	47.25	756.00	70.35	1125.60		
4 Cement Finishers	55.00	1760.00	80.45	2574.40		
1 Gas Engine Vibrator		29.68		32.65	.53	.58
56 L.H., Daily Totals		$2939.68		$4319.05	$52.49	$77.13

Crew C-14H	Hr.	Daily	Hr.	Daily	Bare Costs	Incl. O&P
1 Carpenter Foreman (outside)	$60.60	$484.80	$90.20	$721.60	$57.43	$85.32
2 Carpenters	58.60	937.60	87.25	1396.00		
1 Rodman (reinf.)	64.55	516.40	96.40	771.20		
1 Laborer	47.25	378.00	70.35	562.80		
1 Cement Finisher	55.00	440.00	80.45	643.60		
1 Gas Engine Vibrator		29.68		32.65	.62	.68
48 L.H., Daily Totals		$2786.48		$4127.85	$58.05	$86.00

Crew C-14L	Hr.	Daily	Hr.	Daily	Bare Costs	Incl. O&P
1 Carpenter Foreman (outside)	$60.60	$484.80	$90.20	$721.60	$54.68	$81.30
6 Carpenters	58.60	2812.80	87.25	4188.00		
4 Laborers	47.25	1512.00	70.35	2251.20		
1 Cement Finisher	55.00	440.00	80.45	643.60		
1 Gas Engine Vibrator		29.68		32.65	.31	.34
96 L.H., Daily Totals		$5279.28		$7837.05	$54.99	$81.64

Crew C-14M	Hr.	Daily	Hr.	Daily	Bare Costs	Incl. O&P
1 Carpenter Foreman (outside)	$60.60	$484.80	$90.20	$721.60	$56.86	$84.51
2 Carpenters	58.60	937.60	87.25	1396.00		
1 Rodman (reinf.)	64.55	516.40	96.40	771.20		
2 Laborers	47.25	756.00	70.35	1125.60		
1 Cement Finisher	55.00	440.00	80.45	643.60		
1 Equip. Oper. (medium)	63.05	504.40	93.80	750.40		
1 Gas Engine Vibrator		29.68		32.65		
1 Concrete Pump (Small)		827.49		910.24	13.39	14.73
64 L.H., Daily Totals		$4496.37		$6351.29	$70.26	$99.24

Crew C-15	Hr.	Daily	Hr.	Daily	Bare Costs	Incl. O&P
1 Carpenter Foreman (outside)	$60.60	$484.80	$90.20	$721.60	$54.90	$81.45
2 Carpenters	58.60	937.60	87.25	1396.00		
3 Laborers	47.25	1134.00	70.35	1688.40		
2 Cement Finishers	55.00	880.00	80.45	1287.20		
1 Rodman (reinf.)	64.55	516.40	96.40	771.20		
72 L.H., Daily Totals		$3952.80		$5864.40	$54.90	$81.45

Crew C-16	Hr.	Daily	Hr.	Daily	Bare Costs	Incl. O&P
1 Labor Foreman (outside)	$49.25	$394.00	$73.30	$586.40	$52.01	$77.01
3 Laborers	47.25	1134.00	70.35	1688.40		
2 Cement Finishers	55.00	880.00	80.45	1287.20		
1 Equip. Oper. (medium)	63.05	504.40	93.80	750.40		
1 Gunite Pump Rig		352.58		387.84		
2 -50' Air Hoses, 3/4"		16.32		17.95		
2 -50' Air Hoses, 2"		64.70		71.17	7.74	8.52
56 L.H., Daily Totals		$3346.00		$4789.36	$59.75	$85.52

Crew C-16A	Hr.	Daily	Hr.	Daily	Bare Costs	Incl. O&P
1 Laborer	$47.25	$378.00	$70.35	$562.80	$55.08	$81.26
2 Cement Finishers	55.00	880.00	80.45	1287.20		
1 Equip. Oper. (medium)	63.05	504.40	93.80	750.40		
1 Gunite Pump Rig		352.58		387.84		
2 -50' Air Hoses, 3/4"		16.32		17.95		
2 -50' Air Hoses, 2"		64.70		71.17		
1 Telescoping Boom Lift, to 60'		385.68		424.25	25.60	28.16
32 L.H., Daily Totals		$2581.68		$3501.61	$80.68	$109.43

Crew C-17	Hr.	Daily	Hr.	Daily	Bare Costs	Incl. O&P
2 Skilled Worker Foremen (out)	$63.25	$1012.00	$95.00	$1520.00	$61.65	$92.60
8 Skilled Workers	61.25	3920.00	92.00	5888.00		
80 L.H., Daily Totals		$4932.00		$7408.00	$61.65	$92.60

Crew C-17A	Hr.	Daily	Hr.	Daily	Bare Costs	Incl. O&P
2 Skilled Worker Foremen (out)	$63.25	$1012.00	$95.00	$1520.00	$61.71	$92.68
8 Skilled Workers	61.25	3920.00	92.00	5888.00		
.13 Equip. Oper. (crane)	66.30	68.95	98.65	102.60		
.13 Hyd. Crane, 80 Ton		343.42		377.76	4.24	4.66
81.04 L.H., Daily Totals		$5344.37		$7888.36	$65.95	$97.34

Crew C-17B	Hr.	Daily	Hr.	Daily	Bare Costs	Incl. O&P
2 Skilled Worker Foremen (out)	$63.25	$1012.00	$95.00	$1520.00	$61.76	$92.75
8 Skilled Workers	61.25	3920.00	92.00	5888.00		
.25 Equip. Oper. (crane)	66.30	132.60	98.65	197.30		
.25 Hyd. Crane, 80 Ton		660.42		726.47		
.25 Trowel, 48" Walk-Behind		21.41		23.55	8.31	9.15
82 L.H., Daily Totals		$5746.43		$8355.31	$70.08	$101.89

Crew C-17C	Hr.	Daily	Hr.	Daily	Bare Costs	Incl. O&P
2 Skilled Worker Foremen (out)	$63.25	$1012.00	$95.00	$1520.00	$61.82	$92.82
8 Skilled Workers	61.25	3920.00	92.00	5888.00		
.38 Equip. Oper. (crane)	66.30	201.55	98.65	299.90		
.38 Hyd. Crane, 80 Ton		1003.85		1104.23	12.09	13.30
83.04 L.H., Daily Totals		$6137.40		$8812.13	$73.91	$106.12

Crew C-17D	Hr.	Daily	Hr.	Daily	Bare Costs	Incl. O&P
2 Skilled Worker Foremen (out)	$63.25	$1012.00	$95.00	$1520.00	$61.87	$92.89
8 Skilled Workers	61.25	3920.00	92.00	5888.00		
.5 Equip. Oper. (crane)	66.30	265.20	98.65	394.60		
.5 Hyd. Crane, 80 Ton		1320.85		1452.93	15.72	17.30
84 L.H., Daily Totals		$6518.05		$9255.53	$77.60	$110.18

Crew C-17E	Hr.	Daily	Hr.	Daily	Bare Costs	Incl. O&P
2 Skilled Worker Foremen (out)	$63.25	$1012.00	$95.00	$1520.00	$61.65	$92.60
8 Skilled Workers	61.25	3920.00	92.00	5888.00		
1 Hyd. Jack with Rods		40.57		44.63	.51	.56
80 L.H., Daily Totals		$4972.57		$7452.63	$62.16	$93.16

Crew C-18	Hr.	Daily	Hr.	Daily	Bare Costs	Incl. O&P
.13 Labor Foreman (outside)	$49.25	$51.22	$73.30	$76.23	$47.48	$70.69
1 Laborer	47.25	378.00	70.35	562.80		
1 Concrete Cart, 10 C.F.		149.92		164.91	16.58	18.24
9.04 L.H., Daily Totals		$579.14		$803.94	$64.06	$88.93

Crew C-19	Hr.	Daily	Hr.	Daily	Bare Costs	Incl. O&P
.13 Labor Foreman (outside)	$49.25	$51.22	$73.30	$76.23	$47.48	$70.69
1 Laborer	47.25	378.00	70.35	562.80		
1 Concrete Cart, 18 C.F.		122.73		135.00	13.58	14.93
9.04 L.H., Daily Totals		$551.95		$774.03	$61.06	$85.62

Crew C-20	Hr.	Daily	Hr.	Daily	Bare Costs	Incl. O&P
1 Labor Foreman (outside)	$49.25	$394.00	$73.30	$586.40	$50.44	$74.91
5 Laborers	47.25	1890.00	70.35	2814.00		
1 Cement Finisher	55.00	440.00	80.45	643.60		
1 Equip. Oper. (medium)	63.05	504.40	93.80	750.40		
2 Gas Engine Vibrators		59.36		65.30		
1 Concrete Pump (Small)		827.49		910.24	13.86	15.24
64 L.H., Daily Totals		$4115.25		$5769.94	$64.30	$90.16

Crew C-21	Bare Costs Hr.	Bare Costs Daily	Incl. Subs O&P Hr.	Incl. Subs O&P Daily	Cost Per Labor-Hour Bare Costs	Cost Per Labor-Hour Incl. O&P
1 Labor Foreman (outside)	$49.25	$394.00	$73.30	$586.40	$50.44	$74.91
5 Laborers	47.25	1890.00	70.35	2814.00		
1 Cement Finisher	55.00	440.00	80.45	643.60		
1 Equip. Oper. (medium)	63.05	504.40	93.80	750.40		
2 Gas Engine Vibrators		59.36		65.30		
1 Concrete Conveyer		194.76		214.24	3.97	4.37
64 L.H., Daily Totals		$3482.52		$5073.93	$54.41	$79.28

Crew C-22	Hr.	Daily	Hr.	Daily	Bare Costs	Incl. O&P
1 Rodman Foreman (outside)	$66.55	$532.40	$99.40	$795.20	$64.77	$96.72
4 Rodmen (reinf.)	64.55	2065.60	96.40	3084.80		
.13 Equip. Oper. (crane)	66.30	68.95	98.65	102.60		
.13 Equip. Oper. (oiler)	56.40	58.66	83.90	87.26		
.13 Hyd. Crane, 25 Ton		295.53		325.08	7.02	7.73
42.08 L.H., Daily Totals		$3021.14		$4394.94	$71.80	$104.44

Crew C-23	Hr.	Daily	Hr.	Daily	Bare Costs	Incl. O&P
2 Skilled Worker Foremen (out)	$63.25	$1012.00	$95.00	$1520.00	$61.67	$92.45
6 Skilled Workers	61.25	2940.00	92.00	4416.00		
1 Equip. Oper. (crane)	66.30	530.40	98.65	789.20		
1 Equip. Oper. (oiler)	56.40	451.20	83.90	671.20		
1 Lattice Boom Crane, 90 Ton		2689.54		2958.49	33.62	36.98
80 L.H., Daily Totals		$7623.14		$10354.89	$95.29	$129.44

Crew C-23A	Hr.	Daily	Hr.	Daily	Bare Costs	Incl. O&P
1 Labor Foreman (outside)	$49.25	$394.00	$73.30	$586.40	$53.29	$79.31
2 Laborers	47.25	756.00	70.35	1125.60		
1 Equip. Oper. (crane)	66.30	530.40	98.65	789.20		
1 Equip. Oper. (oiler)	56.40	451.20	83.90	671.20		
1 Crawler Crane, 100 Ton		1552.12		1707.33		
3 Conc. Buckets, 8 C.Y.		425.58		468.14	49.44	54.39
40 L.H., Daily Totals		$4109.30		$5347.87	$102.73	$133.70

Crew C-24	Hr.	Daily	Hr.	Daily	Bare Costs	Incl. O&P
2 Skilled Worker Foremen (out)	$63.25	$1012.00	$95.00	$1520.00	$61.67	$92.45
6 Skilled Workers	61.25	2940.00	92.00	4416.00		
1 Equip. Oper. (crane)	66.30	530.40	98.65	789.20		
1 Equip. Oper. (oiler)	56.40	451.20	83.90	671.20		
1 Lattice Boom Crane, 150 Ton		2585.11		2843.62	32.31	35.55
80 L.H., Daily Totals		$7518.71		$10240.02	$93.98	$128.00

Crew C-25	Hr.	Daily	Hr.	Daily	Bare Costs	Incl. O&P
2 Rodmen (reinf.)	$64.55	$1032.80	$96.40	$1542.40	$51.70	$79.67
2 Rodmen Helpers	38.85	621.60	62.95	1007.20		
32 L.H., Daily Totals		$1654.40		$2549.60	$51.70	$79.67

Crew C-27	Hr.	Daily	Hr.	Daily	Bare Costs	Incl. O&P
2 Cement Finishers	$55.00	$880.00	$80.45	$1287.20	$55.00	$80.45
1 Concrete Saw		176.00		193.60	11.00	12.10
16 L.H., Daily Totals		$1056.00		$1480.80	$66.00	$92.55

Crew C-28	Hr.	Daily	Hr.	Daily	Bare Costs	Incl. O&P
1 Cement Finisher	$55.00	$440.00	$80.45	$643.60	$55.00	$80.45
1 Portable Air Compressor, Gas		34.53		37.98	4.32	4.75
8 L.H., Daily Totals		$474.53		$681.58	$59.32	$85.20

Crew C-29	Hr.	Daily	Hr.	Daily	Bare Costs	Incl. O&P
1 Laborer	$47.25	$378.00	$70.35	$562.80	$47.25	$70.35
1 Pressure Washer		104.23		114.65	13.03	14.33
8 L.H., Daily Totals		$482.23		$677.45	$60.28	$84.68

Crew C-30	Hr.	Daily	Hr.	Daily	Bare Costs	Incl. O&P
1 Laborer	$47.25	$378.00	$70.35	$562.80	$47.25	$70.35
1 Concrete Mixer, 10 C.F.		149.77		164.75	18.72	20.59
8 L.H., Daily Totals		$527.77		$727.55	$65.97	$90.94

Crew C-31	Hr.	Daily	Hr.	Daily	Bare Costs	Incl. O&P
1 Cement Finisher	$55.00	$440.00	$80.45	$643.60	$55.00	$80.45
1 Grout Pump		352.58		387.84	44.07	48.48
8 L.H., Daily Totals		$792.58		$1031.44	$99.07	$128.93

Crew C-32	Hr.	Daily	Hr.	Daily	Bare Costs	Incl. O&P
1 Cement Finisher	$55.00	$440.00	$80.45	$643.60	$51.13	$75.40
1 Laborer	47.25	378.00	70.35	562.80		
1 Crack Chaser Saw, Gas, 6 H.P.		86.61		95.27		
1 Vacuum Pick-Up System		73.53		80.88	10.01	11.01
16 L.H., Daily Totals		$978.14		$1382.55	$61.13	$86.41

Crew D-1	Hr.	Daily	Hr.	Daily	Bare Costs	Incl. O&P
1 Bricklayer	$57.50	$460.00	$86.35	$690.80	$52.08	$78.20
1 Bricklayer Helper	46.65	373.20	70.05	560.40		
16 L.H., Daily Totals		$833.20		$1251.20	$52.08	$78.20

Crew D-2	Hr.	Daily	Hr.	Daily	Bare Costs	Incl. O&P
3 Bricklayers	$57.50	$1380.00	$86.35	$2072.40	$53.65	$80.50
2 Bricklayer Helpers	46.65	746.40	70.05	1120.80		
.5 Carpenter	58.60	234.40	87.25	349.00		
44 L.H., Daily Totals		$2360.80		$3542.20	$53.65	$80.50

Crew D-3	Hr.	Daily	Hr.	Daily	Bare Costs	Incl. O&P
3 Bricklayers	$57.50	$1380.00	$86.35	$2072.40	$53.42	$80.18
2 Bricklayer Helpers	46.65	746.40	70.05	1120.80		
.25 Carpenter	58.60	117.20	87.25	174.50		
42 L.H., Daily Totals		$2243.60		$3367.70	$53.42	$80.18

Crew D-4	Hr.	Daily	Hr.	Daily	Bare Costs	Incl. O&P
1 Bricklayer	$57.50	$460.00	$86.35	$690.80	$52.63	$78.83
2 Bricklayer Helpers	46.65	746.40	70.05	1120.80		
1 Equip. Oper. (light)	59.70	477.60	88.85	710.80		
1 Grout Pump, 50 C.F./hr.		158.45		174.29	4.95	5.45
32 L.H., Daily Totals		$1842.45		$2696.70	$57.58	$84.27

Crew D-5	Hr.	Daily	Hr.	Daily	Bare Costs	Incl. O&P
1 Bricklayer	57.50	460.00	86.35	690.80	57.50	86.35
8 L.H., Daily Totals		$460.00		$690.80	$57.50	$86.35

Crew D-6	Hr.	Daily	Hr.	Daily	Bare Costs	Incl. O&P
3 Bricklayers	$57.50	$1380.00	$86.35	$2072.40	$52.34	$78.56
3 Bricklayer Helpers	46.65	1119.60	70.05	1681.20		
.25 Carpenter	58.60	117.20	87.25	174.50		
50 L.H., Daily Totals		$2616.80		$3928.10	$52.34	$78.56

Crew D-7	Hr.	Daily	Hr.	Daily	Bare Costs	Incl. O&P
1 Tile Layer	$55.30	$442.40	$80.80	$646.40	$49.90	$72.90
1 Tile Layer Helper	44.50	356.00	65.00	520.00		
16 L.H., Daily Totals		$798.40		$1166.40	$49.90	$72.90

Crew D-8	Hr.	Daily	Hr.	Daily	Bare Costs	Incl. O&P
3 Bricklayers	$57.50	$1380.00	$86.35	$2072.40	$53.16	$79.83
2 Bricklayer Helpers	46.65	746.40	70.05	1120.80		
40 L.H., Daily Totals		$2126.40		$3193.20	$53.16	$79.83

Crew No.	Bare Costs Hr.	Bare Costs Daily	Incl. Subs O&P Hr.	Incl. Subs O&P Daily	Cost Per Labor-Hour Bare Costs	Cost Per Labor-Hour Incl. O&P
Crew D-9						
3 Bricklayers	$57.50	$1380.00	$86.35	$2072.40	$52.08	$78.20
3 Bricklayer Helpers	46.65	1119.60	70.05	1681.20		
48 L.H., Daily Totals		$2499.60		$3753.60	$52.08	$78.20

Crew D-10	Hr.	Daily	Hr.	Daily	Bare Costs	Incl. O&P
1 Bricklayer Foreman (outside)	$59.50	$476.00	$89.35	$714.80	$57.49	$86.10
1 Bricklayer	57.50	460.00	86.35	690.80		
1 Bricklayer Helper	46.65	373.20	70.05	560.40		
1 Equip. Oper. (crane)	66.30	530.40	98.65	789.20		
1 S.P. Crane, 4x4, 12 Ton		637.99		701.79	19.94	21.93
32 L.H., Daily Totals		$2477.59		$3456.99	$77.42	$108.03

Crew D-11	Hr.	Daily	Hr.	Daily	Bare Costs	Incl. O&P
1 Bricklayer Foreman (outside)	$59.50	$476.00	$89.35	$714.80	$54.55	$81.92
1 Bricklayer	57.50	460.00	86.35	690.80		
1 Bricklayer Helper	46.65	373.20	70.05	560.40		
24 L.H., Daily Totals		$1309.20		$1966.00	$54.55	$81.92

Crew D-12	Hr.	Daily	Hr.	Daily	Bare Costs	Incl. O&P
1 Bricklayer Foreman (outside)	$59.50	$476.00	$89.35	$714.80	$52.58	$78.95
1 Bricklayer	57.50	460.00	86.35	690.80		
2 Bricklayer Helpers	46.65	746.40	70.05	1120.80		
32 L.H., Daily Totals		$1682.40		$2526.40	$52.58	$78.95

Crew D-13	Hr.	Daily	Hr.	Daily	Bare Costs	Incl. O&P
1 Bricklayer Foreman (outside)	$59.50	$476.00	$89.35	$714.80	$55.87	$83.62
1 Bricklayer	57.50	460.00	86.35	690.80		
2 Bricklayer Helpers	46.65	746.40	70.05	1120.80		
1 Carpenter	58.60	468.80	87.25	698.00		
1 Equip. Oper. (crane)	66.30	530.40	98.65	789.20		
1 S.P. Crane, 4x4, 12 Ton		637.99		701.79	13.29	14.62
48 L.H., Daily Totals		$3319.59		$4715.39	$69.16	$98.24

Crew D-14	Hr.	Daily	Hr.	Daily	Bare Costs	Incl. O&P
3 Bricklayers	$57.50	$1380.00	$86.35	$2072.40	$54.79	$82.28
1 Bricklayer Helper	46.65	373.20	70.05	560.40		
32 L.H., Daily Totals		$1753.20		$2632.80	$54.79	$82.28

Crew E-1	Hr.	Daily	Hr.	Daily	Bare Costs	Incl. O&P
1 Welder Foreman (outside)	$66.55	$532.40	$102.50	$820.00	$63.60	$96.92
1 Welder	64.55	516.40	99.40	795.20		
1 Equip. Oper. (light)	59.70	477.60	88.85	710.80		
1 Welder, Gas Engine, 300 amp		147.09		161.80	6.13	6.74
24 L.H., Daily Totals		$1673.49		$2487.80	$69.73	$103.66

Crew E-2	Hr.	Daily	Hr.	Daily	Bare Costs	Incl. O&P
1 Struc. Steel Foreman (outside)	$66.55	$532.40	$102.50	$820.00	$63.92	$97.52
4 Struc. Steel Workers	64.55	2065.60	99.40	3180.80		
1 Equip. Oper. (crane)	66.30	530.40	98.65	789.20		
1 Equip. Oper. (oiler)	56.40	451.20	83.90	671.20		
1 Lattice Boom Crane, 90 Ton		2689.54		2958.49	48.03	52.83
56 L.H., Daily Totals		$6269.14		$8419.69	$111.95	$150.35

Crew E-3	Hr.	Daily	Hr.	Daily	Bare Costs	Incl. O&P
1 Struc. Steel Foreman (outside)	$66.55	$532.40	$102.50	$820.00	$65.22	$100.43
1 Struc. Steel Worker	64.55	516.40	99.40	795.20		
1 Welder	64.55	516.40	99.40	795.20		
1 Welder, Gas Engine, 300 amp		147.09		161.80	6.13	6.74
24 L.H., Daily Totals		$1712.29		$2572.20	$71.35	$107.17

Crew E-3A	Hr.	Daily	Hr.	Daily	Bare Costs	Incl. O&P
1 Struc. Steel Foreman (outside)	$66.55	$532.40	$102.50	$820.00	$65.22	$100.43
1 Struc. Steel Worker	64.55	516.40	99.40	795.20		
1 Welder	64.55	516.40	99.40	795.20		
1 Welder, Gas Engine, 300 amp		147.09		161.80		
1 Telescoping Boom Lift, to 40'		345.57		380.13	20.53	22.58
24 L.H., Daily Totals		$2057.86		$2952.33	$85.74	$123.01

Crew E-4	Hr.	Daily	Hr.	Daily	Bare Costs	Incl. O&P
1 Struc. Steel Foreman (outside)	$66.55	$532.40	$102.50	$820.00	$65.05	$100.18
3 Struc. Steel Workers	64.55	1549.20	99.40	2385.60		
1 Welder, Gas Engine, 300 amp		147.09		161.80	4.60	5.06
32 L.H., Daily Totals		$2228.69		$3367.40	$69.65	$105.23

Crew E-5	Hr.	Daily	Hr.	Daily	Bare Costs	Incl. O&P
2 Struc. Steel Foremen (outside)	$66.55	$1064.80	$102.50	$1640.00	$64.31	$98.39
5 Struc. Steel Workers	64.55	2582.00	99.40	3976.00		
1 Equip. Oper. (crane)	66.30	530.40	98.65	789.20		
1 Welder	64.55	516.40	99.40	795.20		
1 Equip. Oper. (oiler)	56.40	451.20	83.90	671.20		
1 Lattice Boom Crane, 90 Ton		2689.54		2958.49		
1 Welder, Gas Engine, 300 amp		147.09		161.80	35.46	39.00
80 L.H., Daily Totals		$7981.43		$10991.89	$99.77	$137.40

Crew E-6	Hr.	Daily	Hr.	Daily	Bare Costs	Incl. O&P
3 Struc. Steel Foremen (outside)	$66.55	$1597.20	$102.50	$2460.00	$64.22	$98.31
9 Struc. Steel Workers	64.55	4647.60	99.40	7156.80		
1 Equip. Oper. (crane)	66.30	530.40	98.65	789.20		
1 Welder	64.55	516.40	99.40	795.20		
1 Equip. Oper. (oiler)	56.40	451.20	83.90	671.20		
1 Equip. Oper. (light)	59.70	477.60	88.85	710.80		
1 Lattice Boom Crane, 90 Ton		2689.54		2958.49		
1 Welder, Gas Engine, 300 amp		147.09		161.80		
1 Air Compressor, 160 cfm		244.12		268.53		
2 Impact Wrenches		92.56		101.82	24.79	27.27
128 L.H., Daily Totals		$11393.71		$16073.84	$89.01	$125.58

Crew E-7	Hr.	Daily	Hr.	Daily	Bare Costs	Incl. O&P
1 Struc. Steel Foreman (outside)	$66.55	$532.40	$102.50	$820.00	$64.31	$98.39
4 Struc. Steel Workers	64.55	2065.60	99.40	3180.80		
1 Equip. Oper. (crane)	66.30	530.40	98.65	789.20		
1 Equip. Oper. (oiler)	56.40	451.20	83.90	671.20		
1 Welder Foreman (outside)	66.55	532.40	102.50	820.00		
2 Welders	64.55	1032.80	99.40	1590.40		
1 Lattice Boom Crane, 90 Ton		2689.54		2958.49		
2 Welder, Gas Engine, 300 amp		294.18		323.60	37.30	41.03
80 L.H., Daily Totals		$8128.52		$11153.69	$101.61	$139.42

Crew E-8	Hr.	Daily	Hr.	Daily	Bare Costs	Incl. O&P
1 Struc. Steel Foreman (outside)	$66.55	$532.40	$102.50	$820.00	$63.99	$97.82
4 Struc. Steel Workers	64.55	2065.60	99.40	3180.80		
1 Welder Foreman (outside)	66.55	532.40	102.50	820.00		
4 Welders	64.55	2065.60	99.40	3180.80		
1 Equip. Oper. (crane)	66.30	530.40	98.65	789.20		
1 Equip. Oper. (oiler)	56.40	451.20	83.90	671.20		
1 Equip. Oper. (light)	59.70	477.60	88.85	710.80		
1 Lattice Boom Crane, 90 Ton		2689.54		2958.49		
4 Welder, Gas Engine, 300 amp		588.36		647.20	31.52	34.67
104 L.H., Daily Totals		$9933.10		$13778.49	$95.51	$132.49

Crew No.	Bare Costs		Incl. Subs O&P		Cost Per Labor-Hour	
Crew E-9	**Hr.**	**Daily**	**Hr.**	**Daily**	**Bare Costs**	**Incl. O&P**
2 Struc. Steel Foremen (outside)	$66.55	$1064.80	$102.50	$1640.00	$64.22	$98.31
5 Struc. Steel Workers	64.55	2582.00	99.40	3976.00		
1 Welder Foreman (outside)	66.55	532.40	102.50	820.00		
5 Welders	64.55	2582.00	99.40	3976.00		
1 Equip. Oper. (crane)	66.30	530.40	98.65	789.20		
1 Equip. Oper. (oiler)	56.40	451.20	83.90	671.20		
1 Equip. Oper. (light)	59.70	477.60	88.85	710.80		
1 Lattice Boom Crane, 90 Ton		2689.54		2958.49		
5 Welder, Gas Engine, 300 amp		735.45		809.00	26.76	29.43
128 L.H., Daily Totals		$11645.39		$16350.69	$90.98	$127.74
Crew E-10	**Hr.**	**Daily**	**Hr.**	**Daily**	**Bare Costs**	**Incl. O&P**
1 Welder Foreman (outside)	$66.55	$532.40	$102.50	$820.00	$65.55	$100.95
1 Welder	64.55	516.40	99.40	795.20		
1 Welder, Gas Engine, 300 amp		147.09		161.80		
1 Flatbed Truck, Gas, 3 Ton		391.02		430.12	33.63	37.00
16 L.H., Daily Totals		$1586.91		$2207.12	$99.18	$137.95
Crew E-11	**Hr.**	**Daily**	**Hr.**	**Daily**	**Bare Costs**	**Incl. O&P**
2 Painters, Struc. Steel	$51.20	$819.20	$81.75	$1308.00	$52.34	$80.67
1 Building Laborer	47.25	378.00	70.35	562.80		
1 Equip. Oper. (light)	59.70	477.60	88.85	710.80		
1 Air Compressor, 250 cfm		196.28		215.91		
1 Sandblaster, Portable, 3 C.F.		84.26		92.69		
1 Set Sand Blasting Accessories		17.14		18.85	9.30	10.23
32 L.H., Daily Totals		$1972.48		$2909.05	$61.64	$90.91
Crew E-11A	**Hr.**	**Daily**	**Hr.**	**Daily**	**Bare Costs**	**Incl. O&P**
2 Painters, Struc. Steel	$51.20	$819.20	$81.75	$1308.00	$52.34	$80.67
1 Building Laborer	47.25	378.00	70.35	562.80		
1 Equip. Oper. (light)	59.70	477.60	88.85	710.80		
1 Air Compressor, 250 cfm		196.28		215.91		
1 Sandblaster, Portable, 3 C.F.		84.26		92.69		
1 Set Sand Blasting Accessories		17.14		18.85		
1 Telescoping Boom Lift, to 60'		385.68		424.25	21.36	23.49
32 L.H., Daily Totals		$2358.16		$3333.30	$73.69	$104.17
Crew E-11B	**Hr.**	**Daily**	**Hr.**	**Daily**	**Bare Costs**	**Incl. O&P**
2 Painters, Struc. Steel	$51.20	$819.20	$81.75	$1308.00	$49.88	$77.95
1 Building Laborer	47.25	378.00	70.35	562.80		
2 Paint Sprayer, 8 C.F.M.		104.28		114.71		
1 Telescoping Boom Lift, to 60'		385.68		424.25	20.41	22.46
24 L.H., Daily Totals		$1687.16		$2409.76	$70.30	$100.41
Crew E-12	**Hr.**	**Daily**	**Hr.**	**Daily**	**Bare Costs**	**Incl. O&P**
1 Welder Foreman (outside)	$66.55	$532.40	$102.50	$820.00	$63.13	$95.67
1 Equip. Oper. (light)	59.70	477.60	88.85	710.80		
1 Welder, Gas Engine, 300 amp		147.09		161.80	9.19	10.11
16 L.H., Daily Totals		$1157.09		$1692.60	$72.32	$105.79
Crew E-13	**Hr.**	**Daily**	**Hr.**	**Daily**	**Bare Costs**	**Incl. O&P**
1 Welder Foreman (outside)	$66.55	$532.40	$102.50	$820.00	$64.27	$97.95
.5 Equip. Oper. (light)	59.70	238.80	88.85	355.40		
1 Welder, Gas Engine, 300 amp		147.09		161.80	12.26	13.48
12 L.H., Daily Totals		$918.29		$1337.20	$76.52	$111.43
Crew E-14	**Hr.**	**Daily**	**Hr.**	**Daily**	**Bare Costs**	**Incl. O&P**
1 Welder Foreman (outside)	$66.55	$532.40	$102.50	$820.00	$66.55	$102.50
1 Welder, Gas Engine, 300 amp		147.09		161.80	18.39	20.22
8 L.H., Daily Totals		$679.49		$981.80	$84.94	$122.72

Crew No.	Bare Costs		Incl. Subs O&P		Cost Per Labor-Hour	
Crew E-16	**Hr.**	**Daily**	**Hr.**	**Daily**	**Bare Costs**	**Incl. O&P**
1 Welder Foreman (outside)	$66.55	$532.40	$102.50	$820.00	$65.55	$100.95
1 Welder	64.55	516.40	99.40	795.20		
1 Welder, Gas Engine, 300 amp		147.09		161.80	9.19	10.11
16 L.H., Daily Totals		$1195.89		$1777.00	$74.74	$111.06
Crew E-17	**Hr.**	**Daily**	**Hr.**	**Daily**	**Bare Costs**	**Incl. O&P**
1 Struc. Steel Foreman (outside)	$66.55	$532.40	$102.50	$820.00	$65.55	$100.95
1 Structural Steel Worker	64.55	516.40	99.40	795.20		
16 L.H., Daily Totals		$1048.80		$1615.20	$65.55	$100.95
Crew E-18	**Hr.**	**Daily**	**Hr.**	**Daily**	**Bare Costs**	**Incl. O&P**
1 Struc. Steel Foreman (outside)	$66.55	$532.40	$102.50	$820.00	$64.65	$98.90
3 Structural Steel Workers	64.55	1549.20	99.40	2385.60		
1 Equipment Operator (med.)	63.05	504.40	93.80	750.40		
1 Lattice Boom Crane, 20 Ton		868.10		954.91	21.70	23.87
40 L.H., Daily Totals		$3454.10		$4910.91	$86.35	$122.77
Crew E-19	**Hr.**	**Daily**	**Hr.**	**Daily**	**Bare Costs**	**Incl. O&P**
1 Struc. Steel Foreman (outside)	$66.55	$532.40	$102.50	$820.00	$63.60	$96.92
1 Structural Steel Worker	64.55	516.40	99.40	795.20		
1 Equip. Oper. (light)	59.70	477.60	88.85	710.80		
1 Lattice Boom Crane, 20 Ton		868.10		954.91	36.17	39.79
24 L.H., Daily Totals		$2394.50		$3280.91	$99.77	$136.70
Crew E-20	**Hr.**	**Daily**	**Hr.**	**Daily**	**Bare Costs**	**Incl. O&P**
1 Struc. Steel Foreman (outside)	$66.55	$532.40	$102.50	$820.00	$64.00	$97.76
5 Structural Steel Workers	64.55	2582.00	99.40	3976.00		
1 Equip. Oper. (crane)	66.30	530.40	98.65	789.20		
1 Equip. Oper. (oiler)	56.40	451.20	83.90	671.20		
1 Lattice Boom Crane, 40 Ton		2371.83		2609.01	37.06	40.77
64 L.H., Daily Totals		$6467.83		$8865.41	$101.06	$138.52
Crew E-22	**Hr.**	**Daily**	**Hr.**	**Daily**	**Bare Costs**	**Incl. O&P**
1 Skilled Worker Foreman (out)	$63.25	$506.00	$95.00	$760.00	$61.92	$93.00
2 Skilled Workers	61.25	980.00	92.00	1472.00		
24 L.H., Daily Totals		$1486.00		$2232.00	$61.92	$93.00
Crew E-24	**Hr.**	**Daily**	**Hr.**	**Daily**	**Bare Costs**	**Incl. O&P**
3 Structural Steel Workers	$64.55	$1549.20	$99.40	$2385.60	$64.17	$98.00
1 Equipment Operator (med.)	63.05	504.40	93.80	750.40		
1 Hyd. Crane, 25 Ton		2273.31		2500.64	71.04	78.14
32 L.H., Daily Totals		$4326.91		$5636.64	$135.22	$176.15
Crew E-25	**Hr.**	**Daily**	**Hr.**	**Daily**	**Bare Costs**	**Incl. O&P**
1 Welder Foreman (outside)	$66.55	$532.40	$102.50	$820.00	$66.55	$102.50
1 Cutting Torch		14.24		15.66	1.78	1.96
8 L.H., Daily Totals		$546.64		$835.66	$68.33	$104.46
Crew E-26	**Hr.**	**Daily**	**Hr.**	**Daily**	**Bare Costs**	**Incl. O&P**
1 Struc. Steel Foreman (outside)	$66.55	$532.40	$102.50	$820.00	$65.86	$100.91
1 Struc. Steel Worker	64.55	516.40	99.40	795.20		
1 Welder	64.55	516.40	99.40	795.20		
.25 Electrician	67.35	134.70	100.10	200.20		
.25 Plumber	72.05	144.10	107.45	214.90		
1 Welder, Gas Engine, 300 amp		147.09		161.80	5.25	5.78
28 L.H., Daily Totals		$1991.09		$2987.30	$71.11	$106.69

Crew No.	Bare Costs		Incl. Subs O&P		Cost Per Labor-Hour	
Crew E-27	**Hr.**	**Daily**	**Hr.**	**Daily**	**Bare Costs**	**Incl. O&P**
1 Struc. Steel Foreman (outside)	$66.55	$532.40	$102.50	$820.00	$64.00	$97.76
5 Struc. Steel Workers	64.55	2582.00	99.40	3976.00		
1 Equip. Oper. (crane)	66.30	530.40	98.65	789.20		
1 Equip. Oper. (oiler)	56.40	451.20	83.90	671.20		
1 Hyd. Crane, 12 Ton		2150.65		2365.72		
1 Hyd. Crane, 80 Ton		2641.70		2905.87	74.88	82.37
64 L.H., Daily Totals		$8888.35		$11527.99	$138.88	$180.12

Crew F-3	**Hr.**	**Daily**	**Hr.**	**Daily**	**Bare Costs**	**Incl. O&P**
4 Carpenters	$58.60	$1875.20	$87.25	$2792.00	$60.14	$89.53
1 Equip. Oper. (crane)	66.30	530.40	98.65	789.20		
1 Hyd. Crane, 12 Ton		2150.65		2365.72	53.77	59.14
40 L.H., Daily Totals		$4556.25		$5946.92	$113.91	$148.67

Crew F-4	**Hr.**	**Daily**	**Hr.**	**Daily**	**Bare Costs**	**Incl. O&P**
4 Carpenters	$58.60	$1875.20	$87.25	$2792.00	$59.52	$88.59
1 Equip. Oper. (crane)	66.30	530.40	98.65	789.20		
1 Equip. Oper. (oiler)	56.40	451.20	83.90	671.20		
1 Hyd. Crane, 55 Ton		2461.06		2707.17	51.27	56.40
48 L.H., Daily Totals		$5317.86		$6959.57	$110.79	$144.99

Crew F-5	**Hr.**	**Daily**	**Hr.**	**Daily**	**Bare Costs**	**Incl. O&P**
1 Carpenter Foreman (outside)	$60.60	$484.80	$90.20	$721.60	$59.10	$87.99
3 Carpenters	58.60	1406.40	87.25	2094.00		
32 L.H., Daily Totals		$1891.20		$2815.60	$59.10	$87.99

Crew F-6	**Hr.**	**Daily**	**Hr.**	**Daily**	**Bare Costs**	**Incl. O&P**
2 Carpenters	$58.60	$937.60	$87.25	$1396.00	$55.60	$82.77
2 Building Laborers	47.25	756.00	70.35	1125.60		
1 Equip. Oper. (crane)	66.30	530.40	98.65	789.20		
1 Hyd. Crane, 12 Ton		2150.65		2365.72	53.77	59.14
40 L.H., Daily Totals		$4374.65		$5676.52	$109.37	$141.91

Crew F-7	**Hr.**	**Daily**	**Hr.**	**Daily**	**Bare Costs**	**Incl. O&P**
2 Carpenters	$58.60	$937.60	$87.25	$1396.00	$52.92	$78.80
2 Building Laborers	47.25	756.00	70.35	1125.60		
32 L.H., Daily Totals		$1693.60		$2521.60	$52.92	$78.80

Crew G-1	**Hr.**	**Daily**	**Hr.**	**Daily**	**Bare Costs**	**Incl. O&P**
1 Roofer Foreman (outside)	$53.80	$430.40	$87.20	$697.60	$48.39	$78.41
4 Roofers Composition	51.80	1657.60	83.95	2686.40		
2 Roofer Helpers	38.85	621.60	62.95	1007.20		
1 Application Equipment		189.41		208.35		
1 Tar Kettle/Pot		220.65		242.72		
1 Crew Truck		183.83		202.21	10.61	11.67
56 L.H., Daily Totals		$3303.49		$5044.48	$58.99	$90.08

Crew G-2	**Hr.**	**Daily**	**Hr.**	**Daily**	**Bare Costs**	**Incl. O&P**
1 Plasterer	$53.35	$426.80	$79.30	$634.40	$49.38	$73.43
1 Plasterer Helper	47.55	380.40	70.65	565.20		
1 Building Laborer	47.25	378.00	70.35	562.80		
1 Grout Pump, 50 C.F./hr.		158.45		174.29	6.60	7.26
24 L.H., Daily Totals		$1343.65		$1936.69	$55.99	$80.70

Crew No.	Bare Costs		Incl. Subs O&P		Cost Per Labor-Hour	
Crew G-2A	**Hr.**	**Daily**	**Hr.**	**Daily**	**Bare Costs**	**Incl. O&P**
1 Roofer Composition	$51.80	$414.40	$83.95	$671.60	$45.97	$72.42
1 Roofer Helper	38.85	310.80	62.95	503.60		
1 Building Laborer	47.25	378.00	70.35	562.80		
1 Foam Spray Rig, Trailer-Mtd.		581.75		639.92		
1 Pickup Truck, 3/4 Ton		122.56		134.82	29.35	32.28
24 L.H., Daily Totals		$1807.51		$2512.74	$75.31	$104.70

Crew G-3	**Hr.**	**Daily**	**Hr.**	**Daily**	**Bare Costs**	**Incl. O&P**
2 Sheet Metal Workers	$70.15	$1122.40	$105.70	$1691.20	$58.70	$88.03
2 Building Laborers	47.25	756.00	70.35	1125.60		
32 L.H., Daily Totals		$1878.40		$2816.80	$58.70	$88.03

Crew G-4	**Hr.**	**Daily**	**Hr.**	**Daily**	**Bare Costs**	**Incl. O&P**
1 Labor Foreman (outside)	$49.25	$394.00	$73.30	$586.40	$47.92	$71.33
2 Building Laborers	47.25	756.00	70.35	1125.60		
1 Flatbed Truck, Gas, 1.5 Ton		361.95		398.14		
1 Air Compressor, 160 cfm		244.12		268.53	25.25	27.78
24 L.H., Daily Totals		$1756.07		$2378.68	$73.17	$99.11

Crew G-5	**Hr.**	**Daily**	**Hr.**	**Daily**	**Bare Costs**	**Incl. O&P**
1 Roofer Foreman (outside)	$53.80	$430.40	$87.20	$697.60	$47.02	$76.20
2 Roofers Composition	51.80	828.80	83.95	1343.20		
2 Roofer Helpers	38.85	621.60	62.95	1007.20		
1 Application Equipment		189.41		208.35	4.74	5.21
40 L.H., Daily Totals		$2070.21		$3256.35	$51.76	$81.41

Crew G-6A	**Hr.**	**Daily**	**Hr.**	**Daily**	**Bare Costs**	**Incl. O&P**
2 Roofers Composition	$51.80	$828.80	$83.95	$1343.20	$51.80	$83.95
1 Small Compressor, Electric		32.29		35.52		
2 Pneumatic Nailers		38.40		42.24	4.42	4.86
16 L.H., Daily Totals		$899.49		$1420.96	$56.22	$88.81

Crew G-7	**Hr.**	**Daily**	**Hr.**	**Daily**	**Bare Costs**	**Incl. O&P**
1 Carpenter	$58.60	$468.80	$87.25	$698.00	$58.60	$87.25
1 Small Compressor, Electric		32.29		35.52		
1 Pneumatic Nailer		19.20		21.12	6.44	7.08
8 L.H., Daily Totals		$520.29		$754.64	$65.04	$94.33

Crew H-1	**Hr.**	**Daily**	**Hr.**	**Daily**	**Bare Costs**	**Incl. O&P**
2 Glaziers	$56.05	$896.80	$83.30	$1332.80	$60.30	$91.35
2 Struc. Steel Workers	64.55	1032.80	99.40	1590.40		
32 L.H., Daily Totals		$1929.60		$2923.20	$60.30	$91.35

Crew H-2	**Hr.**	**Daily**	**Hr.**	**Daily**	**Bare Costs**	**Incl. O&P**
2 Glaziers	$56.05	$896.80	$83.30	$1332.80	$53.12	$78.98
1 Building Laborer	47.25	378.00	70.35	562.80		
24 L.H., Daily Totals		$1274.80		$1895.60	$53.12	$78.98

Crew H-3	**Hr.**	**Daily**	**Hr.**	**Daily**	**Bare Costs**	**Incl. O&P**
1 Glazier	$56.05	$448.40	$83.30	$666.40	$50.50	$75.63
1 Helper	44.95	359.60	67.95	543.60		
16 L.H., Daily Totals		$808.00		$1210.00	$50.50	$75.63

Crew H-4	**Hr.**	**Daily**	**Hr.**	**Daily**	**Bare Costs**	**Incl. O&P**
1 Carpenter	$58.60	$468.80	$87.25	$698.00	$54.89	$82.10
1 Carpenter Helper	44.95	359.60	67.95	543.60		
.5 Electrician	67.35	269.40	100.10	400.40		
20 L.H., Daily Totals		$1097.80		$1642.00	$54.89	$82.10

Crew J-1	Bare Costs Hr.	Bare Costs Daily	Incl. Subs O&P Hr.	Incl. Subs O&P Daily	Cost Per Labor-Hour Bare Costs	Cost Per Labor-Hour Incl. O&P
3 Plasterers	$53.35	$1280.40	$79.30	$1903.20	$51.03	$75.84
2 Plasterer Helpers	47.55	760.80	70.65	1130.40		
1 Mixing Machine, 6 C.F.		116.18		127.80	2.90	3.19
40 L.H., Daily Totals		$2157.38		$3161.40	$53.93	$79.03

Crew J-2	Hr.	Daily	Hr.	Daily	Bare Costs	Incl. O&P
3 Plasterers	$53.35	$1280.40	$79.30	$1903.20	$52.27	$77.42
2 Plasterer Helpers	47.55	760.80	70.65	1130.40		
1 Lather	58.45	467.60	85.30	682.40		
1 Mixing Machine, 6 C.F.		116.18		127.80	2.42	2.66
48 L.H., Daily Totals		$2624.98		$3843.80	$54.69	$80.08

Crew J-3	Hr.	Daily	Hr.	Daily	Bare Costs	Incl. O&P
1 Terrazzo Worker	$55.25	$442.00	$80.70	$645.60	$51.02	$74.53
1 Terrazzo Helper	46.80	374.40	68.35	546.80		
1 Floor Grinder, 22" Path		109.91		120.90		
1 Terrazzo Mixer		144.05		158.46	15.87	17.46
16 L.H., Daily Totals		$1070.36		$1471.76	$66.90	$91.98

Crew J-4	Hr.	Daily	Hr.	Daily	Bare Costs	Incl. O&P
2 Cement Finishers	$55.00	$880.00	$80.45	$1287.20	$52.42	$77.08
1 Laborer	47.25	378.00	70.35	562.80		
1 Floor Grinder, 22" Path		109.91		120.90		
1 Floor Edger, 7" Path		52.63		57.89		
1 Vacuum Pick-Up System		73.53		80.88	9.84	10.82
24 L.H., Daily Totals		$1494.07		$2109.68	$62.25	$87.90

Crew J-4A	Hr.	Daily	Hr.	Daily	Bare Costs	Incl. O&P
2 Cement Finishers	$55.00	$880.00	$80.45	$1287.20	$51.13	$75.40
2 Laborers	47.25	756.00	70.35	1125.60		
1 Floor Grinder, 22" Path		109.91		120.90		
1 Floor Edger, 7" Path		52.63		57.89		
1 Vacuum Pick-Up System		73.53		80.88		
1 Floor Auto Scrubber		195.20		214.72	13.48	14.82
32 L.H., Daily Totals		$2067.27		$2887.20	$64.60	$90.22

Crew J-4B	Hr.	Daily	Hr.	Daily	Bare Costs	Incl. O&P
1 Laborer	$47.25	$378.00	$70.35	$562.80	$47.25	$70.35
1 Floor Auto Scrubber		195.20		214.72	24.40	26.84
8 L.H., Daily Totals		$573.20		$777.52	$71.65	$97.19

Crew J-6	Hr.	Daily	Hr.	Daily	Bare Costs	Incl. O&P
2 Painters	$49.65	$794.40	$73.55	$1176.80	$51.56	$76.58
1 Building Laborer	47.25	378.00	70.35	562.80		
1 Equip. Oper. (light)	59.70	477.60	88.85	710.80		
1 Air Compressor, 250 cfm		196.28		215.91		
1 Sandblaster, Portable, 3 C.F.		84.26		92.69		
1 Set Sand Blasting Accessories		17.14		18.85	9.30	10.23
32 L.H., Daily Totals		$1947.68		$2777.85	$60.87	$86.81

Crew J-7	Hr.	Daily	Hr.	Daily	Bare Costs	Incl. O&P
2 Painters	$49.65	$794.40	$73.55	$1176.80	$49.65	$73.55
1 Floor Belt Sander		49.75		54.73		
1 Floor Sanding Edger		26.35		28.98	4.76	5.23
16 L.H., Daily Totals		$870.50		$1260.51	$54.41	$78.78

Crew K-1	Hr.	Daily	Hr.	Daily	Bare Costs	Incl. O&P
1 Carpenter	$58.60	$468.80	$87.25	$698.00	$55.75	$83.13
1 Truck Driver (light)	52.90	423.20	79.00	632.00		
1 Flatbed Truck, Gas, 3 Ton		391.02		430.12	24.44	26.88
16 L.H., Daily Totals		$1283.02		$1760.12	$80.19	$110.01

Crew K-2	Hr.	Daily	Hr.	Daily	Bare Costs	Incl. O&P
1 Struc. Steel Foreman (outside)	$66.55	$532.40	$102.50	$820.00	$61.33	$93.63
1 Struc. Steel Worker	64.55	516.40	99.40	795.20		
1 Truck Driver (light)	52.90	423.20	79.00	632.00		
1 Flatbed Truck, Gas, 3 Ton		391.02		430.12	16.29	17.92
24 L.H., Daily Totals		$1863.02		$2677.32	$77.63	$111.56

Crew L-1	Hr.	Daily	Hr.	Daily	Bare Costs	Incl. O&P
1 Electrician	$67.35	$538.80	$100.10	$800.80	$69.70	$103.78
1 Plumber	72.05	576.40	107.45	859.60		
16 L.H., Daily Totals		$1115.20		$1660.40	$69.70	$103.78

Crew L-2	Hr.	Daily	Hr.	Daily	Bare Costs	Incl. O&P
1 Carpenter	$58.60	$468.80	$87.25	$698.00	$51.77	$77.60
1 Carpenter Helper	44.95	359.60	67.95	543.60		
16 L.H., Daily Totals		$828.40		$1241.60	$51.77	$77.60

Crew L-3	Hr.	Daily	Hr.	Daily	Bare Costs	Incl. O&P
1 Carpenter	$58.60	$468.80	$87.25	$698.00	$63.67	$95.08
.5 Electrician	67.35	269.40	100.10	400.40		
.5 Sheet Metal Worker	70.15	280.60	105.70	422.80		
16 L.H., Daily Totals		$1018.80		$1521.20	$63.67	$95.08

Crew L-3A	Hr.	Daily	Hr.	Daily	Bare Costs	Incl. O&P
1 Carpenter Foreman (outside)	$60.60	$484.80	$90.20	$721.60	$63.78	$95.37
.5 Sheet Metal Worker	70.15	280.60	105.70	422.80		
12 L.H., Daily Totals		$765.40		$1144.40	$63.78	$95.37

Crew L-4	Hr.	Daily	Hr.	Daily	Bare Costs	Incl. O&P
2 Skilled Workers	$61.25	$980.00	$92.00	$1472.00	$55.82	$83.98
1 Helper	44.95	359.60	67.95	543.60		
24 L.H., Daily Totals		$1339.60		$2015.60	$55.82	$83.98

Crew L-5	Hr.	Daily	Hr.	Daily	Bare Costs	Incl. O&P
1 Struc. Steel Foreman (outside)	$66.55	$532.40	$102.50	$820.00	$65.09	$99.74
5 Struc. Steel Workers	64.55	2582.00	99.40	3976.00		
1 Equip. Oper. (crane)	66.30	530.40	98.65	789.20		
1 Hyd. Crane, 25 Ton		2273.31		2500.64	40.59	44.65
56 L.H., Daily Totals		$5918.11		$8085.84	$105.68	$144.39

Crew L-5A	Hr.	Daily	Hr.	Daily	Bare Costs	Incl. O&P
1 Struc. Steel Foreman (outside)	$66.55	$532.40	$102.50	$820.00	$65.49	$99.99
2 Structural Steel Workers	64.55	1032.80	99.40	1590.40		
1 Equip. Oper. (crane)	66.30	530.40	98.65	789.20		
1 S.P. Crane, 4x4, 25 Ton		927.07		1019.78	28.97	31.87
32 L.H., Daily Totals		$3022.67		$4219.38	$94.46	$131.86

Crew No.	Bare Costs		Incl. Subs O&P		Cost Per Labor-Hour	

Crew L-5B	Hr.	Daily	Hr.	Daily	Bare Costs	Incl. O&P
1 Struc. Steel Foreman (outside)	$66.55	$532.40	$102.50	$820.00	$66.46	$100.05
2 Structural Steel Workers	64.55	1032.80	99.40	1590.40		
2 Electricians	67.35	1077.60	100.10	1601.60		
2 Steamfitters/Pipefitters	72.55	1160.80	108.20	1731.20		
1 Equip. Oper. (crane)	66.30	530.40	98.65	789.20		
1 Equip. Oper. (oiler)	56.40	451.20	83.90	671.20		
1 Hyd. Crane, 80 Ton		2641.70		2905.87	36.69	40.36
72 L.H., Daily Totals		$7426.90		$10109.47	$103.15	$140.41

Crew L-6	Hr.	Daily	Hr.	Daily	Bare Costs	Incl. O&P
1 Plumber	$72.05	$576.40	$107.45	$859.60	$70.48	$105.00
.5 Electrician	67.35	269.40	100.10	400.40		
12 L.H., Daily Totals		$845.80		$1260.00	$70.48	$105.00

Crew L-7	Hr.	Daily	Hr.	Daily	Bare Costs	Incl. O&P
2 Carpenters	$58.60	$937.60	$87.25	$1396.00	$56.61	$84.26
1 Building Laborer	47.25	378.00	70.35	562.80		
.5 Electrician	67.35	269.40	100.10	400.40		
28 L.H., Daily Totals		$1585.00		$2359.20	$56.61	$84.26

Crew L-8	Hr.	Daily	Hr.	Daily	Bare Costs	Incl. O&P
2 Carpenters	$58.60	$937.60	$87.25	$1396.00	$61.29	$91.29
.5 Plumber	72.05	288.20	107.45	429.80		
20 L.H., Daily Totals		$1225.80		$1825.80	$61.29	$91.29

Crew L-9	Hr.	Daily	Hr.	Daily	Bare Costs	Incl. O&P
1 Labor Foreman (inside)	$47.75	$382.00	$71.10	$568.80	$53.44	$80.28
2 Building Laborers	47.25	756.00	70.35	1125.60		
1 Struc. Steel Worker	64.55	516.40	99.40	795.20		
.5 Electrician	67.35	269.40	100.10	400.40		
36 L.H., Daily Totals		$1923.80		$2890.00	$53.44	$80.28

Crew L-10	Hr.	Daily	Hr.	Daily	Bare Costs	Incl. O&P
1 Struc. Steel Foreman (outside)	$66.55	$532.40	$102.50	$820.00	$65.80	$100.18
1 Structural Steel Worker	64.55	516.40	99.40	795.20		
1 Equip. Oper. (crane)	66.30	530.40	98.65	789.20		
1 Hyd. Crane, 12 Ton		2150.65		2365.72	89.61	98.57
24 L.H., Daily Totals		$3729.85		$4770.11	$155.41	$198.75

Crew L-11	Hr.	Daily	Hr.	Daily	Bare Costs	Incl. O&P
2 Wreckers	$47.25	$756.00	$71.35	$1141.60	$55.13	$82.55
1 Equip. Oper. (crane)	66.30	530.40	98.65	789.20		
1 Equip. Oper. (light)	59.70	477.60	88.85	710.80		
1 Hyd. Excavator, 2.5 C.Y.		1683.69		1852.06		
1 Loader, Skid Steer, 78 H.P.		429.91		472.90	66.05	72.66
32 L.H., Daily Totals		$3877.60		$4966.56	$121.18	$155.21

Crew M-1	Hr.	Daily	Hr.	Daily	Bare Costs	Incl. O&P
3 Elevator Constructors	$96.60	$2318.40	$143.00	$3432.00	$91.78	$135.86
1 Elevator Apprentice	77.30	618.40	114.45	915.60		
5 Hand Tools		344.60		379.06	10.77	11.85
32 L.H., Daily Totals		$3281.40		$4726.66	$102.54	$147.71

Crew No.	Bare Costs		Incl. Subs O&P		Cost Per Labor-Hour	

Crew M-3	Hr.	Daily	Hr.	Daily	Bare Costs	Incl. O&P
1 Electrician Foreman (outside)	$69.35	$554.80	$103.05	$824.40	$72.06	$106.89
1 Common Laborer	47.25	378.00	70.35	562.80		
.25 Equipment Operator (med.)	63.05	126.10	93.80	187.60		
1 Elevator Constructor	96.60	772.80	143.00	1144.00		
1 Elevator Apprentice	77.30	618.40	114.45	915.60		
.25 S.P. Crane, 4x4, 20 Ton		190.24		209.27	5.60	6.15
34 L.H., Daily Totals		$2640.34		$3843.67	$77.66	$113.05

Crew M-4	Hr.	Daily	Hr.	Daily	Bare Costs	Incl. O&P
1 Electrician Foreman (outside)	$69.35	$554.80	$103.05	$824.40	$71.37	$105.89
1 Common Laborer	47.25	378.00	70.35	562.80		
.25 Equipment Operator, Crane	66.30	132.60	98.65	197.30		
.25 Equip. Oper. (oiler)	56.40	112.80	83.90	167.80		
1 Elevator Constructor	96.60	772.80	143.00	1144.00		
1 Elevator Apprentice	77.30	618.40	114.45	915.60		
.25 S.P. Crane, 4x4, 40 Ton		284.79		313.26	7.91	8.70
36 L.H., Daily Totals		$2854.18		$4125.16	$79.28	$114.59

Crew Q-1	Hr.	Daily	Hr.	Daily	Bare Costs	Incl. O&P
1 Plumber	$72.05	$576.40	$107.45	$859.60	$64.85	$96.70
1 Plumber Apprentice	57.65	461.20	85.95	687.60		
16 L.H., Daily Totals		$1037.60		$1547.20	$64.85	$96.70

Crew Q-1A	Hr.	Daily	Hr.	Daily	Bare Costs	Incl. O&P
.25 Plumber Foreman (outside)	$74.05	$148.10	$110.40	$220.80	$72.45	$108.04
1 Plumber	72.05	576.40	107.45	859.60		
10 L.H., Daily Totals		$724.50		$1080.40	$72.45	$108.04

Crew Q-1C	Hr.	Daily	Hr.	Daily	Bare Costs	Incl. O&P
1 Plumber	$72.05	$576.40	$107.45	$859.60	$64.25	$95.73
1 Plumber Apprentice	57.65	461.20	85.95	687.60		
1 Equip. Oper. (medium)	63.05	504.40	93.80	750.40		
1 Trencher, Chain Type, 8' D		2079.03		2286.93	86.63	95.29
24 L.H., Daily Totals		$3621.03		$4584.53	$150.88	$191.02

Crew Q-2	Hr.	Daily	Hr.	Daily	Bare Costs	Incl. O&P
2 Plumbers	$72.05	$1152.80	$107.45	$1719.20	$67.25	$100.28
1 Plumber Apprentice	57.65	461.20	85.95	687.60		
24 L.H., Daily Totals		$1614.00		$2406.80	$67.25	$100.28

Crew Q-3	Hr.	Daily	Hr.	Daily	Bare Costs	Incl. O&P
1 Plumber Foreman (inside)	$72.55	$580.40	$108.20	$865.60	$68.58	$102.26
2 Plumbers	72.05	1152.80	107.45	1719.20		
1 Plumber Apprentice	57.65	461.20	85.95	687.60		
32 L.H., Daily Totals		$2194.40		$3272.40	$68.58	$102.26

Crew Q-4	Hr.	Daily	Hr.	Daily	Bare Costs	Incl. O&P
1 Plumber Foreman (inside)	$72.55	$580.40	$108.20	$865.60	$68.58	$102.26
1 Plumber	72.05	576.40	107.45	859.60		
1 Welder (plumber)	72.05	576.40	107.45	859.60		
1 Plumber Apprentice	57.65	461.20	85.95	687.60		
1 Welder, Electric, 300 amp		64.17		70.59	2.01	2.21
32 L.H., Daily Totals		$2258.57		$3342.99	$70.58	$104.47

Crew Q-5	Hr.	Daily	Hr.	Daily	Bare Costs	Incl. O&P
1 Steamfitter	$72.55	$580.40	$108.20	$865.60	$65.30	$97.38
1 Steamfitter Apprentice	58.05	464.40	86.55	692.40		
16 L.H., Daily Totals		$1044.80		$1558.00	$65.30	$97.38

Crew No.	Bare Costs		Incl. Subs O&P		Cost Per Labor-Hour	
Crew Q-6	**Hr.**	**Daily**	**Hr.**	**Daily**	**Bare Costs**	**Incl. O&P**
2 Steamfitters	$72.55	$1160.80	$108.20	$1731.20	$67.72	$100.98
1 Steamfitter Apprentice	58.05	464.40	86.55	692.40		
24 L.H., Daily Totals		$1625.20		$2423.60	$67.72	$100.98
Crew Q-7	**Hr.**	**Daily**	**Hr.**	**Daily**	**Bare Costs**	**Incl. O&P**
1 Steamfitter Foreman (inside)	$73.05	$584.40	$108.95	$871.60	$69.05	$102.97
2 Steamfitters	72.55	1160.80	108.20	1731.20		
1 Steamfitter Apprentice	58.05	464.40	86.55	692.40		
32 L.H., Daily Totals		$2209.60		$3295.20	$69.05	$102.97
Crew Q-8	**Hr.**	**Daily**	**Hr.**	**Daily**	**Bare Costs**	**Incl. O&P**
1 Steamfitter Foreman (inside)	$73.05	$584.40	$108.95	$871.60	$69.05	$102.97
1 Steamfitter	72.55	580.40	108.20	865.60		
1 Welder (steamfitter)	72.55	580.40	108.20	865.60		
1 Steamfitter Apprentice	58.05	464.40	86.55	692.40		
1 Welder, Electric, 300 amp		64.17		70.59	2.01	2.21
32 L.H., Daily Totals		$2273.77		$3365.79	$71.06	$105.18
Crew Q-9	**Hr.**	**Daily**	**Hr.**	**Daily**	**Bare Costs**	**Incl. O&P**
1 Sheet Metal Worker	$70.15	$561.20	$105.70	$845.60	$63.13	$95.10
1 Sheet Metal Apprentice	56.10	448.80	84.50	676.00		
16 L.H., Daily Totals		$1010.00		$1521.60	$63.13	$95.10
Crew Q-10	**Hr.**	**Daily**	**Hr.**	**Daily**	**Bare Costs**	**Incl. O&P**
2 Sheet Metal Workers	$70.15	$1122.40	$105.70	$1691.20	$65.47	$98.63
1 Sheet Metal Apprentice	56.10	448.80	84.50	676.00		
24 L.H., Daily Totals		$1571.20		$2367.20	$65.47	$98.63
Crew Q-11	**Hr.**	**Daily**	**Hr.**	**Daily**	**Bare Costs**	**Incl. O&P**
1 Sheet Metal Foreman (inside)	$70.65	$565.20	$106.45	$851.60	$66.76	$100.59
2 Sheet Metal Workers	70.15	1122.40	105.70	1691.20		
1 Sheet Metal Apprentice	56.10	448.80	84.50	676.00		
32 L.H., Daily Totals		$2136.40		$3218.80	$66.76	$100.59
Crew Q-12	**Hr.**	**Daily**	**Hr.**	**Daily**	**Bare Costs**	**Incl. O&P**
1 Sprinkler Installer	$70.80	$566.40	$105.70	$845.60	$63.73	$95.13
1 Sprinkler Apprentice	56.65	453.20	84.55	676.40		
16 L.H., Daily Totals		$1019.60		$1522.00	$63.73	$95.13
Crew Q-13	**Hr.**	**Daily**	**Hr.**	**Daily**	**Bare Costs**	**Incl. O&P**
1 Sprinkler Foreman (inside)	$71.30	$570.40	$106.45	$851.60	$67.39	$100.60
2 Sprinkler Installers	70.80	1132.80	105.70	1691.20		
1 Sprinkler Apprentice	56.65	453.20	84.55	676.40		
32 L.H., Daily Totals		$2156.40		$3219.20	$67.39	$100.60
Crew Q-14	**Hr.**	**Daily**	**Hr.**	**Daily**	**Bare Costs**	**Incl. O&P**
1 Asbestos Worker	$65.25	$522.00	$99.80	$798.40	$58.73	$89.83
1 Asbestos Apprentice	52.20	417.60	79.85	638.80		
16 L.H., Daily Totals		$939.60		$1437.20	$58.73	$89.83
Crew Q-15	**Hr.**	**Daily**	**Hr.**	**Daily**	**Bare Costs**	**Incl. O&P**
1 Plumber	$72.05	$576.40	$107.45	$859.60	$64.85	$96.70
1 Plumber Apprentice	57.65	461.20	85.95	687.60		
1 Welder, Electric, 300 amp		64.17		70.59	4.01	4.41
16 L.H., Daily Totals		$1101.77		$1617.79	$68.86	$101.11
Crew Q-16	**Hr.**	**Daily**	**Hr.**	**Daily**	**Bare Costs**	**Incl. O&P**
2 Plumbers	$72.05	$1152.80	$107.45	$1719.20	$67.25	$100.28
1 Plumber Apprentice	57.65	461.20	85.95	687.60		
1 Welder, Electric, 300 amp		64.17		70.59	2.67	2.94
24 L.H., Daily Totals		$1678.17		$2477.39	$69.92	$103.22
Crew Q-17	**Hr.**	**Daily**	**Hr.**	**Daily**	**Bare Costs**	**Incl. O&P**
1 Steamfitter	$72.55	$580.40	$108.20	$865.60	$65.30	$97.38
1 Steamfitter Apprentice	58.05	464.40	86.55	692.40		
1 Welder, Electric, 300 amp		64.17		70.59	4.01	4.41
16 L.H., Daily Totals		$1108.97		$1628.59	$69.31	$101.79
Crew Q-17A	**Hr.**	**Daily**	**Hr.**	**Daily**	**Bare Costs**	**Incl. O&P**
1 Steamfitter	$72.55	$580.40	$108.20	$865.60	$65.63	$97.80
1 Steamfitter Apprentice	58.05	464.40	86.55	692.40		
1 Equip. Oper. (crane)	66.30	530.40	98.65	789.20		
1 Hyd. Crane, 12 Ton		2150.65		2365.72		
1 Welder, Electric, 300 amp		64.17		70.59	92.28	101.51
24 L.H., Daily Totals		$3790.02		$4783.50	$157.92	$199.31
Crew Q-18	**Hr.**	**Daily**	**Hr.**	**Daily**	**Bare Costs**	**Incl. O&P**
2 Steamfitters	$72.55	$1160.80	$108.20	$1731.20	$67.72	$100.98
1 Steamfitter Apprentice	58.05	464.40	86.55	692.40		
1 Welder, Electric, 300 amp		64.17		70.59	2.67	2.94
24 L.H., Daily Totals		$1689.37		$2494.19	$70.39	$103.92
Crew Q-19	**Hr.**	**Daily**	**Hr.**	**Daily**	**Bare Costs**	**Incl. O&P**
1 Steamfitter	$72.55	$580.40	$108.20	$865.60	$65.98	$98.28
1 Steamfitter Apprentice	58.05	464.40	86.55	692.40		
1 Electrician	67.35	538.80	100.10	800.80		
24 L.H., Daily Totals		$1583.60		$2358.80	$65.98	$98.28
Crew Q-20	**Hr.**	**Daily**	**Hr.**	**Daily**	**Bare Costs**	**Incl. O&P**
1 Sheet Metal Worker	$70.15	$561.20	$105.70	$845.60	$63.97	$96.10
1 Sheet Metal Apprentice	56.10	448.80	84.50	676.00		
.5 Electrician	67.35	269.40	100.10	400.40		
20 L.H., Daily Totals		$1279.40		$1922.00	$63.97	$96.10
Crew Q-21	**Hr.**	**Daily**	**Hr.**	**Daily**	**Bare Costs**	**Incl. O&P**
2 Steamfitters	$72.55	$1160.80	$108.20	$1731.20	$67.63	$100.76
1 Steamfitter Apprentice	58.05	464.40	86.55	692.40		
1 Electrician	67.35	538.80	100.10	800.80		
32 L.H., Daily Totals		$2164.00		$3224.40	$67.63	$100.76
Crew Q-22	**Hr.**	**Daily**	**Hr.**	**Daily**	**Bare Costs**	**Incl. O&P**
1 Plumber	$72.05	$576.40	$107.45	$859.60	$64.85	$96.70
1 Plumber Apprentice	57.65	461.20	85.95	687.60		
1 Hyd. Crane, 12 Ton		2150.65		2365.72	134.42	147.86
16 L.H., Daily Totals		$3188.25		$3912.92	$199.27	$244.56
Crew Q-22A	**Hr.**	**Daily**	**Hr.**	**Daily**	**Bare Costs**	**Incl. O&P**
1 Plumber	$72.05	$576.40	$107.45	$859.60	$60.81	$90.60
1 Plumber Apprentice	57.65	461.20	85.95	687.60		
1 Laborer	47.25	378.00	70.35	562.80		
1 Equip. Oper. (crane)	66.30	530.40	98.65	789.20		
1 Hyd. Crane, 12 Ton		2150.65		2365.72	67.21	73.93
32 L.H., Daily Totals		$4096.65		$5264.92	$128.02	$164.53

Crew No.	Bare Costs		Incl. Subs O&P		Cost Per Labor-Hour	
Crew Q-23	**Hr.**	**Daily**	**Hr.**	**Daily**	**Bare Costs**	**Incl. O&P**
1 Plumber Foreman (outside)	$74.05	$592.40	$110.40	$883.20	$69.72	$103.88
1 Plumber	72.05	576.40	107.45	859.60		
1 Equip. Oper. (medium)	63.05	504.40	93.80	750.40		
1 Lattice Boom Crane, 20 Ton		868.10		954.91	36.17	39.79
24 L.H., Daily Totals		$2541.30		$3448.11	$105.89	$143.67

Crew R-1	Hr.	Daily	Hr.	Daily	Bare Costs	Incl. O&P
1 Electrician Foreman	$67.85	$542.80	$100.85	$806.80	$62.95	$93.56
3 Electricians	67.35	1616.40	100.10	2402.40		
2 Electrician Apprentices	53.90	862.40	80.10	1281.60		
48 L.H., Daily Totals		$3021.60		$4490.80	$62.95	$93.56

Crew R-1A	Hr.	Daily	Hr.	Daily	Bare Costs	Incl. O&P
1 Electrician	$67.35	$538.80	$100.10	$800.80	$60.63	$90.10
1 Electrician Apprentice	53.90	431.20	80.10	640.80		
16 L.H., Daily Totals		$970.00		$1441.60	$60.63	$90.10

Crew R-1B	Hr.	Daily	Hr.	Daily	Bare Costs	Incl. O&P
1 Electrician	$67.35	$538.80	$100.10	$800.80	$58.38	$86.77
2 Electrician Apprentices	53.90	862.40	80.10	1281.60		
24 L.H., Daily Totals		$1401.20		$2082.40	$58.38	$86.77

Crew R-1C	Hr.	Daily	Hr.	Daily	Bare Costs	Incl. O&P
2 Electricians	$67.35	$1077.60	$100.10	$1601.60	$60.63	$90.10
2 Electrician Apprentices	53.90	862.40	80.10	1281.60		
1 Portable cable puller, 8000 lb.		118.26		130.09	3.70	4.07
32 L.H., Daily Totals		$2058.26		$3013.29	$64.32	$94.17

Crew R-2	Hr.	Daily	Hr.	Daily	Bare Costs	Incl. O&P
1 Electrician Foreman	$67.85	$542.80	$100.85	$806.80	$63.43	$94.29
3 Electricians	67.35	1616.40	100.10	2402.40		
2 Electrician Apprentices	53.90	862.40	80.10	1281.60		
1 Equip. Oper. (crane)	66.30	530.40	98.65	789.20		
1 S.P. Crane, 4x4, 5 Ton		385.89		424.48	6.89	7.58
56 L.H., Daily Totals		$3937.89		$5704.48	$70.32	$101.87

Crew R-3	Hr.	Daily	Hr.	Daily	Bare Costs	Incl. O&P
1 Electrician Foreman	$67.85	$542.80	$100.85	$806.80	$67.34	$100.11
1 Electrician	67.35	538.80	100.10	800.80		
.5 Equip. Oper. (crane)	66.30	265.20	98.65	394.60		
.5 S.P. Crane, 4x4, 5 Ton		192.94		212.24	9.65	10.61
20 L.H., Daily Totals		$1539.74		$2214.44	$76.99	$110.72

Crew R-4	Hr.	Daily	Hr.	Daily	Bare Costs	Incl. O&P
1 Struc. Steel Foreman (outside)	$66.55	$532.40	$102.50	$820.00	$65.51	$100.16
3 Struc. Steel Workers	64.55	1549.20	99.40	2385.60		
1 Electrician	67.35	538.80	100.10	800.80		
1 Welder, Gas Engine, 300 amp		147.09		161.80	3.68	4.04
40 L.H., Daily Totals		$2767.49		$4168.20	$69.19	$104.21

Crew R-5	Hr.	Daily	Hr.	Daily	Bare Costs	Incl. O&P
1 Electrician Foreman	$67.85	$542.80	$100.85	$806.80	$59.25	$88.48
4 Electrician Linemen	67.35	2155.20	100.10	3203.20		
2 Electrician Operators	67.35	1077.60	100.10	1601.60		
4 Electrician Groundmen	44.95	1438.40	67.95	2174.40		
1 Crew Truck		183.83		202.21		
1 Flatbed Truck, 20,000 GVW		223.10		245.41		
1 Pickup Truck, 3/4 Ton		122.56		134.82		
.2 Hyd. Crane, 55 Ton		492.21		541.43		
.2 Hyd. Crane, 12 Ton		430.13		473.14		
.2 Earth Auger, Truck-Mtd.		30.79		33.87		
1 Tractor w/Winch		413.43		454.77	21.55	23.70
88 L.H., Daily Totals		$7110.06		$9871.66	$80.80	$112.18

Crew R-6	Hr.	Daily	Hr.	Daily	Bare Costs	Incl. O&P
1 Electrician Foreman	$67.85	$542.80	$100.85	$806.80	$59.25	$88.48
4 Electrician Linemen	67.35	2155.20	100.10	3203.20		
2 Electrician Operators	67.35	1077.60	100.10	1601.60		
4 Electrician Groundmen	44.95	1438.40	67.95	2174.40		
1 Crew Truck		183.83		202.21		
1 Flatbed Truck, 20,000 GVW		223.10		245.41		
1 Pickup Truck, 3/4 Ton		122.56		134.82		
.2 Hyd. Crane, 55 Ton		492.21		541.43		
.2 Hyd. Crane, 12 Ton		430.13		473.14		
.2 Earth Auger, Truck-Mtd.		30.79		33.87		
1 Tractor w/Winch		413.43		454.77		
3 Cable Trailers		609.78		670.76		
.5 Tensioning Rig		76.23		83.86		
.5 Cable Pulling Rig		370.78		407.86	33.56	36.91
88 L.H., Daily Totals		$8166.85		$11034.14	$92.81	$125.39

Crew R-7	Hr.	Daily	Hr.	Daily	Bare Costs	Incl. O&P
1 Electrician Foreman	$67.85	$542.80	$100.85	$806.80	$48.77	$73.43
5 Electrician Groundmen	44.95	1798.00	67.95	2718.00		
1 Crew Truck		183.83		202.21	3.83	4.21
48 L.H., Daily Totals		$2524.63		$3727.01	$52.60	$77.65

Crew R-8	Hr.	Daily	Hr.	Daily	Bare Costs	Incl. O&P
1 Electrician Foreman	$67.85	$542.80	$100.85	$806.80	$59.97	$89.51
3 Electrician Linemen	67.35	1616.40	100.10	2402.40		
2 Electrician Groundmen	44.95	719.20	67.95	1087.20		
1 Pickup Truck, 3/4 Ton		122.56		134.82		
1 Crew Truck		183.83		202.21	6.38	7.02
48 L.H., Daily Totals		$3184.79		$4633.43	$66.35	$96.53

Crew R-9	Hr.	Daily	Hr.	Daily	Bare Costs	Incl. O&P
1 Electrician Foreman	$67.85	$542.80	$100.85	$806.80	$56.21	$84.12
1 Electrician Lineman	67.35	538.80	100.10	800.80		
2 Electrician Operators	67.35	1077.60	100.10	1601.60		
4 Electrician Groundmen	44.95	1438.40	67.95	2174.40		
1 Pickup Truck, 3/4 Ton		122.56		134.82		
1 Crew Truck		183.83		202.21	4.79	5.27
64 L.H., Daily Totals		$3903.99		$5720.63	$61.00	$89.38

Crew R-10	Hr.	Daily	Hr.	Daily	Bare Costs	Incl. O&P
1 Electrician Foreman	$67.85	$542.80	$100.85	$806.80	$63.70	$94.87
4 Electrician Linemen	67.35	2155.20	100.10	3203.20		
1 Electrician Groundman	44.95	359.60	67.95	543.60		
1 Crew Truck		183.83		202.21		
3 Tram Cars		237.63		261.39	8.78	9.66
48 L.H., Daily Totals		$3479.06		$5017.21	$72.48	$104.53

Crew R-11	Bare Costs Hr.	Bare Costs Daily	Incl. Subs O&P Hr.	Incl. Subs O&P Daily	Cost Per Labor-Hour Bare Costs	Cost Per Labor-Hour Incl. O&P
1 Electrician Foreman	$67.85	$542.80	$100.85	$806.80	$64.40	$95.75
4 Electricians	67.35	2155.20	100.10	3203.20		
1 Equip. Oper. (crane)	66.30	530.40	98.65	789.20		
1 Common Laborer	47.25	378.00	70.35	562.80		
1 Crew Truck		183.83		202.21		
1 Hyd. Crane, 12 Ton		2150.65		2365.72	41.69	45.86
56 L.H., Daily Totals		$5940.88		$7929.93	$106.09	$141.61

Crew R-12	Hr.	Daily	Hr.	Daily	Bare Costs	Incl. O&P
1 Carpenter Foreman (inside)	$59.10	$472.80	$88.00	$704.00	$55.46	$82.87
4 Carpenters	58.60	1875.20	87.25	2792.00		
4 Common Laborers	47.25	1512.00	70.35	2251.20		
1 Equip. Oper. (medium)	63.05	504.40	93.80	750.40		
1 Steel Worker	64.55	516.40	99.40	795.20		
1 Dozer, 200 H.P.		1382.36		1520.60		
1 Pickup Truck, 3/4 Ton		122.56		134.82	17.10	18.81
88 L.H., Daily Totals		$6385.72		$8948.21	$72.56	$101.68

Crew R-13	Hr.	Daily	Hr.	Daily	Bare Costs	Incl. O&P
1 Electrician Foreman	$67.85	$542.80	$100.85	$806.80	$65.31	$97.09
3 Electricians	67.35	1616.40	100.10	2402.40		
.25 Equip. Oper. (crane)	66.30	132.60	98.65	197.30		
1 Equipment Oiler	56.40	451.20	83.90	671.20		
.25 Hydraulic Crane, 33 Ton		607.40		668.15	14.46	15.91
42 L.H., Daily Totals		$3350.41		$4745.85	$79.77	$113.00

Crew R-15	Hr.	Daily	Hr.	Daily	Bare Costs	Incl. O&P
1 Electrician Foreman	$67.85	$542.80	$100.85	$806.80	$66.16	$98.35
4 Electricians	67.35	2155.20	100.10	3203.20		
1 Equipment Oper. (light)	59.70	477.60	88.85	710.80		
1 Telescoping Boom Lift, to 40'		345.57		380.13	7.20	7.92
48 L.H., Daily Totals		$3521.17		$5100.93	$73.36	$106.27

Crew R-15A	Hr.	Daily	Hr.	Daily	Bare Costs	Incl. O&P
1 Electrician Foreman	$67.85	$542.80	$100.85	$806.80	$59.46	$88.43
2 Electricians	67.35	1077.60	100.10	1601.60		
2 Common Laborers	47.25	756.00	70.35	1125.60		
1 Equip. Oper. (light)	59.70	477.60	88.85	710.80		
1 Telescoping Boom Lift, to 40'		345.57		380.13	7.20	7.92
48 L.H., Daily Totals		$3199.57		$4624.93	$66.66	$96.35

Crew R-18	Hr.	Daily	Hr.	Daily	Bare Costs	Incl. O&P
.25 Electrician Foreman	$67.85	$135.70	$100.85	$201.70	$59.11	$87.85
1 Electrician	67.35	538.80	100.10	800.80		
2 Electrician Apprentices	53.90	862.40	80.10	1281.60		
26 L.H., Daily Totals		$1536.90		$2284.10	$59.11	$87.85

Crew R-19	Hr.	Daily	Hr.	Daily	Bare Costs	Incl. O&P
.5 Electrician Foreman	$67.85	$271.40	$100.85	$403.40	$67.45	$100.25
2 Electricians	67.35	1077.60	100.10	1601.60		
20 L.H., Daily Totals		$1349.00		$2005.00	$67.45	$100.25

Crew R-21	Hr.	Daily	Hr.	Daily	Bare Costs	Incl. O&P
1 Electrician Foreman	$67.85	$542.80	$100.85	$806.80	$67.37	$100.13
3 Electricians	67.35	1616.40	100.10	2402.40		
.1 Equip. Oper. (medium)	63.05	50.44	93.80	75.04		
.1 S.P. Crane, 4x4, 25 Ton		92.71		101.98	2.83	3.11
32.8 L.H., Daily Totals		$2302.35		$3386.22	$70.19	$103.24

Crew R-22	Hr.	Daily	Hr.	Daily	Bare Costs	Incl. O&P
.66 Electrician Foreman	$67.85	$358.25	$100.85	$532.49	$61.65	$91.62
2 Electricians	67.35	1077.60	100.10	1601.60		
2 Electrician Apprentices	53.90	862.40	80.10	1281.60		
37.28 L.H., Daily Totals		$2298.25		$3415.69	$61.65	$91.62

Crew R-30	Hr.	Daily	Hr.	Daily	Bare Costs	Incl. O&P
.25 Electrician Foreman (outside)	$69.35	$138.70	$103.05	$206.10	$55.13	$82.02
1 Electrician	67.35	538.80	100.10	800.80		
2 Laborers (Semi-Skilled)	47.25	756.00	70.35	1125.60		
26 L.H., Daily Totals		$1433.50		$2132.50	$55.13	$82.02

Crew R-31	Hr.	Daily	Hr.	Daily	Bare Costs	Incl. O&P
1 Electrician	$67.35	$538.80	$100.10	$800.80	$67.35	$100.10
1 Core Drill, Electric, 2.5 H.P.		61.41		67.55	7.68	8.44
8 L.H., Daily Totals		$600.21		$868.35	$75.03	$108.54

Crew W-41E	Hr.	Daily	Hr.	Daily	Bare Costs	Incl. O&P
.5 Plumber Foreman (outside)	$74.05	$296.20	$110.40	$441.60	$62.53	$93.20
1 Plumber	72.05	576.40	107.45	859.60		
1 Laborer	47.25	378.00	70.35	562.80		
20 L.H., Daily Totals		$1250.60		$1864.00	$62.53	$93.20

Historical Cost Indexes

The table below lists both the RSMeans® historical cost index based on Jan. 1, 1993 = 100 as well as the computed value of an index based on Jan. 1, 2023 costs. Since the Jan. 1, 2023 figure is estimated, space is left to write in the actual index figures as they become available through the quarterly *RSMeans Construction Cost Indexes.*

To compute the actual index based on Jan. 1, 2023 = 100, divide the historical cost index for a particular year by the actual Jan. 1, 2023 construction cost index. Space has been left to advance the index figures as the year progresses.

Year	Historical Cost Index Jan. 1, 1993 = 100		Current Index Based on Jan. 1, 2023 = 100	
	Est.	Actual	Est.	Actual
Oct 2023				
July 2023				
April 2023				
Jan 2023	318.8		100.0	
July 2022		297.1	93.2	
2021		257.5	80.8	
2020		234.6	73.6	
2019		232.2	72.8	
2018		222.9	69.9	
2017		213.6	67.0	
2016		207.3	65.0	
2015		206.2	64.7	
2014		204.9	64.3	
2013		201.2	63.1	
2012		194.6	61.0	
2011		191.2	60.0	
2010		183.5	57.6	
2009		180.1	56.5	
2008		180.4	56.6	
2007		169.4	53.1	

Year	Historical Cost Index Jan. 1, 1993 = 100	Current Index Based on Jan. 1, 2023 = 100	
	Actual	Est.	Actual
July 2006	162.0	50.8	
2005	151.6	47.6	
2004	143.7	45.1	
2003	132.0	41.4	
2002	128.7	40.4	
2001	125.1	39.2	
2000	120.9	37.9	
1999	117.6	36.9	
1998	115.1	36.1	
1997	112.8	35.4	
1996	110.2	34.6	
1995	107.6	33.8	
1994	104.4	32.7	
1993	101.7	31.9	
1992	99.4	31.2	
1991	96.8	30.4	
1990	94.3	29.6	
1989	92.1	28.9	
1988	89.9	28.2	
1987	87.7	27.5	

Year	Historical Cost Index Jan. 1, 1993 = 100	Current Index Based on Jan. 1, 2023 = 100	
	Actual	Est.	Actual
July 1986	84.2	26.4	
1985	82.6	25.9	
1984	82.0	25.7	
1983	80.2	25.1	
1982	76.1	23.9	
1981	70.0	22.0	
1980	62.9	19.7	
1979	57.8	18.1	
1978	53.5	16.8	
1977	49.5	15.5	
1976	46.9	14.7	
1975	44.8	14.1	
1974	41.4	13.0	
1973	37.7	11.8	
1972	34.8	10.9	
1971	32.1	10.1	

Adjustments to Costs

The "Historical Cost Index" can be used to convert national average building costs at a particular time to the approximate building costs for some other time.

Time Adjustment Using the Historical Cost Indexes:

$$\frac{\text{Index for Year A}}{\text{Index for Year B}} \times \text{Cost in Year B} = \text{Cost in Year A}$$

Example:

Estimate and compare construction costs for different years in the same city.

To estimate the national average construction cost of a building in 1971, knowing that it cost $900,000 in 2023:

INDEX in 1970 = 32.1

INDEX in 2023 = 318.8

$$\frac{\text{INDEX 1971}}{\text{INDEX 2023}} \times \text{Cost 2023} = \text{Cost 1971}$$

$$\frac{32.1}{318.8} \times \$900{,}000 = .100 \times \$900{,}000 = \$90{,}000$$

The construction cost of the building in 1971 was $90,000.

Note: The city cost indexes for Canada can be used to convert U.S. national averages to local costs in Canadian dollars.

Example:

To estimate and compare the cost of a building in Toronto, ON in 2023 with the known cost of $600,000 (US$) in New York, NY in 2023:

INDEX Toronto = 132.1

INDEX New York = 139.6

$$\frac{\text{INDEX Toronto}}{\text{INDEX New York}} \times \text{Cost New York} = \text{Cost Toronto}$$

$$\frac{132.1}{139.6} \times \$600{,}000 = .947 \times \$600{,}000 = \$568{,}200$$

The construction cost of the building in Toronto is $568,200 (CN$).

*Historical Cost Index updates and other resources are provided on the following website:
rsmeans.com/2023books

How to Use the City Cost Indexes

What you should know before you begin

RSMeans City Cost Indexes (CCI) are an extremely useful tool for when you want to compare costs from city to city and region to region.

This publication contains average construction cost indexes for 731 U.S. and Canadian cities covering over 930 three-digit zip code locations, as listed directly under each city.

Keep in mind that a City Cost Index number is a percentage ratio of a specific city's cost to the national average cost of the same item at a stated time period.

In other words, these index figures represent relative construction factors (or, if you prefer, multipliers) for material and installation costs, as well as the weighted average for Total In Place costs for each CSI MasterFormat division. Installation costs include both labor and equipment rental costs. When estimating equipment rental rates only for a specific location, use 01 54 33 EQUIPMENT RENTAL COSTS in the Reference Section.

The 30 City Average Index is the average of 30 major U.S. cities and serves as a national average. This national average represents the baseline from which all locations are calculated.

Index figures for both material and installation are based on the 30 major city average of 100 and represent the cost relationship as of July 1, 2022. The index for each division is computed from representative material and labor quantities for that division. The weighted average for each city is a weighted total of the components listed above it. It does not include relative productivity between trades or cities.

As changes occur in local material prices, labor rates, and equipment rental rates (including fuel costs), the impact of these changes should be accurately measured by the change in the City Cost Index for each particular city (as compared to the 30 city average).

Therefore, if you know (or have estimated) building costs in one city today, you can easily convert those costs to expected building costs in another city.

In addition, by using the Historical Cost Index, you can easily convert national average building costs at a particular time to the approximate building costs for some other time. The City Cost Indexes can then be applied to calculate the costs for a particular city.

Quick calculations

Location Adjustment Using the City Cost Indexes:

$$\frac{\text{Index for City A}}{\text{Index for City B}} \times \text{Cost in City B} = \text{Cost in City A}$$

Time Adjustment for the National Average Using the Historical Cost Index:

$$\frac{\text{Index for Year A}}{\text{Index for Year B}} \times \text{Cost in Year B} = \text{Cost in Year A}$$

Adjustment from the National Average:

$$\frac{\text{Index for City A}}{100} \times \text{National Average Cost} = \text{Cost in City A}$$

Since each of the other RSMeans data sets contains many different items, any *one* item multiplied by the particular city index may give incorrect results. However, the larger the number of items compiled, the closer the results should be to actual costs for that particular city.

The City Cost Indexes for Canadian cities are calculated using Canadian material and equipment prices and labor rates in Canadian dollars. When compared to the baseline mentioned previously, the resulting index enables the user to convert baseline costs to local costs. Therefore, indexes for Canadian cities can be used to convert U.S. national average prices to local costs in Canadian dollars.

How to use this section

1. Compare costs from city to city.

In using the RSMeans Indexes, remember that an index number is not a fixed number but a ratio: It's a percentage ratio of a building component's cost at any stated time to the national average cost of that same component at the same time period. Put in the form of an equation:

$$\frac{\text{Specific City Cost}}{\text{National Average Cost}} \times 100 = \text{City Index Number}$$

Therefore, when making cost comparisons between cities, do not subtract one city's index number from the index number of another city and read the result as a percentage difference. Instead, divide one city's index number by that of the other city. The resulting number may then be used as a multiplier to calculate cost differences from city to city.

The formula used to find cost differences between cities for the purpose of comparison is as follows:

$$\frac{\text{City A Index}}{\text{City B Index}} \times \text{City B Cost (Known)} = \text{City A Cost (Unknown)}$$

In addition, you can use RSMeans CCI to calculate and compare costs division by division between cities using the same basic formula. (Just be sure that you're comparing similar divisions.)

2. Compare a specific city's construction costs with the national average.

When you're studying construction location feasibility, it's advisable to compare a prospective project's cost index with an index of the national average cost.

For example, divide the weighted average index of construction costs of a specific city by that of the 30 City Average, which = 100.

$$\frac{\text{City Index}}{100} = \text{\% of National Average}$$

As a result, you get a ratio that indicates the relative cost of construction in that city in comparison with the national average.

3. Convert U.S. national average to actual costs in Canadian City.

$$\frac{\text{Index for Canadian City}}{100} \times \text{National Average Cost} = \text{Cost in Canadian City in \$ CAN}$$

4. **Adjust construction cost data based on a national average.**

When you use a source of construction cost data which is based on a national average (such as RSMeans cost data), it is necessary to adjust those costs to a specific location.

$$\frac{\text{City Index}}{100} \times \text{Cost Based on National Average Costs} = \text{City Cost (Unknown)}$$

5. **When applying the City Cost Indexes to demolition projects, use the appropriate division installation index.** For example, for removal of existing doors and windows, use the Division 8 (Openings) index.

What you might like to know about how we developed the Indexes

The information presented in the CCI is organized according to the Construction Specifications Institute (CSI) MasterFormat 2018 classification system.

To create a reliable index, RSMeans researched the building type most often constructed in the United States and Canada. Because it was concluded that no one type of building completely represented the building construction industry, nine different types of buildings were combined to create a composite model.

The exact material, labor, and equipment quantities are based on detailed analyses of these nine building types, and then each quantity is weighted in proportion to expected usage. These various material items, labor hours, and equipment rental rates are thus combined to form a composite building representing as closely as possible the actual usage of materials, labor, and equipment in the North American building construction industry.

The following structures were chosen to make up that composite model:

1. Factory, 1 story
2. Office, 2–4 stories
3. Store, Retail
4. Town Hall, 2–3 stories
5. High School, 2–3 stories
6. Hospital, 4–8 stories
7. Garage, Parking
8. Apartment, 1–3 stories
9. Hotel/Motel, 2–3 stories

For the purposes of ensuring the timeliness of the data, the components of the index for the composite model have been streamlined. They currently consist of:

- specific quantities of 66 commonly used construction materials;
- specific labor-hours for 21 building construction trades; and
- specific days of equipment rental for 6 types of construction equipment (normally used to install the 66 material items by the 21 trades.) Fuel costs and routine maintenance costs are included in the equipment cost.

Material and equipment price quotations are gathered quarterly from cities in the United States and Canada. These prices and the latest negotiated labor wage rates for 21 different building trades are used to compile the quarterly update of the City Cost Index.

The 30 major U.S. cities used to calculate the national average are:

Atlanta, GA	Memphis, TN
Baltimore, MD	Milwaukee, WI
Boston, MA	Minneapolis, MN
Buffalo, NY	Nashville, TN
Chicago, IL	New Orleans, LA
Cincinnati, OH	New York, NY
Cleveland, OH	Philadelphia, PA
Columbus, OH	Phoenix, AZ
Dallas, TX	Pittsburgh, PA
Denver, CO	St. Louis, MO
Detroit, MI	San Antonio, TX
Houston, TX	San Diego, CA
Indianapolis, IN	San Francisco, CA
Kansas City, MO	Seattle, WA
Los Angeles, CA	Washington, DC

What the CCI does not indicate

The weighted average for each city is a total of the divisional components weighted to reflect typical usage. It does not include the productivity variations between trades or cities.

In addition, the CCI does not take into consideration factors such as the following:

- managerial efficiency
- competitive conditions
- automation
- restrictive union practices
- unique local requirements
- regional variations due to specific building codes

	DIVISION	UNITED STATES 30 CITY AVERAGE			ALABAMA ANNISTON 362			BIRMINGHAM 350 - 352			BUTLER 369			DECATUR 356			DOTHAN 363		
		MAT.	INST.	TOTAL	MAT.	INST.	TOTAL	MAT.	INST.	TOTAL	MAT.	INST.	TOTAL	MAT.	INST.	TOTAL	MAT.	INST.	TOTAL
015433	CONTRACTOR EQUIPMENT		100.0	100.0		98.3	98.3		102.9	102.9		96.1	96.1		98.3	98.3		96.1	96.1
0241, 31 - 34	SITE & INFRASTRUCTURE, DEMOLITION	100.0	100.0	100.0	104.1	85.5	92.0	99.0	93.6	95.5	111.3	82.0	92.2	91.3	85.1	87.3	108.9	82.2	91.4
0310	Concrete Forming & Accessories	100.0	100.0	100.0	92.5	63.3	69.9	100.0	67.6	74.9	88.2	65.5	70.6	99.3	61.9	70.3	98.4	69.0	75.5
0320	Concrete Reinforcing	100.0	100.0	100.0	88.0	67.9	82.4	98.0	68.1	89.7	92.9	67.4	85.8	91.4	64.4	83.9	92.9	68.2	86.0
0330	Cast-in-Place Concrete	100.0	100.0	100.0	87.9	65.7	80.0	106.6	70.4	93.8	85.7	65.9	78.7	99.0	65.0	86.9	85.7	67.6	79.3
03	CONCRETE	100.0	100.0	100.0	90.5	66.7	81.1	98.4	70.1	87.2	91.5	67.7	82.1	92.2	65.2	81.5	91.5	70.0	83.0
04	MASONRY	100.0	100.0	100.0	81.2	59.8	68.2	86.2	62.3	71.7	82.5	59.8	68.7	81.8	58.8	67.8	84.4	63.1	71.5
05	METALS	100.0	100.0	100.0	104.2	92.5	101.9	104.6	90.3	101.8	103.2	92.9	101.2	105.9	90.6	102.9	103.3	94.0	101.5
06	WOOD, PLASTICS & COMPOSITES	100.0	100.0	100.0	87.0	63.5	76.4	94.5	67.8	82.5	80.8	65.9	74.1	97.8	61.6	81.6	94.5	69.6	83.3
07	THERMAL & MOISTURE PROTECTION	100.0	100.0	100.0	102.7	59.2	87.2	106.7	66.1	92.2	102.7	62.9	88.5	104.1	62.1	89.1	102.8	64.4	89.1
08	OPENINGS	100.0	100.0	100.0	102.9	65.0	94.4	103.0	67.9	95.1	102.9	66.7	94.8	106.5	63.6	96.8	103.0	68.9	95.3
0920	Plaster & Gypsum Board	100.0	100.0	100.0	92.5	63.0	73.8	93.2	67.1	76.7	90.1	65.5	74.5	92.5	61.1	72.6	101.2	69.3	81.0
0950, 0980	Ceilings & Acoustic Treatment	100.0	100.0	100.0	92.1	63.0	75.8	90.1	67.1	77.2	92.1	65.5	77.2	87.9	61.1	72.9	92.1	69.3	79.3
0960	Flooring	100.0	100.0	100.0	68.1	64.2	67.1	106.5	67.5	96.7	71.7	64.2	69.8	100.1	64.2	91.1	75.8	68.8	74.0
0970, 0990	Wall Finishes & Painting/Coating	100.0	100.0	100.0	96.2	50.1	68.7	99.2	51.1	70.5	96.2	42.4	64.1	88.5	56.4	69.4	96.2	82.0	87.7
09	FINISHES	100.0	100.0	100.0	84.6	62.0	73.3	97.9	65.6	81.7	87.4	62.6	75.0	92.8	61.4	77.0	89.9	70.3	80.0
COVERS	DIVS. 10 - 14, 25, 28, 41, 43, 44, 46	100.0	100.0	100.0	100.0	83.4	96.8	100.0	85.0	97.1	100.0	84.5	97.0	100.0	78.9	95.9	100.0	85.2	97.1
21, 22, 23	FIRE SUPPRESSION, PLUMBING & HVAC	100.0	100.0	100.0	105.5	49.6	85.5	100.0	63.5	86.9	95.9	61.3	83.5	100.0	61.3	86.1	95.9	61.8	83.7
26, 27, 3370	ELECTRICAL, COMMUNICATIONS & UTIL.	100.0	100.0	100.0	98.0	53.3	78.6	100.7	64.2	84.9	99.1	53.5	79.3	98.0	60.3	81.6	98.4	73.4	87.6
MF2018	WEIGHTED AVERAGE	100.0	100.0	100.0	99.2	64.0	86.3	100.6	70.5	89.5	97.5	66.7	86.2	99.3	66.7	87.3	97.8	71.5	88.1

	DIVISION	ALABAMA EVERGREEN 364			GADSDEN 359			HUNTSVILLE 357 - 358			JASPER 355			MOBILE 365 - 366			MONTGOMERY 360 - 361		
		MAT.	INST.	TOTAL	MAT.	INST.	TOTAL	MAT.	INST.	TOTAL	MAT.	INST.	TOTAL	MAT.	INST.	TOTAL	MAT.	INST.	TOTAL
015433	CONTRACTOR EQUIPMENT		96.1	96.1		98.3	98.3		98.3	98.3		98.3	98.3		96.1	96.1		103.7	103.7
0241, 31 - 34	SITE & INFRASTRUCTURE, DEMOLITION	111.8	82.0	92.3	101.5	85.5	91.1	91.0	85.5	87.4	101.4	85.5	91.1	105.7	82.0	90.2	104.4	94.8	98.1
0310	Concrete Forming & Accessories	84.7	63.5	68.3	90.5	65.8	71.3	99.3	72.0	78.1	96.3	64.1	71.3	97.4	66.8	73.6	102.8	67.3	75.2
0320	Concrete Reinforcing	92.9	67.4	85.8	96.5	68.0	88.7	91.4	76.0	87.1	91.4	67.9	84.9	91.0	68.8	84.8	99.8	68.1	91.0
0330	Cast-in-Place Concrete	85.7	65.8	78.7	99.0	67.8	87.9	96.4	67.6	86.2	109.8	66.4	94.3	89.9	66.9	81.7	89.8	68.8	82.3
03	CONCRETE	91.6	66.8	81.8	95.6	68.6	84.9	91.1	72.7	83.8	98.5	67.3	86.2	89.0	68.9	81.1	92.2	69.4	83.2
04	MASONRY	82.5	59.8	68.7	80.4	61.8	69.1	82.7	61.5	69.8	77.9	60.8	67.5	83.9	61.3	70.2	81.4	61.4	69.3
05	METALS	103.3	92.7	101.2	102.9	93.2	101.0	105.9	96.1	103.9	102.8	92.9	100.9	106.1	93.5	103.6	105.7	90.3	102.7
06	WOOD, PLASTICS & COMPOSITES	76.4	63.5	70.6	86.2	65.7	77.0	97.8	74.1	87.2	94.5	63.5	80.6	93.3	67.5	81.7	97.9	67.8	84.4
07	THERMAL & MOISTURE PROTECTION	102.7	61.8	88.1	104.2	64.2	90.0	104.1	65.0	90.1	104.3	62.3	89.3	102.5	63.2	88.5	102.5	65.6	89.3
08	OPENINGS	102.9	65.3	94.5	103.0	66.7	94.8	106.2	73.3	98.8	102.9	65.5	94.5	105.9	67.9	97.3	104.2	67.9	96.0
0920	Plaster & Gypsum Board	89.8	63.0	72.8	83.4	65.3	71.9	92.5	73.9	80.7	87.9	63.0	72.1	98.9	67.1	78.8	101.4	67.1	79.6
0950, 0980	Ceilings & Acoustic Treatment	92.1	63.0	75.8	81.1	65.3	72.2	88.9	73.9	80.5	81.1	63.0	70.9	101.3	67.1	82.1	104.0	67.1	83.3
0960	Flooring	70.0	64.2	68.6	97.0	66.8	89.4	100.1	66.8	91.7	98.7	64.2	90.0	75.7	67.5	73.6	75.0	67.5	73.1
0970, 0990	Wall Finishes & Painting/Coating	96.2	42.4	64.1	88.5	50.1	65.6	88.5	58.8	70.8	88.5	50.1	65.6	99.8	42.4	65.6	101.2	50.1	70.7
09	FINISHES	86.9	61.2	74.0	89.3	64.0	76.6	93.1	69.8	81.4	90.3	62.2	76.2	91.6	64.2	77.8	94.1	65.3	79.6
COVERS	DIVS. 10 - 14, 25, 28, 41, 43, 44, 46	100.0	84.2	96.9	100.0	83.9	96.9	100.0	84.7	97.0	100.0	83.7	96.8	100.0	84.7	97.0	100.0	84.7	97.0
21, 22, 23	FIRE SUPPRESSION, PLUMBING & HVAC	95.9	55.4	81.4	107.1	63.7	91.5	100.0	63.4	86.9	107.1	63.3	91.4	100.1	60.2	85.8	100.1	60.3	85.8
26, 27, 3370	ELECTRICAL, COMMUNICATIONS & UTIL.	97.6	53.5	78.5	98.2	64.2	83.5	98.7	65.6	84.4	97.8	53.3	78.5	99.7	58.6	81.9	100.8	71.1	87.9
MF2018	WEIGHTED AVERAGE	97.3	65.0	85.4	100.2	69.5	88.9	99.3	71.6	89.1	100.6	67.2	88.3	99.4	67.8	87.8	99.8	70.6	89.0

	DIVISION	ALABAMA PHENIX CITY 368			SELMA 367			TUSCALOOSA 354			ALASKA ANCHORAGE 995 - 996			FAIRBANKS 997			JUNEAU 998		
		MAT.	INST.	TOTAL	MAT.	INST.	TOTAL	MAT.	INST.	TOTAL	MAT.	INST.	TOTAL	MAT.	INST.	TOTAL	MAT.	INST.	TOTAL
015433	CONTRACTOR EQUIPMENT		96.1	96.1		96.1	96.1		98.3	98.3		104.7	104.7		109.1	109.1		104.7	104.7
0241, 31 - 34	SITE & INFRASTRUCTURE, DEMOLITION	115.6	81.9	93.7	108.6	81.9	91.2	91.5	85.5	87.6	137.2	112.6	121.2	133.5	118.5	123.7	149.0	112.6	125.3
0310	Concrete Forming & Accessories	92.4	65.3	71.3	89.7	63.8	69.6	99.3	66.9	74.1	96.6	113.8	110.0	100.2	113.7	110.7	96.1	113.8	109.9
0320	Concrete Reinforcing	92.8	64.2	84.9	92.9	67.9	86.0	91.4	68.0	84.9	106.6	117.1	109.5	103.7	117.1	107.4	106.5	117.1	109.4
0330	Cast-in-Place Concrete	85.8	66.2	78.8	85.7	65.9	78.7	100.4	67.5	88.7	131.6	112.9	125.0	130.4	111.0	123.5	131.5	112.9	124.9
03	CONCRETE	94.0	67.2	83.4	90.8	67.0	81.4	92.8	69.0	83.4	116.1	113.4	115.0	108.8	112.8	110.4	120.9	113.4	117.9
04	MASONRY	82.5	59.8	68.7	87.3	59.8	70.6	82.1	61.3	69.5	180.4	113.1	139.5	179.4	113.0	139.1	165.4	113.1	133.6
05	METALS	103.2	91.6	100.9	103.2	93.0	101.2	105.0	93.2	102.7	132.1	101.8	126.1	126.8	104.1	122.3	127.1	101.8	122.1
06	WOOD, PLASTICS & COMPOSITES	86.4	65.4	77.0	82.9	63.5	74.2	97.8	67.5	84.2	107.6	111.8	109.5	120.9	111.7	116.8	112.1	111.8	112.0
07	THERMAL & MOISTURE PROTECTION	103.0	63.3	88.9	102.6	62.6	88.3	104.1	64.1	89.9	119.1	111.1	116.3	119.1	109.8	115.8	114.7	111.1	113.4
08	OPENINGS	102.9	65.6	94.5	102.9	65.5	94.5	106.2	67.7	97.5	121.5	113.6	119.7	124.5	112.2	121.7	123.4	113.6	121.2
0920	Plaster & Gypsum Board	94.2	65.0	75.7	92.0	63.0	73.6	92.5	67.1	76.4	129.5	112.1	118.4	154.7	112.1	127.7	142.9	112.1	123.4
0950, 0980	Ceilings & Acoustic Treatment	92.1	65.0	76.9	92.1	63.0	75.8	88.9	67.1	76.7	112.6	112.1	112.3	103.7	112.1	108.4	123.9	112.1	117.3
0960	Flooring	73.2	64.2	70.9	72.0	64.2	70.0	100.1	66.8	91.7	112.5	109.5	111.7	101.7	109.5	103.6	108.1	109.5	108.4
0970, 0990	Wall Finishes & Painting/Coating	96.2	74.4	83.2	96.2	50.1	68.7	88.5	50.1	65.6	105.1	115.5	111.3	101.8	109.7	106.5	105.1	115.5	111.3
09	FINISHES	88.8	65.8	77.3	87.5	62.0	74.7	93.1	64.9	78.9	113.5	113.3	113.4	111.4	112.7	112.0	116.7	113.3	115.0
COVERS	DIVS. 10 - 14, 25, 28, 41, 43, 44, 46	100.0	80.3	96.2	100.0	83.4	96.8	100.0	83.9	96.9	100.0	111.3	102.2	100.0	111.2	102.2	100.0	111.3	102.2
21, 22, 23	FIRE SUPPRESSION, PLUMBING & HVAC	95.9	60.1	83.1	95.9	60.8	83.3	100.0	63.3	86.8	100.0	107.3	102.6	99.8	107.2	102.5	100.0	107.3	102.6
26, 27, 3370	ELECTRICAL, COMMUNICATIONS & UTIL.	98.8	63.0	83.3	98.3	67.7	85.0	98.5	64.2	83.6	102.4	102.2	102.3	117.4	102.2	110.8	102.4	102.2	102.3
MF2018	WEIGHTED AVERAGE	98.0	67.8	86.9	97.5	68.3	86.7	99.3	69.6	88.4	116.6	109.2	113.9	116.2	109.6	113.8	116.1	109.2	113.5

DIVISION		ALASKA			ARIZONA															
		KETCHIKAN			CHAMBERS			FLAGSTAFF			GLOBE			KINGMAN			MESA/TEMPE		
		999			865			860			855			864			852		
		MAT.	INST.	TOTAL	MAT.	INST.	TOTAL	MAT.	INST.	TOTAL	MAT.	INST.	TOTAL	MAT.	INST.	TOTAL	MAT.	INST.	TOTAL
015433	**CONTRACTOR EQUIPMENT**		109.1	109.1		87.5	87.5		87.5	87.5		89.5	89.5		87.5	87.5		89.5	89.5
0241, 31 - 34	**SITE & INFRASTRUCTURE, DEMOLITION**	186.9	118.5	142.3	74.0	87.4	82.7	94.9	87.7	90.2	105.8	88.8	94.7	74.0	87.7	82.9	99.0	89.1	92.6
0310	Concrete Forming & Accessories	92.6	113.8	109.1	98.6	65.6	72.9	104.8	73.1	80.2	93.0	65.8	71.8	96.5	62.0	69.7	96.3	70.6	76.3
0320	Concrete Reinforcing	80.6	117.1	90.7	93.5	73.7	88.0	93.4	73.3	87.9	104.7	73.7	96.1	93.6	73.7	88.1	105.4	73.7	96.6
0330	Cast-in-Place Concrete	264.1	111.7	209.9	80.9	67.0	75.9	80.9	67.4	76.1	78.5	66.9	74.4	80.6	67.3	75.9	79.2	67.3	75.0
03	**CONCRETE**	175.7	113.1	151.0	89.4	67.6	80.8	104.5	71.2	91.4	95.1	67.8	84.3	89.1	66.2	80.1	89.9	70.1	82.1
04	**MASONRY**	188.4	113.0	142.6	97.3	65.2	77.8	97.5	58.9	74.0	118.6	65.1	86.1	97.3	65.3	77.9	118.8	65.2	86.3
05	**METALS**	127.0	104.1	122.5	98.5	72.4	93.4	99.1	73.0	94.0	95.8	73.8	91.4	99.3	73.4	94.2	96.1	74.8	91.9
06	**WOOD, PLASTICS & COMPOSITES**	110.6	111.7	111.1	104.3	66.3	87.3	112.5	76.2	96.2	91.7	66.5	80.4	98.6	61.2	81.8	96.4	72.7	85.8
07	**THERMAL & MOISTURE PROTECTION**	131.5	109.5	123.6	91.1	68.9	83.2	92.6	68.6	84.1	90.9	67.7	82.6	91.0	68.8	83.1	90.9	68.8	83.0
08	**OPENINGS**	120.5	113.6	118.9	100.3	63.8	92.1	100.4	72.9	94.2	90.9	63.9	84.8	100.4	62.5	91.9	91.0	68.2	85.8
0920	Plaster & Gypsum Board	138.2	112.1	121.6	104.2	65.6	79.7	109.1	75.8	88.0	101.5	65.6	78.8	94.4	60.4	72.8	105.6	72.1	84.3
0950, 0980	Ceilings & Acoustic Treatment	100.7	112.1	107.1	110.8	65.6	85.5	111.7	75.8	91.6	99.0	65.6	80.3	111.7	60.4	82.9	99.0	72.1	83.9
0960	Flooring	101.3	109.5	103.4	90.4	57.7	82.2	92.0	62.8	84.7	93.8	57.7	84.8	89.5	57.7	81.5	94.9	61.7	86.6
0970, 0990	Wall Finishes & Painting/Coating	101.8	115.5	110.0	87.5	55.2	68.2	87.5	55.2	68.2	93.3	55.2	70.6	87.5	55.2	68.2	93.3	55.2	70.6
09	**FINISHES**	112.7	113.3	113.0	97.4	62.6	79.9	100.3	69.4	84.8	98.6	62.8	80.6	96.0	59.7	77.7	98.4	67.3	82.8
COVERS	**DIVS. 10 - 14, 25, 28, 41, 43, 44, 46**	100.0	111.2	102.2	100.0	83.6	96.8	100.0	84.6	97.0	100.0	84.0	96.9	100.0	83.0	96.7	100.0	84.6	97.0
21, 22, 23	**FIRE SUPPRESSION, PLUMBING & HVAC**	93.2	107.2	98.2	94.2	74.1	87.0	100.4	76.2	91.7	92.8	74.2	86.1	94.2	76.2	87.8	100.4	74.2	91.0
26, 27, 3370	**ELECTRICAL, COMMUNICATIONS & UTIL.**	117.4	102.2	110.8	101.9	65.6	86.2	101.4	63.8	85.1	97.7	63.8	83.0	101.9	63.8	85.4	96.1	63.8	82.1
MF2018	**WEIGHTED AVERAGE**	124.5	109.8	119.1	96.2	70.2	86.6	100.3	71.7	89.8	96.3	70.2	86.7	96.2	69.8	86.5	97.1	71.5	87.7

DIVISION		ARIZONA												ARKANSAS					
		PHOENIX			PRESCOTT			SHOW LOW			TUCSON			BATESVILLE			CAMDEN		
		850,853			863			859			856 - 857			725			717		
		MAT.	INST.	TOTAL	MAT.	INST.	TOTAL	MAT.	INST.	TOTAL	MAT.	INST.	TOTAL	MAT.	INST.	TOTAL	MAT.	INST.	TOTAL
015433	**CONTRACTOR EQUIPMENT**		98.6	98.6		87.5	87.5		89.5	89.5		89.5	89.5		87.3	87.3		87.3	87.3
0241, 31 - 34	**SITE & INFRASTRUCTURE, DEMOLITION**	99.8	97.3	98.2	83.3	87.7	86.2	108.0	88.8	95.5	95.0	89.2	91.2	73.4	82.4	79.3	78.5	82.3	81.0
0310	Concrete Forming & Accessories	101.4	71.6	78.3	100.3	68.7	75.8	100.9	65.8	73.6	97.1	77.7	82.0	86.0	56.9	63.4	83.1	57.1	62.9
0320	Concrete Reinforcing	100.7	71.7	92.6	93.4	73.7	88.0	105.4	73.7	96.6	86.5	73.4	82.8	96.2	63.6	87.2	96.0	64.6	87.3
0330	Cast-in-Place Concrete	83.4	71.7	79.2	80.9	67.4	76.1	78.5	66.9	74.4	81.5	67.3	76.5	61.7	71.7	65.2	67.1	71.2	68.6
03	**CONCRETE**	91.0	71.9	83.5	93.5	69.3	83.9	97.1	67.8	85.5	85.9	73.3	80.9	73.1	64.1	69.6	75.3	64.2	70.9
04	**MASONRY**	110.7	65.6	83.3	97.4	65.3	77.9	118.6	65.1	86.1	103.2	58.8	76.2	89.3	58.2	70.4	110.3	58.1	78.6
05	**METALS**	103.4	76.5	98.1	99.2	73.7	94.1	95.5	73.8	91.2	96.9	74.4	92.5	98.5	74.8	93.8	109.3	75.1	102.5
06	**WOOD, PLASTICS & COMPOSITES**	104.1	73.1	90.2	106.4	70.2	90.2	102.3	66.5	86.2	96.9	82.4	90.4	82.0	57.7	71.1	81.7	58.2	71.2
07	**THERMAL & MOISTURE PROTECTION**	91.6	71.0	84.3	91.5	70.5	84.0	91.2	67.7	82.8	91.4	68.1	83.1	106.1	58.8	89.2	100.7	59.1	85.9
08	**OPENINGS**	100.8	70.3	93.9	100.4	66.4	92.7	90.3	65.4	84.7	87.7	76.3	85.2	103.7	56.0	93.0	97.1	56.5	88.0
0920	Plaster & Gypsum Board	116.1	72.1	88.2	104.8	69.7	82.5	108.5	65.6	81.3	110.6	82.0	92.5	74.9	57.0	63.6	84.7	57.5	67.5
0950, 0980	Ceilings & Acoustic Treatment	115.1	72.1	91.0	109.0	69.7	86.9	99.0	65.6	80.3	101.7	82.0	90.7	98.9	57.0	75.4	103.7	57.5	77.8
0960	Flooring	100.1	66.3	91.7	91.1	61.9	83.7	95.9	57.7	86.3	85.0	62.5	79.3	91.2	66.1	84.9	92.8	67.4	86.5
0970, 0990	Wall Finishes & Painting/Coating	101.2	55.0	73.7	87.5	55.2	68.2	93.3	55.2	70.6	93.5	55.2	70.7	95.8	48.8	67.8	97.1	50.4	69.2
09	**FINISHES**	106.2	68.9	87.4	97.6	65.8	81.6	100.3	62.8	81.5	96.7	73.1	84.9	87.8	57.5	72.6	92.1	58.0	75.0
COVERS	**DIVS. 10 - 14, 25, 28, 41, 43, 44, 46**	100.0	86.1	97.3	100.0	84.0	96.9	100.0	84.0	96.9	100.0	85.7	97.2	100.0	78.4	95.8	100.0	78.2	95.8
21, 22, 23	**FIRE SUPPRESSION, PLUMBING & HVAC**	100.1	77.2	91.9	100.4	74.1	91.0	92.8	74.2	86.1	100.3	76.2	91.7	93.0	49.2	77.3	92.6	54.0	78.8
26, 27, 3370	**ELECTRICAL, COMMUNICATIONS & UTIL.**	100.1	63.8	84.4	101.2	63.8	85.0	96.3	63.8	82.2	97.3	57.9	80.2	93.8	53.8	76.5	95.6	51.7	76.6
MF2018	**WEIGHTED AVERAGE**	100.4	73.7	90.6	98.4	70.9	88.3	96.6	70.3	86.9	95.9	72.1	87.1	92.6	60.4	80.7	95.9	61.2	83.1

DIVISION		ARKANSAS																	
		FAYETTEVILLE			FORT SMITH			HARRISON			HOT SPRINGS			JONESBORO			LITTLE ROCK		
		727			729			726			719			724			720 - 722		
		MAT.	INST.	TOTAL	MAT.	INST.	TOTAL	MAT.	INST.	TOTAL	MAT.	INST.	TOTAL	MAT.	INST.	TOTAL	MAT.	INST.	TOTAL
015433	**CONTRACTOR EQUIPMENT**		87.3	87.3		87.3	87.3		87.3	87.3		87.3	87.3		107.9	107.9		93.8	93.8
0241, 31 - 34	**SITE & INFRASTRUCTURE, DEMOLITION**	73.1	82.3	79.1	80.8	82.4	81.8	77.5	82.3	80.6	81.1	82.4	81.9	96.7	97.7	97.3	86.0	92.5	90.2
0310	Concrete Forming & Accessories	80.9	57.1	62.4	103.1	58.1	68.1	91.3	56.9	64.6	79.7	57.4	62.4	89.8	57.6	64.8	102.5	58.7	68.5
0320	Concrete Reinforcing	96.2	61.4	86.6	97.4	63.6	88.1	95.8	64.6	87.2	94.2	64.4	86.0	93.5	65.6	85.8	98.7	66.3	89.7
0330	Cast-in-Place Concrete	61.7	71.2	65.1	70.5	72.5	71.2	68.4	71.2	69.4	68.7	72.0	69.9	67.1	72.9	69.2	68.4	75.1	70.8
03	**CONCRETE**	72.7	63.7	69.1	79.3	64.9	73.6	77.9	64.1	72.5	77.0	64.6	72.1	75.9	66.1	72.0	81.8	66.5	75.7
04	**MASONRY**	81.6	58.1	67.3	91.8	59.0	71.9	89.7	58.1	70.5	82.9	57.4	67.4	83.3	59.7	69.0	88.8	61.6	72.3
05	**METALS**	98.5	74.0	93.6	101.3	74.6	96.0	100.1	74.9	95.2	109.2	74.7	102.4	95.5	89.0	94.2	101.4	74.5	96.1
06	**WOOD, PLASTICS & COMPOSITES**	77.1	58.2	68.6	103.4	59.3	83.7	89.1	58.2	75.2	78.1	58.2	69.2	85.9	58.5	73.6	98.1	59.6	80.8
07	**THERMAL & MOISTURE PROTECTION**	106.7	59.1	89.7	107.2	59.4	90.2	106.4	59.1	89.5	100.9	58.4	85.8	111.8	59.7	93.2	100.8	61.6	86.8
08	**OPENINGS**	103.7	55.7	92.9	105.4	56.8	94.4	104.4	56.4	93.6	97.1	56.0	87.9	109.1	56.9	97.3	98.6	57.3	89.3
0920	Plaster & Gypsum Board	73.4	57.5	63.3	81.5	58.7	67.0	81.1	57.5	66.1	83.5	57.5	67.0	83.1	57.5	66.9	93.2	58.7	71.3
0950, 0980	Ceilings & Acoustic Treatment	98.9	57.5	75.7	101.6	58.7	77.5	101.6	57.5	76.9	103.7	57.5	77.8	100.4	57.5	76.3	109.0	58.7	80.8
0960	Flooring	88.7	67.4	83.4	96.6	74.6	91.1	93.1	67.4	86.6	92.0	63.5	84.9	63.4	74.6	66.2	99.8	80.1	94.9
0970, 0990	Wall Finishes & Painting/Coating	95.8	50.4	68.7	95.8	50.1	68.6	95.8	50.4	68.7	97.1	48.4	68.1	84.3	49.5	63.6	99.1	49.5	69.6
09	**FINISHES**	87.0	58.0	72.4	91.3	60.4	75.7	90.2	58.0	74.1	92.0	57.4	74.6	83.5	59.9	71.6	100.7	61.6	81.1
COVERS	**DIVS. 10 - 14, 25, 28, 41, 43, 44, 46**	100.0	78.1	95.8	100.0	78.6	95.8	100.0	78.2	95.8	100.0	78.7	95.9	100.0	79.2	96.0	100.0	79.3	96.0
21, 22, 23	**FIRE SUPPRESSION, PLUMBING & HVAC**	93.1	58.1	80.6	100.7	47.7	81.7	93.0	46.8	76.4	92.6	47.7	76.5	101.2	48.6	82.4	100.2	50.1	82.2
26, 27, 3370	**ELECTRICAL, COMMUNICATIONS & UTIL.**	90.9	48.0	72.3	92.5	56.8	77.0	93.1	51.2	75.0	96.6	58.0	79.9	99.9	58.3	81.9	100.8	58.5	82.4
MF2018	**WEIGHTED AVERAGE**	91.9	61.4	80.6	96.4	61.1	83.4	93.9	59.6	81.3	95.1	60.6	82.4	95.4	64.2	83.9	97.4	63.4	84.9

City Cost Indexes

DIVISION		ARKANSAS												CALIFORNIA					
		PINE BLUFF			RUSSELLVILLE			TEXARKANA			WEST MEMPHIS			ALHAMBRA			ANAHEIM		
		716			728			718			723			917 - 918			928		
		MAT.	INST.	TOTAL	MAT.	INST.	TOTAL	MAT.	INST.	TOTAL	MAT.	INST.	TOTAL	MAT.	INST.	TOTAL	MAT.	INST.	TOTAL
015433	**CONTRACTOR EQUIPMENT**		87.3	87.3		87.3	87.3		88.4	88.4		107.9	107.9		93.7	93.7		96.6	96.6
0241, 31 - 34	**SITE & INFRASTRUCTURE, DEMOLITION**	86.2	82.4	83.7	74.7	82.4	79.7	94.7	84.2	87.8	99.1	97.5	98.1	113.1	101.2	105.4	110.8	101.5	104.8
0310	Concrete Forming & Accessories	79.5	57.5	62.4	86.9	57.3	63.9	87.3	57.3	64.0	96.1	57.7	66.3	97.0	138.9	129.6	96.1	139.0	129.5
0320	Concrete Reinforcing	95.9	66.1	87.7	96.9	64.4	87.9	95.4	66.1	87.3	93.5	56.9	83.4	99.5	132.7	108.7	79.8	132.6	94.4
0330	Cast-in-Place Concrete	68.7	71.8	69.8	64.6	72.0	67.2	74.8	71.5	73.7	70.4	73.0	71.3	94.3	126.6	105.8	99.3	129.5	110.0
03	**CONCRETE**	77.7	64.8	72.6	75.3	64.5	71.1	77.4	64.7	72.4	80.5	64.7	74.3	101.6	132.4	113.7	99.9	133.5	113.1
04	**MASONRY**	117.5	60.2	82.7	91.1	57.4	70.6	96.6	59.6	74.1	76.2	57.3	64.7	150.7	138.1	143.0	83.0	135.6	114.9
05	**METALS**	110.0	75.7	103.3	98.5	74.5	93.7	100.8	75.8	95.9	94.5	85.5	92.8	95.9	114.8	99.6	110.8	114.9	111.6
06	**WOOD, PLASTICS & COMPOSITES**	77.6	58.2	68.9	83.7	58.2	72.3	88.1	58.2	74.7	93.4	58.5	77.7	94.2	137.6	113.6	102.8	137.8	118.5
07	**THERMAL & MOISTURE PROTECTION**	101.0	60.1	86.4	106.9	58.4	89.6	101.5	59.6	86.6	112.3	58.3	93.0	125.1	129.5	126.7	91.3	131.9	105.8
08	**OPENINGS**	98.2	56.7	88.8	103.7	56.0	93.0	102.3	56.9	92.0	107.0	54.5	95.1	92.0	136.4	102.0	99.6	136.6	107.9
0920	Plaster & Gypsum Board	83.3	57.5	66.9	74.9	57.5	63.9	87.6	57.5	68.5	85.7	57.5	67.8	140.3	139.1	139.5	120.5	139.1	132.3
0950, 0980	Ceilings & Acoustic Treatment	103.7	57.5	77.8	98.9	57.5	75.7	112.8	57.5	81.8	99.8	57.5	76.1	105.4	139.1	124.3	105.3	139.1	124.2
0960	Flooring	91.9	74.6	87.6	90.7	63.5	83.9	93.4	75.7	89.0	65.4	63.5	64.9	91.7	118.3	98.4	89.6	118.3	96.8
0970, 0990	Wall Finishes & Painting/Coating	97.1	51.1	69.7	95.8	48.4	67.6	97.1	50.4	69.2	84.3	48.4	62.9	95.3	127.1	114.2	87.9	127.1	111.2
09	**FINISHES**	92.0	59.8	75.8	87.9	57.4	72.6	95.9	59.8	77.8	85.0	57.7	71.2	104.3	133.9	119.1	98.5	134.0	116.3
COVERS	**DIVS. 10 - 14, 25, 28, 41, 43, 44, 46**	100.0	78.5	95.8	100.0	78.7	95.9	100.0	78.3	95.8	100.0	79.7	96.1	100.0	116.2	103.1	100.0	116.7	103.2
21, 22, 23	**FIRE SUPPRESSION, PLUMBING & HVAC**	100.3	51.1	82.7	93.1	47.2	76.7	100.3	54.8	84.0	93.7	59.4	81.4	92.5	128.4	105.4	99.8	128.4	110.1
26, 27, 3370	**ELECTRICAL, COMMUNICATIONS & UTIL.**	95.6	55.4	78.2	92.5	51.2	74.6	96.5	53.3	77.8	100.7	58.1	82.2	101.3	134.5	115.7	84.4	117.1	98.6
MF2018	**WEIGHTED AVERAGE**	98.5	61.8	85.0	92.9	59.5	80.6	96.7	62.3	84.1	94.0	65.3	83.4	100.4	128.2	110.6	99.9	125.8	109.4

DIVISION		CALIFORNIA																	
		BAKERSFIELD			BERKELEY			EUREKA			FRESNO			INGLEWOOD			LONG BEACH		
		932 - 933			947			955			936 - 938			903 - 905			906 - 908		
		MAT.	INST.	TOTAL	MAT.	INST.	TOTAL	MAT.	INST.	TOTAL	MAT.	INST.	TOTAL	MAT.	INST.	TOTAL	MAT.	INST.	TOTAL
015433	**CONTRACTOR EQUIPMENT**		99.2	99.2		95.8	95.8		94.7	94.7		94.9	94.9		95.8	95.8		95.8	95.8
0241, 31 - 34	**SITE & INFRASTRUCTURE, DEMOLITION**	112.0	107.6	109.1	113.5	102.4	106.3	121.2	99.1	106.8	114.5	99.5	104.7	97.7	98.8	98.4	106.0	98.8	101.3
0310	Concrete Forming & Accessories	101.1	138.0	129.8	112.0	168.4	155.9	103.3	155.6	143.9	102.4	155.0	143.2	103.6	139.3	131.3	97.6	139.3	130.0
0320	Concrete Reinforcing	97.9	132.6	107.5	89.1	138.5	102.7	87.9	134.0	100.7	81.1	133.3	95.5	99.7	132.8	108.9	98.9	132.8	108.3
0330	Cast-in-Place Concrete	95.2	130.3	107.7	109.1	133.0	117.6	107.7	129.4	115.4	103.1	129.1	112.4	107.2	129.0	114.9	122.1	129.0	124.5
03	**CONCRETE**	101.5	133.1	114.0	106.7	148.7	123.3	110.6	141.1	122.6	99.9	140.6	115.9	105.6	133.5	116.6	114.8	133.5	122.2
04	**MASONRY**	111.1	137.1	126.9	105.8	152.0	133.9	101.1	153.7	133.1	116.5	143.3	132.8	84.1	138.2	117.0	94.3	138.2	121.0
05	**METALS**	103.9	112.3	105.6	100.2	116.6	103.5	110.4	117.4	111.8	104.8	115.8	106.9	87.4	116.8	93.2	87.3	116.8	93.1
06	**WOOD, PLASTICS & COMPOSITES**	101.0	136.8	117.1	136.9	174.4	153.7	117.8	159.7	136.6	109.5	159.7	132.0	98.9	137.9	116.4	90.5	137.9	111.7
07	**THERMAL & MOISTURE PROTECTION**	105.3	126.1	112.7	90.6	155.2	113.6	93.9	149.1	113.6	95.7	134.7	109.6	102.8	131.0	112.9	102.9	131.0	112.9
08	**OPENINGS**	98.5	134.9	106.7	91.6	163.2	107.8	98.8	144.0	109.0	100.7	147.5	111.2	86.8	136.6	98.0	86.8	136.6	98.0
0920	Plaster & Gypsum Board	110.5	137.9	127.9	123.1	176.3	156.9	127.6	161.6	149.2	104.4	161.6	140.7	119.8	139.1	132.0	113.2	139.1	129.6
0950, 0980	Ceilings & Acoustic Treatment	113.8	137.9	127.3	93.3	176.3	139.9	111.7	161.6	139.7	101.5	161.6	135.2	100.5	139.1	122.1	100.5	139.1	122.1
0960	Flooring	96.0	118.3	101.6	110.5	143.2	118.7	94.5	143.2	106.7	95.2	123.7	102.3	95.0	118.3	100.8	93.1	118.3	99.4
0970, 0990	Wall Finishes & Painting/Coating	99.1	110.3	105.8	98.4	165.8	138.6	90.1	134.0	116.3	105.9	121.6	115.2	99.8	127.1	116.1	99.8	127.1	116.1
09	**FINISHES**	104.2	131.7	118.0	104.9	165.1	135.1	105.1	152.7	129.0	100.4	148.0	124.3	101.2	134.1	117.7	100.2	134.1	117.3
COVERS	**DIVS. 10 - 14, 25, 28, 41, 43, 44, 46**	100.0	117.8	103.4	100.0	129.9	105.8	100.0	127.1	105.3	100.0	127.0	105.2	100.0	117.0	103.3	100.0	117.0	103.3
21, 22, 23	**FIRE SUPPRESSION, PLUMBING & HVAC**	100.0	128.3	110.1	92.7	167.5	119.5	92.3	130.0	105.8	100.0	132.6	111.7	91.7	128.5	104.9	91.7	128.5	104.9
26, 27, 3370	**ELECTRICAL, COMMUNICATIONS & UTIL.**	98.7	108.0	102.8	99.7	165.2	128.1	91.2	125.7	106.1	87.4	107.6	96.1	100.5	134.5	115.2	100.4	134.5	115.1
MF2018	**WEIGHTED AVERAGE**	102.0	124.3	110.2	99.5	151.3	118.6	101.7	134.0	113.6	100.7	129.9	111.4	94.6	128.5	107.0	96.1	128.5	108.0

DIVISION		CALIFORNIA																	
		LOS ANGELES			MARYSVILLE			MODESTO			MOJAVE			OAKLAND			OXNARD		
		900 - 902			959			953			935			946			930		
		MAT.	INST.	TOTAL	MAT.	INST.	TOTAL	MAT.	INST.	TOTAL	MAT.	INST.	TOTAL	MAT.	INST.	TOTAL	MAT.	INST.	TOTAL
015433	**CONTRACTOR EQUIPMENT**		108.2	108.2		94.7	94.7		94.7	94.7		94.9	94.9		95.8	95.8		93.9	93.9
0241, 31 - 34	**SITE & INFRASTRUCTURE, DEMOLITION**	108.7	112.2	111.0	117.2	99.1	105.4	114.4	99.1	104.4	104.2	99.7	101.2	122.1	102.4	109.2	114.8	98.0	103.9
0310	Concrete Forming & Accessories	101.5	139.7	131.1	93.0	155.2	141.3	88.9	155.2	140.4	110.9	138.0	131.9	99.2	168.4	153.0	102.7	139.1	131.0
0320	Concrete Reinforcing	98.6	134.4	108.5	87.9	133.4	100.5	91.1	133.4	102.8	99.1	132.6	108.4	91.1	138.5	104.2	97.3	132.7	107.1
0330	Cast-in-Place Concrete	110.8	131.4	118.2	120.4	129.2	123.5	107.8	129.2	115.4	89.2	128.7	103.2	103.4	133.0	114.0	103.9	128.9	112.8
03	**CONCRETE**	112.8	135.0	121.6	111.6	140.8	123.1	103.6	140.7	118.3	95.5	132.7	110.2	107.2	148.7	123.6	102.5	133.3	114.6
04	**MASONRY**	102.2	138.3	124.2	102.3	144.3	127.8	106.2	144.3	129.4	114.5	137.0	128.1	113.6	152.0	136.9	117.9	137.2	129.6
05	**METALS**	102.5	120.4	106.1	109.8	116.2	111.1	103.1	116.1	105.6	104.3	114.5	106.3	96.1	116.6	100.1	100.3	114.8	103.1
06	**WOOD, PLASTICS & COMPOSITES**	102.7	138.3	118.7	102.2	159.7	128.0	96.4	159.7	124.8	110.1	136.7	122.0	120.0	174.4	144.4	103.5	137.9	118.9
07	**THERMAL & MOISTURE PROTECTION**	99.9	132.8	111.7	93.3	139.5	109.8	93.0	139.8	109.6	101.4	123.2	109.2	89.8	155.2	113.1	103.1	131.5	113.2
08	**OPENINGS**	101.4	137.2	109.5	98.2	148.4	109.5	97.3	148.4	108.8	95.3	134.8	104.2	91.7	163.2	107.8	98.0	136.6	106.7
0920	Plaster & Gypsum Board	115.4	139.1	130.4	117.6	161.6	145.5	120.5	161.6	146.6	117.1	137.9	130.3	114.3	176.3	153.7	107.9	139.1	127.7
0950, 0980	Ceilings & Acoustic Treatment	112.8	139.1	127.5	110.8	161.6	139.3	105.3	161.6	136.9	107.8	137.9	124.7	94.8	176.3	140.5	104.1	139.1	123.7
0960	Flooring	97.0	118.3	102.4	91.9	130.2	101.5	92.1	133.9	102.6	94.0	118.3	100.1	106.7	143.2	115.8	87.8	118.3	95.4
0970, 0990	Wall Finishes & Painting/Coating	99.1	127.1	115.8	90.1	134.0	116.3	90.1	130.3	114.1	90.4	110.3	102.3	98.4	165.8	138.6	90.4	127.1	112.2
09	**FINISHES**	105.2	134.4	119.9	102.2	150.5	126.4	100.6	150.7	125.8	101.9	131.6	116.8	103.4	165.1	134.4	98.1	134.1	116.2
COVERS	**DIVS. 10 - 14, 25, 28, 41, 43, 44, 46**	100.0	117.8	103.5	100.0	127.1	105.2	100.0	127.0	105.2	100.0	123.8	104.6	100.0	129.9	105.8	100.0	116.8	103.3
21, 22, 23	**FIRE SUPPRESSION, PLUMBING & HVAC**	100.1	128.6	110.3	92.3	130.9	106.1	99.8	132.6	111.6	92.4	128.2	105.2	100.2	167.5	124.3	99.9	128.4	110.1
26, 27, 3370	**ELECTRICAL, COMMUNICATIONS & UTIL.**	99.5	134.5	114.7	89.6	118.5	102.1	91.1	109.8	99.2	86.0	108.0	95.5	99.2	165.2	127.8	94.4	111.7	101.9
MF2018	**WEIGHTED AVERAGE**	102.9	130.2	112.9	101.1	131.6	112.3	100.3	130.8	111.5	97.8	123.9	107.4	100.5	151.3	119.2	100.6	124.8	109.5

	DIVISION	CALIFORNIA																	
		PALM SPRINGS			PALO ALTO			PASADENA			REDDING			RICHMOND			RIVERSIDE		
		922			943			910 - 912			960			948			925		
		MAT.	INST.	TOTAL	MAT.	INST.	TOTAL	MAT.	INST.	TOTAL	MAT.	INST.	TOTAL	MAT.	INST.	TOTAL	MAT.	INST.	TOTAL
015433	CONTRACTOR EQUIPMENT		95.6	95.6		95.8	95.8		93.7	93.7		94.7	94.7		95.8	95.8		95.6	95.6
0241, 31 - 34	SITE & INFRASTRUCTURE, DEMOLITION	99.2	99.8	99.6	110.0	102.4	105.0	109.0	101.2	104.0	136.0	99.1	111.9	118.2	102.3	107.9	109.2	99.8	103.1
0310	Concrete Forming & Accessories	92.8	139.0	128.7	97.2	168.6	152.6	90.7	138.9	128.2	86.8	155.2	139.9	115.2	168.1	156.3	96.8	139.1	129.6
0320	Concrete Reinforcing	92.3	132.7	103.5	89.1	138.5	102.8	101.2	132.7	109.9	88.1	133.4	100.7	89.1	138.5	102.7	89.7	132.7	101.6
0330	Cast-in-Place Concrete	94.6	129.5	107.0	92.2	133.1	106.8	89.4	126.6	102.6	131.5	129.2	130.7	106.1	132.9	115.6	102.9	129.5	112.4
03	CONCRETE	96.7	133.5	111.2	97.5	148.8	117.7	98.0	132.4	111.6	116.9	140.7	126.3	109.1	148.4	124.6	101.9	133.5	114.4
04	MASONRY	80.0	137.2	114.8	91.1	152.0	128.1	132.4	138.1	135.9	112.6	144.3	131.9	105.6	152.0	133.8	81.2	137.2	115.2
05	METALS	111.1	115.0	111.8	93.7	116.7	98.3	87.3	114.8	92.8	105.3	116.1	107.4	93.8	116.2	98.2	109.0	115.1	110.2
06	WOOD, PLASTICS & COMPOSITES	96.3	137.8	114.9	116.6	174.4	142.5	84.6	137.6	108.3	100.9	159.7	127.3	141.4	174.4	156.2	102.8	137.8	118.5
07	THERMAL & MOISTURE PROTECTION	90.8	130.6	105.0	89.1	155.2	112.7	111.7	129.5	118.0	97.3	139.5	112.3	89.9	154.3	112.8	91.5	132.4	106.1
08	OPENINGS	95.8	136.6	105.0	91.7	162.3	107.6	87.7	136.4	98.7	103.8	148.4	113.8	91.7	163.2	107.8	98.4	136.6	107.0
0920	Plaster & Gypsum Board	112.3	139.1	129.3	111.9	176.3	152.8	118.0	139.1	131.4	108.5	161.6	142.2	123.7	176.3	157.1	119.1	139.1	131.8
0950, 0980	Ceilings & Acoustic Treatment	100.8	139.1	122.2	93.8	176.3	140.1	98.1	139.1	121.1	120.7	161.6	143.7	93.8	176.3	140.1	105.4	139.1	124.3
0960	Flooring	93.9	118.3	100.0	105.9	143.2	115.3	88.7	118.3	96.1	71.0	119.0	83.0	111.9	143.2	119.8	94.6	118.3	100.6
0970, 0990	Wall Finishes & Painting/Coating	86.9	127.1	110.8	98.4	165.8	138.6	94.7	127.1	114.0	96.3	134.0	118.8	98.4	165.8	138.6	86.9	127.1	110.8
09	FINISHES	96.8	134.0	115.5	101.9	165.1	133.7	97.8	133.9	115.9	99.1	148.5	123.9	106.0	165.1	135.7	99.5	134.0	116.8
COVERS	DIVS. 10 - 14, 25, 28, 41, 43, 44, 46	100.0	116.7	103.2	100.0	130.0	105.8	100.0	116.2	103.1	100.0	127.1	105.2	100.0	129.8	105.8	100.0	117.6	103.4
21, 22, 23	FIRE SUPPRESSION, PLUMBING & HVAC	92.3	128.4	105.2	92.7	168.7	119.9	92.5	128.4	105.4	99.7	130.9	110.9	92.7	157.7	116.0	99.8	128.4	110.1
26, 27, 3370	ELECTRICAL, COMMUNICATIONS & UTIL.	85.8	118.3	99.9	99.2	181.5	134.8	109.1	134.5	120.1	93.3	118.5	104.2	99.4	139.1	116.6	84.2	118.3	99.0
MF2018	WEIGHTED AVERAGE	97.1	125.9	107.7	95.8	153.9	117.2	96.8	128.2	108.4	103.9	131.4	114.0	98.5	145.5	115.8	99.6	126.0	109.3

	DIVISION	CALIFORNIA																	
		SACRAMENTO			SALINAS			SAN BERNARDINO			SAN DIEGO			SAN FRANCISCO			SAN JOSE		
		942,956 - 958			939			923 - 924			919 - 921			940 - 941			951		
		MAT.	INST.	TOTAL	MAT.	INST.	TOTAL	MAT.	INST.	TOTAL	MAT.	INST.	TOTAL	MAT.	INST.	TOTAL	MAT.	INST.	TOTAL
015433	CONTRACTOR EQUIPMENT		94.8	94.8		94.9	94.9		95.6	95.6		105.6	105.6		112.4	112.4		96.2	96.2
0241, 31 - 34	SITE & INFRASTRUCTURE, DEMOLITION	102.9	107.1	105.7	127.0	99.6	109.1	84.4	99.8	94.5	119.7	112.3	114.9	122.3	117.6	119.2	148.4	94.8	113.5
0310	Concrete Forming & Accessories	98.2	157.5	144.3	107.2	158.0	146.6	100.7	139.0	130.5	101.5	137.7	129.6	101.0	168.9	153.8	94.7	168.3	151.9
0320	Concrete Reinforcing	83.5	133.5	97.3	97.9	133.9	107.9	89.7	132.7	101.6	98.6	129.0	107.0	99.3	139.6	110.4	79.7	138.5	96.0
0330	Cast-in-Place Concrete	87.5	130.2	102.6	102.6	129.5	112.2	71.0	129.5	91.8	102.5	128.4	111.7	115.6	134.7	122.4	125.3	132.1	127.7
03	CONCRETE	98.6	141.6	115.5	110.9	142.2	123.2	79.0	133.5	100.5	109.4	131.9	118.3	117.3	150.2	130.3	108.4	148.8	124.3
04	MASONRY	92.0	144.3	123.8	114.6	149.4	135.8	89.7	137.2	118.6	121.4	133.9	129.0	116.2	155.0	139.7	133.9	152.0	144.9
05	METALS	91.7	108.9	95.1	107.4	117.2	109.4	109.0	115.0	110.1	103.7	114.3	105.8	105.9	126.3	109.9	102.5	124.1	106.8
06	WOOD, PLASTICS & COMPOSITES	113.6	162.7	135.6	110.3	162.4	133.7	107.4	137.8	121.0	102.8	137.7	118.5	121.2	174.4	145.0	108.7	174.1	138.0
07	THERMAL & MOISTURE PROTECTION	98.0	141.1	113.4	102.1	145.6	117.6	90.2	132.4	105.3	105.6	121.9	111.4	95.0	157.3	117.2	90.6	155.2	113.6
08	OPENINGS	103.5	150.0	114.0	99.2	155.5	111.9	95.8	136.6	105.0	99.2	132.6	106.7	103.7	163.4	117.1	89.2	163.0	105.8
0920	Plaster & Gypsum Board	108.0	164.4	143.7	110.1	164.4	144.5	121.5	139.1	132.6	113.6	138.6	129.5	111.8	176.3	152.7	113.3	176.3	153.3
0950, 0980	Ceilings & Acoustic Treatment	93.8	164.4	133.4	107.8	164.4	139.5	105.3	139.1	124.2	105.6	138.6	124.1	113.6	176.3	148.8	99.9	176.3	142.8
0960	Flooring	105.4	130.2	111.6	90.1	143.2	103.4	95.9	118.3	101.5	97.3	118.3	102.6	104.0	142.0	113.5	84.4	143.2	99.2
0970, 0990	Wall Finishes & Painting/Coating	95.4	138.5	121.1	91.3	170.3	138.4	86.9	127.1	110.8	95.2	118.9	109.3	99.1	174.0	143.8	89.8	165.8	135.1
09	FINISHES	100.4	152.7	126.7	102.0	158.3	130.3	98.6	134.0	116.4	102.9	132.6	117.8	107.1	165.8	136.6	97.6	164.9	131.4
COVERS	DIVS. 10 - 14, 25, 28, 41, 43, 44, 46	100.0	127.9	105.4	100.0	127.4	105.3	100.0	115.1	102.9	100.0	116.6	103.2	100.0	130.2	105.8	100.0	129.4	105.7
21, 22, 23	FIRE SUPPRESSION, PLUMBING & HVAC	100.1	130.8	111.1	92.4	138.0	108.7	92.3	128.4	105.2	100.1	127.2	109.8	100.1	180.3	128.8	99.8	168.7	124.5
26, 27, 3370	ELECTRICAL, COMMUNICATIONS & UTIL.	94.3	118.4	104.8	86.9	135.3	107.8	85.8	113.5	97.8	101.0	103.0	101.9	99.7	189.6	138.7	95.5	181.5	132.8
MF2018	WEIGHTED AVERAGE	97.6	132.2	110.3	101.3	137.9	114.7	94.8	125.2	106.0	103.7	123.3	110.9	105.4	160.2	125.6	102.2	153.9	121.3

	DIVISION	CALIFORNIA																	
		SAN LUIS OBISPO			SAN MATEO			SAN RAFAEL			SANTA ANA			SANTA BARBARA			SANTA CRUZ		
		934			944			949			926 - 927			931			950		
		MAT.	INST.	TOTAL	MAT.	INST.	TOTAL	MAT.	INST.	TOTAL	MAT.	INST.	TOTAL	MAT.	INST.	TOTAL	MAT.	INST.	TOTAL
015433	CONTRACTOR EQUIPMENT		94.9	94.9		95.8	95.8		95.1	95.1		95.6	95.6		94.9	94.9		96.2	96.2
0241, 31 - 34	SITE & INFRASTRUCTURE, DEMOLITION	118.0	99.7	106.1	116.0	102.4	107.1	112.1	107.1	108.8	97.4	99.8	99.0	114.8	99.7	104.9	148.5	94.7	113.4
0310	Concrete Forming & Accessories	112.9	139.1	133.3	104.2	168.5	154.1	112.3	168.1	155.7	101.1	139.0	130.6	103.1	139.1	131.0	94.7	158.0	143.9
0320	Concrete Reinforcing	99.1	132.6	108.4	89.1	138.7	102.8	89.4	134.3	101.8	92.6	132.7	103.7	97.3	132.6	107.0	99.1	133.9	108.7
0330	Cast-in-Place Concrete	110.3	128.8	116.9	102.7	133.0	113.5	119.6	132.1	124.0	90.8	129.5	104.5	103.5	128.8	112.5	124.4	131.0	126.8
03	CONCRETE	109.8	133.2	119.0	105.8	148.7	122.7	125.9	147.3	134.3	94.7	133.5	110.0	102.3	133.2	114.5	113.1	143.0	124.9
04	MASONRY	116.3	136.2	128.4	105.2	154.8	135.3	86.1	154.8	127.8	77.7	137.5	114.0	114.7	136.2	127.8	138.1	149.6	145.1
05	METALS	105.7	114.7	107.5	93.6	116.8	98.2	96.6	111.6	99.6	109.0	115.0	110.2	101.9	114.7	104.5	109.1	121.1	111.5
06	WOOD, PLASTICS & COMPOSITES	112.9	137.9	124.1	127.3	174.4	148.4	126.4	174.2	147.8	109.6	137.8	122.2	103.5	137.9	118.9	108.7	162.5	132.8
07	THERMAL & MOISTURE PROTECTION	102.2	130.8	112.3	89.6	155.2	113.0	92.6	154.8	114.7	91.1	131.6	105.5	101.6	130.8	112.0	90.3	147.4	110.6
08	OPENINGS	97.3	135.4	105.9	91.6	162.3	107.6	100.9	161.2	114.5	95.1	136.6	104.5	99.1	136.6	107.6	90.0	155.6	104.8
0920	Plaster & Gypsum Board	118.0	139.1	131.4	120.3	176.3	155.9	124.3	176.3	157.3	122.9	139.1	133.2	107.9	139.1	127.7	121.6	164.4	148.7
0950, 0980	Ceilings & Acoustic Treatment	107.8	139.1	125.3	93.8	176.3	140.1	107.4	176.3	146.0	105.3	139.1	124.2	104.1	139.1	123.7	106.7	164.4	139.0
0960	Flooring	94.6	118.3	100.6	108.1	143.2	116.9	117.5	143.2	123.9	96.3	118.3	101.8	89.5	118.3	96.7	88.1	143.2	101.9
0970, 0990	Wall Finishes & Painting/Coating	90.4	114.0	104.5	98.4	165.8	138.6	94.8	170.3	139.8	86.9	127.1	110.8	90.4	127.1	112.2	89.5	165.8	135.0
09	FINISHES	103.4	132.7	118.1	104.2	165.1	134.8	109.5	165.5	137.6	100.1	134.0	117.1	98.8	134.1	116.5	101.6	157.9	129.9
COVERS	DIVS. 10 - 14, 25, 28, 41, 43, 44, 46	100.0	125.6	105.0	100.0	130.0	105.8	100.0	129.3	105.7	100.0	116.7	103.2	100.0	117.7	103.4	100.0	127.7	105.4
21, 22, 23	FIRE SUPPRESSION, PLUMBING & HVAC	92.4	128.4	105.3	92.7	165.2	118.7	92.7	180.1	124.0	92.3	128.4	105.2	99.9	128.4	110.1	99.8	138.0	113.5
26, 27, 3370	ELECTRICAL, COMMUNICATIONS & UTIL.	86.0	109.0	96.0	99.2	174.5	131.8	91.9	125.7	106.5	85.8	117.1	99.4	85.5	107.5	95.1	95.2	135.3	112.6
MF2018	WEIGHTED AVERAGE	100.5	124.5	109.3	97.7	152.4	117.9	100.4	148.3	118.1	96.6	125.8	107.4	100.0	124.3	108.9	104.7	138.0	117.0

DIVISION		CALIFORNIA															COLORADO		
		SANTA ROSA			STOCKTON			SUSANVILLE			VALLEJO			VAN NUYS			ALAMOSA		
		954			952			961			945			913 - 916			811		
		MAT.	INST.	TOTAL	MAT.	INST.	TOTAL	MAT.	INST.	TOTAL	MAT.	INST.	TOTAL	MAT.	INST.	TOTAL	MAT.	INST.	TOTAL
015433	CONTRACTOR EQUIPMENT		95.2	95.2		94.7	94.7		94.7	94.7		95.1	95.1		93.7	93.7		89.2	89.2
0241, 31 - 34	SITE & INFRASTRUCTURE, DEMOLITION	112.3	99.0	103.6	114.1	99.1	104.3	141.5	99.1	113.8	103.5	107.0	105.8	129.5	101.2	111.1	131.3	81.7	98.9
0310	Concrete Forming & Accessories	93.8	167.3	150.9	93.2	157.2	142.9	88.0	155.2	140.2	101.4	167.2	152.5	97.5	138.9	129.7	99.9	68.7	75.6
0320	Concrete Reinforcing	88.6	134.3	101.2	91.1	133.4	102.8	88.1	133.4	100.7	90.5	134.2	102.6	101.2	132.7	109.9	101.8	63.4	91.2
0330	Cast-in-Place Concrete	118.3	130.5	122.6	105.0	129.2	113.6	119.6	129.2	123.0	95.2	131.3	108.0	94.3	126.6	105.8	90.2	69.2	82.7
03	CONCRETE	111.6	146.9	125.5	102.9	141.6	118.2	117.9	140.8	126.9	103.8	146.5	120.7	110.4	132.4	119.1	104.9	68.6	90.6
04	MASONRY	102.2	153.8	133.6	106.1	144.3	129.3	110.8	144.3	131.2	68.6	153.8	120.4	151.3	138.1	143.3	132.0	67.4	92.8
05	METALS	109.4	118.8	111.2	103.7	116.1	106.2	103.1	116.2	105.6	96.5	111.0	99.3	86.4	114.8	92.0	99.1	78.5	95.0
06	WOOD, PLASTICS & COMPOSITES	98.2	173.9	132.2	103.5	162.4	129.9	102.8	159.7	128.3	111.5	174.2	139.6	94.5	137.6	113.8	99.2	71.1	86.6
07	THERMAL & MOISTURE PROTECTION	91.4	153.8	113.6	93.4	137.7	109.2	97.4	139.5	112.4	91.1	154.0	113.5	112.6	129.5	118.6	99.9	66.9	88.2
08	OPENINGS	96.6	161.9	111.3	97.3	150.8	109.4	103.7	149.3	114.0	102.7	161.2	115.9	87.6	136.4	98.6	91.6	68.2	86.3
0920	Plaster & Gypsum Board	115.9	176.3	154.2	120.5	164.4	148.3	108.9	161.6	142.3	115.9	176.3	154.2	122.9	139.1	133.2	89.0	70.3	77.1
0950, 0980	Ceilings & Acoustic Treatment	105.3	176.3	145.1	109.9	164.4	140.4	115.4	161.6	141.3	108.4	176.3	146.5	94.5	139.1	119.5	105.3	70.3	85.7
0960	Flooring	94.2	133.7	104.1	92.1	133.9	102.6	71.2	119.0	83.2	113.9	143.2	121.3	90.6	118.3	97.5	110.5	79.6	102.7
0970, 0990	Wall Finishes & Painting/Coating	86.9	161.3	131.2	90.1	138.5	119.0	96.3	134.0	118.8	95.7	170.3	140.2	94.7	127.1	114.0	100.7	71.0	83.0
09	FINISHES	99.5	162.4	131.1	101.8	153.2	127.6	98.8	148.5	123.8	106.4	165.2	135.9	99.5	133.9	116.8	104.3	71.2	87.7
COVERS	DIVS. 10 - 14, 25, 28, 41, 43, 44, 46	100.0	128.5	105.5	100.0	125.7	105.0	100.0	127.1	105.3	100.0	129.0	105.6	100.0	116.2	103.1	100.0	84.9	97.1
21, 22, 23	FIRE SUPPRESSION, PLUMBING & HVAC	92.3	174.5	121.8	99.8	132.6	111.6	92.1	132.7	106.7	100.2	146.9	116.9	92.5	128.4	105.4	92.5	66.8	83.3
26, 27, 3370	ELECTRICAL, COMMUNICATIONS & UTIL.	85.9	120.9	101.1	91.1	112.2	100.3	93.5	120.8	105.3	89.9	125.0	105.1	109.0	134.5	120.1	92.6	56.3	76.9
MF2018	WEIGHTED AVERAGE	100.0	145.9	116.9	100.5	131.6	111.9	102.0	132.1	113.1	98.1	140.9	113.8	99.5	128.2	110.1	99.5	69.1	88.3

DIVISION		COLORADO																	
		BOULDER			COLORADO SPRINGS			DENVER			DURANGO			FORT COLLINS			FORT MORGAN		
		803			808 - 809			800 - 802			813			805			807		
		MAT.	INST.	TOTAL	MAT.	INST.	TOTAL	MAT.	INST.	TOTAL	MAT.	INST.	TOTAL	MAT.	INST.	TOTAL	MAT.	INST.	TOTAL
015433	CONTRACTOR EQUIPMENT		90.0	90.0		88.2	88.2		94.7	94.7		89.2	89.2		90.0	90.0		90.0	90.0
0241, 31 - 34	SITE & INFRASTRUCTURE, DEMOLITION	92.5	87.8	89.5	97.5	83.4	88.3	101.3	94.4	96.8	125.4	81.7	96.9	105.8	87.4	93.8	94.2	86.8	89.4
0310	Concrete Forming & Accessories	99.9	71.6	77.9	90.3	68.5	73.4	99.3	68.6	75.5	106.5	68.4	76.9	97.8	68.6	75.2	100.4	68.3	75.5
0320	Concrete Reinforcing	97.1	69.1	89.3	96.5	68.8	88.9	100.8	69.0	92.0	101.8	63.4	91.2	97.1	65.8	88.5	97.2	63.4	87.9
0330	Cast-in-Place Concrete	97.8	75.1	89.7	100.4	71.1	90.0	101.7	73.2	91.6	103.7	69.1	91.4	110.4	71.0	96.4	95.9	68.3	86.1
03	CONCRETE	100.1	72.9	89.3	102.4	70.1	89.7	109.1	70.8	94.0	107.0	68.5	91.8	108.6	69.6	93.2	98.9	68.1	86.7
04	MASONRY	94.2	69.3	79.1	97.8	61.2	75.6	103.9	64.0	79.7	119.1	67.4	87.7	108.5	67.5	83.6	107.7	67.5	83.3
05	METALS	89.5	79.2	87.5	92.9	78.8	90.1	102.0	78.1	97.2	99.1	78.2	95.0	90.7	77.9	88.2	89.2	76.7	86.7
06	WOOD, PLASTICS & COMPOSITES	100.5	72.7	88.0	87.3	70.7	79.9	102.4	70.8	88.2	110.4	71.1	92.8	97.2	70.6	85.3	100.5	70.6	87.1
07	THERMAL & MOISTURE PROTECTION	97.9	72.9	89.0	98.7	68.6	88.0	97.4	72.3	88.5	99.9	66.9	88.2	98.1	70.4	88.3	97.9	68.1	87.3
08	OPENINGS	90.0	71.7	85.9	93.8	70.0	88.4	99.3	70.6	92.8	97.7	68.2	91.0	90.0	69.3	85.3	90.0	68.0	85.0
0920	Plaster & Gypsum Board	114.9	72.4	88.0	99.3	70.3	80.9	110.4	70.3	85.0	107.1	70.3	83.8	105.0	70.3	83.0	114.9	70.3	86.6
0950, 0980	Ceilings & Acoustic Treatment	97.6	72.4	83.5	111.7	70.3	88.5	114.5	70.3	89.7	105.3	70.3	85.7	97.6	70.3	82.3	97.6	70.3	82.3
0960	Flooring	119.9	79.6	109.8	110.4	79.6	102.7	116.5	79.6	107.2	114.2	79.6	105.5	116.8	79.6	107.5	120.2	79.6	110.1
0970, 0990	Wall Finishes & Painting/Coating	90.2	75.4	81.4	89.9	78.3	83.0	99.1	73.2	83.6	100.7	71.0	83.0	90.2	71.0	78.8	90.2	71.0	78.8
09	FINISHES	106.0	73.4	89.6	104.8	71.6	88.2	109.5	71.0	90.2	107.1	71.2	89.1	104.1	70.9	87.4	106.0	70.9	88.4
COVERS	DIVS. 10 - 14, 25, 28, 41, 43, 44, 46	100.0	85.3	97.2	100.0	84.1	96.9	100.0	84.1	96.9	100.0	84.9	97.1	100.0	84.0	96.9	100.0	84.0	96.9
21, 22, 23	FIRE SUPPRESSION, PLUMBING & HVAC	92.6	74.6	86.1	100.3	66.7	88.3	100.1	74.2	90.8	92.5	54.4	78.8	100.1	71.7	89.9	92.6	67.7	83.7
26, 27, 3370	ELECTRICAL, COMMUNICATIONS & UTIL.	96.8	79.8	89.4	98.3	70.0	86.1	99.4	80.0	91.0	92.3	49.4	73.7	96.8	76.9	88.2	97.3	69.5	85.3
MF2018	WEIGHTED AVERAGE	94.9	76.0	87.9	98.2	70.9	88.1	102.2	75.1	92.3	99.9	65.5	87.3	98.5	73.7	89.4	95.3	71.3	86.5

DIVISION		COLORADO																	
		GLENWOOD SPRINGS			GOLDEN			GRAND JUNCTION			GREELEY			MONTROSE			PUEBLO		
		816			804			815			806			814			810		
		MAT.	INST.	TOTAL	MAT.	INST.	TOTAL	MAT.	INST.	TOTAL	MAT.	INST.	TOTAL	MAT.	INST.	TOTAL	MAT.	INST.	TOTAL
015433	CONTRACTOR EQUIPMENT		92.0	92.0		90.0	90.0		92.0	92.0		90.0	90.0		90.6	90.6		89.2	89.2
0241, 31 - 34	SITE & INFRASTRUCTURE, DEMOLITION	139.3	88.3	106.1	103.4	87.0	92.7	128.0	88.9	102.5	94.7	87.5	90.0	133.6	85.3	102.1	121.1	82.1	95.7
0310	Concrete Forming & Accessories	96.3	68.2	74.4	92.8	68.1	73.6	105.2	69.2	77.2	95.5	68.7	74.7	95.9	68.3	74.5	102.4	68.8	76.3
0320	Concrete Reinforcing	101.1	63.4	90.6	97.2	63.2	87.8	101.3	65.7	91.4	97.1	65.8	88.4	101.0	63.4	90.6	97.6	69.0	89.7
0330	Cast-in-Place Concrete	90.1	68.1	82.3	96.0	70.4	86.9	99.8	71.6	89.8	92.2	71.0	84.7	90.1	68.6	82.5	89.5	71.6	83.1
03	CONCRETE	108.5	68.0	92.5	106.9	68.7	91.8	104.2	70.1	90.7	96.1	69.6	85.6	101.7	68.3	88.5	95.9	70.5	85.9
04	MASONRY	104.1	67.4	81.8	110.5	64.0	82.2	139.9	65.7	94.8	102.2	67.5	81.1	111.5	67.4	84.7	100.5	63.8	78.2
05	METALS	98.7	77.8	94.6	89.4	76.6	86.9	100.4	78.9	96.2	90.6	78.0	88.1	97.6	78.0	93.7	102.9	80.6	98.5
06	WOOD, PLASTICS & COMPOSITES	93.6	70.8	83.4	90.3	70.6	81.5	108.7	70.8	91.7	93.9	70.6	83.5	94.1	70.9	83.7	102.6	71.1	88.5
07	THERMAL & MOISTURE PROTECTION	99.8	66.9	88.1	98.6	68.5	87.9	99.2	69.0	88.4	97.6	70.4	87.9	99.9	66.9	88.1	98.8	68.1	87.9
08	OPENINGS	96.7	68.1	90.2	90.0	68.0	85.0	97.3	69.3	91.0	90.0	69.3	85.3	97.8	68.2	91.1	93.0	70.2	87.9
0920	Plaster & Gypsum Board	122.4	70.3	89.4	100.4	70.3	81.3	141.0	70.3	96.2	103.1	70.3	82.3	87.8	70.3	76.7	95.5	70.3	79.5
0950, 0980	Ceilings & Acoustic Treatment	104.4	70.3	85.3	97.6	70.3	82.3	104.4	70.3	85.3	97.6	70.3	82.3	105.3	70.3	85.7	115.3	70.3	90.1
0960	Flooring	109.8	79.6	102.3	114.8	79.6	106.0	113.6	79.6	105.1	115.8	79.6	106.7	112.3	79.6	104.1	111.3	79.6	103.4
0970, 0990	Wall Finishes & Painting/Coating	100.7	71.0	83.0	90.2	71.0	78.8	100.7	71.0	83.0	90.2	71.0	78.8	100.7	71.0	83.0	100.7	71.0	83.0
09	FINISHES	108.8	71.0	89.8	103.5	70.6	87.0	110.8	71.4	91.0	103.0	70.9	86.9	104.7	71.1	87.9	106.6	71.1	88.7
COVERS	DIVS. 10 - 14, 25, 28, 41, 43, 44, 46	100.0	84.3	97.0	100.0	83.7	96.9	100.0	84.8	97.1	100.0	84.0	96.9	100.0	84.6	97.0	100.0	84.8	97.0
21, 22, 23	FIRE SUPPRESSION, PLUMBING & HVAC	92.5	54.4	78.8	92.6	67.3	83.5	100.0	71.3	89.7	100.1	71.7	89.9	92.5	54.4	78.8	100.0	67.6	88.4
26, 27, 3370	ELECTRICAL, COMMUNICATIONS & UTIL.	91.0	49.4	73.0	97.3	71.7	86.2	92.2	54.0	75.6	96.8	76.9	88.2	92.2	49.4	73.6	92.6	62.8	79.7
MF2018	WEIGHTED AVERAGE	99.5	65.9	87.1	96.4	71.2	87.1	102.6	70.5	90.8	96.4	73.7	88.0	98.5	65.7	86.5	99.8	70.4	89.0

DIVISION		COLORADO			CONNECTICUT														
		SALIDA			BRIDGEPORT			BRISTOL			HARTFORD			MERIDEN			NEW BRITAIN		
		812			066			060			061			064			060		
		MAT.	INST.	TOTAL	MAT.	INST.	TOTAL	MAT.	INST.	TOTAL	MAT.	INST.	TOTAL	MAT.	INST.	TOTAL	MAT.	INST.	TOTAL
015433	CONTRACTOR EQUIPMENT		90.6	90.6		93.0	93.0		93.0	93.0		97.4	97.4		93.3	93.3		93.0	93.0
0241, 31 - 34	SITE & INFRASTRUCTURE, DEMOLITION	125.1	85.0	99.0	100.2	93.5	95.8	99.5	93.5	95.6	96.9	101.1	99.6	94.4	94.1	94.2	99.6	93.5	95.6
0310	Concrete Forming & Accessories	105.2	68.6	76.7	103.5	112.3	110.4	103.5	114.6	112.1	104.5	114.8	112.5	103.1	114.5	112.0	104.1	114.6	112.3
0320	Concrete Reinforcing	100.8	63.4	90.5	103.8	139.9	113.8	103.8	139.9	113.8	99.0	139.9	110.3	103.8	139.9	113.8	103.8	139.9	113.8
0330	Cast-in-Place Concrete	103.3	68.7	91.0	81.6	124.8	97.0	76.5	124.8	93.6	77.9	126.4	95.2	73.6	124.7	91.8	77.7	124.8	94.4
03	CONCRETE	103.1	68.4	89.4	96.6	120.9	106.2	94.5	121.9	105.3	95.0	122.5	105.9	93.2	121.9	104.5	95.0	121.9	105.6
04	MASONRY	140.4	67.4	96.1	121.0	128.9	125.8	112.5	128.9	122.4	116.1	129.0	123.9	112.2	128.9	122.3	114.7	128.9	123.3
05	METALS	97.2	78.3	93.4	98.4	116.0	101.8	98.4	115.9	101.8	101.6	114.1	104.1	95.3	115.8	99.4	94.4	115.9	98.6
06	WOOD, PLASTICS & COMPOSITES	104.3	70.9	89.4	110.5	109.2	109.9	110.5	112.4	111.4	102.0	112.6	106.7	110.5	112.4	111.4	110.5	112.4	111.4
07	THERMAL & MOISTURE PROTECTION	99.2	66.9	87.7	96.7	118.4	104.4	96.8	116.7	103.9	101.6	119.1	107.8	96.8	116.7	103.9	96.8	116.7	103.9
08	OPENINGS	91.6	68.2	86.3	95.8	117.0	100.6	95.8	118.3	100.9	97.6	118.4	102.3	97.7	118.8	102.5	95.8	118.3	100.9
0920	Plaster & Gypsum Board	88.0	70.3	76.8	130.8	109.5	117.3	130.8	112.8	119.3	119.8	112.8	115.3	134.2	112.8	120.6	130.8	112.8	119.3
0950, 0980	Ceilings & Acoustic Treatment	105.3	70.3	85.7	95.0	109.5	103.1	95.0	112.8	104.9	96.3	112.8	105.5	105.4	112.8	109.5	95.0	112.8	104.9
0960	Flooring	116.1	79.6	107.0	94.2	121.9	101.1	94.2	121.9	101.1	102.3	125.0	108.0	94.2	111.5	98.5	94.2	121.9	101.1
0970, 0990	Wall Finishes & Painting/Coating	100.7	71.0	83.0	91.3	126.9	112.6	91.3	126.9	112.6	99.1	126.9	115.7	91.3	126.9	112.6	91.3	126.9	112.6
09	FINISHES	105.0	71.1	88.0	99.0	115.3	107.2	99.1	117.1	108.1	102.3	117.8	110.1	102.3	115.3	108.9	99.1	117.1	108.1
COVERS	DIVS. 10 - 14, 25, 28, 41, 43, 44, 46	100.0	84.6	97.0	100.0	110.9	102.1	100.0	111.3	102.2	100.0	111.7	102.3	100.0	111.2	102.2	100.0	111.3	102.2
21, 22, 23	FIRE SUPPRESSION, PLUMBING & HVAC	92.5	67.8	83.6	100.2	117.5	106.4	100.2	117.5	106.4	100.1	117.5	106.3	92.6	117.5	101.5	100.2	117.5	106.4
26, 27, 3370	ELECTRICAL, COMMUNICATIONS & UTIL.	92.3	56.3	76.7	96.6	101.3	98.6	96.6	103.3	99.5	99.9	105.1	102.1	96.5	94.2	95.5	96.6	103.3	99.5
MF2018	WEIGHTED AVERAGE	99.1	69.5	88.2	99.3	114.2	104.8	98.7	114.9	104.7	100.3	115.8	106.0	96.5	113.4	102.7	98.0	114.9	104.2

DIVISION		CONNECTICUT																	
		NEW HAVEN			NEW LONDON			NORWALK			STAMFORD			WATERBURY			WILLIMANTIC		
		065			063			068			069			067			062		
		MAT.	INST.	TOTAL	MAT.	INST.	TOTAL	MAT.	INST.	TOTAL	MAT.	INST.	TOTAL	MAT.	INST.	TOTAL	MAT.	INST.	TOTAL
015433	CONTRACTOR EQUIPMENT		93.3	93.3		93.3	93.3		93.0	93.0		93.0	93.0		93.0	93.0		93.0	93.0
0241, 31 - 34	SITE & INFRASTRUCTURE, DEMOLITION	99.5	94.0	95.9	90.2	94.0	92.6	100.0	93.4	95.7	100.5	93.4	95.8	99.9	93.5	95.7	100.0	93.2	95.6
0310	Concrete Forming & Accessories	103.1	114.5	112.0	103.1	114.4	111.9	103.5	112.3	110.3	103.4	112.3	110.3	103.5	114.6	112.1	103.4	114.3	111.9
0320	Concrete Reinforcing	103.8	139.9	113.8	81.4	139.9	97.6	103.8	139.8	113.8	103.8	139.8	113.8	103.8	139.9	113.8	103.8	139.9	113.8
0330	Cast-in-Place Concrete	79.1	122.1	94.3	67.4	122.0	86.8	80.3	123.2	95.5	81.6	123.2	96.4	81.6	124.8	97.0	76.2	118.5	91.2
03	CONCRETE	106.9	120.9	112.4	82.4	120.8	97.6	96.0	120.3	105.6	96.6	120.3	105.9	96.6	121.9	106.6	94.3	119.6	104.3
04	MASONRY	112.7	128.9	122.5	111.0	128.9	121.8	112.0	127.1	121.2	113.0	127.1	121.5	113.0	128.9	122.6	112.3	128.9	122.4
05	METALS	94.6	115.8	98.8	94.3	115.7	98.5	98.4	115.8	101.8	98.4	115.8	101.8	98.4	115.9	101.8	98.1	115.6	101.6
06	WOOD, PLASTICS & COMPOSITES	110.5	112.4	111.4	110.5	112.4	111.4	110.5	109.2	109.9	110.5	109.2	109.9	110.5	112.4	111.4	110.5	112.4	111.4
07	THERMAL & MOISTURE PROTECTION	96.9	116.3	103.8	96.7	116.4	103.7	96.9	117.7	104.3	96.8	117.7	104.2	96.8	116.7	103.9	97.0	115.6	103.6
08	OPENINGS	95.8	118.8	101.0	98.3	116.5	102.4	95.8	117.0	100.6	95.8	117.0	100.6	95.8	118.8	101.0	98.3	118.8	102.9
0920	Plaster & Gypsum Board	130.8	112.8	119.3	130.8	112.8	119.3	130.8	109.5	117.3	130.8	109.5	117.3	130.8	112.8	119.3	130.8	112.8	119.3
0950, 0980	Ceilings & Acoustic Treatment	95.0	112.8	104.9	94.5	112.8	104.7	95.0	109.5	103.1	95.0	109.5	103.1	95.0	112.8	104.9	94.5	112.8	104.7
0960	Flooring	94.2	121.9	101.1	94.2	113.7	99.1	94.2	121.9	101.1	94.2	121.9	101.1	94.2	121.9	101.1	94.2	108.5	97.8
0970, 0990	Wall Finishes & Painting/Coating	91.3	122.0	109.6	91.3	118.3	107.4	91.3	126.9	112.6	91.3	126.9	112.6	91.3	126.9	112.6	91.3	126.9	112.6
09	FINISHES	99.1	116.6	107.9	98.5	114.8	106.7	99.1	115.3	107.2	99.1	115.3	107.2	99.0	117.1	108.1	99.0	114.8	106.9
COVERS	DIVS. 10 - 14, 25, 28, 41, 43, 44, 46	100.0	111.3	102.2	100.0	111.2	102.2	100.0	110.9	102.1	100.0	110.9	102.1	100.0	111.3	102.2	100.0	111.2	102.2
21, 22, 23	FIRE SUPPRESSION, PLUMBING & HVAC	100.2	117.5	106.4	92.6	117.4	101.5	100.2	117.5	106.4	100.2	117.5	106.4	100.2	117.5	106.4	100.2	117.4	106.3
26, 27, 3370	ELECTRICAL, COMMUNICATIONS & UTIL.	96.5	101.7	98.7	95.0	96.1	95.5	96.6	101.3	98.6	96.6	104.0	99.8	96.3	101.7	98.6	96.6	99.0	97.6
MF2018	WEIGHTED AVERAGE	99.4	114.5	104.9	94.4	113.4	101.4	98.9	113.9	104.4	99.0	114.3	104.6	98.9	114.7	104.7	98.8	113.6	104.3

DIVISION		D.C.			DELAWARE									FLORIDA					
		WASHINGTON			DOVER			NEWARK			WILMINGTON			DAYTONA BEACH			FORT LAUDERDALE		
		200 - 205			199			197			198			321			333		
		MAT.	INST.	TOTAL	MAT.	INST.	TOTAL	MAT.	INST.	TOTAL	MAT.	INST.	TOTAL	MAT.	INST.	TOTAL	MAT.	INST.	TOTAL
015433	CONTRACTOR EQUIPMENT		104.8	104.8		113.6	113.6		113.7	113.7		113.8	113.8		96.1	96.1		90.1	90.1
0241, 31 - 34	SITE & INFRASTRUCTURE, DEMOLITION	111.7	99.1	103.5	111.9	103.6	106.5	109.7	103.0	105.3	107.6	104.7	105.7	127.6	81.5	97.5	105.8	71.5	83.4
0310	Concrete Forming & Accessories	99.1	74.2	79.8	104.2	95.1	97.2	99.4	94.8	95.8	104.2	95.4	97.4	99.0	60.8	69.3	94.3	60.1	67.7
0320	Concrete Reinforcing	100.4	89.8	97.5	98.7	114.5	103.1	97.6	114.5	102.3	98.5	114.6	103.0	90.5	58.2	81.5	89.3	60.9	81.5
0330	Cast-in-Place Concrete	129.2	79.9	111.7	119.7	104.9	114.5	99.8	102.5	100.7	116.4	105.0	112.3	90.2	66.2	81.7	92.9	62.7	82.2
03	CONCRETE	105.6	79.7	95.4	102.0	102.9	102.4	93.8	102.1	97.1	100.6	103.1	101.6	89.5	64.0	79.4	90.7	63.0	79.8
04	MASONRY	108.1	87.7	95.7	106.2	100.9	103.0	103.4	100.8	101.8	106.0	100.9	102.9	87.1	61.9	71.8	101.3	56.6	74.1
05	METALS	102.3	95.3	100.9	101.1	119.5	104.7	102.6	122.8	106.6	102.7	119.8	106.1	107.4	86.8	103.4	104.6	88.8	101.5
06	WOOD, PLASTICS & COMPOSITES	97.0	72.6	86.0	101.5	92.2	97.4	97.0	91.9	94.7	101.5	92.2	97.4	96.0	59.0	79.4	82.7	60.2	72.6
07	THERMAL & MOISTURE PROTECTION	101.8	87.4	96.6	103.2	111.7	106.2	106.2	110.0	107.5	102.9	111.7	106.0	92.2	65.9	82.8	94.4	59.1	81.8
08	OPENINGS	104.7	75.6	98.2	98.1	104.1	99.5	95.2	103.9	97.1	98.1	104.1	99.5	93.6	58.0	85.5	96.1	59.3	87.8
0920	Plaster & Gypsum Board	109.8	71.8	85.7	125.6	91.9	104.2	121.9	91.9	102.8	125.6	91.9	104.2	92.7	58.4	70.9	111.6	59.7	78.7
0950, 0980	Ceilings & Acoustic Treatment	96.8	71.8	82.8	110.0	91.9	99.8	108.1	91.9	99.0	110.0	91.9	99.8	73.1	58.4	64.9	88.2	59.7	72.2
0960	Flooring	97.6	74.4	91.8	105.5	109.5	106.5	96.6	109.5	99.8	105.8	109.5	106.8	102.8	57.3	91.4	107.1	61.4	95.6
0970, 0990	Wall Finishes & Painting/Coating	94.9	68.7	79.3	99.1	116.8	109.6	89.0	116.8	105.5	99.1	116.8	109.6	102.0	57.9	75.7	92.6	57.3	71.5
09	FINISHES	99.9	72.6	86.2	108.1	99.0	103.5	100.9	98.7	99.8	108.5	99.0	103.7	93.5	59.2	76.3	99.3	59.5	79.3
COVERS	DIVS. 10 - 14, 25, 28, 41, 43, 44, 46	100.0	95.6	99.2	100.0	94.5	98.9	100.0	93.7	98.8	100.0	107.5	101.5	100.0	82.0	96.5	100.0	82.2	96.5
21, 22, 23	FIRE SUPPRESSION, PLUMBING & HVAC	100.0	93.1	97.5	99.9	117.6	106.3	100.3	117.5	106.5	100.0	117.6	106.3	99.9	75.6	91.2	99.9	67.1	88.1
26, 27, 3370	ELECTRICAL, COMMUNICATIONS & UTIL.	99.9	98.9	99.5	101.3	106.2	103.4	100.3	106.2	102.9	100.1	106.2	102.7	97.2	59.6	80.9	95.4	69.2	84.1
MF2018	WEIGHTED AVERAGE	102.2	88.6	97.2	101.7	107.3	103.7	100.1	107.3	102.8	101.7	107.8	103.9	98.9	68.8	87.9	98.9	67.0	87.1

DIVISION		FLORIDA																	
		FORT MYERS			GAINESVILLE			JACKSONVILLE			LAKELAND			MELBOURNE			MIAMI		
		339,341			326,344			320,322			338			329			330 - 332,340		
		MAT.	INST.	TOTAL	MAT.	INST.	TOTAL	MAT.	INST.	TOTAL	MAT.	INST.	TOTAL	MAT.	INST.	TOTAL	MAT.	INST.	TOTAL
015433	**CONTRACTOR EQUIPMENT**		96.1	96.1		96.1	96.1		96.1	96.1		96.1	96.1		96.1	96.1		96.3	96.3
0241, 31 - 34	**SITE & INFRASTRUCTURE, DEMOLITION**	117.1	81.8	94.1	134.0	81.7	99.9	127.6	81.2	97.3	119.0	81.7	94.7	135.3	81.5	100.2	108.1	83.4	92.0
0310	Concrete Forming & Accessories	89.5	61.6	67.8	93.4	62.2	69.2	98.8	63.3	71.2	85.5	63.8	68.7	94.8	63.6	70.5	103.3	62.6	71.7
0320	Concrete Reinforcing	90.3	73.5	85.7	95.9	60.8	86.2	90.5	60.6	82.2	92.6	71.8	86.8	91.5	67.4	84.8	99.7	60.8	88.9
0330	Cast-in-Place Concrete	96.9	65.4	85.7	103.6	65.5	90.1	91.1	64.9	81.8	99.1	65.9	87.3	108.8	66.3	93.7	90.0	69.0	82.5
03	**CONCRETE**	91.4	66.7	81.7	99.0	64.8	85.5	89.8	65.0	80.0	93.0	67.6	82.9	99.0	66.8	86.3	93.5	66.0	82.6
04	**MASONRY**	96.9	56.6	72.4	96.7	60.2	74.5	86.8	56.9	68.7	117.3	60.3	82.7	80.2	61.9	69.1	109.5	61.2	80.2
05	**METALS**	106.3	92.9	103.7	105.9	88.2	102.4	106.1	86.5	102.2	106.1	92.4	103.4	114.9	90.3	110.0	104.6	85.0	100.7
06	**WOOD, PLASTICS & COMPOSITES**	79.0	60.7	70.8	88.5	61.6	76.4	96.0	63.4	81.4	73.6	64.2	69.4	90.7	62.4	78.0	98.2	60.6	81.3
07	**THERMAL & MOISTURE PROTECTION**	94.2	61.1	82.4	92.5	62.6	81.8	92.5	62.0	81.6	94.1	62.5	82.8	92.6	64.5	82.6	95.4	63.9	84.2
08	**OPENINGS**	97.4	62.5	89.5	93.2	60.0	85.7	93.6	61.0	86.2	97.4	64.0	89.8	93.0	62.0	86.0	98.3	59.5	89.5
0920	Plaster & Gypsum Board	105.8	60.1	76.8	89.0	61.0	71.3	92.7	62.9	73.8	102.9	63.8	78.1	89.0	61.9	71.8	102.2	59.7	75.2
0950, 0980	Ceilings & Acoustic Treatment	82.6	60.1	70.0	70.1	61.0	65.0	73.1	62.9	67.4	82.6	63.8	72.1	72.7	61.9	66.6	88.6	59.7	72.4
0960	Flooring	104.9	69.2	96.0	101.1	59.6	90.7	102.8	60.2	92.1	103.6	63.9	93.6	101.3	62.0	91.5	105.7	60.2	94.3
0970, 0990	Wall Finishes & Painting/Coating	97.2	61.7	76.0	102.0	61.1	77.6	102.0	61.1	77.6	97.2	61.7	76.0	102.0	79.8	88.8	99.1	57.3	74.2
09	**FINISHES**	98.7	62.6	80.6	92.8	61.2	76.9	93.6	62.4	77.9	98.0	63.4	80.6	93.2	64.5	78.8	99.4	60.9	80.1
COVERS	**DIVS. 10 - 14, 25, 28, 41, 43, 44, 46**	100.0	80.5	96.2	100.0	80.2	96.2	100.0	80.4	96.2	100.0	81.8	96.5	100.0	82.4	96.6	100.0	84.9	97.1
21, 22, 23	**FIRE SUPPRESSION, PLUMBING & HVAC**	95.8	57.7	82.1	95.6	64.2	84.3	99.9	63.8	87.0	95.8	57.2	81.9	99.9	75.8	91.3	99.9	64.2	87.1
26, 27, 3370	**ELECTRICAL, COMMUNICATIONS & UTIL.**	96.3	60.1	80.6	97.3	58.2	80.4	97.0	64.4	82.9	95.6	52.1	76.7	98.0	67.9	85.0	98.1	74.9	88.0
MF2018	**WEIGHTED AVERAGE**	98.6	66.0	86.6	99.2	66.5	87.2	98.7	67.0	87.0	99.4	65.4	86.9	101.6	71.6	90.6	100.2	69.1	88.8

DIVISION		FLORIDA																	
		ORLANDO			PANAMA CITY			PENSACOLA			SARASOTA			ST. PETERSBURG			TALLAHASSEE		
		327 - 328,347			324			325			342			337			323		
		MAT.	INST.	TOTAL	MAT.	INST.	TOTAL	MAT.	INST.	TOTAL	MAT.	INST.	TOTAL	MAT.	INST.	TOTAL	MAT.	INST.	TOTAL
015433	**CONTRACTOR EQUIPMENT**		103.7	103.7		96.1	96.1		96.1	96.1		96.1	96.1		96.1	96.1		103.7	103.7
0241, 31 - 34	**SITE & INFRASTRUCTURE, DEMOLITION**	126.6	94.4	105.6	141.2	81.6	102.4	140.8	81.4	102.0	128.0	81.7	97.8	122.4	81.5	95.7	123.0	94.3	104.3
0310	Concrete Forming & Accessories	104.5	64.9	73.8	98.0	64.9	72.2	95.3	68.9	74.8	98.9	63.6	71.5	93.8	59.8	67.4	104.5	64.0	73.0
0320	Concrete Reinforcing	100.4	63.2	90.1	94.5	67.7	87.1	96.8	65.5	88.2	91.5	68.7	85.2	92.6	70.8	86.5	100.6	60.8	89.6
0330	Cast-in-Place Concrete	111.7	68.6	96.4	95.8	66.3	85.3	118.4	64.7	99.3	106.9	65.8	92.3	100.2	63.9	87.3	93.6	68.9	84.8
03	**CONCRETE**	102.7	67.3	88.8	97.0	67.5	85.4	106.0	68.3	91.2	95.8	66.9	84.4	94.5	64.9	82.8	96.3	66.6	84.6
04	**MASONRY**	94.0	62.0	74.5	90.3	60.3	72.1	114.0	59.2	80.7	86.6	60.3	70.6	165.0	57.3	99.6	82.5	60.1	68.9
05	**METALS**	105.3	85.6	101.4	106.6	90.3	103.4	107.7	89.0	104.0	105.1	90.6	102.3	107.0	91.0	103.8	104.4	84.5	100.5
06	**WOOD, PLASTICS & COMPOSITES**	99.4	64.6	83.8	94.5	64.6	81.1	93.0	71.2	83.3	95.1	64.2	81.3	84.6	59.0	73.1	99.2	63.7	83.3
07	**THERMAL & MOISTURE PROTECTION**	95.6	68.0	85.8	92.7	62.8	82.0	92.6	62.1	81.8	101.8	62.5	87.8	94.3	58.9	81.7	95.3	64.3	84.2
08	**OPENINGS**	98.3	62.2	90.2	91.9	63.3	85.5	91.9	66.4	86.1	98.4	62.9	90.4	96.4	60.9	88.4	98.4	61.2	90.0
0920	Plaster & Gypsum Board	103.9	63.8	78.5	91.6	64.2	74.2	105.4	71.0	83.6	97.1	63.8	76.0	108.9	58.4	76.9	104.8	62.9	78.2
0950, 0980	Ceilings & Acoustic Treatment	84.1	63.8	72.7	72.7	64.2	67.9	72.7	71.0	71.7	86.8	63.8	73.9	83.6	58.4	69.5	90.0	62.9	74.8
0960	Flooring	104.5	59.6	93.3	102.6	73.8	95.4	99.7	60.8	89.9	106.9	49.1	92.4	106.3	53.9	93.2	100.6	61.6	90.8
0970, 0990	Wall Finishes & Painting/Coating	99.1	83.4	89.7	102.0	61.1	77.6	102.0	61.1	77.6	101.1	61.7	77.6	97.2	61.1	75.7	101.2	61.1	77.3
09	**FINISHES**	99.9	65.8	82.8	94.7	65.7	80.1	95.3	66.9	81.0	100.3	60.8	80.5	100.0	58.5	79.2	100.0	63.1	81.4
COVERS	**DIVS. 10 - 14, 25, 28, 41, 43, 44, 46**	100.0	83.4	96.8	100.0	81.6	96.4	100.0	81.7	96.5	100.0	80.5	96.2	100.0	80.2	96.2	100.0	81.4	96.4
21, 22, 23	**FIRE SUPPRESSION, PLUMBING & HVAC**	100.1	55.7	84.2	99.9	64.4	87.2	99.9	61.3	86.0	99.6	53.2	83.0	99.9	55.5	84.0	100.0	64.3	87.2
26, 27, 3370	**ELECTRICAL, COMMUNICATIONS & UTIL.**	100.1	62.3	83.7	96.4	56.9	79.3	98.6	49.8	77.5	97.8	52.1	78.0	95.6	58.9	79.7	100.7	55.8	81.2
MF2018	**WEIGHTED AVERAGE**	101.7	67.5	89.1	100.0	67.7	88.1	102.5	66.3	89.1	100.4	63.9	87.0	102.8	64.3	88.6	100.2	67.5	88.2

DIVISION		FLORIDA						GEORGIA											
		TAMPA			WEST PALM BEACH			ALBANY			ATHENS			ATLANTA			AUGUSTA		
		335 - 336,346			334,349			317,398			306			300 - 303,399			308 - 309		
		MAT.	INST.	TOTAL	MAT.	INST.	TOTAL	MAT.	INST.	TOTAL	MAT.	INST.	TOTAL	MAT.	INST.	TOTAL	MAT.	INST.	TOTAL
015433	**CONTRACTOR EQUIPMENT**		96.1	96.1		90.1	90.1		90.9	90.9		89.4	89.4		97.5	97.5		89.4	89.4
0241, 31 - 34	**SITE & INFRASTRUCTURE, DEMOLITION**	122.8	81.9	96.1	100.7	71.5	81.6	116.4	74.1	88.8	136.8	86.7	104.1	134.8	97.8	110.7	129.0	87.4	101.9
0310	Concrete Forming & Accessories	96.9	64.9	72.1	98.6	59.6	68.3	94.1	68.7	74.4	96.9	39.8	52.5	103.2	75.2	81.4	98.1	71.0	77.0
0320	Concrete Reinforcing	89.3	71.8	84.5	91.8	51.7	80.7	92.3	71.6	86.5	91.9	56.7	82.2	100.3	70.4	92.0	92.1	68.4	85.6
0330	Cast-in-Place Concrete	97.9	67.5	87.1	88.3	62.5	79.2	90.9	67.3	82.5	125.9	66.2	104.7	129.9	71.5	109.2	118.9	69.3	101.3
03	**CONCRETE**	93.0	68.6	83.4	88.7	61.1	77.8	86.7	70.4	80.3	98.3	53.4	80.6	102.5	73.6	91.1	93.6	70.7	84.5
04	**MASONRY**	102.2	63.1	78.4	100.8	51.6	70.9	83.5	67.6	73.8	73.8	64.1	67.9	84.5	68.0	74.5	85.7	69.9	76.1
05	**METALS**	106.4	92.5	103.7	103.0	84.9	99.4	107.4	96.8	105.3	91.9	75.3	88.7	97.8	82.1	94.7	91.7	82.1	89.8
06	**WOOD, PLASTICS & COMPOSITES**	89.6	64.2	78.2	88.4	60.2	75.8	86.2	69.6	78.8	91.2	32.7	65.0	101.4	78.3	91.0	93.0	72.9	84.0
07	**THERMAL & MOISTURE PROTECTION**	94.6	63.8	83.6	94.2	58.6	81.5	104.8	66.9	91.3	91.6	61.6	80.9	92.3	72.1	85.1	91.5	70.8	84.1
08	**OPENINGS**	97.4	64.0	89.8	95.7	57.3	87.1	87.8	71.5	84.1	88.5	46.9	79.1	100.5	75.6	94.9	88.5	72.1	84.8
0920	Plaster & Gypsum Board	112.8	63.8	81.7	116.4	59.7	80.4	95.9	69.4	79.1	93.4	31.2	54.0	99.2	77.9	85.7	94.8	72.7	80.8
0950, 0980	Ceilings & Acoustic Treatment	88.2	63.8	74.5	82.6	59.7	69.8	73.6	69.4	71.3	92.5	31.2	58.1	85.0	77.9	81.0	93.5	72.7	81.8
0960	Flooring	107.1	63.9	96.3	108.3	49.1	93.5	105.8	66.8	96.0	92.2	66.8	85.9	97.6	70.2	90.7	92.3	72.2	87.3
0970, 0990	Wall Finishes & Painting/Coating	97.2	61.7	76.0	92.6	57.0	71.4	96.9	96.8	96.9	94.5	83.5	87.9	101.2	95.6	97.9	94.5	81.7	86.9
09	**FINISHES**	102.0	64.1	83.0	98.6	57.0	77.7	94.2	71.0	82.5	97.1	47.3	72.1	97.7	76.6	87.1	96.6	72.4	84.4
COVERS	**DIVS. 10 - 14, 25, 28, 41, 43, 44, 46**	100.0	81.5	96.4	100.0	82.1	96.5	100.0	84.3	97.0	100.0	79.7	96.1	100.0	86.1	97.3	100.0	84.8	97.1
21, 22, 23	**FIRE SUPPRESSION, PLUMBING & HVAC**	99.9	58.7	85.1	95.8	55.1	81.2	99.9	71.0	89.6	92.6	59.6	80.8	100.1	71.7	89.9	100.1	65.8	87.8
26, 27, 3370	**ELECTRICAL, COMMUNICATIONS & UTIL.**	94.9	64.4	81.7	96.2	60.0	80.5	97.0	57.4	79.8	99.8	56.9	81.2	100.1	69.6	86.9	100.1	64.6	84.7
MF2018	**WEIGHTED AVERAGE**	100.3	68.1	88.4	97.3	61.6	84.2	98.0	71.6	88.3	94.8	60.7	82.2	99.8	75.6	90.9	96.1	71.8	87.2

DIVISION		GEORGIA																	
		COLUMBUS			DALTON			GAINESVILLE			MACON			SAVANNAH			STATESBORO		
		318 - 319			307			305			310 - 312			313 - 314			304		
		MAT.	INST.	TOTAL	MAT.	INST.	TOTAL	MAT.	INST.	TOTAL	MAT.	INST.	TOTAL	MAT.	INST.	TOTAL	MAT.	INST.	TOTAL
015433	CONTRACTOR EQUIPMENT		90.9	90.9		102.8	102.8		89.4	89.4		99.4	99.4		98.2	98.2		92.0	92.0
0241, 31 - 34	SITE & INFRASTRUCTURE, DEMOLITION	116.3	74.5	89.0	136.7	91.2	107.1	135.2	86.6	103.5	118.1	87.2	98.0	118.4	86.6	97.7	138.6	74.1	96.6
0310	Concrete Forming & Accessories	94.0	70.0	75.4	87.9	58.6	65.1	101.4	37.8	52.0	93.9	70.0	75.3	101.7	70.4	77.4	82.2	68.6	71.7
0320	Concrete Reinforcing	92.9	71.8	87.1	91.6	54.4	81.3	91.8	56.7	82.1	94.1	71.8	87.9	100.1	68.3	91.3	91.4	63.6	83.7
0330	Cast-in-Place Concrete	90.6	70.0	83.3	122.3	64.8	101.9	132.3	65.8	108.7	89.4	68.2	81.9	91.8	70.6	84.3	125.6	65.5	104.3
03	CONCRETE	86.8	72.0	80.9	96.6	62.0	82.9	100.9	52.4	81.8	86.5	71.4	80.6	88.5	71.5	81.8	97.1	68.4	85.8
04	MASONRY	82.7	70.0	75.0	72.4	62.6	66.5	82.8	63.2	70.9	95.1	69.4	79.5	77.9	68.1	72.0	75.7	64.0	68.6
05	METALS	107.1	98.2	105.3	92.7	88.8	92.0	91.2	75.4	88.1	101.7	98.2	101.0	104.0	92.6	101.7	96.0	93.4	95.5
06	WOOD, PLASTICS & COMPOSITES	86.2	71.1	79.4	74.7	59.2	67.7	96.0	30.3	66.6	90.5	71.8	82.1	98.8	71.9	86.7	66.8	71.6	69.0
07	THERMAL & MOISTURE PROTECTION	104.7	69.1	92.0	93.4	63.1	82.6	91.6	60.9	80.7	103.3	69.7	91.4	101.9	70.3	90.6	92.0	63.5	81.9
08	OPENINGS	87.8	72.2	84.3	90.0	61.0	83.4	88.4	45.6	78.8	87.8	72.3	84.3	97.8	71.6	91.9	90.8	70.2	86.2
0920	Plaster & Gypsum Board	95.9	70.9	80.0	82.9	58.6	67.5	95.8	28.8	53.3	97.0	71.5	80.9	99.6	71.4	81.7	82.8	71.4	75.6
0950, 0980	Ceilings & Acoustic Treatment	73.6	70.9	72.1	101.5	58.6	77.5	92.5	28.8	56.8	70.5	71.5	71.1	90.4	71.4	79.7	99.7	71.4	83.8
0960	Flooring	105.8	72.2	97.4	92.4	66.8	86.0	93.6	66.8	86.8	83.3	66.8	79.1	99.6	69.4	92.1	112.2	66.8	100.8
0970, 0990	Wall Finishes & Painting/Coating	96.9	85.0	89.8	84.1	62.2	71.1	94.5	83.5	87.9	99.2	96.8	97.8	99.1	82.0	88.9	92.7	62.2	74.5
09	FINISHES	94.1	71.7	82.8	104.3	60.2	82.2	97.5	45.7	71.5	83.2	71.9	77.5	97.9	71.3	84.6	108.8	67.8	88.2
COVERS	DIVS. 10 - 14, 25, 28, 41, 43, 44, 46	100.0	84.5	97.0	100.0	76.2	95.4	100.0	79.3	96.0	100.0	84.2	96.9	100.0	85.4	97.2	100.0	83.8	96.9
21, 22, 23	FIRE SUPPRESSION, PLUMBING & HVAC	100.0	66.3	87.9	92.6	54.6	79.0	92.6	59.1	80.6	100.0	68.3	88.6	100.1	66.8	88.1	94.5	62.6	83.1
26, 27, 3370	ELECTRICAL, COMMUNICATIONS & UTIL.	96.8	68.1	84.3	112.5	55.4	87.8	99.8	65.4	84.9	94.3	58.1	78.6	99.1	59.8	82.1	101.2	58.6	82.8
MF2018	WEIGHTED AVERAGE	97.9	72.9	88.7	96.6	64.5	84.8	95.3	61.2	82.8	96.2	72.8	87.6	98.7	72.0	88.9	97.1	68.5	86.5

DIVISION		GEORGIA						HAWAII									IDAHO		
		VALDOSTA			WAYCROSS			HILO			HONOLULU			STATES & POSS., GUAM			BOISE		
		316			315			967			968			969			836 - 837		
		MAT.	INST.	TOTAL	MAT.	INST.	TOTAL	MAT.	INST.	TOTAL	MAT.	INST.	TOTAL	MAT.	INST.	TOTAL	MAT.	INST.	TOTAL
015433	CONTRACTOR EQUIPMENT		90.9	90.9		90.9	90.9		95.8	95.8		101.5	101.5		151.9	151.9		93.2	93.2
0241, 31 - 34	SITE & INFRASTRUCTURE, DEMOLITION	126.9	74.1	92.4	121.4	73.6	90.2	158.4	99.2	119.8	165.4	109.9	129.2	209.0	96.2	135.4	89.8	88.9	89.2
0310	Concrete Forming & Accessories	83.1	70.0	72.9	85.2	68.3	72.1	89.8	119.1	112.6	100.4	119.2	115.0	92.0	59.7	66.9	97.7	81.4	85.1
0320	Concrete Reinforcing	94.6	60.7	85.2	94.6	53.4	83.2	91.7	120.4	99.6	104.7	120.4	109.0	154.3	41.3	123.0	96.4	76.3	90.8
0330	Cast-in-Place Concrete	89.0	67.3	81.3	100.6	65.4	88.1	221.5	120.3	185.6	172.8	121.6	154.6	191.9	99.1	158.9	81.6	99.0	87.8
03	CONCRETE	89.3	69.1	81.3	92.7	66.2	82.3	152.3	119.0	139.1	144.2	119.3	134.4	156.5	71.2	122.8	93.0	86.9	90.6
04	MASONRY	87.6	70.3	77.1	88.5	64.0	73.6	140.7	119.3	127.7	135.1	119.5	125.6	208.8	45.9	109.8	127.7	84.6	101.5
05	METALS	105.7	92.5	103.1	104.8	84.3	100.8	111.0	106.2	110.0	125.4	104.0	121.2	141.4	79.4	129.2	106.0	82.2	101.3
06	WOOD, PLASTICS & COMPOSITES	71.7	71.6	71.6	73.8	71.6	72.8	104.6	119.4	111.2	123.8	119.4	121.8	116.8	59.9	91.3	95.6	79.6	88.4
07	THERMAL & MOISTURE PROTECTION	104.8	69.0	92.1	104.7	63.8	90.1	96.6	114.4	102.9	107.8	116.2	110.8	111.2	65.9	95.1	92.2	85.7	89.9
08	OPENINGS	84.6	69.4	81.2	84.8	65.4	80.5	101.4	118.3	105.2	112.3	118.3	113.7	106.0	49.8	93.4	92.0	74.9	88.1
0920	Plaster & Gypsum Board	86.8	71.4	77.0	86.8	71.4	77.0	110.9	120.0	116.7	142.8	120.0	128.3	239.6	49.7	119.1	99.1	79.2	86.5
0950, 0980	Ceilings & Acoustic Treatment	72.3	71.4	71.8	71.2	71.4	71.3	109.5	120.0	115.3	121.4	120.0	120.6	254.0	49.7	139.5	111.3	79.2	93.3
0960	Flooring	101.5	72.9	94.3	102.4	66.8	93.5	79.0	135.4	93.1	100.8	135.4	109.5	96.5	44.4	83.4	94.2	84.7	91.8
0970, 0990	Wall Finishes & Painting/Coating	96.9	86.9	90.9	96.9	62.2	76.2	91.4	128.8	113.7	104.7	128.8	119.1	96.3	36.9	60.9	92.1	61.4	73.8
09	FINISHES	92.2	72.3	82.2	91.8	67.8	79.7	99.8	123.6	111.7	115.1	123.6	119.4	187.1	54.8	120.7	99.0	79.9	89.4
COVERS	DIVS. 10 - 14, 25, 28, 41, 43, 44, 46	100.0	84.5	97.0	100.0	77.9	95.7	100.0	110.8	102.1	100.0	110.8	102.1	100.0	87.6	97.6	100.0	90.2	98.1
21, 22, 23	FIRE SUPPRESSION, PLUMBING & HVAC	100.0	70.7	89.5	95.5	57.1	81.7	99.7	106.8	102.2	99.7	106.8	102.3	101.7	49.6	83.0	100.2	74.1	90.8
26, 27, 3370	ELECTRICAL, COMMUNICATIONS & UTIL.	95.9	52.5	77.1	97.8	58.6	80.8	101.2	114.9	107.1	102.0	114.9	107.6	142.1	45.5	100.2	100.0	73.1	88.3
MF2018	WEIGHTED AVERAGE	97.7	70.7	87.8	97.1	65.8	85.6	111.8	113.3	112.3	116.5	114.1	115.6	134.9	60.4	107.5	100.3	80.3	93.0

DIVISION		IDAHO															ILLINOIS		
		COEUR D'ALENE			IDAHO FALLS			LEWISTON			POCATELLO			TWIN FALLS			BLOOMINGTON		
		838			834			835			832			833			617		
		MAT.	INST.	TOTAL	MAT.	INST.	TOTAL	MAT.	INST.	TOTAL	MAT.	INST.	TOTAL	MAT.	INST.	TOTAL	MAT.	INST.	TOTAL
015433	CONTRACTOR EQUIPMENT		88.7	88.7		93.2	93.2		88.7	88.7		93.2	93.2		93.2	93.2		98.1	98.1
0241, 31 - 34	SITE & INFRASTRUCTURE, DEMOLITION	90.4	85.9	87.5	90.5	89.0	89.5	99.2	84.4	89.6	91.1	88.9	89.7	97.3	88.4	91.5	86.6	91.5	89.8
0310	Concrete Forming & Accessories	99.5	82.0	85.9	90.9	77.2	80.2	105.2	81.7	87.0	97.9	80.8	84.6	99.1	76.7	81.7	85.3	115.5	108.8
0320	Concrete Reinforcing	101.3	97.0	100.1	97.6	74.1	91.1	101.3	96.9	100.1	96.6	76.3	91.0	97.8	73.0	91.0	98.5	102.7	99.6
0330	Cast-in-Place Concrete	88.2	81.3	85.8	77.7	94.6	83.7	91.7	82.8	88.6	83.9	98.8	89.2	86.1	94.0	88.9	88.3	110.9	96.3
03	CONCRETE	98.1	84.5	92.7	86.8	83.1	85.3	101.1	84.9	94.7	92.4	86.5	90.1	98.3	82.5	92.1	89.9	112.5	98.8
04	MASONRY	130.2	84.8	102.6	123.1	86.1	100.6	130.7	83.2	101.9	125.6	86.3	101.7	128.7	79.1	98.5	114.2	109.7	111.5
05	METALS	99.0	89.5	97.1	112.9	81.3	106.7	98.4	89.1	96.6	113.4	81.7	107.1	113.0	80.5	106.6	94.4	122.9	100.0
06	WOOD, PLASTICS & COMPOSITES	93.3	81.0	87.8	87.1	75.2	81.8	100.9	81.0	92.0	95.6	79.6	88.4	96.8	75.2	87.1	77.0	115.3	94.2
07	THERMAL & MOISTURE PROTECTION	136.7	80.9	116.8	91.1	78.3	86.5	137.1	79.8	116.7	91.6	75.5	85.9	92.2	81.3	88.4	101.3	107.3	103.5
08	OPENINGS	107.4	75.9	100.3	94.7	70.3	89.2	101.4	79.5	96.4	92.6	67.9	87.0	95.3	70.9	89.8	88.9	119.5	95.8
0920	Plaster & Gypsum Board	155.5	80.8	108.1	88.3	74.6	79.7	157.7	80.8	108.9	91.2	79.2	83.6	94.1	74.6	81.7	78.0	116.1	102.2
0950, 0980	Ceilings & Acoustic Treatment	131.0	80.8	102.9	107.2	74.6	88.9	131.0	80.8	102.9	115.3	79.2	95.1	110.8	74.6	90.5	89.8	116.1	104.6
0960	Flooring	136.5	90.1	124.8	95.2	76.2	90.4	138.8	74.7	122.7	97.6	74.7	91.9	98.5	79.7	93.8	90.7	124.5	99.2
0970, 0990	Wall Finishes & Painting/Coating	109.4	68.2	84.8	92.2	41.9	62.2	109.4	59.6	79.7	92.0	57.9	71.7	92.2	57.9	71.7	87.9	119.7	106.9
09	FINISHES	156.4	82.0	119.0	96.4	73.0	84.7	157.5	77.8	117.5	100.1	77.5	88.8	100.1	75.3	87.6	88.3	118.1	103.3
COVERS	DIVS. 10 - 14, 25, 28, 41, 43, 44, 46	100.0	97.6	99.5	100.0	89.1	97.9	100.0	97.5	99.5	100.0	90.1	98.1	100.0	88.8	97.8	100.0	105.0	101.0
21, 22, 23	FIRE SUPPRESSION, PLUMBING & HVAC	96.8	86.6	93.1	103.6	77.2	94.1	101.3	83.1	94.8	100.0	71.9	89.9	100.0	69.0	88.9	92.4	103.0	96.2
26, 27, 3370	ELECTRICAL, COMMUNICATIONS & UTIL.	84.2	78.3	81.7	83.9	67.9	77.0	83.3	81.2	82.4	95.2	67.9	83.4	84.6	70.1	78.3	92.5	95.7	93.9
MF2018	WEIGHTED AVERAGE	103.8	84.3	96.6	99.8	78.5	92.0	104.8	83.3	96.9	101.3	78.3	92.9	101.4	76.5	92.2	93.4	107.8	98.7

DIVISION		ILLINOIS																	
		CARBONDALE			CENTRALIA			CHAMPAIGN			CHICAGO			DECATUR			EAST ST. LOUIS		
		629			628			618 - 619			606 - 608			625			620 - 622		
		MAT.	INST.	TOTAL	MAT.	INST.	TOTAL	MAT.	INST.	TOTAL	MAT.	INST.	TOTAL	MAT.	INST.	TOTAL	MAT.	INST.	TOTAL
015433	CONTRACTOR EQUIPMENT		105.5	105.5		105.5	105.5		98.9	98.9		98.7	98.7		98.9	98.9		105.5	105.5
0241, 31 - 34	SITE & INFRASTRUCTURE, DEMOLITION	93.1	92.3	92.5	93.4	93.0	93.1	93.1	93.7	93.5	92.1	103.0	99.2	92.9	92.4	92.6	98.3	93.1	94.9
0310	Concrete Forming & Accessories	97.5	105.8	104.0	99.8	109.3	107.2	92.7	126.9	119.3	100.7	158.5	145.6	101.3	114.9	111.8	94.4	111.5	107.7
0320	Concrete Reinforcing	101.6	93.2	99.3	101.6	93.8	99.5	98.5	98.9	98.6	98.0	150.7	112.6	99.4	98.5	99.1	101.6	104.5	102.4
0330	Cast-in-Place Concrete	86.0	100.7	91.2	86.4	108.7	94.3	102.3	119.6	108.5	107.9	153.7	124.2	93.9	111.1	100.0	87.9	115.4	97.7
03	CONCRETE	85.3	103.3	92.4	85.8	107.8	94.5	99.6	119.9	107.6	101.3	154.8	122.4	92.9	111.4	100.2	86.3	113.1	96.9
04	MASONRY	98.7	110.2	105.7	98.8	116.9	109.8	138.3	133.9	135.6	107.2	163.8	141.6	93.4	119.2	109.1	99.0	120.3	112.0
05	METALS	98.9	123.5	103.7	98.9	126.1	104.3	94.4	120.6	99.6	98.1	145.2	107.4	104.5	119.0	107.4	100.0	131.8	106.3
06	WOOD, PLASTICS & COMPOSITES	97.8	103.5	100.4	101.6	108.3	104.6	86.0	126.3	104.1	98.4	157.7	125.0	102.1	114.1	107.5	93.8	108.3	100.3
07	THERMAL & MOISTURE PROTECTION	93.7	95.7	94.4	93.8	106.8	98.4	102.0	118.1	107.7	105.6	148.6	120.9	98.4	110.2	102.6	93.7	107.8	98.7
08	OPENINGS	87.9	107.9	92.4	87.9	110.5	93.0	89.4	121.9	96.8	99.2	168.1	114.7	98.8	115.2	102.5	88.0	117.3	94.6
0920	Plaster & Gypsum Board	84.2	104.0	96.8	85.6	109.0	100.4	80.0	127.5	110.1	83.7	159.5	131.8	89.2	114.9	105.5	83.0	109.0	99.5
0950, 0980	Ceilings & Acoustic Treatment	94.5	104.0	99.8	94.5	109.0	102.6	89.8	127.5	110.9	92.2	159.5	129.9	105.9	114.9	110.9	94.5	109.0	102.6
0960	Flooring	116.5	110.3	114.9	117.3	102.5	113.6	93.3	125.6	101.4	98.8	160.9	114.4	103.2	120.3	107.5	115.6	102.5	112.4
0970, 0990	Wall Finishes & Painting/Coating	101.3	102.5	102.0	101.3	108.4	105.5	87.9	125.6	110.4	99.1	161.8	136.5	94.2	104.7	100.4	101.3	110.8	107.0
09	FINISHES	96.2	106.3	101.3	96.7	108.1	102.4	89.9	127.6	108.8	94.1	160.1	127.2	97.4	115.4	106.5	95.9	109.6	102.8
COVERS	DIVS. 10 - 14, 25, 28, 41, 43, 44, 46	100.0	104.7	100.9	100.0	104.9	100.9	100.0	109.2	101.8	100.0	126.9	105.2	100.0	105.7	101.1	100.0	109.3	101.8
21, 22, 23	FIRE SUPPRESSION, PLUMBING & HVAC	92.4	99.8	95.1	92.4	88.2	90.9	92.4	106.2	97.3	99.9	134.9	112.4	100.0	95.6	98.4	99.9	95.3	98.3
26, 27, 3370	ELECTRICAL, COMMUNICATIONS & UTIL.	92.3	107.1	98.7	93.0	94.6	93.7	94.1	95.7	94.8	99.2	133.2	113.9	94.4	88.9	92.0	92.8	103.2	97.3
MF2018	WEIGHTED AVERAGE	93.8	105.2	98.0	94.0	103.3	97.4	96.0	113.7	102.6	99.4	143.7	115.7	98.8	105.4	101.2	95.9	108.2	100.5

DIVISION		ILLINOIS																	
		EFFINGHAM			GALESBURG			JOLIET			KANKAKEE			LA SALLE			NORTH SUBURBAN		
		624			614			604			609			613			600 - 603		
		MAT.	INST.	TOTAL	MAT.	INST.	TOTAL	MAT.	INST.	TOTAL	MAT.	INST.	TOTAL	MAT.	INST.	TOTAL	MAT.	INST.	TOTAL
015433	CONTRACTOR EQUIPMENT		98.9	98.9		98.1	98.1		90.0	90.0		90.0	90.0		98.1	98.1		90.0	90.0
0241, 31 - 34	SITE & INFRASTRUCTURE, DEMOLITION	92.3	92.2	92.2	88.3	91.6	90.5	88.5	93.6	91.9	81.2	92.1	88.3	88.0	93.0	91.3	88.2	93.0	91.3
0310	Concrete Forming & Accessories	106.5	105.7	105.8	92.6	116.2	110.9	99.0	161.0	147.2	91.9	144.4	132.7	108.6	124.8	121.2	98.2	157.9	144.5
0320	Concrete Reinforcing	102.3	84.2	97.3	98.1	103.1	99.5	108.1	139.2	116.7	108.5	131.4	114.8	98.2	129.7	107.0	108.1	150.6	119.8
0330	Cast-in-Place Concrete	93.6	107.1	98.4	90.9	108.0	97.0	98.1	150.9	116.8	91.4	132.3	105.9	90.8	125.8	103.2	98.1	143.1	114.1
03	CONCRETE	94.1	103.4	97.7	92.4	111.8	100.0	97.7	153.0	119.5	93.0	137.4	110.5	93.7	126.8	106.7	97.7	150.7	118.6
04	MASONRY	102.6	107.8	105.8	114.4	121.9	118.9	106.2	163.1	140.8	102.8	145.4	128.7	114.4	132.7	125.5	103.3	163.5	139.9
05	METALS	101.1	110.6	103.0	94.4	122.8	100.0	90.3	139.3	100.0	90.3	130.8	98.3	94.5	141.2	103.7	91.3	142.2	101.4
06	WOOD, PLASTICS & COMPOSITES	105.5	103.3	104.5	85.8	115.3	99.0	90.6	161.7	122.5	82.0	143.8	109.7	105.8	121.7	112.9	89.6	157.3	120.0
07	THERMAL & MOISTURE PROTECTION	98.0	100.1	98.8	101.5	106.1	103.1	112.1	146.4	124.3	111.4	137.4	120.6	101.9	120.6	108.6	112.6	147.4	125.0
08	OPENINGS	94.5	104.9	96.8	88.9	115.2	94.8	93.4	166.6	109.9	86.9	154.6	102.2	88.9	131.2	98.5	93.5	167.9	110.3
0920	Plaster & Gypsum Board	87.1	103.7	97.7	80.0	116.2	102.9	78.3	164.0	132.7	77.9	145.5	120.8	87.7	122.7	109.9	82.7	159.5	131.4
0950, 0980	Ceilings & Acoustic Treatment	94.5	103.7	99.7	89.8	116.2	104.6	94.8	164.0	133.6	94.8	145.5	123.2	89.8	122.7	108.2	94.8	159.5	131.1
0960	Flooring	104.2	111.6	106.1	93.1	124.5	101.0	97.5	160.9	113.4	95.0	144.4	107.3	98.3	128.8	105.9	98.0	160.9	113.7
0970, 0990	Wall Finishes & Painting/Coating	94.2	106.3	101.4	87.9	95.4	92.3	88.1	161.8	132.0	88.1	129.4	112.7	87.9	129.4	112.6	90.2	161.8	132.9
09	FINISHES	94.4	107.1	100.8	89.4	116.3	102.9	91.8	162.2	127.2	90.7	143.5	117.2	92.0	125.5	108.8	92.6	159.8	126.4
COVERS	DIVS. 10 - 14, 25, 28, 41, 43, 44, 46	100.0	104.0	100.8	100.0	106.2	101.2	100.0	126.2	105.1	100.0	113.0	102.5	100.0	108.2	101.6	100.0	126.0	105.0
21, 22, 23	FIRE SUPPRESSION, PLUMBING & HVAC	92.5	95.9	93.7	92.4	100.6	95.3	99.9	134.3	112.2	92.4	126.9	104.8	92.4	127.6	105.0	99.8	135.1	112.5
26, 27, 3370	ELECTRICAL, COMMUNICATIONS & UTIL.	93.4	107.0	99.3	93.0	92.7	92.9	97.7	134.5	113.6	94.8	133.9	111.8	91.6	133.9	109.9	98.0	133.1	113.2
MF2018	WEIGHTED AVERAGE	96.2	103.0	98.7	93.9	107.6	99.0	96.4	142.3	113.3	92.9	132.1	107.3	94.3	126.4	106.1	96.6	142.0	113.3

DIVISION		ILLINOIS																	
		PEORIA			QUINCY			ROCK ISLAND			ROCKFORD			SOUTH SUBURBAN			SPRINGFIELD		
		615 - 616			623			612			610 - 611			605			626 - 627		
		MAT.	INST.	TOTAL	MAT.	INST.	TOTAL	MAT.	INST.	TOTAL	MAT.	INST.	TOTAL	MAT.	INST.	TOTAL	MAT.	INST.	TOTAL
015433	CONTRACTOR EQUIPMENT		98.1	98.1		98.9	98.9		98.1	98.1		98.1	98.1		90.0	90.0		104.6	104.6
0241, 31 - 34	SITE & INFRASTRUCTURE, DEMOLITION	92.4	91.7	92.0	91.2	93.1	92.5	87.0	90.5	89.3	92.0	93.4	92.9	88.2	92.8	91.2	96.3	102.0	100.0
0310	Concrete Forming & Accessories	96.7	117.4	112.8	103.6	111.5	109.7	94.4	102.7	100.9	101.0	133.3	126.1	98.2	157.9	144.6	101.8	115.4	112.4
0320	Concrete Reinforcing	95.7	103.2	97.8	102.1	78.1	95.5	98.1	96.0	97.6	90.1	135.5	102.7	108.1	150.6	119.8	99.1	98.5	98.9
0330	Cast-in-Place Concrete	88.2	115.3	97.8	93.7	116.0	101.6	88.9	100.8	93.1	90.2	131.5	104.9	98.1	150.4	116.7	89.3	109.9	96.6
03	CONCRETE	90.1	114.9	99.9	93.7	108.1	99.4	90.9	101.9	95.2	89.9	133.6	107.1	97.7	153.2	119.6	91.6	111.0	99.3
04	MASONRY	113.3	123.1	119.2	136.3	121.9	127.5	114.2	105.1	108.7	88.7	145.5	123.2	103.3	163.5	139.8	109.1	119.9	115.7
05	METALS	97.5	123.6	102.7	101.1	111.1	103.1	94.5	116.3	98.8	97.5	144.0	106.7	91.3	142.1	101.3	102.0	116.5	104.9
06	WOOD, PLASTICS & COMPOSITES	96.5	115.3	104.9	101.9	108.9	105.1	88.0	101.8	94.2	96.4	130.5	111.7	89.6	157.3	120.0	99.9	114.4	106.4
07	THERMAL & MOISTURE PROTECTION	102.2	111.5	105.5	98.0	105.0	100.5	101.5	95.8	99.5	104.6	132.8	114.7	112.6	147.4	125.0	102.7	112.2	106.1
08	OPENINGS	93.9	119.5	99.7	95.1	105.9	97.5	88.9	105.7	92.7	93.9	140.2	104.3	93.5	167.9	110.3	98.6	115.4	102.4
0920	Plaster & Gypsum Board	86.1	116.2	105.2	85.6	109.6	100.8	80.0	102.2	94.1	86.1	131.8	115.1	82.7	159.5	131.4	90.2	114.9	105.9
0950, 0980	Ceilings & Acoustic Treatment	98.0	116.2	108.2	94.5	109.6	103.0	89.8	102.2	96.8	98.0	131.8	116.9	94.8	159.5	131.1	109.5	114.9	112.5
0960	Flooring	95.9	124.5	103.0	103.2	102.5	103.1	93.9	96.0	94.5	95.9	129.0	104.2	98.0	160.9	113.7	103.0	122.4	107.9
0970, 0990	Wall Finishes & Painting/Coating	87.9	129.4	112.6	94.2	108.4	102.7	87.9	95.4	92.3	87.9	140.0	119.0	90.2	161.8	132.9	99.1	107.5	104.1
09	FINISHES	93.3	120.3	106.8	93.9	109.7	101.8	89.6	100.8	95.2	93.3	133.2	113.3	92.6	159.8	126.4	101.3	116.6	109.0
COVERS	DIVS. 10 - 14, 25, 28, 41, 43, 44, 46	100.0	106.6	101.3	100.0	105.8	101.1	100.0	98.6	99.7	100.0	113.4	102.6	100.0	126.0	105.0	100.0	106.6	101.3
21, 22, 23	FIRE SUPPRESSION, PLUMBING & HVAC	99.9	99.9	99.9	92.5	95.0	93.4	92.4	97.0	94.0	100.1	118.6	106.7	99.8	135.1	112.5	100.0	99.7	99.9
26, 27, 3370	ELECTRICAL, COMMUNICATIONS & UTIL.	93.4	92.2	92.9	92.2	103.2	97.0	89.0	91.6	90.2	93.7	131.0	109.8	98.0	133.1	113.2	101.0	87.4	95.1
MF2018	WEIGHTED AVERAGE	96.9	108.8	101.3	97.3	105.1	100.1	93.3	99.9	95.7	96.0	128.6	108.0	96.6	142.3	113.4	99.8	106.8	102.4

DIVISION		INDIANA																	
		ANDERSON			BLOOMINGTON			COLUMBUS			EVANSVILLE			FORT WAYNE			GARY		
		460			474			472			476 - 477			467 - 468			463 - 464		
		MAT.	INST.	TOTAL	MAT.	INST.	TOTAL	MAT.	INST.	TOTAL	MAT.	INST.	TOTAL	MAT.	INST.	TOTAL	MAT.	INST.	TOTAL
015433	CONTRACTOR EQUIPMENT		92.4	92.4		81.1	81.1		81.1	81.1		106.9	106.9		92.4	92.4		92.4	92.4
0241, 31 - 34	SITE & INFRASTRUCTURE, DEMOLITION	93.0	86.1	88.5	80.6	84.7	83.3	74.7	84.3	81.0	84.9	109.7	101.1	94.4	85.6	88.7	93.5	88.8	90.4
0310	Concrete Forming & Accessories	93.1	74.5	78.7	100.8	78.7	83.6	94.5	74.9	79.2	93.6	78.9	82.2	91.5	78.2	81.2	93.2	102.5	100.4
0320	Concrete Reinforcing	100.3	79.3	94.5	91.6	82.1	88.9	92.0	80.0	88.7	100.2	93.9	98.4	100.3	76.8	93.8	100.3	106.0	101.9
0330	Cast-in-Place Concrete	89.4	72.4	83.3	96.9	74.1	88.8	96.5	70.1	87.1	92.6	81.8	88.8	95.0	71.5	86.6	93.4	103.8	97.1
03	CONCRETE	92.6	75.4	85.8	95.3	77.5	88.3	94.6	74.0	86.5	96.2	82.9	91.0	94.8	76.3	87.5	94.2	103.6	98.0
04	MASONRY	92.3	74.5	81.5	92.0	69.7	78.4	91.8	68.7	77.8	87.5	78.1	81.8	98.3	70.3	81.3	93.8	101.4	98.4
05	METALS	97.6	88.5	95.8	97.5	76.2	93.3	97.5	74.2	92.9	91.9	90.2	91.6	97.6	86.7	95.4	97.6	103.1	98.7
06	WOOD, PLASTICS & COMPOSITES	88.6	74.6	82.3	105.7	79.5	94.0	99.1	75.3	88.4	88.4	78.0	83.7	88.5	80.9	85.1	86.5	100.9	93.0
07	THERMAL & MOISTURE PROTECTION	110.5	71.8	96.7	97.3	74.5	89.2	96.8	72.0	87.9	101.4	80.7	94.0	110.3	75.6	97.9	109.3	97.1	105.0
08	OPENINGS	91.5	72.8	87.3	95.4	76.6	91.2	91.9	73.6	87.8	90.2	79.0	87.7	91.5	75.0	87.8	91.5	105.9	94.7
0920	Plaster & Gypsum Board	101.1	74.3	84.1	91.6	79.8	84.1	88.0	75.3	80.0	86.3	77.2	80.5	100.4	80.8	88.0	93.9	101.4	98.6
0950, 0980	Ceilings & Acoustic Treatment	93.8	74.3	82.9	80.9	79.8	80.2	80.9	75.3	77.8	83.4	77.2	79.9	93.8	80.8	86.5	93.8	101.4	98.0
0960	Flooring	98.4	71.3	91.6	99.7	76.8	94.0	95.7	76.8	90.9	94.9	71.3	89.0	98.4	72.1	91.8	98.4	101.0	99.0
0970, 0990	Wall Finishes & Painting/Coating	93.0	69.2	78.8	85.2	76.6	80.1	85.2	74.4	78.7	91.3	82.3	85.9	93.0	68.2	78.2	93.0	109.4	102.8
09	FINISHES	94.4	73.2	83.7	91.2	78.2	84.7	89.5	75.2	82.3	89.8	77.5	83.6	94.2	76.6	85.3	93.3	102.8	98.1
COVERS	DIVS. 10 - 14, 25, 28, 41, 43, 44, 46	100.0	88.7	97.8	100.0	88.8	97.8	100.0	88.1	97.7	100.0	89.4	97.9	100.0	90.0	98.1	100.0	96.7	99.4
21, 22, 23	FIRE SUPPRESSION, PLUMBING & HVAC	99.9	72.4	90.0	99.6	75.1	90.8	92.1	72.6	85.1	100.0	78.3	92.2	99.9	71.2	89.6	99.9	97.3	99.0
26, 27, 3370	ELECTRICAL, COMMUNICATIONS & UTIL.	83.5	78.6	81.3	100.7	82.7	92.9	100.2	80.5	91.7	94.6	80.0	88.3	84.6	79.3	82.3	94.3	99.9	96.7
MF2018	WEIGHTED AVERAGE	95.4	77.1	88.7	97.1	77.7	89.9	94.6	75.5	87.6	94.7	83.1	90.4	96.0	77.2	89.1	96.7	99.9	97.9

DIVISION		INDIANA																	
		INDIANAPOLIS			KOKOMO			LAFAYETTE			LAWRENCEBURG			MUNCIE			NEW ALBANY		
		461 - 462			469			479			470			473			471		
		MAT.	INST.	TOTAL	MAT.	INST.	TOTAL	MAT.	INST.	TOTAL	MAT.	INST.	TOTAL	MAT.	INST.	TOTAL	MAT.	INST.	TOTAL
015433	CONTRACTOR EQUIPMENT		91.2	91.2		92.4	92.4		81.1	81.1		98.2	98.2		91.2	91.2		89.3	89.3
0241, 31 - 34	SITE & INFRASTRUCTURE, DEMOLITION	92.9	96.6	95.3	86.7	85.4	85.8	75.0	84.3	81.1	75.9	97.4	89.9	81.2	85.4	83.9	72.5	86.3	81.5
0310	Concrete Forming & Accessories	93.8	84.8	86.8	96.3	72.8	78.0	91.7	77.1	80.3	90.6	73.0	77.0	90.9	74.1	77.9	90.4	71.7	75.9
0320	Concrete Reinforcing	99.9	87.5	96.5	90.7	80.3	87.8	91.6	80.2	88.4	91.2	73.5	86.3	101.3	79.2	95.2	92.2	75.7	87.6
0330	Cast-in-Place Concrete	86.8	87.1	86.9	88.5	77.1	84.4	97.0	74.9	89.1	90.7	69.6	83.2	101.8	71.7	91.1	93.6	69.5	85.1
03	CONCRETE	96.7	85.6	92.3	88.7	76.4	83.9	94.6	76.7	87.5	89.3	72.7	82.8	95.9	75.0	87.6	93.4	72.2	85.0
04	MASONRY	104.8	80.4	90.0	91.8	71.4	79.4	96.6	71.6	81.4	76.3	68.6	71.6	93.9	74.6	82.2	83.1	66.1	72.8
05	METALS	98.7	78.2	94.7	93.2	87.6	92.1	95.3	74.8	91.3	92.8	84.3	91.1	99.3	88.5	97.2	94.3	80.6	91.6
06	WOOD, PLASTICS & COMPOSITES	89.7	85.0	87.6	91.6	72.1	82.9	95.6	78.1	87.7	86.3	73.2	80.4	95.6	74.2	86.0	89.2	72.5	81.7
07	THERMAL & MOISTURE PROTECTION	105.6	81.2	96.9	109.7	71.8	96.2	96.7	74.2	88.7	102.2	71.4	91.2	99.5	73.1	90.1	90.9	68.9	83.1
08	OPENINGS	99.3	81.4	95.2	87.1	71.8	83.7	90.7	75.2	87.2	91.8	71.0	87.1	88.8	72.6	85.2	89.9	68.9	85.1
0920	Plaster & Gypsum Board	87.7	84.5	85.7	105.8	71.7	84.2	84.9	78.3	80.7	71.8	73.1	72.6	86.3	74.3	78.7	83.4	72.3	76.3
0950, 0980	Ceilings & Acoustic Treatment	101.3	84.5	91.9	94.2	71.7	81.6	76.3	78.3	77.4	90.2	73.1	80.6	80.9	74.3	77.2	83.4	72.3	77.2
0960	Flooring	102.3	84.0	97.7	101.5	82.5	96.7	94.7	76.8	90.2	68.9	76.8	70.9	95.5	71.3	89.5	92.5	48.4	81.5
0970, 0990	Wall Finishes & Painting/Coating	97.1	81.3	87.7	93.0	62.7	75.0	85.2	76.7	80.2	85.6	67.0	74.5	85.2	69.2	75.7	91.3	60.1	72.7
09	FINISHES	98.0	84.4	91.2	96.0	73.3	84.6	87.5	77.1	82.3	81.6	73.2	77.4	88.9	72.9	80.9	88.9	66.0	77.4
COVERS	DIVS. 10 - 14, 25, 28, 41, 43, 44, 46	100.0	92.4	98.5	100.0	88.5	97.8	100.0	88.3	97.7	100.0	83.6	96.8	100.0	87.8	97.6	100.0	83.4	96.8
21, 22, 23	FIRE SUPPRESSION, PLUMBING & HVAC	99.9	80.2	92.8	92.4	72.7	85.3	92.1	73.5	85.4	93.3	69.6	84.8	99.6	72.3	89.8	92.4	72.4	85.2
26, 27, 3370	ELECTRICAL, COMMUNICATIONS & UTIL.	98.5	87.6	93.8	85.7	71.6	79.6	100.0	74.3	88.8	92.7	68.4	82.1	90.4	70.0	81.6	94.0	69.2	83.2
MF2018	WEIGHTED AVERAGE	99.0	84.2	93.5	92.1	75.8	86.1	94.0	75.9	87.4	91.3	74.3	85.1	95.8	75.7	88.4	92.3	72.4	85.0

DIVISION		INDIANA									IOWA								
		SOUTH BEND			TERRE HAUTE			WASHINGTON			BURLINGTON			CARROLL			CEDAR RAPIDS		
		465 - 466			478			475			526			514			522 - 524		
		MAT.	INST.	TOTAL	MAT.	INST.	TOTAL	MAT.	INST.	TOTAL	MAT.	INST.	TOTAL	MAT.	INST.	TOTAL	MAT.	INST.	TOTAL
015433	CONTRACTOR EQUIPMENT		108.7	108.7		106.9	106.9		106.9	106.9		95.2	95.2		95.2	95.2		92.4	92.4
0241, 31 - 34	SITE & INFRASTRUCTURE, DEMOLITION	92.8	97.4	95.8	86.0	109.6	101.4	81.6	109.8	100.0	84.6	86.9	86.1	77.3	87.6	84.0	88.9	87.2	87.8
0310	Concrete Forming & Accessories	99.4	73.4	79.2	94.6	74.0	78.6	95.4	76.8	81.0	96.4	85.3	87.7	82.4	76.0	77.4	103.1	80.8	85.7
0320	Concrete Reinforcing	98.9	78.1	93.1	100.2	79.1	94.3	92.7	80.0	89.2	93.4	87.7	91.8	94.0	77.0	89.3	94.0	93.6	93.9
0330	Cast-in-Place Concrete	89.5	77.2	85.1	89.6	75.3	84.5	97.5	81.7	91.9	118.2	50.5	94.1	118.2	75.0	102.8	118.5	80.2	104.8
03	CONCRETE	99.7	77.0	90.7	98.0	75.9	89.3	101.3	79.5	92.7	103.3	74.2	91.8	101.9	76.7	92.0	103.8	83.6	95.8
04	MASONRY	92.1	70.9	79.2	95.2	70.9	80.5	87.6	73.6	79.1	107.6	64.8	81.6	108.8	65.2	82.3	113.3	77.8	91.7
05	METALS	101.3	98.2	100.7	92.5	84.3	90.9	85.6	85.2	85.5	88.0	93.9	89.1	88.0	90.6	88.5	90.8	98.6	92.3
06	WOOD, PLASTICS & COMPOSITES	96.7	72.6	85.9	91.3	73.8	83.4	91.6	76.0	84.6	94.1	89.0	91.8	76.3	80.2	78.0	103.1	80.4	92.9
07	THERMAL & MOISTURE PROTECTION	101.9	75.3	92.4	101.5	75.3	92.2	101.4	77.7	93.0	105.3	69.1	92.4	105.3	70.7	93.0	106.1	76.4	95.6
08	OPENINGS	98.4	72.1	92.5	90.6	72.1	86.5	88.0	75.9	85.3	91.1	86.8	90.2	95.2	76.3	90.9	95.6	82.6	92.6
0920	Plaster & Gypsum Board	91.0	71.8	78.9	86.3	72.8	77.7	86.4	75.2	79.3	100.0	89.1	93.0	95.6	80.0	85.7	106.5	80.3	89.9
0950, 0980	Ceilings & Acoustic Treatment	85.3	71.8	77.7	83.4	72.8	77.5	78.4	75.2	76.6	108.4	89.1	97.6	108.4	80.0	92.5	111.6	80.3	94.1
0960	Flooring	99.9	81.9	95.4	94.9	71.9	89.2	95.6	76.8	90.9	98.5	61.9	89.4	94.1	71.2	88.3	114.7	82.5	106.6
0970, 0990	Wall Finishes & Painting/Coating	99.1	77.8	86.4	91.3	73.8	80.8	91.3	80.7	85.0	93.6	75.2	82.6	93.6	75.2	82.6	95.8	67.4	78.9
09	FINISHES	93.6	75.1	84.3	89.8	73.3	81.5	88.9	77.0	82.9	98.9	80.9	89.9	96.0	75.4	85.7	105.6	79.6	92.5
COVERS	DIVS. 10 - 14, 25, 28, 41, 43, 44, 46	100.0	90.7	98.2	100.0	89.9	98.0	100.0	88.8	97.8	100.0	92.3	98.5	100.0	88.5	97.8	100.0	91.6	98.4
21, 22, 23	FIRE SUPPRESSION, PLUMBING & HVAC	99.8	71.6	89.7	100.0	73.7	90.5	92.4	75.4	86.4	92.5	75.3	86.4	92.5	69.9	84.4	100.1	79.6	92.7
26, 27, 3370	ELECTRICAL, COMMUNICATIONS & UTIL.	99.7	82.1	92.1	93.9	78.9	87.4	94.1	77.5	86.9	96.3	64.3	82.4	96.7	68.5	84.4	95.1	74.1	86.0
MF2018	WEIGHTED AVERAGE	99.1	79.4	91.9	95.4	78.7	89.2	92.0	80.4	87.7	94.9	76.9	88.3	94.6	75.2	87.5	98.4	82.0	92.4

DIVISION		IOWA																	
		COUNCIL BLUFFS			CRESTON			DAVENPORT			DECORAH			DES MOINES			DUBUQUE		
		515			508			527 - 528			521			500 - 503,509			520		
		MAT.	INST.	TOTAL	MAT.	INST.	TOTAL	MAT.	INST.	TOTAL	MAT.	INST.	TOTAL	MAT.	INST.	TOTAL	MAT.	INST.	TOTAL
015433	CONTRACTOR EQUIPMENT		91.9	91.9		95.2	95.2		95.2	95.2		95.2	95.2		101.2	101.2		91.4	91.4
0241, 31 - 34	SITE & INFRASTRUCTURE, DEMOLITION	89.6	84.6	86.3	81.4	88.5	86.0	88.5	90.4	89.8	83.6	86.7	85.6	88.0	99.2	95.3	87.1	84.8	85.6
0310	Concrete Forming & Accessories	81.5	72.3	74.3	81.0	78.5	79.1	102.4	94.4	96.2	93.6	65.1	71.5	102.1	89.1	92.0	83.2	78.2	79.3
0320	Concrete Reinforcing	95.9	82.4	92.2	89.3	77.1	85.9	94.0	94.1	94.0	93.4	76.5	88.7	98.4	99.0	98.5	92.7	76.1	88.1
0330	Cast-in-Place Concrete	123.2	84.1	109.3	121.3	78.1	106.0	114.1	91.4	106.0	115.0	69.5	98.8	103.4	92.8	99.6	116.0	79.6	103.1
03	CONCRETE	105.3	79.2	95.0	101.8	79.0	92.8	101.9	94.0	98.8	101.4	69.8	88.9	101.7	92.6	98.1	100.1	79.2	91.8
04	MASONRY	113.1	74.1	89.4	112.1	71.9	87.7	108.4	89.4	96.9	129.7	62.3	88.8	98.7	88.4	92.5	114.3	65.8	84.9
05	METALS	94.4	93.9	94.3	93.1	91.1	92.7	90.8	104.0	93.4	88.1	89.5	88.4	99.2	101.3	99.6	89.0	90.6	89.3
06	WOOD, PLASTICS & COMPOSITES	74.6	70.6	72.8	74.5	80.2	77.1	103.1	94.1	99.1	90.2	64.4	78.6	99.4	88.2	94.4	77.0	79.0	77.9
07	THERMAL & MOISTURE PROTECTION	105.4	71.4	93.3	110.0	73.7	97.1	105.7	88.0	99.4	105.4	62.7	90.2	102.4	87.1	96.9	105.6	72.2	93.7
08	OPENINGS	94.8	77.0	90.8	105.5	77.9	99.3	95.6	95.8	95.6	93.9	70.6	88.6	97.3	93.8	96.5	94.8	79.1	91.3
0920	Plaster & Gypsum Board	95.6	70.3	79.5	95.9	80.0	85.8	106.5	94.4	98.8	99.0	63.7	76.6	90.2	88.0	88.8	95.6	79.0	85.1
0950, 0980	Ceilings & Acoustic Treatment	108.4	70.3	87.0	99.7	80.0	88.7	111.6	94.4	101.9	108.4	63.7	83.3	104.2	88.0	95.1	108.4	79.0	91.9
0960	Flooring	93.4	80.1	90.0	90.4	61.9	83.2	100.4	85.0	96.5	98.6	61.9	89.4	102.4	89.8	99.3	107.5	67.0	97.4
0970, 0990	Wall Finishes & Painting/Coating	90.8	57.5	70.9	87.4	75.2	80.1	93.6	86.8	89.6	93.6	75.2	82.6	99.1	82.1	89.0	95.4	74.0	82.6
09	FINISHES	96.6	71.6	84.0	91.9	75.2	83.5	101.2	91.9	96.5	98.8	65.3	82.0	99.2	88.3	93.7	101.0	75.7	88.3
COVERS	DIVS. 10 - 14, 25, 28, 41, 43, 44, 46	100.0	89.5	98.0	100.0	90.7	98.2	100.0	95.6	99.1	100.0	88.1	97.7	100.0	94.8	99.0	100.0	90.6	98.2
21, 22, 23	FIRE SUPPRESSION, PLUMBING & HVAC	100.1	75.6	91.3	92.5	71.7	85.0	100.1	90.1	96.5	92.5	66.9	83.3	99.9	85.0	94.6	100.1	72.0	90.0
26, 27, 3370	ELECTRICAL, COMMUNICATIONS & UTIL.	97.8	81.6	90.8	90.2	68.5	80.8	92.7	81.5	87.8	95.1	42.1	72.1	99.5	89.6	95.2	97.0	71.2	85.8
MF2018	WEIGHTED AVERAGE	98.7	79.0	91.4	96.0	76.8	88.9	97.4	91.3	95.1	95.6	67.4	85.2	99.4	90.8	96.2	97.1	76.4	89.5

DIVISION		IOWA																	
		FORT DODGE			MASON CITY			OTTUMWA			SHENANDOAH			SIBLEY			SIOUX CITY		
		505			504			525			516			512			510 - 511		
		MAT.	INST.	TOTAL	MAT.	INST.	TOTAL	MAT.	INST.	TOTAL	MAT.	INST.	TOTAL	MAT.	INST.	TOTAL	MAT.	INST.	TOTAL
015433	CONTRACTOR EQUIPMENT		95.2	95.2		95.2	95.2		91.4	91.4		91.9	91.9		95.2	95.2		95.2	95.2
0241, 31 - 34	SITE & INFRASTRUCTURE, DEMOLITION	86.0	85.7	85.8	86.1	86.6	86.4	83.9	82.4	83.0	85.1	84.2	84.5	91.2	86.6	88.2	96.2	88.6	91.3
0310	Concrete Forming & Accessories	81.6	70.7	73.1	86.3	64.7	69.5	91.2	79.0	81.7	83.5	70.0	73.0	84.1	34.5	45.6	103.1	70.9	78.0
0320	Concrete Reinforcing	89.3	76.4	85.7	89.2	76.5	85.6	93.4	87.9	91.8	95.9	77.0	90.7	95.9	76.4	90.5	94.0	92.2	93.5
0330	Cast-in-Place Concrete	113.8	38.9	87.2	113.8	65.2	96.6	118.9	58.8	97.6	119.1	75.6	103.7	116.7	51.1	93.4	117.4	82.8	105.1
03	CONCRETE	97.7	61.7	83.5	98.1	68.1	86.2	102.8	74.4	91.6	103.1	74.3	91.8	102.2	49.6	81.4	103.2	79.8	94.0
04	MASONRY	111.0	46.8	72.0	124.8	61.2	86.2	110.2	49.8	73.5	112.5	67.1	85.0	133.1	47.0	80.8	106.8	64.3	81.0
05	METALS	93.2	89.2	92.5	93.3	89.5	92.5	87.9	95.1	89.3	93.4	91.3	93.0	88.2	88.7	88.3	90.8	97.6	92.1
06	WOOD, PLASTICS & COMPOSITES	75.1	80.2	77.4	80.8	64.4	73.5	86.7	88.8	87.7	77.0	71.2	74.4	78.1	31.2	57.1	103.1	70.1	88.3
07	THERMAL & MOISTURE PROTECTION	109.5	58.5	91.3	109.2	63.3	92.8	105.8	63.1	90.6	104.9	65.8	90.9	105.1	49.6	85.3	105.7	67.2	92.0
08	OPENINGS	99.5	68.8	92.6	91.8	70.6	87.0	95.2	84.1	92.7	87.1	69.3	83.1	92.2	41.8	80.8	95.6	76.1	91.2
0920	Plaster & Gypsum Board	95.9	80.0	85.8	95.9	63.7	75.5	96.1	89.1	91.6	95.6	70.9	80.0	95.6	29.5	53.7	106.5	69.6	83.1
0950, 0980	Ceilings & Acoustic Treatment	99.7	80.0	88.7	99.7	63.7	79.5	108.4	89.1	97.6	108.4	70.9	87.4	108.4	29.5	64.2	111.6	69.6	88.0
0960	Flooring	91.8	61.9	84.3	93.5	61.9	85.6	109.9	61.9	97.9	93.9	66.2	87.0	94.8	61.9	86.6	100.5	67.0	92.1
0970, 0990	Wall Finishes & Painting/Coating	87.4	72.2	78.3	87.4	75.2	80.1	95.4	75.2	83.3	90.8	75.2	81.5	93.6	74.3	82.1	93.6	84.0	87.9
09	FINISHES	93.2	70.4	81.8	93.7	65.0	79.3	101.9	76.5	89.1	96.6	69.6	83.0	98.2	41.9	69.9	102.2	71.0	86.5
COVERS	DIVS. 10 - 14, 25, 28, 41, 43, 44, 46	100.0	84.7	97.0	100.0	87.7	97.6	100.0	86.2	97.3	100.0	87.4	97.6	100.0	79.5	96.0	100.0	89.2	97.9
21, 22, 23	FIRE SUPPRESSION, PLUMBING & HVAC	92.5	64.2	82.3	92.5	69.8	84.3	92.5	65.7	82.9	92.5	75.4	86.4	92.5	64.2	82.4	100.1	74.4	90.9
26, 27, 3370	ELECTRICAL, COMMUNICATIONS & UTIL.	93.3	61.8	79.6	92.9	42.1	70.9	96.2	63.2	81.9	95.1	69.8	84.1	95.1	42.0	72.1	95.1	68.5	83.6
MF2018	WEIGHTED AVERAGE	95.5	67.4	85.1	95.4	67.7	85.2	95.4	71.9	86.8	95.5	74.8	87.9	95.7	57.3	81.6	98.0	76.4	90.1

DIVISION		IOWA						KANSAS											
		SPENCER			WATERLOO			BELLEVILLE			COLBY			DODGE CITY			EMPORIA		
		513			506 - 507			669			677			678			668		
		MAT.	INST.	TOTAL	MAT.	INST.	TOTAL	MAT.	INST.	TOTAL	MAT.	INST.	TOTAL	MAT.	INST.	TOTAL	MAT.	INST.	TOTAL
015433	CONTRACTOR EQUIPMENT		95.2	95.2		95.2	95.2		99.6	99.6		99.6	99.6		99.6	99.6		98.1	98.1
0241, 31 - 34	SITE & INFRASTRUCTURE, DEMOLITION	91.3	85.5	87.5	93.6	88.3	90.1	97.4	87.2	90.7	92.1	87.6	89.2	97.3	87.9	91.2	92.0	85.0	87.4
0310	Concrete Forming & Accessories	91.0	34.2	46.9	99.5	66.0	73.5	97.2	50.1	60.6	103.9	55.7	66.4	95.7	57.3	65.9	87.2	63.6	68.8
0320	Concrete Reinforcing	95.9	76.3	90.5	89.9	76.4	86.2	101.9	93.9	99.7	110.5	93.9	105.9	107.8	93.7	103.9	100.5	94.0	98.7
0330	Cast-in-Place Concrete	116.7	60.1	96.6	122.0	80.5	107.2	106.0	77.3	95.8	101.7	79.5	93.8	103.5	83.6	96.4	102.5	79.6	94.3
03	CONCRETE	102.8	52.5	82.9	103.8	74.1	92.1	103.7	68.8	89.9	103.7	72.1	91.2	103.8	74.2	92.1	97.7	75.7	89.0
04	MASONRY	133.1	47.0	80.8	111.9	71.8	87.6	105.0	54.5	74.3	89.9	58.2	70.6	97.4	56.2	72.4	111.6	59.5	79.9
05	METALS	88.2	88.4	88.2	96.0	91.3	95.1	96.9	94.7	96.4	97.2	95.4	96.8	98.5	95.1	97.9	96.5	95.6	96.3
06	WOOD, PLASTICS & COMPOSITES	86.5	31.2	61.7	98.3	61.9	82.0	90.6	46.6	70.8	95.6	52.2	76.1	85.4	52.9	70.8	79.1	62.5	71.7
07	THERMAL & MOISTURE PROTECTION	105.9	50.1	86.0	109.5	73.0	96.5	99.9	57.3	84.7	104.3	59.4	88.3	104.3	63.1	89.6	98.3	67.6	87.4
08	OPENINGS	102.5	41.8	88.8	92.1	70.1	87.1	89.3	57.1	82.0	95.4	60.1	87.5	95.4	60.6	87.5	87.5	67.8	83.1
0920	Plaster & Gypsum Board	96.1	29.5	53.8	104.5	61.1	77.0	79.9	45.3	57.9	88.5	51.0	64.7	81.8	51.8	62.8	76.3	61.7	67.1
0950, 0980	Ceilings & Acoustic Treatment	108.4	29.5	64.2	102.4	61.1	79.3	87.3	45.3	63.7	83.6	51.0	65.3	83.6	51.8	65.8	87.3	61.7	73.0
0960	Flooring	96.9	61.9	88.1	98.0	75.0	92.3	92.7	61.2	84.8	84.3	61.2	78.5	81.7	62.4	76.9	88.9	61.2	82.0
0970, 0990	Wall Finishes & Painting/Coating	93.6	50.8	68.1	87.4	78.9	82.3	92.7	91.5	92.0	97.3	91.5	93.9	97.3	91.5	93.9	92.7	91.5	92.0
09	FINISHES	98.9	38.3	68.5	97.1	68.0	82.5	88.7	55.2	71.9	86.2	59.3	72.7	84.6	60.5	72.5	86.2	65.4	75.8
COVERS	DIVS. 10 - 14, 25, 28, 41, 43, 44, 46	100.0	79.5	96.0	100.0	89.3	97.9	100.0	75.0	95.2	100.0	76.8	95.5	100.0	80.5	96.2	100.0	76.6	95.5
21, 22, 23	FIRE SUPPRESSION, PLUMBING & HVAC	92.5	64.2	82.4	100.0	76.4	91.5	92.2	64.1	82.2	92.6	63.9	82.3	100.2	72.0	90.1	92.2	66.1	82.8
26, 27, 3370	ELECTRICAL, COMMUNICATIONS & UTIL.	95.9	42.0	72.6	91.2	59.3	77.4	97.0	55.8	79.1	99.0	60.4	82.3	97.5	65.8	83.8	95.5	59.6	79.9
MF2018	WEIGHTED AVERAGE	96.9	57.1	82.3	98.3	74.3	89.5	96.0	65.7	84.9	96.2	68.1	85.9	98.2	71.1	88.2	94.7	70.3	85.7

DIVISION		KANSAS																	
		FORT SCOTT			HAYS			HUTCHINSON			INDEPENDENCE			KANSAS CITY			LIBERAL		
		667			676			675			673			660 - 662			679		
		MAT.	INST.	TOTAL	MAT.	INST.	TOTAL	MAT.	INST.	TOTAL	MAT.	INST.	TOTAL	MAT.	INST.	TOTAL	MAT.	INST.	TOTAL
015433	CONTRACTOR EQUIPMENT		98.8	98.8		99.6	99.6		99.6	99.6		99.6	99.6		96.7	96.7		99.6	99.6
0241, 31 - 34	SITE & INFRASTRUCTURE, DEMOLITION	89.5	85.1	86.6	95.0	87.5	90.1	80.8	87.8	85.4	94.5	87.8	90.1	89.8	86.5	87.7	94.7	87.4	90.0
0310	Concrete Forming & Accessories	106.7	75.1	82.1	100.9	54.4	64.7	89.1	51.6	60.0	114.0	61.6	73.3	102.7	98.9	99.7	96.1	53.6	63.1
0320	Concrete Reinforcing	99.8	90.4	97.2	107.8	93.9	103.9	107.8	93.9	103.9	107.1	90.4	102.5	96.9	101.2	98.1	109.3	93.6	105.0
0330	Cast-in-Place Concrete	95.0	75.3	88.0	80.2	77.6	79.3	74.3	79.4	76.1	103.9	79.5	95.3	81.4	96.1	86.6	80.2	76.4	78.9
03	CONCRETE	94.9	78.8	88.5	96.4	70.8	86.3	83.9	70.2	78.5	105.4	74.1	93.1	88.2	98.7	92.3	97.7	70.0	86.8
04	MASONRY	115.0	50.6	75.9	96.4	54.7	71.0	90.3	58.1	70.8	87.1	58.1	69.5	113.3	96.8	103.3	95.2	48.3	66.7
05	METALS	96.5	94.1	96.0	96.6	95.4	96.4	96.4	95.0	96.1	96.3	94.2	95.9	106.4	104.4	106.0	97.0	94.7	96.5
06	WOOD, PLASTICS & COMPOSITES	103.9	82.1	94.2	91.9	52.2	74.1	78.6	46.8	64.3	109.0	59.8	87.0	99.2	98.8	99.0	86.0	52.2	70.8
07	THERMAL & MOISTURE PROTECTION	99.3	65.3	87.2	104.6	57.9	88.0	103.2	58.5	87.2	104.5	67.2	91.2	99.0	97.2	98.4	104.7	55.4	87.1
08	OPENINGS	87.5	77.8	85.4	95.4	60.1	87.4	95.4	57.2	86.7	93.5	63.6	86.8	88.3	97.3	90.3	95.4	60.1	87.5
0920	Plaster & Gypsum Board	83.1	81.9	82.3	86.1	51.0	63.9	80.8	45.5	58.4	97.7	58.9	73.1	77.2	99.1	91.1	82.3	51.0	62.4
0950, 0980	Ceilings & Acoustic Treatment	87.3	81.9	84.3	83.6	51.0	65.3	83.6	45.5	62.2	83.6	58.9	69.8	87.3	99.1	93.9	83.6	51.0	65.3
0960	Flooring	102.2	59.9	91.6	83.5	61.2	77.9	79.6	61.2	75.0	87.3	59.9	80.4	80.8	95.6	84.5	81.8	61.2	76.7
0970, 0990	Wall Finishes & Painting/Coating	94.2	68.8	79.1	97.3	91.5	93.9	97.3	91.5	93.9	97.3	91.5	93.9	100.6	105.3	103.4	97.3	91.5	93.9
09	FINISHES	91.3	72.8	82.0	86.0	58.5	72.2	82.7	56.2	69.4	88.4	64.1	76.2	86.2	99.0	92.6	85.2	58.0	71.5
COVERS	DIVS. 10 - 14, 25, 28, 41, 43, 44, 46	100.0	77.5	95.6	100.0	75.6	95.3	100.0	76.2	95.4	100.0	77.6	95.7	100.0	96.1	99.2	100.0	75.0	95.2
21, 22, 23	FIRE SUPPRESSION, PLUMBING & HVAC	92.2	60.6	80.9	92.6	61.6	81.5	92.6	63.9	82.3	92.6	63.3	82.1	99.7	103.5	101.1	92.6	62.3	81.8
26, 27, 3370	ELECTRICAL, COMMUNICATIONS & UTIL.	95.1	60.4	80.1	98.5	60.4	82.0	96.2	54.3	78.0	97.2	64.8	83.2	97.6	92.3	95.3	97.5	60.4	81.5
MF2018	WEIGHTED AVERAGE	95.0	70.2	85.9	95.5	66.9	84.9	92.7	66.3	83.0	96.1	69.8	86.5	97.9	98.0	98.0	95.4	66.1	84.6

DIVISION		KANSAS									KENTUCKY								
		SALINA			TOPEKA			WICHITA			ASHLAND			BOWLING GREEN			CAMPTON		
		674			664 - 666			670 - 672			411 - 412			421 - 422			413 - 414		
		MAT.	INST.	TOTAL	MAT.	INST.	TOTAL	MAT.	INST.	TOTAL	MAT.	INST.	TOTAL	MAT.	INST.	TOTAL	MAT.	INST.	TOTAL
015433	CONTRACTOR EQUIPMENT		99.6	99.6		104.6	104.6		104.7	104.7		95.4	95.4		89.3	89.3		94.8	94.8
0241, 31 - 34	SITE & INFRASTRUCTURE, DEMOLITION	90.5	87.5	88.6	93.0	96.6	95.4	89.7	97.0	94.5	98.5	76.1	83.9	75.8	86.5	82.8	79.5	86.8	84.2
0310	Concrete Forming & Accessories	91.5	58.1	65.6	98.8	64.2	71.9	101.0	55.6	65.7	85.3	81.2	82.1	86.4	77.7	79.6	88.1	73.8	77.0
0320	Concrete Reinforcing	107.1	93.8	103.4	98.5	95.2	97.6	99.5	97.4	98.9	92.9	86.0	91.0	90.8	74.7	86.4	91.7	83.5	89.4
0330	Cast-in-Place Concrete	89.8	80.2	86.4	90.2	85.5	88.5	84.1	76.4	81.3	85.2	86.4	85.6	84.5	65.5	77.8	94.3	62.8	83.1
03	CONCRETE	94.1	73.4	85.9	92.3	78.0	86.7	90.2	71.3	82.8	89.6	85.2	87.8	88.3	73.4	82.5	91.7	72.2	84.0
04	MASONRY	109.5	51.8	74.4	107.6	61.2	79.4	88.0	52.4	66.4	94.2	82.9	87.3	96.2	65.4	77.5	93.0	49.3	66.4
05	METALS	98.3	95.8	97.8	101.0	94.9	99.8	100.8	94.8	99.6	93.7	102.9	95.5	95.0	83.4	92.7	94.3	86.6	92.8
06	WOOD, PLASTICS & COMPOSITES	80.7	57.1	70.1	95.5	62.9	80.9	98.7	52.8	78.1	71.4	79.6	75.1	82.8	80.2	81.7	80.8	80.2	80.5
07	THERMAL & MOISTURE PROTECTION	103.7	58.7	87.7	101.9	79.7	94.0	101.6	60.3	86.9	93.3	80.0	88.6	90.9	73.4	84.6	101.5	60.9	87.0
08	OPENINGS	95.4	63.3	88.1	98.0	70.5	91.8	98.0	62.0	89.9	89.2	81.0	87.3	89.9	75.7	86.7	91.1	79.2	88.4
0920	Plaster & Gypsum Board	80.8	56.2	65.2	89.1	61.7	71.7	87.6	51.3	64.6	59.4	79.4	72.1	78.6	80.2	79.6	78.6	79.4	79.1
0950, 0980	Ceilings & Acoustic Treatment	83.6	56.2	68.2	106.8	61.7	81.5	101.8	51.3	73.5	80.9	79.4	80.0	83.4	80.2	81.6	83.4	79.4	81.2
0960	Flooring	80.6	62.4	76.0	95.1	62.4	86.9	91.2	66.4	85.0	73.1	72.8	73.1	90.8	56.6	82.3	92.9	57.6	84.1
0970, 0990	Wall Finishes & Painting/Coating	97.3	91.5	93.9	99.1	91.5	94.6	99.1	99.6	99.4	92.7	80.3	85.3	91.3	62.4	74.1	91.3	47.9	65.4
09	FINISHES	83.6	61.4	72.4	98.0	65.5	81.7	95.3	60.8	78.0	77.6	79.5	78.6	87.6	72.3	79.9	88.4	68.5	78.4
COVERS	DIVS. 10 - 14, 25, 28, 41, 43, 44, 46	100.0	85.1	97.1	100.0	81.2	96.4	100.0	85.7	97.2	100.0	78.8	95.9	100.0	88.3	97.7	100.0	86.6	97.4
21, 22, 23	FIRE SUPPRESSION, PLUMBING & HVAC	100.2	65.5	87.7	99.9	70.3	89.3	99.9	68.2	88.5	92.1	76.4	86.5	100.0	73.5	90.5	92.5	68.7	83.9
26, 27, 3370	ELECTRICAL, COMMUNICATIONS & UTIL.	97.4	71.6	86.2	99.5	66.5	85.2	99.5	71.6	87.4	91.8	78.6	86.1	94.3	70.7	84.1	93.0	78.5	86.7
MF2018	WEIGHTED AVERAGE	97.2	70.3	87.3	99.0	74.1	89.9	97.7	71.2	88.0	91.5	81.8	87.9	94.0	74.7	86.9	92.9	72.6	85.4

DIVISION		KENTUCKY																	
		CORBIN			COVINGTON			ELIZABETHTOWN			FRANKFORT			HAZARD			HENDERSON		
		407 - 409			410			427			406			417 - 418			424		
		MAT.	INST.	TOTAL	MAT.	INST.	TOTAL	MAT.	INST.	TOTAL	MAT.	INST.	TOTAL	MAT.	INST.	TOTAL	MAT.	INST.	TOTAL
015433	CONTRACTOR EQUIPMENT		94.8	94.8		98.2	98.2		89.3	89.3		99.9	99.9		94.8	94.8		106.9	106.9
0241, 31 - 34	SITE & INFRASTRUCTURE, DEMOLITION	81.6	87.2	85.3	76.9	96.8	89.9	68.3	85.8	79.7	81.9	97.9	92.3	77.9	87.7	84.3	73.8	108.2	96.2
0310	Concrete Forming & Accessories	85.0	68.9	72.5	83.5	64.3	68.6	80.8	65.7	69.1	101.8	71.5	78.2	84.2	74.6	76.8	91.3	69.8	74.6
0320	Concrete Reinforcing	89.5	82.8	87.6	90.8	70.5	85.2	91.3	75.1	86.8	98.1	75.4	91.9	92.2	83.0	89.6	90.9	75.7	86.7
0330	Cast-in-Place Concrete	87.6	66.6	80.2	90.2	74.7	84.7	76.4	62.5	71.5	87.8	71.0	81.9	90.7	64.2	81.3	74.7	77.3	75.6
03	CONCRETE	83.6	71.2	78.7	89.9	70.1	82.1	82.1	67.1	76.2	89.4	72.5	82.8	89.2	73.0	82.8	85.7	74.1	81.1
04	MASONRY	100.0	54.0	72.1	107.0	64.8	81.4	80.2	55.7	65.4	96.8	66.9	78.7	91.4	51.1	66.9	99.3	70.9	82.1
05	METALS	97.7	85.7	95.3	92.8	84.7	91.2	94.2	83.0	92.0	100.8	81.7	97.0	94.3	86.5	92.8	85.3	83.6	85.0
06	WOOD, PLASTICS & COMPOSITES	71.8	70.5	71.2	77.3	62.1	70.5	76.3	67.2	72.2	98.6	70.5	86.0	76.7	80.2	78.3	85.6	68.9	78.1
07	THERMAL & MOISTURE PROTECTION	103.8	62.5	89.1	102.4	65.4	89.2	90.4	61.6	80.1	102.7	69.1	90.7	101.3	62.5	87.5	100.8	74.3	91.4
08	OPENINGS	91.4	63.9	85.2	92.7	66.7	86.8	89.9	66.2	84.5	98.4	72.5	92.6	91.4	79.1	88.6	88.4	71.1	84.5
0920	Plaster & Gypsum Board	88.3	69.4	76.3	67.9	61.6	63.9	76.9	66.8	70.5	96.6	69.4	79.3	76.9	79.4	78.5	81.8	67.8	72.9
0950, 0980	Ceilings & Acoustic Treatment	73.2	69.4	71.1	90.2	61.6	74.2	83.4	66.8	74.1	94.1	69.4	80.2	83.4	79.4	81.2	78.4	67.8	72.4
0960	Flooring	89.0	57.6	81.1	66.9	74.8	68.9	88.7	66.1	83.0	102.2	70.4	94.2	91.5	57.6	83.0	94.2	68.1	87.6
0970, 0990	Wall Finishes & Painting/Coating	87.7	55.1	68.2	85.6	63.2	72.2	91.3	60.5	73.0	99.1	81.5	88.6	91.3	47.9	65.4	91.3	77.1	82.8
09	FINISHES	83.8	65.4	74.6	80.7	65.6	73.1	86.5	64.6	75.5	97.4	72.3	84.8	87.6	69.0	78.3	87.3	70.3	78.7
COVERS	DIVS. 10 - 14, 25, 28, 41, 43, 44, 46	100.0	87.9	97.7	100.0	86.8	97.4	100.0	85.2	97.1	100.0	89.7	98.0	100.0	83.1	96.7	100.0	50.2	90.3
21, 22, 23	FIRE SUPPRESSION, PLUMBING & HVAC	92.8	66.7	83.4	93.3	68.3	84.3	92.7	70.1	84.6	100.1	72.8	90.3	92.5	69.7	84.3	92.7	71.3	85.0
26, 27, 3370	ELECTRICAL, COMMUNICATIONS & UTIL.	93.3	78.5	86.9	94.0	64.5	81.2	92.8	69.3	82.7	100.6	69.3	87.1	93.0	78.5	86.7	94.0	69.3	83.3
MF2018	WEIGHTED AVERAGE	92.7	71.4	84.9	92.6	71.4	84.8	90.3	69.9	82.8	98.2	74.8	89.6	92.4	73.1	85.3	90.2	74.6	84.5

	DIVISION	KENTUCKY																	
		LEXINGTON 403 - 405			LOUISVILLE 400 - 402			OWENSBORO 423			PADUCAH 420			PIKEVILLE 415 - 416			SOMERSET 425 - 426		
		MAT.	INST.	TOTAL	MAT.	INST.	TOTAL	MAT.	INST.	TOTAL	MAT.	INST.	TOTAL	MAT.	INST.	TOTAL	MAT.	INST.	TOTAL
015433	CONTRACTOR EQUIPMENT		94.8	94.8		96.9	96.9		106.9	106.9		106.9	106.9		95.4	95.4		94.8	94.8
0241, 31 - 34	SITE & INFRASTRUCTURE, DEMOLITION	86.9	89.7	88.7	80.5	98.5	92.2	84.3	109.7	100.8	75.1	108.4	96.8	105.9	75.4	86.0	72.6	87.2	82.1
0310	Concrete Forming & Accessories	98.4	70.7	76.9	98.9	78.7	83.2	89.5	73.9	77.4	87.3	73.6	76.6	94.9	77.5	81.4	85.3	69.5	73.0
0320	Concrete Reinforcing	98.2	84.9	94.5	97.5	85.0	94.1	90.9	75.2	86.6	91.5	74.0	86.6	93.4	85.9	91.3	91.3	83.0	89.0
0330	Cast-in-Place Concrete	89.7	79.9	86.2	84.4	70.7	79.5	87.1	80.0	84.6	79.6	74.3	77.7	93.7	81.7	89.4	74.7	80.4	76.7
03	CONCRETE	87.8	77.1	83.6	87.6	77.3	83.5	94.8	76.9	87.7	89.1	74.5	83.3	100.0	81.9	92.8	78.8	76.3	77.8
04	MASONRY	98.6	67.4	79.7	96.4	69.4	80.0	91.7	75.2	81.7	94.9	71.3	80.6	91.1	75.0	81.3	86.4	57.0	68.5
05	METALS	100.6	88.0	98.1	101.6	86.0	98.5	86.8	85.5	86.5	83.8	84.0	83.9	93.6	102.7	95.4	94.2	86.3	92.7
06	WOOD, PLASTICS & COMPOSITES	90.1	68.8	80.6	94.6	80.6	88.3	83.0	72.9	78.5	80.1	74.0	77.4	83.8	79.6	81.9	77.4	70.5	74.3
07	THERMAL & MOISTURE PROTECTION	104.2	74.3	93.5	100.4	74.3	91.1	101.4	77.1	92.7	100.9	74.2	91.4	94.1	72.3	86.3	100.8	64.6	87.9
08	OPENINGS	91.5	72.8	87.3	98.2	76.8	93.4	88.4	74.7	85.3	87.7	73.5	84.5	89.8	78.0	87.1	90.6	69.9	85.9
0920	Plaster & Gypsum Board	100.4	67.7	79.7	96.6	80.2	86.2	80.2	71.9	74.9	79.2	73.0	75.3	64.0	79.4	73.8	76.9	69.4	72.2
0950, 0980	Ceilings & Acoustic Treatment	76.4	67.7	71.6	94.1	80.2	86.3	78.4	71.9	74.8	78.4	73.0	75.4	80.9	79.4	80.0	83.4	69.4	75.6
0960	Flooring	93.0	59.9	84.7	93.8	58.2	84.9	93.7	56.6	84.4	92.9	68.1	86.7	76.5	57.6	71.8	91.7	57.6	83.2
0970, 0990	Wall Finishes & Painting/Coating	87.7	75.1	80.2	94.9	66.1	77.8	91.3	84.6	87.3	91.3	65.0	75.6	92.7	81.5	86.0	91.3	60.5	73.0
09	FINISHES	87.6	68.4	78.0	94.3	73.5	83.9	87.3	71.3	79.3	86.7	71.7	79.1	79.9	74.5	77.2	87.2	66.1	76.6
COVERS	DIVS. 10 - 14, 25, 28, 41, 43, 44, 46	100.0	89.5	98.0	100.0	89.5	98.0	100.0	90.4	98.1	100.0	81.4	96.4	100.0	43.4	89.0	100.0	88.1	97.7
21, 22, 23	FIRE SUPPRESSION, PLUMBING & HVAC	100.3	72.6	90.4	100.0	76.7	91.6	100.0	73.5	90.5	92.7	70.3	84.7	92.1	73.9	85.6	92.7	66.5	83.3
26, 27, 3370	ELECTRICAL, COMMUNICATIONS & UTIL.	94.7	70.5	84.2	100.6	73.6	88.9	94.0	68.3	82.9	95.3	68.8	83.8	93.4	78.6	87.0	93.2	78.5	86.8
MF2018	WEIGHTED AVERAGE	96.2	75.2	88.5	97.7	78.2	90.5	93.1	77.7	87.5	90.1	75.8	84.9	93.3	77.8	87.6	90.8	72.8	84.1

	DIVISION	LOUISIANA																	
		ALEXANDRIA 713 - 714			BATON ROUGE 707 - 708			HAMMOND 704			LAFAYETTE 705			LAKE CHARLES 706			MONROE 712		
		MAT.	INST.	TOTAL	MAT.	INST.	TOTAL	MAT.	INST.	TOTAL	MAT.	INST.	TOTAL	MAT.	INST.	TOTAL	MAT.	INST.	TOTAL
015433	CONTRACTOR EQUIPMENT		88.4	88.4		95.2	95.2		87.3	87.3		87.3	87.3		86.8	86.8		88.4	88.4
0241, 31 - 34	SITE & INFRASTRUCTURE, DEMOLITION	99.8	84.9	90.1	102.2	96.3	98.3	96.9	84.4	88.8	101.2	84.6	90.4	101.8	84.0	90.2	99.8	84.8	90.0
0310	Concrete Forming & Accessories	81.9	57.8	63.1	99.2	67.6	74.7	78.3	51.6	57.5	96.9	61.9	69.7	97.0	65.2	72.3	81.4	57.3	62.7
0320	Concrete Reinforcing	97.3	50.7	84.4	98.7	50.8	85.5	93.7	48.9	81.3	95.1	48.9	82.3	95.1	50.7	82.8	96.2	50.7	83.6
0330	Cast-in-Place Concrete	78.2	64.5	73.3	87.8	67.7	80.6	83.1	63.3	76.0	82.7	64.9	76.4	87.0	65.8	79.5	78.2	63.8	73.1
03	CONCRETE	80.8	59.8	72.5	88.3	65.4	79.3	83.3	56.2	72.6	85.0	61.5	75.7	86.8	63.6	77.6	80.5	59.4	72.2
04	MASONRY	114.1	60.7	81.6	84.5	58.6	68.8	89.0	58.5	70.5	88.9	61.5	72.3	88.6	62.9	73.0	108.8	59.5	78.8
05	METALS	99.1	70.3	93.4	101.8	72.8	96.1	89.3	68.4	85.2	88.6	68.5	84.6	88.6	69.2	84.8	99.0	70.3	93.3
06	WOOD, PLASTICS & COMPOSITES	82.1	56.6	70.7	94.5	70.6	83.8	73.6	49.4	62.7	97.8	61.8	81.6	95.6	65.4	82.1	81.3	56.6	70.2
07	THERMAL & MOISTURE PROTECTION	101.9	62.2	87.7	97.6	64.7	85.9	96.9	59.6	83.6	97.4	63.1	85.2	97.3	64.1	85.5	101.8	61.7	87.5
08	OPENINGS	103.7	56.1	92.9	98.0	67.7	91.2	94.8	49.8	84.7	98.3	56.4	88.8	98.3	59.5	89.5	103.6	54.6	92.6
0920	Plaster & Gypsum Board	83.9	55.9	66.1	95.2	69.9	79.2	89.6	48.4	63.5	98.9	61.2	75.0	98.9	65.0	77.4	83.7	55.9	66.0
0950, 0980	Ceilings & Acoustic Treatment	105.0	55.9	77.5	95.0	69.9	80.9	92.4	48.4	67.7	88.3	61.2	73.1	88.8	65.0	75.5	105.0	55.9	77.5
0960	Flooring	92.0	63.4	84.8	99.6	63.4	90.6	92.7	63.4	85.4	99.4	63.4	90.4	99.4	63.4	90.4	91.8	63.4	84.7
0970, 0990	Wall Finishes & Painting/Coating	97.1	56.3	72.8	99.1	56.3	73.6	102.9	53.2	73.3	102.9	53.1	73.2	102.9	56.3	75.1	97.1	58.0	73.8
09	FINISHES	93.4	58.3	75.8	98.8	66.0	82.3	95.0	53.1	74.0	97.2	61.2	79.1	97.3	64.0	80.6	93.3	58.2	75.7
COVERS	DIVS. 10 - 14, 25, 28, 41, 43, 44, 46	100.0	77.9	95.7	100.0	84.6	97.0	100.0	81.6	96.4	100.0	83.9	96.9	100.0	84.7	97.0	100.0	77.5	95.6
21, 22, 23	FIRE SUPPRESSION, PLUMBING & HVAC	100.3	59.5	85.7	100.1	58.2	85.1	92.6	56.6	79.7	100.1	57.8	85.0	100.1	60.6	86.0	100.3	58.4	85.3
26, 27, 3370	ELECTRICAL, COMMUNICATIONS & UTIL.	92.8	50.8	74.6	100.7	54.8	80.8	96.3	62.0	81.4	96.9	56.8	79.5	96.6	61.1	81.2	93.7	54.1	76.6
MF2018	WEIGHTED AVERAGE	97.0	61.8	84.1	98.2	65.6	86.2	92.0	60.8	80.5	94.6	63.0	83.0	94.7	65.3	83.9	96.9	61.7	83.9

	DIVISION	LOUISIANA									MAINE								
		NEW ORLEANS 700 - 701			SHREVEPORT 710 - 711			THIBODAUX 703			AUGUSTA 043			BANGOR 044			BATH 045		
		MAT.	INST.	TOTAL	MAT.	INST.	TOTAL	MAT.	INST.	TOTAL	MAT.	INST.	TOTAL	MAT.	INST.	TOTAL	MAT.	INST.	TOTAL
015433	CONTRACTOR EQUIPMENT		91.1	91.1		96.9	96.9		87.3	87.3		98.6	98.6		93.0	93.0		93.0	93.0
0241, 31 - 34	SITE & INFRASTRUCTURE, DEMOLITION	101.6	96.5	98.3	102.0	97.6	99.1	99.0	84.4	89.5	89.0	102.1	97.5	90.0	91.3	90.9	84.9	89.7	88.0
0310	Concrete Forming & Accessories	100.7	69.5	76.4	102.3	59.1	68.8	89.3	58.9	65.7	101.8	74.6	80.6	95.7	77.0	81.2	90.8	74.2	77.9
0320	Concrete Reinforcing	99.2	70.8	91.4	98.7	49.9	85.2	93.7	48.9	81.3	99.0	80.5	93.9	84.5	80.7	83.5	83.7	80.3	82.7
0330	Cast-in-Place Concrete	80.3	71.9	77.3	80.9	66.6	75.8	89.3	63.0	79.9	74.4	106.5	85.8	58.8	110.2	77.0	58.8	105.3	75.3
03	CONCRETE	87.9	70.5	81.0	86.4	60.9	76.4	87.4	59.4	76.4	93.4	87.3	91.0	84.0	89.9	86.3	83.7	86.9	84.9
04	MASONRY	92.7	63.4	74.9	96.5	59.9	74.3	111.4	58.1	79.0	113.3	89.3	98.7	126.9	91.7	105.5	134.3	86.9	105.5
05	METALS	99.3	69.9	93.5	101.9	68.2	95.2	89.3	68.4	85.2	105.2	90.8	102.4	91.3	93.6	91.7	89.7	92.4	90.2
06	WOOD, PLASTICS & COMPOSITES	98.4	71.6	86.4	98.7	58.8	80.8	82.2	59.6	72.1	100.8	71.3	87.6	95.1	74.0	85.7	87.5	71.3	80.2
07	THERMAL & MOISTURE PROTECTION	95.1	68.7	85.7	99.4	63.7	86.7	97.1	60.5	84.0	82.4	95.7	87.2	89.5	99.2	93.0	89.4	93.6	90.9
08	OPENINGS	100.0	68.5	92.9	98.1	54.4	88.2	99.0	51.6	88.4	98.2	75.6	93.1	95.2	80.2	91.8	95.2	74.7	90.6
0920	Plaster & Gypsum Board	87.0	70.9	76.8	100.9	57.7	73.5	91.1	58.9	70.7	91.3	70.3	78.0	96.0	73.2	81.5	89.7	70.3	77.4
0950, 0980	Ceilings & Acoustic Treatment	85.5	70.9	77.3	119.0	57.7	84.7	92.4	58.9	73.6	108.2	70.3	87.0	77.3	73.2	75.0	77.3	70.3	73.4
0960	Flooring	102.8	68.6	94.3	99.2	63.4	90.3	97.1	62.9	88.5	107.7	103.1	106.6	99.3	103.1	100.2	97.8	99.1	98.1
0970, 0990	Wall Finishes & Painting/Coating	113.5	59.9	81.5	99.1	58.0	74.6	102.9	53.2	73.3	113.5	83.8	95.8	99.1	93.6	95.8	99.1	79.0	87.1
09	FINISHES	98.8	68.5	83.6	105.1	59.6	82.2	96.7	58.9	77.7	105.3	79.8	92.5	92.0	82.5	87.2	90.7	78.5	84.6
COVERS	DIVS. 10 - 14, 25, 28, 41, 43, 44, 46	100.0	85.3	97.2	100.0	78.7	95.9	100.0	82.5	96.6	100.0	95.0	99.0	100.0	99.9	100.0	100.0	90.9	98.2
21, 22, 23	FIRE SUPPRESSION, PLUMBING & HVAC	99.7	60.9	85.8	100.1	59.1	85.4	92.6	56.3	79.6	99.7	71.6	89.6	100.2	75.4	91.3	92.7	71.6	85.1
26, 27, 3370	ELECTRICAL, COMMUNICATIONS & UTIL.	104.5	67.7	88.5	101.3	60.7	83.7	95.6	62.0	81.0	104.3	72.5	90.5	100.0	65.5	85.1	98.9	72.5	87.5
MF2018	WEIGHTED AVERAGE	98.3	69.5	87.7	99.0	64.1	86.2	93.9	62.2	82.2	100.7	82.4	94.0	95.7	83.1	91.0	93.5	80.9	88.9

	DIVISION	MAINE																	
		HOULTON			KITTERY			LEWISTON			MACHIAS			PORTLAND			ROCKLAND		
		047			039			042			046			040 - 041			048		
		MAT.	INST.	TOTAL	MAT.	INST.	TOTAL	MAT.	INST.	TOTAL	MAT.	INST.	TOTAL	MAT.	INST.	TOTAL	MAT.	INST.	TOTAL
015433	CONTRACTOR EQUIPMENT		93.0	93.0		93.0	93.0		93.0	93.0		93.0	93.0		95.9	95.9		93.0	93.0
0241, 31 - 34	SITE & INFRASTRUCTURE, DEMOLITION	86.4	89.7	88.6	75.5	89.7	84.8	88.8	91.3	90.5	85.8	89.7	88.4	89.5	97.7	94.8	83.3	89.7	87.5
0310	Concrete Forming & Accessories	100.3	74.1	80.0	91.8	74.3	78.2	102.2	77.0	82.6	96.7	74.1	79.2	104.7	77.7	83.7	98.0	74.2	79.5
0320	Concrete Reinforcing	84.5	80.3	83.4	84.5	80.3	83.3	103.9	80.7	97.5	84.5	80.3	83.4	97.8	80.9	93.1	84.5	80.3	83.4
0330	Cast-in-Place Concrete	58.8	104.3	74.9	58.9	105.3	75.4	60.0	110.2	77.8	58.8	105.3	75.3	71.1	111.5	85.4	60.0	105.3	76.1
03	CONCRETE	85.0	86.5	85.6	79.4	86.9	82.4	86.9	89.9	88.1	84.4	86.8	85.4	91.9	90.6	91.4	82.1	86.9	84.0
04	MASONRY	106.4	86.9	94.5	122.5	86.9	100.8	107.2	91.7	97.8	106.4	86.9	94.5	108.1	91.8	98.2	100.0	86.9	92.0
05	METALS	90.0	92.3	90.4	85.6	92.5	87.0	95.7	93.6	95.3	90.0	92.3	90.5	100.8	92.2	99.1	89.8	92.4	90.3
06	WOOD, PLASTICS & COMPOSITES	100.3	71.3	87.3	90.1	71.3	81.6	103.0	74.0	90.0	96.4	71.3	85.1	102.6	74.1	89.8	97.7	71.3	85.8
07	THERMAL & MOISTURE PROTECTION	89.6	93.6	91.0	95.3	93.6	94.7	89.4	99.2	92.9	89.6	93.6	91.0	101.2	100.7	101.0	89.3	93.6	90.8
08	OPENINGS	95.2	74.7	90.6	97.7	77.9	93.2	98.0	80.2	94.0	95.2	74.7	90.6	98.6	80.2	94.4	95.2	74.7	90.6
0920	Plaster & Gypsum Board	97.9	70.3	80.4	102.9	70.3	82.2	103.4	73.2	84.2	97.0	70.3	80.1	108.1	73.2	85.9	97.0	70.3	80.1
0950, 0980	Ceilings & Acoustic Treatment	77.3	70.3	73.4	88.2	70.3	78.2	90.9	73.2	81.0	77.3	70.3	73.4	86.8	73.2	79.2	77.3	70.3	73.4
0960	Flooring	100.5	99.1	100.1	97.1	99.1	97.6	101.8	103.1	102.1	99.8	99.1	99.6	102.5	166.4	118.5	100.1	99.1	99.8
0970, 0990	Wall Finishes & Painting/Coating	99.1	79.0	87.1	82.5	90.7	87.4	99.1	93.6	95.8	99.1	79.0	87.1	99.1	93.6	95.8	99.1	79.0	87.1
09	FINISHES	92.6	78.5	85.5	94.8	79.8	87.2	97.1	82.5	89.8	92.3	78.5	85.3	97.4	95.5	96.4	92.1	78.5	85.2
COVERS	DIVS. 10 - 14, 25, 28, 41, 43, 44, 46	100.0	88.0	97.7	100.0	90.9	98.2	100.0	99.9	100.0	100.0	88.1	97.7	100.0	100.0	100.0	100.0	90.9	98.2
21, 22, 23	FIRE SUPPRESSION, PLUMBING & HVAC	92.7	71.6	85.1	92.8	71.6	85.2	100.2	75.4	91.3	92.7	71.6	85.1	100.1	75.5	91.3	92.7	71.6	85.1
26, 27, 3370	ELECTRICAL, COMMUNICATIONS & UTIL.	101.1	72.5	88.7	100.3	72.5	88.3	101.1	74.8	89.7	101.1	72.5	88.7	101.4	74.8	89.9	101.0	72.5	88.7
MF2018	WEIGHTED AVERAGE	93.2	80.7	88.6	92.3	81.2	88.2	97.0	84.4	92.4	93.1	80.8	88.5	99.2	86.6	94.5	92.4	80.9	88.2

	DIVISION	MAINE			MARYLAND														
		WATERVILLE			ANNAPOLIS			BALTIMORE			COLLEGE PARK			CUMBERLAND			EASTON		
		049			214			210 - 212			207 - 208			215			216		
		MAT.	INST.	TOTAL	MAT.	INST.	TOTAL	MAT.	INST.	TOTAL	MAT.	INST.	TOTAL	MAT.	INST.	TOTAL	MAT.	INST.	TOTAL
015433	CONTRACTOR EQUIPMENT		93.0	93.0		107.1	107.1		105.3	105.3		104.4	104.4		100.8	100.8		100.8	100.8
0241, 31 - 34	SITE & INFRASTRUCTURE, DEMOLITION	86.1	89.7	88.5	109.6	97.1	101.4	110.6	98.5	102.7	105.5	89.4	95.0	98.2	87.2	91.1	104.8	85.6	92.3
0310	Concrete Forming & Accessories	90.2	74.1	77.7	103.0	70.3	77.6	102.9	74.9	81.2	82.5	69.4	72.3	93.3	76.3	80.1	91.2	67.3	72.6
0320	Concrete Reinforcing	84.5	80.3	83.4	98.2	88.7	95.6	100.4	90.6	97.7	97.7	97.0	97.6	87.5	84.7	86.7	86.8	78.2	84.4
0330	Cast-in-Place Concrete	58.8	105.3	75.3	103.7	74.5	93.3	111.4	77.8	99.4	136.4	70.3	112.9	86.0	82.0	84.6	95.6	61.0	83.3
03	CONCRETE	85.1	86.8	85.8	95.1	76.3	87.7	101.7	79.6	93.0	106.4	76.2	94.5	83.5	81.1	82.6	89.2	68.6	81.1
04	MASONRY	118.0	86.9	99.1	98.1	68.6	80.2	105.6	73.9	86.3	123.1	67.3	89.2	100.6	84.5	90.8	114.9	53.1	77.4
05	METALS	89.9	92.3	90.4	101.0	101.1	101.0	100.4	97.8	99.9	84.1	108.6	88.9	95.7	102.1	97.0	96.0	98.5	96.5
06	WOOD, PLASTICS & COMPOSITES	86.6	71.3	79.7	99.6	70.6	86.6	100.6	74.6	89.0	70.9	68.7	69.9	85.4	73.6	80.1	82.6	73.5	78.5
07	THERMAL & MOISTURE PROTECTION	89.5	93.6	91.0	107.6	78.8	97.3	102.8	82.4	95.5	101.3	74.5	91.7	101.6	76.8	92.8	101.8	67.4	89.5
08	OPENINGS	95.2	74.7	90.6	98.5	79.7	94.2	99.7	80.3	95.3	92.9	78.6	89.6	93.4	78.3	90.0	91.8	76.3	88.3
0920	Plaster & Gypsum Board	89.7	70.3	77.4	115.1	69.7	86.3	115.1	73.7	88.8	98.6	68.1	79.3	114.5	73.2	88.3	114.5	73.1	88.2
0950, 0980	Ceilings & Acoustic Treatment	77.3	70.3	73.4	96.8	69.7	81.6	96.8	73.7	83.8	98.3	68.1	81.4	101.8	73.2	85.8	101.8	73.1	85.7
0960	Flooring	97.6	99.1	98.0	108.4	71.2	99.1	96.0	75.3	90.8	92.5	70.3	86.9	96.0	88.5	94.1	95.3	67.8	88.4
0970, 0990	Wall Finishes & Painting/Coating	99.1	79.0	87.1	99.1	64.8	78.6	99.1	68.5	80.8	93.9	64.8	76.5	93.6	75.2	82.6	93.6	64.8	76.4
09	FINISHES	90.8	78.5	84.6	104.4	69.1	86.7	100.3	73.7	86.9	96.4	68.3	82.3	102.3	78.3	90.2	102.5	67.3	84.8
COVERS	DIVS. 10 - 14, 25, 28, 41, 43, 44, 46	100.0	87.9	97.7	100.0	87.5	97.6	100.0	89.6	98.0	100.0	77.5	95.6	100.0	90.6	98.2	100.0	79.1	95.9
21, 22, 23	FIRE SUPPRESSION, PLUMBING & HVAC	92.7	71.6	85.1	100.0	78.6	92.3	100.1	84.1	94.3	92.6	78.8	87.6	92.3	67.3	83.3	92.3	65.5	82.7
26, 27, 3370	ELECTRICAL, COMMUNICATIONS & UTIL.	101.1	72.5	88.7	100.0	82.1	92.3	100.0	87.0	94.4	100.3	98.9	99.7	99.5	75.9	89.2	99.2	55.5	80.3
MF2018	WEIGHTED AVERAGE	93.4	80.8	88.7	100.2	80.3	92.9	100.9	83.8	94.6	95.6	82.1	90.6	94.8	79.8	89.3	96.1	69.1	86.2

	DIVISION	MARYLAND															MASSACHUSETTS		
		ELKTON			HAGERSTOWN			SALISBURY			SILVER SPRING			WALDORF			BOSTON		
		219			217			218			209			206			020 - 022, 024		
		MAT.	INST.	TOTAL	MAT.	INST.	TOTAL	MAT.	INST.	TOTAL	MAT.	INST.	TOTAL	MAT.	INST.	TOTAL	MAT.	INST.	TOTAL
015433	CONTRACTOR EQUIPMENT		100.8	100.8		100.8	100.8		100.8	100.8		97.2	97.2		97.2	97.2		103.3	103.3
0241, 31 - 34	SITE & INFRASTRUCTURE, DEMOLITION	92.6	86.1	88.3	99.7	87.5	91.8	104.8	85.4	92.1	92.9	82.3	86.0	99.0	82.1	88.0	89.8	103.7	98.8
0310	Concrete Forming & Accessories	97.9	83.8	86.9	92.2	80.7	83.3	107.6	46.1	59.8	90.8	68.7	73.6	98.6	68.6	75.3	106.5	137.3	130.4
0320	Concrete Reinforcing	86.8	105.3	91.9	87.5	84.7	86.7	86.8	58.6	79.0	97.0	97.0	97.0	97.7	96.9	97.5	101.1	149.3	114.4
0330	Cast-in-Place Concrete	77.4	66.9	73.6	82.0	82.1	82.0	95.6	59.1	82.6	139.6	70.6	115.1	156.5	70.4	125.9	80.3	140.6	101.7
03	CONCRETE	78.3	82.8	80.1	80.9	83.2	81.8	90.6	55.0	76.5	106.2	75.8	94.2	115.9	75.7	100.0	96.7	139.9	113.7
04	MASONRY	100.1	60.5	76.0	106.2	84.5	93.0	114.0	50.0	75.1	122.4	67.6	89.1	105.7	67.5	82.5	121.3	144.5	135.4
05	METALS	96.0	109.3	98.6	95.8	102.5	97.1	96.0	90.0	94.8	89.0	104.9	92.2	89.0	104.4	92.1	98.7	132.8	105.4
06	WOOD, PLASTICS & COMPOSITES	91.4	91.9	91.7	84.3	79.1	81.9	105.4	46.9	79.1	78.5	68.1	73.8	86.7	68.1	78.3	104.9	136.7	119.1
07	THERMAL & MOISTURE PROTECTION	101.4	72.9	91.2	101.9	82.3	94.9	102.1	63.1	88.2	104.0	78.8	95.0	104.5	78.8	95.4	96.5	137.7	111.2
08	OPENINGS	91.8	93.6	92.2	91.8	81.3	89.4	92.0	56.2	84.0	84.9	78.2	83.4	85.5	78.2	83.8	98.6	143.4	108.7
0920	Plaster & Gypsum Board	117.9	92.1	101.5	114.5	78.9	91.9	130.2	45.6	76.6	108.2	68.1	82.8	111.1	68.1	83.8	123.5	137.7	132.5
0950, 0980	Ceilings & Acoustic Treatment	101.8	92.1	96.4	103.3	78.9	89.6	101.8	45.6	70.3	107.4	68.1	85.4	107.4	68.1	85.4	101.3	137.7	121.7
0960	Flooring	97.3	67.8	89.9	95.6	88.5	93.8	100.4	67.8	92.2	98.2	70.3	91.2	100.8	70.3	93.2	104.8	159.0	118.4
0970, 0990	Wall Finishes & Painting/Coating	93.6	64.8	76.4	93.6	67.2	77.8	93.6	64.8	76.4	100.6	64.8	79.2	100.6	64.8	79.2	99.1	156.1	133.1
09	FINISHES	102.7	79.9	91.3	102.3	80.6	91.4	106.2	50.8	78.4	98.0	67.7	82.8	99.5	67.8	83.6	104.2	143.9	124.1
COVERS	DIVS. 10 - 14, 25, 28, 41, 43, 44, 46	100.0	51.1	90.5	100.0	91.2	98.3	100.0	75.2	95.2	100.0	76.2	95.4	100.0	74.3	95.0	100.0	116.7	103.2
21, 22, 23	FIRE SUPPRESSION, PLUMBING & HVAC	92.3	70.8	84.6	99.8	83.9	94.1	92.3	63.7	82.0	92.6	79.2	87.8	92.6	79.1	87.8	100.2	133.0	111.9
26, 27, 3370	ELECTRICAL, COMMUNICATIONS & UTIL.	100.1	77.4	90.3	99.4	75.9	89.2	98.6	53.5	79.1	95.9	98.9	97.2	94.6	98.9	96.5	102.6	126.4	112.9
MF2018	WEIGHTED AVERAGE	94.2	78.8	88.5	96.3	84.3	91.9	96.7	62.0	83.9	95.5	81.2	90.2	96.3	81.1	90.7	100.3	133.3	112.5

	DIVISION	MASSACHUSETTS																	
		BROCKTON			BUZZARDS BAY			FALL RIVER			FITCHBURG			FRAMINGHAM			GREENFIELD		
		023			025			027			014			017			013		
		MAT.	INST.	TOTAL	MAT.	INST.	TOTAL	MAT.	INST.	TOTAL	MAT.	INST.	TOTAL	MAT.	INST.	TOTAL	MAT.	INST.	TOTAL
015433	CONTRACTOR EQUIPMENT		96.0	96.0		96.0	96.0		96.8	96.8		93.0	93.0		94.5	94.5		93.0	93.0
0241, 31 - 34	SITE & INFRASTRUCTURE, DEMOLITION	88.1	94.3	92.2	77.1	94.0	88.1	87.4	94.4	92.0	79.1	93.6	88.6	76.7	93.1	87.4	82.3	92.2	88.7
0310	Concrete Forming & Accessories	98.0	115.4	111.5	95.7	114.6	110.4	98.0	115.1	111.3	94.9	108.2	105.2	103.2	115.3	112.6	93.0	111.8	107.6
0320	Concrete Reinforcing	98.5	135.8	108.9	79.0	114.2	88.7	98.5	114.3	102.9	81.3	127.9	94.2	81.3	135.6	96.3	83.5	113.8	91.9
0330	Cast-in-Place Concrete	69.1	125.5	89.2	57.5	125.2	81.5	66.9	125.7	87.8	63.2	125.1	85.2	63.2	125.3	85.3	64.9	111.2	81.4
03	CONCRETE	88.3	122.4	101.7	74.7	118.2	91.8	86.3	118.6	99.0	75.8	117.4	92.2	78.3	122.2	95.6	78.6	111.6	91.7
04	MASONRY	119.6	128.1	124.8	110.6	128.1	121.2	120.0	128.1	124.9	107.1	120.4	115.2	114.0	124.2	120.2	112.5	111.4	111.8
05	METALS	94.4	124.2	100.3	87.7	114.7	93.0	94.4	115.3	98.5	92.2	116.8	97.0	92.2	123.2	98.4	96.2	108.5	98.6
06	WOOD, PLASTICS & COMPOSITES	95.7	114.6	104.2	91.4	114.6	101.8	95.7	114.8	104.3	95.2	105.6	99.9	103.8	114.4	108.5	92.5	114.9	102.5
07	THERMAL & MOISTURE PROTECTION	93.5	119.4	102.7	92.5	116.3	101.0	93.3	116.2	101.5	92.6	112.4	99.7	92.8	117.2	101.5	92.6	103.1	96.4
08	OPENINGS	94.9	122.6	101.2	91.3	112.2	96.0	94.9	113.2	99.0	97.8	115.6	101.8	88.2	122.5	96.0	97.8	113.7	101.4
0920	Plaster & Gypsum Board	109.0	115.0	112.8	99.4	115.0	109.3	109.0	115.0	112.8	108.2	105.7	106.6	113.1	115.0	114.3	110.3	115.3	113.5
0950, 0980	Ceilings & Acoustic Treatment	104.8	115.0	110.5	86.1	115.0	102.3	104.8	115.0	110.5	85.4	105.7	96.8	85.4	115.0	102.0	97.2	115.3	107.4
0960	Flooring	102.9	149.0	114.5	100.5	149.0	112.7	101.5	149.0	113.5	96.7	149.0	109.8	97.6	149.0	110.5	96.0	128.3	104.1
0970, 0990	Wall Finishes & Painting/Coating	87.3	129.5	112.5	87.3	129.5	112.5	87.3	129.5	112.5	89.2	129.5	113.3	90.0	129.5	113.6	89.2	107.2	99.9
09	FINISHES	100.7	123.3	112.0	93.2	123.3	108.3	100.3	123.4	111.9	93.0	118.0	105.6	93.8	123.1	108.5	96.5	115.3	105.9
COVERS	DIVS. 10 - 14, 25, 28, 41, 43, 44, 46	100.0	110.7	102.1	100.0	110.7	102.1	100.0	111.1	102.2	100.0	99.8	100.0	100.0	110.2	102.0	100.0	103.4	100.7
21, 22, 23	FIRE SUPPRESSION, PLUMBING & HVAC	100.6	98.5	99.8	93.1	93.9	93.3	100.6	98.2	99.7	93.0	94.9	93.7	93.0	109.8	99.0	93.0	92.7	92.9
26, 27, 3370	ELECTRICAL, COMMUNICATIONS & UTIL.	101.6	92.3	97.6	100.0	89.2	95.3	101.1	93.6	97.8	100.5	92.7	97.1	98.7	110.7	103.9	100.5	93.9	97.6
MF2018	WEIGHTED AVERAGE	97.5	111.2	102.6	91.1	107.8	97.2	97.2	109.5	101.7	92.7	106.7	97.9	92.4	115.5	100.9	94.4	103.4	97.7

	DIVISION	MASSACHUSETTS																	
		HYANNIS			LAWRENCE			LOWELL			NEW BEDFORD			PITTSFIELD			SPRINGFIELD		
		026			019			018			027			012			010 - 011		
		MAT.	INST.	TOTAL	MAT.	INST.	TOTAL	MAT.	INST.	TOTAL	MAT.	INST.	TOTAL	MAT.	INST.	TOTAL	MAT.	INST.	TOTAL
015433	CONTRACTOR EQUIPMENT		96.0	96.0		95.1	95.1		93.0	93.0		96.8	96.8		93.0	93.0		93.0	93.0
0241, 31 - 34	SITE & INFRASTRUCTURE, DEMOLITION	85.0	94.2	91.0	89.6	93.7	92.3	88.8	94.0	92.2	86.4	94.4	91.6	89.5	92.3	91.3	89.1	92.6	91.4
0310	Concrete Forming & Accessories	89.3	115.0	109.3	104.6	115.8	113.3	100.7	117.6	113.8	98.0	115.2	111.4	100.7	100.1	100.3	101.0	113.0	110.3
0320	Concrete Reinforcing	79.0	114.3	88.8	100.5	133.5	109.7	101.4	133.3	110.2	98.5	114.2	102.9	82.9	110.6	90.6	101.4	113.8	104.9
0330	Cast-in-Place Concrete	63.1	125.4	85.2	73.1	125.5	91.7	66.5	128.2	88.4	58.9	125.8	82.7	72.5	109.5	85.7	69.2	112.9	84.7
03	CONCRETE	78.8	118.4	94.4	91.8	122.1	103.8	85.7	123.7	100.7	84.1	118.7	97.7	83.3	105.3	92.0	86.8	112.8	97.1
04	MASONRY	118.4	128.1	124.3	120.4	130.5	126.5	106.1	131.5	121.6	118.7	126.7	123.6	106.7	106.5	106.6	106.4	114.5	111.3
05	METALS	89.2	115.1	94.3	96.6	123.3	101.9	96.6	120.3	101.3	94.4	115.3	98.5	96.4	106.9	98.4	99.5	108.6	101.3
06	WOOD, PLASTICS & COMPOSITES	83.6	114.6	97.5	105.0	114.6	109.3	103.5	114.6	108.4	95.7	114.8	104.3	103.5	100.4	102.1	103.5	114.9	108.6
07	THERMAL & MOISTURE PROTECTION	92.9	118.6	102.0	93.2	120.1	102.8	93.0	121.1	103.0	93.3	115.8	101.3	93.1	99.7	95.4	93.0	104.5	97.1
08	OPENINGS	91.8	113.4	96.7	91.6	121.9	98.4	98.9	121.9	104.1	94.9	117.3	100.0	98.9	104.9	100.2	98.9	113.7	102.2
0920	Plaster & Gypsum Board	94.4	115.0	107.4	117.5	115.0	115.9	117.5	115.0	115.9	109.0	115.0	112.8	117.5	100.4	106.6	117.5	115.3	116.1
0950, 0980	Ceilings & Acoustic Treatment	91.2	115.0	104.5	97.7	115.0	107.4	97.7	115.0	107.4	104.8	115.0	110.5	97.7	100.4	99.2	97.7	115.3	107.6
0960	Flooring	98.3	149.0	111.0	98.5	149.0	111.2	98.5	149.0	111.2	101.5	149.0	113.5	98.7	123.4	104.9	97.9	128.3	105.5
0970, 0990	Wall Finishes & Painting/Coating	87.3	129.5	112.5	89.3	129.5	113.3	89.2	129.5	113.3	87.3	129.5	112.5	89.2	107.2	99.9	89.9	107.2	100.2
09	FINISHES	93.5	123.3	108.5	98.5	123.3	110.9	98.5	124.5	111.5	100.2	123.4	111.9	98.5	105.3	101.9	98.3	116.1	107.3
COVERS	DIVS. 10 - 14, 25, 28, 41, 43, 44, 46	100.0	110.7	102.1	100.0	110.7	102.1	100.0	112.3	102.4	100.0	111.1	102.2	100.0	101.1	100.2	100.0	104.4	100.9
21, 22, 23	FIRE SUPPRESSION, PLUMBING & HVAC	100.6	102.4	101.3	100.0	113.5	104.8	100.0	119.4	107.0	100.6	98.2	99.7	100.0	89.8	96.4	100.0	94.3	97.9
26, 27, 3370	ELECTRICAL, COMMUNICATIONS & UTIL.	100.8	93.5	97.6	100.0	116.1	107.0	100.2	115.0	106.6	102.5	95.4	99.4	100.2	93.9	97.5	100.3	95.1	98.0
MF2018	WEIGHTED AVERAGE	94.1	110.4	100.1	97.8	117.8	105.2	97.1	119.2	105.2	97.0	109.8	101.7	96.9	99.3	97.7	97.9	104.6	100.4

	DIVISION	MASSACHUSETTS			MICHIGAN														
		WORCESTER			ANN ARBOR			BATTLE CREEK			BAY CITY			DEARBORN			DETROIT		
		015 - 016			481			490			487			481			482		
		MAT.	INST.	TOTAL	MAT.	INST.	TOTAL	MAT.	INST.	TOTAL	MAT.	INST.	TOTAL	MAT.	INST.	TOTAL	MAT.	INST.	TOTAL
015433	CONTRACTOR EQUIPMENT		93.0	93.0		104.6	104.6		94.2	94.2		104.6	104.6		104.6	104.6		95.0	95.0
0241, 31 - 34	SITE & INFRASTRUCTURE, DEMOLITION	89.1	93.6	92.0	82.5	88.4	86.4	86.1	79.0	81.5	77.1	87.1	83.6	82.3	88.5	86.4	94.4	98.7	97.2
0310	Concrete Forming & Accessories	101.3	116.5	113.1	98.0	99.0	98.8	103.1	78.9	84.3	98.1	75.4	80.5	97.9	99.7	99.3	95.6	104.4	102.4
0320	Concrete Reinforcing	101.4	140.0	112.1	97.1	98.7	97.6	94.6	76.8	89.7	97.1	98.0	97.4	97.1	99.9	97.9	100.7	100.4	100.6
0330	Cast-in-Place Concrete	68.8	125.2	88.8	91.2	93.9	92.2	80.8	89.3	83.8	87.3	82.0	85.4	89.2	94.7	91.2	108.6	99.4	105.4
03	CONCRETE	86.7	123.3	101.1	88.9	98.2	92.5	84.9	82.1	83.8	87.2	83.2	85.6	88.0	99.0	92.4	98.8	101.4	99.8
04	MASONRY	106.1	126.7	118.6	104.1	94.0	98.0	100.8	74.0	84.5	103.6	78.6	88.4	103.9	116.0	111.3	108.0	97.3	101.5
05	METALS	99.6	122.5	104.1	95.0	113.9	98.7	101.5	81.9	97.7	95.6	110.1	98.5	95.1	115.7	99.1	95.8	92.5	95.2
06	WOOD, PLASTICS & COMPOSITES	104.1	116.3	109.6	93.3	100.5	96.5	98.6	78.5	89.6	93.3	74.3	84.8	93.3	100.5	96.5	92.3	106.7	98.8
07	THERMAL & MOISTURE PROTECTION	93.0	115.3	101.0	109.4	93.9	103.9	104.1	75.1	93.8	107.2	79.9	97.5	108.0	101.2	105.6	108.2	103.9	106.7
08	OPENINGS	98.9	124.7	104.7	91.3	96.0	92.4	84.5	73.6	82.1	91.3	78.6	88.4	91.3	96.0	92.4	98.6	101.3	99.2
0920	Plaster & Gypsum Board	117.5	116.7	117.0	103.5	100.4	101.5	86.2	75.1	79.1	103.5	73.5	84.5	103.5	100.4	101.5	109.5	107.0	107.9
0950, 0980	Ceilings & Acoustic Treatment	97.7	116.7	108.4	101.1	100.4	100.7	82.2	75.1	78.2	101.6	73.5	85.8	101.1	100.4	100.7	113.1	107.0	109.7
0960	Flooring	98.5	150.2	111.4	92.6	104.0	95.5	101.3	63.1	91.7	92.6	80.2	89.5	91.6	98.5	93.3	97.8	103.4	99.2
0970, 0990	Wall Finishes & Painting/Coating	89.2	129.5	113.3	86.1	93.7	90.6	88.7	67.7	76.2	86.1	76.9	80.6	86.1	92.0	89.6	99.1	95.5	97.0
09	FINISHES	98.5	124.5	111.5	97.3	99.5	98.4	90.7	74.5	82.6	97.1	75.7	86.3	97.0	98.7	97.8	103.8	103.7	103.8
COVERS	DIVS. 10 - 14, 25, 28, 41, 43, 44, 46	100.0	105.4	101.1	100.0	100.0	100.0	100.0	101.1	100.2	100.0	94.4	98.9	100.0	100.4	100.1	100.0	100.6	100.1
21, 22, 23	FIRE SUPPRESSION, PLUMBING & HVAC	100.0	99.2	99.7	100.2	88.7	96.1	99.9	76.2	91.4	100.2	78.6	92.5	100.2	97.2	99.1	100.1	100.2	100.1
26, 27, 3370	ELECTRICAL, COMMUNICATIONS & UTIL.	100.3	98.3	99.4	96.1	97.3	96.6	93.7	69.2	83.1	95.0	73.4	85.7	96.1	92.6	94.6	100.6	100.0	100.3
MF2018	WEIGHTED AVERAGE	97.9	111.9	103.1	96.2	96.4	96.3	95.7	77.0	88.8	95.8	82.2	90.8	96.1	100.1	97.5	99.5	99.9	99.7

	DIVISION	MICHIGAN																	
		FLINT			GAYLORD			GRAND RAPIDS			IRON MOUNTAIN			JACKSON			KALAMAZOO		
		484 - 485			497			493,495			498 - 499			492			491		
		MAT.	INST.	TOTAL	MAT.	INST.	TOTAL	MAT.	INST.	TOTAL	MAT.	INST.	TOTAL	MAT.	INST.	TOTAL	MAT.	INST.	TOTAL
015433	CONTRACTOR EQUIPMENT		104.6	104.6		100.9	100.9		99.4	99.4		89.7	89.7		100.9	100.9		94.2	94.2
0241, 31 - 34	SITE & INFRASTRUCTURE, DEMOLITION	75.3	87.4	83.2	82.8	76.8	78.9	85.1	91.0	89.0	85.2	84.8	84.9	94.4	78.4	84.0	86.3	79.0	81.6
0310	Concrete Forming & Accessories	101.4	83.8	87.7	101.6	67.3	74.9	100.7	75.0	80.8	95.1	71.4	76.7	97.9	74.8	80.0	103.1	79.2	84.5
0320	Concrete Reinforcing	97.1	98.3	97.5	88.4	83.4	87.0	98.7	76.8	92.7	87.6	76.3	84.4	85.8	97.9	89.1	94.6	75.5	89.4
0330	Cast-in-Place Concrete	91.8	84.7	89.3	80.6	72.0	77.5	84.9	86.4	85.5	95.4	62.3	83.7	80.5	85.5	82.2	82.4	89.4	84.9
03	CONCRETE	89.4	88.0	88.8	81.7	73.5	78.5	91.4	79.3	86.6	88.1	70.0	81.0	77.9	84.0	80.3	87.1	82.1	85.1
04	MASONRY	104.1	87.0	93.7	111.9	65.5	83.7	97.9	72.2	82.3	96.3	71.8	81.4	90.1	78.2	82.9	99.1	80.4	87.7
05	METALS	95.1	110.7	98.2	103.0	105.5	103.5	97.9	80.5	94.5	102.2	87.4	99.3	103.3	108.6	104.4	101.5	82.0	97.7
06	WOOD, PLASTICS & COMPOSITES	98.0	83.6	91.5	92.0	66.7	80.7	97.8	74.0	87.1	92.0	71.7	82.9	90.6	72.5	82.4	98.6	78.5	89.6
07	THERMAL & MOISTURE PROTECTION	107.5	85.1	99.5	102.7	67.1	90.0	105.7	69.8	92.9	106.0	67.1	92.2	102.1	79.6	94.1	104.1	77.1	94.5
08	OPENINGS	91.3	83.0	89.4	83.6	71.4	80.8	98.8	72.8	93.0	89.5	63.3	83.6	82.8	78.8	81.9	84.5	74.7	82.3
0920	Plaster & Gypsum Board	105.9	83.0	91.4	85.5	65.0	72.5	93.9	70.9	79.3	55.4	71.5	65.7	84.1	70.9	75.7	86.2	75.1	79.1
0950, 0980	Ceilings & Acoustic Treatment	101.1	83.0	91.0	79.9	65.0	71.6	90.9	70.9	79.7	80.6	71.5	75.5	79.9	70.9	74.9	82.2	75.1	78.2
0960	Flooring	92.6	85.2	90.8	93.2	76.7	89.1	103.9	82.6	98.6	117.8	81.5	108.7	92.2	70.4	86.8	101.3	70.7	93.7
0970, 0990	Wall Finishes & Painting/Coating	86.1	75.6	79.8	84.4	72.5	77.3	99.1	72.5	83.3	103.1	61.9	78.5	84.4	83.3	83.8	88.7	73.4	79.6
09	FINISHES	96.9	82.8	89.8	89.3	68.8	79.0	97.0	75.8	86.3	93.5	72.2	82.8	89.8	73.9	81.8	90.7	76.6	83.6
COVERS	DIVS. 10 - 14, 25, 28, 41, 43, 44, 46	100.0	96.6	99.3	100.0	93.5	98.7	100.0	99.2	99.8	100.0	91.9	98.4	100.0	96.3	99.3	100.0	101.1	100.2
21, 22, 23	FIRE SUPPRESSION, PLUMBING & HVAC	100.2	83.6	94.2	92.9	71.0	85.0	99.9	80.7	93.0	92.6	75.4	86.4	92.9	77.2	87.2	99.9	77.8	92.0
26, 27, 3370	ELECTRICAL, COMMUNICATIONS & UTIL.	96.1	88.9	93.0	92.9	67.9	82.1	99.3	79.9	90.9	96.9	71.8	86.0	94.9	91.7	93.5	93.4	76.6	86.1
MF2018	WEIGHTED AVERAGE	96.1	88.4	93.3	94.0	74.3	86.7	97.8	79.6	91.1	95.3	75.0	87.8	93.3	83.5	89.7	95.8	79.4	89.8

	DIVISION	MICHIGAN															MINNESOTA		
		LANSING			MUSKEGON			ROYAL OAK			SAGINAW			TRAVERSE CITY			BEMIDJI		
		488 - 489			494			480,483			486			496			566		
		MAT.	INST.	TOTAL	MAT.	INST.	TOTAL	MAT.	INST.	TOTAL	MAT.	INST.	TOTAL	MAT.	INST.	TOTAL	MAT.	INST.	TOTAL
015433	CONTRACTOR EQUIPMENT		109.0	109.0		94.2	94.2		87.3	87.3		104.6	104.6		89.7	89.7		94.2	94.2
0241, 31 - 34	SITE & INFRASTRUCTURE, DEMOLITION	89.5	99.0	95.6	84.7	79.0	81.0	80.5	87.1	84.8	78.0	87.1	84.0	74.8	83.9	80.7	82.0	91.0	87.9
0310	Concrete Forming & Accessories	100.6	78.6	83.5	103.6	78.1	83.8	93.6	97.9	96.9	98.0	79.8	83.9	95.1	65.8	72.3	86.7	88.6	88.1
0320	Concrete Reinforcing	99.6	98.1	99.2	95.5	77.2	90.4	88.0	94.0	89.7	97.1	98.0	97.4	88.9	72.0	84.3	95.9	103.8	98.1
0330	Cast-in-Place Concrete	100.6	84.5	94.9	80.5	88.1	83.2	79.8	88.7	83.0	90.1	82.0	87.2	74.4	73.5	74.1	112.1	96.0	106.4
03	CONCRETE	94.3	85.3	90.7	84.1	81.4	83.0	77.8	93.5	84.0	88.4	85.2	87.1	75.8	70.6	73.8	99.0	95.1	97.5
04	MASONRY	99.6	85.4	91.0	98.2	78.9	86.5	97.9	89.7	92.9	105.9	78.6	89.3	94.4	67.4	78.0	106.4	104.8	105.4
05	METALS	97.3	106.4	99.1	100.2	82.5	96.7	97.6	87.6	95.6	95.1	110.0	98.0	102.1	85.4	98.8	91.1	119.6	96.7
06	WOOD, PLASTICS & COMPOSITES	97.8	76.8	88.4	97.3	77.0	88.2	88.8	100.5	94.0	90.9	80.4	86.2	92.0	65.4	80.1	70.5	84.7	76.9
07	THERMAL & MOISTURE PROTECTION	105.2	82.9	97.3	103.2	71.7	92.0	105.8	90.9	100.5	108.1	80.5	98.3	105.2	66.9	91.5	107.1	91.1	101.4
08	OPENINGS	98.7	79.4	94.4	83.7	74.5	81.6	91.1	93.9	91.7	89.7	82.0	88.0	89.5	59.4	82.7	95.8	106.6	98.2
0920	Plaster & Gypsum Board	89.5	76.1	81.0	68.9	73.5	71.8	100.2	100.4	100.3	103.5	79.8	88.4	55.4	65.0	61.5	94.4	84.9	88.3
0950, 0980	Ceilings & Acoustic Treatment	102.2	76.1	87.6	82.2	73.5	77.3	100.3	100.4	100.3	101.1	79.8	89.2	80.6	65.0	71.9	119.3	84.9	100.0
0960	Flooring	93.9	82.6	91.1	100.2	82.6	95.8	90.4	95.5	91.7	92.6	80.2	89.5	117.8	76.7	107.5	96.3	107.4	99.0
0970, 0990	Wall Finishes & Painting/Coating	99.1	73.9	84.1	87.0	73.7	79.1	87.8	83.3	85.2	86.1	76.9	80.6	103.1	35.0	62.5	90.8	94.2	92.8
09	FINISHES	97.2	78.2	87.6	87.4	78.2	82.8	96.1	96.2	96.2	97.0	79.2	88.1	92.7	64.1	78.3	100.1	92.2	96.1
COVERS	DIVS. 10 - 14, 25, 28, 41, 43, 44, 46	100.0	95.8	99.2	100.0	100.9	100.2	100.0	99.6	99.9	100.0	95.1	99.1	100.0	90.7	98.2	100.0	98.8	99.8
21, 22, 23	FIRE SUPPRESSION, PLUMBING & HVAC	99.9	85.1	94.6	99.8	81.7	93.3	93.1	91.1	92.4	100.2	78.2	92.3	92.6	70.9	84.8	92.8	85.0	90.0
26, 27, 3370	ELECTRICAL, COMMUNICATIONS & UTIL.	99.3	87.4	94.1	94.0	73.1	84.9	97.2	91.8	94.9	95.0	80.8	88.8	94.5	67.9	82.9	100.4	79.8	91.4
MF2018	WEIGHTED AVERAGE	98.2	87.6	94.3	94.8	79.6	89.2	93.5	91.9	92.9	95.8	84.1	91.5	93.2	71.6	85.2	95.8	93.7	95.0

	DIVISION	MINNESOTA																	
		BRAINERD			DETROIT LAKES			DULUTH			MANKATO			MINNEAPOLIS			ROCHESTER		
		564			565			556 - 558			560			553 - 555			559		
		MAT.	INST.	TOTAL	MAT.	INST.	TOTAL	MAT.	INST.	TOTAL	MAT.	INST.	TOTAL	MAT.	INST.	TOTAL	MAT.	INST.	TOTAL
015433	CONTRACTOR EQUIPMENT		96.5	96.5		94.2	94.2		102.3	102.3		96.5	96.5		102.8	102.8		96.9	96.9
0241, 31 - 34	SITE & INFRASTRUCTURE, DEMOLITION	84.9	95.4	91.8	80.7	90.6	87.2	92.6	102.0	98.8	82.4	94.7	90.4	88.3	102.1	97.3	90.7	93.8	92.7
0310	Concrete Forming & Accessories	86.6	91.3	90.3	83.1	76.6	78.1	101.4	104.4	103.8	95.8	101.1	99.9	101.7	120.8	116.6	101.8	104.7	104.0
0320	Concrete Reinforcing	95.2	103.9	97.6	95.9	103.5	98.0	99.0	104.5	100.6	95.1	107.0	98.4	99.3	107.9	101.7	95.5	107.5	98.9
0330	Cast-in-Place Concrete	122.0	100.5	114.4	108.9	97.0	104.7	141.0	107.1	129.0	112.3	101.1	108.3	124.8	119.7	123.0	134.6	102.1	123.0
03	CONCRETE	102.7	97.9	100.8	96.7	90.0	94.1	120.3	106.2	114.7	98.9	103.1	100.6	114.5	118.6	116.1	110.3	105.3	108.3
04	MASONRY	133.3	113.0	121.0	131.9	102.3	113.9	112.8	118.3	116.1	120.9	107.8	113.0	109.4	123.6	118.0	109.2	115.3	112.9
05	METALS	91.9	119.6	97.4	91.0	118.2	96.4	98.4	120.2	102.7	91.8	121.2	97.6	96.9	123.8	102.2	95.9	124.0	101.4
06	WOOD, PLASTICS & COMPOSITES	82.8	84.6	83.6	66.8	67.6	67.1	98.8	102.4	100.4	94.8	99.9	97.1	98.8	119.6	108.1	100.6	103.4	101.8
07	THERMAL & MOISTURE PROTECTION	104.7	98.7	102.6	106.9	94.5	102.5	105.2	106.8	105.8	105.2	93.1	100.9	106.6	121.0	111.7	111.3	100.3	107.4
08	OPENINGS	83.2	106.5	88.5	95.7	97.1	96.0	98.4	113.2	101.7	87.6	115.2	93.8	98.9	127.9	105.5	95.3	117.9	100.4
0920	Plaster & Gypsum Board	79.1	84.9	82.8	93.9	67.2	76.9	91.2	102.8	98.6	83.5	100.6	94.4	88.3	120.3	108.6	94.6	104.1	100.6
0950, 0980	Ceilings & Acoustic Treatment	63.9	84.9	75.6	119.3	67.2	90.1	110.4	102.8	106.1	63.9	100.6	84.5	100.9	120.3	111.8	99.9	104.1	102.3
0960	Flooring	95.3	107.0	98.2	95.2	76.6	90.6	100.6	107.0	102.2	96.2	94.0	95.7	95.5	125.3	103.0	95.5	95.9	95.6
0970, 0990	Wall Finishes & Painting/Coating	84.8	94.2	90.4	90.8	94.2	92.8	99.1	114.7	108.4	96.6	98.4	97.7	99.1	129.3	117.1	89.3	103.3	97.6
09	FINISHES	82.5	93.8	88.2	99.6	77.4	88.5	101.2	106.1	103.7	83.9	100.1	92.0	96.7	122.5	109.7	94.9	103.2	99.1
COVERS	DIVS. 10 - 14, 25, 28, 41, 43, 44, 46	100.0	100.9	100.2	100.0	97.8	99.6	100.0	103.2	100.6	100.0	101.3	100.2	100.0	107.6	101.5	100.0	102.1	100.4
21, 22, 23	FIRE SUPPRESSION, PLUMBING & HVAC	91.8	88.7	90.7	92.8	86.4	90.5	99.9	98.3	99.3	91.8	90.3	91.3	100.0	116.6	105.9	100.0	100.0	100.0
26, 27, 3370	ELECTRICAL, COMMUNICATIONS & UTIL.	99.5	100.9	100.1	100.2	77.9	90.5	99.7	100.9	100.2	102.9	96.1	99.9	99.5	118.1	107.6	98.8	96.1	97.6
MF2018	WEIGHTED AVERAGE	94.9	99.5	96.6	96.3	90.2	94.1	102.4	106.1	103.8	94.8	100.6	97.0	100.9	118.4	107.4	99.9	104.7	101.7

	DIVISION	MINNESOTA															MISSISSIPPI		
		SAINT PAUL 550 - 551			ST. CLOUD 563			THIEF RIVER FALLS 567			WILLMAR 562			WINDOM 561			BILOXI 395		
		MAT.	INST.	TOTAL	MAT.	INST.	TOTAL	MAT.	INST.	TOTAL	MAT.	INST.	TOTAL	MAT.	INST.	TOTAL	MAT.	INST.	TOTAL
015433	CONTRACTOR EQUIPMENT		102.2	102.2		96.5	96.5		94.2	94.2		96.5	96.5		96.5	96.5		96.7	96.7
0241, 31 - 34	SITE & INFRASTRUCTURE, DEMOLITION	90.7	102.8	98.6	84.8	96.1	92.2	81.4	90.6	87.4	80.9	95.0	90.1	76.4	93.9	87.8	111.8	82.8	92.9
0310	Concrete Forming & Accessories	96.8	118.9	113.9	83.6	115.4	108.3	87.5	88.2	88.1	83.3	97.0	93.9	88.1	76.6	79.2	101.2	65.3	73.3
0320	Concrete Reinforcing	99.8	107.8	102.0	95.2	107.5	98.6	96.1	103.5	98.1	94.9	107.3	98.4	94.9	105.8	98.0	87.4	60.9	80.1
0330	Cast-in-Place Concrete	141.5	119.7	133.8	107.5	115.1	110.2	111.2	89.3	103.4	109.2	110.2	109.6	94.5	78.8	88.9	128.8	65.8	106.4
03	CONCRETE	120.1	117.7	119.1	94.8	114.5	102.6	98.0	92.5	95.8	94.9	104.5	98.7	87.0	84.0	85.8	100.8	66.4	87.2
04	MASONRY	110.6	124.9	119.3	116.1	118.3	117.4	106.4	99.9	102.5	119.1	114.9	116.6	131.5	83.7	102.5	76.9	60.7	67.0
05	METALS	98.3	122.9	103.2	92.6	122.8	98.5	91.2	118.1	96.5	91.7	122.0	97.7	91.6	117.8	96.8	92.3	88.8	91.6
06	WOOD, PLASTICS & COMPOSITES	93.5	116.2	103.7	79.0	113.7	94.5	72.1	84.7	77.8	78.6	91.6	84.4	84.6	72.5	79.2	97.1	65.7	83.0
07	THERMAL & MOISTURE PROTECTION	105.1	119.7	110.3	104.8	113.2	107.8	107.9	91.2	102.0	104.7	104.4	104.6	104.7	76.5	94.6	102.1	61.2	87.5
08	OPENINGS	98.3	125.0	104.3	87.9	123.7	96.0	95.8	106.6	98.2	85.1	111.4	91.0	88.4	96.1	90.1	96.2	60.3	88.1
0920	Plaster & Gypsum Board	88.3	117.0	106.5	79.1	114.9	101.8	94.4	84.9	88.3	79.1	92.1	87.4	79.1	72.4	74.9	109.6	65.3	81.5
0950, 0980	Ceilings & Acoustic Treatment	102.4	117.0	110.6	63.9	114.9	92.5	119.3	84.9	100.0	63.9	92.1	79.7	63.9	72.4	68.7	85.0	65.3	74.0
0960	Flooring	100.9	120.8	105.9	92.3	88.1	91.3	95.9	76.6	91.1	93.9	90.2	93.0	95.9	76.6	91.1	101.7	60.4	91.3
0970, 0990	Wall Finishes & Painting/Coating	98.4	127.2	115.6	96.6	126.7	114.5	90.8	94.2	92.8	90.8	94.2	92.8	90.8	98.4	95.3	91.9	46.0	64.5
09	FINISHES	98.7	120.1	109.4	82.0	112.1	97.1	99.9	86.9	93.4	82.2	95.0	88.6	82.4	78.3	80.3	95.7	62.4	79.0
COVERS	DIVS. 10 - 14, 25, 28, 41, 43, 44, 46	100.0	107.5	101.5	100.0	105.2	101.0	100.0	98.8	99.8	100.0	101.6	100.3	100.0	95.6	99.2	100.0	82.1	96.5
21, 22, 23	FIRE SUPPRESSION, PLUMBING & HVAC	99.9	116.7	105.9	99.3	113.3	104.3	92.8	85.2	90.1	91.8	105.6	96.7	91.8	78.8	87.1	100.0	53.7	83.4
26, 27, 3370	ELECTRICAL, COMMUNICATIONS & UTIL.	99.5	118.1	107.6	99.5	118.1	107.6	99.1	77.9	89.9	99.5	92.8	96.6	102.9	96.1	99.9	98.8	51.9	78.5
MF2018	WEIGHTED AVERAGE	102.0	117.9	107.9	95.4	114.2	102.3	95.6	91.8	94.2	93.4	103.8	97.2	93.5	88.3	91.6	97.1	64.0	84.9

	DIVISION	MISSISSIPPI																	
		CLARKSDALE 386			COLUMBUS 397			GREENVILLE 387			GREENWOOD 389			JACKSON 390 - 392			LAUREL 394		
		MAT.	INST.	TOTAL	MAT.	INST.	TOTAL	MAT.	INST.	TOTAL	MAT.	INST.	TOTAL	MAT.	INST.	TOTAL	MAT.	INST.	TOTAL
015433	CONTRACTOR EQUIPMENT		96.7	96.7		96.7	96.7		96.7	96.7		96.7	96.7		101.6	101.6		96.7	96.7
0241, 31 - 34	SITE & INFRASTRUCTURE, DEMOLITION	108.1	80.9	90.4	108.7	81.6	91.0	116.5	82.8	94.5	111.6	80.7	91.4	107.7	91.4	97.1	114.2	81.0	92.5
0310	Concrete Forming & Accessories	86.4	40.2	50.5	87.4	42.3	52.3	82.7	59.2	64.4	97.2	40.4	53.1	103.9	67.3	75.5	87.6	54.3	61.8
0320	Concrete Reinforcing	98.6	59.8	87.9	93.5	59.9	84.2	99.2	60.0	88.4	98.6	59.8	87.9	98.6	65.0	89.3	94.1	29.5	76.2
0330	Cast-in-Place Concrete	105.9	55.1	87.9	131.4	57.1	105.0	109.1	64.3	93.2	113.9	54.9	92.9	111.0	70.3	96.5	128.4	56.3	102.8
03	CONCRETE	95.3	51.0	77.8	102.5	52.7	82.8	99.2	63.0	84.9	100.9	51.0	81.2	98.6	69.4	87.1	103.6	52.6	83.5
04	MASONRY	87.0	47.0	62.7	96.2	49.5	67.9	126.1	61.2	86.7	87.7	46.9	63.0	82.0	64.2	71.2	92.9	49.5	66.5
05	METALS	95.5	84.1	93.2	88.6	86.4	88.2	96.5	88.4	94.9	95.5	83.9	93.2	98.1	87.8	96.1	88.7	73.7	85.8
06	WOOD, PLASTICS & COMPOSITES	78.3	40.4	61.3	77.9	41.2	61.4	73.7	57.1	66.3	93.6	40.4	69.8	101.9	67.6	86.5	79.5	58.6	70.1
07	THERMAL & MOISTURE PROTECTION	99.7	47.2	81.0	101.9	50.3	83.5	100.0	60.6	86.0	100.1	49.2	82.0	99.8	64.6	87.2	102.0	52.3	84.3
08	OPENINGS	95.6	43.7	83.9	95.9	44.1	84.2	95.4	53.4	85.9	95.6	43.7	83.9	98.3	60.3	89.7	93.6	47.0	83.1
0920	Plaster & Gypsum Board	88.8	39.3	57.4	96.9	40.0	60.8	87.9	56.4	67.9	101.4	39.3	62.0	94.9	66.9	77.1	96.9	58.0	72.2
0950, 0980	Ceilings & Acoustic Treatment	85.0	39.3	59.4	78.6	40.0	57.0	86.0	56.4	69.4	85.0	39.3	59.4	89.1	66.9	76.6	78.6	58.0	67.0
0960	Flooring	102.7	60.4	92.1	97.5	60.4	88.2	101.4	60.4	91.1	106.9	60.4	95.2	98.8	65.3	90.4	96.6	60.4	87.5
0970, 0990	Wall Finishes & Painting/Coating	96.5	41.7	63.8	91.9	41.7	61.9	96.5	54.5	71.5	96.5	41.7	63.8	99.1	54.5	72.5	91.9	41.7	61.9
09	FINISHES	94.6	43.8	69.1	91.1	44.8	67.9	95.0	58.5	76.6	97.9	43.8	70.7	96.2	65.7	80.9	91.4	55.1	73.1
COVERS	DIVS. 10 - 14, 25, 28, 41, 43, 44, 46	100.0	43.2	89.0	100.0	44.1	89.2	100.0	81.4	96.4	100.0	43.2	89.0	100.0	83.3	96.8	100.0	31.0	86.6
21, 22, 23	FIRE SUPPRESSION, PLUMBING & HVAC	96.3	46.1	78.3	95.8	47.9	78.6	100.1	54.1	83.6	96.3	46.5	78.5	100.1	59.7	85.6	95.9	42.8	76.9
26, 27, 3370	ELECTRICAL, COMMUNICATIONS & UTIL.	98.0	37.0	71.6	97.5	49.0	76.5	98.0	56.1	79.8	98.0	34.7	70.6	101.3	56.1	81.7	98.3	51.6	78.0
MF2018	WEIGHTED AVERAGE	96.2	51.3	79.7	95.6	54.4	80.4	99.4	63.3	86.1	97.3	51.0	80.3	98.7	67.8	87.3	95.7	53.7	80.2

	DIVISION	MISSISSIPPI									MISSOURI								
		MCCOMB 396			MERIDIAN 393			TUPELO 388			BOWLING GREEN 633			CAPE GIRARDEAU 637			CHILLICOTHE 646		
		MAT.	INST.	TOTAL	MAT.	INST.	TOTAL	MAT.	INST.	TOTAL	MAT.	INST.	TOTAL	MAT.	INST.	TOTAL	MAT.	INST.	TOTAL
015433	CONTRACTOR EQUIPMENT		96.7	96.7		96.7	96.7		96.7	96.7		103.2	103.2		103.2	103.2		97.8	97.8
0241, 31 - 34	SITE & INFRASTRUCTURE, DEMOLITION	101.2	80.8	87.9	107.2	82.8	91.3	106.2	80.8	89.7	83.6	85.6	84.9	88.0	85.7	86.5	98.1	84.0	88.9
0310	Concrete Forming & Accessories	87.5	41.5	51.7	84.2	66.1	70.1	83.2	41.7	51.0	96.6	85.3	87.8	88.6	76.7	79.3	86.7	86.8	86.8
0320	Concrete Reinforcing	94.7	30.9	77.0	93.5	64.8	85.6	96.5	59.7	86.3	102.9	86.6	98.4	104.2	80.0	97.5	101.5	92.1	98.9
0330	Cast-in-Place Concrete	114.0	54.7	92.9	122.0	66.0	102.1	105.9	55.9	88.1	79.5	87.1	82.2	78.7	80.8	79.4	93.4	78.6	88.1
03	CONCRETE	93.6	46.4	75.0	97.2	67.5	85.5	94.5	51.9	77.7	90.0	87.8	89.1	89.2	80.6	85.8	95.5	85.9	91.7
04	MASONRY	96.4	46.5	66.1	76.4	60.9	67.0	115.4	48.0	74.4	106.6	88.2	95.4	104.1	75.3	86.6	101.7	83.0	90.4
05	METALS	88.9	72.8	85.7	89.7	90.4	89.9	95.3	83.7	93.0	85.8	111.3	90.8	86.8	107.8	91.0	81.2	104.8	85.9
06	WOOD, PLASTICS & COMPOSITES	77.9	42.6	62.1	74.1	66.3	70.6	74.5	41.2	59.5	95.4	85.7	91.0	85.3	74.9	80.6	84.7	88.0	86.2
07	THERMAL & MOISTURE PROTECTION	101.5	49.2	82.9	101.6	61.7	87.4	99.7	47.5	81.1	101.4	88.9	97.0	100.8	78.0	92.7	99.4	83.1	93.6
08	OPENINGS	96.0	37.5	82.8	95.7	62.6	88.2	95.6	46.6	84.6	93.1	89.0	92.2	93.1	73.4	88.7	85.6	87.1	85.9
0920	Plaster & Gypsum Board	96.9	41.5	61.7	96.9	66.0	77.3	87.9	40.0	57.5	79.1	85.8	83.3	78.7	74.6	76.1	74.0	87.8	82.8
0950, 0980	Ceilings & Acoustic Treatment	78.6	41.5	57.8	79.1	66.0	71.7	85.0	40.0	59.8	90.5	85.8	87.9	90.5	74.6	81.6	87.9	87.8	87.8
0960	Flooring	97.5	60.4	88.2	96.6	60.4	87.5	101.6	60.4	91.3	100.4	86.8	97.0	97.5	79.4	93.0	104.7	89.3	100.8
0970, 0990	Wall Finishes & Painting/Coating	91.9	41.7	61.9	91.9	53.5	69.0	96.5	40.2	62.9	95.0	94.4	94.7	95.0	71.6	81.0	93.0	91.7	92.2
09	FINISHES	90.5	45.0	67.6	90.7	63.7	77.1	94.2	44.6	69.3	93.9	86.3	90.1	92.9	75.9	84.4	94.8	88.0	91.4
COVERS	DIVS. 10 - 14, 25, 28, 41, 43, 44, 46	100.0	45.7	89.5	100.0	82.2	96.6	100.0	44.1	89.2	100.0	95.5	99.1	100.0	94.4	98.9	100.0	95.2	99.1
21, 22, 23	FIRE SUPPRESSION, PLUMBING & HVAC	95.8	45.6	77.8	100.0	58.0	84.9	96.5	47.4	78.9	92.4	89.4	91.3	99.9	92.7	97.3	92.5	89.8	91.5
26, 27, 3370	ELECTRICAL, COMMUNICATIONS & UTIL.	96.7	49.8	76.4	98.3	53.7	79.0	97.9	49.0	76.7	95.5	68.4	83.8	95.5	87.7	92.1	93.7	67.5	82.3
MF2018	WEIGHTED AVERAGE	94.2	51.3	78.4	95.3	65.8	84.4	97.0	53.7	81.1	92.4	87.5	90.6	94.0	85.9	91.0	91.3	86.0	89.4

DIVISION		MISSOURI																	
		COLUMBIA			FLAT RIVER			HANNIBAL			HARRISONVILLE			JEFFERSON CITY			JOPLIN		
		652			636			634			647			650 - 651			648		
		MAT.	INST.	TOTAL	MAT.	INST.	TOTAL	MAT.	INST.	TOTAL	MAT.	INST.	TOTAL	MAT.	INST.	TOTAL	MAT.	INST.	TOTAL
015433	**CONTRACTOR EQUIPMENT**		105.5	105.5		103.2	103.2		103.2	103.2		97.8	97.8		112.0	112.0		100.8	100.8
0241, 31 - 34	**SITE & INFRASTRUCTURE, DEMOLITION**	88.2	90.1	89.4	85.6	85.3	85.4	81.7	85.4	84.1	91.2	85.0	87.1	89.0	101.2	97.0	102.7	88.4	93.4
0310	Concrete Forming & Accessories	84.6	83.3	83.6	104.1	80.0	85.4	94.9	75.0	79.4	83.6	89.8	88.4	101.5	80.3	85.0	98.7	71.4	77.5
0320	Concrete Reinforcing	94.9	99.7	96.2	104.2	92.3	100.9	102.3	86.6	98.0	101.3	99.5	100.8	99.1	96.4	98.4	104.9	96.6	102.6
0330	Cast-in-Place Concrete	78.2	83.4	80.1	82.1	82.6	82.3	75.3	85.3	78.8	95.6	90.8	93.9	83.0	86.2	84.2	101.1	71.4	90.6
03	**CONCRETE**	80.7	87.9	83.6	92.7	84.8	89.6	87.0	82.5	85.2	92.9	92.8	92.9	88.3	86.7	87.7	96.8	77.0	89.0
04	**MASONRY**	126.2	86.8	102.3	104.2	68.8	82.7	98.4	85.2	90.4	95.8	89.6	92.0	88.3	87.0	87.5	95.2	79.2	85.5
05	**METALS**	97.2	117.9	101.3	85.7	112.4	90.9	85.8	110.9	90.7	81.6	108.9	87.0	97.2	113.3	100.3	83.6	103.2	87.5
06	**WOOD, PLASTICS & COMPOSITES**	76.4	81.5	78.7	105.8	81.3	94.8	93.0	73.7	84.3	80.7	89.5	84.7	99.0	77.2	89.2	98.5	70.7	86.0
07	**THERMAL & MOISTURE PROTECTION**	95.3	85.3	91.7	101.6	81.6	94.5	101.2	83.8	95.0	98.8	90.3	95.8	100.6	86.7	95.6	98.8	76.8	91.0
08	**OPENINGS**	97.9	85.1	95.0	93.1	88.3	92.0	93.1	75.9	89.2	85.5	93.5	87.3	97.6	81.9	94.1	86.5	73.8	83.6
0920	Plaster & Gypsum Board	75.0	81.3	79.0	85.7	81.2	82.9	78.9	73.4	75.4	72.4	89.4	83.2	84.2	76.4	79.3	80.9	69.9	73.9
0950, 0980	Ceilings & Acoustic Treatment	88.6	81.3	84.5	90.5	81.2	85.3	90.5	73.4	80.9	87.9	89.4	88.7	95.4	76.4	84.8	89.2	69.9	78.4
0960	Flooring	96.5	99.0	97.2	103.3	75.7	96.4	99.8	86.8	96.5	99.1	90.2	96.9	100.4	96.1	99.3	133.8	67.1	117.1
0970, 0990	Wall Finishes & Painting/Coating	98.3	81.1	88.1	95.0	63.7	76.4	95.0	83.6	88.2	97.5	95.8	96.5	99.1	81.1	88.4	92.7	67.4	77.6
09	**FINISHES**	87.8	85.4	86.6	95.7	76.8	86.2	93.5	77.0	85.2	92.6	90.3	91.4	95.4	82.3	88.8	103.6	70.2	86.8
COVERS	**DIVS. 10 - 14, 25, 28, 41, 43, 44, 46**	100.0	94.7	99.0	100.0	89.2	97.9	100.0	93.3	98.7	100.0	96.5	99.3	100.0	96.6	99.3	100.0	92.2	98.5
21, 22, 23	**FIRE SUPPRESSION, PLUMBING & HVAC**	99.9	94.2	97.8	92.4	87.0	90.4	92.4	87.8	90.7	92.5	90.6	91.8	99.9	97.8	99.2	100.1	66.0	87.8
26, 27, 3370	**ELECTRICAL, COMMUNICATIONS & UTIL.**	92.9	80.9	87.7	97.9	87.7	93.4	94.9	68.4	83.4	97.0	90.1	94.0	97.9	80.9	90.5	92.5	69.1	82.4
MF2018	**WEIGHTED AVERAGE**	95.6	90.7	93.8	93.1	85.8	90.4	91.5	84.0	88.8	90.8	92.2	91.3	96.5	91.3	94.6	94.2	76.5	87.7

DIVISION		MISSOURI																	
		KANSAS CITY			KIRKSVILLE			POPLAR BLUFF			ROLLA			SEDALIA			SIKESTON		
		640 - 641			635			639			654 - 655			653			638		
		MAT.	INST.	TOTAL	MAT.	INST.	TOTAL	MAT.	INST.	TOTAL	MAT.	INST.	TOTAL	MAT.	INST.	TOTAL	MAT.	INST.	TOTAL
015433	**CONTRACTOR EQUIPMENT**		103.4	103.4		94.5	94.5		96.5	96.5		105.5	105.5		96.7	96.7		96.5	96.5
0241, 31 - 34	**SITE & INFRASTRUCTURE, DEMOLITION**	96.1	97.8	97.2	83.4	81.0	81.8	73.4	84.2	80.5	84.0	89.5	87.6	83.2	84.7	84.2	76.1	84.8	81.8
0310	Concrete Forming & Accessories	99.0	101.5	100.9	86.7	71.2	74.7	86.9	71.9	75.3	93.3	92.2	92.4	91.4	71.0	75.5	87.7	71.9	75.5
0320	Concrete Reinforcing	99.7	107.7	101.9	102.5	74.8	94.8	105.7	68.2	95.3	95.4	95.3	95.4	93.6	98.9	95.1	105.0	68.2	94.8
0330	Cast-in-Place Concrete	99.2	100.5	99.7	82.0	75.2	79.6	63.1	76.3	67.8	80.1	91.9	84.3	83.6	74.3	80.3	67.5	76.3	70.6
03	**CONCRETE**	96.6	102.6	99.0	100.4	74.7	90.2	82.4	74.2	79.2	82.5	94.1	87.1	91.4	78.4	86.3	85.1	74.2	80.8
04	**MASONRY**	101.4	98.6	99.7	110.3	76.4	89.7	102.3	66.7	80.7	102.6	83.4	90.9	108.4	73.5	87.2	102.0	66.7	80.6
05	**METALS**	97.0	109.7	99.5	86.2	96.1	88.2	86.7	93.0	87.9	96.5	115.4	100.2	97.5	106.6	99.3	87.6	93.0	88.6
06	**WOOD, PLASTICS & COMPOSITES**	96.7	102.0	99.0	79.2	69.5	74.8	77.9	72.6	75.5	86.2	94.0	89.7	81.0	69.7	75.9	79.9	72.6	76.6
07	**THERMAL & MOISTURE PROTECTION**	100.2	103.6	101.4	106.6	81.4	97.7	105.1	74.5	94.2	95.6	89.7	93.5	100.3	78.7	92.6	105.2	73.7	94.0
08	**OPENINGS**	100.6	101.5	100.8	98.1	71.5	92.1	99.0	68.2	92.0	97.9	90.7	96.2	103.8	78.8	98.2	99.0	68.2	92.0
0920	Plaster & Gypsum Board	82.0	102.0	94.7	73.0	69.1	70.5	73.6	72.3	72.8	76.4	94.2	87.7	71.8	69.1	70.1	76.0	72.3	73.7
0950, 0980	Ceilings & Acoustic Treatment	94.1	102.0	98.5	88.7	69.1	77.7	90.5	72.3	80.3	88.6	94.2	91.7	88.6	69.1	77.7	90.5	72.3	80.3
0960	Flooring	103.3	99.3	102.3	75.8	86.4	78.4	91.6	75.7	87.6	99.1	90.6	97.0	74.2	65.3	71.9	92.1	75.7	88.0
0970, 0990	Wall Finishes & Painting/Coating	99.1	109.2	105.1	90.6	69.6	78.1	89.9	59.6	71.8	98.3	87.2	91.7	98.3	91.7	94.4	89.9	59.6	71.8
09	**FINISHES**	96.5	102.0	99.3	89.9	73.2	81.5	91.6	70.7	81.1	88.8	91.3	90.1	84.7	71.3	78.0	92.2	71.0	81.6
COVERS	**DIVS. 10 - 14, 25, 28, 41, 43, 44, 46**	100.0	99.5	99.9	100.0	92.8	98.6	100.0	92.0	98.4	100.0	97.0	99.4	100.0	90.9	98.2	100.0	87.6	97.6
21, 22, 23	**FIRE SUPPRESSION, PLUMBING & HVAC**	99.8	101.3	100.4	92.4	87.3	90.6	92.4	85.3	89.9	92.3	95.5	93.5	92.3	85.3	89.8	92.4	85.3	89.9
26, 27, 3370	**ELECTRICAL, COMMUNICATIONS & UTIL.**	99.4	97.3	98.5	93.9	68.3	82.8	94.5	87.6	91.5	92.2	76.2	85.3	91.9	90.1	91.1	94.1	87.6	91.3
MF2018	**WEIGHTED AVERAGE**	98.6	101.2	99.6	93.8	79.5	88.5	91.4	80.1	87.2	93.1	91.8	92.6	94.8	83.5	90.7	92.0	80.0	87.6

DIVISION		MISSOURI									MONTANA								
		SPRINGFIELD			ST. JOSEPH			ST. LOUIS			BILLINGS			BUTTE			GREAT FALLS		
		656 - 658			644 - 645			630 - 631			590 - 591			597			594		
		MAT.	INST.	TOTAL	MAT.	INST.	TOTAL	MAT.	INST.	TOTAL	MAT.	INST.	TOTAL	MAT.	INST.	TOTAL	MAT.	INST.	TOTAL
015433	**CONTRACTOR EQUIPMENT**		98.8	98.8		97.8	97.8		107.6	107.6		94.4	94.4		94.2	94.2		94.2	94.2
0241, 31 - 34	**SITE & INFRASTRUCTURE, DEMOLITION**	88.1	88.8	88.6	97.8	83.6	88.5	93.6	99.1	97.2	85.5	89.4	88.0	88.0	88.6	88.4	91.0	88.9	89.6
0310	Concrete Forming & Accessories	100.5	77.4	82.6	97.5	89.9	91.6	101.4	102.6	102.4	100.9	68.0	75.4	86.2	65.3	69.9	101.0	65.4	73.4
0320	Concrete Reinforcing	90.9	99.3	93.3	98.3	102.4	99.4	100.1	103.8	101.1	91.0	80.3	88.1	98.9	79.6	93.6	91.2	80.0	88.1
0330	Cast-in-Place Concrete	85.0	76.5	82.0	93.9	95.0	94.3	88.9	103.6	94.1	126.3	71.2	106.7	139.1	67.2	113.5	147.0	68.9	119.2
03	**CONCRETE**	88.9	82.0	86.2	92.3	94.8	93.3	93.2	104.1	97.5	103.8	72.2	91.4	108.2	69.5	92.9	112.2	70.2	95.6
04	**MASONRY**	82.9	84.7	84.0	96.4	87.7	91.1	84.0	105.4	97.0	146.7	84.3	108.8	142.4	71.7	99.4	147.9	76.5	104.6
05	**METALS**	104.4	105.0	104.5	88.5	110.5	92.8	97.5	116.7	101.3	104.6	89.5	101.6	98.4	88.1	96.4	101.7	89.0	99.2
06	**WOOD, PLASTICS & COMPOSITES**	90.3	75.1	83.5	98.5	90.3	94.8	100.3	101.6	100.9	99.2	64.1	83.5	82.2	62.6	73.4	100.9	62.6	83.7
07	**THERMAL & MOISTURE PROTECTION**	99.0	77.9	91.5	99.2	87.8	95.1	101.1	103.3	101.9	101.8	72.9	91.5	101.5	65.6	88.7	102.1	68.5	90.1
08	**OPENINGS**	105.9	87.4	101.7	89.8	95.8	91.2	99.1	105.7	100.6	101.7	64.9	93.4	100.0	63.4	91.8	102.9	67.6	94.9
0920	Plaster & Gypsum Board	77.6	74.7	75.7	83.4	90.2	87.7	81.7	102.0	94.5	121.4	63.6	84.7	114.5	62.0	81.2	127.7	62.0	86.0
0950, 0980	Ceilings & Acoustic Treatment	88.6	74.7	80.8	96.9	90.2	93.2	87.2	102.0	95.5	108.1	63.6	83.2	111.4	62.0	83.7	113.7	62.0	84.7
0960	Flooring	96.0	73.4	90.3	108.7	93.7	104.9	102.0	96.8	100.7	95.5	77.5	91.0	94.9	74.6	89.8	99.9	72.3	93.0
0970, 0990	Wall Finishes & Painting/Coating	92.2	101.4	97.7	93.0	106.7	101.2	99.1	105.6	103.0	92.2	86.5	88.8	90.5	60.2	72.4	90.5	85.0	87.2
09	**FINISHES**	90.1	79.3	84.7	99.1	92.5	95.8	94.3	101.5	97.9	99.8	70.9	85.3	99.4	65.9	82.5	103.4	67.9	85.6
COVERS	**DIVS. 10 - 14, 25, 28, 41, 43, 44, 46**	100.0	94.1	98.8	100.0	96.1	99.2	100.0	101.3	100.3	100.0	94.4	98.9	100.0	93.3	98.7	100.0	93.0	98.7
21, 22, 23	**FIRE SUPPRESSION, PLUMBING & HVAC**	99.9	72.5	90.1	100.1	85.6	94.9	99.9	104.4	101.5	99.9	75.5	91.2	99.9	64.6	87.3	99.9	71.0	89.6
26, 27, 3370	**ELECTRICAL, COMMUNICATIONS & UTIL.**	94.2	67.8	82.8	97.1	74.0	87.1	99.2	102.8	100.8	95.1	72.9	85.5	98.3	65.2	83.9	94.6	67.8	83.0
MF2018	**WEIGHTED AVERAGE**	97.7	81.0	91.6	95.1	89.3	93.0	97.3	104.5	99.9	102.5	77.4	93.3	101.6	71.1	90.4	103.4	74.1	92.6

DIVISION		MONTANA																	
		HAVRE			HELENA			KALISPELL			MILES CITY			MISSOULA			WOLF POINT		
		595			596			599			593			598			592		
		MAT.	INST.	TOTAL	MAT.	INST.	TOTAL	MAT.	INST.	TOTAL	MAT.	INST.	TOTAL	MAT.	INST.	TOTAL	MAT.	INST.	TOTAL
015433	CONTRACTOR EQUIPMENT		94.2	94.2		101.0	101.0		94.2	94.2		94.2	94.2		94.2	94.2		94.2	94.2
0241, 31 - 34	SITE & INFRASTRUCTURE, DEMOLITION	89.4	88.0	88.5	83.2	99.3	93.7	77.5	88.2	84.5	81.8	88.1	85.9	75.8	88.2	83.9	93.0	88.1	89.8
0310	Concrete Forming & Accessories	78.2	63.8	67.0	103.5	65.0	73.6	90.0	64.8	70.4	99.0	64.0	71.8	90.0	65.2	70.7	90.5	64.0	69.9
0320	Concrete Reinforcing	99.7	80.3	94.3	101.3	80.2	95.4	101.5	81.9	96.1	99.1	80.4	93.9	100.6	81.7	95.3	100.5	80.4	95.0
0330	Cast-in-Place Concrete	149.8	65.2	119.7	107.1	68.5	93.4	120.7	66.3	101.4	132.2	65.3	108.4	102.4	66.9	89.8	148.1	64.3	118.3
03	CONCRETE	115.0	68.2	96.5	103.8	69.7	90.3	99.5	69.3	87.6	105.9	68.3	91.0	89.3	69.6	81.5	118.1	68.0	98.3
04	MASONRY	143.6	72.6	100.5	128.9	70.6	93.5	141.1	74.4	100.6	150.1	72.6	103.0	172.0	71.4	110.9	151.6	72.6	103.6
05	METALS	94.6	87.3	93.2	100.0	84.9	97.0	94.5	88.0	93.2	93.9	87.4	92.6	95.0	87.8	93.6	94.0	87.4	92.7
06	WOOD, PLASTICS & COMPOSITES	71.2	62.6	67.4	104.9	62.9	86.0	86.8	62.6	76.0	96.8	62.6	81.5	86.8	62.6	76.0	85.4	62.6	75.2
07	THERMAL & MOISTURE PROTECTION	101.7	59.9	86.8	103.0	66.7	90.1	101.2	66.5	88.8	101.5	61.1	87.1	100.9	67.6	89.0	102.2	61.0	87.5
08	OPENINGS	100.5	63.5	92.2	99.4	63.7	91.3	100.5	63.8	92.2	100.0	63.5	91.8	100.1	63.8	91.9	100.0	63.5	91.8
0920	Plaster & Gypsum Board	108.9	62.0	79.2	117.5	62.0	82.3	114.5	62.0	81.2	125.3	62.0	85.1	114.5	62.0	81.2	117.3	62.0	82.2
0950, 0980	Ceilings & Acoustic Treatment	111.4	62.0	83.7	115.4	62.0	85.5	111.4	62.0	83.7	106.0	62.0	81.3	111.4	62.0	83.7	106.0	62.0	81.3
0960	Flooring	93.3	81.4	90.3	106.4	74.6	98.4	96.3	81.4	92.5	99.9	81.4	95.2	96.3	74.6	90.8	97.2	81.4	93.3
0970, 0990	Wall Finishes & Painting/Coating	90.5	60.2	72.4	99.1	53.4	71.8	90.5	80.9	84.7	90.5	60.2	72.4	90.5	80.9	84.7	90.5	60.2	72.4
09	FINISHES	98.6	66.6	82.5	107.3	65.1	86.1	99.3	69.3	84.3	100.7	66.6	83.6	98.9	68.1	83.5	99.9	66.6	83.2
COVERS	DIVS. 10 - 14, 25, 28, 41, 43, 44, 46	100.0	79.7	96.1	100.0	87.1	97.5	100.0	80.3	96.2	100.0	79.7	96.1	100.0	86.7	97.4	100.0	79.7	96.1
21, 22, 23	FIRE SUPPRESSION, PLUMBING & HVAC	92.4	62.0	81.5	100.1	64.2	87.2	92.4	62.4	81.6	92.4	67.7	83.6	99.9	64.5	87.2	92.4	67.7	83.6
26, 27, 3370	ELECTRICAL, COMMUNICATIONS & UTIL.	94.6	61.6	80.3	101.2	65.5	85.7	96.7	60.6	81.1	94.6	66.3	82.3	97.2	63.9	82.8	94.6	66.3	82.3
MF2018	WEIGHTED AVERAGE	99.5	69.4	88.4	101.9	71.3	90.6	97.6	70.3	87.6	98.7	71.3	88.6	99.3	71.0	88.9	100.4	71.3	89.6

DIVISION		NEBRASKA																	
		ALLIANCE			COLUMBUS			GRAND ISLAND			HASTINGS			LINCOLN			MCCOOK		
		693			686			688			689			683 - 685			690		
		MAT.	INST.	TOTAL	MAT.	INST.	TOTAL	MAT.	INST.	TOTAL	MAT.	INST.	TOTAL	MAT.	INST.	TOTAL	MAT.	INST.	TOTAL
015433	CONTRACTOR EQUIPMENT		92.1	92.1		98.1	98.1		98.1	98.1		98.1	98.1		104.1	104.1		98.1	98.1
0241, 31 - 34	SITE & INFRASTRUCTURE, DEMOLITION	92.5	90.8	91.4	91.9	85.8	87.9	98.8	86.7	90.9	94.5	85.8	88.8	91.0	97.0	94.9	91.4	85.8	87.8
0310	Concrete Forming & Accessories	89.6	50.3	59.1	101.0	68.1	75.4	100.5	77.8	82.9	104.5	65.8	74.5	100.3	70.2	76.9	95.3	50.8	60.7
0320	Concrete Reinforcing	110.9	78.4	101.9	100.5	77.1	94.0	99.9	78.4	94.0	99.9	68.3	91.2	98.6	78.7	93.1	106.2	68.5	95.8
0330	Cast-in-Place Concrete	97.4	74.7	89.4	97.8	74.7	89.6	103.5	73.1	92.7	103.5	67.8	90.8	81.9	79.3	81.0	105.3	67.7	91.9
03	CONCRETE	108.2	64.7	91.0	97.3	73.3	87.8	100.8	77.4	91.5	101.1	68.3	88.2	91.0	75.9	85.0	101.0	61.5	85.4
04	MASONRY	109.3	69.8	85.3	104.4	69.7	83.3	97.8	69.4	80.6	104.6	66.6	81.6	88.5	73.5	79.4	104.2	69.7	83.3
05	METALS	97.9	81.5	94.6	92.9	93.1	93.0	94.7	94.7	94.7	95.2	89.2	94.0	102.6	92.2	100.5	92.9	89.2	92.2
06	WOOD, PLASTICS & COMPOSITES	81.1	44.4	64.6	93.9	68.0	82.3	93.0	78.6	86.5	97.9	65.4	83.3	97.0	68.3	84.1	89.3	45.2	69.6
07	THERMAL & MOISTURE PROTECTION	105.6	68.0	92.2	105.5	72.1	93.6	105.7	75.7	95.0	105.7	69.6	92.9	101.1	75.3	91.9	101.9	68.2	89.9
08	OPENINGS	88.4	52.7	80.3	88.4	66.8	83.5	88.4	76.9	85.8	88.4	63.3	82.7	98.1	65.0	90.7	88.9	50.6	80.3
0920	Plaster & Gypsum Board	73.3	43.0	54.1	91.3	67.3	76.1	90.5	78.3	82.8	92.2	64.7	74.8	103.9	67.3	80.7	80.0	43.9	57.1
0950, 0980	Ceilings & Acoustic Treatment	92.0	43.0	64.6	88.8	67.3	76.8	88.8	78.3	82.9	88.8	64.7	75.3	115.4	67.3	88.5	89.8	43.9	64.1
0960	Flooring	97.2	78.2	92.4	87.3	78.2	85.0	87.1	70.7	83.0	88.1	72.8	84.2	100.1	77.5	94.4	93.8	78.2	89.9
0970, 0990	Wall Finishes & Painting/Coating	158.6	45.9	91.4	74.2	53.4	61.8	74.2	73.3	73.6	74.2	53.4	61.8	99.1	70.5	82.0	87.9	40.0	59.3
09	FINISHES	93.3	53.5	73.3	87.9	68.2	78.0	87.9	76.0	81.9	88.5	65.6	77.0	104.1	71.1	87.5	90.1	53.3	71.6
COVERS	DIVS. 10 - 14, 25, 28, 41, 43, 44, 46	100.0	84.2	96.9	100.0	86.9	97.5	100.0	89.3	97.9	100.0	86.6	97.4	100.0	88.9	97.8	100.0	84.4	97.0
21, 22, 23	FIRE SUPPRESSION, PLUMBING & HVAC	93.8	67.4	84.3	92.6	67.7	83.7	100.2	77.9	92.2	92.6	67.0	83.5	99.9	78.0	92.1	92.4	67.6	83.5
26, 27, 3370	ELECTRICAL, COMMUNICATIONS & UTIL.	90.2	58.4	76.4	91.3	72.5	83.1	90.6	61.1	77.8	90.3	70.7	81.8	99.7	61.1	82.9	91.2	58.5	77.0
MF2018	WEIGHTED AVERAGE	96.8	67.0	85.9	93.8	73.9	86.5	96.1	76.9	89.0	94.8	71.5	86.2	98.9	76.4	90.6	94.2	66.9	84.2

DIVISION		NEBRASKA												NEVADA					
		NORFOLK			NORTH PLATTE			OMAHA			VALENTINE			CARSON CITY			ELKO		
		687			691			680 - 681			692			897			898		
		MAT.	INST.	TOTAL	MAT.	INST.	TOTAL	MAT.	INST.	TOTAL	MAT.	INST.	TOTAL	MAT.	INST.	TOTAL	MAT.	INST.	TOTAL
015433	CONTRACTOR EQUIPMENT		88.9	88.9		98.1	98.1		96.2	96.2		91.9	91.9		98.2	98.2		93.2	93.2
0241, 31 - 34	SITE & INFRASTRUCTURE, DEMOLITION	76.6	85.0	82.1	95.8	85.7	89.2	86.7	97.1	93.5	79.4	89.9	86.3	85.6	97.0	93.1	71.1	87.5	81.8
0310	Concrete Forming & Accessories	86.4	67.2	71.5	98.3	69.0	75.6	101.0	76.5	82.0	86.1	48.6	56.9	102.0	79.6	84.6	105.8	87.0	91.2
0320	Concrete Reinforcing	100.6	59.7	89.3	105.7	73.3	96.7	100.0	79.1	94.2	106.3	59.6	93.3	101.9	110.9	104.4	102.9	85.0	97.9
0330	Cast-in-Place Concrete	98.4	65.2	86.6	105.3	63.1	90.3	80.9	81.8	81.2	92.9	50.0	77.7	88.8	80.8	86.0	83.2	66.5	77.3
03	CONCRETE	95.7	66.0	84.0	101.1	69.0	88.4	91.0	79.2	86.3	98.1	52.3	80.0	102.0	85.5	95.5	93.1	79.6	87.8
04	MASONRY	109.2	69.7	85.2	93.3	69.2	78.7	89.5	80.5	84.0	104.3	69.2	83.0	131.3	63.2	89.9	141.6	61.0	92.6
05	METALS	96.2	77.0	92.4	92.5	91.4	92.2	103.1	85.1	99.5	103.5	76.4	98.2	103.3	92.4	101.2	107.5	83.7	102.8
06	WOOD, PLASTICS & COMPOSITES	78.2	67.6	73.4	92.1	69.8	82.1	98.6	76.1	88.5	77.1	43.2	61.9	102.1	80.4	92.4	114.4	92.8	104.7
07	THERMAL & MOISTURE PROTECTION	104.4	70.2	92.2	101.8	71.9	91.1	104.0	81.8	96.1	101.3	66.3	88.9	97.6	77.7	90.5	94.2	66.1	84.2
08	OPENINGS	89.1	62.2	83.1	88.3	70.0	84.2	98.1	77.5	93.5	89.8	48.5	80.4	97.8	78.8	93.5	98.5	80.1	94.3
0920	Plaster & Gypsum Board	92.0	67.3	76.3	80.0	69.2	73.2	99.2	75.8	84.3	82.7	42.2	57.0	117.4	79.8	93.6	129.8	92.8	106.4
0950, 0980	Ceilings & Acoustic Treatment	102.0	67.3	82.6	89.8	69.2	78.3	103.3	75.8	87.9	105.0	42.2	69.8	108.8	79.8	92.5	103.7	92.8	97.6
0960	Flooring	113.5	78.2	104.6	94.7	70.7	88.7	100.1	90.0	97.5	124.7	78.2	113.1	101.0	60.1	90.7	98.5	60.1	88.9
0970, 0990	Wall Finishes & Painting/Coating	133.8	53.4	85.8	87.9	69.1	76.7	99.1	58.6	74.9	157.4	54.2	95.9	99.1	79.4	87.4	94.5	70.5	80.2
09	FINISHES	106.5	67.8	87.1	90.4	69.3	79.8	99.9	76.9	88.3	111.7	53.5	82.5	103.9	75.6	89.7	100.6	81.6	91.0
COVERS	DIVS. 10 - 14, 25, 28, 41, 43, 44, 46	100.0	86.0	97.3	100.0	86.9	97.5	100.0	89.0	97.9	100.0	83.1	96.7	100.0	99.8	100.0	100.0	81.3	96.4
21, 22, 23	FIRE SUPPRESSION, PLUMBING & HVAC	92.2	66.8	83.1	99.9	69.6	89.0	99.9	76.6	91.6	91.8	66.1	82.6	100.1	76.8	91.7	96.1	69.0	86.4
26, 27, 3370	ELECTRICAL, COMMUNICATIONS & UTIL.	90.6	72.4	82.7	90.4	61.1	77.7	99.5	82.6	92.2	88.7	58.5	75.6	99.9	85.1	93.5	95.8	78.6	88.3
MF2018	WEIGHTED AVERAGE	95.2	70.8	86.2	95.4	72.1	86.8	98.7	81.2	92.3	97.0	64.2	85.0	101.9	81.5	94.4	100.3	76.4	91.5

DIVISION		NEVADA									NEW HAMPSHIRE								
		ELY			LAS VEGAS			RENO			CHARLESTON			CLAREMONT			CONCORD		
		893			889 - 891			894 - 895			036			037			032 - 033		
		MAT.	INST.	TOTAL	MAT.	INST.	TOTAL	MAT.	INST.	TOTAL	MAT.	INST.	TOTAL	MAT.	INST.	TOTAL	MAT.	INST.	TOTAL
015433	CONTRACTOR EQUIPMENT		93.2	93.2		93.2	93.2		93.2	93.2		93.0	93.0		93.0	93.0		97.1	97.1
0241, 31 - 34	SITE & INFRASTRUCTURE, DEMOLITION	76.1	88.5	84.2	80.5	92.9	88.6	77.8	89.2	85.2	77.0	91.2	86.2	72.6	91.2	84.7	88.1	101.3	96.7
0310	Concrete Forming & Accessories	97.4	91.7	93.0	98.7	108.4	106.2	94.0	79.6	82.8	89.0	78.1	80.5	96.1	78.1	82.1	104.6	91.5	94.4
0320	Concrete Reinforcing	101.7	85.2	97.1	94.1	125.2	102.7	96.2	123.1	103.6	84.5	86.6	85.1	84.5	86.6	85.1	97.6	87.1	94.7
0330	Cast-in-Place Concrete	89.3	86.8	88.4	86.5	109.4	94.6	94.5	78.6	88.8	70.4	105.6	82.9	64.7	105.6	79.2	85.7	113.3	95.5
03	CONCRETE	99.2	88.9	95.1	94.5	111.2	101.1	97.9	86.9	93.6	85.5	89.6	87.1	80.1	89.6	83.8	97.9	98.3	98.1
04	MASONRY	147.1	67.4	98.7	130.9	107.0	116.4	139.9	63.1	93.2	99.2	89.6	93.4	100.5	89.6	93.9	111.2	100.2	104.5
05	METALS	107.4	86.4	103.3	116.7	106.7	114.7	109.3	98.4	107.1	91.3	90.8	91.2	91.3	90.8	91.2	98.6	90.2	96.9
06	WOOD, PLASTICS & COMPOSITES	101.1	94.7	98.3	99.7	105.6	102.3	94.0	80.2	87.8	87.5	75.7	82.2	96.2	75.7	87.0	102.6	90.2	97.0
07	THERMAL & MOISTURE PROTECTION	94.5	82.7	90.3	103.5	102.2	103.1	94.1	75.4	87.4	94.9	96.8	95.6	94.8	96.8	95.5	97.8	107.1	101.1
08	OPENINGS	98.4	81.2	94.5	97.5	112.1	100.8	96.4	81.4	93.0	97.7	76.8	93.0	98.7	76.8	93.8	97.9	88.0	95.7
0920	Plaster & Gypsum Board	122.6	94.8	105.0	113.3	106.0	108.6	107.2	79.8	89.8	102.9	74.9	85.1	103.9	74.9	85.5	102.1	89.9	94.4
0950, 0980	Ceilings & Acoustic Treatment	103.7	94.8	98.7	111.8	106.0	108.5	107.7	79.8	92.1	88.2	74.9	80.7	88.2	74.9	80.7	82.7	89.9	86.8
0960	Flooring	96.9	60.1	87.7	88.7	104.7	92.7	94.8	60.1	86.1	95.8	101.3	97.2	98.0	101.3	98.8	103.1	105.4	103.7
0970, 0990	Wall Finishes & Painting/Coating	94.5	99.5	97.5	97.3	120.9	111.3	94.5	79.4	85.5	82.5	80.0	81.0	82.5	80.0	81.0	99.1	97.2	98.0
09	FINISHES	99.6	87.5	93.5	98.2	108.8	103.5	97.8	75.4	86.6	93.7	81.9	87.8	94.1	81.9	88.0	95.9	94.2	95.1
COVERS	DIVS. 10 - 14, 25, 28, 41, 43, 44, 46	100.0	63.4	92.9	100.0	106.1	101.2	100.0	99.3	99.9	100.0	79.4	96.0	100.0	79.4	96.0	100.0	106.3	101.2
21, 22, 23	FIRE SUPPRESSION, PLUMBING & HVAC	96.1	86.2	92.6	100.2	105.4	102.1	100.1	76.8	91.7	92.8	73.9	86.1	92.8	74.0	86.1	100.2	87.7	95.7
26, 27, 3370	ELECTRICAL, COMMUNICATIONS & UTIL.	96.1	82.8	90.3	101.9	107.8	104.5	96.1	85.1	91.3	101.0	67.0	86.3	101.0	67.0	86.3	101.6	74.7	90.0
MF2018	WEIGHTED AVERAGE	101.1	83.6	94.7	103.7	106.4	104.7	101.7	81.6	94.3	93.4	81.5	89.0	92.9	81.5	88.7	99.3	91.9	96.5

DIVISION		NEW HAMPSHIRE															NEW JERSEY		
		KEENE			LITTLETON			MANCHESTER			NASHUA			PORTSMOUTH			ATLANTIC CITY		
		034			035			031			030			038			082,084		
		MAT.	INST.	TOTAL	MAT.	INST.	TOTAL	MAT.	INST.	TOTAL	MAT.	INST.	TOTAL	MAT.	INST.	TOTAL	MAT.	INST.	TOTAL
015433	CONTRACTOR EQUIPMENT		93.0	93.0		93.0	93.0		97.4	97.4		93.0	93.0		93.0	93.0		90.8	90.8
0241, 31 - 34	SITE & INFRASTRUCTURE, DEMOLITION	82.4	91.2	88.1	72.8	90.3	84.2	85.6	101.3	95.8	87.6	92.0	90.5	82.2	92.6	89.0	87.6	95.5	92.7
0310	Concrete Forming & Accessories	94.4	78.3	81.9	108.4	72.8	80.8	104.6	91.9	94.8	104.2	91.7	94.5	90.7	90.3	90.4	115.4	140.6	135.0
0320	Concrete Reinforcing	84.5	86.6	85.1	85.2	86.6	85.6	99.5	87.2	96.1	105.5	87.1	100.4	84.5	87.1	85.2	76.5	134.6	92.6
0330	Cast-in-Place Concrete	70.7	105.7	83.1	63.5	97.8	75.7	80.8	115.6	93.2	67.0	114.4	83.8	63.5	113.5	81.3	65.4	132.9	89.4
03	CONCRETE	85.4	89.7	87.1	80.3	84.5	81.9	96.4	99.3	97.5	89.3	98.9	93.1	79.5	98.0	86.8	83.2	135.6	103.9
04	MASONRY	101.5	89.6	94.3	114.4	75.7	90.9	111.0	100.2	104.4	106.0	100.1	102.4	100.7	97.3	98.6	108.1	137.2	125.8
05	METALS	92.0	91.2	91.9	92.1	90.8	91.8	100.1	91.2	98.3	99.5	92.6	98.1	93.6	94.1	93.7	96.2	114.5	99.8
06	WOOD, PLASTICS & COMPOSITES	94.1	75.7	85.9	109.2	75.7	94.2	102.6	90.3	97.1	107.6	90.3	99.9	89.4	90.3	89.8	124.3	141.6	132.0
07	THERMAL & MOISTURE PROTECTION	95.5	96.9	96.0	95.0	90.6	93.4	100.6	107.3	103.0	95.9	105.8	99.4	95.3	101.5	97.5	99.9	132.8	111.6
08	OPENINGS	96.4	80.0	92.7	99.6	76.8	94.5	97.6	90.8	96.1	100.6	87.5	97.6	101.1	79.0	96.1	97.8	137.6	106.8
0920	Plaster & Gypsum Board	103.4	74.9	85.3	125.1	74.9	93.2	107.8	89.9	96.4	118.0	89.9	100.2	102.9	89.9	94.7	131.5	142.8	138.7
0950, 0980	Ceilings & Acoustic Treatment	88.2	74.9	80.7	88.2	74.9	80.7	100.9	89.9	94.7	101.5	89.9	95.0	88.8	89.9	89.4	102.3	142.8	125.0
0960	Flooring	97.7	101.3	98.6	107.3	101.3	105.8	103.1	110.7	105.0	101.0	103.3	101.6	96.0	103.3	97.8	104.3	152.0	116.3
0970, 0990	Wall Finishes & Painting/Coating	82.5	91.8	88.1	82.5	80.0	81.0	99.1	113.4	107.6	82.5	110.1	98.9	82.5	90.8	87.5	82.6	143.0	118.6
09	FINISHES	95.3	83.2	89.2	99.7	78.4	89.0	101.4	97.2	99.3	101.8	95.3	98.5	94.4	92.4	93.4	102.4	144.2	123.4
COVERS	DIVS. 10 - 14, 25, 28, 41, 43, 44, 46	100.0	84.9	97.1	100.0	85.7	97.2	100.0	106.5	101.3	100.0	106.5	101.3	100.0	105.5	101.1	100.0	114.9	102.9
21, 22, 23	FIRE SUPPRESSION, PLUMBING & HVAC	92.8	74.0	86.1	92.8	66.7	83.5	100.2	87.7	95.7	100.4	87.8	95.8	100.4	86.0	95.2	99.3	132.7	111.3
26, 27, 3370	ELECTRICAL, COMMUNICATIONS & UTIL.	101.0	67.0	86.3	101.5	43.8	76.5	101.6	76.6	90.8	102.2	76.6	91.1	101.2	71.7	88.4	93.1	134.1	110.9
MF2018	WEIGHTED AVERAGE	93.8	82.1	89.5	94.3	74.1	86.9	99.8	92.9	97.3	99.0	91.8	96.3	95.4	89.6	93.3	96.5	130.3	108.9

DIVISION		NEW JERSEY																	
		CAMDEN			DOVER			ELIZABETH			HACKENSACK			JERSEY CITY			LONG BRANCH		
		081			078			072			076			073			077		
		MAT.	INST.	TOTAL	MAT.	INST.	TOTAL	MAT.	INST.	TOTAL	MAT.	INST.	TOTAL	MAT.	INST.	TOTAL	MAT.	INST.	TOTAL
015433	CONTRACTOR EQUIPMENT		90.8	90.8		93.0	93.0		93.0	93.0		93.0	93.0		90.8	90.8		90.5	90.5
0241, 31 - 34	SITE & INFRASTRUCTURE, DEMOLITION	89.1	95.8	93.5	100.3	96.8	98.0	104.4	96.8	99.5	101.3	96.8	98.4	93.8	96.8	95.7	96.5	96.5	96.5
0310	Concrete Forming & Accessories	104.8	140.8	132.7	94.2	141.9	131.2	106.4	142.0	134.1	94.2	141.8	131.2	98.6	142.1	132.4	99.3	141.0	131.7
0320	Concrete Reinforcing	100.5	134.6	109.9	73.9	148.3	94.5	73.9	148.3	94.5	73.9	148.3	94.5	95.9	148.3	110.4	73.9	148.2	94.5
0330	Cast-in-Place Concrete	63.4	133.0	88.1	67.6	134.5	91.4	58.1	134.2	85.2	66.1	134.1	90.3	52.8	134.6	81.8	58.7	132.8	85.0
03	CONCRETE	86.9	135.6	106.2	80.9	139.2	103.9	79.4	139.1	103.0	79.7	139.0	103.1	80.9	139.1	103.8	80.5	138.0	103.2
04	MASONRY	97.2	137.2	121.5	95.2	139.0	121.8	111.7	139.0	128.3	99.3	139.0	123.4	89.1	139.0	119.4	104.2	137.2	124.2
05	METALS	104.0	114.6	106.1	94.2	122.6	99.8	95.7	122.7	101.0	94.3	122.5	99.9	102.1	120.0	105.6	94.3	119.6	99.3
06	WOOD, PLASTICS & COMPOSITES	109.1	141.6	123.7	91.2	141.6	113.8	108.0	141.6	123.0	91.2	141.6	113.8	92.4	141.6	114.5	93.6	141.6	115.1
07	THERMAL & MOISTURE PROTECTION	99.7	133.5	111.7	97.8	134.3	110.8	98.1	137.4	112.1	97.6	132.5	110.0	97.4	137.4	111.6	97.5	131.3	109.6
08	OPENINGS	99.6	137.6	108.2	100.4	139.3	109.2	98.8	139.3	107.9	98.1	139.3	107.4	96.4	139.3	106.1	92.9	139.3	103.4
0920	Plaster & Gypsum Board	128.0	142.8	137.4	119.7	142.8	134.4	129.6	142.8	138.0	119.7	142.8	134.4	126.0	142.8	136.7	122.2	142.8	135.3
0950, 0980	Ceilings & Acoustic Treatment	120.1	142.8	132.8	97.7	142.8	123.0	98.2	142.8	123.2	97.7	142.8	123.0	113.6	142.8	130.0	97.7	142.8	123.0
0960	Flooring	101.5	152.0	114.2	86.4	176.5	108.9	90.8	176.5	112.3	86.4	176.5	108.9	87.2	176.5	109.6	87.5	176.5	109.8
0970, 0990	Wall Finishes & Painting/Coating	82.6	143.0	118.6	81.8	140.9	117.0	81.8	140.9	117.0	81.8	140.9	117.0	81.9	140.9	117.1	81.9	143.0	118.3
09	FINISHES	105.8	144.2	125.1	95.7	148.2	122.1	99.0	148.8	124.0	95.6	148.2	122.0	100.9	148.9	125.0	96.6	148.4	122.6
COVERS	DIVS. 10 - 14, 25, 28, 41, 43, 44, 46	100.0	114.9	102.9	100.0	127.4	105.3	100.0	127.4	105.3	100.0	127.4	105.3	100.0	127.4	105.3	100.0	114.8	102.9
21, 22, 23	FIRE SUPPRESSION, PLUMBING & HVAC	99.9	132.9	111.7	99.3	134.8	112.0	99.9	133.9	112.1	99.3	134.8	112.0	99.9	134.9	112.4	99.3	132.8	111.3
26, 27, 3370	ELECTRICAL, COMMUNICATIONS & UTIL.	95.5	134.1	112.2	92.4	136.6	111.5	92.7	136.6	111.7	92.4	136.0	111.3	94.8	136.0	112.7	92.3	131.3	109.2
MF2018	WEIGHTED AVERAGE	98.9	130.4	110.5	94.9	133.7	109.1	96.2	133.6	110.0	94.7	133.5	109.0	96.6	133.5	110.2	94.5	131.4	108.1

	DIVISION	NEW JERSEY																	
		NEW BRUNSWICK			NEWARK			PATERSON			POINT PLEASANT			SUMMIT			TRENTON		
		088 - 089			070 - 071			074 - 075			087			079			085 - 086		
		MAT.	INST.	TOTAL	MAT.	INST.	TOTAL	MAT.	INST.	TOTAL	MAT.	INST.	TOTAL	MAT.	INST.	TOTAL	MAT.	INST.	TOTAL
015433	CONTRACTOR EQUIPMENT		90.5	90.5		98.0	98.0		93.0	93.0		90.5	90.5		93.0	93.0		96.1	96.1
0241, 31 - 34	SITE & INFRASTRUCTURE, DEMOLITION	97.4	96.7	96.9	107.4	104.5	105.5	103.4	96.8	99.1	98.5	96.1	96.9	102.2	96.8	98.7	88.5	105.5	99.6
0310	Concrete Forming & Accessories	108.5	142.0	134.5	99.0	142.3	132.7	96.2	142.0	131.7	101.8	126.7	121.1	96.9	141.8	131.8	103.6	140.9	132.6
0320	Concrete Reinforcing	77.4	148.3	97.0	99.7	148.3	113.1	95.9	148.3	110.4	77.4	147.6	96.8	73.9	148.3	94.5	100.0	134.7	109.6
0330	Cast-in-Place Concrete	80.8	133.9	99.7	76.5	136.3	97.7	67.2	134.2	91.0	80.8	123.7	96.1	56.2	134.1	83.9	77.4	133.9	97.5
03	CONCRETE	95.7	138.8	112.7	92.7	139.9	111.3	86.6	139.1	107.3	95.1	128.3	108.2	76.9	139.0	101.4	93.6	136.0	110.3
04	MASONRY	105.6	139.0	125.9	99.9	139.1	123.7	96.0	139.0	122.1	93.8	122.1	111.0	98.2	139.0	122.9	104.5	137.3	124.4
05	METALS	96.3	119.9	100.9	103.1	121.1	106.7	98.1	122.7	102.9	96.3	118.4	100.7	94.2	122.5	99.8	103.2	114.0	105.3
06	WOOD, PLASTICS & COMPOSITES	115.8	141.6	127.3	94.8	141.9	115.9	94.1	141.6	115.4	105.7	126.2	114.9	95.4	141.6	116.1	100.8	141.6	119.1
07	THERMAL & MOISTURE PROTECTION	100.1	136.6	113.1	100.4	138.9	114.1	97.9	132.5	110.2	100.1	121.8	107.8	98.1	137.4	112.1	101.2	134.8	113.2
08	OPENINGS	92.9	139.3	103.4	98.7	139.4	107.9	103.0	139.3	111.2	94.7	132.3	103.2	104.7	139.3	112.5	97.8	136.1	106.4
0920	Plaster & Gypsum Board	128.8	142.8	137.7	117.7	142.8	133.6	126.0	142.8	136.7	121.1	127.0	124.9	122.2	142.8	135.3	120.1	142.8	134.5
0950, 0980	Ceilings & Acoustic Treatment	102.3	142.8	125.0	114.0	142.8	130.2	113.6	142.8	130.0	102.3	127.0	116.1	97.7	142.8	123.0	113.5	142.8	130.0
0960	Flooring	102.6	176.5	121.1	104.1	176.5	122.2	87.2	176.5	109.6	100.6	152.0	113.5	87.5	176.5	109.8	106.4	176.5	124.0
0970, 0990	Wall Finishes & Painting/Coating	82.6	140.9	117.4	94.9	140.9	122.4	81.8	140.9	117.0	82.6	143.0	118.6	81.8	140.9	117.0	99.1	143.0	125.3
09	FINISHES	102.5	148.8	125.8	107.0	149.1	128.1	101.0	148.9	125.1	100.9	133.5	117.3	96.7	148.2	122.5	107.7	148.5	128.2
COVERS	DIVS. 10 - 14, 25, 28, 41, 43, 44, 46	100.0	127.3	105.3	100.0	128.1	105.4	100.0	127.4	105.3	100.0	99.5	99.9	100.0	127.4	105.3	100.0	114.9	102.9
21, 22, 23	FIRE SUPPRESSION, PLUMBING & HVAC	99.3	133.7	111.7	99.9	134.9	112.5	99.9	134.9	112.4	99.3	129.1	110.0	99.4	130.1	110.4	99.9	132.7	111.7
26, 27, 3370	ELECTRICAL, COMMUNICATIONS & UTIL.	93.5	134.1	111.1	100.3	136.0	115.8	94.8	136.6	112.9	93.1	131.3	109.7	92.7	136.6	111.7	100.2	126.7	111.7
MF2018	WEIGHTED AVERAGE	97.7	132.9	110.7	100.4	134.5	112.9	97.5	133.7	110.8	97.1	124.5	107.2	95.1	132.7	108.9	100.2	130.6	111.4

	DIVISION	NEW JERSEY			NEW MEXICO														
		VINELAND			ALBUQUERQUE			CARRIZOZO			CLOVIS			FARMINGTON			GALLUP		
		080,083			870 - 872			883			881			874			873		
		MAT.	INST.	TOTAL	MAT.	INST.	TOTAL	MAT.	INST.	TOTAL	MAT.	INST.	TOTAL	MAT.	INST.	TOTAL	MAT.	INST.	TOTAL
015433	CONTRACTOR EQUIPMENT		90.8	90.8		104.7	104.7		104.7	104.7		104.7	104.7		104.7	104.7		104.7	104.7
0241, 31 - 34	SITE & INFRASTRUCTURE, DEMOLITION	90.9	95.8	94.1	93.8	94.0	93.9	107.4	94.0	98.6	95.8	94.0	94.6	98.9	94.0	95.7	105.1	94.0	97.9
0310	Concrete Forming & Accessories	98.4	140.7	131.3	99.7	68.7	75.6	96.1	68.7	74.8	96.1	68.5	74.7	99.8	68.7	75.6	99.8	68.7	75.6
0320	Concrete Reinforcing	76.5	134.6	92.6	94.2	68.8	87.2	103.8	68.8	94.1	105.0	68.7	94.9	103.0	68.8	93.5	98.6	68.8	90.3
0330	Cast-in-Place Concrete	70.5	132.9	92.7	82.6	69.5	78.0	85.4	69.5	79.7	85.3	69.4	79.7	83.4	69.5	78.5	78.5	69.5	75.3
03	CONCRETE	85.9	135.6	105.5	90.2	70.3	82.4	107.9	70.3	93.0	99.2	70.2	87.7	94.3	70.3	84.8	98.2	70.3	87.2
04	MASONRY	96.1	137.2	121.1	101.6	60.1	76.4	109.6	60.1	79.6	109.7	60.1	79.6	107.1	60.1	78.6	99.0	60.1	75.4
05	METALS	96.1	114.5	99.8	105.8	91.0	102.9	101.2	91.0	99.2	100.8	90.9	98.9	102.5	91.0	100.2	101.6	91.0	99.6
06	WOOD, PLASTICS & COMPOSITES	101.4	141.6	119.4	102.2	70.0	87.8	95.6	70.0	84.1	95.6	70.0	84.1	102.4	70.0	87.9	102.4	70.0	87.9
07	THERMAL & MOISTURE PROTECTION	99.6	132.8	111.4	100.9	70.7	90.1	95.5	70.7	86.6	94.5	70.7	86.0	101.1	70.7	90.3	102.0	70.7	90.9
08	OPENINGS	94.3	137.6	104.0	97.9	67.8	91.1	91.6	67.8	86.3	91.8	67.8	86.4	100.2	67.8	92.9	100.2	67.8	92.9
0920	Plaster & Gypsum Board	118.5	142.8	133.9	99.4	69.1	80.2	88.0	69.1	76.0	88.0	69.1	76.0	90.1	69.1	76.8	90.1	69.1	76.8
0950, 0980	Ceilings & Acoustic Treatment	102.3	142.8	125.0	122.6	69.1	92.6	105.3	69.1	85.0	105.3	69.1	85.0	114.6	69.1	89.1	114.6	69.1	89.1
0960	Flooring	100.1	152.0	113.1	94.1	66.7	87.2	99.0	66.7	90.9	99.0	66.7	90.9	95.6	66.7	88.4	95.6	66.7	88.4
0970, 0990	Wall Finishes & Painting/Coating	82.6	143.0	118.6	94.1	51.0	68.4	92.2	51.0	67.6	92.2	51.0	67.6	88.2	51.0	66.0	88.2	51.0	66.0
09	FINISHES	99.7	144.2	122.1	101.6	66.5	83.9	98.9	66.5	82.6	97.8	66.5	82.1	98.6	66.5	82.4	99.7	66.5	83.0
COVERS	DIVS. 10 - 14, 25, 28, 41, 43, 44, 46	100.0	114.9	102.9	100.0	86.7	97.4	100.0	86.7	97.4	100.0	86.7	97.4	100.0	86.7	97.4	100.0	86.7	97.4
21, 22, 23	FIRE SUPPRESSION, PLUMBING & HVAC	99.3	132.7	111.3	100.3	67.8	88.6	95.4	67.8	85.5	95.4	67.5	85.4	100.2	67.8	88.6	95.5	67.8	85.6
26, 27, 3370	ELECTRICAL, COMMUNICATIONS & UTIL.	93.1	134.1	110.9	83.3	69.0	77.1	85.6	69.0	78.4	84.4	69.0	77.7	82.1	69.0	76.4	81.7	69.0	76.2
MF2018	WEIGHTED AVERAGE	95.7	130.4	108.5	98.2	72.3	88.7	98.3	72.3	88.7	96.6	72.2	87.6	98.2	72.3	88.6	97.4	72.3	88.1

	DIVISION	NEW MEXICO																	
		LAS CRUCES			LAS VEGAS			ROSWELL			SANTA FE			SOCORRO			TRUTH/CONSEQUENCES		
		880			877			882			875			878			879		
		MAT.	INST.	TOTAL	MAT.	INST.	TOTAL	MAT.	INST.	TOTAL	MAT.	INST.	TOTAL	MAT.	INST.	TOTAL	MAT.	INST.	TOTAL
015433	CONTRACTOR EQUIPMENT		83.2	83.2		104.7	104.7		104.7	104.7		108.5	108.5		104.7	104.7		83.3	83.3
0241, 31 - 34	SITE & INFRASTRUCTURE, DEMOLITION	98.4	76.0	83.8	95.8	94.0	94.6	99.9	94.0	96.0	99.7	100.4	100.2	93.0	94.0	93.7	108.3	76.0	87.3
0310	Concrete Forming & Accessories	92.8	67.7	73.3	99.8	68.7	75.6	96.1	68.7	74.8	100.4	68.9	75.9	99.8	68.7	75.6	97.8	67.7	74.4
0320	Concrete Reinforcing	102.9	68.5	93.4	100.3	68.8	91.6	105.0	68.8	94.9	100.3	68.8	91.6	102.2	68.8	93.0	97.8	68.6	89.7
0330	Cast-in-Place Concrete	80.6	63.2	74.4	81.1	69.5	77.0	85.3	69.5	79.7	86.2	71.8	81.1	79.5	69.5	75.9	87.1	63.2	78.6
03	CONCRETE	82.7	67.3	76.6	92.0	70.3	83.4	99.8	70.3	88.2	97.0	71.0	86.8	91.5	70.3	83.1	86.3	67.3	78.8
04	MASONRY	105.0	57.8	76.3	99.3	60.1	75.5	121.0	60.1	84.0	95.8	60.3	74.2	99.2	60.1	75.5	95.4	59.9	73.8
05	METALS	99.1	83.9	96.1	101.3	91.0	99.3	102.1	91.0	99.9	100.0	88.5	97.7	101.7	91.0	99.6	100.6	84.1	97.3
06	WOOD, PLASTICS & COMPOSITES	86.3	69.1	78.6	102.4	70.0	87.9	95.6	70.0	84.1	98.7	70.3	85.9	102.4	70.0	87.9	95.6	69.1	83.7
07	THERMAL & MOISTURE PROTECTION	86.3	66.0	79.1	100.8	70.7	90.1	94.6	70.7	86.1	103.7	73.0	92.8	100.8	70.7	90.1	91.7	66.6	82.7
08	OPENINGS	87.2	67.3	82.7	97.0	67.8	90.4	91.6	67.8	86.2	98.4	67.9	91.5	96.8	67.8	90.3	90.1	67.3	84.9
0920	Plaster & Gypsum Board	86.8	69.1	75.6	90.1	69.1	76.8	88.0	69.1	76.0	95.3	69.1	78.7	90.1	69.1	76.8	93.1	69.1	77.9
0950, 0980	Ceilings & Acoustic Treatment	101.6	69.1	83.4	114.6	69.1	89.1	105.3	69.1	85.0	112.8	69.1	88.3	114.6	69.1	89.1	113.4	69.1	88.6
0960	Flooring	129.2	66.7	113.6	95.6	66.7	88.4	99.0	66.7	90.9	105.3	66.7	95.6	95.6	66.7	88.4	123.4	66.7	109.2
0970, 0990	Wall Finishes & Painting/Coating	80.6	51.0	62.9	88.2	51.0	66.0	92.2	51.0	67.6	99.1	51.0	70.4	88.2	51.0	66.0	80.6	51.0	62.9
09	FINISHES	109.2	65.6	87.3	98.4	66.5	82.4	97.9	66.5	82.1	104.0	66.6	85.2	98.4	66.5	82.3	111.8	65.8	88.7
COVERS	DIVS. 10 - 14, 25, 28, 41, 43, 44, 46	100.0	84.6	97.0	100.0	86.7	97.4	100.0	86.7	97.4	100.0	87.2	97.5	100.0	86.7	97.4	100.0	84.5	97.0
21, 22, 23	FIRE SUPPRESSION, PLUMBING & HVAC	100.7	67.6	88.8	95.5	67.8	85.6	100.0	67.8	88.5	100.1	67.9	88.6	95.5	67.8	85.6	94.4	67.6	84.8
26, 27, 3370	ELECTRICAL, COMMUNICATIONS & UTIL.	88.0	74.6	82.2	82.8	69.0	76.8	85.1	69.0	78.1	100.8	69.0	87.0	81.9	69.0	76.3	85.9	69.0	78.6
MF2018	WEIGHTED AVERAGE	95.8	70.0	86.3	96.0	72.3	87.3	98.6	72.3	88.9	99.8	72.8	89.9	95.9	72.3	87.2	95.5	69.4	85.9

DIVISION		NEW MEXICO			NEW YORK														
		TUCUMCARI			ALBANY			BINGHAMTON			BRONX			BROOKLYN			BUFFALO		
		884			120 - 122			137 - 139			104			112			140 - 142		
		MAT.	INST.	TOTAL	MAT.	INST.	TOTAL	MAT.	INST.	TOTAL	MAT.	INST.	TOTAL	MAT.	INST.	TOTAL	MAT.	INST.	TOTAL
015433	CONTRACTOR EQUIPMENT		104.7	104.7		111.6	111.6		112.7	112.7		100.4	100.4		105.3	105.3		96.9	96.9
0241, 31 - 34	SITE & INFRASTRUCTURE, DEMOLITION	95.4	94.0	94.5	78.6	103.0	94.5	91.8	86.1	88.1	93.3	104.2	100.4	109.7	114.3	112.7	90.5	97.5	95.1
0310	Concrete Forming & Accessories	96.1	68.5	74.7	104.7	102.5	103.0	100.4	88.6	91.3	90.9	177.7	158.3	106.4	174.2	159.1	105.1	109.7	108.7
0320	Concrete Reinforcing	102.9	68.7	93.4	99.2	110.4	102.3	95.6	106.0	98.5	91.8	163.7	111.7	96.0	238.8	135.5	99.6	109.0	102.2
0330	Cast-in-Place Concrete	85.3	69.4	79.7	76.3	114.3	89.8	105.5	101.0	103.9	69.6	159.4	101.5	107.4	158.2	125.4	126.3	117.2	123.0
03	CONCRETE	98.3	70.2	87.2	92.9	108.9	99.2	95.4	98.2	96.5	76.7	168.4	112.9	104.1	178.3	133.4	121.3	111.9	117.6
04	MASONRY	121.0	60.1	84.0	115.4	115.2	115.3	109.4	99.5	103.4	86.5	181.9	144.5	121.5	181.9	158.2	117.1	119.3	118.5
05	METALS	100.8	90.9	98.9	99.2	120.3	103.4	91.3	131.6	99.2	83.8	164.7	99.8	97.4	173.2	112.4	97.0	103.8	98.3
06	WOOD, PLASTICS & COMPOSITES	95.6	70.0	84.1	103.2	98.4	101.0	103.5	85.3	95.3	103.1	175.8	135.7	107.7	170.5	135.8	102.6	108.0	105.0
07	THERMAL & MOISTURE PROTECTION	94.5	70.7	86.0	97.6	107.3	101.1	106.3	90.5	100.7	97.2	160.1	119.6	105.1	159.0	124.3	99.8	106.9	102.3
08	OPENINGS	91.6	67.8	86.2	97.9	100.6	98.5	91.0	91.2	91.0	94.7	184.5	115.0	88.7	186.7	110.8	100.1	104.5	101.1
0920	Plaster & Gypsum Board	88.0	69.1	76.0	104.0	98.2	100.3	122.7	84.8	98.7	98.7	178.2	149.1	115.9	173.0	152.1	111.6	108.2	109.5
0950, 0980	Ceilings & Acoustic Treatment	105.3	69.1	85.0	95.4	98.2	97.0	104.8	84.8	93.6	77.7	178.2	134.1	97.1	173.0	139.7	95.4	108.2	102.6
0960	Flooring	99.0	66.7	90.9	100.6	104.5	101.6	109.9	95.7	106.3	96.3	180.0	117.3	117.0	180.0	132.8	99.3	115.4	103.3
0970, 0990	Wall Finishes & Painting/Coating	92.2	51.0	67.6	99.1	98.7	98.9	87.1	96.3	92.6	100.0	161.9	136.9	113.0	161.9	142.2	99.1	108.7	104.8
09	FINISHES	97.8	66.5	82.0	98.4	101.8	100.1	101.9	89.9	95.8	93.2	177.0	135.3	111.5	173.9	142.8	98.7	111.0	104.9
COVERS	DIVS. 10 - 14, 25, 28, 41, 43, 44, 46	100.0	86.7	97.4	100.0	101.2	100.2	100.0	97.2	99.5	100.0	139.3	107.6	100.0	138.1	107.4	100.0	105.8	101.1
21, 22, 23	FIRE SUPPRESSION, PLUMBING & HVAC	95.4	67.5	85.4	100.2	107.1	102.7	100.9	95.5	98.9	100.2	169.2	124.9	99.8	169.4	124.7	100.2	98.5	99.6
26, 27, 3370	ELECTRICAL, COMMUNICATIONS & UTIL.	85.6	69.0	78.4	100.6	105.1	102.5	100.3	96.1	98.5	98.0	171.2	129.7	103.1	171.2	132.6	100.9	99.3	100.2
MF2018	WEIGHTED AVERAGE	97.0	72.2	87.9	98.8	107.5	102.0	97.5	97.8	97.6	91.8	165.6	119.0	101.4	168.1	126.0	102.4	105.4	103.5

DIVISION		NEW YORK																	
		ELMIRA			FAR ROCKAWAY			FLUSHING			GLENS FALLS			HICKSVILLE			JAMAICA		
		148 - 149			116			113			128			115,117,118			114		
		MAT.	INST.	TOTAL	MAT.	INST.	TOTAL	MAT.	INST.	TOTAL	MAT.	INST.	TOTAL	MAT.	INST.	TOTAL	MAT.	INST.	TOTAL
015433	CONTRACTOR EQUIPMENT		115.1	115.1		105.3	105.3		105.3	105.3		108.2	108.2		105.3	105.3		105.3	105.3
0241, 31 - 34	SITE & INFRASTRUCTURE, DEMOLITION	86.3	87.0	86.8	108.9	114.3	112.4	108.9	114.3	112.4	68.8	94.3	85.4	104.4	112.6	109.7	104.4	114.3	110.9
0310	Concrete Forming & Accessories	82.4	91.3	89.3	91.7	178.0	158.7	95.9	178.0	159.7	85.1	90.6	89.4	87.8	146.4	133.3	95.9	178.0	159.7
0320	Concrete Reinforcing	99.4	105.0	100.9	96.0	238.8	135.5	97.7	238.8	136.8	96.3	101.5	97.7	96.0	165.0	115.1	96.0	238.8	135.5
0330	Cast-in-Place Concrete	111.0	100.5	107.3	116.2	158.2	131.1	116.2	158.2	131.1	73.5	107.4	85.5	98.6	147.4	116.0	107.4	158.2	125.5
03	CONCRETE	104.1	99.2	102.2	108.6	180.0	136.8	109.4	180.0	137.3	81.7	99.8	88.8	96.8	149.3	117.5	103.2	180.0	133.5
04	MASONRY	109.4	100.2	103.8	124.6	181.9	159.4	118.0	181.9	156.8	120.5	107.8	112.8	114.5	164.6	144.9	124.0	181.9	159.2
05	METALS	90.7	133.4	99.1	97.5	173.2	112.4	97.5	173.2	112.4	93.3	118.0	98.1	98.9	143.0	107.6	97.5	173.2	112.4
06	WOOD, PLASTICS & COMPOSITES	76.2	89.3	82.0	87.0	175.6	126.7	93.0	175.6	130.0	84.4	87.2	85.7	82.7	143.7	110.1	93.0	175.6	130.0
07	THERMAL & MOISTURE PROTECTION	99.1	90.6	96.1	104.9	159.9	124.5	105.0	159.9	124.6	91.4	98.5	94.0	104.6	147.6	119.9	104.8	159.9	124.5
08	OPENINGS	93.6	93.1	93.5	87.5	189.5	110.5	87.5	189.5	110.5	92.0	89.7	91.5	87.8	153.9	102.7	87.5	189.5	110.5
0920	Plaster & Gypsum Board	107.7	89.1	95.9	97.1	178.2	148.6	101.5	178.2	150.2	86.5	87.0	86.8	96.6	145.4	127.6	101.5	178.2	150.2
0950, 0980	Ceilings & Acoustic Treatment	99.4	89.1	93.6	80.3	178.2	135.2	80.3	178.2	135.2	85.0	87.0	86.1	79.8	145.4	116.6	80.3	178.2	135.2
0960	Flooring	95.5	95.7	95.6	112.7	180.0	129.6	113.9	180.0	130.5	90.3	96.5	91.8	111.8	172.4	127.0	113.9	180.0	130.5
0970, 0990	Wall Finishes & Painting/Coating	94.3	86.9	89.9	113.0	161.9	142.2	113.0	161.9	142.2	89.8	101.7	96.9	113.0	161.9	142.2	113.0	161.9	142.2
09	FINISHES	96.1	91.1	93.6	103.6	176.8	140.4	104.5	176.8	140.8	88.8	92.1	90.5	102.4	152.4	127.5	104.2	176.8	140.7
COVERS	DIVS. 10 - 14, 25, 28, 41, 43, 44, 46	100.0	96.1	99.2	100.0	138.7	107.5	100.0	138.7	107.5	100.0	86.4	97.4	100.0	123.8	104.6	100.0	138.7	107.5
21, 22, 23	FIRE SUPPRESSION, PLUMBING & HVAC	92.8	91.3	92.3	92.0	169.4	119.7	92.0	169.4	119.7	92.7	101.0	95.7	99.8	149.8	117.7	92.0	169.4	119.7
26, 27, 3370	ELECTRICAL, COMMUNICATIONS & UTIL.	97.8	99.7	98.6	106.6	171.2	134.6	106.6	171.2	134.6	95.0	93.5	94.3	102.5	134.8	116.5	101.9	171.2	131.9
MF2018	WEIGHTED AVERAGE	95.6	98.2	96.5	99.8	169.0	125.3	99.8	169.0	125.3	92.3	99.2	94.9	99.4	145.1	116.2	98.6	169.0	124.5

DIVISION		NEW YORK																	
		JAMESTOWN			KINGSTON			LONG ISLAND CITY			MONTICELLO			MOUNT VERNON			NEW ROCHELLE		
		147			124			111			127			105			108		
		MAT.	INST.	TOTAL	MAT.	INST.	TOTAL	MAT.	INST.	TOTAL	MAT.	INST.	TOTAL	MAT.	INST.	TOTAL	MAT.	INST.	TOTAL
015433	CONTRACTOR EQUIPMENT		88.8	88.8		105.3	105.3		105.3	105.3		105.3	105.3		100.4	100.4		100.4	100.4
0241, 31 - 34	SITE & INFRASTRUCTURE, DEMOLITION	87.6	85.7	86.4	121.9	108.8	113.4	110.8	114.3	113.1	118.4	108.8	112.1	94.4	99.9	98.0	93.8	99.9	97.8
0310	Concrete Forming & Accessories	82.4	81.6	81.8	86.5	118.3	111.2	100.7	178.0	160.7	95.2	118.3	113.1	81.8	127.2	117.1	95.8	124.1	117.8
0320	Concrete Reinforcing	99.5	99.8	99.6	96.9	143.8	109.9	96.0	238.8	135.5	96.0	143.9	109.3	91.7	163.9	111.7	91.8	163.8	111.7
0330	Cast-in-Place Concrete	115.2	95.8	108.3	99.2	132.5	111.0	110.8	158.2	127.7	92.9	132.5	107.0	77.7	140.1	99.9	77.7	139.8	99.8
03	CONCRETE	107.1	90.1	100.3	98.4	127.6	109.9	105.9	180.0	135.2	94.7	127.6	107.7	82.1	138.9	104.5	82.4	137.4	104.1
04	MASONRY	118.6	94.2	103.8	139.4	139.9	139.7	118.3	181.9	156.9	132.2	139.9	136.9	91.9	146.7	125.2	91.9	146.7	125.2
05	METALS	88.7	97.0	90.3	99.5	127.7	105.0	97.4	173.2	112.4	99.4	127.9	105.0	83.6	163.0	99.2	83.9	162.3	99.3
06	WOOD, PLASTICS & COMPOSITES	74.9	78.2	76.4	86.0	112.4	97.8	100.4	175.6	134.1	96.2	112.4	103.5	93.0	120.0	105.1	111.1	116.6	113.6
07	THERMAL & MOISTURE PROTECTION	98.6	85.5	94.0	108.4	131.4	116.6	105.0	159.9	124.6	108.2	131.4	116.5	97.8	136.4	111.6	98.0	134.2	110.9
08	OPENINGS	93.4	84.3	91.4	94.6	131.8	103.0	87.5	189.5	110.5	90.7	131.8	100.0	94.7	157.7	108.9	94.8	155.8	108.6
0920	Plaster & Gypsum Board	92.5	77.7	83.1	85.0	113.1	102.8	108.5	178.2	152.7	85.7	113.1	103.1	92.7	120.7	110.4	110.1	117.1	114.6
0950, 0980	Ceilings & Acoustic Treatment	94.9	77.7	85.3	70.0	113.1	94.2	80.3	178.2	135.2	70.0	113.1	94.2	75.0	120.7	100.6	75.0	117.1	98.6
0960	Flooring	98.8	91.8	97.0	108.8	143.8	117.5	115.4	180.0	131.6	110.5	143.8	118.9	88.1	160.9	106.4	95.0	146.9	108.0
0970, 0990	Wall Finishes & Painting/Coating	96.0	89.4	92.1	117.2	116.3	116.6	113.0	161.9	142.2	117.2	109.6	112.7	98.3	161.9	136.2	98.3	161.9	136.2
09	FINISHES	94.0	83.5	88.7	99.3	122.0	110.7	105.7	176.8	141.4	99.7	121.2	110.5	89.8	135.6	112.8	94.0	130.8	112.5
COVERS	DIVS. 10 - 14, 25, 28, 41, 43, 44, 46	100.0	94.6	98.9	100.0	108.0	101.5	100.0	138.7	107.5	100.0	108.0	101.5	100.0	116.1	103.1	100.0	101.8	100.3
21, 22, 23	FIRE SUPPRESSION, PLUMBING & HVAC	92.6	84.1	89.6	92.4	120.9	102.7	99.8	169.4	124.7	92.4	124.8	104.0	92.5	142.2	110.3	92.5	141.9	110.2
26, 27, 3370	ELECTRICAL, COMMUNICATIONS & UTIL.	96.5	84.5	91.3	96.6	103.5	99.6	102.2	171.2	132.1	96.6	103.5	99.6	94.9	151.8	119.6	94.9	126.1	108.5
MF2018	WEIGHTED AVERAGE	95.5	87.5	92.6	99.3	121.3	107.4	100.8	169.0	125.9	98.3	122.0	107.0	90.3	140.7	108.9	90.9	135.5	107.3

	DIVISION	NEW YORK																	
		NEW YORK			NIAGARA FALLS			PLATTSBURGH			POUGHKEEPSIE			QUEENS			RIVERHEAD		
		100 - 102			143			129			125 - 126			110			119		
		MAT.	INST.	TOTAL	MAT.	INST.	TOTAL	MAT.	INST.	TOTAL	MAT.	INST.	TOTAL	MAT.	INST.	TOTAL	MAT.	INST.	TOTAL
015433	CONTRACTOR EQUIPMENT		102.4	102.4		88.8	88.8		92.0	92.0		105.3	105.3		105.3	105.3		105.3	105.3
0241, 31 - 34	SITE & INFRASTRUCTURE, DEMOLITION	101.6	107.8	105.6	89.1	86.6	87.5	101.5	91.7	95.1	119.3	108.0	111.9	106.7	114.3	111.7	105.0	112.6	110.0
0310	Concrete Forming & Accessories	99.4	177.9	160.4	82.4	102.4	97.9	91.9	82.7	84.7	86.5	151.7	137.1	88.0	178.0	157.9	92.9	147.0	135.0
0320	Concrete Reinforcing	100.8	165.3	118.7	98.1	100.5	98.8	99.2	100.5	99.6	96.9	144.0	109.9	97.7	238.8	136.8	97.9	230.0	134.4
0330	Cast-in-Place Concrete	80.6	161.7	109.4	119.2	112.7	116.9	89.8	91.6	90.4	96.1	122.9	105.6	102.0	158.2	122.0	100.3	147.8	117.2
03	CONCRETE	87.4	169.6	119.8	109.1	105.5	107.7	92.6	89.0	91.2	96.2	139.4	113.3	99.7	180.0	131.4	97.9	160.8	122.7
04	MASONRY	101.3	182.0	150.3	125.6	112.7	117.8	114.6	87.7	98.2	130.4	133.0	132.0	112.6	181.9	154.7	120.0	164.6	147.1
05	METALS	101.6	166.2	114.4	90.9	97.5	92.2	95.8	94.4	95.5	99.5	128.6	105.2	97.4	173.2	112.4	99.6	166.6	112.8
06	WOOD, PLASTICS & COMPOSITES	112.0	176.1	140.7	74.8	98.2	85.3	92.8	80.0	87.1	86.0	162.4	120.2	82.9	175.6	124.4	89.1	143.7	113.6
07	THERMAL & MOISTURE PROTECTION	101.5	162.6	123.2	98.7	98.6	98.7	104.6	87.1	98.4	108.3	132.6	117.0	104.6	159.9	124.3	106.0	149.0	121.3
08	OPENINGS	102.7	188.2	122.0	93.4	94.8	93.7	99.2	85.8	96.2	94.6	154.3	108.1	87.5	189.5	110.5	87.8	169.8	106.3
0920	Plaster & Gypsum Board	110.6	178.2	153.5	92.5	98.2	96.1	112.4	79.2	91.3	85.0	164.6	135.5	96.6	178.2	148.4	98.4	145.4	128.2
0950, 0980	Ceilings & Acoustic Treatment	101.5	178.2	144.5	94.9	98.2	96.8	97.7	79.2	87.3	70.0	164.6	123.1	80.3	178.2	135.2	80.7	145.4	117.0
0960	Flooring	96.5	177.3	116.8	98.8	100.4	99.2	116.5	94.1	110.9	108.8	142.1	117.1	111.8	180.0	128.9	112.7	172.4	127.7
0970, 0990	Wall Finishes & Painting/Coating	99.1	161.9	136.6	96.0	108.7	103.6	112.9	84.5	96.0	117.2	109.6	112.7	113.0	161.9	142.2	113.0	161.9	142.2
09	FINISHES	101.7	176.7	139.4	94.1	102.8	98.5	101.8	84.4	93.1	99.2	147.9	123.6	102.7	176.8	139.9	103.1	152.4	127.9
COVERS	DIVS. 10 - 14, 25, 28, 41, 43, 44, 46	100.0	139.6	107.7	100.0	101.7	100.3	100.0	82.8	96.7	100.0	117.9	103.5	100.0	138.7	107.5	100.0	123.8	104.6
21, 22, 23	FIRE SUPPRESSION, PLUMBING & HVAC	100.1	169.4	124.9	92.6	94.5	93.3	92.6	90.1	91.7	92.4	108.1	98.1	99.8	169.4	124.7	100.1	150.4	118.1
26, 27, 3370	ELECTRICAL, COMMUNICATIONS & UTIL.	101.2	176.5	133.8	95.8	88.0	92.4	88.8	81.7	85.7	96.6	107.9	101.5	102.5	171.2	132.2	103.3	135.0	117.1
MF2018	WEIGHTED AVERAGE	99.6	167.2	124.5	96.5	98.0	97.1	96.1	87.7	93.0	98.7	125.3	108.5	99.4	169.0	125.0	100.2	149.7	118.4

	DIVISION	NEW YORK																	
		ROCHESTER			SCHENECTADY			STATEN ISLAND			SUFFERN			SYRACUSE			UTICA		
		144 - 146			123			103			109			130 - 132			133 - 135		
		MAT.	INST.	TOTAL	MAT.	INST.	TOTAL	MAT.	INST.	TOTAL	MAT.	INST.	TOTAL	MAT.	INST.	TOTAL	MAT.	INST.	TOTAL
015433	CONTRACTOR EQUIPMENT		111.6	111.6		108.2	108.2		100.4	100.4		100.4	100.4		108.2	108.2		108.2	108.2
0241, 31 - 34	SITE & INFRASTRUCTURE, DEMOLITION	83.7	100.0	94.3	80.1	95.9	90.4	101.3	104.2	103.2	91.6	97.6	95.5	90.6	94.8	93.4	74.0	94.5	87.4
0310	Concrete Forming & Accessories	101.1	96.3	97.4	105.1	102.3	102.9	81.2	174.1	153.4	89.5	127.3	118.9	99.7	90.8	92.8	100.4	89.9	92.2
0320	Concrete Reinforcing	99.6	105.1	101.1	95.3	110.4	99.4	91.8	194.2	120.1	91.8	136.3	104.1	96.6	106.2	99.2	96.6	105.1	98.9
0330	Cast-in-Place Concrete	106.6	104.2	105.7	88.7	112.2	97.1	77.7	159.4	106.8	75.4	125.7	93.3	97.9	105.0	100.4	89.5	104.8	94.9
03	CONCRETE	112.0	101.7	108.0	93.1	108.3	99.1	83.0	171.5	117.9	80.4	127.9	99.2	97.1	99.8	98.2	95.1	99.1	96.7
04	MASONRY	104.3	103.7	103.9	117.6	115.1	116.1	98.6	181.9	149.2	92.0	128.0	113.9	102.4	105.6	104.4	92.8	105.7	100.7
05	METALS	101.7	117.9	104.9	98.5	123.6	103.5	82.3	164.9	98.6	82.3	123.8	90.5	95.9	119.6	100.6	94.0	119.1	98.9
06	WOOD, PLASTICS & COMPOSITES	96.7	94.0	95.5	111.0	98.1	105.2	91.6	170.8	127.1	102.8	129.1	114.5	100.6	86.9	94.5	100.6	85.2	93.7
07	THERMAL & MOISTURE PROTECTION	98.6	98.8	98.6	92.9	105.6	97.4	97.4	159.6	119.6	97.8	127.7	108.5	101.4	96.2	99.6	92.3	96.2	93.7
08	OPENINGS	98.0	96.0	97.6	97.0	99.4	97.5	94.7	181.8	114.3	94.8	139.2	104.8	92.8	90.4	92.3	95.6	89.2	94.1
0920	Plaster & Gypsum Board	112.7	93.8	100.7	101.9	98.2	99.6	93.4	173.0	143.9	97.3	130.0	118.1	111.5	86.6	95.7	111.5	84.9	94.6
0950, 0980	Ceilings & Acoustic Treatment	95.4	93.8	94.5	97.2	98.2	97.8	77.7	173.0	131.1	75.0	130.0	105.8	104.8	86.6	94.6	104.8	84.9	93.6
0960	Flooring	103.1	103.0	103.1	95.7	104.5	97.9	92.2	180.0	114.2	91.3	153.7	106.9	96.1	95.4	95.9	93.6	95.5	94.1
0970, 0990	Wall Finishes & Painting/Coating	94.9	97.7	96.6	89.8	98.7	95.1	100.0	161.9	136.9	98.3	112.8	106.9	89.9	98.8	95.2	83.6	98.8	92.6
09	FINISHES	99.6	97.4	98.5	96.3	101.6	99.0	92.2	174.1	133.3	91.0	131.3	111.3	99.2	91.7	95.4	97.6	90.9	94.3
COVERS	DIVS. 10 - 14, 25, 28, 41, 43, 44, 46	100.0	101.4	100.3	100.0	100.7	100.1	100.0	138.8	107.5	100.0	102.1	100.4	100.0	98.0	99.6	100.0	94.3	98.9
21, 22, 23	FIRE SUPPRESSION, PLUMBING & HVAC	100.1	90.4	96.6	100.2	107.0	102.6	100.2	169.3	124.9	92.5	111.1	99.2	100.4	92.8	97.7	100.4	99.0	99.9
26, 27, 3370	ELECTRICAL, COMMUNICATIONS & UTIL.	100.6	92.3	97.0	97.3	105.1	100.7	98.0	171.2	129.7	98.5	102.0	100.0	100.0	102.5	101.1	96.9	102.5	99.3
MF2018	WEIGHTED AVERAGE	101.4	98.6	100.4	98.2	107.0	101.4	92.7	165.5	119.5	90.3	118.0	100.5	98.1	99.0	98.4	96.2	99.9	97.5

	DIVISION	NEW YORK									NORTH CAROLINA								
		WATERTOWN			WHITE PLAINS			YONKERS			ASHEVILLE			CHARLOTTE			DURHAM		
		136			106			107			287 - 288			281 - 282			277		
		MAT.	INST.	TOTAL	MAT.	INST.	TOTAL	MAT.	INST.	TOTAL	MAT.	INST.	TOTAL	MAT.	INST.	TOTAL	MAT.	INST.	TOTAL
015433	CONTRACTOR EQUIPMENT		108.2	108.2		100.4	100.4		100.4	100.4		97.1	97.1		102.2	102.2		101.7	101.7
0241, 31 - 34	SITE & INFRASTRUCTURE, DEMOLITION	80.2	94.5	89.5	93.0	100.0	97.5	99.9	100.0	99.9	102.2	76.7	85.6	104.4	87.1	93.1	107.0	84.4	92.3
0310	Concrete Forming & Accessories	83.8	91.7	90.0	94.4	137.6	127.9	94.7	138.3	128.6	95.9	59.4	67.6	102.0	62.8	71.6	102.0	59.9	69.3
0320	Concrete Reinforcing	97.2	106.1	99.7	91.8	164.0	111.8	95.4	164.0	114.4	97.3	59.4	86.8	99.7	65.7	90.3	98.4	60.1	87.8
0330	Cast-in-Place Concrete	104.3	105.3	104.6	69.1	140.2	94.3	77.2	140.3	99.7	111.5	69.2	96.4	113.7	72.6	99.1	126.0	69.2	105.9
03	CONCRETE	104.7	100.3	103.0	76.7	143.7	103.1	83.1	144.1	107.1	92.8	64.6	81.7	95.2	68.2	84.5	101.0	64.9	86.7
04	MASONRY	94.2	106.8	101.8	91.6	146.7	125.1	95.2	146.7	126.5	79.6	61.3	68.5	81.3	63.6	70.5	82.6	61.3	69.7
05	METALS	94.0	119.3	99.0	83.8	163.4	99.5	93.7	163.7	107.5	99.7	87.7	97.3	101.0	87.3	98.3	115.1	88.0	109.7
06	WOOD, PLASTICS & COMPOSITES	78.4	87.6	82.5	108.8	133.5	119.9	108.7	134.2	120.1	96.9	57.4	79.2	98.8	60.8	81.7	101.5	57.9	82.0
07	THERMAL & MOISTURE PROTECTION	92.5	96.9	94.0	97.7	139.4	112.6	98.0	140.1	113.0	110.0	59.3	91.9	102.6	64.8	89.1	106.7	59.4	89.9
08	OPENINGS	95.6	92.3	94.8	94.8	165.2	110.7	98.0	165.6	113.2	88.7	56.3	81.4	98.7	61.4	90.3	96.7	56.8	87.7
0920	Plaster & Gypsum Board	98.5	87.4	91.4	102.2	134.6	122.7	111.0	135.3	126.4	107.8	56.1	75.0	102.3	59.5	75.1	102.8	56.7	73.6
0950, 0980	Ceilings & Acoustic Treatment	104.8	87.4	95.0	75.0	134.6	108.4	104.0	135.3	121.6	102.0	56.1	76.3	104.1	59.5	79.1	91.7	56.7	72.1
0960	Flooring	88.1	94.6	89.7	93.5	172.4	113.2	92.9	180.0	114.7	100.0	59.8	89.9	103.4	65.5	93.9	111.4	59.8	98.5
0970, 0990	Wall Finishes & Painting/Coating	83.6	96.7	91.4	98.3	161.9	136.2	98.3	161.9	136.2	103.1	50.7	71.9	99.1	64.4	78.4	102.8	50.7	71.8
09	FINISHES	94.7	92.2	93.4	91.9	146.0	119.1	101.3	147.9	124.7	102.0	58.2	80.0	102.8	63.1	82.8	100.7	58.5	79.5
COVERS	DIVS. 10 - 14, 25, 28, 41, 43, 44, 46	100.0	98.6	99.7	100.0	120.1	103.9	100.0	128.5	105.5	100.0	84.0	96.9	100.0	85.1	97.1	100.0	84.0	96.9
21, 22, 23	FIRE SUPPRESSION, PLUMBING & HVAC	100.4	87.0	95.6	100.3	142.4	115.4	100.3	142.5	115.4	100.9	60.2	86.3	100.1	62.7	86.7	101.0	60.2	86.4
26, 27, 3370	ELECTRICAL, COMMUNICATIONS & UTIL.	100.0	87.3	94.5	94.9	153.7	120.4	98.6	158.9	124.7	99.8	51.5	78.9	100.6	81.2	92.2	94.4	51.1	75.6
MF2018	WEIGHTED AVERAGE	97.5	95.9	96.9	91.7	143.7	110.8	96.3	145.1	114.2	98.0	63.8	85.4	99.3	71.1	88.9	102.5	64.5	88.5

	DIVISION	NORTH CAROLINA																	
		ELIZABETH CITY			FAYETTEVILLE			GASTONIA			GREENSBORO			HICKORY			KINSTON		
		279			283			280			270,272 - 274			286			285		
		MAT.	INST.	TOTAL	MAT.	INST.	TOTAL	MAT.	INST.	TOTAL	MAT.	INST.	TOTAL	MAT.	INST.	TOTAL	MAT.	INST.	TOTAL
015433	CONTRACTOR EQUIPMENT		105.2	105.2		101.7	101.7		97.1	97.1		101.7	101.7		101.7	101.7		101.7	101.7
0241, 31 - 34	SITE & INFRASTRUCTURE, DEMOLITION	107.8	85.6	93.3	101.6	84.1	90.2	102.1	76.7	85.5	106.9	84.4	92.2	98.0	84.1	89.0	96.8	84.1	88.5
0310	Concrete Forming & Accessories	85.3	58.2	64.2	95.4	58.1	66.5	103.1	60.1	69.7	101.7	59.9	69.2	91.4	59.9	67.0	87.2	58.1	64.6
0320	Concrete Reinforcing	96.8	62.8	87.4	100.6	60.1	89.4	97.7	60.1	87.3	97.7	60.1	87.3	97.3	60.1	87.0	96.8	60.1	86.6
0330	Cast-in-Place Concrete	126.3	68.8	105.8	116.9	66.7	99.0	108.9	69.3	94.9	125.1	69.2	105.2	111.4	69.0	96.4	107.6	66.7	93.0
03	CONCRETE	99.8	64.5	85.9	95.4	63.3	82.7	92.1	65.1	81.5	100.4	64.9	86.4	92.4	64.9	81.5	89.9	63.3	79.4
04	MASONRY	92.9	56.7	70.9	83.7	56.8	67.3	84.8	61.3	70.6	81.9	61.3	69.4	70.1	61.2	64.7	76.0	56.8	64.3
05	METALS	100.7	89.9	98.6	118.8	88.0	112.7	100.6	88.2	98.2	106.3	88.0	102.7	99.8	87.4	97.3	98.7	88.0	96.6
06	WOOD, PLASTICS & COMPOSITES	79.9	57.7	70.0	95.1	57.9	78.5	107.3	57.9	85.2	101.2	57.9	81.8	89.7	57.9	75.4	85.2	57.9	73.0
07	THERMAL & MOISTURE PROTECTION	105.6	57.1	88.3	109.3	57.3	90.7	110.2	59.4	92.1	106.2	59.4	89.5	110.2	59.4	92.1	110.1	57.3	91.3
08	OPENINGS	94.0	57.2	85.7	88.8	56.8	81.6	91.9	56.8	84.0	96.7	56.8	87.7	88.8	56.8	81.6	88.9	56.8	81.6
0920	Plaster & Gypsum Board	94.2	55.9	69.9	111.5	56.7	76.7	116.4	56.7	78.5	103.4	56.7	73.8	107.8	56.7	75.4	108.4	56.7	75.6
0950, 0980	Ceilings & Acoustic Treatment	91.7	55.9	71.6	106.5	56.7	78.6	110.2	56.7	80.2	91.7	56.7	72.1	102.0	56.7	76.6	110.2	56.7	80.2
0960	Flooring	104.4	59.8	93.2	100.1	59.8	90.0	102.8	59.8	92.0	111.4	59.8	98.5	99.9	59.8	89.9	97.4	59.8	88.0
0970, 0990	Wall Finishes & Painting/Coating	102.8	50.7	71.8	103.1	50.7	71.9	103.1	50.7	71.9	102.8	50.7	71.8	103.1	50.7	71.9	103.1	50.7	71.9
09	FINISHES	97.8	57.3	77.5	103.7	57.4	80.4	106.1	58.5	82.2	100.8	58.5	79.6	102.1	58.5	80.2	103.5	57.4	80.3
COVERS	DIVS. 10 - 14, 25, 28, 41, 43, 44, 46	100.0	83.9	96.9	100.0	82.5	96.6	100.0	84.2	96.9	100.0	84.0	96.9	100.0	84.2	96.9	100.0	82.5	96.6
21, 22, 23	FIRE SUPPRESSION, PLUMBING & HVAC	93.3	58.0	80.7	100.7	57.8	85.3	100.9	60.2	86.3	100.8	60.2	86.3	93.4	60.2	81.5	93.4	57.8	80.6
26, 27, 3370	ELECTRICAL, COMMUNICATIONS & UTIL.	93.7	61.6	79.8	102.1	51.1	80.0	99.5	81.5	91.7	93.7	51.5	75.4	98.6	81.5	91.2	98.5	49.7	77.4
MF2018	WEIGHTED AVERAGE	97.2	65.0	85.4	102.9	63.0	88.2	98.9	68.2	87.6	100.4	64.5	87.2	95.7	68.7	85.7	95.4	62.8	83.4

	DIVISION	NORTH CAROLINA															NORTH DAKOTA		
		MURPHY			RALEIGH			ROCKY MOUNT			WILMINGTON			WINSTON-SALEM			BISMARCK		
		289			275 - 276			278			284			271			585		
		MAT.	INST.	TOTAL	MAT.	INST.	TOTAL	MAT.	INST.	TOTAL	MAT.	INST.	TOTAL	MAT.	INST.	TOTAL	MAT.	INST.	TOTAL
015433	CONTRACTOR EQUIPMENT		97.1	97.1		107.8	107.8		101.7	101.7		97.1	97.1		101.7	101.7		100.3	100.3
0241, 31 - 34	SITE & INFRASTRUCTURE, DEMOLITION	100.1	76.4	84.7	106.0	96.3	99.7	105.9	84.1	91.7	103.1	76.4	85.7	107.2	84.4	92.4	89.2	99.1	95.7
0310	Concrete Forming & Accessories	103.8	54.9	65.8	101.7	59.6	69.0	92.7	59.3	66.8	97.3	58.1	66.9	103.7	59.9	69.6	101.7	75.7	81.5
0320	Concrete Reinforcing	96.8	57.9	86.0	98.9	60.1	88.2	96.8	60.1	86.7	98.1	60.1	87.6	97.7	60.1	87.3	98.8	97.4	98.4
0330	Cast-in-Place Concrete	115.3	66.6	98.0	129.7	70.3	108.6	123.5	68.3	103.9	111.0	66.7	95.3	128.2	69.2	107.3	111.8	91.0	104.4
03	CONCRETE	95.3	61.4	81.9	101.6	65.0	87.1	100.0	64.3	85.9	92.9	63.3	81.2	101.8	64.9	87.3	106.1	85.3	97.9
04	MASONRY	72.5	56.8	62.9	83.1	60.3	69.3	73.4	60.1	65.3	70.8	56.8	62.3	82.2	61.3	69.5	103.4	82.6	90.7
05	METALS	97.7	87.2	95.6	99.8	84.8	96.9	99.8	87.2	97.3	99.4	88.0	97.2	103.8	88.0	100.7	102.1	92.3	100.2
06	WOOD, PLASTICS & COMPOSITES	108.3	53.6	83.8	97.8	58.1	80.0	89.6	57.9	75.4	98.9	57.9	80.5	101.2	57.9	81.8	102.1	70.9	88.1
07	THERMAL & MOISTURE PROTECTION	110.2	56.6	91.1	101.4	60.5	86.8	106.1	58.8	89.3	110.0	57.3	91.2	106.2	59.4	89.5	105.8	84.5	98.2
08	OPENINGS	88.7	53.9	80.9	98.7	56.9	89.2	93.4	56.8	85.1	88.9	56.8	81.6	96.7	56.8	87.7	98.2	80.9	94.3
0920	Plaster & Gypsum Board	113.8	52.2	74.8	98.9	56.7	72.1	95.4	56.7	70.9	109.9	56.7	76.2	103.4	56.7	73.8	108.6	70.2	84.3
0950, 0980	Ceilings & Acoustic Treatment	102.0	52.2	74.1	88.2	56.7	70.5	88.5	56.7	70.7	106.5	56.7	78.6	91.7	56.7	72.1	113.8	70.2	89.4
0960	Flooring	103.1	59.8	92.2	102.4	59.8	91.7	107.5	59.8	95.5	100.5	59.8	90.3	111.4	59.8	98.5	100.2	51.6	88.0
0970, 0990	Wall Finishes & Painting/Coating	103.1	50.7	71.9	99.1	50.7	70.3	102.8	50.7	71.8	103.1	50.7	71.9	102.8	50.7	71.8	98.4	58.6	74.7
09	FINISHES	103.9	54.8	79.3	98.0	58.4	78.1	98.2	58.2	78.1	103.6	57.4	80.4	100.8	58.5	79.6	104.1	69.8	86.9
COVERS	DIVS. 10 - 14, 25, 28, 41, 43, 44, 46	100.0	82.1	96.5	100.0	84.0	96.9	100.0	83.7	96.8	100.0	82.5	96.6	100.0	84.0	96.9	100.0	91.9	98.4
21, 22, 23	FIRE SUPPRESSION, PLUMBING & HVAC	93.4	57.8	80.6	100.1	59.6	85.6	93.3	59.6	81.2	100.9	57.8	85.5	100.8	60.2	86.3	100.0	76.6	91.6
26, 27, 3370	ELECTRICAL, COMMUNICATIONS & UTIL.	100.3	49.7	78.4	99.9	50.1	78.3	94.7	51.1	75.8	100.4	49.7	78.4	93.7	51.5	75.4	99.8	86.1	93.8
MF2018	WEIGHTED AVERAGE	96.2	61.4	83.4	99.4	64.8	86.7	96.4	64.0	84.5	97.8	62.2	84.7	100.0	64.5	87.0	101.4	82.9	94.6

	DIVISION	NORTH DAKOTA																	
		DEVILS LAKE			DICKINSON			FARGO			GRAND FORKS			JAMESTOWN			MINOT		
		583			586			580 - 581			582			584			587		
		MAT.	INST.	TOTAL	MAT.	INST.	TOTAL	MAT.	INST.	TOTAL	MAT.	INST.	TOTAL	MAT.	INST.	TOTAL	MAT.	INST.	TOTAL
015433	CONTRACTOR EQUIPMENT		94.2	94.2		94.2	94.2		100.6	100.6		94.2	94.2		94.2	94.2		94.2	94.2
0241, 31 - 34	SITE & INFRASTRUCTURE, DEMOLITION	89.1	88.6	88.8	93.4	88.5	90.2	89.2	99.2	95.7	94.4	89.2	91.0	88.3	88.6	88.5	92.9	89.3	90.5
0310	Concrete Forming & Accessories	105.5	65.2	74.2	93.1	65.1	71.4	101.7	66.0	73.9	97.8	71.7	77.5	95.0	65.2	71.8	92.6	65.4	71.5
0320	Concrete Reinforcing	102.1	97.3	100.8	103.1	97.2	101.5	99.0	97.9	98.7	100.5	97.4	99.7	102.7	97.8	101.3	104.1	97.2	102.2
0330	Cast-in-Place Concrete	131.2	74.6	111.1	118.7	74.5	103.0	108.6	81.6	99.0	118.7	80.6	105.1	129.6	74.6	110.1	118.7	74.9	103.1
03	CONCRETE	111.2	74.9	96.9	109.2	74.8	95.7	107.5	77.7	95.7	107.0	80.0	96.3	109.6	75.0	95.9	106.3	75.2	94.0
04	MASONRY	111.2	77.5	90.7	113.0	75.9	90.4	92.4	85.8	88.4	105.6	80.4	90.3	123.1	85.6	100.3	103.4	74.4	85.8
05	METALS	98.5	93.0	97.4	98.4	92.6	97.2	102.1	92.5	100.2	98.4	93.7	97.5	98.4	93.5	97.4	98.7	93.7	97.7
06	WOOD, PLASTICS & COMPOSITES	103.1	61.3	84.4	87.1	61.3	75.5	98.8	61.7	82.2	93.2	68.2	82.0	89.7	61.3	77.0	86.7	61.3	75.3
07	THERMAL & MOISTURE PROTECTION	105.7	76.0	95.1	106.0	77.5	95.8	101.4	81.2	94.2	105.8	79.0	96.2	105.4	78.7	95.9	105.5	77.7	95.6
08	OPENINGS	96.1	75.6	91.4	96.0	75.6	91.4	96.9	75.8	92.1	94.9	79.4	91.4	96.0	75.6	91.4	95.0	75.6	90.6
0920	Plaster & Gypsum Board	110.9	60.7	79.1	100.0	60.7	75.1	93.8	60.7	72.8	101.7	67.8	80.2	101.2	60.7	75.5	100.0	60.7	75.1
0950, 0980	Ceilings & Acoustic Treatment	105.8	60.7	80.5	105.8	60.7	80.5	113.6	60.7	83.9	105.8	67.8	84.5	105.8	60.7	80.5	105.8	60.7	80.5
0960	Flooring	101.1	51.6	88.6	96.2	51.6	85.0	100.6	51.6	88.3	97.5	51.6	86.0	96.7	51.6	85.4	96.0	51.6	84.8
0970, 0990	Wall Finishes & Painting/Coating	89.9	50.1	66.1	89.9	50.1	66.1	99.1	59.8	75.7	89.9	58.7	71.3	89.9	50.1	66.1	89.9	51.1	66.7
09	FINISHES	99.4	61.3	80.3	97.1	61.3	79.1	102.4	62.7	82.4	97.4	67.0	82.1	96.8	61.3	79.0	96.5	61.4	78.9
COVERS	DIVS. 10 - 14, 25, 28, 41, 43, 44, 46	100.0	77.9	95.7	100.0	77.9	95.7	100.0	88.6	97.8	100.0	85.3	97.2	100.0	77.8	95.7	100.0	87.8	97.6
21, 22, 23	FIRE SUPPRESSION, PLUMBING & HVAC	92.5	70.6	84.7	92.5	65.9	83.0	99.9	66.7	88.0	100.1	73.6	90.6	92.5	65.0	82.7	100.1	64.9	87.5
26, 27, 3370	ELECTRICAL, COMMUNICATIONS & UTIL.	93.3	64.8	80.9	97.7	64.5	83.3	99.6	61.8	83.2	95.1	64.8	81.9	93.3	60.8	79.2	96.7	65.2	83.1
MF2018	WEIGHTED AVERAGE	98.6	73.8	89.5	98.7	72.6	89.1	100.7	75.3	91.3	99.5	76.9	91.2	98.5	73.0	89.2	99.5	72.9	89.7

DIVISION		NORTH DAKOTA			OHIO															
		WILLISTON			AKRON			ATHENS			CANTON			CHILLICOTHE			CINCINNATI			
		588			442 - 443			457			446 - 447			456			451 - 452			
		MAT.	INST.	TOTAL	MAT.	INST.	TOTAL	MAT.	INST.	TOTAL	MAT.	INST.	TOTAL	MAT.	INST.	TOTAL	MAT.	INST.	TOTAL	
015433	CONTRACTOR EQUIPMENT		94.2	94.2		88.0	88.0		84.2	84.2		88.0	88.0		93.6	93.6		97.6	97.6	
0241, 31 - 34	SITE & INFRASTRUCTURE, DEMOLITION	89.5	89.3	89.4	86.2	90.8	89.2	87.8	82.4	84.3	86.3	90.7	89.2	82.0	90.6	87.6	84.8	99.4	94.3	
0310	Concrete Forming & Accessories	99.8	71.7	78.0	98.6	82.4	86.0	88.2	83.2	84.3	98.6	74.4	79.8	90.8	74.1	77.8	94.4	73.1	77.9	
0320	Concrete Reinforcing	105.0	97.2	102.8	102.1	90.5	98.9	97.1	80.1	92.4	102.1	73.2	94.1	95.5	79.7	91.1	99.2	79.4	93.7	
0330	Cast-in-Place Concrete	118.7	80.6	105.1	100.9	85.7	95.5	111.6	88.6	103.5	101.9	84.3	95.6	101.3	84.5	95.3	96.8	79.9	90.8	
03	CONCRETE	107.7	80.0	96.8	96.6	84.7	91.9	103.4	84.4	95.9	97.0	77.6	89.3	98.5	79.3	91.0	97.4	76.9	89.3	
04	MASONRY	99.1	77.2	85.8	96.4	88.9	91.8	60.0	89.5	77.9	97.0	81.0	87.3	65.2	81.5	75.1	69.1	81.9	76.9	
05	METALS	98.6	93.5	97.6	91.4	82.3	89.6	95.8	78.7	92.4	91.4	75.3	88.2	89.2	86.9	88.7	97.6	82.5	94.6	
06	WOOD, PLASTICS & COMPOSITES	95.4	68.2	83.2	98.9	81.3	91.0	77.0	81.2	78.9	99.4	72.5	87.3	87.2	70.8	79.9	91.4	70.9	82.2	
07	THERMAL & MOISTURE PROTECTION	105.7	79.0	96.2	101.7	88.3	96.9	98.3	87.3	94.4	102.6	84.8	96.2	100.8	80.1	93.4	99.8	81.2	93.1	
08	OPENINGS	96.1	79.4	92.3	101.5	82.2	97.1	93.5	76.7	89.7	95.7	69.6	89.8	84.9	70.7	81.7	99.0	71.5	92.8	
0920	Plaster & Gypsum Board	101.7	67.8	80.2	85.8	80.8	82.7	84.4	80.7	82.1	87.5	71.7	77.5	87.7	70.5	76.8	84.8	70.2	75.5	
0950, 0980	Ceilings & Acoustic Treatment	105.8	67.8	84.5	95.1	80.8	87.1	114.2	80.7	95.4	95.1	71.7	82.0	108.2	70.5	87.1	97.2	70.2	82.1	
0960	Flooring	98.2	51.6	86.5	89.3	75.1	85.8	111.2	74.4	102.0	89.6	68.0	84.2	90.0	67.4	84.4	93.8	77.8	89.8	
0970, 0990	Wall Finishes & Painting/Coating	89.9	56.4	69.9	95.0	86.6	90.0	102.6	82.9	90.9	95.0	72.1	81.4	99.7	79.2	87.5	99.1	71.6	82.7	
09	FINISHES	97.5	66.9	82.1	92.2	81.5	86.8	99.9	81.3	90.6	92.5	72.2	82.3	96.6	72.5	84.5	94.0	73.3	83.6	
COVERS	DIVS. 10 - 14, 25, 28, 41, 43, 44, 46	100.0	87.4	97.6	100.0	92.1	98.5	100.0	91.3	98.3	100.0	90.5	98.2	100.0	88.1	97.7	100.0	88.2	97.7	
21, 22, 23	FIRE SUPPRESSION, PLUMBING & HVAC	92.5	70.5	84.6	100.0	86.4	95.1	92.6	79.2	87.8	100.0	76.3	91.5	93.3	83.1	89.6	100.0	77.0	91.8	
26, 27, 3370	ELECTRICAL, COMMUNICATIONS & UTIL.	95.3	65.2	82.3	99.3	80.8	91.3	102.5	87.5	96.0	99.0	80.7	91.1	99.1	79.9	90.8	99.4	75.8	89.2	
MF2018	WEIGHTED AVERAGE	97.8	76.0	89.8	96.8	85.0	92.4	95.5	83.1	90.9	96.4	78.5	89.8	92.5	81.0	88.3	96.9	79.3	90.4	

DIVISION		OHIO																	
		CLEVELAND			COLUMBUS			DAYTON			HAMILTON			LIMA			LORAIN		
		441			430 - 432			453 - 454			450			458			440		
		MAT.	INST.	TOTAL	MAT.	INST.	TOTAL	MAT.	INST.	TOTAL	MAT.	INST.	TOTAL	MAT.	INST.	TOTAL	MAT.	INST.	TOTAL
015433	CONTRACTOR EQUIPMENT		93.9	93.9		97.1	97.1		87.7	87.7		93.6	93.6		87.1	87.1		88.0	88.0
0241, 31 - 34	SITE & INFRASTRUCTURE, DEMOLITION	85.8	97.8	93.6	83.6	97.6	92.7	82.8	90.6	87.9	82.9	90.3	87.7	83.8	81.7	82.4	85.6	90.7	88.9
0310	Concrete Forming & Accessories	98.5	88.7	90.9	93.5	85.4	87.2	92.7	77.1	80.6	92.8	70.5	75.4	88.1	69.6	73.7	98.7	76.4	81.4
0320	Concrete Reinforcing	100.5	91.7	98.1	100.8	80.1	95.1	101.2	78.0	94.8	101.2	69.3	92.4	97.1	77.8	91.8	102.1	90.5	98.9
0330	Cast-in-Place Concrete	100.6	97.2	99.4	99.4	90.9	96.4	86.8	81.5	84.9	93.0	76.0	86.9	102.5	82.1	95.3	96.0	88.4	93.3
03	CONCRETE	95.8	91.8	94.2	94.5	86.3	91.3	92.2	78.9	86.9	94.8	73.0	86.2	97.4	75.8	88.9	94.6	82.9	90.0
04	MASONRY	100.8	98.2	99.2	76.0	89.0	83.9	64.2	77.3	72.2	64.6	73.2	69.8	77.4	70.4	73.2	93.3	87.9	90.0
05	METALS	97.6	85.0	95.1	97.6	81.8	94.5	91.1	78.2	88.6	91.0	83.0	89.4	95.8	80.4	92.8	92.0	82.2	90.1
06	WOOD, PLASTICS & COMPOSITES	96.3	86.3	91.8	90.7	85.0	88.1	90.7	77.2	84.7	89.9	70.1	81.0	76.9	68.2	73.0	98.9	74.4	87.9
07	THERMAL & MOISTURE PROTECTION	100.5	96.4	99.0	102.0	87.9	97.0	104.3	78.0	95.0	100.9	74.4	91.4	97.9	79.4	91.4	102.5	85.0	96.3
08	OPENINGS	98.9	85.2	95.8	98.6	78.8	94.1	91.9	74.6	88.0	89.6	69.3	85.1	93.5	68.4	87.8	95.7	78.4	91.8
0920	Plaster & Gypsum Board	85.6	85.9	85.8	87.8	84.4	85.6	88.9	77.1	81.4	88.9	69.7	76.7	84.4	67.3	73.6	85.8	73.7	78.2
0950, 0980	Ceilings & Acoustic Treatment	93.6	85.9	89.3	95.4	84.4	89.2	108.2	77.1	90.8	108.2	69.7	86.6	114.2	67.3	87.9	95.1	73.7	83.1
0960	Flooring	93.8	96.0	94.3	91.2	76.6	87.6	93.4	71.4	87.9	91.0	70.3	85.8	110.7	69.1	100.3	89.6	83.8	88.1
0970, 0990	Wall Finishes & Painting/Coating	99.1	86.6	91.6	94.9	78.0	84.8	99.7	68.5	81.1	99.7	63.4	78.0	102.6	68.0	81.9	95.0	84.9	89.0
09	FINISHES	93.2	89.5	91.4	92.8	82.9	87.9	97.6	75.0	86.2	96.8	69.4	83.1	99.5	68.6	83.9	92.3	78.2	85.2
COVERS	DIVS. 10 - 14, 25, 28, 41, 43, 44, 46	100.0	96.9	99.4	100.0	91.4	98.3	100.0	87.6	97.6	100.0	86.0	97.3	100.0	90.0	98.1	100.0	92.9	98.6
21, 22, 23	FIRE SUPPRESSION, PLUMBING & HVAC	100.0	91.5	97.0	100.0	90.8	96.7	101.0	78.6	93.0	100.8	67.4	88.8	92.6	82.5	89.0	100.0	76.7	91.6
26, 27, 3370	ELECTRICAL, COMMUNICATIONS & UTIL.	99.6	88.6	94.8	99.2	83.0	92.2	97.6	75.4	88.0	97.9	67.2	84.6	102.8	67.4	87.4	99.1	73.9	88.2
MF2018	WEIGHTED AVERAGE	98.0	91.4	95.6	96.8	87.0	93.2	94.5	78.6	88.6	94.4	73.1	86.6	95.3	75.6	88.1	96.0	80.9	90.5

DIVISION		OHIO																	
		MANSFIELD			MARION			SPRINGFIELD			STEUBENVILLE			TOLEDO			YOUNGSTOWN		
		448 - 449			433			455			439			434 - 436			444 - 445		
		MAT.	INST.	TOTAL	MAT.	INST.	TOTAL	MAT.	INST.	TOTAL	MAT.	INST.	TOTAL	MAT.	INST.	TOTAL	MAT.	INST.	TOTAL
015433	CONTRACTOR EQUIPMENT		88.0	88.0		89.0	89.0		87.7	87.7		92.2	92.2		92.3	92.3		88.0	88.0
0241, 31 - 34	SITE & INFRASTRUCTURE, DEMOLITION	79.8	90.2	86.6	75.7	87.6	83.5	83.1	90.5	88.0	98.5	94.7	96.0	81.3	88.4	86.0	86.1	90.4	88.9
0310	Concrete Forming & Accessories	87.4	74.9	77.7	91.1	72.2	76.4	92.7	75.8	79.6	91.0	72.0	76.2	94.8	88.4	89.8	98.6	75.3	80.5
0320	Concrete Reinforcing	93.0	71.0	86.9	97.2	70.9	89.9	101.2	78.0	94.8	95.4	91.8	94.4	105.4	86.2	100.1	102.1	81.1	96.3
0330	Cast-in-Place Concrete	93.4	80.7	88.9	86.0	80.9	84.2	89.1	81.7	86.5	93.4	82.3	89.5	94.2	89.9	92.7	99.9	84.4	94.4
03	CONCRETE	88.6	76.2	83.7	84.7	75.3	81.0	93.1	78.3	87.3	87.7	79.0	84.3	92.1	88.6	90.8	96.2	79.4	89.6
04	MASONRY	95.3	80.1	86.1	79.0	80.9	80.2	64.4	77.7	72.4	70.8	82.1	77.7	83.8	90.1	87.6	96.6	83.6	88.7
05	METALS	92.6	74.7	89.0	92.9	77.1	89.8	91.1	78.1	88.6	90.4	82.7	88.9	93.4	88.4	92.4	91.5	78.3	88.9
06	WOOD, PLASTICS & COMPOSITES	83.6	74.4	79.5	84.0	70.5	78.0	91.6	75.3	84.3	79.1	69.5	74.8	88.6	89.4	89.0	98.9	73.6	87.5
07	THERMAL & MOISTURE PROTECTION	101.0	83.1	94.6	97.9	80.6	91.7	104.2	78.0	94.9	109.3	79.2	98.5	98.0	89.8	95.1	102.7	85.6	96.6
08	OPENINGS	96.5	70.3	90.6	87.5	68.1	83.1	90.1	73.7	86.4	87.5	72.9	84.2	89.9	84.2	88.6	95.7	78.4	91.8
0920	Plaster & Gypsum Board	78.3	73.7	75.4	87.1	69.8	76.1	88.9	75.1	80.1	83.5	68.3	73.8	89.0	89.3	89.2	85.8	72.9	77.6
0950, 0980	Ceilings & Acoustic Treatment	96.4	73.7	83.7	100.6	69.8	83.3	108.2	75.1	89.7	99.1	68.3	81.8	100.6	89.3	94.3	95.1	72.9	82.6
0960	Flooring	85.1	87.4	85.7	87.9	87.4	87.8	93.4	71.4	87.9	115.3	85.2	107.8	88.3	92.4	89.3	89.6	86.1	88.7
0970, 0990	Wall Finishes & Painting/Coating	95.0	69.1	79.6	96.8	69.1	80.3	99.7	68.5	81.1	110.3	77.4	90.7	96.8	82.0	87.9	95.0	75.3	83.2
09	FINISHES	90.1	76.3	83.2	93.7	74.3	83.9	97.6	73.9	85.7	109.1	74.1	91.5	94.3	88.6	91.4	92.4	76.7	84.5
COVERS	DIVS. 10 - 14, 25, 28, 41, 43, 44, 46	100.0	89.8	98.0	100.0	87.4	97.6	100.0	87.4	97.6	100.0	86.5	97.4	100.0	93.9	98.8	100.0	90.3	98.1
21, 22, 23	FIRE SUPPRESSION, PLUMBING & HVAC	92.5	75.2	86.3	92.5	83.7	89.3	101.0	76.5	92.2	93.2	82.2	89.3	100.0	91.7	97.0	100.0	79.8	92.8
26, 27, 3370	ELECTRICAL, COMMUNICATIONS & UTIL.	97.9	80.8	90.5	97.3	80.8	90.2	97.6	77.4	88.8	90.1	94.8	92.1	100.8	92.5	97.2	99.1	80.7	91.1
MF2018	WEIGHTED AVERAGE	93.3	78.4	87.8	91.6	79.6	87.2	94.5	78.2	88.5	92.4	83.1	89.0	95.2	90.0	93.3	96.3	80.9	90.6

DIVISION		OHIO			OKLAHOMA														
		ZANESVILLE			ARDMORE			CLINTON			DURANT			ENID			GUYMON		
		437 - 438			734			736			747			737			739		
		MAT.	INST.	TOTAL	MAT.	INST.	TOTAL	MAT.	INST.	TOTAL	MAT.	INST.	TOTAL	MAT.	INST.	TOTAL	MAT.	INST.	TOTAL
015433	CONTRACTOR EQUIPMENT		89.0	89.0		79.3	79.3		78.5	78.5		78.5	78.5		78.5	78.5		78.5	78.5
0241, 31 - 34	SITE & INFRASTRUCTURE, DEMOLITION	77.5	87.5	84.0	93.2	88.5	90.1	94.4	87.2	89.7	91.8	86.9	88.6	99.2	87.2	91.4	98.2	86.4	90.5
0310	Concrete Forming & Accessories	88.2	71.2	75.0	89.2	52.3	60.5	87.6	52.3	60.2	84.4	50.5	58.1	91.6	52.6	61.3	94.8	50.4	60.3
0320	Concrete Reinforcing	96.6	83.1	92.9	88.3	65.1	81.9	88.8	65.1	82.2	96.0	57.2	85.3	88.3	65.1	81.9	88.8	56.8	80.0
0330	Cast-in-Place Concrete	90.6	79.5	86.7	83.7	70.2	78.9	80.9	70.2	77.1	81.1	67.8	76.4	80.9	73.7	78.3	80.9	67.2	76.0
03	CONCRETE	87.3	76.5	83.0	82.3	61.0	73.9	81.8	61.0	73.6	83.0	58.0	73.1	82.2	62.3	74.3	84.2	57.6	73.7
04	MASONRY	76.9	78.0	77.6	94.0	60.6	73.7	118.4	60.6	83.3	87.2	56.0	68.3	100.7	60.6	76.3	95.6	49.9	67.9
05	METALS	94.1	84.2	92.2	97.0	63.0	90.3	97.1	63.0	90.4	91.6	60.0	85.3	98.5	63.3	91.6	97.7	58.1	89.9
06	WOOD, PLASTICS & COMPOSITES	78.8	70.5	75.1	90.9	49.5	72.4	89.9	49.5	71.8	81.1	49.5	66.9	94.0	49.5	74.1	98.4	49.5	76.5
07	THERMAL & MOISTURE PROTECTION	97.9	77.2	90.5	103.5	62.3	88.8	103.6	62.3	88.9	97.9	60.1	84.4	103.7	62.3	89.0	104.0	56.1	87.0
08	OPENINGS	87.5	73.2	84.3	102.2	50.8	90.6	102.2	50.8	90.6	93.2	49.0	83.2	103.2	52.4	91.8	102.3	49.0	90.3
0920	Plaster & Gypsum Board	81.8	69.8	74.2	90.9	48.7	64.1	90.7	48.7	64.0	73.2	48.7	57.6	91.9	48.7	64.5	91.9	48.7	64.5
0950, 0980	Ceilings & Acoustic Treatment	100.6	69.8	83.3	101.9	48.7	72.1	101.9	48.7	72.1	83.6	48.7	64.0	101.9	48.7	72.1	101.9	48.7	72.1
0960	Flooring	86.7	67.4	81.9	94.7	51.3	83.8	93.9	51.3	83.2	96.0	46.3	83.6	95.1	69.2	88.6	96.3	51.3	85.0
0970, 0990	Wall Finishes & Painting/Coating	96.8	79.2	86.3	92.9	42.3	62.7	92.9	42.3	62.7	96.4	42.3	64.1	92.9	42.3	62.7	92.9	37.5	59.9
09	FINISHES	92.7	70.6	81.6	95.5	49.6	72.5	95.5	49.6	72.4	87.9	47.6	67.7	96.0	53.3	74.6	96.8	49.2	72.9
COVERS	DIVS. 10 - 14, 25, 28, 41, 43, 44, 46	100.0	86.5	97.4	100.0	78.2	95.8	100.0	78.2	95.8	100.0	76.8	95.5	100.0	78.2	95.8	100.0	76.8	95.5
21, 22, 23	FIRE SUPPRESSION, PLUMBING & HVAC	92.5	80.8	88.3	92.7	66.2	83.2	92.7	66.2	83.2	92.6	63.9	82.3	100.2	66.2	88.0	92.7	61.8	81.6
26, 27, 3370	ELECTRICAL, COMMUNICATIONS & UTIL.	97.7	79.9	90.0	92.8	70.8	83.3	93.4	70.8	83.6	96.3	61.6	81.3	93.4	70.8	83.6	94.2	58.4	78.7
MF2018	WEIGHTED AVERAGE	92.0	79.0	87.2	94.3	64.4	83.3	95.3	64.3	83.9	91.7	60.9	80.4	96.9	65.0	85.2	95.2	59.2	82.0

DIVISION		OKLAHOMA																	
		LAWTON			MCALESTER			MIAMI			MUSKOGEE			OKLAHOMA CITY			PONCA CITY		
		735			745			743			744			730 - 731			746		
		MAT.	INST.	TOTAL	MAT.	INST.	TOTAL	MAT.	INST.	TOTAL	MAT.	INST.	TOTAL	MAT.	INST.	TOTAL	MAT.	INST.	TOTAL
015433	CONTRACTOR EQUIPMENT		79.3	79.3		78.5	78.5		88.4	88.4		88.4	88.4		90.9	90.9		78.5	78.5
0241, 31 - 34	SITE & INFRASTRUCTURE, DEMOLITION	95.9	88.6	91.1	86.0	87.1	86.7	86.7	84.4	85.2	90.5	84.3	86.5	95.8	101.6	99.6	92.4	86.9	88.8
0310	Concrete Forming & Accessories	94.6	56.2	64.8	82.4	55.1	61.2	96.7	50.5	60.8	101.7	54.1	64.7	98.4	62.0	70.1	91.7	50.6	59.7
0320	Concrete Reinforcing	88.5	65.1	82.0	95.7	68.1	88.1	94.2	65.0	86.1	95.1	62.7	86.2	99.7	65.2	90.1	95.1	65.0	86.8
0330	Cast-in-Place Concrete	78.2	73.8	76.6	71.1	70.5	70.9	74.5	68.7	72.4	75.4	69.2	73.2	82.2	72.1	78.6	83.3	67.9	77.8
03	CONCRETE	79.8	64.0	73.6	76.2	62.8	71.0	79.8	60.5	72.2	81.4	61.9	73.7	87.7	66.1	79.2	84.7	59.4	74.7
04	MASONRY	95.6	60.6	74.3	103.4	57.9	75.8	90.0	56.5	69.6	103.7	57.7	75.7	94.7	58.0	72.4	81.9	56.4	66.4
05	METALS	103.1	63.3	95.2	91.5	64.2	86.1	91.5	76.5	88.5	92.9	75.6	89.5	97.2	65.5	91.0	91.5	62.9	85.8
06	WOOD, PLASTICS & COMPOSITES	97.2	54.4	78.0	78.3	54.5	67.6	96.5	49.6	75.5	102.2	53.5	80.4	94.7	63.5	80.7	90.7	49.5	72.2
07	THERMAL & MOISTURE PROTECTION	103.6	63.0	89.1	97.6	61.7	84.8	98.1	61.0	84.8	98.4	60.2	84.8	95.4	64.3	84.3	98.1	60.4	84.7
08	OPENINGS	104.5	55.1	93.3	93.2	55.4	84.7	93.2	50.9	83.6	94.2	52.5	84.8	98.0	60.1	89.4	93.2	50.8	83.6
0920	Plaster & Gypsum Board	97.0	53.7	69.6	73.0	53.8	60.8	79.5	48.7	59.9	84.5	52.7	64.3	96.7	62.7	75.2	78.0	48.7	59.4
0950, 0980	Ceilings & Acoustic Treatment	118.3	53.7	82.1	83.6	53.8	66.9	83.6	48.7	64.0	99.5	52.7	73.2	106.8	62.7	82.1	83.6	48.7	64.0
0960	Flooring	96.4	69.2	89.6	95.3	65.6	87.9	100.5	46.3	86.9	102.3	60.9	91.9	99.9	69.2	92.2	98.4	51.3	86.6
0970, 0990	Wall Finishes & Painting/Coating	92.9	42.3	62.7	96.4	46.2	66.4	96.4	37.5	61.3	96.4	37.5	61.3	99.1	42.3	65.2	96.4	42.3	64.1
09	FINISHES	101.0	56.2	78.5	87.1	55.3	71.1	89.4	47.1	68.2	95.0	52.7	73.7	101.5	60.9	81.1	89.4	49.5	69.3
COVERS	DIVS. 10 - 14, 25, 28, 41, 43, 44, 46	100.0	78.8	95.9	100.0	77.9	95.7	100.0	77.2	95.6	100.0	78.0	95.7	100.0	79.6	96.1	100.0	76.8	95.5
21, 22, 23	FIRE SUPPRESSION, PLUMBING & HVAC	100.2	66.2	88.0	92.6	60.8	81.2	92.6	57.3	79.9	100.1	60.6	86.0	100.1	64.9	87.5	92.6	57.3	79.9
26, 27, 3370	ELECTRICAL, COMMUNICATIONS & UTIL.	94.2	70.8	84.1	95.4	67.7	83.4	96.2	67.8	83.9	95.2	82.6	89.7	99.9	70.9	87.3	95.2	58.4	79.3
MF2018	WEIGHTED AVERAGE	97.9	65.9	86.1	91.2	63.7	81.1	91.5	62.1	80.7	94.8	65.9	84.2	97.4	67.9	86.5	91.8	59.8	80.0

DIVISION		OKLAHOMA												OREGON					
		POTEAU			SHAWNEE			TULSA			WOODWARD			BEND			EUGENE		
		749			748			740 - 741			738			977			974		
		MAT.	INST.	TOTAL	MAT.	INST.	TOTAL	MAT.	INST.	TOTAL	MAT.	INST.	TOTAL	MAT.	INST.	TOTAL	MAT.	INST.	TOTAL
015433	CONTRACTOR EQUIPMENT		87.3	87.3		78.5	78.5		88.4	88.4		78.5	78.5		94.9	94.9		94.9	94.9
0241, 31 - 34	SITE & INFRASTRUCTURE, DEMOLITION	75.7	82.6	80.2	94.8	87.0	89.7	95.8	84.5	88.5	94.8	87.2	89.9	122.1	94.6	104.1	114.0	94.6	101.3
0310	Concrete Forming & Accessories	89.4	50.6	59.2	84.3	50.6	58.1	101.6	55.1	65.5	87.8	56.7	63.6	100.0	99.3	99.5	96.3	99.5	98.8
0320	Concrete Reinforcing	96.2	65.1	87.6	95.1	59.1	85.1	95.3	65.1	87.0	88.3	65.1	81.9	88.4	112.6	95.1	91.8	112.6	97.5
0330	Cast-in-Place Concrete	74.5	68.7	72.5	85.9	67.9	79.5	82.1	71.4	78.3	80.9	71.2	77.4	133.1	100.6	121.6	128.9	100.7	118.9
03	CONCRETE	81.3	60.5	73.1	85.6	58.4	74.9	85.2	63.6	76.6	81.9	63.3	74.5	116.8	101.6	110.8	109.4	101.8	106.4
04	MASONRY	90.3	56.5	69.7	104.7	56.4	75.4	91.0	57.8	70.8	89.7	60.6	72.0	114.9	102.9	107.6	111.2	102.9	106.1
05	METALS	91.5	76.5	88.6	91.4	60.8	85.4	97.2	77.0	93.2	97.2	63.3	90.5	110.2	96.9	107.6	110.9	97.2	108.2
06	WOOD, PLASTICS & COMPOSITES	86.7	49.6	70.1	80.9	49.5	66.8	101.2	54.6	80.3	90.0	55.2	74.4	107.3	99.5	103.8	101.9	99.5	100.8
07	THERMAL & MOISTURE PROTECTION	98.1	60.9	84.9	98.1	58.7	84.0	98.4	63.4	85.9	103.7	63.1	89.2	95.3	99.9	97.0	94.6	101.7	97.2
08	OPENINGS	93.2	50.9	83.6	93.2	49.4	83.3	95.5	55.1	86.4	102.3	55.1	91.6	92.2	102.6	94.5	92.4	102.6	94.7
0920	Plaster & Gypsum Board	76.3	48.7	58.8	73.2	48.7	57.6	84.5	53.8	65.0	90.7	54.5	67.7	123.3	99.5	108.2	120.1	99.5	107.0
0950, 0980	Ceilings & Acoustic Treatment	83.6	48.7	64.0	83.6	48.7	64.0	99.5	53.8	73.9	101.9	54.5	75.3	94.5	99.5	97.3	94.5	99.5	97.3
0960	Flooring	97.9	46.3	84.9	96.0	51.3	84.8	101.4	60.1	91.1	93.9	65.9	86.9	106.9	101.7	105.6	105.8	101.7	104.8
0970, 0990	Wall Finishes & Painting/Coating	96.4	42.3	64.1	96.4	37.5	61.3	96.4	56.0	72.3	92.9	42.3	62.7	97.7	74.2	83.7	97.7	62.2	76.5
09	FINISHES	87.5	47.7	67.5	88.2	48.1	68.0	94.9	55.2	75.0	95.5	55.9	75.6	106.3	97.0	101.6	104.3	95.7	100.0
COVERS	DIVS. 10 - 14, 25, 28, 41, 43, 44, 46	100.0	77.1	95.6	100.0	76.9	95.5	100.0	78.2	95.8	100.0	78.8	95.9	100.0	101.9	100.4	100.0	101.9	100.4
21, 22, 23	FIRE SUPPRESSION, PLUMBING & HVAC	92.6	57.3	79.9	92.6	63.9	82.3	100.1	60.7	86.0	92.7	66.2	83.2	92.6	97.6	94.4	100.1	108.7	103.2
26, 27, 3370	ELECTRICAL, COMMUNICATIONS & UTIL.	95.3	67.8	83.4	96.3	70.8	85.3	96.3	64.7	82.6	94.1	70.8	84.0	93.5	91.5	92.6	92.8	91.5	92.2
MF2018	WEIGHTED AVERAGE	91.1	62.0	80.4	92.8	62.4	81.6	96.0	64.4	84.4	94.3	65.7	83.8	102.7	97.9	100.9	103.1	100.1	102.0

DIVISION		OREGON																	
		KLAMATH FALLS			MEDFORD			PENDLETON			PORTLAND			SALEM			VALE		
		976			975			978			970 - 972			973			979		
		MAT.	INST.	TOTAL	MAT.	INST.	TOTAL	MAT.	INST.	TOTAL	MAT.	INST.	TOTAL	MAT.	INST.	TOTAL	MAT.	INST.	TOTAL
015433	CONTRACTOR EQUIPMENT		94.9	94.9		94.9	94.9		92.7	92.7		94.9	94.9		99.4	99.4		92.7	92.7
0241, 31 - 34	SITE & INFRASTRUCTURE, DEMOLITION	126.7	94.5	105.7	122.6	94.5	104.3	121.0	88.7	99.9	116.3	94.6	102.1	109.3	101.7	104.3	107.2	88.6	95.1
0310	Concrete Forming & Accessories	92.6	99.0	97.5	91.5	99.1	97.4	94.8	99.1	98.2	97.7	99.7	99.2	96.0	99.7	98.9	101.8	97.9	98.8
0320	Concrete Reinforcing	88.4	112.5	95.1	89.9	112.5	96.2	88.8	112.5	95.4	92.6	112.6	98.1	98.6	112.6	102.5	86.6	112.3	93.7
0330	Cast-in-Place Concrete	133.1	92.1	118.5	133.1	100.5	121.5	134.0	92.5	119.3	132.5	100.8	121.2	121.8	102.7	115.0	105.4	92.7	100.9
03	CONCRETE	118.8	98.5	110.8	114.5	101.5	109.4	103.6	98.7	101.7	111.2	101.9	107.5	109.7	102.4	106.8	88.3	98.2	92.2
04	MASONRY	129.2	102.9	113.2	107.3	102.9	104.6	118.7	103.0	109.1	113.4	102.9	107.0	114.9	103.0	107.7	116.1	103.0	108.1
05	METALS	110.2	96.6	107.5	110.5	96.7	107.7	117.8	97.1	113.7	112.8	97.3	109.7	118.8	95.3	114.2	117.5	95.8	113.2
06	WOOD, PLASTICS & COMPOSITES	95.6	99.5	97.3	94.3	99.5	96.6	99.3	99.6	99.4	103.4	99.5	101.7	95.5	99.7	97.3	109.9	99.6	105.3
07	THERMAL & MOISTURE PROTECTION	95.4	95.1	95.3	95.1	94.5	94.9	90.8	92.0	91.2	94.6	100.5	96.7	91.3	101.8	95.0	90.4	88.4	89.7
08	OPENINGS	92.2	102.6	94.5	94.8	102.6	96.5	89.1	102.7	92.1	90.5	102.6	93.2	97.5	102.7	98.7	89.0	89.8	89.2
0920	Plaster & Gypsum Board	115.6	99.5	105.4	114.9	99.5	105.1	102.6	99.5	100.6	118.3	99.5	106.4	117.6	99.5	106.1	111.8	99.5	104.0
0950, 0980	Ceilings & Acoustic Treatment	105.4	99.5	102.1	108.4	99.5	103.4	72.5	99.5	87.6	96.5	99.5	98.2	115.0	99.5	106.3	72.5	99.5	87.6
0960	Flooring	104.8	101.7	104.0	104.4	101.7	103.7	71.1	101.7	78.8	103.0	101.7	102.7	105.8	101.7	104.8	72.6	101.7	79.9
0970, 0990	Wall Finishes & Painting/Coating	97.7	71.7	82.2	97.7	71.7	82.2	89.0	77.7	82.3	97.2	77.7	85.6	99.1	69.5	81.4	89.0	74.2	80.2
09	FINISHES	108.0	96.7	102.3	107.7	96.7	102.2	76.2	97.5	86.9	103.8	97.4	100.6	108.1	96.6	102.3	76.9	97.1	87.0
COVERS	DIVS. 10 - 14, 25, 28, 41, 43, 44, 46	100.0	101.8	100.4	100.0	101.8	100.4	100.0	99.9	100.0	100.0	102.0	100.4	100.0	102.4	100.5	100.0	102.0	100.4
21, 22, 23	FIRE SUPPRESSION, PLUMBING & HVAC	92.6	97.5	94.3	100.1	103.0	101.1	99.9	103.6	101.2	100.1	108.8	103.2	100.1	108.8	103.2	99.9	66.9	88.0
26, 27, 3370	ELECTRICAL, COMMUNICATIONS & UTIL.	92.9	79.5	87.1	94.5	79.5	88.0	86.5	86.2	86.4	93.5	115.4	103.0	100.9	91.5	96.8	86.5	60.6	75.3
MF2018	WEIGHTED AVERAGE	103.6	95.5	100.6	104.2	97.1	101.6	101.1	97.4	99.7	103.7	103.8	103.7	106.3	100.8	104.3	98.9	85.1	93.9

DIVISION		PENNSYLVANIA																	
		ALLENTOWN			ALTOONA			BEDFORD			BRADFORD			BUTLER			CHAMBERSBURG		
		181			166			155			167			160			172		
		MAT.	INST.	TOTAL	MAT.	INST.	TOTAL	MAT.	INST.	TOTAL	MAT.	INST.	TOTAL	MAT.	INST.	TOTAL	MAT.	INST.	TOTAL
015433	CONTRACTOR EQUIPMENT		108.2	108.2		108.2	108.2		106.9	106.9		108.2	108.2		108.2	108.2		107.5	107.5
0241, 31 - 34	SITE & INFRASTRUCTURE, DEMOLITION	89.4	93.6	92.1	91.3	93.4	92.6	89.9	90.3	90.1	84.9	91.0	88.9	81.1	93.0	88.9	85.0	90.4	88.5
0310	Concrete Forming & Accessories	99.0	104.7	103.4	82.4	83.9	83.6	80.9	73.9	75.4	85.0	87.6	87.0	83.8	87.8	86.9	85.6	69.7	73.2
0320	Concrete Reinforcing	96.6	108.3	99.8	93.6	99.1	95.1	95.5	94.9	95.3	95.6	94.9	95.4	94.2	114.1	99.7	94.3	100.7	96.0
0330	Cast-in-Place Concrete	88.7	100.4	92.8	98.8	88.4	95.1	101.9	78.6	93.6	94.4	82.8	90.3	87.2	93.9	89.6	94.0	85.5	91.0
03	CONCRETE	92.6	104.8	97.4	88.9	89.5	89.1	98.7	80.7	91.6	93.6	88.4	91.5	82.5	95.8	87.7	95.7	82.4	90.5
04	MASONRY	97.3	95.0	95.9	100.0	86.9	92.0	97.9	72.3	82.3	97.7	73.8	83.2	101.9	89.7	94.5	100.5	71.3	82.8
05	METALS	95.1	119.3	99.9	90.2	112.3	94.5	92.4	107.7	95.4	92.5	107.3	95.4	89.9	117.9	95.4	92.8	112.1	96.6
06	WOOD, PLASTICS & COMPOSITES	99.8	105.6	102.4	75.3	82.3	78.4	71.4	74.2	72.7	81.2	91.8	86.0	77.1	85.3	80.8	79.5	68.7	74.6
07	THERMAL & MOISTURE PROTECTION	101.4	109.2	104.2	99.4	91.5	96.6	102.6	79.9	94.5	101.1	81.1	94.0	99.0	90.7	96.0	98.6	74.5	90.0
08	OPENINGS	92.8	104.4	95.4	86.6	85.4	86.3	91.2	80.0	88.6	93.0	88.8	92.0	86.6	94.6	88.4	87.2	73.8	84.2
0920	Plaster & Gypsum Board	107.7	105.9	106.5	96.0	81.9	87.1	108.8	73.6	86.5	96.8	91.7	93.6	96.0	85.0	89.0	102.5	67.8	80.5
0950, 0980	Ceilings & Acoustic Treatment	92.5	105.9	100.0	96.6	81.9	88.4	108.0	73.6	88.7	96.7	91.7	93.9	97.1	85.0	90.4	88.8	67.8	77.1
0960	Flooring	96.1	93.6	95.5	89.6	100.2	92.3	96.1	92.9	95.3	91.5	92.9	91.8	90.4	94.3	91.4	99.1	69.8	91.8
0970, 0990	Wall Finishes & Painting/Coating	89.9	109.8	101.8	85.6	107.1	98.4	92.3	93.9	93.2	89.9	93.9	92.2	85.6	94.3	90.8	91.6	89.5	90.3
09	FINISHES	95.4	103.1	99.2	93.2	88.7	90.9	101.0	78.8	89.9	93.7	89.6	91.6	93.1	89.1	91.1	93.9	71.1	82.4
COVERS	DIVS. 10 - 14, 25, 28, 41, 43, 44, 46	100.0	102.3	100.4	100.0	97.6	99.5	100.0	93.8	98.8	100.0	96.3	99.3	100.0	99.3	99.9	100.0	91.5	98.3
21, 22, 23	FIRE SUPPRESSION, PLUMBING & HVAC	100.4	113.6	105.2	99.8	85.4	94.6	92.8	76.0	86.7	92.9	81.4	88.8	92.2	89.0	91.1	92.8	80.6	88.5
26, 27, 3370	ELECTRICAL, COMMUNICATIONS & UTIL.	99.3	94.2	97.1	91.2	107.9	98.4	100.1	107.8	103.5	96.0	107.8	101.1	91.5	95.9	93.4	93.5	76.4	86.1
MF2018	WEIGHTED AVERAGE	96.8	104.4	99.6	93.5	93.3	93.4	95.4	86.0	92.0	94.0	90.4	92.6	90.8	94.5	92.2	93.6	81.5	89.1

DIVISION		PENNSYLVANIA																	
		DOYLESTOWN			DUBOIS			ERIE			GREENSBURG			HARRISBURG			HAZLETON		
		189			158			164 - 165			156			170 - 171			182		
		MAT.	INST.	TOTAL	MAT.	INST.	TOTAL	MAT.	INST.	TOTAL	MAT.	INST.	TOTAL	MAT.	INST.	TOTAL	MAT.	INST.	TOTAL
015433	CONTRACTOR EQUIPMENT		89.3	89.3		106.9	106.9		108.2	108.2		106.9	106.9		111.3	111.3		108.2	108.2
0241, 31 - 34	SITE & INFRASTRUCTURE, DEMOLITION	96.8	81.9	87.1	93.2	90.6	91.5	89.0	93.1	91.7	86.8	92.3	90.4	90.3	100.3	96.8	80.8	91.9	88.1
0310	Concrete Forming & Accessories	81.6	114.7	107.3	80.4	76.2	77.2	98.0	88.4	90.5	87.6	83.0	84.0	98.9	90.9	92.7	79.2	80.5	80.2
0320	Concrete Reinforcing	93.2	135.3	104.9	94.8	107.1	98.2	95.6	107.8	98.9	94.8	113.9	100.1	98.2	114.6	102.7	93.7	101.4	95.9
0330	Cast-in-Place Concrete	83.7	117.6	95.8	98.2	88.8	94.9	97.1	89.8	94.5	94.5	93.6	94.2	92.7	101.8	95.9	83.7	87.2	84.9
03	CONCRETE	87.7	118.9	100.0	99.9	87.4	95.0	89.1	93.5	90.8	94.9	93.3	94.3	92.6	99.9	95.5	85.7	88.0	86.6
04	MASONRY	100.2	121.5	113.1	98.2	84.1	89.6	90.3	91.8	91.2	107.2	86.2	94.4	96.5	96.1	96.3	109.1	80.6	91.8
05	METALS	93.0	116.8	97.7	92.4	112.8	96.4	90.6	115.2	95.4	92.4	116.4	97.1	99.8	117.6	103.3	94.8	113.0	98.4
06	WOOD, PLASTICS & COMPOSITES	76.2	114.0	93.1	70.3	74.2	72.0	96.7	87.4	92.5	78.8	79.1	78.9	95.7	87.6	92.0	74.3	79.0	76.4
07	THERMAL & MOISTURE PROTECTION	98.2	117.9	105.2	102.9	86.6	97.1	99.9	91.7	97.0	102.6	88.7	97.6	102.3	109.3	104.8	100.6	90.3	96.9
08	OPENINGS	95.0	120.6	100.8	91.2	82.8	89.3	86.7	90.9	87.6	91.1	91.2	91.1	98.4	89.0	96.3	93.3	84.5	91.4
0920	Plaster & Gypsum Board	94.2	114.6	107.1	107.4	73.6	85.9	107.7	87.1	94.6	109.5	78.6	89.9	111.6	87.1	96.1	94.7	78.5	84.4
0950, 0980	Ceilings & Acoustic Treatment	91.7	114.6	104.5	108.0	73.6	88.7	92.5	87.1	89.5	108.0	78.6	91.5	96.8	87.1	91.4	93.0	78.5	84.9
0960	Flooring	80.8	124.8	91.8	95.9	92.9	95.2	92.6	101.4	94.8	98.9	69.8	91.6	107.7	95.6	104.7	89.1	80.0	86.8
0970, 0990	Wall Finishes & Painting/Coating	89.9	127.7	112.4	92.3	109.8	102.7	95.9	90.3	92.6	92.3	94.3	93.5	98.4	91.2	94.1	89.9	92.5	91.4
09	FINISHES	86.8	117.6	102.2	101.1	81.8	91.4	95.1	90.6	92.8	101.7	80.9	91.3	101.8	91.1	96.4	91.3	81.4	86.3
COVERS	DIVS. 10 - 14, 25, 28, 41, 43, 44, 46	100.0	112.8	102.5	100.0	95.5	99.1	100.0	98.7	99.8	100.0	98.6	99.7	100.0	98.9	99.8	100.0	97.0	99.4
21, 22, 23	FIRE SUPPRESSION, PLUMBING & HVAC	92.2	119.1	101.9	92.8	78.7	87.7	99.8	94.1	97.7	92.8	81.7	88.8	100.2	98.1	99.5	92.9	85.9	90.4
26, 27, 3370	ELECTRICAL, COMMUNICATIONS & UTIL.	94.8	117.8	104.8	100.4	107.8	103.6	92.3	88.9	90.8	100.4	107.9	103.6	100.3	91.0	96.3	96.4	80.1	89.4
MF2018	WEIGHTED AVERAGE	93.0	115.6	101.3	95.7	89.9	93.6	93.6	94.3	93.9	95.4	92.4	94.3	98.8	98.0	98.5	93.7	87.5	91.4

DIVISION		PENNSYLVANIA																	
		INDIANA			JOHNSTOWN			KITTANNING			LANCASTER			LEHIGH VALLEY			MONTROSE		
		157			159			162			175 - 176			180			188		
		MAT.	INST.	TOTAL	MAT.	INST.	TOTAL	MAT.	INST.	TOTAL	MAT.	INST.	TOTAL	MAT.	INST.	TOTAL	MAT.	INST.	TOTAL
015433	CONTRACTOR EQUIPMENT		106.9	106.9		106.9	106.9		108.2	108.2		107.5	107.5		108.2	108.2		108.2	108.2
0241, 31 - 34	SITE & INFRASTRUCTURE, DEMOLITION	85.5	91.6	89.5	90.3	92.6	91.8	83.0	93.4	89.8	78.5	93.3	88.1	83.9	92.3	89.4	82.5	92.1	88.7
0310	Concrete Forming & Accessories	81.6	87.5	86.2	80.4	83.4	82.7	83.8	84.7	84.5	87.5	89.8	89.3	91.8	99.9	98.1	80.1	81.0	80.8
0320	Concrete Reinforcing	94.1	114.2	99.7	95.5	114.1	100.6	94.2	114.0	99.7	93.9	106.1	97.3	93.7	96.9	94.6	98.2	104.3	99.9
0330	Cast-in-Place Concrete	92.6	93.4	92.9	102.8	87.5	97.3	90.7	93.6	91.7	79.9	98.4	86.5	90.7	90.4	90.6	88.9	84.8	87.5
03	CONCRETE	92.6	95.4	93.7	99.5	91.4	96.3	84.6	94.2	88.4	86.2	97.1	90.5	91.3	97.1	93.6	90.4	87.8	89.4
04	MASONRY	95.6	91.9	93.3	96.5	83.8	88.8	104.5	87.6	94.3	107.0	90.0	96.7	97.3	86.9	91.0	97.2	82.4	88.2
05	METALS	92.5	116.3	97.2	92.5	116.5	97.2	90.0	116.9	95.3	92.8	119.2	98.0	94.7	112.4	98.2	92.6	113.7	96.7
06	WOOD, PLASTICS & COMPOSITES	72.3	85.3	78.1	70.3	82.3	75.7	77.1	81.1	78.9	83.0	87.3	85.0	89.3	102.1	95.0	75.2	79.0	76.9
07	THERMAL & MOISTURE PROTECTION	102.4	91.3	98.5	102.6	87.4	97.2	99.1	89.7	95.7	98.1	107.2	101.3	101.1	100.3	100.8	100.7	81.6	93.9
08	OPENINGS	91.2	90.6	91.0	91.2	88.9	90.6	86.6	92.3	87.9	87.2	87.1	87.2	93.3	96.6	94.1	90.3	83.2	88.7
0920	Plaster & Gypsum Board	109.1	85.0	93.8	107.4	81.9	91.2	96.0	80.6	86.2	106.8	87.1	94.3	97.3	102.3	100.5	95.8	78.5	84.8
0950, 0980	Ceilings & Acoustic Treatment	108.0	85.0	95.1	108.0	81.9	93.4	97.1	80.6	87.9	88.8	87.1	87.9	93.0	102.3	98.2	96.7	78.5	86.5
0960	Flooring	96.5	92.9	95.6	95.9	97.3	96.3	90.4	92.9	91.0	100.0	95.6	98.9	93.7	84.3	91.3	89.7	92.9	90.5
0970, 0990	Wall Finishes & Painting/Coating	92.3	109.8	102.7	92.3	107.1	101.1	85.6	109.8	100.0	91.6	83.5	86.8	89.9	89.7	89.8	89.9	92.5	91.4
09	FINISHES	100.9	90.3	95.5	100.8	87.8	94.2	93.2	87.8	90.5	94.2	89.5	91.8	93.3	96.0	94.7	92.8	83.6	88.2
COVERS	DIVS. 10 - 14, 25, 28, 41, 43, 44, 46	100.0	99.2	99.9	100.0	97.0	99.4	100.0	98.9	99.8	100.0	97.5	99.5	100.0	101.0	100.2	100.0	97.7	99.5
21, 22, 23	FIRE SUPPRESSION, PLUMBING & HVAC	92.8	80.9	88.5	92.8	84.8	89.9	92.2	85.7	89.9	92.8	96.9	94.3	92.9	105.6	97.4	92.9	85.2	90.1
26, 27, 3370	ELECTRICAL, COMMUNICATIONS & UTIL.	100.4	107.8	103.6	100.4	107.9	103.6	91.2	107.8	98.4	94.3	89.2	92.1	96.4	115.2	104.6	96.0	84.8	91.1
MF2018	WEIGHTED AVERAGE	94.6	94.4	94.5	95.5	93.4	94.7	91.2	94.7	92.5	92.6	95.7	93.8	94.2	101.6	96.9	93.2	88.3	91.4

DIVISION		PENNSYLVANIA																	
		NEW CASTLE			NORRISTOWN			OIL CITY			PHILADELPHIA			PITTSBURGH			POTTSVILLE		
		161			194			163			190 - 191			150 - 152			179		
		MAT.	INST.	TOTAL	MAT.	INST.	TOTAL	MAT.	INST.	TOTAL	MAT.	INST.	TOTAL	MAT.	INST.	TOTAL	MAT.	INST.	TOTAL
015433	CONTRACTOR EQUIPMENT		108.2	108.2		94.4	94.4		108.2	108.2		101.1	101.1		98.4	98.4		107.5	107.5
0241, 31 - 34	SITE & INFRASTRUCTURE, DEMOLITION	81.4	93.7	89.4	99.8	90.0	93.4	80.3	91.3	87.4	105.3	103.9	104.4	94.0	95.7	95.1	80.9	90.9	87.4
0310	Concrete Forming & Accessories	83.8	91.6	89.9	83.7	119.0	111.1	83.8	84.2	84.1	99.8	136.4	128.2	99.7	98.5	98.8	79.0	79.6	79.5
0320	Concrete Reinforcing	93.1	95.4	93.8	96.3	135.3	107.1	94.2	85.2	91.7	101.0	152.1	115.1	100.4	122.8	106.6	93.2	102.4	95.7
0330	Cast-in-Place Concrete	88.1	93.8	90.1	94.2	115.5	101.8	85.5	86.1	85.7	105.7	133.5	115.6	101.4	100.6	101.1	85.2	95.1	88.7
03	CONCRETE	82.6	94.3	87.2	88.6	120.2	101.1	81.5	86.6	83.5	99.3	137.0	114.2	101.1	103.3	102.0	88.7	90.5	89.4
04	MASONRY	101.5	92.5	96.0	110.3	118.1	115.1	101.0	79.9	88.2	96.9	134.1	119.5	90.5	100.4	96.5	100.7	78.9	87.4
05	METALS	90.0	111.4	94.2	97.5	116.8	101.3	90.0	109.1	93.8	100.9	123.8	105.4	100.8	107.6	102.1	93.1	113.8	97.1
06	WOOD, PLASTICS & COMPOSITES	77.1	90.5	83.1	77.4	121.6	97.2	77.1	85.3	80.8	97.0	136.2	114.6	96.9	98.5	97.6	71.4	77.3	74.0
07	THERMAL & MOISTURE PROTECTION	99.0	90.9	96.1	105.1	117.3	109.5	98.9	83.1	93.3	101.2	137.2	114.0	104.8	100.3	103.2	98.1	90.4	95.4
08	OPENINGS	86.6	93.6	88.1	90.1	124.8	97.9	86.6	87.2	86.7	99.0	139.9	108.2	99.1	104.6	100.3	87.2	84.3	86.6
0920	Plaster & Gypsum Board	96.0	90.3	92.4	104.2	122.5	115.8	96.0	85.0	89.0	121.1	137.2	131.3	114.7	98.4	104.3	98.6	76.7	84.7
0950, 0980	Ceilings & Acoustic Treatment	97.1	90.3	93.3	100.9	122.5	113.0	97.1	85.0	90.4	106.8	137.2	123.9	102.2	98.4	100.1	88.8	76.7	82.0
0960	Flooring	90.4	97.0	92.1	93.7	124.8	101.5	90.4	92.9	91.0	101.7	147.9	113.3	101.9	106.8	103.1	96.5	92.9	95.6
0970, 0990	Wall Finishes & Painting/Coating	85.6	101.9	95.3	90.0	127.7	112.5	85.6	109.8	100.0	98.4	188.7	152.2	98.4	109.8	105.2	91.6	92.5	92.1
09	FINISHES	93.1	93.5	93.3	95.4	121.2	108.3	93.0	88.4	90.7	105.4	144.0	124.8	102.2	100.7	101.4	92.2	82.3	87.3
COVERS	DIVS. 10 - 14, 25, 28, 41, 43, 44, 46	100.0	99.9	100.0	100.0	112.3	102.4	100.0	96.7	99.4	100.0	118.5	103.6	100.0	103.4	100.7	100.0	96.9	99.4
21, 22, 23	FIRE SUPPRESSION, PLUMBING & HVAC	92.2	92.4	92.3	92.6	117.3	101.4	92.2	84.7	89.5	100.2	141.7	115.0	100.2	99.5	100.0	92.8	86.1	90.4
26, 27, 3370	ELECTRICAL, COMMUNICATIONS & UTIL.	91.5	93.2	92.2	97.9	126.4	110.2	92.6	95.9	94.0	100.6	160.7	126.6	100.8	114.6	106.8	93.3	81.3	88.1
MF2018	WEIGHTED AVERAGE	90.9	95.0	92.4	95.4	117.6	103.6	90.8	89.7	90.4	100.5	137.6	114.2	100.1	103.2	101.3	92.4	88.0	90.8

DIVISION		PENNSYLVANIA																	
		READING			SCRANTON			STATE COLLEGE			STROUDSBURG			SUNBURY			UNIONTOWN		
		195 - 196			184 - 185			168			183			178			154		
		MAT.	INST.	TOTAL	MAT.	INST.	TOTAL	MAT.	INST.	TOTAL	MAT.	INST.	TOTAL	MAT.	INST.	TOTAL	MAT.	INST.	TOTAL
015433	CONTRACTOR EQUIPMENT		113.7	113.7		108.2	108.2		107.5	107.5		108.2	108.2		108.2	108.2		106.9	106.9
0241, 31 - 34	SITE & INFRASTRUCTURE, DEMOLITION	106.9	102.6	104.1	89.8	93.0	91.9	78.7	92.2	87.5	82.1	92.2	88.7	90.1	91.6	91.1	85.8	92.2	90.0
0310	Concrete Forming & Accessories	101.5	85.8	89.3	99.2	86.5	89.4	85.3	84.3	84.5	85.8	82.1	82.9	89.2	76.8	79.6	74.6	87.8	84.8
0320	Concrete Reinforcing	97.6	108.2	100.5	96.6	108.0	99.7	94.9	99.3	96.1	96.9	104.4	99.0	95.8	100.7	97.2	94.8	114.2	100.2
0330	Cast-in-Place Concrete	84.4	94.0	87.8	92.6	90.5	91.8	89.3	89.1	89.2	87.2	86.2	86.9	93.1	86.5	90.8	92.6	93.5	93.0
03	CONCRETE	87.6	94.0	90.2	94.2	93.1	93.7	93.3	90.0	92.0	89.4	88.8	89.2	92.6	86.0	90.0	92.2	95.5	93.5
04	MASONRY	100.0	88.4	93.0	97.7	90.1	93.1	102.3	88.8	94.1	94.5	86.7	89.8	100.1	72.9	83.6	108.6	91.9	98.4
05	METALS	97.9	119.1	102.1	97.1	117.3	101.1	92.3	112.9	96.3	94.8	114.1	98.6	92.7	112.7	96.7	92.2	116.8	97.1
06	WOOD, PLASTICS & COMPOSITES	100.5	82.8	92.6	99.8	84.8	93.1	83.4	82.3	82.9	82.2	79.0	80.8	80.6	77.3	79.1	62.9	85.3	72.9
07	THERMAL & MOISTURE PROTECTION	106.1	104.1	105.4	101.3	89.2	97.0	100.4	101.5	100.8	100.9	81.9	94.1	99.2	83.1	93.5	102.3	91.3	98.4
08	OPENINGS	94.9	91.8	94.2	92.8	88.9	91.9	90.2	85.4	89.1	93.4	85.7	91.6	87.3	81.5	86.0	91.1	91.6	91.2
0920	Plaster & Gypsum Board	115.7	82.5	94.7	111.5	84.4	94.3	97.2	81.9	87.5	95.4	78.5	84.7	97.3	76.7	84.3	103.5	85.0	91.8
0950, 0980	Ceilings & Acoustic Treatment	88.1	82.5	85.0	104.8	84.4	93.4	92.6	81.9	86.6	91.7	78.5	84.3	84.7	76.7	80.3	108.0	85.0	95.1
0960	Flooring	96.6	90.5	95.1	96.1	98.0	96.6	94.2	92.4	93.7	91.9	84.3	90.0	97.0	92.9	96.0	93.5	103.4	96.0
0970, 0990	Wall Finishes & Painting/Coating	89.0	103.5	97.6	89.9	103.5	98.0	89.9	107.1	100.1	89.9	92.5	91.4	91.6	92.5	92.1	92.3	101.9	98.0
09	FINISHES	94.6	87.2	90.9	99.1	89.9	94.5	92.7	87.6	90.1	92.0	82.8	87.4	92.2	80.8	86.5	99.2	91.2	95.2
COVERS	DIVS. 10 - 14, 25, 28, 41, 43, 44, 46	100.0	98.0	99.6	100.0	98.7	99.7	100.0	95.8	99.2	100.0	98.6	99.7	100.0	92.9	98.6	100.0	99.3	99.9
21, 22, 23	FIRE SUPPRESSION, PLUMBING & HVAC	100.4	111.2	104.3	100.4	94.8	98.4	92.9	94.8	93.6	92.9	88.0	91.1	92.8	78.5	87.7	92.8	85.7	90.2
26, 27, 3370	ELECTRICAL, COMMUNICATIONS & UTIL.	101.9	93.3	98.2	99.3	89.8	95.2	95.1	107.9	100.6	96.4	126.2	109.3	94.0	81.8	88.7	98.8	107.9	102.7
MF2018	WEIGHTED AVERAGE	97.9	99.3	98.4	97.7	94.3	96.5	93.5	95.6	94.3	93.7	95.4	94.4	93.2	84.6	90.0	94.6	95.7	95.0

	DIVISION	PENNSYLVANIA																	
		WASHINGTON			WELLSBORO			WESTCHESTER			WILKES-BARRE			WILLIAMSPORT			YORK		
		153			169			193			186 - 187			177			173 - 174		
		MAT.	INST.	TOTAL	MAT.	INST.	TOTAL	MAT.	INST.	TOTAL	MAT.	INST.	TOTAL	MAT.	INST.	TOTAL	MAT.	INST.	TOTAL
015433	CONTRACTOR EQUIPMENT		106.9	106.9		108.2	108.2		94.4	94.4		108.2	108.2		108.2	108.2		107.5	107.5
0241, 31 - 34	SITE & INFRASTRUCTURE, DEMOLITION	85.9	93.0	90.5	87.5	91.6	90.2	105.7	90.9	96.1	80.1	92.7	88.3	82.7	92.8	89.3	85.0	93.3	90.4
0310	Concrete Forming & Accessories	81.8	93.7	91.0	84.3	76.3	78.0	91.0	114.5	109.2	88.9	84.9	85.8	85.9	82.2	83.0	82.4	86.4	85.5
0320	Concrete Reinforcing	94.8	114.5	100.2	94.9	104.2	97.4	95.5	135.3	106.5	95.6	110.3	99.6	95.1	110.1	99.2	95.8	110.1	99.8
0330	Cast-in-Place Concrete	92.6	94.1	93.2	93.6	80.5	88.9	104.4	117.4	109.0	83.7	88.8	85.5	78.8	87.5	81.9	85.6	98.4	90.1
03	CONCRETE	92.8	98.5	95.1	95.1	84.2	90.8	95.1	118.7	104.4	87.0	92.0	89.0	82.7	90.4	85.8	90.1	96.1	92.5
04	MASONRY	96.2	94.3	95.0	104.3	73.3	85.5	104.5	121.5	114.8	109.4	92.9	99.4	92.2	87.2	89.2	101.0	90.0	94.3
05	METALS	92.2	118.0	97.3	92.4	112.9	96.4	97.5	116.8	101.3	92.5	117.9	97.5	92.8	118.6	97.9	94.4	119.1	99.3
06	WOOD, PLASTICS & COMPOSITES	72.3	92.8	81.5	80.5	76.6	78.7	86.2	113.9	98.6	85.3	83.1	84.3	76.7	80.9	78.6	75.2	82.9	78.6
07	THERMAL & MOISTURE PROTECTION	102.4	93.4	99.2	101.4	77.1	92.7	105.6	113.8	108.5	100.7	90.0	96.9	98.6	87.6	94.7	98.2	104.5	100.4
08	OPENINGS	91.1	98.7	92.8	93.0	81.5	90.4	90.1	120.5	97.0	90.3	88.1	89.8	87.3	86.9	87.2	87.2	85.4	86.8
0920	Plaster & Gypsum Board	109.1	92.7	98.7	95.5	76.0	83.2	104.7	114.6	111.0	97.0	82.7	87.9	98.6	80.5	87.1	98.6	82.5	88.4
0950, 0980	Ceilings & Acoustic Treatment	108.0	92.7	99.4	92.6	76.0	83.3	100.9	114.6	108.6	96.7	82.7	88.8	88.8	80.5	84.2	87.8	82.5	84.8
0960	Flooring	96.6	103.4	98.3	91.2	92.9	91.6	96.0	124.8	103.2	92.6	98.0	93.9	96.1	88.6	94.2	97.7	95.6	97.2
0970, 0990	Wall Finishes & Painting/Coating	92.3	101.9	98.0	89.9	92.5	91.4	90.0	127.7	112.5	89.9	106.2	99.6	91.6	106.2	100.3	91.6	86.7	88.7
09	FINISHES	100.9	95.9	98.4	92.6	80.8	86.7	96.6	117.5	107.1	93.6	88.9	91.3	92.6	85.3	88.9	92.3	87.2	89.8
COVERS	DIVS. 10 - 14, 25, 28, 41, 43, 44, 46	100.0	100.1	100.0	100.0	92.9	98.6	100.0	112.6	102.4	100.0	98.1	99.6	100.0	94.9	99.0	100.0	97.0	99.4
21, 22, 23	FIRE SUPPRESSION, PLUMBING & HVAC	92.8	89.0	91.4	92.9	78.5	87.7	92.6	119.1	102.1	92.9	94.4	93.4	92.8	93.6	93.1	100.3	96.9	99.1
26, 27, 3370	ELECTRICAL, COMMUNICATIONS & UTIL.	100.1	107.9	103.5	96.0	84.8	91.1	97.8	117.8	106.5	96.4	85.1	91.5	94.2	78.7	87.5	94.3	79.2	87.7
MF2018	WEIGHTED AVERAGE	94.5	98.3	95.9	94.4	84.6	90.8	96.3	116.1	103.6	93.4	93.5	93.4	91.6	91.0	91.4	94.8	93.7	94.4

	DIVISION	PUERTO RICO			RHODE ISLAND						SOUTH CAROLINA								
		SAN JUAN			NEWPORT			PROVIDENCE			AIKEN			BEAUFORT			CHARLESTON		
		009			028			029			298			299			294		
		MAT.	INST.	TOTAL	MAT.	INST.	TOTAL	MAT.	INST.	TOTAL	MAT.	INST.	TOTAL	MAT.	INST.	TOTAL	MAT.	INST.	TOTAL
015433	CONTRACTOR EQUIPMENT		91.1	91.1		95.8	95.8		100.9	100.9		101.3	101.3		101.3	101.3		101.3	101.3
0241, 31 - 34	SITE & INFRASTRUCTURE, DEMOLITION	125.9	88.5	101.5	84.4	93.9	90.6	87.6	103.4	97.9	131.9	83.3	100.2	127.3	83.3	98.6	115.8	83.7	94.9
0310	Concrete Forming & Accessories	77.0	20.5	33.1	97.9	116.4	112.2	95.3	116.5	111.8	95.5	59.0	67.2	94.4	61.3	68.7	93.4	62.4	69.3
0320	Concrete Reinforcing	107.9	17.3	82.8	98.5	115.1	103.1	98.7	115.1	103.3	98.3	54.2	86.1	97.4	59.7	86.9	97.2	64.1	88.0
0330	Cast-in-Place Concrete	90.5	32.5	69.9	56.3	112.1	76.1	77.2	113.5	90.1	97.4	64.2	85.6	97.4	64.3	85.6	114.4	66.6	97.4
03	CONCRETE	97.7	25.5	69.2	83.0	114.5	95.4	93.9	114.9	102.2	95.8	61.8	82.4	94.1	63.8	82.1	95.1	65.9	83.6
04	MASONRY	121.2	22.1	61.0	112.4	118.9	116.4	124.6	119.0	121.2	82.6	53.9	65.2	98.1	53.9	71.3	99.8	64.8	78.6
05	METALS	104.0	43.2	92.0	94.4	112.6	98.0	99.2	110.4	101.4	98.0	85.7	95.6	98.0	87.7	96.0	100.4	91.3	98.6
06	WOOD, PLASTICS & COMPOSITES	81.2	19.6	53.5	95.6	115.4	104.5	93.5	115.5	103.4	93.1	60.8	78.6	91.2	63.7	78.9	89.6	63.7	78.0
07	THERMAL & MOISTURE PROTECTION	143.0	26.1	101.4	93.0	113.3	100.2	97.7	114.7	103.8	108.3	56.9	90.0	108.0	57.9	90.1	107.1	63.5	91.5
08	OPENINGS	159.8	18.0	127.8	94.9	116.2	99.7	97.4	116.3	101.7	92.7	56.7	84.6	92.7	59.5	85.2	96.1	61.9	88.4
0920	Plaster & Gypsum Board	156.5	17.2	68.1	106.5	115.8	112.4	120.0	115.8	117.3	101.5	59.6	74.9	109.0	62.6	79.6	109.2	62.6	79.6
0950, 0980	Ceilings & Acoustic Treatment	227.8	17.2	109.7	91.6	115.8	105.1	113.1	115.8	114.6	96.0	59.6	75.6	106.9	62.6	82.1	106.9	62.6	82.1
0960	Flooring	194.8	26.6	152.6	101.5	126.3	107.8	108.2	126.3	112.7	107.7	80.4	100.8	109.0	67.9	98.7	108.7	79.7	101.4
0970, 0990	Wall Finishes & Painting/Coating	200.1	20.6	93.1	87.3	114.6	103.6	98.4	114.6	108.1	94.3	58.7	73.1	94.3	50.5	68.2	94.3	66.0	77.4
09	FINISHES	197.7	21.5	109.2	96.4	118.4	107.5	107.9	118.5	113.2	103.5	62.9	83.1	107.4	61.6	84.4	105.2	66.0	85.5
COVERS	DIVS. 10 - 14, 25, 28, 41, 43, 44, 46	100.0	24.9	85.4	100.0	106.1	101.2	100.0	106.4	101.2	100.0	82.5	96.6	100.0	75.5	95.3	100.0	83.3	96.8
21, 22, 23	FIRE SUPPRESSION, PLUMBING & HVAC	117.6	17.3	81.6	100.6	110.9	104.3	100.2	110.9	104.0	93.0	49.8	77.5	93.0	54.9	79.4	100.5	57.7	85.2
26, 27, 3370	ELECTRICAL, COMMUNICATIONS & UTIL.	120.3	22.3	77.9	102.5	94.8	99.2	101.1	94.8	98.3	94.0	55.1	77.1	95.9	59.1	79.9	95.1	61.6	80.6
MF2018	WEIGHTED AVERAGE	121.3	28.7	87.2	96.3	109.9	101.3	100.1	110.6	104.0	96.8	61.8	84.0	97.6	63.7	85.1	99.6	67.5	87.8

	DIVISION	SOUTH CAROLINA															SOUTH DAKOTA		
		COLUMBIA			FLORENCE			GREENVILLE			ROCK HILL			SPARTANBURG			ABERDEEN		
		290 - 292			295			296			297			293			574		
		MAT.	INST.	TOTAL	MAT.	INST.	TOTAL	MAT.	INST.	TOTAL	MAT.	INST.	TOTAL	MAT.	INST.	TOTAL	MAT.	INST.	TOTAL
015433	CONTRACTOR EQUIPMENT		106.4	106.4		101.3	101.3		101.3	101.3		101.3	101.3		101.3	101.3		94.2	94.2
0241, 31 - 34	SITE & INFRASTRUCTURE, DEMOLITION	115.4	96.0	102.7	124.8	83.2	97.7	120.1	83.5	96.3	114.4	83.2	94.1	119.9	83.5	96.2	89.1	88.8	88.9
0310	Concrete Forming & Accessories	97.1	57.3	66.2	80.6	57.2	62.5	93.0	57.4	65.3	91.0	58.8	66.0	96.0	57.4	66.0	96.9	64.0	71.4
0320	Concrete Reinforcing	99.9	63.9	90.0	96.7	64.0	87.7	96.7	58.1	86.0	97.5	58.9	86.8	96.7	60.6	86.7	97.7	70.0	90.1
0330	Cast-in-Place Concrete	115.8	66.3	98.2	97.4	66.1	86.3	97.4	66.6	86.4	97.4	63.8	85.4	97.4	66.6	86.4	125.0	75.6	107.5
03	CONCRETE	95.7	63.2	82.9	90.5	63.3	79.7	90.4	62.6	79.5	89.5	62.3	78.8	90.7	63.0	79.8	108.1	70.1	93.1
04	MASONRY	92.4	63.2	74.7	82.8	64.7	71.8	80.9	64.8	71.1	104.6	53.2	73.4	82.7	64.8	71.9	125.1	70.6	92.0
05	METALS	98.2	87.1	96.0	98.8	89.7	97.0	98.8	89.3	96.9	98.0	87.3	95.9	98.8	89.7	97.0	95.6	82.4	93.0
06	WOOD, PLASTICS & COMPOSITES	94.3	57.0	77.6	73.9	57.1	66.3	89.4	57.1	74.9	87.6	60.8	75.6	94.0	57.1	77.5	95.9	59.0	79.3
07	THERMAL & MOISTURE PROTECTION	103.4	63.4	89.2	107.3	62.8	91.5	107.3	62.8	91.5	107.2	52.4	87.7	107.4	62.8	91.5	103.6	71.1	92.0
08	OPENINGS	98.3	58.3	89.3	92.8	58.3	85.0	92.7	57.3	84.7	92.7	57.8	84.8	92.7	57.5	84.8	92.8	70.4	87.7
0920	Plaster & Gypsum Board	108.4	55.8	75.1	94.9	55.8	70.1	99.6	55.8	71.8	99.1	59.6	74.1	102.5	55.8	72.9	109.7	58.3	77.1
0950, 0980	Ceilings & Acoustic Treatment	108.6	55.8	79.0	98.8	55.8	74.7	96.0	55.8	73.5	96.0	59.6	75.6	96.0	55.8	73.5	104.3	58.3	78.5
0960	Flooring	102.4	75.1	95.6	101.2	75.1	94.7	106.7	75.1	98.8	105.8	67.9	96.3	107.9	75.1	99.7	93.1	65.0	86.0
0970, 0990	Wall Finishes & Painting/Coating	94.9	66.0	77.7	94.3	66.0	77.4	94.3	66.0	77.4	94.3	58.7	73.1	94.3	66.0	77.4	85.1	72.9	77.8
09	FINISHES	104.9	61.2	82.9	100.1	61.4	80.7	101.2	61.4	81.2	100.6	60.6	80.5	102.0	61.4	81.6	95.8	65.3	80.5
COVERS	DIVS. 10 - 14, 25, 28, 41, 43, 44, 46	100.0	82.5	96.6	100.0	82.6	96.6	100.0	82.7	96.6	100.0	82.4	96.6	100.0	82.7	96.6	100.0	80.9	96.3
21, 22, 23	FIRE SUPPRESSION, PLUMBING & HVAC	100.0	54.1	83.6	100.5	54.1	83.9	100.5	53.2	83.6	93.0	49.4	77.4	100.5	53.2	83.6	100.1	77.1	91.9
26, 27, 3370	ELECTRICAL, COMMUNICATIONS & UTIL.	100.2	55.9	81.0	94.0	55.9	77.5	95.1	78.7	88.0	95.1	80.7	88.9	95.1	78.7	88.0	92.9	67.2	81.8
MF2018	WEIGHTED AVERAGE	99.5	65.1	86.8	97.4	64.5	85.3	97.5	67.4	86.5	96.3	65.2	84.8	97.7	67.5	86.6	99.1	73.5	89.7

DIVISION		SOUTH DAKOTA																	
		MITCHELL			MOBRIDGE			PIERRE			RAPID CITY			SIOUX FALLS			WATERTOWN		
		573			576			575			577			570 - 571			572		
		MAT.	INST.	TOTAL	MAT.	INST.	TOTAL	MAT.	INST.	TOTAL	MAT.	INST.	TOTAL	MAT.	INST.	TOTAL	MAT.	INST.	TOTAL
015433	CONTRACTOR EQUIPMENT		94.2	94.2		94.2	94.2		100.3	100.3		94.2	94.2		100.3	100.3		94.2	94.2
0241, 31 - 34	SITE & INFRASTRUCTURE, DEMOLITION	83.3	88.2	86.5	83.3	88.2	86.5	89.3	98.0	95.0	88.1	88.5	88.4	84.3	98.9	93.8	83.2	88.2	86.4
0310	Concrete Forming & Accessories	95.8	41.2	53.4	85.5	41.7	51.5	99.0	79.6	83.9	104.7	52.5	64.2	97.3	80.1	84.0	81.7	68.2	71.2
0320	Concrete Reinforcing	97.2	69.9	89.6	99.7	69.8	91.4	100.0	72.2	92.3	91.3	71.9	85.9	100.3	95.9	99.1	94.5	69.7	87.6
0330	Cast-in-Place Concrete	121.5	48.6	95.6	121.5	74.2	104.7	126.9	78.3	109.6	120.5	74.8	104.3	99.8	80.3	92.9	121.5	73.9	104.6
03	CONCRETE	105.8	50.4	83.9	105.6	59.5	87.4	112.0	78.2	98.6	104.7	64.9	89.0	100.7	83.3	93.8	103.9	71.3	91.1
04	MASONRY	110.9	69.8	85.9	119.4	65.6	86.7	111.9	74.3	89.1	118.5	68.3	88.0	113.9	75.5	90.6	147.9	66.4	98.4
05	METALS	94.6	81.2	92.0	94.7	81.6	92.1	99.5	79.8	95.6	97.9	81.3	94.6	98.8	90.4	97.2	94.6	81.0	91.9
06	WOOD, PLASTICS & COMPOSITES	94.6	30.7	66.0	80.5	30.5	58.1	100.0	79.2	90.6	101.8	43.7	75.7	94.3	79.0	87.4	75.5	67.4	71.9
07	THERMAL & MOISTURE PROTECTION	103.5	65.9	90.1	103.4	68.9	91.1	104.1	79.4	95.3	104.0	72.5	92.8	104.5	81.8	96.4	103.2	70.3	91.4
08	OPENINGS	91.9	54.8	83.6	94.3	54.7	85.4	97.0	82.5	93.7	96.1	62.9	88.6	97.6	87.4	95.3	91.9	57.2	84.1
0920	Plaster & Gypsum Board	107.7	29.2	57.9	101.2	29.0	55.4	108.2	78.7	89.5	109.8	42.5	67.1	99.2	78.5	86.1	98.3	67.0	78.4
0950, 0980	Ceilings & Acoustic Treatment	99.8	29.2	60.2	104.3	29.0	62.1	111.9	78.7	93.3	107.1	42.5	70.9	110.4	78.5	92.5	99.8	67.0	81.4
0960	Flooring	92.8	70.3	87.1	89.4	41.6	77.4	102.4	69.6	94.2	92.5	65.0	85.6	99.9	74.2	93.4	88.3	39.2	76.0
0970, 0990	Wall Finishes & Painting/Coating	85.1	72.9	77.8	85.1	72.9	77.8	99.1	114.6	108.4	85.1	114.6	102.7	94.9	114.6	106.7	85.1	72.9	77.8
09	FINISHES	94.1	48.0	71.0	93.5	44.0	68.6	103.9	82.8	93.3	96.3	60.8	78.5	101.2	82.6	91.8	91.5	65.2	78.3
COVERS	DIVS. 10 - 14, 25, 28, 41, 43, 44, 46	100.0	73.3	94.8	100.0	73.1	94.8	100.0	88.1	97.7	100.0	83.0	96.7	100.0	88.2	97.7	100.0	76.6	95.5
21, 22, 23	FIRE SUPPRESSION, PLUMBING & HVAC	92.6	44.2	75.2	92.6	68.4	83.9	100.1	70.3	89.4	100.1	69.4	89.1	100.0	70.6	89.5	92.6	47.0	76.2
26, 27, 3370	ELECTRICAL, COMMUNICATIONS & UTIL.	92.1	67.2	81.3	92.9	35.4	68.0	99.5	42.5	74.8	91.2	42.5	70.1	99.6	67.2	85.6	91.6	67.2	81.0
MF2018	WEIGHTED AVERAGE	96.0	60.0	82.8	96.4	61.1	83.4	101.6	73.9	91.4	99.1	66.3	87.1	99.9	79.6	92.4	96.8	66.0	85.5

DIVISION		TENNESSEE																	
		CHATTANOOGA			COLUMBIA			COOKEVILLE			JACKSON			JOHNSON CITY			KNOXVILLE		
		373 - 374			384			385			383			376			377 - 379		
		MAT.	INST.	TOTAL	MAT.	INST.	TOTAL	MAT.	INST.	TOTAL	MAT.	INST.	TOTAL	MAT.	INST.	TOTAL	MAT.	INST.	TOTAL
015433	CONTRACTOR EQUIPMENT		101.0	101.0		96.1	96.1		96.1	96.1		101.5	101.5		95.7	95.7		95.7	95.7
0241, 31 - 34	SITE & INFRASTRUCTURE, DEMOLITION	102.4	90.0	94.3	97.2	81.1	86.7	103.4	80.3	88.3	109.9	90.6	97.3	107.4	80.4	89.8	91.3	81.2	84.7
0310	Concrete Forming & Accessories	100.6	58.5	67.9	82.9	56.9	62.7	83.0	30.0	41.8	90.9	66.6	72.0	85.2	56.5	62.9	99.2	63.3	71.3
0320	Concrete Reinforcing	93.1	64.4	85.1	86.0	58.4	78.3	86.0	58.1	78.3	86.0	65.3	80.2	93.5	60.6	84.4	93.1	66.8	85.8
0330	Cast-in-Place Concrete	94.9	61.1	82.9	94.4	60.5	82.3	107.0	54.1	88.2	104.5	63.6	90.0	76.3	55.8	69.0	89.2	64.1	80.2
03	CONCRETE	94.8	62.2	81.9	90.7	60.2	78.6	98.8	45.8	77.9	92.7	66.9	82.5	100.8	58.8	84.2	92.6	65.8	82.0
04	MASONRY	96.3	53.5	70.3	104.9	50.0	71.5	101.1	35.5	61.3	105.5	55.6	75.2	108.2	41.3	67.5	74.7	55.5	63.1
05	METALS	96.3	88.1	94.7	95.5	85.0	93.4	95.6	84.3	93.4	99.2	87.9	96.9	92.1	86.3	91.0	96.3	88.9	94.8
06	WOOD, PLASTICS & COMPOSITES	99.9	59.0	81.5	68.0	57.6	63.4	68.3	26.9	49.8	82.5	67.7	75.9	73.1	61.4	67.9	91.1	64.1	79.0
07	THERMAL & MOISTURE PROTECTION	107.9	59.0	90.5	98.0	56.7	83.3	98.4	47.5	80.3	99.9	62.0	86.4	103.6	53.8	85.9	101.9	62.6	87.9
08	OPENINGS	98.4	57.8	89.2	91.7	48.4	81.9	91.7	32.3	78.3	98.1	61.7	89.9	95.3	58.5	87.0	92.8	57.6	84.9
0920	Plaster & Gypsum Board	77.4	58.4	65.3	84.1	57.0	66.9	84.1	25.4	46.9	87.5	67.4	74.7	84.6	60.9	69.6	93.2	63.6	74.4
0950, 0980	Ceilings & Acoustic Treatment	98.0	58.4	75.8	75.4	57.0	65.1	75.4	25.4	47.4	80.5	67.4	73.1	94.1	60.9	75.5	95.9	63.6	77.8
0960	Flooring	102.4	57.7	91.2	87.8	48.3	77.9	87.8	44.8	77.0	83.9	52.7	76.1	102.4	52.7	90.0	106.5	56.8	94.1
0970, 0990	Wall Finishes & Painting/Coating	95.2	52.9	70.0	86.7	50.2	64.9	86.7	50.2	64.9	89.4	56.5	69.8	92.0	52.9	68.7	92.0	54.5	69.6
09	FINISHES	96.2	57.4	76.7	88.9	54.3	71.5	89.4	32.8	61.0	88.0	63.1	75.5	99.2	55.4	77.2	93.9	61.0	77.3
COVERS	DIVS. 10 - 14, 25, 28, 41, 43, 44, 46	100.0	80.4	96.2	100.0	80.1	96.2	100.0	73.2	94.8	100.0	82.9	96.7	100.0	77.5	95.6	100.0	81.7	96.5
21, 22, 23	FIRE SUPPRESSION, PLUMBING & HVAC	100.2	53.6	83.5	94.4	66.2	84.3	94.4	60.4	82.2	100.1	63.0	86.8	100.0	50.1	82.1	100.0	62.7	86.6
26, 27, 3370	ELECTRICAL, COMMUNICATIONS & UTIL.	103.8	73.8	90.8	96.0	45.0	73.9	96.8	54.6	78.5	103.7	58.5	84.1	93.6	46.7	73.3	96.7	57.0	79.5
MF2018	WEIGHTED AVERAGE	98.8	65.4	86.5	94.5	61.5	82.3	95.7	53.8	80.3	98.6	67.2	87.1	97.6	57.8	82.9	95.7	65.6	84.6

DIVISION		TENNESSEE									TEXAS								
		MCKENZIE			MEMPHIS			NASHVILLE			ABILENE			AMARILLO			AUSTIN		
		382			375,380 - 381			370 - 372			795 - 796			790 - 791			786 - 787		
		MAT.	INST.	TOTAL	MAT.	INST.	TOTAL	MAT.	INST.	TOTAL	MAT.	INST.	TOTAL	MAT.	INST.	TOTAL	MAT.	INST.	TOTAL
015433	CONTRACTOR EQUIPMENT		96.1	96.1		97.2	97.2		103.4	103.4		88.4	88.4		95.3	95.3		95.6	95.6
0241, 31 - 34	SITE & INFRASTRUCTURE, DEMOLITION	102.9	80.5	88.3	90.3	90.1	90.2	100.2	97.6	98.5	95.4	84.5	88.3	95.5	94.8	95.0	90.8	94.2	93.0
0310	Concrete Forming & Accessories	92.1	32.0	45.4	100.2	67.6	74.9	101.2	71.0	77.7	100.8	58.5	67.9	102.4	53.3	64.2	97.6	53.3	63.2
0320	Concrete Reinforcing	86.1	58.9	78.6	100.1	70.0	91.7	101.0	68.3	92.0	98.9	49.7	85.3	99.2	48.5	85.1	99.6	47.7	85.2
0330	Cast-in-Place Concrete	104.7	55.1	87.1	92.0	69.1	83.8	86.9	70.4	81.0	77.3	64.2	72.6	75.5	70.2	73.6	83.8	66.5	77.7
03	CONCRETE	98.1	47.2	78.0	97.9	69.5	86.7	97.3	71.3	87.0	84.5	59.9	74.8	88.8	59.3	77.2	88.3	57.8	76.3
04	MASONRY	104.1	40.6	65.6	81.7	57.7	67.1	97.0	63.5	76.6	94.3	59.6	73.2	88.0	61.9	72.2	91.0	60.7	72.6
05	METALS	95.6	84.9	93.5	100.4	82.0	96.8	100.4	84.0	97.2	108.8	71.0	101.4	104.5	68.8	97.4	101.5	67.7	94.8
06	WOOD, PLASTICS & COMPOSITES	79.7	29.0	57.0	95.8	67.2	83.0	98.0	71.6	86.1	101.1	60.3	82.8	98.7	51.3	77.4	94.7	52.8	76.0
07	THERMAL & MOISTURE PROTECTION	98.5	48.4	80.6	106.1	66.4	91.9	105.3	69.2	92.5	96.5	61.6	84.1	93.1	63.7	82.6	90.9	64.3	81.4
08	OPENINGS	91.7	33.8	78.6	100.3	63.5	92.0	99.2	68.1	92.2	100.8	56.0	90.7	98.9	51.0	88.1	98.4	50.7	87.6
0920	Plaster & Gypsum Board	88.2	27.5	49.7	87.8	66.4	74.2	81.2	70.8	74.6	91.3	59.7	71.2	104.4	50.0	69.9	92.0	51.6	66.4
0950, 0980	Ceilings & Acoustic Treatment	75.4	27.5	48.5	111.8	66.4	86.3	86.8	70.8	77.8	105.1	59.7	79.6	101.4	50.0	72.6	98.2	51.6	72.1
0960	Flooring	89.9	48.3	79.5	103.1	55.3	91.1	108.4	64.1	97.3	96.3	66.9	88.9	98.6	64.9	90.2	103.9	64.3	94.0
0970, 0990	Wall Finishes & Painting/Coating	86.7	39.2	58.4	95.5	74.1	82.7	98.7	65.9	79.2	98.8	53.2	71.6	104.7	51.7	73.1	104.7	43.4	68.1
09	FINISHES	90.5	34.0	62.1	101.8	65.7	83.7	97.8	69.1	83.4	95.5	59.5	77.4	101.2	54.6	77.8	99.2	54.0	76.5
COVERS	DIVS. 10 - 14, 25, 28, 41, 43, 44, 46	100.0	73.9	94.9	100.0	84.3	97.0	100.0	84.9	97.1	100.0	79.1	95.9	100.0	80.1	96.1	100.0	80.4	96.2
21, 22, 23	FIRE SUPPRESSION, PLUMBING & HVAC	94.4	52.7	79.5	100.1	73.5	90.5	100.1	73.0	90.4	100.1	49.4	81.9	100.0	53.2	83.2	99.7	58.5	84.9
26, 27, 3370	ELECTRICAL, COMMUNICATIONS & UTIL.	96.7	49.3	76.1	99.2	63.9	83.9	104.0	64.2	86.8	97.4	51.0	77.3	100.8	58.3	82.3	98.4	56.0	80.1
MF2018	WEIGHTED AVERAGE	95.8	52.5	79.9	99.1	70.7	88.7	100.0	73.1	90.1	99.1	59.8	84.7	98.9	61.6	85.2	97.6	61.9	84.4

DIVISION		TEXAS																	
		BEAUMONT			BROWNWOOD			BRYAN			CHILDRESS			CORPUS CHRISTI			DALLAS		
		776 - 777			768			778			792			783 - 784			752 - 753		
		MAT.	INST.	TOTAL	MAT.	INST.	TOTAL	MAT.	INST.	TOTAL	MAT.	INST.	TOTAL	MAT.	INST.	TOTAL	MAT.	INST.	TOTAL
015433	CONTRACTOR EQUIPMENT		91.2	91.2		88.4	88.4		91.2	91.2		88.4	88.4		97.6	97.6		108.2	108.2
0241, 31 - 34	SITE & INFRASTRUCTURE, DEMOLITION	92.5	87.3	89.1	100.0	84.4	89.8	81.0	87.0	84.9	101.7	84.4	90.4	123.8	80.1	95.3	111.7	100.4	104.3
0310	Concrete Forming & Accessories	104.4	54.9	65.9	97.4	55.4	64.8	82.9	53.0	59.7	99.0	55.5	65.2	102.5	51.7	63.0	97.7	61.6	69.6
0320	Concrete Reinforcing	100.0	70.5	91.8	89.8	46.0	77.6	101.4	46.0	86.1	99.0	46.0	84.3	87.9	48.8	77.0	100.3	50.7	86.6
0330	Cast-in-Place Concrete	72.0	66.7	70.1	96.7	54.6	81.7	57.7	54.6	56.6	79.3	54.7	70.5	102.0	64.3	88.6	101.8	69.1	90.2
03	CONCRETE	85.4	62.7	76.4	90.4	54.5	76.3	74.2	53.5	66.0	90.4	54.6	76.3	91.9	57.6	78.4	95.9	63.7	83.2
04	MASONRY	94.9	60.8	74.2	116.2	54.8	78.9	126.2	54.6	82.7	97.4	54.4	71.2	81.1	57.9	67.0	112.3	57.9	79.3
05	METALS	93.4	79.1	90.6	100.0	68.9	93.8	92.8	69.0	88.1	105.4	69.0	98.3	95.8	83.5	93.4	101.2	79.7	96.9
06	WOOD, PLASTICS & COMPOSITES	106.5	54.0	82.9	101.2	57.4	81.6	72.9	53.9	64.4	100.3	57.4	81.1	113.1	51.5	85.5	95.3	63.4	81.0
07	THERMAL & MOISTURE PROTECTION	96.1	64.6	84.9	91.7	58.0	79.7	89.4	58.4	78.3	97.1	57.9	83.1	97.4	60.1	84.1	91.8	65.3	82.3
08	OPENINGS	86.5	58.5	80.2	98.5	52.5	88.1	87.4	50.7	79.1	96.0	52.5	86.2	96.0	49.4	85.5	98.1	59.1	89.3
0920	Plaster & Gypsum Board	97.0	53.3	69.3	81.5	56.7	65.7	81.7	53.2	63.6	89.4	56.7	68.6	95.1	50.5	66.8	93.9	62.1	73.7
0950, 0980	Ceilings & Acoustic Treatment	107.0	53.3	76.9	84.9	56.7	69.1	96.3	53.2	72.1	99.2	56.7	75.4	100.8	50.5	72.6	103.2	62.1	80.1
0960	Flooring	109.9	72.4	100.5	82.3	48.9	73.9	85.5	60.0	79.1	95.0	48.9	83.5	114.6	70.6	103.6	103.1	67.5	94.2
0970, 0990	Wall Finishes & Painting/Coating	94.2	55.5	71.1	91.8	45.9	64.4	91.5	51.0	67.4	98.8	45.9	67.3	112.4	42.5	70.7	104.7	52.2	73.4
09	FINISHES	97.6	57.5	77.4	84.0	53.1	68.5	84.9	53.6	69.2	94.6	53.1	73.7	103.7	53.7	78.6	102.2	61.6	81.8
COVERS	DIVS. 10 - 14, 25, 28, 41, 43, 44, 46	100.0	75.9	95.3	100.0	78.4	95.8	100.0	75.1	95.2	100.0	78.4	95.8	100.0	77.5	95.6	100.0	81.3	96.4
21, 22, 23	FIRE SUPPRESSION, PLUMBING & HVAC	99.7	63.6	86.8	92.2	44.8	75.2	92.2	59.2	80.3	92.6	48.8	76.9	99.8	57.0	84.4	100.0	60.2	85.7
26, 27, 3370	ELECTRICAL, COMMUNICATIONS & UTIL.	96.6	65.1	83.0	95.0	41.1	71.7	97.5	56.4	79.7	97.4	49.7	76.7	97.2	61.1	81.5	93.4	60.5	79.1
MF2018	WEIGHTED AVERAGE	94.6	66.0	84.1	95.7	54.9	80.7	91.2	60.0	79.7	97.3	56.9	82.4	97.6	61.9	84.5	99.5	66.4	87.3

DIVISION		TEXAS																	
		DEL RIO			DENTON			EASTLAND			EL PASO			FORT WORTH			GALVESTON		
		788			762			764			798 - 799,885			760 - 761			775		
		MAT.	INST.	TOTAL	MAT.	INST.	TOTAL	MAT.	INST.	TOTAL	MAT.	INST.	TOTAL	MAT.	INST.	TOTAL	MAT.	INST.	TOTAL
015433	CONTRACTOR EQUIPMENT		88.2	88.2		96.7	96.7		88.4	88.4		95.4	95.4		96.9	96.9		102.5	102.5
0241, 31 - 34	SITE & INFRASTRUCTURE, DEMOLITION	105.5	82.7	90.6	100.2	79.3	86.6	102.3	84.4	90.6	91.4	94.7	93.6	98.9	97.2	97.8	106.1	85.8	92.9
0310	Concrete Forming & Accessories	98.7	46.7	58.3	105.7	55.7	66.9	98.4	55.4	65.0	103.1	58.4	68.4	98.0	59.3	67.9	92.3	50.8	60.1
0320	Concrete Reinforcing	88.2	42.7	75.6	90.6	46.4	78.4	89.9	46.0	77.8	100.7	49.9	86.6	99.6	49.7	85.8	101.1	53.6	87.9
0330	Cast-in-Place Concrete	109.8	54.0	90.0	74.8	55.6	68.0	102.2	54.6	85.3	68.4	66.6	67.7	87.0	66.1	79.5	76.6	55.5	69.1
03	CONCRETE	106.4	49.7	84.0	75.7	56.0	67.9	94.0	54.6	78.4	87.1	60.6	76.7	88.4	60.8	77.5	85.9	55.1	73.7
04	MASONRY	93.6	54.5	69.9	122.9	60.2	84.8	90.5	54.8	68.8	93.4	63.7	75.4	90.6	61.6	73.0	90.4	54.7	68.7
05	METALS	94.3	65.6	88.7	99.3	83.3	96.1	99.7	69.0	93.7	105.0	69.7	98.0	102.5	69.7	96.0	94.5	86.6	93.0
06	WOOD, PLASTICS & COMPOSITES	96.5	45.9	73.8	115.3	57.5	89.4	107.5	57.4	85.1	98.7	58.9	80.9	95.5	60.7	79.9	87.1	50.8	70.8
07	THERMAL & MOISTURE PROTECTION	94.8	56.9	81.3	89.8	60.3	79.3	92.0	58.0	79.9	98.3	64.9	86.4	88.8	65.5	80.5	88.8	58.7	78.1
08	OPENINGS	91.9	43.4	81.0	116.5	52.2	102.0	67.3	52.5	64.0	98.8	53.7	88.6	98.2	56.2	88.7	90.8	50.8	81.8
0920	Plaster & Gypsum Board	90.3	44.8	61.5	86.9	56.7	67.7	81.5	56.7	65.7	87.6	57.8	68.7	90.4	59.7	70.9	89.6	49.8	64.4
0950, 0980	Ceilings & Acoustic Treatment	95.2	44.8	67.0	89.9	56.7	71.3	84.9	56.7	69.1	105.8	57.8	78.9	98.2	59.7	76.6	102.2	49.8	72.9
0960	Flooring	96.4	48.9	84.5	77.3	48.9	70.2	104.9	48.9	90.9	98.6	75.6	92.9	104.1	69.0	95.3	98.8	60.0	89.1
0970, 0990	Wall Finishes & Painting/Coating	101.1	37.8	63.4	102.0	43.4	67.1	93.3	45.9	65.1	104.7	48.7	71.3	104.7	50.8	72.6	103.5	47.7	70.2
09	FINISHES	94.9	45.5	70.1	82.8	52.9	67.8	91.2	53.1	72.1	99.8	60.3	80.0	100.0	60.1	79.9	95.1	51.4	73.2
COVERS	DIVS. 10 - 14, 25, 28, 41, 43, 44, 46	100.0	72.8	94.7	100.0	78.7	95.9	100.0	78.4	95.8	100.0	81.2	96.4	100.0	80.1	96.1	100.0	75.1	95.2
21, 22, 23	FIRE SUPPRESSION, PLUMBING & HVAC	92.2	53.6	78.4	92.2	50.4	77.2	92.2	44.8	75.2	99.9	61.8	86.2	99.7	58.0	84.8	92.1	59.3	80.4
26, 27, 3370	ELECTRICAL, COMMUNICATIONS & UTIL.	98.3	53.3	78.8	97.9	52.2	78.1	94.9	52.2	76.4	100.0	47.5	77.2	94.8	55.3	77.7	97.9	56.5	80.0
MF2018	WEIGHTED AVERAGE	96.3	55.7	81.3	95.8	59.4	82.4	93.1	56.5	79.6	98.9	63.3	85.8	97.6	63.7	85.1	93.4	61.5	81.6

DIVISION		TEXAS																	
		GIDDINGS			GREENVILLE			HOUSTON			HUNTSVILLE			LAREDO			LONGVIEW		
		789			754			770 - 772			773			780			756		
		MAT.	INST.	TOTAL	MAT.	INST.	TOTAL	MAT.	INST.	TOTAL	MAT.	INST.	TOTAL	MAT.	INST.	TOTAL	MAT.	INST.	TOTAL
015433	CONTRACTOR EQUIPMENT		88.2	88.2		97.2	97.2		100.9	100.9		91.2	91.2		88.2	88.2		89.4	89.4
0241, 31 - 34	SITE & INFRASTRUCTURE, DEMOLITION	94.0	83.0	86.8	98.8	81.8	87.7	108.7	94.0	99.1	94.0	87.0	89.5	92.5	83.3	86.5	96.1	87.2	90.3
0310	Concrete Forming & Accessories	96.4	46.9	57.9	87.3	52.6	60.3	98.2	59.7	68.3	90.8	49.4	58.6	98.8	52.1	62.5	82.9	55.6	61.7
0320	Concrete Reinforcing	88.6	43.5	76.1	101.0	46.4	85.8	99.7	52.1	86.5	101.6	45.9	86.2	88.2	48.8	77.3	100.6	45.7	85.4
0330	Cast-in-Place Concrete	93.0	54.3	79.3	104.2	55.6	87.0	71.3	69.8	70.7	79.3	54.6	70.5	78.6	65.0	73.8	121.3	54.6	97.6
03	CONCRETE	89.4	50.1	73.9	93.8	54.5	78.3	84.0	62.9	75.7	90.2	51.8	75.1	85.0	57.1	74.0	106.2	54.5	85.8
04	MASONRY	99.0	54.6	72.1	178.5	60.1	106.6	89.1	64.4	74.1	125.9	54.6	82.6	87.8	59.9	70.8	173.6	53.5	100.6
05	METALS	93.7	66.6	88.4	94.2	82.0	91.8	101.2	75.1	96.0	92.7	68.9	88.0	97.3	69.8	91.9	87.2	67.9	83.4
06	WOOD, PLASTICS & COMPOSITES	95.9	45.9	73.5	79.3	53.2	67.6	95.5	59.5	79.4	83.7	49.1	68.2	96.5	51.4	76.3	72.2	57.5	65.6
07	THERMAL & MOISTURE PROTECTION	95.1	57.5	81.7	90.9	59.3	79.6	90.2	69.1	82.7	90.3	57.9	78.8	94.1	62.6	82.9	92.2	57.2	79.7
08	OPENINGS	91.1	44.2	80.5	89.8	50.2	80.9	98.8	56.7	89.3	87.4	47.6	78.4	91.9	49.2	82.2	81.1	52.1	74.5
0920	Plaster & Gypsum Board	89.4	44.8	61.1	79.3	52.1	62.0	90.4	58.3	70.0	85.3	48.2	61.8	92.5	50.5	65.8	76.6	56.7	63.9
0950, 0980	Ceilings & Acoustic Treatment	95.2	44.8	67.0	95.8	52.1	71.3	98.2	58.3	75.8	96.3	48.2	69.4	102.0	50.5	73.1	87.2	56.7	70.1
0960	Flooring	97.8	48.9	85.5	94.7	48.9	83.2	103.1	74.9	96.0	88.2	48.9	78.4	96.2	64.3	88.2	100.0	48.9	87.2
0970, 0990	Wall Finishes & Painting/Coating	101.1	39.3	64.2	94.5	45.9	65.5	104.7	57.4	76.5	91.5	51.0	67.4	101.1	43.8	66.9	86.7	43.4	60.9
09	FINISHES	94.3	45.6	69.8	94.5	50.7	72.5	100.7	62.0	81.3	87.2	48.8	67.9	95.6	52.8	74.1	97.5	52.9	75.1
COVERS	DIVS. 10 - 14, 25, 28, 41, 43, 44, 46	100.0	78.3	95.8	100.0	78.4	95.8	100.0	82.5	96.6	100.0	74.6	95.1	100.0	77.7	95.7	100.0	78.6	95.8
21, 22, 23	FIRE SUPPRESSION, PLUMBING & HVAC	92.3	58.4	80.1	92.5	52.4	78.1	99.7	62.6	86.4	92.2	59.2	80.3	99.7	59.3	85.2	92.5	52.0	77.9
26, 27, 3370	ELECTRICAL, COMMUNICATIONS & UTIL.	96.4	49.5	76.1	91.7	52.2	74.6	99.4	64.2	84.1	97.5	52.6	78.0	98.4	55.7	79.9	90.6	45.3	71.0
MF2018	WEIGHTED AVERAGE	93.7	56.6	80.1	96.7	59.2	82.9	97.6	67.2	86.4	93.7	58.4	80.7	95.5	60.7	82.7	95.8	57.0	81.5

	DIVISION	TEXAS																	
		LUBBOCK			LUFKIN			MCALLEN			MCKINNEY			MIDLAND			ODESSA		
		793 - 794			759			785			750			797			797		
		MAT.	INST.	TOTAL	MAT.	INST.	TOTAL	MAT.	INST.	TOTAL	MAT.	INST.	TOTAL	MAT.	INST.	TOTAL	MAT.	INST.	TOTAL
015433	CONTRACTOR EQUIPMENT		99.1	99.1		89.4	89.4		97.8	97.8		97.2	97.2		99.1	99.1		88.4	88.4
0241, 31 - 34	SITE & INFRASTRUCTURE, DEMOLITION	118.1	83.7	95.6	91.3	86.5	88.2	123.9	80.3	95.4	95.5	81.8	86.6	117.4	83.6	95.3	95.7	84.6	88.5
0310	Concrete Forming & Accessories	100.8	54.0	64.4	86.1	49.5	57.7	102.6	47.5	59.8	86.4	52.6	60.1	105.2	60.7	70.6	100.7	60.4	69.4
0320	Concrete Reinforcing	99.7	49.7	85.9	102.4	59.9	90.6	87.9	48.7	77.1	101.0	46.4	85.8	100.3	49.8	86.3	98.9	49.7	85.3
0330	Cast-in-Place Concrete	77.4	67.9	74.1	108.4	53.9	89.1	110.8	56.2	91.4	97.7	55.6	82.8	82.3	68.1	77.3	77.3	64.1	72.6
03	CONCRETE	83.8	60.1	74.5	99.9	53.8	81.7	97.7	52.8	80.0	89.8	54.5	75.9	87.2	63.2	77.7	84.5	60.7	75.1
04	MASONRY	93.9	62.6	74.9	132.3	54.5	85.0	92.9	59.1	72.4	192.1	60.1	112.0	108.8	60.9	79.7	94.3	60.8	74.0
05	METALS	112.4	84.8	107.0	94.4	71.0	89.8	94.2	82.9	91.9	94.1	82.0	91.7	110.6	85.0	105.5	108.0	71.0	100.7
06	WOOD, PLASTICS & COMPOSITES	103.2	52.3	80.4	78.8	49.3	65.6	111.1	46.0	81.9	78.0	53.2	66.9	109.0	62.1	88.0	101.1	62.0	83.6
07	THERMAL & MOISTURE PROTECTION	87.4	63.1	78.8	92.0	56.7	79.4	97.4	59.9	84.0	90.7	59.3	79.5	87.7	63.3	79.0	96.5	62.5	84.4
08	OPENINGS	108.6	52.9	96.0	61.0	51.3	58.8	95.3	44.8	83.9	89.8	50.2	80.9	109.9	57.7	98.1	100.8	57.6	91.1
0920	Plaster & Gypsum Board	91.7	51.4	66.1	74.3	48.2	57.8	96.3	44.8	63.7	79.3	52.1	62.0	91.6	61.4	72.5	91.3	61.4	72.3
0950, 0980	Ceilings & Acoustic Treatment	106.5	51.4	75.6	79.9	48.2	62.2	102.0	44.8	70.0	95.8	52.1	71.3	101.5	61.4	79.0	105.1	61.4	80.6
0960	Flooring	91.3	67.5	85.4	134.3	48.9	112.9	114.3	70.6	103.3	94.3	48.9	82.9	92.1	66.8	85.8	96.3	62.5	87.8
0970, 0990	Wall Finishes & Painting/Coating	109.9	51.7	75.2	86.7	45.9	62.4	112.4	37.8	67.9	94.5	45.9	65.5	109.9	52.7	75.8	98.8	52.7	71.3
09	FINISHES	98.5	55.7	77.0	105.2	48.7	76.8	104.4	50.3	77.3	94.1	50.7	72.3	97.8	61.0	79.3	95.5	60.0	77.7
COVERS	DIVS. 10 - 14, 25, 28, 41, 43, 44, 46	100.0	79.6	96.0	100.0	75.0	95.1	100.0	77.3	95.6	100.0	78.4	95.8	100.0	80.1	96.1	100.0	79.8	96.1
21, 22, 23	FIRE SUPPRESSION, PLUMBING & HVAC	99.5	50.2	81.8	92.5	52.4	78.1	92.3	44.8	75.2	92.5	54.4	78.8	92.0	53.5	78.2	100.1	48.5	81.6
26, 27, 3370	ELECTRICAL, COMMUNICATIONS & UTIL.	96.1	50.5	76.4	91.4	54.6	75.4	97.0	28.2	67.2	91.8	52.2	74.6	96.1	58.4	79.8	97.6	58.4	80.6
MF2018	WEIGHTED AVERAGE	100.7	60.8	86.0	93.9	57.8	80.6	96.7	53.4	80.8	96.6	59.6	83.0	99.7	63.9	86.5	99.0	61.1	85.0

	DIVISION	TEXAS																	
		PALESTINE			SAN ANGELO			SAN ANTONIO			TEMPLE			TEXARKANA			TYLER		
		758			769			781 - 782			765			755			757		
		MAT.	INST.	TOTAL	MAT.	INST.	TOTAL	MAT.	INST.	TOTAL	MAT.	INST.	TOTAL	MAT.	INST.	TOTAL	MAT.	INST.	TOTAL
015433	CONTRACTOR EQUIPMENT		89.4	89.4		88.4	88.4		94.9	94.9		88.4	88.4		89.4	89.4		89.4	89.4
0241, 31 - 34	SITE & INFRASTRUCTURE, DEMOLITION	96.1	87.2	90.3	96.8	84.4	88.7	90.7	94.5	93.2	87.2	83.8	85.0	86.7	87.4	87.1	95.3	87.3	90.1
0310	Concrete Forming & Accessories	76.9	55.5	60.3	97.8	47.5	58.7	97.7	55.8	65.1	101.5	46.8	59.0	94.1	59.2	67.0	87.9	56.2	63.3
0320	Concrete Reinforcing	99.9	45.9	84.9	89.7	50.9	79.0	101.5	50.3	87.3	89.8	45.7	77.6	99.7	49.5	85.8	100.6	49.2	86.3
0330	Cast-in-Place Concrete	99.1	54.6	83.3	91.2	65.6	82.1	74.9	70.3	73.2	74.7	54.0	67.4	99.8	64.1	87.1	119.1	55.4	96.5
03	CONCRETE	98.7	54.5	81.3	87.1	55.6	74.7	85.9	60.6	75.9	77.2	50.3	66.6	94.0	60.1	80.6	105.8	55.7	86.0
04	MASONRY	126.1	53.5	82.0	113.2	78.9	92.4	93.9	63.0	75.1	121.8	54.6	81.0	196.9	58.6	112.9	185.0	54.8	105.9
05	METALS	94.2	68.0	89.0	100.2	72.4	94.7	101.3	66.9	94.5	99.8	67.1	93.3	87.0	70.1	83.7	94.0	69.4	89.1
06	WOOD, PLASTICS & COMPOSITES	67.8	57.5	63.2	101.6	45.9	76.6	95.3	54.8	77.2	111.1	45.9	81.9	87.3	60.8	75.4	81.0	57.5	70.4
07	THERMAL & MOISTURE PROTECTION	92.4	56.9	79.7	91.5	64.7	81.9	90.9	67.1	82.4	91.1	56.6	78.8	91.9	62.2	81.3	92.3	59.3	80.5
08	OPENINGS	60.9	52.5	59.0	98.5	47.0	86.9	98.8	52.1	88.2	63.9	46.1	59.9	81.0	56.5	75.5	60.9	54.7	59.5
0920	Plaster & Gypsum Board	74.1	56.7	63.0	81.5	44.8	58.2	93.4	53.5	68.1	81.5	44.8	58.2	82.6	60.1	68.4	74.3	56.7	63.1
0950, 0980	Ceilings & Acoustic Treatment	79.9	56.7	66.9	84.9	44.8	62.5	91.4	53.5	70.2	84.9	44.8	62.5	87.2	60.1	72.0	79.9	56.7	66.9
0960	Flooring	128.2	48.9	108.3	82.4	48.9	74.0	103.1	73.6	95.7	106.1	48.9	91.7	105.6	64.0	95.1	135.9	48.9	114.1
0970, 0990	Wall Finishes & Painting/Coating	86.7	45.9	62.4	91.8	45.9	64.4	104.7	45.1	69.2	93.3	39.3	61.1	86.7	51.7	65.8	86.7	51.7	65.8
09	FINISHES	104.0	53.2	78.5	83.8	46.4	65.0	97.5	57.5	77.4	90.3	45.6	67.9	99.3	59.2	79.2	106.0	54.1	80.0
COVERS	DIVS. 10 - 14, 25, 28, 41, 43, 44, 46	100.0	78.6	95.8	100.0	78.3	95.8	100.0	79.8	96.1	100.0	77.2	95.6	100.0	79.4	96.0	100.0	79.0	95.9
21, 22, 23	FIRE SUPPRESSION, PLUMBING & HVAC	92.5	51.2	77.7	92.2	48.8	76.7	99.7	62.6	86.4	92.2	48.0	76.4	92.5	54.1	78.7	92.5	53.2	78.4
26, 27, 3370	ELECTRICAL, COMMUNICATIONS & UTIL.	89.1	43.1	69.2	97.4	48.6	76.3	99.7	59.7	82.4	95.7	46.3	74.3	91.3	54.7	75.4	90.6	47.9	72.1
MF2018	WEIGHTED AVERAGE	93.2	56.5	79.7	95.4	58.7	81.9	97.4	64.4	85.3	91.7	54.1	77.8	95.3	61.4	82.8	96.7	58.4	82.6

	DIVISION	TEXAS															UTAH		
		VICTORIA			WACO			WAXAHACHIE			WHARTON			WICHITA FALLS			LOGAN		
		779			766 - 767			751			774			763			843		
		MAT.	INST.	TOTAL	MAT.	INST.	TOTAL	MAT.	INST.	TOTAL	MAT.	INST.	TOTAL	MAT.	INST.	TOTAL	MAT.	INST.	TOTAL
015433	CONTRACTOR EQUIPMENT		101.4	101.4		88.4	88.4		97.2	97.2		102.5	102.5		88.4	88.4		92.5	92.5
0241, 31 - 34	SITE & INFRASTRUCTURE, DEMOLITION	110.3	83.7	93.0	97.6	84.1	88.8	97.3	82.2	87.4	115.2	85.6	95.9	98.3	84.5	89.3	101.3	86.7	91.8
0310	Concrete Forming & Accessories	91.8	46.9	57.0	100.0	59.6	68.6	86.4	62.7	67.9	86.5	48.4	56.9	99.9	58.7	67.9	99.9	68.9	75.8
0320	Concrete Reinforcing	97.1	45.7	82.9	89.6	49.7	78.6	101.0	53.2	87.7	101.0	45.7	85.7	89.6	49.7	78.5	96.6	82.6	92.7
0330	Cast-in-Place Concrete	85.9	55.5	75.1	80.9	64.1	74.9	103.1	64.6	89.4	88.3	54.6	76.3	86.4	68.3	80.0	77.8	73.2	76.2
03	CONCRETE	90.4	52.0	75.2	81.8	60.3	73.3	92.9	63.4	81.3	93.6	52.3	77.3	84.1	61.4	75.1	98.3	73.4	88.5
04	MASONRY	105.4	54.7	74.6	88.7	59.9	71.2	179.2	62.8	108.5	91.4	54.6	69.0	89.2	58.4	70.5	110.9	60.9	80.5
05	METALS	92.9	83.5	91.0	102.9	70.0	96.4	94.2	85.4	92.4	94.5	83.0	92.3	102.8	71.1	96.6	104.5	83.6	100.4
06	WOOD, PLASTICS & COMPOSITES	89.9	45.9	70.2	108.7	61.4	87.5	78.0	64.5	71.9	79.2	47.9	65.2	108.7	60.3	87.0	90.0	69.1	80.6
07	THERMAL & MOISTURE PROTECTION	91.8	56.0	79.1	91.8	62.6	81.4	90.8	64.0	81.3	89.1	58.3	78.1	91.8	61.3	81.0	93.0	67.1	83.8
08	OPENINGS	90.7	46.3	80.7	74.6	57.6	70.8	89.8	60.5	83.2	90.8	47.4	81.0	74.6	56.0	70.4	87.6	70.5	83.7
0920	Plaster & Gypsum Board	85.5	44.8	59.7	81.8	60.9	68.5	80.1	63.8	69.8	84.8	46.9	60.7	81.8	59.7	67.7	88.6	68.4	75.8
0950, 0980	Ceilings & Acoustic Treatment	104.5	44.8	71.1	85.8	60.9	71.8	98.6	63.8	79.1	102.2	46.9	71.2	85.8	59.7	71.2	107.2	68.4	85.4
0960	Flooring	99.6	48.9	86.9	105.6	67.3	96.0	94.3	61.9	86.2	97.0	59.6	87.7	106.1	69.7	97.0	99.0	62.1	89.8
0970, 0990	Wall Finishes & Painting/Coating	103.7	51.0	72.3	93.3	54.8	70.4	94.5	56.5	71.8	103.5	49.5	71.3	95.1	50.7	68.6	92.2	60.2	73.1
09	FINISHES	94.1	47.0	70.4	90.9	60.5	75.6	95.2	61.8	78.4	94.7	49.8	72.2	91.2	59.8	75.4	98.9	66.4	82.6
COVERS	DIVS. 10 - 14, 25, 28, 41, 43, 44, 46	100.0	74.5	95.1	100.0	79.3	96.0	100.0	80.5	96.2	100.0	74.7	95.1	100.0	79.1	95.9	100.0	85.3	97.1
21, 22, 23	FIRE SUPPRESSION, PLUMBING & HVAC	92.2	59.2	80.4	99.7	59.4	85.3	92.5	63.1	82.0	92.1	55.8	79.1	99.7	54.7	83.6	100.0	72.0	90.0
26, 27, 3370	ELECTRICAL, COMMUNICATIONS & UTIL.	101.4	48.1	78.3	97.6	54.0	78.7	91.8	62.3	79.0	100.1	52.7	79.5	100.3	51.8	79.3	93.0	70.9	83.5
MF2018	WEIGHTED AVERAGE	94.6	58.5	81.3	94.7	62.5	82.9	96.6	66.9	85.7	94.7	59.1	81.6	95.3	61.2	82.7	99.1	72.6	89.3

		UTAH												VERMONT					
DIVISION		OGDEN			PRICE			PROVO			SALT LAKE CITY			BELLOWS FALLS			BENNINGTON		
		842,844			845			846 - 847			840 - 841			051			052		
		MAT.	INST.	TOTAL	MAT.	INST.	TOTAL	MAT.	INST.	TOTAL	MAT.	INST.	TOTAL	MAT.	INST.	TOTAL	MAT.	INST.	TOTAL
015433	CONTRACTOR EQUIPMENT		92.5	92.5		91.7	91.7		91.7	91.7		92.5	92.5		93.0	93.0		93.0	93.0
0241, 31 - 34	SITE & INFRASTRUCTURE, DEMOLITION	90.3	86.7	87.9	97.0	84.3	88.7	97.8	85.3	89.7	90.0	86.6	87.8	82.7	91.5	88.4	82.2	91.5	88.2
0310	Concrete Forming & Accessories	99.9	68.9	75.8	102.7	59.8	69.4	101.9	68.9	76.2	102.2	68.9	76.3	101.7	92.8	94.8	98.6	92.6	94.0
0320	Concrete Reinforcing	96.4	82.6	92.6	103.7	80.4	97.3	104.6	82.5	98.5	98.8	82.5	94.3	80.2	78.2	79.6	80.2	78.2	79.6
0330	Cast-in-Place Concrete	79.0	73.2	77.0	77.9	68.0	74.4	77.9	73.2	76.2	86.3	73.2	81.7	71.1	110.7	85.1	71.1	110.6	85.1
03	CONCRETE	90.5	73.4	83.7	100.5	67.0	87.3	99.4	73.3	89.1	105.6	73.3	92.9	82.6	96.6	88.2	82.4	96.5	88.0
04	MASONRY	105.2	60.9	78.3	116.7	62.3	83.7	116.8	60.9	82.8	119.4	60.9	83.8	103.5	89.4	94.9	115.1	89.4	99.5
05	METALS	105.0	83.6	100.8	101.4	81.6	97.5	102.3	83.5	98.6	109.1	83.6	104.1	91.1	89.5	90.8	91.0	89.4	90.7
06	WOOD, PLASTICS & COMPOSITES	90.0	69.1	80.6	94.2	58.2	78.1	92.0	69.1	81.8	92.5	69.1	82.1	107.6	96.8	102.8	103.9	96.8	100.7
07	THERMAL & MOISTURE PROTECTION	92.1	67.1	83.2	94.3	63.0	83.2	94.4	67.1	84.7	98.6	67.1	87.4	90.1	83.8	87.9	90.0	83.8	87.8
08	OPENINGS	87.6	70.5	83.7	91.1	70.3	86.4	91.1	70.5	86.5	89.1	70.5	84.9	95.6	88.4	93.9	95.6	88.4	93.9
0920	Plaster & Gypsum Board	88.6	68.4	75.8	92.9	57.2	70.3	89.6	68.4	76.2	96.5	68.4	78.7	99.9	96.6	97.8	98.7	96.6	97.4
0950, 0980	Ceilings & Acoustic Treatment	107.2	68.4	85.4	107.2	57.2	79.1	107.2	68.4	85.4	103.1	68.4	83.7	72.8	96.6	86.2	72.8	96.6	86.2
0960	Flooring	96.5	62.1	87.9	99.8	50.2	87.3	99.7	62.1	90.2	100.3	62.1	90.7	91.2	109.2	95.7	90.5	109.2	95.2
0970, 0990	Wall Finishes & Painting/Coating	92.2	60.2	73.1	92.2	53.9	69.4	92.2	58.5	72.1	95.3	59.1	73.7	89.3	90.2	89.8	89.3	90.2	89.8
09	FINISHES	97.0	66.4	81.7	100.0	56.7	78.3	99.5	66.2	82.8	98.7	66.3	82.4	85.7	96.0	90.9	85.4	96.0	90.7
COVERS	DIVS. 10 - 14, 25, 28, 41, 43, 44, 46	100.0	85.3	97.1	100.0	83.8	96.9	100.0	85.2	97.1	100.0	85.3	97.1	100.0	98.9	99.8	100.0	98.8	99.8
21, 22, 23	FIRE SUPPRESSION, PLUMBING & HVAC	100.0	72.0	90.0	95.9	58.7	82.6	100.0	72.0	90.0	100.2	72.0	90.1	92.6	78.9	87.7	92.6	78.9	87.7
26, 27, 3370	ELECTRICAL, COMMUNICATIONS & UTIL.	93.6	70.9	83.8	95.6	61.2	80.7	93.2	66.2	81.5	96.5	68.7	84.5	101.6	70.8	88.2	101.6	48.5	78.6
MF2018	WEIGHTED AVERAGE	97.7	72.6	88.4	98.6	65.8	86.5	99.3	71.8	89.2	101.7	72.3	90.9	92.6	86.7	90.4	92.9	83.5	89.5

		VERMONT																	
DIVISION		BRATTLEBORO			BURLINGTON			GUILDHALL			MONTPELIER			RUTLAND			ST. JOHNSBURY		
		053			054			059			056			057			058		
		MAT.	INST.	TOTAL	MAT.	INST.	TOTAL	MAT.	INST.	TOTAL	MAT.	INST.	TOTAL	MAT.	INST.	TOTAL	MAT.	INST.	TOTAL
015433	CONTRACTOR EQUIPMENT		93.0	93.0		97.6	97.6		93.0	93.0		97.6	97.6		93.0	93.0		93.0	93.0
0241, 31 - 34	SITE & INFRASTRUCTURE, DEMOLITION	83.3	91.5	88.6	90.6	101.7	97.9	82.1	91.1	88.0	86.0	100.9	95.7	89.2	92.5	91.4	82.2	90.6	87.7
0310	Concrete Forming & Accessories	102.0	92.8	94.8	103.7	83.2	87.8	98.5	87.5	90.0	103.7	94.5	96.5	102.3	83.2	87.5	96.0	87.5	89.4
0320	Concrete Reinforcing	79.3	78.2	79.0	98.7	82.1	94.1	80.9	78.2	80.1	97.9	82.1	93.5	100.2	82.1	95.2	79.3	78.2	79.0
0330	Cast-in-Place Concrete	73.3	110.7	86.6	88.1	114.2	97.4	68.9	103.2	81.1	81.7	114.2	93.3	69.6	113.1	85.1	68.9	103.1	81.1
03	CONCRETE	84.0	96.6	89.0	99.2	94.1	97.2	80.7	91.6	85.0	96.4	99.1	97.5	88.0	93.8	90.3	80.1	91.6	84.6
04	MASONRY	114.9	89.4	99.4	117.0	94.0	103.0	115.3	76.2	91.6	113.3	94.0	101.6	94.2	93.9	94.0	145.4	76.2	103.4
05	METALS	91.0	89.5	90.7	99.8	88.8	97.6	91.1	89.2	90.7	97.8	88.7	96.0	98.6	90.9	97.1	91.1	89.2	90.7
06	WOOD, PLASTICS & COMPOSITES	108.1	96.8	103.0	102.5	81.5	93.1	101.8	96.8	99.6	102.5	96.8	99.9	108.3	81.5	96.3	94.7	96.8	95.6
07	THERMAL & MOISTURE PROTECTION	90.2	83.8	87.9	95.2	95.9	95.5	89.9	77.9	85.6	94.8	97.6	95.8	90.3	94.4	91.7	89.7	77.9	85.5
08	OPENINGS	95.6	88.6	94.0	97.8	82.0	94.2	95.6	89.6	94.2	98.0	90.5	96.3	98.2	82.0	94.6	95.6	89.6	94.2
0920	Plaster & Gypsum Board	99.9	96.6	97.8	107.9	80.9	90.8	110.0	96.6	101.5	107.9	96.6	100.8	100.5	80.9	88.0	113.4	96.6	102.8
0950, 0980	Ceilings & Acoustic Treatment	72.8	96.6	86.2	81.2	80.9	81.0	72.8	96.6	86.2	80.7	96.6	89.6	78.2	80.9	79.7	72.8	96.6	86.2
0960	Flooring	91.4	109.2	95.8	99.2	109.2	101.7	93.5	109.2	97.4	99.2	109.2	101.7	91.2	109.2	95.7	96.0	109.2	99.3
0970, 0990	Wall Finishes & Painting/Coating	89.3	90.2	89.8	104.7	97.6	100.5	89.3	97.6	94.2	104.7	97.6	100.5	89.3	97.6	94.2	89.3	97.6	94.2
09	FINISHES	85.9	96.0	91.0	95.1	89.0	92.0	87.7	93.5	90.6	95.0	97.9	96.5	87.4	89.0	88.2	88.9	93.5	91.2
COVERS	DIVS. 10 - 14, 25, 28, 41, 43, 44, 46	100.0	98.9	99.8	100.0	98.7	99.8	100.0	94.4	98.9	100.0	100.4	100.1	100.0	98.7	99.7	100.0	94.4	98.9
21, 22, 23	FIRE SUPPRESSION, PLUMBING & HVAC	92.6	78.9	87.7	99.9	66.5	87.9	92.6	57.2	79.9	92.5	66.5	83.2	100.1	66.5	88.1	92.6	57.2	79.9
26, 27, 3370	ELECTRICAL, COMMUNICATIONS & UTIL.	101.6	70.8	88.2	101.0	51.9	79.7	101.6	48.5	78.6	101.1	51.9	79.8	101.6	51.9	80.1	101.6	48.5	78.6
MF2018	WEIGHTED AVERAGE	93.2	86.7	90.8	99.7	81.3	92.9	92.9	76.4	86.8	97.1	83.7	92.1	96.7	80.7	90.8	94.0	76.3	87.5

		VERMONT			VIRGINIA														
DIVISION		WHITE RIVER JCT.			ALEXANDRIA			ARLINGTON			BRISTOL			CHARLOTTESVILLE			CULPEPER		
		050			223			222			242			229			227		
		MAT.	INST.	TOTAL	MAT.	INST.	TOTAL	MAT.	INST.	TOTAL	MAT.	INST.	TOTAL	MAT.	INST.	TOTAL	MAT.	INST.	TOTAL
015433	CONTRACTOR EQUIPMENT		93.0	93.0		102.8	102.8		101.7	101.7		101.7	101.7		105.3	105.3		101.7	101.7
0241, 31 - 34	SITE & INFRASTRUCTURE, DEMOLITION	85.1	90.7	88.7	120.0	85.7	97.6	129.9	83.7	99.8	112.6	83.8	93.8	116.5	85.5	96.3	114.8	83.3	94.3
0310	Concrete Forming & Accessories	95.5	87.9	89.6	94.2	68.8	74.4	92.2	59.1	66.5	87.6	56.2	63.2	85.8	57.9	64.1	82.4	64.9	68.8
0320	Concrete Reinforcing	80.2	78.2	79.6	82.6	88.0	84.1	93.2	85.4	91.0	93.4	66.3	85.9	92.8	67.7	85.8	93.2	87.8	91.7
0330	Cast-in-Place Concrete	73.3	103.8	84.1	116.7	73.4	101.3	113.5	73.5	99.3	113.1	48.3	90.1	117.7	71.0	101.1	116.2	71.4	100.3
03	CONCRETE	85.3	92.0	88.0	95.8	75.2	87.7	99.6	70.5	88.1	97.3	57.1	81.4	98.2	66.1	85.5	96.2	72.7	86.9
04	MASONRY	129.5	77.5	97.9	89.1	71.4	78.4	99.6	71.0	82.2	90.6	52.4	67.4	114.1	53.4	77.2	104.1	66.1	81.1
05	METALS	91.1	89.2	90.7	102.4	101.2	102.2	100.4	100.4	100.4	99.2	91.4	97.6	99.5	94.1	98.4	99.6	100.0	99.6
06	WOOD, PLASTICS & COMPOSITES	99.5	96.8	98.3	94.9	67.5	82.6	90.7	54.5	74.5	81.1	54.4	69.1	79.1	54.9	68.3	77.3	63.8	71.2
07	THERMAL & MOISTURE PROTECTION	90.2	78.4	86.0	103.4	75.9	93.6	105.1	74.5	94.2	104.5	58.5	88.1	104.1	66.1	90.6	104.2	73.0	93.1
08	OPENINGS	95.6	89.6	94.2	94.7	72.6	89.7	93.0	65.3	86.8	95.8	61.0	87.9	94.1	61.6	86.8	94.4	70.6	89.0
0920	Plaster & Gypsum Board	97.0	96.6	96.8	109.7	66.5	82.3	105.1	53.2	72.2	99.8	53.0	70.1	99.8	53.0	70.1	100.0	62.7	76.4
0950, 0980	Ceilings & Acoustic Treatment	72.8	96.6	86.2	102.0	66.5	82.1	98.8	53.2	73.2	97.9	53.0	72.8	97.9	53.0	72.8	98.8	62.7	78.6
0960	Flooring	89.8	109.2	94.7	105.7	70.7	96.9	104.4	73.4	96.6	101.5	51.7	89.0	100.2	51.7	88.1	100.2	66.7	91.8
0970, 0990	Wall Finishes & Painting/Coating	89.3	97.6	94.2	116.2	65.4	85.9	116.2	68.1	87.5	102.1	69.9	82.9	102.1	56.0	74.6	116.2	65.2	85.8
09	FINISHES	85.2	93.8	89.5	104.7	67.9	86.3	104.1	61.2	82.6	100.8	56.5	78.6	100.5	55.3	77.8	101.1	64.3	82.6
COVERS	DIVS. 10 - 14, 25, 28, 41, 43, 44, 46	100.0	94.8	99.0	100.0	87.8	97.6	100.0	86.3	97.3	100.0	81.6	96.4	100.0	82.9	96.7	100.0	86.6	97.4
21, 22, 23	FIRE SUPPRESSION, PLUMBING & HVAC	92.6	57.9	80.2	100.4	81.4	93.6	100.4	83.3	94.3	92.9	47.3	76.5	92.9	66.8	83.5	92.9	78.6	87.8
26, 27, 3370	ELECTRICAL, COMMUNICATIONS & UTIL.	101.6	48.4	78.5	96.2	93.2	94.9	94.6	97.3	95.8	95.7	32.4	68.2	95.7	68.5	83.9	96.9	90.0	93.9
MF2018	WEIGHTED AVERAGE	93.9	76.7	87.5	99.7	81.2	92.9	100.1	79.9	92.6	97.1	57.2	82.4	98.1	68.2	87.1	97.6	78.3	90.5

	DIVISION	VIRGINIA																	
		FAIRFAX			FARMVILLE			FREDERICKSBURG			GRUNDY			HARRISONBURG			LYNCHBURG		
		220 - 221			239			224 - 225			246			228			245		
		MAT.	INST.	TOTAL	MAT.	INST.	TOTAL	MAT.	INST.	TOTAL	MAT.	INST.	TOTAL	MAT.	INST.	TOTAL	MAT.	INST.	TOTAL
015433	CONTRACTOR EQUIPMENT		101.7	101.7		105.3	105.3		101.7	101.7		101.7	101.7		101.7	101.7		101.7	101.7
0241, 31 - 34	SITE & INFRASTRUCTURE, DEMOLITION	125.5	83.8	98.3	113.2	84.4	94.4	114.4	83.2	94.1	110.5	82.4	92.2	122.4	83.6	97.1	111.1	84.0	93.4
0310	Concrete Forming & Accessories	85.9	61.6	67.0	102.9	57.0	67.3	85.9	59.7	65.5	91.3	55.3	63.3	81.3	58.2	63.3	87.6	57.5	64.2
0320	Concrete Reinforcing	93.2	88.1	91.8	90.1	61.2	82.1	93.9	72.9	88.1	92.1	39.8	77.6	93.2	75.9	88.4	92.8	66.6	85.5
0330	Cast-in-Place Concrete	113.5	74.5	99.6	117.4	80.3	104.2	115.3	69.5	99.0	113.1	48.4	90.1	113.5	72.7	99.0	113.1	71.7	98.4
03	CONCRETE	99.0	72.4	88.5	99.4	67.7	86.9	96.1	67.2	84.7	96.5	51.9	78.9	97.5	68.1	85.9	96.3	66.0	84.3
04	MASONRY	99.4	72.7	83.2	92.7	53.5	68.8	102.9	76.7	87.0	94.9	53.4	69.7	99.2	67.9	80.1	107.2	53.4	74.5
05	METALS	99.7	101.4	100.0	95.9	87.8	94.3	99.6	95.4	98.8	99.2	73.7	94.2	99.5	96.5	98.9	99.4	92.9	98.1
06	WOOD, PLASTICS & COMPOSITES	81.1	57.0	70.3	100.1	54.9	79.8	81.1	58.8	71.1	85.0	54.4	71.3	76.0	54.5	66.4	81.1	54.5	69.2
07	THERMAL & MOISTURE PROTECTION	104.8	76.6	94.7	99.6	65.9	87.6	104.3	74.7	93.7	104.5	56.0	87.2	104.6	75.0	94.0	104.3	65.9	90.6
08	OPENINGS	93.0	67.2	87.2	94.4	50.2	84.4	94.1	63.6	87.2	95.8	42.0	83.6	94.4	63.1	87.3	94.4	61.1	86.9
0920	Plaster & Gypsum Board	100.0	55.7	71.9	114.5	53.0	75.5	100.0	57.6	73.1	99.8	53.0	70.1	99.8	53.2	70.2	99.8	53.2	70.2
0950, 0980	Ceilings & Acoustic Treatment	98.8	55.7	74.6	99.7	53.0	73.6	98.8	57.6	75.7	97.9	53.0	72.8	97.9	53.2	72.8	97.9	53.2	72.8
0960	Flooring	101.7	75.8	95.2	103.4	51.7	90.4	101.7	64.8	92.5	102.6	51.7	89.8	100.0	72.2	93.0	101.5	51.7	89.0
0970, 0990	Wall Finishes & Painting/Coating	116.2	68.1	87.5	103.0	50.8	71.9	116.2	50.6	77.1	102.1	27.8	57.8	116.2	54.9	79.7	102.1	69.9	82.9
09	FINISHES	102.7	63.4	83.0	103.1	54.8	78.9	101.5	58.8	80.0	100.9	51.9	76.3	101.4	59.1	80.2	100.6	56.5	78.5
COVERS	DIVS. 10 - 14, 25, 28, 41, 43, 44, 46	100.0	87.1	97.5	100.0	79.2	96.0	100.0	70.2	94.2	100.0	77.9	95.7	100.0	81.8	96.5	100.0	81.6	96.4
21, 22, 23	FIRE SUPPRESSION, PLUMBING & HVAC	92.9	84.2	89.8	92.7	50.3	77.5	92.9	71.8	85.3	92.9	59.9	81.1	92.9	71.2	85.1	92.9	66.8	83.5
26, 27, 3370	ELECTRICAL, COMMUNICATIONS & UTIL.	96.2	95.9	96.1	92.0	64.6	80.1	94.7	97.3	95.8	95.7	64.6	82.2	95.8	72.4	85.6	96.2	60.3	80.7
MF2018	WEIGHTED AVERAGE	98.0	80.9	91.7	96.4	63.1	84.1	97.4	76.2	89.6	97.1	60.5	83.7	97.7	72.3	88.3	97.5	66.9	86.3

	DIVISION	VIRGINIA																	
		NEWPORT NEWS			NORFOLK			PETERSBURG			PORTSMOUTH			PULASKI			RICHMOND		
		236			233 - 235			238			237			243			230 - 232		
		MAT.	INST.	TOTAL	MAT.	INST.	TOTAL	MAT.	INST.	TOTAL	MAT.	INST.	TOTAL	MAT.	INST.	TOTAL	MAT.	INST.	TOTAL
015433	CONTRACTOR EQUIPMENT		105.3	105.3		105.3	105.3		105.3	105.3		105.2	105.2		101.7	101.7		105.3	105.3
0241, 31 - 34	SITE & INFRASTRUCTURE, DEMOLITION	115.4	85.6	96.0	115.3	90.5	99.1	115.7	85.6	96.1	114.1	85.1	95.2	109.9	82.7	92.1	107.9	90.5	96.6
0310	Concrete Forming & Accessories	101.9	60.5	69.7	102.1	60.2	69.5	94.2	58.0	66.1	89.2	57.2	64.3	91.3	55.7	63.7	102.2	60.6	69.9
0320	Concrete Reinforcing	89.9	63.8	82.7	98.8	63.7	89.1	89.5	67.8	83.5	89.5	63.0	82.2	92.1	75.4	87.5	98.7	67.8	90.2
0330	Cast-in-Place Concrete	114.1	73.7	99.7	126.7	75.4	108.5	121.2	73.9	104.4	113.0	62.7	95.1	113.1	76.7	100.2	96.5	75.6	89.1
03	CONCRETE	97.2	67.5	85.5	104.6	67.7	90.1	101.0	67.1	87.6	95.5	62.0	82.3	96.5	68.2	85.3	92.1	68.7	82.9
04	MASONRY	90.2	54.0	68.2	90.4	54.1	68.3	99.2	55.2	72.4	94.3	52.6	69.0	86.5	50.3	64.5	90.5	55.3	69.1
05	METALS	98.8	92.5	97.6	100.1	88.6	97.8	96.0	94.3	95.6	97.7	91.5	96.5	99.2	92.6	97.9	100.3	90.5	98.4
06	WOOD, PLASTICS & COMPOSITES	98.4	58.8	80.6	98.8	58.5	80.7	87.2	54.9	72.8	82.3	54.9	70.1	85.0	54.4	71.3	98.8	58.5	80.7
07	THERMAL & MOISTURE PROTECTION	99.5	64.9	87.2	98.1	68.1	87.4	99.5	67.0	87.9	99.5	63.0	86.5	104.5	64.6	90.2	97.2	69.1	87.2
08	OPENINGS	94.6	62.3	87.3	98.5	62.6	90.4	94.1	61.6	86.8	94.7	60.0	86.9	95.8	52.8	86.1	98.3	63.5	90.5
0920	Plaster & Gypsum Board	117.2	57.0	79.0	111.8	57.0	77.0	106.8	53.0	72.7	108.8	53.0	73.4	99.8	53.0	70.1	108.6	57.0	75.9
0950, 0980	Ceilings & Acoustic Treatment	108.4	57.0	79.6	102.5	57.0	77.0	102.0	53.0	74.6	108.4	53.0	77.3	97.9	53.0	72.8	103.0	57.0	77.2
0960	Flooring	103.4	52.7	90.7	106.0	52.7	92.6	99.9	54.8	88.6	97.4	51.7	85.9	102.6	51.7	89.8	101.2	54.8	89.6
0970, 0990	Wall Finishes & Painting/Coating	103.0	54.1	73.8	104.7	54.9	75.0	103.0	56.0	75.0	103.0	54.9	74.3	102.1	42.9	66.8	104.7	56.0	75.7
09	FINISHES	105.6	57.5	81.5	105.0	57.5	81.1	101.9	55.9	78.8	102.7	55.0	78.8	100.9	52.7	76.7	103.3	58.0	80.5
COVERS	DIVS. 10 - 14, 25, 28, 41, 43, 44, 46	100.0	83.3	96.8	100.0	83.3	96.8	100.0	82.9	96.7	100.0	83.1	96.7	100.0	80.8	96.3	100.0	82.8	96.7
21, 22, 23	FIRE SUPPRESSION, PLUMBING & HVAC	100.2	62.6	86.7	99.7	62.1	86.2	92.7	66.9	83.4	100.2	62.2	86.6	92.9	60.3	81.2	99.7	66.8	87.9
26, 27, 3370	ELECTRICAL, COMMUNICATIONS & UTIL.	93.5	64.4	80.9	100.0	61.8	83.5	93.5	68.5	82.7	92.6	61.8	79.2	95.7	74.2	86.4	99.3	68.4	85.9
MF2018	WEIGHTED AVERAGE	98.7	67.2	87.1	100.7	66.9	88.3	96.8	68.7	86.5	97.9	65.2	85.9	96.8	66.5	85.7	98.8	69.4	88.0

	DIVISION	VIRGINIA									WASHINGTON								
		ROANOKE			STAUNTON			WINCHESTER			CLARKSTON			EVERETT			OLYMPIA		
		240 - 241			244			226			994			982			985		
		MAT.	INST.	TOTAL	MAT.	INST.	TOTAL	MAT.	INST.	TOTAL	MAT.	INST.	TOTAL	MAT.	INST.	TOTAL	MAT.	INST.	TOTAL
015433	CONTRACTOR EQUIPMENT		101.7	101.7		105.3	105.3		101.7	101.7		88.6	88.6		96.9	96.9		99.6	99.6
0241, 31 - 34	SITE & INFRASTRUCTURE, DEMOLITION	113.5	84.0	94.3	113.3	84.2	94.3	121.2	83.3	96.5	108.8	82.8	91.9	107.9	101.4	103.7	109.4	105.0	106.5
0310	Concrete Forming & Accessories	98.7	57.8	66.9	90.9	57.0	64.6	84.0	60.3	65.6	83.6	58.5	64.1	116.4	103.9	106.7	100.4	103.1	102.5
0320	Concrete Reinforcing	93.1	66.7	85.8	92.8	65.3	85.2	92.6	72.0	86.9	77.0	96.2	82.3	93.3	114.3	99.1	100.0	113.8	103.8
0330	Cast-in-Place Concrete	128.5	80.4	111.4	117.7	80.2	104.4	113.5	59.0	94.2	97.8	76.1	90.1	111.7	110.2	111.2	98.4	111.0	102.9
03	CONCRETE	102.1	69.1	89.1	98.1	68.3	86.3	97.3	63.6	84.0	90.8	71.8	83.3	101.1	107.5	103.6	100.7	107.1	103.2
04	MASONRY	96.5	54.4	70.9	104.2	53.4	73.4	96.8	62.8	76.2	94.7	82.6	87.3	119.1	105.5	110.8	141.2	96.2	113.9
05	METALS	102.3	93.0	100.5	99.5	88.9	97.4	99.6	93.8	98.5	100.6	86.6	97.9	107.1	100.2	105.7	109.1	97.1	106.7
06	WOOD, PLASTICS & COMPOSITES	96.1	54.5	77.5	85.0	54.9	71.5	79.1	59.0	70.1	97.3	53.3	77.6	130.8	102.5	118.1	103.8	102.7	103.3
07	THERMAL & MOISTURE PROTECTION	104.3	67.6	91.2	104.1	65.9	90.5	104.7	69.8	92.2	84.3	74.4	80.8	99.8	106.7	102.3	96.9	105.4	99.9
08	OPENINGS	94.7	61.1	87.1	94.4	51.0	84.6	95.8	62.0	88.2	108.2	61.2	97.6	97.9	107.3	100.0	98.2	106.2	100.0
0920	Plaster & Gypsum Board	109.7	53.2	73.9	99.8	53.0	70.1	100.0	57.8	73.2	130.2	51.9	80.5	127.5	102.8	111.8	117.6	102.8	108.2
0950, 0980	Ceilings & Acoustic Treatment	102.0	53.2	74.6	97.9	53.0	72.8	98.8	57.8	75.8	86.6	51.9	67.1	98.7	102.8	101.0	106.2	102.8	104.3
0960	Flooring	105.7	53.2	92.6	102.1	51.7	89.5	101.2	66.7	92.6	82.7	69.4	79.4	99.8	101.6	100.2	100.3	86.0	96.7
0970, 0990	Wall Finishes & Painting/Coating	102.1	69.9	82.9	102.1	27.3	57.5	116.2	68.9	88.0	82.6	64.1	71.6	96.3	95.5	95.8	104.7	90.9	96.5
09	FINISHES	103.8	56.9	80.3	100.8	52.2	76.4	102.0	61.7	81.8	94.4	59.4	76.8	104.7	101.9	103.3	104.8	98.0	101.4
COVERS	DIVS. 10 - 14, 25, 28, 41, 43, 44, 46	100.0	81.8	96.5	100.0	79.2	96.0	100.0	74.0	95.0	100.0	92.5	98.5	100.0	102.2	100.4	100.0	102.2	100.4
21, 22, 23	FIRE SUPPRESSION, PLUMBING & HVAC	100.4	63.8	87.3	92.9	54.0	79.0	92.9	73.2	85.8	92.1	72.5	85.1	100.1	108.1	103.0	100.0	108.5	103.0
26, 27, 3370	ELECTRICAL, COMMUNICATIONS & UTIL.	95.7	55.2	78.1	95.1	74.9	86.4	95.0	81.7	89.2	83.4	85.1	84.2	104.1	103.5	103.8	100.9	101.3	101.1
MF2018	WEIGHTED AVERAGE	100.5	66.2	87.9	97.6	65.2	85.7	97.6	72.6	88.4	95.3	75.6	88.1	103.5	104.7	104.0	104.1	102.9	103.7

City Cost Indexes

		WASHINGTON																	
DIVISION		RICHLAND			SEATTLE			SPOKANE			TACOMA			VANCOUVER			WENATCHEE		
		993			980 - 981,987			990 - 992			983 - 984			986			988		
		MAT.	INST.	TOTAL	MAT.	INST.	TOTAL	MAT.	INST.	TOTAL	MAT.	INST.	TOTAL	MAT.	INST.	TOTAL	MAT.	INST.	TOTAL
015433	CONTRACTOR EQUIPMENT		88.6	88.6		99.2	99.2		88.6	88.6		96.9	96.9		93.7	93.7		96.9	96.9
0241, 31 - 34	SITE & INFRASTRUCTURE, DEMOLITION	113.9	83.9	94.4	113.0	103.0	106.5	113.7	83.9	94.2	111.3	101.1	104.7	122.7	89.8	101.3	118.6	98.6	105.6
0310	Concrete Forming & Accessories	83.7	82.7	82.9	104.7	108.4	107.5	89.2	82.3	83.9	105.5	103.1	103.6	105.3	95.7	97.9	107.1	74.9	82.0
0320	Concrete Reinforcing	73.8	96.3	80.1	99.5	119.4	105.0	74.3	96.9	80.6	92.6	114.3	98.6	93.1	114.2	98.9	93.1	86.2	91.2
0330	Cast-in-Place Concrete	98.0	84.3	93.1	117.8	112.0	115.8	101.9	84.1	95.6	114.9	109.1	112.8	128.3	99.9	118.2	117.3	84.1	105.5
03	CONCRETE	90.2	85.6	88.4	110.4	111.0	110.6	92.4	85.5	89.7	102.4	106.7	104.1	111.5	100.3	107.0	109.1	80.5	97.8
04	MASONRY	95.8	85.6	89.6	104.2	105.6	105.0	96.5	96.4	96.5	122.7	103.8	111.2	121.5	104.2	111.0	127.1	85.1	101.6
05	METALS	101.0	88.5	98.5	105.5	103.3	105.1	102.2	88.8	99.5	109.5	99.7	107.6	109.4	100.3	107.6	106.3	87.2	102.5
06	WOOD, PLASTICS & COMPOSITES	97.5	81.7	90.4	122.8	107.6	116.0	107.0	81.7	95.6	116.4	102.5	110.1	109.9	94.7	103.1	118.6	73.3	98.3
07	THERMAL & MOISTURE PROTECTION	92.6	84.2	89.6	99.7	110.0	103.4	91.3	84.8	89.0	99.7	106.9	102.3	99.9	100.7	100.2	99.3	79.9	92.4
08	OPENINGS	106.4	78.2	100.0	103.6	111.2	105.3	107.0	77.0	100.2	98.5	106.1	100.2	93.5	101.0	95.2	98.1	69.8	91.7
0920	Plaster & Gypsum Board	130.2	81.1	99.1	116.2	108.0	111.0	127.0	81.1	97.9	119.4	102.8	108.9	115.8	95.1	102.7	124.5	72.7	91.7
0950, 0980	Ceilings & Acoustic Treatment	89.6	81.1	84.9	100.7	108.0	104.8	87.6	81.1	84.0	103.2	102.8	103.0	95.8	95.1	95.4	94.0	72.7	82.1
0960	Flooring	82.8	77.1	81.4	92.2	103.4	95.0	81.0	93.9	84.3	95.1	95.2	95.1	100.3	98.7	99.9	97.0	69.4	90.1
0970, 0990	Wall Finishes & Painting/Coating	82.6	62.7	70.8	104.7	95.5	99.2	83.0	73.8	77.5	96.3	90.9	93.1	97.8	80.9	87.7	96.3	94.0	95.0
09	FINISHES	95.4	78.8	87.1	101.0	105.3	103.2	94.0	83.4	88.7	103.6	99.7	101.7	100.4	94.2	97.3	103.5	74.9	89.2
COVERS	DIVS. 10 - 14, 25, 28, 41, 43, 44, 46	100.0	97.3	99.5	100.0	103.2	100.6	100.0	97.2	99.5	100.0	101.7	100.3	100.0	95.4	99.1	100.0	94.8	99.0
21, 22, 23	FIRE SUPPRESSION, PLUMBING & HVAC	99.9	106.2	102.2	100.1	122.3	108.0	99.9	81.8	93.4	100.2	108.5	103.2	100.2	108.1	103.0	92.7	82.7	89.1
26, 27, 3370	ELECTRICAL, COMMUNICATIONS & UTIL.	79.7	97.9	87.6	100.9	126.4	112.0	81.0	80.1	80.6	104.0	101.3	102.9	113.5	100.9	108.1	104.5	84.1	95.7
MF2018	WEIGHTED AVERAGE	97.0	91.0	94.8	103.6	112.6	106.9	97.6	84.9	93.0	104.3	103.8	104.1	105.9	100.6	103.9	103.1	83.2	95.8

		WASHINGTON			WEST VIRGINIA														
DIVISION		YAKIMA			BECKLEY			BLUEFIELD			BUCKHANNON			CHARLESTON			CLARKSBURG		
		989			258 - 259			247 - 248			262			250 - 253			263 - 264		
		MAT.	INST.	TOTAL	MAT.	INST.	TOTAL	MAT.	INST.	TOTAL	MAT.	INST.	TOTAL	MAT.	INST.	TOTAL	MAT.	INST.	TOTAL
015433	CONTRACTOR EQUIPMENT		96.9	96.9		101.7	101.7		101.7	101.7		101.7	101.7		104.3	104.3		101.7	101.7
0241, 31 - 34	SITE & INFRASTRUCTURE, DEMOLITION	113.9	100.6	105.2	104.8	84.4	91.5	104.7	84.4	91.4	110.5	84.7	93.7	106.2	92.6	97.3	111.2	84.7	93.9
0310	Concrete Forming & Accessories	105.8	78.1	84.3	87.3	79.5	81.2	87.6	79.2	81.1	86.9	79.7	81.3	103.0	86.0	89.8	84.1	79.9	80.8
0320	Concrete Reinforcing	92.9	97.1	94.0	93.6	81.7	90.3	91.8	74.1	86.9	92.4	81.6	89.4	99.1	82.1	94.4	92.4	92.5	92.4
0330	Cast-in-Place Concrete	122.7	85.9	109.7	109.1	85.1	100.5	110.6	85.0	101.5	110.3	87.7	102.3	105.6	88.0	99.3	120.9	83.9	107.8
03	CONCRETE	106.8	84.4	97.9	92.2	83.1	88.6	93.4	81.7	88.8	95.1	84.2	90.8	94.2	86.9	91.3	99.1	84.7	93.4
04	MASONRY	115.3	96.8	104.1	85.2	80.3	82.2	87.7	80.3	83.2	97.9	86.0	90.7	83.3	86.2	85.1	100.9	86.0	91.9
05	METALS	107.0	92.7	104.1	99.2	100.9	99.5	99.5	98.1	99.2	99.7	101.2	100.0	97.9	98.6	98.1	99.7	105.0	100.7
06	WOOD, PLASTICS & COMPOSITES	116.9	73.3	97.4	84.8	79.4	82.4	83.3	79.4	81.5	82.3	77.0	79.9	99.4	86.2	93.5	78.1	77.0	77.6
07	THERMAL & MOISTURE PROTECTION	99.8	87.4	95.4	104.9	78.9	95.6	104.2	78.9	95.2	104.5	82.7	96.7	101.5	85.0	95.6	104.4	82.4	96.6
08	OPENINGS	98.1	84.0	94.9	97.7	76.6	92.9	96.2	74.8	91.4	96.2	75.2	91.5	97.9	80.3	93.9	96.2	79.9	92.6
0920	Plaster & Gypsum Board	118.7	72.7	89.6	90.2	78.8	83.0	97.8	78.8	85.7	99.0	76.4	84.7	102.3	85.7	91.8	96.4	76.4	83.7
0950, 0980	Ceilings & Acoustic Treatment	95.0	72.7	82.5	74.0	78.8	76.7	93.8	78.8	85.4	97.9	76.4	85.8	85.5	85.7	85.6	97.9	76.4	85.8
0960	Flooring	95.6	93.9	95.2	104.6	95.1	102.2	99.5	95.1	98.4	99.2	90.7	97.1	106.2	95.1	103.4	98.4	90.7	96.4
0970, 0990	Wall Finishes & Painting/Coating	96.3	73.8	82.9	101.9	81.9	89.9	102.1	79.8	88.8	102.1	85.5	92.2	104.7	87.9	94.7	102.1	85.5	92.2
09	FINISHES	101.7	78.8	90.2	92.5	82.7	87.6	98.2	82.5	90.3	99.9	82.0	90.9	99.1	87.9	93.5	99.2	82.0	90.6
COVERS	DIVS. 10 - 14, 25, 28, 41, 43, 44, 46	100.0	96.3	99.3	100.0	86.3	97.3	100.0	90.4	98.1	100.0	91.7	98.4	100.0	92.1	98.5	100.0	91.7	98.4
21, 22, 23	FIRE SUPPRESSION, PLUMBING & HVAC	100.2	107.3	102.7	92.7	87.1	90.7	92.9	75.6	86.7	92.9	89.7	91.7	99.7	88.9	95.8	92.9	89.9	91.8
26, 27, 3370	ELECTRICAL, COMMUNICATIONS & UTIL.	105.6	102.5	104.3	93.8	74.9	85.6	95.1	74.9	86.4	95.9	88.9	92.8	100.8	83.5	93.3	95.9	88.9	92.8
MF2018	WEIGHTED AVERAGE	104.0	94.7	100.6	95.4	83.9	91.2	96.2	81.0	90.6	97.2	87.2	93.5	98.2	88.3	94.5	97.7	87.9	94.1

		WEST VIRGINIA																	
DIVISION		GASSAWAY			HUNTINGTON			LEWISBURG			MARTINSBURG			MORGANTOWN			PARKERSBURG		
		266			255 - 257			249			254			265			261		
		MAT.	INST.	TOTAL	MAT.	INST.	TOTAL	MAT.	INST.	TOTAL	MAT.	INST.	TOTAL	MAT.	INST.	TOTAL	MAT.	INST.	TOTAL
015433	CONTRACTOR EQUIPMENT		101.7	101.7		101.7	101.7		101.7	101.7		101.7	101.7		101.7	101.7		101.7	101.7
0241, 31 - 34	SITE & INFRASTRUCTURE, DEMOLITION	108.1	84.7	92.8	112.3	85.6	94.9	119.7	84.4	96.7	108.4	84.6	92.9	105.5	85.8	92.7	116.6	85.8	96.5
0310	Concrete Forming & Accessories	86.3	80.4	81.7	101.2	83.1	87.1	84.5	79.3	80.5	87.4	72.2	75.6	84.5	80.3	81.2	89.3	86.3	87.0
0320	Concrete Reinforcing	92.4	82.3	89.6	94.9	85.1	92.2	92.4	74.1	87.3	93.6	85.4	91.3	92.4	92.5	92.4	91.8	81.5	88.9
0330	Cast-in-Place Concrete	115.5	87.6	105.6	118.9	89.8	108.6	110.7	85.0	101.6	114.3	80.9	102.4	110.3	92.7	104.0	112.7	88.1	104.0
03	CONCRETE	96.3	84.5	91.6	97.8	87.0	93.5	98.8	81.8	92.1	95.0	78.9	88.7	93.2	88.0	91.1	96.7	87.3	93.0
04	MASONRY	101.8	84.9	91.5	87.5	86.7	87.0	94.3	80.3	85.8	87.5	75.6	80.3	118.9	86.0	98.9	79.7	78.4	78.9
05	METALS	99.6	101.1	99.9	102.3	102.7	102.4	99.6	98.2	99.3	99.6	99.8	99.6	99.7	105.4	100.9	100.3	101.3	100.5
06	WOOD, PLASTICS & COMPOSITES	81.2	78.3	79.9	99.4	82.1	91.6	78.5	79.4	78.9	84.8	71.4	78.8	78.5	77.0	77.8	82.9	87.9	85.2
07	THERMAL & MOISTURE PROTECTION	104.2	83.0	96.7	105.2	82.5	97.1	105.0	78.9	95.7	105.1	72.5	93.5	104.2	83.7	96.9	104.5	81.7	96.4
08	OPENINGS	94.5	76.1	90.4	96.8	78.7	92.7	96.2	74.8	91.4	99.5	67.0	92.2	97.4	79.9	93.4	95.2	80.9	92.0
0920	Plaster & Gypsum Board	97.8	77.7	85.0	98.2	81.6	87.6	96.4	78.8	85.2	90.2	70.6	77.8	96.4	76.4	83.7	99.8	87.6	92.1
0950, 0980	Ceilings & Acoustic Treatment	97.9	77.7	86.6	74.0	81.6	78.2	97.9	78.8	87.2	74.0	70.6	72.1	97.9	76.4	85.8	97.9	87.6	92.1
0960	Flooring	99.1	95.1	98.1	111.2	94.3	106.9	98.5	95.1	97.7	104.6	88.6	100.6	98.5	90.7	96.6	101.8	94.2	99.9
0970, 0990	Wall Finishes & Painting/Coating	102.1	87.9	93.7	101.9	83.2	90.7	102.1	57.3	75.4	101.9	74.4	85.5	102.1	85.5	92.2	102.1	87.2	93.2
09	FINISHES	99.4	83.9	91.6	95.5	85.1	90.2	100.4	80.0	90.2	92.7	74.9	83.8	98.8	82.0	90.3	100.9	88.2	94.5
COVERS	DIVS. 10 - 14, 25, 28, 41, 43, 44, 46	100.0	91.8	98.4	100.0	91.8	98.4	100.0	90.4	98.1	100.0	89.0	97.9	100.0	91.7	98.4	100.0	91.4	98.3
21, 22, 23	FIRE SUPPRESSION, PLUMBING & HVAC	92.9	77.9	87.5	100.2	86.4	95.3	92.9	87.0	90.8	92.7	72.8	85.6	92.9	90.2	91.9	100.4	85.5	95.0
26, 27, 3370	ELECTRICAL, COMMUNICATIONS & UTIL.	95.9	83.5	90.5	95.9	83.0	90.3	93.8	74.9	85.6	97.0	68.4	84.6	96.0	88.9	92.9	95.9	84.4	90.9
MF2018	WEIGHTED AVERAGE	97.2	84.2	92.4	99.2	87.0	94.7	97.5	83.1	92.2	96.6	77.2	89.4	97.6	88.6	94.3	98.6	86.6	94.2

		WEST VIRGINIA									WISCONSIN								
DIVISION		PETERSBURG			ROMNEY			WHEELING			BELOIT			EAU CLAIRE			GREEN BAY		
		268			267			260			535			547			541 - 543		
		MAT.	INST.	TOTAL	MAT.	INST.	TOTAL	MAT.	INST.	TOTAL	MAT.	INST.	TOTAL	MAT.	INST.	TOTAL	MAT.	INST.	TOTAL
015433	CONTRACTOR EQUIPMENT		101.7	101.7		101.7	101.7		101.7	101.7		95.4	95.4		96.2	96.2		94.2	94.2
0241, 31 - 34	SITE & INFRASTRUCTURE, DEMOLITION	104.9	85.5	92.3	107.7	85.5	93.2	117.2	85.6	96.6	85.3	96.0	92.3	86.2	95.3	92.1	88.6	91.7	90.6
0310	Concrete Forming & Accessories	88.1	81.1	82.7	83.6	81.0	81.6	91.4	79.4	82.1	95.4	87.7	89.4	98.2	92.8	94.0	110.6	102.7	104.5
0320	Concrete Reinforcing	91.8	82.3	89.2	92.4	85.7	90.5	91.2	92.4	91.6	100.2	138.6	110.8	91.8	109.2	96.6	90.7	106.2	95.0
0330	Cast-in-Place Concrete	110.3	87.6	102.2	115.5	80.0	102.9	112.7	89.8	104.6	89.9	91.6	90.5	110.0	99.3	106.2	113.8	99.0	108.5
03	CONCRETE	93.3	84.9	90.0	96.0	82.7	90.8	96.7	86.6	92.7	95.9	98.1	96.7	100.2	98.3	99.5	103.5	102.1	102.9
04	MASONRY	94.0	86.0	89.2	94.7	84.9	88.8	100.4	83.4	90.1	99.9	103.2	101.9	97.5	104.4	101.7	128.8	98.4	110.4
05	METALS	99.8	101.1	100.1	99.9	102.0	100.3	100.5	105.1	101.4	92.7	113.1	96.7	91.5	105.1	94.2	96.2	104.2	97.8
06	WOOD, PLASTICS & COMPOSITES	83.6	79.4	81.7	77.4	79.4	78.3	85.0	77.0	81.4	93.0	85.4	89.6	101.3	90.5	96.5	115.6	103.8	110.3
07	THERMAL & MOISTURE PROTECTION	104.3	78.1	95.0	104.4	77.7	94.9	104.7	81.1	96.3	102.0	87.8	96.9	104.7	99.9	103.0	107.0	99.3	104.3
08	OPENINGS	97.4	75.8	92.5	97.3	76.6	92.6	95.9	79.9	92.3	93.9	101.5	95.6	99.8	92.4	98.2	95.4	103.3	97.2
0920	Plaster & Gypsum Board	99.0	78.8	86.2	95.9	78.8	85.1	99.8	76.4	84.9	82.0	85.6	84.3	97.2	90.8	93.2	95.5	104.5	101.2
0950, 0980	Ceilings & Acoustic Treatment	97.9	78.8	87.2	97.9	78.8	87.2	97.9	76.4	85.8	89.9	85.6	87.5	93.9	90.8	92.2	87.8	104.5	97.1
0960	Flooring	100.0	90.7	97.6	98.3	88.6	95.9	102.6	90.7	99.6	96.3	106.1	98.8	83.8	115.1	91.7	100.3	116.7	104.4
0970, 0990	Wall Finishes & Painting/Coating	102.1	85.5	92.2	102.1	85.5	92.2	102.1	85.5	92.2	97.2	92.0	94.1	85.4	79.5	81.9	92.9	117.9	107.8
09	FINISHES	99.6	83.3	91.4	98.9	82.9	90.9	101.1	81.6	91.3	92.0	90.8	91.4	89.5	95.1	92.3	93.4	107.3	100.4
COVERS	DIVS. 10 - 14, 25, 28, 41, 43, 44, 46	100.0	89.8	98.0	100.0	91.9	98.4	100.0	86.4	97.4	100.0	96.7	99.4	100.0	93.3	98.7	100.0	97.6	99.5
21, 22, 23	FIRE SUPPRESSION, PLUMBING & HVAC	92.9	78.4	87.7	92.9	78.1	87.6	100.4	89.1	96.3	99.7	86.2	94.9	100.0	85.9	94.9	100.3	92.6	97.6
26, 27, 3370	ELECTRICAL, COMMUNICATIONS & UTIL.	97.6	68.5	85.0	97.2	68.4	84.7	94.5	88.9	92.1	98.9	75.0	88.6	97.6	98.3	97.9	95.4	100.3	97.5
MF2018	WEIGHTED AVERAGE	96.9	82.2	91.5	97.2	81.8	91.6	99.4	87.6	95.0	96.3	92.8	95.0	96.9	95.8	96.5	99.5	99.3	99.4

		WISCONSIN																	
DIVISION		KENOSHA			LA CROSSE			LANCASTER			MADISON			MILWAUKEE			NEW RICHMOND		
		531			546			538			537			530,532			540		
		MAT.	INST.	TOTAL	MAT.	INST.	TOTAL	MAT.	INST.	TOTAL	MAT.	INST.	TOTAL	MAT.	INST.	TOTAL	MAT.	INST.	TOTAL
015433	CONTRACTOR EQUIPMENT		93.7	93.7		96.2	96.2		95.4	95.4		99.4	99.4		88.6	88.6		96.5	96.5
0241, 31 - 34	SITE & INFRASTRUCTURE, DEMOLITION	88.8	94.6	92.6	81.6	95.3	90.5	80.9	95.5	90.4	85.1	103.1	96.8	82.1	93.8	89.8	83.0	94.2	90.3
0310	Concrete Forming & Accessories	106.8	107.7	107.5	83.0	92.9	90.7	94.7	86.5	88.4	100.1	102.3	101.8	100.5	116.0	112.6	92.0	83.8	85.7
0320	Concrete Reinforcing	100.1	109.7	102.7	91.6	105.0	95.3	100.9	96.1	99.6	98.7	105.2	100.5	98.7	116.4	103.6	90.2	103.3	93.8
0330	Cast-in-Place Concrete	97.8	103.0	99.6	98.9	99.4	99.1	89.3	91.1	90.0	82.8	104.9	90.6	83.3	113.1	93.9	114.5	93.7	107.1
03	CONCRETE	100.0	106.2	102.5	92.0	97.6	94.2	95.6	90.2	93.5	96.4	103.5	99.2	96.7	114.1	103.5	98.4	91.3	95.6
04	MASONRY	97.9	108.9	104.6	96.4	99.0	98.0	100.0	103.2	101.9	114.4	103.0	107.5	88.6	119.7	107.5	123.0	103.3	111.0
05	METALS	94.7	103.9	96.5	91.4	103.5	93.8	89.3	97.1	90.9	97.4	99.6	97.9	96.9	98.8	97.3	93.4	101.6	95.0
06	WOOD, PLASTICS & COMPOSITES	106.2	107.8	106.9	81.6	90.5	85.6	91.9	85.4	89.0	98.9	101.7	100.1	98.9	114.2	105.7	88.7	81.8	85.6
07	THERMAL & MOISTURE PROTECTION	102.9	104.1	103.3	104.1	97.8	101.9	101.8	87.5	96.7	99.5	102.7	100.6	101.3	115.1	106.2	104.9	93.8	101.0
08	OPENINGS	88.2	107.0	92.5	99.8	90.5	97.7	90.2	83.3	88.6	98.7	102.4	99.6	100.1	113.4	103.1	85.4	81.8	84.6
0920	Plaster & Gypsum Board	74.3	108.7	96.1	92.1	90.8	91.3	79.6	85.6	83.4	86.4	102.1	96.3	86.4	114.8	104.4	79.2	82.0	81.0
0950, 0980	Ceilings & Acoustic Treatment	89.9	108.7	100.5	92.1	90.8	91.4	82.2	85.6	84.1	94.8	102.1	98.9	99.9	114.8	108.2	62.5	82.0	73.4
0960	Flooring	115.7	111.0	114.6	79.4	116.7	88.7	96.0	99.4	96.9	103.1	114.8	106.0	95.4	121.9	102.1	94.9	102.6	96.8
0970, 0990	Wall Finishes & Painting/Coating	107.2	114.2	111.4	85.4	117.5	104.5	97.2	86.8	91.0	104.7	97.7	100.5	104.7	124.7	116.6	96.6	72.6	82.3
09	FINISHES	97.4	109.5	103.5	86.7	99.6	93.2	89.5	88.7	89.1	96.5	104.4	100.5	95.9	118.3	107.1	82.6	85.8	84.2
COVERS	DIVS. 10 - 14, 25, 28, 41, 43, 44, 46	100.0	99.5	99.9	100.0	98.6	99.7	100.0	96.7	99.4	100.0	101.2	100.2	100.0	103.8	100.7	100.0	84.8	97.1
21, 22, 23	FIRE SUPPRESSION, PLUMBING & HVAC	99.9	96.5	98.7	100.0	85.8	94.9	92.2	80.2	87.9	99.7	95.2	98.1	99.7	109.6	103.2	91.8	79.9	87.5
26, 27, 3370	ELECTRICAL, COMMUNICATIONS & UTIL.	99.0	95.2	97.4	97.8	100.3	98.9	98.5	75.5	88.6	98.4	98.3	98.3	98.3	102.8	100.3	96.9	75.6	87.7
MF2018	WEIGHTED AVERAGE	97.4	101.9	99.0	95.3	95.9	95.5	93.2	88.0	91.3	98.6	100.5	99.3	97.6	109.3	101.9	94.2	87.7	91.8

		WISCONSIN																	
DIVISION		OSHKOSH			PORTAGE			RACINE			RHINELANDER			SUPERIOR			WAUSAU		
		549			539			534			545			548			544		
		MAT.	INST.	TOTAL	MAT.	INST.	TOTAL	MAT.	INST.	TOTAL	MAT.	INST.	TOTAL	MAT.	INST.	TOTAL	MAT.	INST.	TOTAL
015433	CONTRACTOR EQUIPMENT		94.2	94.2		95.4	95.4		95.4	95.4		94.2	94.2		96.5	96.5		94.2	94.2
0241, 31 - 34	SITE & INFRASTRUCTURE, DEMOLITION	79.1	90.7	86.6	75.0	96.3	88.9	85.2	97.8	93.4	87.3	90.3	89.2	80.6	93.9	89.3	76.2	91.3	86.0
0310	Concrete Forming & Accessories	91.2	87.1	88.0	86.3	87.2	87.0	95.8	107.7	105.0	88.5	86.0	86.6	89.7	80.7	82.7	90.6	88.7	89.1
0320	Concrete Reinforcing	90.8	99.4	93.2	101.0	96.3	99.7	100.2	109.7	102.8	90.9	96.4	92.4	90.2	112.5	96.4	90.9	105.2	94.9
0330	Cast-in-Place Concrete	105.5	90.7	100.2	76.8	89.9	81.4	88.2	102.7	93.3	119.6	89.5	108.9	107.9	89.9	101.5	98.3	84.7	93.5
03	CONCRETE	94.1	91.0	92.9	85.7	90.3	87.5	95.2	106.2	99.5	104.5	89.6	98.6	93.6	90.1	92.2	89.7	90.6	90.1
04	MASONRY	111.3	104.6	107.2	98.9	103.2	101.5	99.9	108.9	105.4	132.4	102.6	114.3	122.1	101.1	109.4	110.7	102.6	105.8
05	METALS	93.7	100.5	95.0	90.1	100.9	92.2	94.3	104.0	96.2	93.1	99.2	94.3	94.5	105.4	96.7	93.0	102.9	95.0
06	WOOD, PLASTICS & COMPOSITES	89.7	85.5	87.8	80.4	85.4	82.6	93.3	107.8	99.8	86.2	85.5	85.9	86.6	77.8	82.7	88.9	88.1	88.6
07	THERMAL & MOISTURE PROTECTION	106.1	80.1	96.8	101.3	93.3	98.5	102.1	104.3	102.9	106.7	78.5	96.7	104.6	88.9	99.0	105.9	89.3	100.0
08	OPENINGS	92.2	87.2	91.0	90.3	90.3	90.3	93.9	107.0	96.8	92.2	83.3	90.2	84.7	90.0	85.9	92.3	90.1	91.8
0920	Plaster & Gypsum Board	81.5	85.6	84.1	73.5	85.6	81.2	82.0	108.7	99.0	81.5	85.6	84.1	79.6	77.9	78.5	81.5	88.4	85.9
0950, 0980	Ceilings & Acoustic Treatment	87.8	85.6	86.6	87.7	85.6	86.5	89.9	108.7	100.5	87.8	85.6	86.6	63.9	77.9	71.7	87.8	88.4	88.1
0960	Flooring	93.9	102.8	96.2	93.1	102.6	95.4	96.3	111.0	100.0	93.5	102.6	95.8	96.3	110.2	99.8	93.9	102.6	96.1
0970, 0990	Wall Finishes & Painting/Coating	90.8	99.1	95.8	97.2	86.8	91.0	97.2	116.4	108.6	90.8	71.1	79.0	84.8	94.0	90.3	90.8	74.0	80.7
09	FINISHES	89.1	91.3	90.2	88.9	89.6	89.2	92.0	109.7	100.9	89.7	87.7	88.7	82.5	86.9	84.7	88.9	89.6	89.2
COVERS	DIVS. 10 - 14, 25, 28, 41, 43, 44, 46	100.0	95.2	99.1	100.0	96.8	99.4	100.0	99.5	99.9	100.0	94.5	98.9	100.0	83.7	96.8	100.0	94.8	99.0
21, 22, 23	FIRE SUPPRESSION, PLUMBING & HVAC	92.8	79.6	88.1	92.2	86.1	90.0	99.7	96.5	98.6	92.8	79.7	88.1	91.8	82.1	88.3	92.8	80.2	88.3
26, 27, 3370	ELECTRICAL, COMMUNICATIONS & UTIL.	97.2	75.0	87.6	100.9	83.7	93.4	99.0	92.3	96.1	96.8	69.5	85.0	99.4	87.7	94.4	97.8	69.5	85.5
MF2018	WEIGHTED AVERAGE	94.6	88.2	92.2	92.1	91.4	91.8	96.5	101.8	98.5	96.7	86.2	92.8	94.0	90.1	92.6	93.9	87.7	91.6

	DIVISION	WYOMING																	
		CASPER			CHEYENNE			NEWCASTLE			RAWLINS			RIVERTON			ROCK SPRINGS		
		826			820			827			823			825			829 - 831		
		MAT.	INST.	TOTAL	MAT.	INST.	TOTAL	MAT.	INST.	TOTAL	MAT.	INST.	TOTAL	MAT.	INST.	TOTAL	MAT.	INST.	TOTAL
015433	CONTRACTOR EQUIPMENT		99.7	99.7		93.2	93.2		93.2	93.2		93.2	93.2		93.2	93.2		93.2	93.2
0241, 31 - 34	SITE & INFRASTRUCTURE, DEMOLITION	102.3	98.5	99.8	96.7	87.2	90.5	87.2	86.9	87.0	100.0	86.9	91.4	94.3	86.9	89.4	91.9	86.9	88.7
0310	Concrete Forming & Accessories	103.3	62.8	71.8	105.9	62.5	72.2	94.4	60.8	68.3	99.3	60.8	69.4	93.1	60.6	67.9	101.6	62.7	71.4
0320	Concrete Reinforcing	101.2	82.3	96.0	92.5	82.6	89.7	99.8	82.4	95.0	99.5	82.4	94.8	100.4	82.4	95.4	100.4	79.0	94.5
0330	Cast-in-Place Concrete	95.9	78.8	89.8	90.4	77.3	85.7	91.3	75.8	85.8	91.4	75.8	85.8	91.3	75.7	85.8	91.3	76.3	86.0
03	CONCRETE	102.3	72.3	90.4	96.1	71.8	86.5	96.9	70.5	86.5	107.8	70.5	93.0	103.4	70.4	90.4	97.7	71.0	87.1
04	MASONRY	91.2	64.4	75.0	93.0	68.3	78.0	90.2	64.0	74.2	90.1	64.0	74.2	90.2	64.0	74.3	142.3	59.1	91.8
05	METALS	105.3	79.7	100.2	107.3	82.2	102.3	103.3	81.8	99.1	103.4	81.8	99.1	103.5	81.6	99.2	104.2	80.3	99.5
06	WOOD, PLASTICS & COMPOSITES	102.9	59.7	83.5	104.1	59.1	83.9	90.1	58.3	75.8	95.7	58.3	78.9	88.5	58.3	75.0	101.1	60.6	82.9
07	THERMAL & MOISTURE PROTECTION	97.5	67.7	86.9	93.4	67.6	84.2	94.1	63.9	83.3	95.3	63.9	84.1	94.8	66.9	84.8	94.2	66.7	84.4
08	OPENINGS	97.9	65.6	90.6	96.0	65.3	89.0	99.4	62.9	91.2	99.2	62.9	91.0	99.3	62.9	91.1	99.7	64.6	91.8
0920	Plaster & Gypsum Board	111.2	58.4	77.7	98.6	58.0	72.9	95.8	57.3	71.4	95.8	57.3	71.4	95.8	57.3	71.4	112.0	59.6	78.7
0950, 0980	Ceilings & Acoustic Treatment	99.1	58.4	76.3	84.4	58.0	69.6	85.4	57.3	69.6	85.4	57.3	69.6	85.4	57.3	69.6	85.4	59.6	70.9
0960	Flooring	103.1	75.3	96.1	101.8	75.3	95.2	96.4	63.5	88.1	98.5	63.5	89.7	95.9	63.5	87.8	100.2	55.8	89.1
0970, 0990	Wall Finishes & Painting/Coating	104.7	56.4	75.9	103.7	56.4	75.5	99.9	69.6	81.9	99.9	69.6	81.9	99.9	53.7	72.4	99.9	71.0	82.7
09	FINISHES	102.4	63.8	83.0	96.8	63.4	80.0	92.4	61.3	76.8	94.2	61.3	77.7	93.0	59.6	76.2	95.7	61.5	78.6
COVERS	DIVS. 10 - 14, 25, 28, 41, 43, 44, 46	100.0	84.4	97.0	100.0	88.0	97.7	100.0	92.6	98.6	100.0	92.6	98.6	100.0	82.2	96.6	100.0	86.8	97.4
21, 22, 23	FIRE SUPPRESSION, PLUMBING & HVAC	99.9	71.9	89.9	100.2	77.8	92.2	96.0	74.5	88.3	96.0	74.5	88.3	96.0	74.4	88.3	100.1	75.0	91.1
26, 27, 3370	ELECTRICAL, COMMUNICATIONS & UTIL.	97.7	59.3	81.1	95.2	65.1	82.2	93.4	55.5	77.0	93.4	55.5	77.0	93.4	59.4	78.7	92.5	62.4	79.5
MF2018	WEIGHTED AVERAGE	100.8	71.1	89.9	99.6	72.8	89.7	97.2	69.8	87.1	99.0	69.8	88.3	98.2	69.8	87.8	100.8	70.3	89.6

	DIVISION	WYOMING												CANADA					
		SHERIDAN			WHEATLAND			WORLAND			YELLOWSTONE NAT'L PA			BARRIE, ONTARIO			BATHURST, NEW BRUNSWICK		
		828			822			824			821								
		MAT.	INST.	TOTAL	MAT.	INST.	TOTAL	MAT.	INST.	TOTAL	MAT.	INST.	TOTAL	MAT.	INST.	TOTAL	MAT.	INST.	TOTAL
015433	CONTRACTOR EQUIPMENT		93.2	93.2		93.2	93.2		93.2	93.2		93.2	93.2		97.9	97.9		98.6	98.6
0241, 31 - 34	SITE & INFRASTRUCTURE, DEMOLITION	94.5	87.2	89.7	91.1	86.9	88.3	88.5	86.9	87.4	88.6	86.9	87.5	122.1	90.8	101.7	116.5	87.8	97.8
0310	Concrete Forming & Accessories	103.7	61.7	71.1	96.6	60.5	68.6	96.7	60.8	68.8	96.7	60.7	68.7	124.9	77.5	88.1	91.1	54.6	62.8
0320	Concrete Reinforcing	100.4	82.4	95.4	99.8	81.7	94.8	100.4	82.4	95.4	102.1	79.4	95.8	151.8	81.2	132.3	70.2	53.8	65.6
0330	Cast-in-Place Concrete	94.4	77.2	88.3	95.3	75.7	88.3	91.3	75.8	85.8	91.3	75.7	85.8	165.1	77.7	134.1	115.6	53.8	93.6
03	CONCRETE	104.0	71.4	91.1	101.0	70.2	88.8	97.3	70.5	86.7	97.7	69.9	86.7	150.7	78.9	122.4	104.1	55.4	84.9
04	MASONRY	90.5	66.5	75.9	90.5	52.9	67.7	90.2	64.0	74.3	90.2	64.0	74.3	171.6	83.8	118.3	156.6	53.9	94.2
05	METALS	107.3	81.7	102.2	103.3	80.7	98.8	103.5	81.8	99.2	104.2	80.7	99.5	114.3	89.5	109.4	128.6	73.0	117.6
06	WOOD, PLASTICS & COMPOSITES	106.1	58.3	84.7	92.8	58.3	77.3	92.9	58.3	77.4	92.9	58.3	77.4	117.3	76.4	99.0	91.3	54.8	74.9
07	THERMAL & MOISTURE PROTECTION	95.4	67.0	85.3	94.3	60.8	82.4	94.1	63.9	83.3	93.8	63.9	83.1	113.9	80.1	101.9	118.3	54.4	95.6
08	OPENINGS	100.0	62.9	91.6	98.3	62.9	90.3	99.6	62.9	91.3	93.8	62.2	86.7	89.2	76.4	86.3	84.8	48.4	76.6
0920	Plaster & Gypsum Board	118.7	57.3	79.7	95.8	57.3	71.4	95.8	57.3	71.4	96.1	57.3	71.5	153.8	75.9	104.4	119.8	53.5	77.8
0950, 0980	Ceilings & Acoustic Treatment	87.4	57.3	70.5	85.4	57.3	69.6	85.4	57.3	69.6	86.3	57.3	70.0	92.9	75.9	83.3	91.7	53.5	70.3
0960	Flooring	100.6	54.0	88.9	97.4	63.5	88.9	97.4	63.5	88.9	97.4	63.5	88.9	120.7	81.5	110.9	95.7	38.7	81.4
0970, 0990	Wall Finishes & Painting/Coating	102.6	56.4	75.1	99.9	51.9	71.3	99.9	69.6	81.9	99.9	53.7	72.4	106.8	77.6	89.4	112.3	44.4	71.8
09	FINISHES	99.8	59.3	79.4	93.0	59.4	76.1	92.7	61.3	77.0	93.0	59.6	76.2	112.4	78.5	95.4	98.0	50.7	74.2
COVERS	DIVS. 10 - 14, 25, 28, 41, 43, 44, 46	100.0	83.7	96.9	100.0	82.9	96.7	100.0	92.7	98.6	100.0	92.7	98.6	139.3	60.6	124.0	131.1	54.1	116.2
21, 22, 23	FIRE SUPPRESSION, PLUMBING & HVAC	96.0	75.9	88.8	96.0	74.4	88.3	96.0	74.5	88.3	96.0	74.4	88.3	110.3	87.6	102.2	110.6	60.7	92.7
26, 27, 3370	ELECTRICAL, COMMUNICATIONS & UTIL.	95.3	59.4	79.7	93.4	59.4	78.7	93.4	59.4	78.7	92.9	59.4	78.4	124.9	76.9	104.1	137.5	51.8	100.4
MF2018	WEIGHTED AVERAGE	100.1	70.6	89.2	97.8	68.4	87.0	97.4	70.3	87.4	97.1	69.9	87.1	121.0	82.1	106.7	117.1	59.1	95.7

	DIVISION	CANADA																	
		BRANDON, MANITOBA			BRANTFORD, ONTARIO			BRIDGEWATER, NOVA SCOTIA			CALGARY, ALBERTA			CAP-DE-LA-MADELEINE, QUEBEC			CHARLESBOURG, QUEBEC		
		MAT.	INST.	TOTAL	MAT.	INST.	TOTAL	MAT.	INST.	TOTAL	MAT.	INST.	TOTAL	MAT.	INST.	TOTAL	MAT.	INST.	TOTAL
015433	CONTRACTOR EQUIPMENT		97.2	97.2		97.8	97.8		98.1	98.1		119.7	119.7		99.0	99.0		99.0	99.0
0241, 31 - 34	SITE & INFRASTRUCTURE, DEMOLITION	126.4	87.8	101.2	126.1	91.0	103.2	110.6	89.1	96.6	118.5	108.8	112.2	106.2	90.6	96.0	106.2	90.6	96.0
0310	Concrete Forming & Accessories	129.6	62.2	77.3	112.0	84.0	90.2	84.9	64.1	68.7	119.6	87.1	94.3	117.3	74.7	84.2	117.3	74.7	84.2
0320	Concrete Reinforcing	87.1	51.0	77.1	84.1	80.0	83.0	72.3	44.6	64.6	75.3	74.9	75.2	72.3	67.7	71.0	72.3	67.7	71.0
0330	Cast-in-Place Concrete	124.7	66.2	103.9	149.0	96.1	130.2	153.2	63.7	121.4	145.8	93.5	127.2	120.2	82.9	107.0	120.2	82.9	107.0
03	CONCRETE	131.8	62.8	104.5	134.4	88.1	116.1	132.5	61.7	104.6	183.8	88.1	146.0	119.9	77.1	103.0	119.9	77.1	103.0
04	MASONRY	219.9	56.9	120.9	172.2	87.6	120.8	167.4	61.5	103.1	230.3	80.8	139.5	167.6	71.6	109.3	167.6	71.6	109.3
05	METALS	143.1	75.9	129.9	128.1	90.0	120.6	126.9	75.1	116.7	154.9	95.9	143.2	125.4	83.8	117.2	125.4	83.8	117.2
06	WOOD, PLASTICS & COMPOSITES	135.6	63.1	103.1	114.0	82.9	100.1	82.0	63.8	73.9	103.2	87.2	96.0	125.8	74.8	102.9	125.8	74.8	102.9
07	THERMAL & MOISTURE PROTECTION	133.6	63.8	108.7	126.8	85.1	111.9	121.7	63.0	100.8	147.2	89.3	126.5	120.7	78.4	105.6	120.7	78.4	105.6
08	OPENINGS	100.3	56.5	90.4	88.0	81.8	86.6	83.7	57.9	77.9	91.0	77.1	87.9	89.6	68.3	84.8	89.6	68.3	84.8
0920	Plaster & Gypsum Board	100.6	61.9	76.1	117.8	82.6	95.5	114.7	62.8	81.8	120.5	86.0	98.6	146.5	74.0	100.5	146.5	74.0	100.5
0950, 0980	Ceilings & Acoustic Treatment	94.0	61.9	76.0	78.3	82.6	80.7	78.3	62.8	69.6	105.8	86.0	94.7	78.3	74.0	75.9	78.3	74.0	75.9
0960	Flooring	123.0	57.8	106.7	107.9	81.5	101.3	94.1	55.0	84.3	126.8	77.8	114.5	107.9	80.2	100.9	107.9	80.2	100.9
0970, 0990	Wall Finishes & Painting/Coating	118.1	50.1	77.5	110.9	85.2	95.6	110.9	54.9	77.5	111.0	94.5	101.2	110.9	77.4	90.9	110.9	77.4	90.9
09	FINISHES	109.7	60.4	84.9	99.3	83.9	91.6	94.3	61.7	77.9	119.9	86.7	103.3	102.6	76.3	89.4	102.6	76.3	89.4
COVERS	DIVS. 10 - 14, 25, 28, 41, 43, 44, 46	131.1	55.8	116.5	131.1	62.3	117.8	131.1	56.8	116.7	131.1	84.5	122.1	131.1	70.4	119.4	131.1	70.4	119.4
21, 22, 23	FIRE SUPPRESSION, PLUMBING & HVAC	117.2	73.8	101.7	110.5	90.2	103.2	110.5	74.5	97.6	109.8	81.1	99.5	110.2	78.9	99.0	110.2	78.9	99.0
26, 27, 3370	ELECTRICAL, COMMUNICATIONS & UTIL.	130.8	58.5	99.5	134.6	76.5	109.4	135.4	54.4	100.3	134.7	83.6	112.5	129.3	60.5	99.5	129.3	60.5	99.5
MF2018	WEIGHTED AVERAGE	130.0	66.3	106.6	122.0	85.5	108.5	119.8	66.5	100.2	137.9	86.9	119.1	118.6	75.6	102.8	118.6	75.6	102.8

CANADA

	DIVISION	CHARLOTTETOWN, PRINCE EDWARD ISLAND			CHICOUTIMI, QUEBEC			CORNER BROOK, NEWFOUNDLAND			CORNWALL, ONTARIO			DALHOUSIE, NEW BRUNSWICK			DARTMOUTH, NOVA SCOTIA		
		MAT.	INST.	TOTAL	MAT.	INST.	TOTAL	MAT.	INST.	TOTAL	MAT.	INST.	TOTAL	MAT.	INST.	TOTAL	MAT.	INST.	TOTAL
015433	CONTRACTOR EQUIPMENT		122.2	122.2		99.2	99.2		96.8	96.8		97.8	97.8		97.9	97.9		95.3	95.3
0241, 31 - 34	SITE & INFRASTRUCTURE, DEMOLITION	145.2	107.9	120.9	113.2	91.0	98.7	131.7	86.3	102.1	124.2	90.6	102.3	109.2	87.3	94.9	123.0	87.3	99.7
0310	Concrete Forming & Accessories	112.5	50.5	64.4	117.8	86.2	93.3	105.9	71.0	78.8	109.8	77.7	84.8	90.6	54.8	62.8	95.8	63.9	71.0
0320	Concrete Reinforcing	60.5	43.6	55.9	52.9	90.0	63.2	80.2	45.6	70.6	84.1	79.7	82.9	75.6	53.8	69.6	83.6	44.6	72.8
0330	Cast-in-Place Concrete	136.8	57.4	108.6	108.8	91.3	102.6	145.2	60.2	115.0	134.0	87.7	117.6	129.4	53.7	102.5	140.1	63.1	112.8
03	CONCRETE	121.8	53.6	94.9	96.4	89.0	93.4	169.1	63.7	127.5	128.0	82.2	109.9	138.6	55.4	105.8	147.6	61.4	113.6
04	MASONRY	167.4	51.6	97.1	158.1	85.9	114.2	215.3	69.6	126.8	170.9	80.3	115.9	172.1	53.9	100.3	229.0	61.5	127.3
05	METALS	147.7	78.4	134.0	128.5	91.5	121.2	143.6	73.4	129.8	127.9	88.8	120.2	119.3	72.8	110.1	144.0	73.7	130.2
06	WOOD, PLASTICS & COMPOSITES	110.2	50.1	83.3	125.4	86.9	108.2	113.8	76.7	97.2	112.2	77.1	96.5	94.1	54.8	76.5	102.1	63.7	84.9
07	THERMAL & MOISTURE PROTECTION	146.1	54.9	113.6	118.8	91.4	109.0	136.8	61.3	109.9	126.4	80.2	109.9	124.2	54.4	99.3	134.7	62.9	109.1
08	OPENINGS	92.5	43.5	81.4	88.2	73.3	84.9	105.7	62.7	96.0	89.6	76.1	86.5	88.5	48.4	79.5	92.5	57.8	84.7
0920	Plaster & Gypsum Board	154.2	47.7	86.7	147.0	86.6	108.7	129.8	76.1	95.8	171.2	76.6	111.2	125.7	53.5	79.9	126.8	62.8	86.2
0950, 0980	Ceilings & Acoustic Treatment	107.0	47.7	73.8	90.8	86.6	88.4	94.0	76.1	84.0	81.5	76.6	78.7	78.4	53.5	64.5	100.8	62.8	79.5
0960	Flooring	123.1	51.6	105.2	107.9	80.2	101.0	108.9	46.2	93.2	107.9	80.3	101.0	102.9	59.2	92.0	105.0	55.0	92.5
0970, 0990	Wall Finishes & Painting/Coating	112.9	36.9	67.6	112.3	98.3	104.0	117.9	52.3	78.8	110.9	79.3	92.1	114.6	44.4	72.7	117.9	54.9	80.4
09	FINISHES	125.3	49.6	87.3	104.8	87.4	96.0	109.6	65.8	87.6	107.2	78.5	92.8	101.0	54.8	77.8	108.8	61.6	85.1
COVERS	DIVS. 10 - 14, 25, 28, 41, 43, 44, 46	131.1	55.4	116.5	131.1	75.3	120.3	131.1	56.3	116.6	131.1	60.2	117.4	131.1	54.0	116.2	131.1	56.5	116.7
21, 22, 23	FIRE SUPPRESSION, PLUMBING & HVAC	117.1	55.4	94.9	110.6	77.3	98.7	117.2	61.7	97.3	110.2	88.3	102.4	111.1	60.7	93.0	117.2	74.4	101.9
26, 27, 3370	ELECTRICAL, COMMUNICATIONS & UTIL.	148.2	44.1	103.1	130.8	79.5	108.6	125.0	47.8	91.6	132.4	77.4	108.5	134.6	49.0	97.5	127.7	54.4	96.0
MF2018	WEIGHTED AVERAGE	130.7	58.1	104.0	116.5	84.0	104.6	134.3	64.4	108.5	121.4	82.3	107.1	120.2	59.1	97.7	131.0	66.1	107.2

CANADA

	DIVISION	EDMONTON, ALBERTA			FORT MCMURRAY, ALBERTA			FREDERICTON, NEW BRUNSWICK			GATINEAU, QUEBEC			GRANBY, QUEBEC			HALIFAX, NOVA SCOTIA		
		MAT.	INST.	TOTAL	MAT.	INST.	TOTAL	MAT.	INST.	TOTAL	MAT.	INST.	TOTAL	MAT.	INST.	TOTAL	MAT.	INST.	TOTAL
015433	CONTRACTOR EQUIPMENT		120.6	120.6		99.4	99.4		121.9	121.9		99.0	99.0		99.0	99.0		119.5	119.5
0241, 31 - 34	SITE & INFRASTRUCTURE, DEMOLITION	124.6	110.3	115.3	129.8	91.5	104.8	150.0	108.6	123.0	106.0	90.6	95.9	106.4	90.6	96.1	114.2	108.2	110.3
0310	Concrete Forming & Accessories	112.2	86.5	92.2	110.4	82.3	88.5	112.5	55.9	68.6	117.3	74.6	84.1	117.3	74.5	84.1	112.5	81.3	88.2
0320	Concrete Reinforcing	73.3	74.9	73.7	78.2	74.8	77.2	58.7	54.1	57.4	76.2	67.7	73.8	76.2	67.7	73.8	60.7	73.2	64.2
0330	Cast-in-Place Concrete	163.8	93.5	138.8	198.0	87.4	158.7	155.3	58.0	120.7	118.6	82.9	105.9	122.5	82.9	108.4	143.9	76.4	119.9
03	CONCRETE	190.1	87.8	149.7	152.9	83.3	125.5	129.0	58.0	101.0	120.2	77.1	103.2	121.9	77.0	104.2	124.8	79.3	106.9
04	MASONRY	227.7	80.8	138.4	213.4	78.8	131.6	179.7	55.3	104.1	167.5	71.6	109.2	167.7	71.6	109.4	176.9	79.4	117.7
05	METALS	148.5	96.0	138.1	159.2	87.8	145.2	144.6	83.1	132.5	125.4	83.7	117.2	125.7	83.6	117.4	147.4	96.5	137.4
06	WOOD, PLASTICS & COMPOSITES	102.1	86.4	95.1	107.8	81.9	96.2	101.3	55.7	80.9	125.8	74.8	102.9	125.8	74.8	102.9	101.3	81.6	92.5
07	THERMAL & MOISTURE PROTECTION	147.0	89.2	126.4	135.0	84.4	117.0	146.1	56.7	114.3	120.7	78.4	105.6	120.9	77.0	105.3	149.6	82.2	125.6
08	OPENINGS	91.4	76.7	88.1	89.6	74.2	86.1	92.0	47.9	82.1	89.6	64.2	83.9	89.6	64.2	83.9	91.8	73.8	87.7
0920	Plaster & Gypsum Board	157.4	85.2	111.6	115.4	81.3	93.8	123.8	53.5	79.2	121.2	74.0	91.2	121.2	74.0	91.2	123.7	80.3	96.2
0950, 0980	Ceilings & Acoustic Treatment	100.3	85.2	91.8	85.1	81.3	83.0	99.4	53.5	73.7	78.3	74.0	75.9	78.3	74.0	75.9	100.9	80.3	89.4
0960	Flooring	127.5	77.8	115.0	107.9	77.8	100.3	121.5	61.8	106.6	107.9	80.2	100.9	107.9	80.2	100.9	116.3	74.8	105.9
0970, 0990	Wall Finishes & Painting/Coating	113.8	94.5	102.3	111.0	81.8	93.6	113.7	56.5	79.6	110.9	77.4	90.9	110.9	77.4	90.9	113.4	82.6	95.0
09	FINISHES	123.8	86.2	104.9	101.9	81.7	91.7	113.5	57.3	85.3	99.2	76.3	87.7	99.2	76.3	87.7	109.5	80.7	95.1
COVERS	DIVS. 10 - 14, 25, 28, 41, 43, 44, 46	131.1	85.5	122.3	131.1	82.9	121.8	131.1	55.9	116.6	131.1	70.4	119.4	131.1	70.4	119.4	131.1	63.9	118.1
21, 22, 23	FIRE SUPPRESSION, PLUMBING & HVAC	109.8	81.1	99.5	110.9	87.2	102.4	117.1	69.2	99.9	110.2	78.8	99.0	110.5	78.8	99.1	110.7	75.2	97.9
26, 27, 3370	ELECTRICAL, COMMUNICATIONS & UTIL.	134.8	83.6	112.6	125.1	71.9	102.0	148.5	64.7	112.1	129.3	60.5	99.5	130.9	60.5	100.4	114.4	81.0	99.9
MF2018	WEIGHTED AVERAGE	137.6	86.9	118.9	132.2	82.5	113.9	130.6	66.7	107.0	118.4	75.4	102.6	118.9	75.3	102.9	124.4	82.1	108.8

CANADA

	DIVISION	HAMILTON, ONTARIO			HULL, QUEBEC			JOLIETTE, QUEBEC			KAMLOOPS, BRITISH COLUMBIA			KINGSTON, ONTARIO			KITCHENER, ONTARIO		
		MAT.	INST.	TOTAL	MAT.	INST.	TOTAL	MAT.	INST.	TOTAL	MAT.	INST.	TOTAL	MAT.	INST.	TOTAL	MAT.	INST.	TOTAL
015433	CONTRACTOR EQUIPMENT		118.0	118.0		99.0	99.0		99.0	99.0		101.6	101.6		99.7	99.7		100.9	100.9
0241, 31 - 34	SITE & INFRASTRUCTURE, DEMOLITION	118.6	107.9	111.6	105.9	90.6	95.9	106.5	90.6	96.1	127.3	93.6	105.3	124.2	93.9	104.4	106.6	96.8	100.2
0310	Concrete Forming & Accessories	118.8	89.0	95.7	117.3	74.6	84.1	117.3	74.7	84.2	105.7	77.5	83.8	110.0	77.7	84.9	103.5	84.7	88.9
0320	Concrete Reinforcing	73.8	96.8	80.2	76.2	67.7	73.8	72.3	67.7	71.0	56.4	70.9	60.4	84.1	79.7	82.9	50.7	96.6	63.4
0330	Cast-in-Place Concrete	151.6	100.5	133.5	118.6	82.9	105.9	123.5	82.9	109.1	106.9	86.8	99.8	134.0	87.7	117.6	141.2	93.6	124.3
03	CONCRETE	136.1	95.2	119.9	120.2	77.1	103.2	121.3	77.1	103.8	133.6	80.3	112.6	130.4	82.2	111.4	108.7	90.3	101.5
04	MASONRY	183.4	96.7	130.7	167.4	71.6	109.2	167.8	71.6	109.4	174.2	78.8	116.3	177.7	80.4	118.6	152.4	94.2	117.1
05	METALS	153.6	105.3	144.1	125.7	83.7	117.4	125.7	83.8	117.4	129.2	85.7	120.6	130.3	88.8	122.1	145.0	97.4	135.6
06	WOOD, PLASTICS & COMPOSITES	104.0	87.7	96.7	125.8	74.8	102.9	125.8	74.8	102.9	95.1	76.3	86.7	112.2	77.2	96.5	95.5	83.0	89.9
07	THERMAL & MOISTURE PROTECTION	146.8	97.7	129.3	120.9	78.4	105.7	120.9	78.4	105.7	136.7	76.1	115.1	126.4	81.3	110.3	127.2	93.8	115.3
08	OPENINGS	87.4	87.1	87.3	89.6	64.2	83.9	89.6	68.3	84.8	86.9	74.1	84.0	89.6	75.8	86.5	78.4	83.0	79.4
0920	Plaster & Gypsum Board	125.1	86.5	100.6	121.2	74.0	91.2	146.5	74.0	100.5	99.4	75.3	84.1	174.4	76.7	112.5	108.2	82.6	91.9
0950, 0980	Ceilings & Acoustic Treatment	106.9	86.5	95.5	78.3	74.0	75.9	78.3	74.0	75.9	78.3	75.3	76.6	91.9	76.7	83.4	82.5	82.6	82.5
0960	Flooring	121.0	87.1	112.5	107.9	80.2	100.9	107.9	80.2	100.9	108.5	45.9	92.8	107.9	80.3	101.0	95.2	87.2	93.2
0970, 0990	Wall Finishes & Painting/Coating	110.4	97.6	102.7	110.9	77.4	90.9	110.9	77.4	90.9	110.9	70.8	87.0	110.9	73.3	88.5	105.3	88.3	95.2
09	FINISHES	113.4	89.3	101.3	99.2	76.3	87.7	102.6	76.3	89.4	98.5	71.2	84.8	110.5	77.9	94.1	93.0	85.0	89.0
COVERS	DIVS. 10 - 14, 25, 28, 41, 43, 44, 46	131.1	85.8	122.4	131.1	70.4	119.4	131.1	70.4	119.4	131.1	78.5	120.9	131.1	60.2	117.4	131.1	82.8	121.8
21, 22, 23	FIRE SUPPRESSION, PLUMBING & HVAC	109.9	88.5	102.2	110.5	78.8	99.1	110.5	78.9	99.1	110.5	82.0	100.2	110.2	88.4	102.4	109.1	88.1	101.6
26, 27, 3370	ELECTRICAL, COMMUNICATIONS & UTIL.	135.2	98.2	119.2	134.0	60.5	102.1	130.9	60.5	100.4	136.4	68.8	107.1	132.4	76.2	108.1	136.2	96.1	118.8
MF2018	WEIGHTED AVERAGE	129.4	94.9	116.7	119.0	75.4	103.0	119.1	75.6	103.1	122.4	78.8	106.3	122.7	82.4	107.9	119.8	91.0	109.2

DIVISION		CANADA																	
		LAVAL, QUEBEC			LETHBRIDGE, ALBERTA			LLOYDMINSTER, ALBERTA			LONDON, ONTARIO			MEDICINE HAT, ALBERTA			MONCTON, NEW BRUNSWICK		
		MAT.	INST.	TOTAL	MAT.	INST.	TOTAL	MAT.	INST.	TOTAL	MAT.	INST.	TOTAL	MAT.	INST.	TOTAL	MAT.	INST.	TOTAL
015433	CONTRACTOR EQUIPMENT		99.0	99.0		99.4	99.4		99.4	99.4		118.6	118.6		99.4	99.4		98.6	98.6
0241, 31 - 34	SITE & INFRASTRUCTURE, DEMOLITION	106.4	90.6	96.1	122.7	92.0	102.7	122.4	91.5	102.2	120.2	107.4	111.8	121.3	91.5	101.9	116.0	90.0	99.1
0310	Concrete Forming & Accessories	117.5	75.2	84.6	111.3	82.3	88.8	109.6	73.6	81.6	119.2	85.3	92.9	111.3	73.6	82.0	91.1	61.7	68.3
0320	Concrete Reinforcing	76.2	68.4	74.0	78.2	74.8	77.2	78.2	74.7	77.2	73.4	95.7	79.6	78.2	74.7	77.2	70.2	65.4	68.8
0330	Cast-in-Place Concrete	122.5	83.5	108.7	148.4	87.4	126.7	137.7	84.1	118.6	151.7	98.7	132.9	137.7	84.1	118.6	111.3	65.4	95.0
03	CONCRETE	121.9	77.7	104.4	132.6	83.4	113.1	128.0	78.3	108.4	136.1	92.7	119.0	128.1	78.2	108.4	102.3	64.9	87.6
04	MASONRY	167.8	72.3	109.8	186.0	78.8	120.9	167.7	73.0	110.2	190.8	95.1	132.7	167.6	73.0	110.1	156.2	71.3	104.6
05	METALS	125.5	84.0	117.3	149.9	87.9	137.6	129.1	87.7	120.9	152.0	105.9	142.9	129.3	87.7	121.1	128.6	85.8	120.1
06	WOOD, PLASTICS & COMPOSITES	125.8	75.4	103.2	111.4	81.9	98.2	107.8	73.2	92.3	104.0	83.3	94.7	111.4	73.2	94.3	91.3	59.2	76.9
07	THERMAL & MOISTURE PROTECTION	122.5	78.8	106.9	132.8	84.4	115.6	129.7	80.4	112.1	147.1	95.4	128.7	135.2	80.4	115.6	121.9	68.1	102.7
08	OPENINGS	89.6	64.8	84.0	89.6	74.2	86.1	89.6	69.4	85.0	88.0	83.7	87.0	89.6	69.4	85.0	84.8	56.9	78.5
0920	Plaster & Gypsum Board	121.2	74.7	91.7	108.8	81.3	91.3	103.8	72.3	83.8	125.1	82.0	97.8	106.7	72.3	84.9	119.8	58.0	80.6
0950, 0980	Ceilings & Acoustic Treatment	78.3	74.7	76.3	85.1	81.3	83.0	78.3	72.3	74.9	106.9	82.0	92.9	78.3	72.3	74.9	91.7	58.0	72.8
0960	Flooring	107.9	81.1	101.1	107.9	77.8	100.3	107.9	77.8	100.3	100.9	87.2	97.5	107.9	77.8	100.3	95.7	60.5	86.9
0970, 0990	Wall Finishes & Painting/Coating	110.9	78.1	91.3	110.8	89.3	98.0	111.0	69.5	86.3	113.0	94.6	102.0	110.8	69.5	86.2	112.3	74.2	89.6
09	FINISHES	99.2	76.9	88.0	100.2	82.5	91.3	97.8	73.8	85.8	107.7	86.2	96.9	98.1	73.8	85.9	98.0	62.3	80.0
COVERS	DIVS. 10 - 14, 25, 28, 41, 43, 44, 46	131.1	71.0	119.5	131.1	81.8	121.6	131.1	80.1	121.3	131.1	85.0	122.2	131.1	79.0	121.0	131.1	57.1	116.8
21, 22, 23	FIRE SUPPRESSION, PLUMBING & HVAC	109.3	79.6	98.7	110.7	84.2	101.2	110.2	84.2	100.9	109.9	86.6	101.5	110.5	81.2	100.0	110.6	75.3	97.9
26, 27, 3370	ELECTRICAL, COMMUNICATIONS & UTIL.	131.1	61.0	100.7	129.0	71.9	104.3	124.0	71.9	101.4	134.9	95.9	118.0	124.0	71.9	101.4	138.9	85.2	115.6
MF2018	WEIGHTED AVERAGE	118.7	75.9	103.0	126.7	82.0	110.3	120.0	79.1	104.9	128.9	93.0	115.7	120.3	78.4	104.9	117.1	73.6	101.1

DIVISION		CANADA																	
		MONTREAL, QUEBEC			MOOSE JAW, SASKATCHEWAN			NEW GLASGOW, NOVA SCOTIA			NEWCASTLE, NEW BRUNSWICK			NORTH BAY, ONTARIO			OSHAWA, ONTARIO		
		MAT.	INST.	TOTAL	MAT.	INST.	TOTAL	MAT.	INST.	TOTAL	MAT.	INST.	TOTAL	MAT.	INST.	TOTAL	MAT.	INST.	TOTAL
015433	CONTRACTOR EQUIPMENT		120.6	120.6		96.5	96.5		95.3	95.3		98.6	98.6		95.2	95.2		100.9	100.9
0241, 31 - 34	SITE & INFRASTRUCTURE, DEMOLITION	129.1	107.0	114.7	122.1	86.6	98.9	115.6	87.3	97.1	116.5	87.8	97.8	128.3	88.5	102.3	116.5	96.9	103.7
0310	Concrete Forming & Accessories	113.1	87.2	93.0	94.7	51.5	61.2	95.7	63.9	71.0	91.1	54.8	62.9	130.3	75.3	87.6	108.5	87.8	92.4
0320	Concrete Reinforcing	61.6	90.2	69.5	55.2	57.4	55.8	80.2	44.6	70.3	70.2	53.8	65.6	94.2	79.3	90.0	80.3	98.9	85.4
0330	Cast-in-Place Concrete	117.7	96.2	110.0	133.6	60.6	107.6	140.1	63.1	112.8	115.6	53.9	93.6	135.0	75.5	113.8	163.4	102.7	141.8
03	CONCRETE	111.2	91.7	103.5	111.6	56.9	90.0	146.7	61.4	113.0	104.1	55.5	84.9	148.7	76.7	120.3	132.2	95.3	117.6
04	MASONRY	173.4	86.1	120.4	165.8	52.9	97.2	214.9	61.5	121.7	156.6	53.9	94.2	221.5	76.8	133.6	156.4	97.4	120.6
05	METALS	164.9	101.5	152.4	124.2	73.9	114.3	140.6	73.7	127.4	128.6	73.2	117.6	141.9	87.2	131.1	134.1	98.6	127.1
06	WOOD, PLASTICS & COMPOSITES	99.5	87.8	94.3	92.2	50.4	73.4	102.1	63.7	84.9	91.3	54.8	74.9	138.3	75.8	110.3	102.7	86.4	95.4
07	THERMAL & MOISTURE PROTECTION	144.5	93.6	126.4	120.0	55.9	97.2	134.7	62.9	109.1	121.9	54.4	97.9	140.4	76.9	117.8	127.9	98.3	117.4
08	OPENINGS	88.6	75.6	85.6	86.1	48.5	77.6	92.5	57.8	84.7	84.8	48.4	76.6	98.4	73.8	92.9	82.5	86.4	83.4
0920	Plaster & Gypsum Board	122.8	86.6	99.8	97.6	49.0	66.8	124.7	62.8	85.4	119.8	53.5	77.8	122.4	75.3	92.6	112.7	86.1	95.9
0950, 0980	Ceilings & Acoustic Treatment	113.2	86.6	98.3	78.3	49.0	61.9	94.0	62.8	76.5	91.7	53.5	70.3	94.0	75.3	83.5	79.3	86.1	83.1
0960	Flooring	103.2	83.0	98.2	100.2	50.1	87.7	105.0	55.0	92.5	95.7	59.2	86.6	123.0	80.3	112.3	97.4	89.2	95.3
0970, 0990	Wall Finishes & Painting/Coating	119.3	98.3	106.8	110.9	56.5	78.5	117.9	54.9	80.4	112.3	44.4	71.8	117.9	78.7	94.6	105.3	101.3	102.9
09	FINISHES	110.2	88.5	99.3	94.6	51.5	73.0	106.6	61.6	84.0	98.0	54.8	76.3	112.3	76.9	94.6	93.8	89.1	91.5
COVERS	DIVS. 10 - 14, 25, 28, 41, 43, 44, 46	131.1	77.4	120.7	131.1	53.6	116.1	131.1	56.5	116.7	131.1	54.1	116.2	131.1	58.8	117.1	131.1	83.5	121.9
21, 22, 23	FIRE SUPPRESSION, PLUMBING & HVAC	109.2	77.6	97.9	110.2	65.9	94.3	117.2	74.4	101.9	110.6	60.7	92.7	117.2	86.5	106.2	109.1	84.4	100.3
26, 27, 3370	ELECTRICAL, COMMUNICATIONS & UTIL.	148.0	79.5	118.3	136.4	52.3	99.9	125.8	54.4	94.9	137.2	51.8	100.2	130.0	77.3	107.1	136.6	97.3	119.5
MF2018	WEIGHTED AVERAGE	129.7	87.0	114.0	117.3	60.4	96.3	129.1	66.1	105.9	117.2	59.6	96.0	132.0	80.1	112.9	121.1	92.4	110.6

DIVISION		CANADA																	
		OTTAWA, ONTARIO			OWEN SOUND, ONTARIO			PETERBOROUGH, ONTARIO			PORTAGE LA PRAIRIE, MANITOBA			PRINCE ALBERT, SASKATCHEWAN			PRINCE GEORGE, BRITISH COLUMBIA		
		MAT.	INST.	TOTAL	MAT.	INST.	TOTAL	MAT.	INST.	TOTAL	MAT.	INST.	TOTAL	MAT.	INST.	TOTAL	MAT.	INST.	TOTAL
015433	CONTRACTOR EQUIPMENT		120.2	120.2		97.9	97.9		97.8	97.8		99.8	99.8		96.5	96.5		101.6	101.6
0241, 31 - 34	SITE & INFRASTRUCTURE, DEMOLITION	119.6	108.0	112.0	122.1	90.7	101.6	126.1	90.5	102.9	123.0	89.5	101.2	118.6	86.7	97.8	130.6	93.6	106.5
0310	Concrete Forming & Accessories	113.1	89.6	94.8	124.9	74.2	85.5	112.0	76.4	84.3	111.5	62.0	73.0	94.7	51.4	61.0	100.4	73.1	79.2
0320	Concrete Reinforcing	65.6	95.7	73.9	151.8	81.2	132.3	84.1	79.8	82.9	78.2	51.0	70.7	57.6	57.4	57.6	56.4	70.9	60.4
0330	Cast-in-Place Concrete	137.9	101.9	125.1	165.1	72.6	132.2	149.0	77.4	123.6	137.7	66.2	112.3	121.0	60.5	99.5	134.0	86.9	117.3
03	CONCRETE	127.8	95.9	115.2	150.7	75.6	121.0	134.4	78.0	112.2	120.4	62.7	97.7	107.1	56.8	87.2	144.4	78.3	118.3
04	MASONRY	189.2	96.0	132.6	171.6	81.7	117.0	172.2	82.6	117.8	170.7	56.1	101.0	164.8	52.9	96.9	176.7	78.8	117.2
05	METALS	153.6	107.3	144.5	114.3	89.3	109.3	128.1	89.0	120.4	129.3	77.2	119.0	124.2	73.8	114.3	129.2	85.8	120.6
06	WOOD, PLASTICS & COMPOSITES	93.8	88.8	91.6	117.3	73.1	97.5	114.0	74.7	96.4	111.4	63.2	89.8	92.2	50.4	73.4	95.1	70.1	83.9
07	THERMAL & MOISTURE PROTECTION	147.2	97.2	129.4	113.9	77.7	101.0	126.8	82.0	110.8	120.7	63.5	100.3	119.9	54.9	96.8	131.8	75.4	111.7
08	OPENINGS	87.8	86.7	87.5	89.2	73.3	85.6	88.0	75.5	85.2	89.6	56.6	82.2	85.2	48.5	76.9	86.9	70.7	83.3
0920	Plaster & Gypsum Board	125.1	87.5	101.3	153.8	72.4	102.2	117.8	74.2	90.1	106.4	61.9	78.2	97.6	49.0	66.8	99.4	69.0	80.1
0950, 0980	Ceilings & Acoustic Treatment	106.9	87.5	96.1	92.9	72.4	81.4	78.3	74.2	76.0	78.3	61.9	69.1	78.3	49.0	61.9	78.3	69.0	73.1
0960	Flooring	100.9	83.1	96.4	120.7	81.5	110.9	107.9	80.3	101.0	107.9	57.8	95.3	100.2	50.1	87.7	104.3	62.9	94.0
0970, 0990	Wall Finishes & Painting/Coating	113.5	89.8	99.3	106.8	77.6	89.4	110.9	80.7	92.9	111.0	50.1	74.7	110.9	48.2	73.5	110.9	70.8	87.0
09	FINISHES	107.8	88.3	98.0	112.4	76.0	94.1	99.3	77.6	88.4	98.0	60.3	79.1	94.6	50.6	72.5	97.3	70.5	83.8
COVERS	DIVS. 10 - 14, 25, 28, 41, 43, 44, 46	131.1	84.1	122.0	139.3	59.5	123.8	131.1	60.4	117.4	131.1	55.8	116.5	131.1	53.6	116.1	131.1	77.8	120.8
21, 22, 23	FIRE SUPPRESSION, PLUMBING & HVAC	109.9	87.3	101.8	110.3	86.5	101.8	110.5	89.7	103.0	110.5	73.4	97.2	110.2	59.3	92.0	110.5	82.0	100.3
26, 27, 3370	ELECTRICAL, COMMUNICATIONS & UTIL.	135.2	96.5	118.5	127.1	76.2	105.1	134.6	76.9	109.6	135.7	50.5	98.8	136.4	52.3	99.9	134.2	68.8	105.9
MF2018	WEIGHTED AVERAGE	128.2	94.4	115.7	121.3	80.5	106.3	122.0	82.1	107.3	120.4	65.3	100.1	116.5	58.9	95.3	123.4	78.2	106.7

City Cost Indexes

	DIVISION	CANADA																	
		QUEBEC CITY, QUEBEC			RED DEER, ALBERTA			REGINA, SASKATCHEWAN			RIMOUSKI, QUEBEC			ROUYN-NORANDA, QUEBEC			SAINT HYACINTHE, QUEBEC		
		MAT.	INST.	TOTAL	MAT.	INST.	TOTAL	MAT.	INST.	TOTAL	MAT.	INST.	TOTAL	MAT.	INST.	TOTAL	MAT.	INST.	TOTAL
015433	CONTRACTOR EQUIPMENT		122.1	122.1		99.4	99.4		127.3	127.3		99.0	99.0		99.0	99.0		99.0	99.0
0241, 31 - 34	SITE & INFRASTRUCTURE, DEMOLITION	129.6	107.3	115.1	121.3	91.5	101.9	138.5	118.0	125.1	106.1	90.8	96.2	105.9	90.6	95.9	106.4	90.6	96.1
0310	Concrete Forming & Accessories	113.0	87.4	93.1	119.0	73.6	83.7	120.1	83.4	91.6	117.3	86.2	93.2	117.3	74.6	84.1	117.3	74.6	84.1
0320	Concrete Reinforcing	62.6	90.2	70.3	78.2	74.7	77.2	71.7	79.8	73.9	54.5	90.0	64.3	76.2	67.7	73.8	76.2	67.7	73.8
0330	Cast-in-Place Concrete	117.6	96.4	110.1	137.7	84.1	118.6	176.1	92.3	146.3	124.8	91.2	112.8	118.6	82.9	105.9	122.5	82.9	108.5
03	CONCRETE	111.5	92.0	103.8	128.8	78.2	108.8	180.3	86.9	143.5	117.2	89.0	106.0	120.2	77.1	103.2	121.9	77.1	104.2
04	MASONRY	183.9	86.1	124.5	167.6	73.0	110.1	220.1	78.6	134.1	166.8	85.9	117.7	167.4	71.6	109.2	167.7	71.6	109.3
05	METALS	164.9	103.3	152.8	129.3	87.7	121.1	153.7	98.3	142.8	125.2	91.4	118.5	125.7	83.7	117.4	125.7	83.7	117.4
06	WOOD, PLASTICS & COMPOSITES	100.2	87.8	94.7	111.4	73.2	94.3	122.3	83.9	105.1	125.8	86.9	108.4	125.8	74.8	102.9	125.8	74.8	102.9
07	THERMAL & MOISTURE PROTECTION	143.5	93.7	125.7	143.0	80.4	120.7	147.2	79.3	123.0	120.9	91.3	110.4	120.9	78.4	105.7	122.5	78.4	106.8
08	OPENINGS	89.5	82.4	87.9	89.6	69.4	85.0	93.0	72.8	88.4	89.1	73.3	85.6	89.6	64.2	83.9	89.6	64.2	83.9
0920	Plaster & Gypsum Board	118.5	86.6	98.2	106.7	72.3	84.9	134.9	82.6	101.7	146.4	86.6	108.4	121.0	74.0	91.2	121.0	74.0	91.2
0950, 0980	Ceilings & Acoustic Treatment	107.5	86.6	95.8	78.3	72.3	74.9	113.8	82.6	96.3	77.8	86.6	82.7	77.8	74.0	75.7	77.8	74.0	75.7
0960	Flooring	102.9	83.0	97.9	111.0	77.8	102.7	122.7	87.2	113.8	109.0	80.2	101.8	107.9	80.2	100.9	107.9	80.2	100.9
0970, 0990	Wall Finishes & Painting/Coating	120.3	98.3	107.2	110.8	69.5	86.2	113.5	79.1	93.0	114.1	98.3	104.7	110.9	77.4	90.9	110.9	77.4	90.9
09	FINISHES	108.1	88.5	98.3	99.0	73.8	86.4	118.4	84.4	101.3	103.0	87.4	95.1	99.0	76.3	87.6	99.0	76.3	87.6
COVERS	DIVS. 10 - 14, 25, 28, 41, 43, 44, 46	131.1	77.4	120.7	131.1	79.0	121.0	131.1	65.0	118.3	131.1	75.3	120.3	131.1	70.4	119.4	131.1	70.4	119.4
21, 22, 23	FIRE SUPPRESSION, PLUMBING & HVAC	108.9	77.6	97.7	110.5	81.2	100.0	109.8	78.2	98.5	110.5	77.3	98.6	110.5	78.8	99.1	106.2	78.8	96.4
26, 27, 3370	ELECTRICAL, COMMUNICATIONS & UTIL.	148.0	79.6	118.3	124.0	71.9	101.4	134.4	81.5	111.5	130.9	79.5	108.6	130.9	60.5	100.4	131.4	60.5	100.7
MF2018	WEIGHTED AVERAGE	130.0	87.5	114.4	120.7	78.4	105.1	137.5	85.1	118.2	118.5	84.0	105.8	118.7	75.4	102.8	118.1	75.4	102.4

	DIVISION	CANADA																	
		SAINT JOHN, NEW BRUNSWICK			SARNIA, ONTARIO			SASKATOON, SASKATCHEWAN			SAULT STE MARIE, ONTARIO			SHERBROOKE, QUEBEC			SOREL, QUEBEC		
		MAT.	INST.	TOTAL	MAT.	INST.	TOTAL	MAT.	INST.	TOTAL	MAT.	INST.	TOTAL	MAT.	INST.	TOTAL	MAT.	INST.	TOTAL
015433	CONTRACTOR EQUIPMENT		98.6	98.6		97.8	97.8		96.1	96.1		97.8	97.8		99.0	99.0		99.0	99.0
0241, 31 - 34	SITE & INFRASTRUCTURE, DEMOLITION	116.6	90.0	99.3	124.6	90.6	102.4	119.3	89.4	99.8	115.2	90.2	98.9	106.5	90.6	96.1	106.5	90.6	96.1
0310	Concrete Forming & Accessories	109.8	65.7	75.5	110.7	82.6	88.9	94.6	82.3	85.0	100.2	82.6	86.5	117.3	74.6	84.1	117.3	74.7	84.2
0320	Concrete Reinforcing	70.2	65.4	68.8	61.2	81.1	66.7	60.1	79.6	65.5	54.0	80.1	61.2	76.2	67.7	73.8	72.3	67.7	71.0
0330	Cast-in-Place Concrete	113.9	65.4	96.6	137.5	89.0	120.3	132.9	86.1	116.3	123.5	76.3	106.7	122.5	82.9	108.5	123.5	82.9	109.1
03	CONCRETE	105.1	66.7	90.0	123.6	85.1	108.4	121.5	83.6	106.5	107.6	80.6	97.0	121.9	77.1	104.2	121.3	77.1	103.8
04	MASONRY	175.6	71.3	112.2	183.2	85.0	123.5	180.4	78.3	118.4	167.9	87.8	119.3	167.8	71.6	109.4	167.8	71.6	109.4
05	METALS	128.5	85.8	120.0	128.1	89.3	120.4	120.4	86.6	113.7	127.3	92.9	120.5	125.4	83.7	117.2	125.7	83.8	117.4
06	WOOD, PLASTICS & COMPOSITES	114.4	64.6	92.1	113.0	82.0	99.1	94.7	82.9	89.4	99.7	84.7	93.0	125.8	74.8	102.9	125.8	74.8	102.9
07	THERMAL & MOISTURE PROTECTION	122.3	68.3	103.1	126.8	85.2	112.0	122.2	76.0	105.8	125.8	82.4	110.4	120.7	78.4	105.6	120.9	78.4	105.7
08	OPENINGS	84.8	58.9	78.9	91.1	78.9	88.3	88.3	72.2	84.6	83.1	81.9	82.8	89.6	64.2	83.9	89.6	68.3	84.8
0920	Plaster & Gypsum Board	138.8	63.6	91.1	140.0	81.6	103.0	115.1	82.6	94.5	107.6	84.5	92.9	121.0	74.0	91.2	146.4	74.0	100.5
0950, 0980	Ceilings & Acoustic Treatment	95.4	63.6	77.6	82.8	81.6	82.2	92.9	82.6	87.1	78.3	84.5	81.7	77.8	74.0	75.7	77.8	74.0	75.7
0960	Flooring	104.7	60.5	93.6	107.9	87.8	102.8	106.5	87.2	101.7	102.4	84.9	98.1	107.9	80.2	100.9	107.9	80.2	100.9
0970, 0990	Wall Finishes & Painting/Coating	112.3	74.2	89.6	110.9	91.2	99.2	114.6	79.1	93.4	110.9	84.6	95.2	110.9	77.4	90.9	110.9	77.4	90.9
09	FINISHES	104.2	65.4	84.7	103.5	84.8	94.1	105.1	83.6	94.3	95.7	83.7	89.7	99.0	76.3	87.6	102.4	76.3	89.3
COVERS	DIVS. 10 - 14, 25, 28, 41, 43, 44, 46	131.1	58.0	117.0	131.1	61.6	117.7	131.1	63.0	117.9	131.1	80.8	121.4	131.1	70.4	119.4	131.1	70.4	119.4
21, 22, 23	FIRE SUPPRESSION, PLUMBING & HVAC	110.6	75.3	97.9	110.5	95.1	104.9	109.5	77.9	98.2	110.5	85.2	101.4	110.2	78.8	99.0	110.5	78.9	99.1
26, 27, 3370	ELECTRICAL, COMMUNICATIONS & UTIL.	140.2	85.2	116.4	141.8	78.8	114.5	135.8	81.4	112.2	138.6	77.3	112.0	130.8	60.5	100.4	130.9	60.5	100.4
MF2018	WEIGHTED AVERAGE	119.0	74.5	102.6	122.4	86.0	109.0	118.9	81.0	105.0	117.7	84.3	105.4	118.8	75.4	102.8	119.1	75.6	103.1

	DIVISION	CANADA																	
		ST CATHARINES, ONTARIO			ST JEROME, QUEBEC			ST JOHN'S, NEWFOUNDLAND			SUDBURY, ONTARIO			SUMMERSIDE, PRINCE EDWARD ISLAND			SYDNEY, NOVA SCOTIA		
		MAT.	INST.	TOTAL	MAT.	INST.	TOTAL	MAT.	INST.	TOTAL	MAT.	INST.	TOTAL	MAT.	INST.	TOTAL	MAT.	INST.	TOTAL
015433	CONTRACTOR EQUIPMENT		99.1	99.1		99.0	99.0		122.4	122.4		99.1	99.1		95.3	95.3		95.3	95.3
0241, 31 - 34	SITE & INFRASTRUCTURE, DEMOLITION	106.2	93.8	98.1	105.9	90.6	95.9	116.2	112.3	113.7	106.3	93.5	97.9	124.1	84.9	98.6	111.6	87.3	95.7
0310	Concrete Forming & Accessories	101.5	89.7	92.3	117.3	74.6	84.1	112.3	79.5	86.8	97.5	85.5	88.2	96.0	49.5	59.9	95.7	63.9	71.0
0320	Concrete Reinforcing	51.1	96.6	63.7	76.2	67.7	73.8	120.0	77.6	108.2	51.5	93.3	63.1	79.0	43.4	69.1	80.2	44.6	70.3
0330	Cast-in-Place Concrete	134.9	95.1	120.7	118.6	82.9	105.9	136.7	94.9	121.8	136.0	92.0	120.4	133.0	51.8	104.2	108.1	63.1	92.1
03	CONCRETE	106.0	93.1	101.0	120.2	77.1	103.2	141.0	85.7	119.1	106.3	89.6	99.7	157.6	50.5	115.3	133.5	61.4	105.0
04	MASONRY	151.8	96.4	118.1	167.4	71.6	109.2	195.1	85.1	128.3	151.8	93.2	116.2	213.9	51.5	115.3	212.0	61.5	120.6
05	METALS	134.0	97.4	126.8	125.7	83.7	117.4	142.4	96.0	133.2	133.5	96.2	126.1	140.6	67.5	126.2	140.6	73.7	127.4
06	WOOD, PLASTICS & COMPOSITES	93.1	89.3	91.4	125.8	74.8	102.9	102.0	77.6	91.0	88.8	84.8	87.0	102.7	49.1	78.7	102.1	63.7	84.9
07	THERMAL & MOISTURE PROTECTION	127.2	96.7	116.4	120.9	78.4	105.7	146.2	88.8	125.7	125.3	92.2	113.5	134.2	53.2	105.3	134.7	62.9	109.1
08	OPENINGS	77.7	86.8	79.8	89.6	64.2	83.9	91.7	69.4	86.7	78.3	82.3	79.2	102.2	42.9	88.8	92.5	57.8	84.7
0920	Plaster & Gypsum Board	102.6	89.1	94.0	121.0	74.0	91.2	146.5	76.1	101.8	100.7	84.5	90.4	125.9	47.7	76.3	124.7	62.8	85.4
0950, 0980	Ceilings & Acoustic Treatment	79.3	89.1	84.8	77.8	74.0	75.7	111.3	76.1	91.6	75.2	84.5	80.4	94.0	47.7	68.1	94.0	62.8	76.5
0960	Flooring	94.3	84.3	91.8	107.9	80.2	100.9	119.5	47.9	101.6	92.9	84.9	90.9	105.0	51.6	91.6	105.0	55.0	92.5
0970, 0990	Wall Finishes & Painting/Coating	105.3	97.6	100.7	110.9	77.4	90.9	115.3	91.6	101.2	105.3	89.2	95.7	117.9	36.9	69.6	117.9	54.9	80.4
09	FINISHES	91.1	89.6	90.3	99.0	76.3	87.6	116.8	74.7	95.7	89.3	85.5	87.4	107.6	48.8	78.1	106.6	61.6	84.0
COVERS	DIVS. 10 - 14, 25, 28, 41, 43, 44, 46	131.1	64.7	118.3	131.1	70.4	119.4	131.1	63.4	118.0	131.1	82.7	121.8	131.1	53.0	116.0	131.1	56.5	116.7
21, 22, 23	FIRE SUPPRESSION, PLUMBING & HVAC	109.1	87.3	101.3	110.5	78.8	99.1	109.6	78.1	98.3	109.3	85.4	100.8	117.2	55.1	95.0	117.2	74.4	101.9
26, 27, 3370	ELECTRICAL, COMMUNICATIONS & UTIL.	140.3	96.8	121.4	132.4	60.5	101.2	150.1	72.4	116.5	135.9	96.9	119.0	123.6	44.0	89.1	125.8	54.4	94.9
MF2018	WEIGHTED AVERAGE	117.3	91.6	107.8	118.9	75.4	102.9	130.0	82.4	112.5	116.6	90.0	106.8	131.2	54.5	103.0	127.3	66.1	104.8

DIVISION		CANADA																	
		THUNDER BAY, ONTARIO			TIMMINS, ONTARIO			TORONTO, ONTARIO			TROIS RIVIERES, QUEBEC			TRURO, NOVA SCOTIA			VANCOUVER, BRITISH COLUMBIA		
		MAT.	INST.	TOTAL	MAT.	INST.	TOTAL	MAT.	INST.	TOTAL	MAT.	INST.	TOTAL	MAT.	INST.	TOTAL	MAT.	INST.	TOTAL
015433	**CONTRACTOR EQUIPMENT**		99.1	99.1		97.8	97.8		118.9	118.9		96.2	96.2		98.1	98.1		135.4	135.4
0241, 31 - 34	**SITE & INFRASTRUCTURE, DEMOLITION**	110.9	93.6	99.6	126.1	90.2	102.7	117.7	108.1	111.4	111.6	88.7	96.6	110.8	89.1	96.7	122.0	122.1	122.1
0310	Concrete Forming & Accessories	108.5	87.7	92.3	112.0	75.4	83.6	112.7	98.6	101.8	137.2	74.5	88.5	84.9	64.1	68.7	118.1	85.6	92.8
0320	Concrete Reinforcing	45.7	96.2	59.7	84.1	79.3	82.8	65.5	99.2	74.8	80.2	67.7	76.7	72.3	44.6	64.6	71.9	89.3	76.7
0330	Cast-in-Place Concrete	148.5	94.5	129.3	149.0	76.0	123.1	137.8	111.6	128.5	111.9	82.3	101.4	154.8	63.7	122.4	142.1	96.9	126.1
03	**CONCRETE**	114.2	91.9	105.4	134.4	77.0	111.8	127.7	103.9	118.3	136.1	76.8	112.7	133.2	61.8	105.0	135.7	91.5	118.3
04	**MASONRY**	152.6	94.7	117.4	172.2	76.9	114.3	185.6	104.2	136.2	216.0	71.6	128.3	167.6	61.5	103.1	183.7	89.2	126.3
05	**METALS**	134.0	96.5	126.6	128.1	88.5	120.3	149.5	108.4	141.4	139.3	82.3	128.1	126.9	75.2	116.7	151.5	108.9	143.1
06	**WOOD, PLASTICS & COMPOSITES**	102.7	87.1	95.7	114.0	75.9	96.9	93.8	97.0	95.2	152.2	74.6	117.4	82.0	63.8	73.9	120.1	84.7	104.2
07	**THERMAL & MOISTURE PROTECTION**	127.5	93.7	115.4	126.8	77.0	109.0	147.1	105.5	132.3	133.8	78.2	114.0	121.7	63.0	100.8	147.4	87.4	126.0
08	**OPENINGS**	77.1	85.1	78.9	88.0	73.9	84.8	87.1	94.6	88.7	100.3	68.2	93.1	83.7	57.9	77.9	93.1	82.6	90.8
0920	Plaster & Gypsum Board	127.3	86.9	101.7	117.8	75.3	90.9	126.9	96.1	107.4	150.6	74.0	102.0	114.7	62.8	81.8	133.3	83.1	101.4
0950, 0980	Ceilings & Acoustic Treatment	75.2	86.9	81.8	78.3	75.3	76.6	113.8	96.1	103.9	92.6	74.0	82.2	78.3	62.8	69.6	113.8	83.1	96.6
0960	Flooring	97.4	90.3	95.6	107.9	80.3	101.0	120.8	92.5	113.7	123.0	80.2	112.3	94.1	55.0	84.3	112.5	81.2	104.7
0970, 0990	Wall Finishes & Painting/Coating	105.3	90.1	96.3	110.9	78.7	91.7	109.7	101.3	104.7	117.9	77.4	93.8	110.9	54.9	77.5	109.2	91.8	98.8
09	**FINISHES**	94.5	88.3	91.4	99.3	77.0	88.1	115.3	97.7	106.5	115.1	76.2	95.5	94.3	61.7	77.9	114.5	85.2	99.8
COVERS	**DIVS. 10 - 14, 25, 28, 41, 43, 44, 46**	131.1	64.2	118.2	131.1	59.1	117.2	131.1	88.7	122.9	131.1	70.1	119.3	131.1	56.8	116.7	131.1	83.6	121.9
21, 22, 23	**FIRE SUPPRESSION, PLUMBING & HVAC**	109.1	86.5	101.0	110.5	86.5	101.9	109.9	97.6	105.5	117.2	78.8	103.4	110.5	74.5	97.6	109.9	84.1	100.6
26, 27, 3370	**ELECTRICAL, COMMUNICATIONS & UTIL.**	136.2	96.0	118.8	138.6	77.3	112.0	134.9	98.4	119.1	126.5	60.5	97.9	130.0	54.4	97.3	135.1	75.4	109.3
MF2018	**WEIGHTED AVERAGE**	118.2	90.6	108.1	122.4	80.4	106.9	127.5	100.9	117.7	129.3	75.2	109.4	119.3	66.5	99.9	129.7	89.8	115.0

DIVISION		CANADA																	
		VICTORIA, BRITISH COLUMBIA			WHITEHORSE, YUKON			WINDSOR, ONTARIO			WINNIPEG, MANITOBA			YARMOUTH, NOVA SCOTIA			YELLOWKNIFE, NWT		
		MAT.	INST.	TOTAL	MAT.	INST.	TOTAL	MAT.	INST.	TOTAL	MAT.	INST.	TOTAL	MAT.	INST.	TOTAL	MAT.	INST.	TOTAL
015433	**CONTRACTOR EQUIPMENT**		103.8	103.8		130.8	130.8		99.1	99.1		125.6	125.6		95.3	95.3		123.8	123.8
0241, 31 - 34	**SITE & INFRASTRUCTURE, DEMOLITION**	129.7	97.9	109.0	134.3	117.0	123.0	103.6	93.8	97.2	125.5	114.3	118.2	115.4	87.3	97.1	147.3	113.1	125.0
0310	Concrete Forming & Accessories	100.0	82.7	86.6	115.3	53.7	67.5	108.6	86.1	91.1	112.6	60.9	72.5	95.7	63.9	71.0	121.5	71.7	82.8
0320	Concrete Reinforcing	58.8	89.1	67.2	84.8	59.2	77.7	50.1	95.5	62.6	69.0	56.1	65.4	80.2	44.6	70.3	74.7	61.6	71.0
0330	Cast-in-Place Concrete	137.7	91.2	121.2	178.6	69.2	139.8	138.2	96.0	123.2	172.0	69.3	135.5	138.7	63.1	111.8	199.5	84.5	158.6
03	**CONCRETE**	163.9	87.2	133.6	178.8	62.0	132.7	107.7	91.6	101.4	149.4	64.6	115.9	146.1	61.4	112.7	171.7	75.7	133.8
04	**MASONRY**	183.3	89.0	126.0	260.7	54.6	135.5	152.0	95.7	117.8	211.8	60.3	119.7	214.7	61.5	121.7	246.4	64.8	136.1
05	**METALS**	122.9	92.0	116.8	152.6	87.3	139.7	134.0	96.9	126.7	153.3	85.3	139.9	140.6	73.7	127.4	154.5	89.1	141.6
06	**WOOD, PLASTICS & COMPOSITES**	99.0	82.0	91.4	110.2	52.6	84.4	102.7	84.6	94.6	109.9	61.7	88.3	102.1	63.7	84.9	117.1	73.1	97.4
07	**THERMAL & MOISTURE PROTECTION**	132.4	82.7	114.7	150.0	60.6	118.1	127.3	94.0	115.4	147.6	65.9	118.5	134.7	62.9	109.1	152.0	75.0	124.6
08	**OPENINGS**	89.6	77.4	86.8	103.1	50.2	91.2	77.0	84.1	78.6	94.0	55.6	85.3	92.5	57.8	84.7	94.6	62.1	87.2
0920	Plaster & Gypsum Board	108.3	81.2	91.1	159.5	50.1	90.1	113.0	84.3	94.8	134.9	59.6	87.1	124.7	62.8	85.4	162.8	71.3	104.8
0950, 0980	Ceilings & Acoustic Treatment	78.0	81.2	79.8	131.2	50.1	85.7	75.2	84.3	80.3	113.8	59.6	83.4	94.0	62.8	76.5	129.0	71.3	96.7
0960	Flooring	110.7	62.9	98.7	125.5	51.5	107.0	97.4	87.9	95.0	140.4	62.8	120.9	105.0	55.0	92.5	120.8	77.4	109.9
0970, 0990	Wall Finishes & Painting/Coating	114.6	91.8	101.0	121.1	49.2	78.2	105.3	91.0	96.8	109.4	48.6	73.2	117.9	54.9	80.4	125.1	70.4	92.4
09	**FINISHES**	102.7	80.2	91.4	135.5	52.6	93.9	92.3	86.7	89.5	123.2	60.3	91.6	106.6	61.6	84.0	132.6	72.1	102.2
COVERS	**DIVS. 10 - 14, 25, 28, 41, 43, 44, 46**	131.1	60.8	117.5	131.1	56.9	116.8	131.1	64.2	118.2	131.1	59.1	117.2	131.1	56.5	116.7	131.1	59.9	117.3
21, 22, 23	**FIRE SUPPRESSION, PLUMBING & HVAC**	111.1	81.7	100.6	117.7	67.1	99.6	109.1	88.0	101.6	110.0	59.5	91.9	117.2	74.4	101.9	118.2	83.0	105.6
26, 27, 3370	**ELECTRICAL, COMMUNICATIONS & UTIL.**	133.4	76.1	108.6	166.0	53.0	117.0	147.7	96.7	125.6	135.2	58.1	101.8	125.8	54.4	94.9	157.1	71.9	120.2
MF2018	**WEIGHTED AVERAGE**	125.3	83.6	110.0	145.7	65.7	116.3	118.3	90.8	108.2	133.5	66.9	109.0	129.0	66.1	105.9	143.4	78.2	119.4

Location Factors - Commercial

Costs shown in RSMeans cost data publications are based on national averages for materials and installation. To adjust these costs to a specific location, simply multiply the base cost by the factor and divide by 100 for that city. The data is arranged alphabetically by state and postal zip code numbers. For a city not listed, use the factor for a nearby city with similar economic characteristics.

STATE/ZIP	CITY	MAT.	INST.	TOTAL
ALABAMA				
350-352	Birmingham	100.6	70.5	89.5
354	Tuscaloosa	99.3	69.6	88.4
355	Jasper	100.6	67.2	88.3
356	Decatur	99.3	66.7	87.3
357-358	Huntsville	99.3	71.6	89.1
359	Gadsden	100.2	69.5	88.9
360-361	Montgomery	99.8	70.6	89.0
362	Anniston	99.2	64.0	86.3
363	Dothan	97.8	71.5	88.1
364	Evergreen	97.3	65.0	85.4
365-366	Mobile	99.4	67.8	87.8
367	Selma	97.5	68.3	86.7
368	Phenix City	98.0	67.8	86.9
369	Butler	97.5	66.7	86.2
ALASKA				
995-996	Anchorage	116.6	109.2	113.9
997	Fairbanks	116.2	109.6	113.8
998	Juneau	116.1	109.2	113.5
999	Ketchikan	124.5	109.8	119.1
ARIZONA				
850,853	Phoenix	100.4	73.7	90.6
851,852	Mesa/Tempe	97.1	71.5	87.7
855	Globe	96.3	70.2	86.7
856-857	Tucson	95.9	72.1	87.1
859	Show Low	96.6	70.3	86.9
860	Flagstaff	100.3	71.7	89.8
863	Prescott	98.4	70.9	88.3
864	Kingman	96.2	69.8	86.5
865	Chambers	96.2	70.2	86.6
ARKANSAS				
716	Pine Bluff	98.5	61.8	85.0
717	Camden	95.9	61.2	83.1
718	Texarkana	96.7	62.3	84.1
719	Hot Springs	95.1	60.6	82.4
720-722	Little Rock	97.4	63.4	84.9
723	West Memphis	94.0	65.3	83.4
724	Jonesboro	95.4	64.2	83.9
725	Batesville	92.6	60.4	80.7
726	Harrison	93.9	59.6	81.3
727	Fayetteville	91.9	61.4	80.6
728	Russellville	92.9	59.5	80.6
729	Fort Smith	96.4	61.1	83.4
CALIFORNIA				
900-902	Los Angeles	102.9	130.2	112.9
903-905	Inglewood	94.6	128.5	107.0
906-908	Long Beach	96.1	128.5	108.0
910-912	Pasadena	96.8	128.2	108.4
913-916	Van Nuys	99.5	128.2	110.1
917-918	Alhambra	100.4	128.2	110.6
919-921	San Diego	103.7	123.3	110.9
922	Palm Springs	97.1	125.9	107.7
923-924	San Bernardino	94.8	125.2	106.0
925	Riverside	99.6	126.0	109.3
926-927	Santa Ana	96.6	125.8	107.4
928	Anaheim	99.9	125.8	109.4
930	Oxnard	100.6	124.8	109.5
931	Santa Barbara	100.0	124.3	108.9
932-933	Bakersfield	102.0	124.3	110.2
934	San Luis Obispo	100.5	124.5	109.3
935	Mojave	97.8	123.9	107.4
936-938	Fresno	100.7	129.9	111.4
939	Salinas	101.3	137.9	114.7
940-941	San Francisco	105.4	160.2	125.6
942,956-958	Sacramento	97.6	132.2	110.3
943	Palo Alto	95.8	153.9	117.2
944	San Mateo	97.7	152.4	117.9
945	Vallejo	98.1	140.9	113.8
946	Oakland	100.5	151.3	119.2
947	Berkeley	99.5	151.3	118.6
948	Richmond	98.5	145.5	115.8
949	San Rafael	100.4	148.3	118.1
950	Santa Cruz	104.7	138.0	117.0

STATE/ZIP	CITY	MAT.	INST.	TOTAL
CALIFORNIA (CONT'D)				
951	San Jose	102.2	153.9	121.3
952	Stockton	100.5	131.6	111.9
953	Modesto	100.3	130.8	111.5
954	Santa Rosa	100.0	145.9	116.9
955	Eureka	101.7	134.0	113.6
959	Marysville	101.1	131.6	112.3
960	Redding	103.9	131.4	114.0
961	Susanville	102.0	132.1	113.1
COLORADO				
800-802	Denver	102.2	75.1	92.3
803	Boulder	94.9	76.0	87.9
804	Golden	96.4	71.2	87.1
805	Fort Collins	98.5	73.7	89.4
806	Greeley	96.4	73.7	88.0
807	Fort Morgan	95.3	71.3	86.5
808-809	Colorado Springs	98.2	70.9	88.1
810	Pueblo	99.8	70.4	89.0
811	Alamosa	99.5	69.1	88.3
812	Salida	99.1	69.5	88.2
813	Durango	99.9	65.5	87.3
814	Montrose	98.5	65.7	86.5
815	Grand Junction	102.6	70.5	90.8
816	Glenwood Springs	99.5	65.9	87.1
CONNECTICUT				
060	New Britain	98.0	114.9	104.2
061	Hartford	100.3	115.8	106.0
062	Willimantic	98.8	113.6	104.3
063	New London	94.4	113.4	101.4
064	Meriden	96.5	113.4	102.7
065	New Haven	99.4	114.5	104.9
066	Bridgeport	99.3	114.2	104.8
067	Waterbury	98.9	114.7	104.7
068	Norwalk	98.9	113.9	104.4
069	Stamford	99.0	114.3	104.6
D.C.				
200-205	Washington	102.2	88.6	97.2
DELAWARE				
197	Newark	100.1	107.3	102.8
198	Wilmington	101.7	107.8	103.9
199	Dover	101.7	107.3	103.7
FLORIDA				
320,322	Jacksonville	98.7	67.0	87.0
321	Daytona Beach	98.9	68.8	87.9
323	Tallahassee	100.2	67.5	88.2
324	Panama City	100.0	67.7	88.1
325	Pensacola	102.5	66.3	89.1
326,344	Gainesville	99.2	66.5	87.2
327-328,347	Orlando	101.7	67.5	89.1
329	Melbourne	101.6	71.6	90.6
330-332,340	Miami	100.2	69.1	88.8
333	Fort Lauderdale	98.9	67.0	87.1
334,349	West Palm Beach	97.3	61.6	84.2
335-336,346	Tampa	100.3	68.1	88.4
337	St. Petersburg	102.8	64.3	88.6
338	Lakeland	99.4	65.4	86.9
339,341	Fort Myers	98.6	66.0	86.6
342	Sarasota	100.4	63.9	87.0
GEORGIA				
300-303,399	Atlanta	99.8	75.6	90.9
304	Statesboro	97.1	68.5	86.5
305	Gainesville	95.3	61.2	82.8
306	Athens	94.8	60.7	82.2
307	Dalton	96.6	64.5	84.8
308-309	Augusta	96.1	71.8	87.2
310-312	Macon	96.2	72.8	87.6
313-314	Savannah	98.7	72.0	88.9
315	Waycross	97.1	65.8	85.6
316	Valdosta	97.7	70.7	87.8
317,398	Albany	98.0	71.6	88.3
318-319	Columbus	97.9	72.9	88.7

Location Factors - Commercial

STATE/ZIP	CITY	MAT.	INST.	TOTAL
HAWAII				
967	Hilo	111.8	113.3	112.3
968	Honolulu	116.5	114.1	115.6
STATES & POSS.				
969	Guam	134.9	60.4	107.5
IDAHO				
832	Pocatello	101.3	78.3	92.9
833	Twin Falls	101.4	76.5	92.2
834	Idaho Falls	99.8	78.5	92.0
835	Lewiston	104.8	83.3	96.9
836-837	Boise	100.3	80.3	93.0
838	Coeur d'Alene	103.8	84.3	96.6
ILLINOIS				
600-603	North Suburban	96.6	142.0	113.3
604	Joliet	96.4	142.3	113.3
605	South Suburban	96.6	142.3	113.4
606-608	Chicago	99.4	143.7	115.7
609	Kankakee	92.9	132.1	107.3
610-611	Rockford	96.0	128.6	108.0
612	Rock Island	93.3	99.9	95.7
613	La Salle	94.3	126.4	106.1
614	Galesburg	93.9	107.6	99.0
615-616	Peoria	96.9	108.8	101.3
617	Bloomington	93.4	107.8	98.7
618-619	Champaign	96.0	113.7	102.6
620-622	East St. Louis	95.9	108.2	100.5
623	Quincy	97.3	105.1	100.1
624	Effingham	96.2	103.0	98.7
625	Decatur	98.8	105.4	101.2
626-627	Springfield	99.8	106.8	102.4
628	Centralia	94.0	103.3	97.4
629	Carbondale	93.8	105.2	98.0
INDIANA				
460	Anderson	95.4	77.1	88.7
461-462	Indianapolis	99.0	84.2	93.5
463-464	Gary	96.7	99.9	97.9
465-466	South Bend	99.1	79.4	91.9
467-468	Fort Wayne	96.0	77.2	89.1
469	Kokomo	92.1	75.8	86.1
470	Lawrenceburg	91.3	74.3	85.1
471	New Albany	92.3	72.4	85.0
472	Columbus	94.6	75.5	87.6
473	Muncie	95.8	75.7	88.4
474	Bloomington	97.1	77.7	89.9
475	Washington	92.0	80.4	87.7
476-477	Evansville	94.7	83.1	90.4
478	Terre Haute	95.4	78.7	89.2
479	Lafayette	94.0	75.9	87.4
IOWA				
500-503,509	Des Moines	99.4	90.8	96.2
504	Mason City	95.4	67.7	85.2
505	Fort Dodge	95.5	67.4	85.1
506-507	Waterloo	98.3	74.3	89.5
508	Creston	96.0	76.8	88.9
510-511	Sioux City	98.0	76.4	90.1
512	Sibley	95.7	57.3	81.6
513	Spencer	96.9	57.1	82.3
514	Carroll	94.6	75.2	87.5
515	Council Bluffs	98.7	79.0	91.4
516	Shenandoah	95.5	74.8	87.9
520	Dubuque	97.1	76.4	89.5
521	Decorah	95.6	67.4	85.2
522-524	Cedar Rapids	98.4	82.0	92.4
525	Ottumwa	95.4	71.9	86.8
526	Burlington	94.9	76.9	88.3
527-528	Davenport	97.4	91.3	95.1
KANSAS				
660-662	Kansas City	97.9	98.0	98.0
664-666	Topeka	99.0	74.1	89.9
667	Fort Scott	95.0	70.2	85.9
668	Emporia	94.7	70.3	85.7
669	Belleville	96.0	65.7	84.9
670-672	Wichita	97.7	71.2	88.0
673	Independence	96.1	69.8	86.5
674	Salina	97.2	70.3	87.3
675	Hutchinson	92.7	66.3	83.0
676	Hays	95.5	66.9	84.9
677	Colby	96.2	68.1	85.9

STATE/ZIP	CITY	MAT.	INST.	TOTAL
KANSAS (CONT'D)				
678	Dodge City	98.2	71.1	88.2
679	Liberal	95.4	66.1	84.6
KENTUCKY				
400-402	Louisville	97.7	78.2	90.5
403-405	Lexington	96.2	75.2	88.5
406	Frankfort	98.2	74.8	89.6
407-409	Corbin	92.7	71.4	84.9
410	Covington	92.6	71.4	84.8
411-412	Ashland	91.5	81.8	87.9
413-414	Campton	92.9	72.6	85.4
415-416	Pikeville	93.3	77.8	87.6
417-418	Hazard	92.4	73.1	85.3
420	Paducah	90.1	75.8	84.9
421-422	Bowling Green	94.0	74.7	86.9
423	Owensboro	93.1	77.7	87.5
424	Henderson	90.2	74.6	84.5
425-426	Somerset	90.8	72.8	84.1
427	Elizabethtown	90.3	69.9	82.8
LOUISIANA				
700-701	New Orleans	98.3	69.5	87.7
703	Thibodaux	93.9	62.2	82.2
704	Hammond	92.0	60.8	80.5
705	Lafayette	94.6	63.0	83.0
706	Lake Charles	94.7	65.3	83.9
707-708	Baton Rouge	98.2	65.6	86.2
710-711	Shreveport	99.0	64.1	86.2
712	Monroe	96.9	61.7	83.9
713-714	Alexandria	97.0	61.8	84.1
MAINE				
039	Kittery	92.3	81.2	88.2
040-041	Portland	99.2	86.6	94.5
042	Lewiston	97.0	84.4	92.4
043	Augusta	100.7	82.4	94.0
044	Bangor	95.7	83.1	91.0
045	Bath	93.5	80.9	88.9
046	Machias	93.1	80.8	88.5
047	Houlton	93.2	80.7	88.6
048	Rockland	92.4	80.9	88.2
049	Waterville	93.4	80.8	88.7
MARYLAND				
206	Waldorf	96.3	81.1	90.7
207-208	College Park	95.6	82.1	90.6
209	Silver Spring	95.5	81.2	90.2
210-212	Baltimore	100.9	83.8	94.6
214	Annapolis	100.2	80.3	92.9
215	Cumberland	94.8	79.8	89.3
216	Easton	96.1	69.1	86.2
217	Hagerstown	96.3	84.3	91.9
218	Salisbury	96.7	62.0	83.9
219	Elkton	94.2	78.8	88.5
MASSACHUSETTS				
010-011	Springfield	97.9	104.6	100.4
012	Pittsfield	96.9	99.3	97.7
013	Greenfield	94.4	103.4	97.7
014	Fitchburg	92.7	106.7	97.9
015-016	Worcester	97.9	111.9	103.1
017	Framingham	92.4	115.5	100.9
018	Lowell	97.1	119.2	105.2
019	Lawrence	97.8	117.8	105.2
020-022, 024	Boston	100.3	133.3	112.5
023	Brockton	97.5	111.2	102.6
025	Buzzards Bay	91.1	107.8	97.2
026	Hyannis	94.1	110.4	100.1
027	New Bedford	97.0	109.8	101.7
MICHIGAN				
480,483	Royal Oak	93.5	91.9	92.9
481	Ann Arbor	96.2	96.4	96.3
482	Detroit	99.5	99.9	99.7
484-485	Flint	96.1	88.4	93.3
486	Saginaw	95.8	84.1	91.5
487	Bay City	95.8	82.2	90.8
488-489	Lansing	98.2	87.6	94.3
490	Battle Creek	95.7	77.0	88.8
491	Kalamazoo	95.8	79.4	89.8
492	Jackson	93.3	83.5	89.7
493,495	Grand Rapids	97.8	79.6	91.1
494	Muskegon	94.8	79.6	89.2

STATE/ZIP	CITY	MAT.	INST.	TOTAL
MICHIGAN (CONT'D)				
496	Traverse City	93.2	71.6	85.2
497	Gaylord	94.0	74.3	86.7
498-499	Iron Mountain	95.3	75.0	87.8
MINNESOTA				
550-551	Saint Paul	102.0	117.9	107.9
553-555	Minneapolis	100.9	118.4	107.4
556-558	Duluth	102.4	106.1	103.8
559	Rochester	99.9	104.7	101.7
560	Mankato	94.8	100.6	97.0
561	Windom	93.5	88.3	91.6
562	Willmar	93.4	103.8	97.2
563	St. Cloud	95.4	114.2	102.3
564	Brainerd	94.9	99.5	96.6
565	Detroit Lakes	96.3	90.2	94.1
566	Bemidji	95.8	93.7	95.0
567	Thief River Falls	95.6	91.8	94.2
MISSISSIPPI				
386	Clarksdale	96.2	51.3	79.7
387	Greenville	99.4	63.3	86.1
388	Tupelo	97.0	53.7	81.1
389	Greenwood	97.3	51.0	80.3
390-392	Jackson	98.7	67.8	87.3
393	Meridian	95.3	65.8	84.4
394	Laurel	95.7	53.7	80.2
395	Biloxi	97.1	64.0	84.9
396	McComb	94.2	51.3	78.4
397	Columbus	95.6	54.4	80.4
MISSOURI				
630-631	St. Louis	97.3	104.5	99.9
633	Bowling Green	92.4	87.5	90.6
634	Hannibal	91.5	84.0	88.8
635	Kirksville	93.8	79.5	88.5
636	Flat River	93.1	85.8	90.4
637	Cape Girardeau	94.0	85.9	91.0
638	Sikeston	92.0	80.0	87.6
639	Poplar Bluff	91.4	80.1	87.2
640-641	Kansas City	98.6	101.2	99.6
644-645	St. Joseph	95.1	89.3	93.0
646	Chillicothe	91.3	86.0	89.4
647	Harrisonville	90.8	92.2	91.3
648	Joplin	94.2	76.5	87.7
650-651	Jefferson City	96.5	91.3	94.6
652	Columbia	95.6	90.7	93.8
653	Sedalia	94.8	83.5	90.7
654-655	Rolla	93.1	91.8	92.6
656-658	Springfield	97.7	81.0	91.6
MONTANA				
590-591	Billings	102.5	77.4	93.3
592	Wolf Point	100.4	71.3	89.6
593	Miles City	98.7	71.3	88.6
594	Great Falls	103.4	74.1	92.6
595	Havre	99.5	69.4	88.4
596	Helena	101.9	71.3	90.6
597	Butte	101.6	71.1	90.4
598	Missoula	99.3	71.0	88.9
599	Kalispell	97.6	70.3	87.6
NEBRASKA				
680-681	Omaha	98.7	81.2	92.3
683-685	Lincoln	98.9	76.4	90.6
686	Columbus	93.8	73.9	86.5
687	Norfolk	95.2	70.8	86.2
688	Grand Island	96.1	76.9	89.0
689	Hastings	94.8	71.5	86.2
690	McCook	94.2	66.9	84.2
691	North Platte	95.4	72.1	86.8
692	Valentine	97.0	64.2	85.0
693	Alliance	96.8	67.0	85.9
NEVADA				
889-891	Las Vegas	103.7	106.4	104.7
893	Ely	101.1	83.6	94.7
894-895	Reno	101.7	81.6	94.3
897	Carson City	101.9	81.5	94.4
898	Elko	100.3	76.4	91.5
NEW HAMPSHIRE				
030	Nashua	99.0	91.8	96.3
031	Manchester	99.8	92.9	97.3

STATE/ZIP	CITY	MAT.	INST.	TOTAL
NEW HAMPSHIRE (CONT'D)				
032-033	Concord	99.3	91.9	96.5
034	Keene	93.8	82.1	89.5
035	Littleton	94.3	74.1	86.9
036	Charleston	93.4	81.5	89.0
037	Claremont	92.9	81.5	88.7
038	Portsmouth	95.4	89.6	93.3
NEW JERSEY				
070-071	Newark	100.4	134.5	112.9
072	Elizabeth	96.2	133.6	110.0
073	Jersey City	96.6	133.5	110.2
074-075	Paterson	97.5	133.7	110.8
076	Hackensack	94.7	133.5	109.0
077	Long Branch	94.5	131.4	108.1
078	Dover	94.9	133.7	109.1
079	Summit	95.1	132.7	108.9
080,083	Vineland	95.7	130.4	108.5
081	Camden	98.9	130.4	110.5
082,084	Atlantic City	96.5	130.3	108.9
085-086	Trenton	100.2	130.6	111.4
087	Point Pleasant	97.1	124.5	107.2
088-089	New Brunswick	97.7	132.9	110.7
NEW MEXICO				
870-872	Albuquerque	98.2	72.3	88.7
873	Gallup	97.4	72.3	88.1
874	Farmington	98.2	72.3	88.6
875	Santa Fe	99.8	72.8	89.9
877	Las Vegas	96.0	72.3	87.3
878	Socorro	95.9	72.3	87.2
879	Truth/Consequences	95.5	69.4	85.9
880	Las Cruces	95.8	70.0	86.3
881	Clovis	96.6	72.2	87.6
882	Roswell	98.6	72.3	88.9
883	Carrizozo	98.3	72.3	88.7
884	Tucumcari	97.0	72.2	87.9
NEW YORK				
100-102	New York	99.6	167.2	124.5
103	Staten Island	92.7	165.5	119.5
104	Bronx	91.8	165.6	119.0
105	Mount Vernon	90.3	140.7	108.9
106	White Plains	91.7	143.7	110.8
107	Yonkers	96.3	145.1	114.2
108	New Rochelle	90.9	135.5	107.3
109	Suffern	90.3	118.0	100.5
110	Queens	99.4	169.0	125.0
111	Long Island City	100.8	169.0	125.9
112	Brooklyn	101.4	168.1	126.0
113	Flushing	99.8	169.0	125.3
114	Jamaica	98.6	169.0	124.5
115,117,118	Hicksville	99.4	145.1	116.2
116	Far Rockaway	99.8	169.0	125.3
119	Riverhead	100.2	149.7	118.4
120-122	Albany	98.8	107.5	102.0
123	Schenectady	98.2	107.0	101.4
124	Kingston	99.3	121.3	107.4
125-126	Poughkeepsie	98.7	125.3	108.5
127	Monticello	98.3	122.0	107.0
128	Glens Falls	92.3	99.2	94.9
129	Plattsburgh	96.1	87.7	93.0
130-132	Syracuse	98.1	99.0	98.4
133-135	Utica	96.2	99.9	97.5
136	Watertown	97.5	95.9	96.9
137-139	Binghamton	97.5	97.8	97.6
140-142	Buffalo	102.4	105.4	103.5
143	Niagara Falls	96.5	98.0	97.1
144-146	Rochester	101.4	98.6	100.4
147	Jamestown	95.5	87.5	92.6
148-149	Elmira	95.6	98.2	96.5
NORTH CAROLINA				
270,272-274	Greensboro	100.4	64.5	87.2
271	Winston-Salem	100.0	64.5	87.0
275-276	Raleigh	99.4	64.8	86.7
277	Durham	102.5	64.5	88.5
278	Rocky Mount	96.4	64.0	84.5
279	Elizabeth City	97.2	65.0	85.4
280	Gastonia	98.9	68.2	87.6
281-282	Charlotte	99.3	71.1	88.9
283	Fayetteville	102.9	63.0	88.2
284	Wilmington	97.8	62.2	84.7
285	Kinston	95.4	62.8	83.4

Location Factors - Commercial

STATE/ZIP	CITY	MAT.	INST.	TOTAL
NORTH CAROLINA (CONT'D)				
286	Hickory	95.7	68.7	85.7
287-288	Asheville	98.0	63.8	85.4
289	Murphy	96.2	61.4	83.4
NORTH DAKOTA				
580-581	Fargo	100.7	75.3	91.3
582	Grand Forks	99.5	76.9	91.2
583	Devils Lake	98.6	73.8	89.5
584	Jamestown	98.5	73.0	89.2
585	Bismarck	101.4	82.9	94.6
586	Dickinson	98.7	72.6	89.1
587	Minot	99.5	72.9	89.7
588	Williston	97.8	76.0	89.8
OHIO				
430-432	Columbus	96.8	87.0	93.2
433	Marion	91.6	79.6	87.2
434-436	Toledo	95.2	90.0	93.3
437-438	Zanesville	92.0	79.0	87.2
439	Steubenville	92.4	83.1	89.0
440	Lorain	96.0	80.9	90.5
441	Cleveland	98.0	91.4	95.6
442-443	Akron	96.8	85.0	92.4
444-445	Youngstown	96.3	80.9	90.6
446-447	Canton	96.4	78.5	89.8
448-449	Mansfield	93.3	78.4	87.8
450	Hamilton	94.4	73.1	86.6
451-452	Cincinnati	96.9	79.3	90.4
453-454	Dayton	94.5	78.6	88.6
455	Springfield	94.5	78.2	88.5
456	Chillicothe	92.5	81.0	88.3
457	Athens	95.5	83.1	90.9
458	Lima	95.3	75.6	88.1
OKLAHOMA				
730-731	Oklahoma City	97.4	67.9	86.5
734	Ardmore	94.3	64.4	83.3
735	Lawton	97.9	65.9	86.1
736	Clinton	95.3	64.3	83.9
737	Enid	96.9	65.0	85.2
738	Woodward	94.3	65.7	83.8
739	Guymon	95.2	59.2	82.0
740-741	Tulsa	96.0	64.4	84.4
743	Miami	91.5	62.1	80.7
744	Muskogee	94.8	65.9	84.2
745	McAlester	91.2	63.7	81.1
746	Ponca City	91.8	59.8	80.0
747	Durant	91.7	60.9	80.4
748	Shawnee	92.8	62.4	81.6
749	Poteau	91.1	62.0	80.4
OREGON				
970-972	Portland	103.7	103.8	103.7
973	Salem	106.3	100.8	104.3
974	Eugene	103.1	100.1	102.0
975	Medford	104.2	97.1	101.6
976	Klamath Falls	103.6	95.5	100.6
977	Bend	102.7	97.9	100.9
978	Pendleton	101.1	97.4	99.7
979	Vale	98.9	85.1	93.9
PENNSYLVANIA				
150-152	Pittsburgh	100.1	103.2	101.3
153	Washington	94.5	98.3	95.9
154	Uniontown	94.6	95.7	95.0
155	Bedford	95.4	86.0	92.0
156	Greensburg	95.4	92.4	94.3
157	Indiana	94.6	94.4	94.5
158	Dubois	95.7	89.9	93.6
159	Johnstown	95.5	93.4	94.7
160	Butler	90.8	94.5	92.2
161	New Castle	90.9	95.0	92.4
162	Kittanning	91.2	94.7	92.5
163	Oil City	90.8	89.7	90.4
164-165	Erie	93.6	94.3	93.9
166	Altoona	93.5	93.3	93.4
167	Bradford	94.0	90.4	92.6
168	State College	93.5	95.6	94.3
169	Wellsboro	94.4	84.6	90.8
170-171	Harrisburg	98.8	98.0	98.5
172	Chambersburg	93.6	81.5	89.1
173-174	York	94.8	93.7	94.4
175-176	Lancaster	92.6	95.7	93.8

STATE/ZIP	CITY	MAT.	INST.	TOTAL
PENNSYLVANIA (CONT'D)				
177	Williamsport	91.6	91.0	91.4
178	Sunbury	93.2	84.6	90.0
179	Pottsville	92.4	88.0	90.8
180	Lehigh Valley	94.2	101.6	96.9
181	Allentown	96.8	104.4	99.6
182	Hazleton	93.7	87.5	91.4
183	Stroudsburg	93.7	95.4	94.4
184-185	Scranton	97.7	94.3	96.5
186-187	Wilkes-Barre	93.4	93.5	93.4
188	Montrose	93.2	88.3	91.4
189	Doylestown	93.0	115.6	101.3
190-191	Philadelphia	100.5	137.6	114.2
193	Westchester	96.3	116.1	103.6
194	Norristown	95.4	117.6	103.6
195-196	Reading	97.9	99.3	98.4
PUERTO RICO				
009	San Juan	121.3	28.7	87.2
RHODE ISLAND				
028	Newport	96.3	109.9	101.3
029	Providence	100.1	110.6	104.0
SOUTH CAROLINA				
290-292	Columbia	99.5	65.1	86.8
293	Spartanburg	97.7	67.5	86.6
294	Charleston	99.6	67.5	87.8
295	Florence	97.4	64.5	85.3
296	Greenville	97.5	67.4	86.5
297	Rock Hill	96.3	65.2	84.8
298	Aiken	96.8	61.8	84.0
299	Beaufort	97.6	63.7	85.1
SOUTH DAKOTA				
570-571	Sioux Falls	99.9	79.6	92.4
572	Watertown	96.8	66.0	85.5
573	Mitchell	96.0	60.0	82.8
574	Aberdeen	99.1	73.5	89.7
575	Pierre	101.6	73.9	91.4
576	Mobridge	96.4	61.1	83.4
577	Rapid City	99.1	66.3	87.1
TENNESSEE				
370-372	Nashville	100.0	73.1	90.1
373-374	Chattanooga	98.8	65.4	86.5
375,380-381	Memphis	99.1	70.7	88.7
376	Johnson City	97.6	57.8	82.9
377-379	Knoxville	95.7	65.6	84.6
382	McKenzie	95.8	52.5	79.9
383	Jackson	98.6	67.2	87.1
384	Columbia	94.5	61.5	82.3
385	Cookeville	95.7	53.8	80.3
TEXAS				
750	McKinney	96.6	59.6	83.0
751	Waxahachie	96.6	66.9	85.7
752-753	Dallas	99.5	66.4	87.3
754	Greenville	96.7	59.2	82.9
755	Texarkana	95.3	61.4	82.8
756	Longview	95.8	57.0	81.5
757	Tyler	96.7	58.4	82.6
758	Palestine	93.2	56.5	79.7
759	Lufkin	93.9	57.8	80.6
760-761	Fort Worth	97.6	63.7	85.1
762	Denton	95.8	59.4	82.4
763	Wichita Falls	95.3	61.2	82.7
764	Eastland	93.1	56.5	79.6
765	Temple	91.7	54.1	77.8
766-767	Waco	94.7	62.5	82.9
768	Brownwood	95.7	54.9	80.7
769	San Angelo	95.4	58.7	81.9
770-772	Houston	97.6	67.2	86.4
773	Huntsville	93.7	58.4	80.7
774	Wharton	94.7	59.1	81.6
775	Galveston	93.4	61.5	81.6
776-777	Beaumont	94.6	66.0	84.1
778	Bryan	91.2	60.0	79.7
779	Victoria	94.6	58.5	81.3
780	Laredo	95.5	60.7	82.7
781-782	San Antonio	97.4	64.4	85.3
783-784	Corpus Christi	97.6	61.9	84.5
785	McAllen	96.7	53.4	80.8
786-787	Austin	97.6	61.9	84.4

STATE/ZIP	CITY	MAT.	INST.	TOTAL
TEXAS (CONT'D)				
788	Del Rio	96.3	55.7	81.3
789	Giddings	93.7	56.6	80.1
790-791	Amarillo	98.9	61.6	85.2
792	Childress	97.3	56.9	82.4
793-794	Lubbock	100.7	60.8	86.0
795-796	Abilene	99.1	59.8	84.7
797	Midland	99.7	63.9	86.5
798-799,885	El Paso	98.9	63.3	85.8
UTAH				
840-841	Salt Lake City	101.7	72.3	90.9
842,844	Ogden	97.7	72.6	88.4
843	Logan	99.1	72.6	89.3
845	Price	98.6	65.8	86.5
846-847	Provo	99.3	71.8	89.2
VERMONT				
050	White River Jct.	93.9	76.7	87.5
051	Bellows Falls	92.6	86.7	90.4
052	Bennington	92.9	83.5	89.5
053	Brattleboro	93.2	86.7	90.8
054	Burlington	99.7	81.3	92.9
056	Montpelier	97.1	83.7	92.1
057	Rutland	96.7	80.7	90.8
058	St. Johnsbury	94.0	76.3	87.5
059	Guildhall	92.9	76.4	86.8
VIRGINIA				
220-221	Fairfax	98.0	80.9	91.7
222	Arlington	100.1	79.9	92.6
223	Alexandria	99.7	81.2	92.9
224-225	Fredericksburg	97.4	76.2	89.6
226	Winchester	97.6	72.6	88.4
227	Culpeper	97.6	78.3	90.5
228	Harrisonburg	97.7	72.3	88.3
229	Charlottesville	98.1	68.2	87.1
230-232	Richmond	98.8	69.4	88.0
233-235	Norfolk	100.7	66.9	88.3
236	Newport News	98.7	67.2	87.1
237	Portsmouth	97.9	65.2	85.9
238	Petersburg	96.8	68.7	86.5
239	Farmville	96.4	63.1	84.1
240-241	Roanoke	100.5	66.2	87.9
242	Bristol	97.1	57.2	82.4
243	Pulaski	96.8	66.5	85.7
244	Staunton	97.6	65.2	85.7
245	Lynchburg	97.5	66.9	86.3
246	Grundy	97.1	60.5	83.7
WASHINGTON				
980-981,987	Seattle	103.6	112.6	106.9
982	Everett	103.5	104.7	104.0
983-984	Tacoma	104.3	103.8	104.1
985	Olympia	104.1	102.9	103.7
986	Vancouver	105.9	100.6	103.9
988	Wenatchee	103.1	83.2	95.8
989	Yakima	104.0	94.7	100.6
990-992	Spokane	97.6	84.9	93.0
993	Richland	97.0	91.0	94.8
994	Clarkston	95.3	75.6	88.1
WEST VIRGINIA				
247-248	Bluefield	96.2	81.0	90.6
249	Lewisburg	97.5	83.1	92.2
250-253	Charleston	98.2	88.3	94.5
254	Martinsburg	96.6	77.2	89.4
255-257	Huntington	99.2	87.0	94.7
258-259	Beckley	95.4	83.9	91.2
260	Wheeling	99.4	87.6	95.0
261	Parkersburg	98.6	86.6	94.2
262	Buckhannon	97.2	87.2	93.5
263-264	Clarksburg	97.7	87.9	94.1
265	Morgantown	97.6	88.6	94.3
266	Gassaway	97.2	84.2	92.4
267	Romney	97.2	81.8	91.6
268	Petersburg	96.9	82.2	91.5
WISCONSIN				
530,532	Milwaukee	97.6	109.3	101.9
531	Kenosha	97.4	101.9	99.0
534	Racine	96.5	101.8	98.5
535	Beloit	96.3	92.8	95.0
537	Madison	98.6	100.5	99.3

STATE/ZIP	CITY	MAT.	INST.	TOTAL
WISCONSIN (CONT'D)				
538	Lancaster	93.2	88.0	91.3
539	Portage	92.1	91.4	91.8
540	New Richmond	94.2	87.7	91.8
541-543	Green Bay	99.5	99.3	99.4
544	Wausau	93.9	87.7	91.6
545	Rhinelander	96.7	86.2	92.8
546	La Crosse	95.3	95.9	95.5
547	Eau Claire	96.9	95.8	96.5
548	Superior	94.0	90.1	92.6
549	Oshkosh	94.6	88.2	92.2
WYOMING				
820	Cheyenne	99.6	72.8	89.7
821	Yellowstone Nat'l Park	97.1	69.9	87.1
822	Wheatland	97.8	68.4	87.0
823	Rawlins	99.0	69.8	88.3
824	Worland	97.4	70.3	87.4
825	Riverton	98.2	69.8	87.8
826	Casper	100.8	71.1	89.9
827	Newcastle	97.2	69.8	87.1
828	Sheridan	100.1	70.6	89.2
829-831	Rock Springs	100.8	70.3	89.6
CANADIAN FACTORS (reflect Canadian currency)				
ALBERTA				
	Calgary	137.9	86.9	119.1
	Edmonton	137.6	86.9	118.9
	Fort McMurray	132.2	82.5	113.9
	Lethbridge	126.7	82.0	110.3
	Lloydminster	120.0	79.1	104.9
	Medicine Hat	120.3	78.4	104.9
	Red Deer	120.7	78.4	105.1
BRITISH COLUMBIA				
	Kamloops	122.4	78.8	106.3
	Prince George	123.4	78.2	106.7
	Vancouver	129.7	89.8	115.0
	Victoria	125.3	83.6	110.0
MANITOBA				
	Brandon	130.0	66.3	106.6
	Portage la Prairie	120.4	65.3	100.1
	Winnipeg	133.5	66.9	109.0
NEW BRUNSWICK				
	Bathurst	117.1	59.1	95.7
	Dalhousie	120.2	59.1	97.7
	Fredericton	130.6	66.7	107.0
	Moncton	117.1	73.6	101.1
	Newcastle	117.2	59.6	96.0
	St. John	119.0	74.5	102.6
NEWFOUNDLAND				
	Corner Brook	134.3	64.4	108.5
	St. Johns	130.0	82.4	112.5
NORTHWEST TERRITORIES				
	Yellowknife	143.4	78.2	119.4
NOVA SCOTIA				
	Bridgewater	119.8	66.5	100.2
	Dartmouth	131.0	66.1	107.2
	Halifax	124.4	82.1	108.8
	New Glasgow	129.1	66.1	105.9
	Sydney	127.3	66.1	104.8
	Truro	119.3	66.5	99.9
	Yarmouth	129.0	66.1	105.9
ONTARIO				
	Barrie	121.0	82.1	106.7
	Brantford	122.0	85.5	108.5
	Cornwall	121.4	82.3	107.1
	Hamilton	129.4	94.9	116.7
	Kingston	122.7	82.4	107.9
	Kitchener	119.8	91.0	109.2
	London	128.9	93.0	115.7
	North Bay	132.0	80.1	112.9
	Oshawa	121.1	92.4	110.6
	Ottawa	128.2	94.4	115.7
	Owen Sound	121.3	80.5	106.3
	Peterborough	122.0	82.1	107.3
	Sarnia	122.4	86.0	109.0

STATE/ZIP	CITY	MAT.	INST.	TOTAL
ONTARIO (CONT'D)				
	Sault Ste. Marie	117.7	84.3	105.4
	St. Catharines	117.3	91.6	107.8
	Sudbury	116.6	90.0	106.8
	Thunder Bay	118.2	90.6	108.1
	Timmins	122.4	80.4	106.9
	Toronto	127.5	100.9	117.7
	Windsor	118.3	90.8	108.2
PRINCE EDWARD ISLAND				
	Charlottetown	130.7	58.1	104.0
	Summerside	131.2	54.5	103.0
QUEBEC				
	Cap-de-la-Madeleine	118.6	75.6	102.8
	Charlesbourg	118.6	75.6	102.8
	Chicoutimi	116.5	84.0	104.6
	Gatineau	118.4	75.4	102.6
	Granby	118.9	75.3	102.9
	Hull	119.0	75.4	103.0
	Joliette	119.1	75.6	103.1
	Laval	118.7	75.9	103.0
	Montreal	129.7	87.0	114.0
	Quebec City	130.0	87.5	114.4
	Rimouski	118.5	84.0	105.8
	Rouyn-Noranda	118.7	75.4	102.8
	Saint-Hyacinthe	118.1	75.4	102.4
	Sherbrooke	118.8	75.4	102.8
	Sorel	119.1	75.6	103.1
	Saint-Jerome	118.9	75.4	102.9
	Trois-Rivieres	129.3	75.2	109.4
SASKATCHEWAN				
	Moose Jaw	117.3	60.4	96.3
	Prince Albert	116.5	58.9	95.3
	Regina	137.5	85.1	118.2
	Saskatoon	118.9	81.0	105.0
YUKON				
	Whitehorse	145.7	65.7	116.3

R011105-05 Tips for Accurate Estimating

1. Use computer applications or pre-printed forms for orderly sequence of dimensions and locations. Keep track of phone conversations by recording (with permission) or note taking on computer applications or pre-printed forms.
2. Use only the front side if pre-printed forms are necessary. Label all pre-printed forms with the same convention.
3. Be consistent in listing dimensions: For example, length x width x height. This helps in rechecking to ensure that, the total length of partitions is appropriate for the building area.
4. Use printed (rather than measured) dimensions where given.
5. Add up multiple printed dimensions for a single entry where possible.
6. Measure all other dimensions carefully.
7. Use each set of dimensions to calculate multiple related quantities.
8. Convert foot and inch measurements to decimal feet when listing. Memorize decimal equivalents to .01 parts of a foot (1/8″ equals approximately .01′).
9. Do not "round off" quantities until the final summary.
10. Mark drawings with different colors as items are taken off.
11. Keep similar items together, different items separate.
12. Identify location and drawing numbers to aid in future checking for completeness.
13. Measure or list everything on the drawings or mentioned in the specifications.
14. It may be necessary to list items not called for to make the job complete.
15. Be alert for: Notes on plans such as N.T.S. (not to scale); changes in scale throughout the drawings; reduced size drawings; discrepancies between the specifications and the drawings.
16. Develop a consistent pattern of performing an estimate. For example:
    a. Start the quantity takeoff at the lower floor and move to the next higher floor.
    b. Proceed from the main section of the building to the wings.
    c. Proceed from south to north or vice versa, clockwise or counterclockwise.
    d. Take off floor plan quantities first, elevations next, then detail drawings.
17. List all gross dimensions that can be either used again for different quantities, or used as a rough check of other quantities for verification (exterior perimeter, gross floor area, individual floor areas, etc.).
18. Utilize design symmetry or repetition (repetitive floors, repetitive wings, symmetrical design around a center line, similar room layouts, etc.). Note: Extreme caution is needed here so as not to omit or duplicate an area.
19. Do not convert units until the final total is obtained. For instance, when estimating concrete work, keep all units to the nearest cubic foot, then summarize and convert to cubic yards.
20. When figuring alternatives, it is best to total all items involved in the basic system, then total all items involved in the alternates. Therefore you work with positive numbers in all cases. When adds and deducts are used, it is often confusing whether to add or subtract a portion of an item; especially on a complicated or involved alternate.

R011105-10 Unit Gross Area Requirements

The figures in the table below indicate typical ranges in square feet as a function of the "occupant" unit. This table is best used in the preliminary design stages to help determine the probable size requirement for the total project.

Building Type	Unit	Gross Area in S.F. 1/4	Median	3/4
Apartments	Unit	660	860	1,100
Auditorium & Play Theaters	Seat	18	25	38
Bowling Alleys	Lane		940	
Churches & Synagogues	Seat	20	28	39
Dormitories	Bed	200	230	275
Fraternity & Sorority Houses	Bed	220	315	370
Garages, Parking	Car	325	355	385
Hospitals	Bed	685	850	1,075
Hotels	Rental Unit	475	600	710
Housing for the elderly	Unit	515	635	755
Housing, Public	Unit	700	875	1,030
Ice Skating Rinks	Total	27,000	30,000	36,000
Motels	Rental Unit	360	465	620
Nursing Homes	Bed	290	350	450
Restaurants	Seat	23	29	39
Schools, Elementary	Pupil	65	77	90
Junior High & Middle	↓	85	110	129
Senior High	↓	102	130	145
Vocational	↓	110	135	195
Shooting Ranges	Point		450	
Theaters & Movies	Seat		15	

R011105-50 Metric Conversion Factors

Description: This table is primarily for converting customary U.S. units in the left hand column to SI metric units in the right hand column. In addition, conversion factors for some commonly encountered Canadian and non-SI metric units are included.

	If You Know		Multiply By		To Find
Length	Inches	x	25.4[a]	=	Millimeters
	Feet	x	0.3048[a]	=	Meters
	Yards	x	0.9144[a]	=	Meters
	Miles (statute)	x	1.609	=	Kilometers
Area	Square inches	x	645.2	=	Square millimeters
	Square feet	x	0.0929	=	Square meters
	Square yards	x	0.8361	=	Square meters
Volume (Capacity)	Cubic inches	x	16,387	=	Cubic millimeters
	Cubic feet	x	0.02832	=	Cubic meters
	Cubic yards	x	0.7646	=	Cubic meters
	Gallons (U.S. liquids)[b]	x	0.003785	=	Cubic meters[c]
	Gallons (Canadian liquid)[b]	x	0.004546	=	Cubic meters[c]
	Ounces (U.S. liquid)[b]	x	29.57	=	Milliliters[c, d]
	Quarts (U.S. liquid)[b]	x	0.9464	=	Liters[c, d]
	Gallons (U.S. liquid)[b]	x	3.785	=	Liters[c, d]
Force	Kilograms force[d]	x	9.807	=	Newtons
	Pounds force	x	4.448	=	Newtons
	Pounds force	x	0.4536	=	Kilograms force[d]
	Kips	x	4448	=	Newtons
	Kips	x	453.6	=	Kilograms force[d]
Pressure, Stress, Strength (Force per unit area)	Kilograms force per square centimeter[d]	x	0.09807	=	Megapascals
	Pounds force per square inch (psi)	x	0.006895	=	Megapascals
	Kips per square inch	x	6.895	=	Megapascals
	Pounds force per square inch (psi)	x	0.07031	=	Kilograms force per square centimeter[d]
	Pounds force per square foot	x	47.88	=	Pascals
	Pounds force per square foot	x	4.882	=	Kilograms force per square meter[d]
Flow	Cubic feet per minute	x	0.4719	=	Liters per second
	Gallons per minute	x	0.0631	=	Liters per second
	Gallons per hour	x	1.05	=	Milliliters per second
Bending Moment Or Torque	Inch-pounds force	x	0.01152	=	Meter-kilograms force[d]
	Inch-pounds force	x	0.1130	=	Newton-meters
	Foot-pounds force	x	0.1383	=	Meter-kilograms force[d]
	Foot-pounds force	x	1.356	=	Newton-meters
	Meter-kilograms force[d]	x	9.807	=	Newton-meters
Mass	Ounces (avoirdupois)	x	28.35	=	Grams
	Pounds (avoirdupois)	x	0.4536	=	Kilograms
	Tons (metric)	x	1000	=	Kilograms
	Tons, short (2000 pounds)	x	907.2	=	Kilograms
	Tons, short (2000 pounds)	x	0.9072	=	Megagrams[e]
Mass per Unit Volume	Pounds mass per cubic foot	x	16.02	=	Kilograms per cubic meter
	Pounds mass per cubic yard	x	0.5933	=	Kilograms per cubic meter
	Pounds mass per gallon (U.S. liquid)[b]	x	119.8	=	Kilograms per cubic meter
	Pounds mass per gallon (Canadian liquid)[b]	x	99.78	=	Kilograms per cubic meter
Temperature	Degrees Fahrenheit		(F-32)/1.8	=	Degrees Celsius
	Degrees Fahrenheit		(F+459.67)/1.8	=	Degrees Kelvin
	Degrees Celsius		C+273.15	=	Degrees Kelvin

[a]The factor given is exact
[b]One U.S. gallon = 0.8327 Canadian gallon
[c]1 liter = 1000 milliliters = 1000 cubic centimeters
1 cubic decimeter = 0.001 cubic meter
[d]Metric but not SI unit
[e]Called "tonne" in England and "metric ton" in other metric countries

R011105-60 Weights and Measures

Measures of Length
1 Mile = 1760 Yards = 5280 Feet
1 Yard = 3 Feet = 36 inches
1 Foot = 12 Inches
1 Mil = 0.001 Inch
1 Fathom = 2 Yards = 6 Feet
1 Rod = 5.5 Yards = 16.5 Feet
1 Hand = 4 Inches
1 Span = 9 Inches
1 Micro-inch = One Millionth Inch or 0.000001 Inch
1 Micron = One Millionth Meter + 0.00003937 Inch

Surveyor's Measure
1 Mile = 8 Furlongs = 80 Chains
1 Furlong = 10 Chains = 220 Yards
1 Chain = 4 Rods = 22 Yards = 66 Feet = 100 Links
1 Link = 7.92 Inches

Square Measure
1 Square Mile = 640 Acres = 6400 Square Chains
1 Acre = 10 Square Chains = 4840 Square Yards = 43,560 Sq. Ft.
1 Square Chain = 16 Square Rods = 484 Square Yards = 4356 Sq. Ft.
1 Square Rod = 30.25 Square Yards = 272.25 Square Feet = 625 Square Lines
1 Square Yard = 9 Square Feet
1 Square Foot = 144 Square Inches
An Acre equals a Square 208.7 Feet per Side

Cubic Measure
1 Cubic Yard = 27 Cubic Feet
1 Cubic Foot = 1728 Cubic Inches
1 Cord of Wood = 4 x 4 x 8 Feet = 128 Cubic Feet
1 Perch of Masonry = 16½ x 1½ x 1 Foot = 24.75 Cubic Feet

Avoirdupois or Commercial Weight
1 Gross or Long Ton = 2240 Pounds
1 Net or Short Ton = 2000 Pounds
1 Pound = 16 Ounces = 7000 Grains
1 Ounce = 16 Drachms = 437.5 Grains
1 Stone = 14 Pounds

Power
1 British Thermal Unit per Hour = 0.2931 Watts
1 Ton (Refrigeration) = 3.517 Kilowatts
1 Horsepower (Boiler) = 9.81 Kilowatts
1 Horsepower (550 ft-lb/s) = 0.746 Kilowatts

Shipping Measure
For Measuring Internal Capacity of a Vessel:
1 Register Ton = 100 Cubic Feet

For Measurement of Cargo:
Approximately 40 Cubic Feet of Merchandise is considered a Shipping Ton, unless that bulk would weigh more than 2000 Pounds, in which case Freight Charge may be based upon weight.

40 Cubic Feet = 32.143 U.S. Bushels = 31.16 Imp. Bushels

Liquid Measure
1 Imperial Gallon = 1.2009 U.S. Gallon = 277.42 Cu. In.
1 Cubic Foot = 7.48 U.S. Gallons

R011110-30 Engineering Fees

Typical **Structural Engineering Fees** based on type of construction and total project size. These fees are included in Architectural Fees.

Type of Construction	Total Project Size (in thousands of dollars)			
	$500	$500-$1,000	$1,000-$5,000	Over $5000
Industrial buildings, factories & warehouses	Technical payroll times 2.0 to 2.5	1.60%	1.25%	1.00%
Hotels, apartments, offices, dormitories, hospitals, public buildings, food stores	↓	2.00%	1.70%	1.20%
Museums, banks, churches and cathedrals	↓	2.00%	1.75%	1.25%
Thin shells, prestressed concrete, earthquake resistive	↓	2.00%	1.75%	1.50%
Parking ramps, auditoriums, stadiums, convention halls, hangars & boiler houses	↓	2.50%	2.00%	1.75%
Special buildings, major alterations, underpinning & future expansion	↓	Add to above 0.5%	Add to above 0.5%	Add to above 0.5%

For complex reinforced concrete or unusually complicated structures, add 20% to 50%.

Typical **Mechanical and Electrical Engineering Fees** are based on the size of the subcontract. The fee structure for both is shown below. These fees are included in Architectural Fees.

Type of Construction	Subcontract Size							
	$25,000	$50,000	$100,000	$225,000	$350,000	$500,000	$750,000	$1,000,000
Simple structures	6.4%	5.7%	4.8%	4.5%	4.4%	4.3%	4.2%	4.1%
Intermediate structures	8.0	7.3	6.5	5.6	5.1	5.0	4.9	4.8
Complex structures	10.1	9.0	9.0	8.0	7.5	7.5	7.0	7.0

For renovations, add 15% to 25% to applicable fee.

R012153-10 Repair and Remodeling

Cost figures are based on new construction utilizing the most cost-effective combination of labor, equipment and material with the work scheduled in proper sequence to allow the various trades to accomplish their work in an efficient manner.

The costs for repair and remodeling work must be modified due to the following factors that may be present in any given repair and remodeling project.

1. Equipment usage curtailment due to the physical limitations of the project, with only hand-operated equipment being used.
2. Increased requirement for shoring and bracing to hold up the building while structural changes are being made and to allow for temporary storage of construction materials on above-grade floors.
3. Material handling becomes more costly due to having to move within the confines of an enclosed building. For multi-story construction, low capacity elevators and stairwells may be the only access to the upper floors.
4. Large amounts of cutting and patching and attempting to match the existing construction is required. It is often more economical to remove entire walls rather than create many new door and window openings. This sort of trade-off has to be carefully analyzed.
5. Cost of protection of completed work is increased since the usual sequence of construction usually cannot be accomplished.
6. Economies of scale usually associated with new construction may not be present. If small quantities of components must be custom fabricated due to job requirements, unit costs will naturally increase. Also, if only small work areas are available at a given time, job scheduling between trades becomes difficult and subcontractor quotations may reflect the excessive start-up and shut-down phases of the job.
7. Work may have to be done on other than normal shifts and may have to be done around an existing production facility which has to stay in production during the course of the repair and remodeling.
8. Dust and noise protection of adjoining non-construction areas can involve substantial special protection and alter usual construction methods.
9. Job may be delayed due to unexpected conditions discovered during demolition or removal. These delays ultimately increase construction costs.
10. Piping and ductwork runs may not be as simple as for new construction. Wiring may have to be snaked through walls and floors.
11. Matching "existing construction" may be impossible because materials may no longer be manufactured. Substitutions may be expensive.
12. Weather protection of existing structure requires additional temporary structures to protect building at openings.
13. On small projects, because of local conditions, it may be necessary to pay a tradesman for a minimum of four hours for a task that is completed in one hour.

All of the above areas can contribute to increased costs for a repair and remodeling project. Each of the above factors should be considered in the planning, bidding and construction stage in order to minimize the increased costs associated with repair and remodeling jobs.

R012153-60 Security Factors

Contractors entering, working in, and exiting secure facilities often lose productive time during a normal workday. The recommended allowances in this section are intended to provide for the loss of productivity by increasing labor costs. Note that different costs are associated with searches upon entry only and searches upon entry and exit. Time spent in a queue is unpredictable and not part of these allowances. Contractors should plan ahead for this situation.

Security checkpoints are designed to reflect the level of security required to gain access or egress. An extreme example is when contractors, along with any materials, tools, equipment, and vehicles, must be physically searched and have all materials, tools, equipment, and vehicles inventoried and documented prior to both entry and exit.

Physical searches without going through the documentation process represent the next level and take up less time.

Electronic searches—passing through a detector or x-ray machine with no documentation of materials, tools, equipment, and vehicles—take less time than physical searches.

Visual searches of materials, tools, equipment, and vehicles represent the next level of security.

Finally, access by means of an ID card or displayed sticker takes the least amount of time.

Another consideration is if the searches described above are performed each and every day, or if they are performed only on the first day with access granted by ID card or displayed sticker for the remainder of the project. The figures for this situation have been calculated to represent the initial check-in as described and subsequent entry by ID card or displayed sticker for up to 20 days on site. For the situation described above, where the time period is beyond 20 days, the impact on labor cost is negligible.

There are situations where tradespeople must be accompanied by an escort and observed during the work day. The loss of freedom of movement will slow down productivity for the tradesperson. Costs for the observer have not been included. Those costs are normally born by the owner.

R012153-65 Infectious Disease Precautions

Contractors entering and working on job sites may be required to take precautions to prevent the spread of infectious diseases. Those precautions will reduce the amount of productive time during a normal workday. The recommended allowances in this section are intended to provide for the loss of productive time by increasing labor costs.

The estimator should be aware that one, many or none of these precautions apply to the line items in an estimate. Job site requirements and sound judgement must be applied.

Labor cost implications are based upon:

Temperature checks	Once per day
Donning/doffing masks and gloves	Four times per day (2 times each)
Washing hands (additional over normal)	Eight times per day
Informational meetings	Once per day
Maintaining social distance	Throughout the day
Disinfecting tools or equipment	Throughout the day

R012909-80 Sales Tax by State

State sales tax on materials is tabulated below (5 states have no sales tax). Many states allow local jurisdictions, such as a county or city, to levy additional sales tax.

Some projects may be sales tax exempt, particularly those constructed with public funds.

State	Tax (%)	State	Tax (%)	State	Tax (%)	State	Tax (%)
Alabama	4	Illinois	6.25	Montana	0	Rhode Island	7
Alaska	0	Indiana	7	Nebraska	5.5	South Carolina	6
Arizona	5.6	Iowa	6	Nevada	6.85	South Dakota	4.5
Arkansas	6.5	Kansas	6.5	New Hampshire	0	Tennessee	7
California	7.25	Kentucky	6	New Jersey	6.625	Texas	6.25
Colorado	2.9	Louisiana	4.45	New Mexico	5.125	Utah	6.10
Connecticut	6.35	Maine	5.5	New York	4	Vermont	6
Delaware	0	Maryland	6	North Carolina	4.75	Virginia	5.3
District of Columbia	6	Massachusetts	6.25	North Dakota	5	Washington	6.5
Florida	6	Michigan	6	Ohio	5.75	West Virginia	6
Georgia	4	Minnesota	6.875	Oklahoma	4.5	Wisconsin	5
Hawaii	4	Mississippi	7	Oregon	0	Wyoming	4
Idaho	6	Missouri	4.225	Pennsylvania	6	Average	5.11 %

Sales Tax by Province (Canada)

GST - a value-added tax, which the government imposes on most goods and services provided in or imported into Canada. PST - a retail sales tax, which five of the provinces impose on the prices of most goods and some services. QST - a value-added tax, similar to the federal GST, which Quebec imposes. HST - Three provinces have combined their retail sales taxes with the federal GST into one harmonized tax.

Province	PST (%)	QST(%)	GST(%)	HST(%)
Alberta	0	0	5	0
British Columbia	7	0	5	0
Manitoba	7	0	5	0
New Brunswick	0	0	0	15
Newfoundland	0	0	0	15
Northwest Territories	0	0	5	0
Nova Scotia	0	0	0	15
Ontario	0	0	0	13
Prince Edward Island	0	0	0	15
Quebec	9.975	0	5	0
Saskatchewan	6	0	5	0
Yukon	0	0	5	0

R012909-85 Unemployment Taxes and Social Security Taxes

State unemployment tax rates vary not only from state to state, but also with the experience rating of the contractor. The federal unemployment tax rate is 6.2% of the first $7,000 of wages. This is reduced by a credit of up to 5.4% for timely payment to the state. The minimum federal unemployment tax is 0.6% after all credits.

Social security (FICA) for 2023 is estimated at time of publication to be 7.65% of wages up to $147,000.

R012909-86 Unemployment Tax by State

Information is from the U.S. Department of Labor, state unemployment tax rates.

State	Tax (%)	State	Tax (%)	State	Tax (%)	State	Tax (%)
Alabama	6.10	Illinois	7.625	Montana	6.30	Rhode Island	9.80
Alaska	5.4	Indiana	7.4	Nebraska	5.4	South Carolina	5.46
Arizona	20.93	Iowa	7.5	Nevada	5.4	South Dakota	9.3
Arkansas	14.2	Kansas	7.6	New Hampshire	8.5	Tennessee	10.0
California	6.2	Kentucky	9.5	New Jersey	5.8	Texas	6.3
Colorado	10.39	Louisiana	6.2	New Mexico	6.4	Utah	7.3
Connecticut	6.8	Maine	6.16	New York	9.9	Vermont	6.5
Delaware	8.20	Maryland	10.50	North Carolina	5.76	Virginia	6.43
District of Columbia	7.6	Massachusetts	14.37	North Dakota	9.69	Washington	6.02
Florida	5.4	Michigan	10.3	Ohio	10.2	West Virginia	8.5
Georgia	8.1	Minnesota	9.5	Oklahoma	7.5	Wisconsin	8.5
Hawaii	5.8	Mississippi	5.6	Oregon	5.4	Wyoming	8.5
Idaho	5.4	Missouri	6.75	Pennsylvania	9.93	Median	7.50 %

R012909-90 Overtime

One way to improve the completion date of a project or eliminate negative float from a schedule is to compress activity duration times. This can be achieved by increasing the crew size or working overtime with the proposed crew.

To determine the costs of working overtime to compress activity duration times, consider the following examples. Below is an overtime efficiency and cost chart based on a five, six, or seven day week with an eight through twelve hour day. Payroll percentage increases for time and one half and double times are shown for the various working days.

Days per Week	Hours per Day	Production Efficiency					Payroll Cost Factors	
		1st Week	2nd Week	3rd Week	4th Week	Average 4 Weeks	@ 1-1/2 Times	@ 2 Times
5	8	100%	100%	100%	100%	100%	1.000	1.000
	9	100	100	95	90	96	1.056	1.111
	10	100	95	90	85	93	1.100	1.200
	11	95	90	75	65	81	1.136	1.273
	12	90	85	70	60	76	1.167	1.333
6	8	100	100	95	90	96	1.083	1.167
	9	100	95	90	85	93	1.130	1.259
	10	95	90	85	80	88	1.167	1.333
	11	95	85	70	65	79	1.197	1.394
	12	90	80	65	60	74	1.222	1.444
7	8	100	95	85	75	89	1.143	1.286
	9	95	90	80	70	84	1.183	1.365
	10	90	85	75	65	79	1.214	1.429
	11	85	80	65	60	73	1.240	1.481
	12	85	75	60	55	69	1.262	1.524

R013113-40 Builder's Risk Insurance

Builder's risk insurance is insurance on a building during construction. Premiums are paid by the owner or the contractor. Blasting, collapse and underground insurance would raise total insurance costs.

R013113-50 General Contractor's Overhead

There are two distinct types of overhead on a construction project: Project overhead and main office overhead. Project overhead includes those costs at a construction site not directly associated with the installation of construction materials. Examples of project overhead costs include the following:

1. Superintendent
2. Construction office and storage trailers
3. Temporary sanitary facilities
4. Temporary utilities
5. Security fencing
6. Photographs
7. Cleanup
8. Performance and payment bonds

The above project overhead items are also referred to as general requirements and therefore are estimated in Division 1. Division 1 is the first division listed in the CSI MasterFormat but it is usually the last division estimated. The sum of the costs in Divisions 1 through 49 is referred to as the sum of the direct costs.

All construction projects also include indirect costs. The primary components of indirect costs are the contractor's main office overhead and profit. The amount of the main office overhead expense varies depending on the following:

1. Owner's compensation
2. Project managers' and estimators' wages
3. Clerical support wages
4. Office rent and utilities
5. Corporate legal and accounting costs
6. Advertising
7. Automobile expenses
8. Association dues
9. Travel and entertainment expenses

These costs are usually calculated as a percentage of annual sales volume. This percentage can range from 35% for a small contractor doing less than $500,000 to 5% for a large contractor with sales in excess of $100 million.

R013113-55 Installing Contractor's Overhead

Installing contractors (subcontractors) also incur costs for general requirements and main office overhead.

Included within the total incl. overhead and profit costs is a percent mark-up for overhead that includes:

1. Compensation and benefits for office staff and project managers
2. Office rent, utilities, business equipment, and maintenance
3. Corporate legal and accounting costs
4. Advertising
5. Vehicle expenses (for office staff and project managers)
6. Association dues
7. Travel, entertainment
8. Insurance
9. Small tools and equipment

R013113-60 Workers' Compensation Insurance Rates by Trade

The table below tabulates the national averages for Workers' Compensation insurance rates by trade and type of building. The average "Insurance Rate" is multiplied by the "% of Building Cost" for each trade. This produces the "Workers' Compensation Cost" by % of total labor cost, to be added for each trade by building type to determine the weighted average Workers' Compensation rate for the building types analyzed.

Trade	Insurance Rate (% Labor Cost)		% of Building Cost			Workers' Compensation		
	Range	Average	Office Bldgs.	Schools & Apts.	Mfg.	Office Bldgs.	Schools & Apts.	Mfg.
Excavation, Grading, etc.	1.9 % to 14.7%	8.3%	4.8%	4.9%	4.5%	0.40%	0.41%	0.37%
Piles & Foundations	2.1 to 32.0	17.0	7.1	5.2	8.7	1.21	0.88	1.48
Concrete	2.6 to 26.5	14.5	5.0	14.8	3.7	0.73	2.15	0.54
Masonry	2.9 to 48.0	25.5	6.9	7.5	1.9	1.76	1.91	0.48
Structural Steel	2.3 to 30.9	16.6	10.7	3.9	17.6	1.78	0.65	2.92
Miscellaneous & Ornamental Metals	2.2 to 22.6	12.4	2.8	4.0	3.6	0.35	0.50	0.45
Carpentry & Millwork	2.7 to 25.2	14.0	3.7	4.0	0.5	0.52	0.56	0.07
Metal or Composition Siding	3.2 to 129.7	66.4	2.3	0.3	4.3	1.53	0.20	2.86
Roofing	4.0 to 101.9	52.9	2.3	2.6	3.1	1.22	1.38	1.64
Doors & Hardware	2.5 to 26.3	14.4	0.9	1.4	0.4	0.13	0.20	0.06
Sash & Glazing	3.1 to 18.1	10.6	3.5	4.0	1.0	0.37	0.42	0.11
Lath & Plaster	1.2 to 32.4	16.8	3.3	6.9	0.8	0.55	1.16	0.13
Tile, Marble & Floors	1.7 to 19.5	10.6	2.6	3.0	0.5	0.28	0.32	0.05
Acoustical Ceilings	1.4 to 18.3	9.9	2.4	0.2	0.3	0.24	0.02	0.03
Painting	2.1 to 35.8	18.9	1.5	1.6	1.6	0.28	0.30	0.30
Interior Partitions	2.7 to 26.8	14.7	3.9	4.3	4.4	0.57	0.63	0.65
Miscellaneous Items	1.3 to 97.7	49.5	5.2	3.7	9.7	2.57	1.83	4.80
Elevators	1.2 to 8.3	4.8	2.1	1.1	2.2	0.10	0.05	0.11
Sprinklers	1.5 to 13.2	7.3	0.5	—	2.0	0.04	—	0.15
Plumbing	1.3 to 12.6	6.9	4.9	7.2	5.2	0.34	0.50	0.36
Heat., Vent., Air Conditioning	2.1 to 14.7	8.4	13.5	11.0	12.9	1.13	0.92	1.08
Electrical	1.4 to 9.5	5.5	10.1	8.4	11.1	0.56	0.46	0.61
Total	1.2 % to 129.7%	65.4	100.0%	100.0%	100.0%	16.66%	15.45%	19.25%
		Overall Weighted Average	17.12%					

Workers' Compensation Insurance Rates by States

The table below lists the weighted average Workers' Compensation base rate for each state with a factor comparing this with the national average of 8.4%.

State	Weighted Average	Factor	State	Weighted Average	Factor	State	Weighted Average	Factor
Alabama	21.1%	251	Kentucky	21.0%	250	North Dakota	7.6%	90
Alaska	13.3	158	Louisiana	31.3	373	Ohio	7.8	93
Arizona	11.6	138	Maine	14.9	177	Oklahoma	14.3	170
Arkansas	8.4	100	Maryland	15.8	188	Oregon	12.5	149
California	35.8	426	Massachusetts	16.1	192	Pennsylvania	34.9	415
Colorado	7.2	86	Michigan	9.0	107	Rhode Island	14.7	175
Connecticut	23.9	285	Minnesota	22.7	270	South Carolina	31.6	376
Delaware	15.9	189	Mississippi	15.1	180	South Dakota	13.3	158
District of Columbia	12.8	152	Missouri	23.1	275	Tennessee	9.6	114
Florida	13.4	160	Montana	14.6	174	Texas	5.7	68
Georgia	55.3	658	Nebraska	18.1	215	Utah	7.9	94
Hawaii	16.8	200	Nevada	13.5	161	Vermont	15.6	186
Idaho	14.2	169	New Hampshire	14.9	177	Virginia	10.4	124
Illinois	34.5	411	New Jersey	23.2	276	Washington	11.8	140
Indiana	5.8	69	New Mexico	23.7	282	West Virginia	6.6	79
Iowa	17.2	205	New York	28.2	336	Wisconsin	17.1	204
Kansas	10.3	123	North Carolina	20.8	248	Wyoming	8.4	100
			Weighted Average for U.S. is	17.1% of payroll = 100%				

The weighted average skilled worker rate for 35 trades is 17.12%. For bidding purposes, apply the full value of Workers' Compensation directly to total labor costs, or if labor is 38%, materials 42% and overhead and profit 20% of total cost, carry 38/80 x 17.12% = 8.13% of cost (before overhead and profit) into overhead. Rates vary not only from state to state but also with the experience rating of the contractor.

Rates are the most current available at the time of publication.

General Requirements — R0131 Project Management & Coordination

R013113-80 Performance Bond

This table shows the cost of a Performance Bond for a construction job scheduled to be completed in 12 months. Add 1% of the premium cost per month for jobs requiring more than 12 months to complete. The rates are "standard" rates offered to contractors that the bonding company considers financially sound and capable of doing the work. Preferred rates are offered by some bonding companies based upon financial strength of the contractor. Actual rates vary from contractor to contractor and from bonding company to bonding company. Contractors should prequalify through a bonding agency before submitting a bid on a contract that requires a bond.

Contract Amount	Building Construction Class B Projects	Highways & Bridges	
		Class A New Construction	Class A-1 Highway Resurfacing
First $ 100,000 bid	$25.00 per M	$15.00 per M	$9.40 per M
Next 400,000 bid	$ 2,500 plus $15.00 per M	$ 1,500 plus $10.00 per M	$ 940 plus $7.20 per M
Next 2,000,000 bid	8,500 plus 10.00 per M	5,500 plus 7.00 per M	3,820 plus 5.00 per M
Next 2,500,000 bid	28,500 plus 7.50 per M	19,500 plus 5.50 per M	15,820 plus 4.50 per M
Next 2,500,000 bid	47,250 plus 7.00 per M	33,250 plus 5.00 per M	28,320 plus 4.50 per M
Over 7,500,000 bid	64,750 plus 6.00 per M	45,750 plus 4.50 per M	39,570 plus 4.00 per M

General Requirements — R0151 Temporary Utilities

R015113-65 Temporary Power Equipment

Cost data for the temporary equipment was developed utilizing the following information.

1) Re-usable material-services, transformers, equipment and cords are based on new purchase and prorated to three projects.
2) PVC feeder includes trench and backfill.
3) Connections include disconnects and fuses.
4) Labor units include an allowance for removal.
5) No utility company charges or fees are included.
6) Concrete pads or vaults are not included.
7) Utility company conduits not included.

R015423-10 Steel Tubular Scaffolding

On new construction, tubular scaffolding is efficient up to 60′ high or five stories. Above this it is usually better to use hung scaffolding if construction permits. Swing scaffolding operations may interfere with tenants. In this case, the tubular is more practical at all heights.

In repairing or cleaning the front of an existing building the cost of tubular scaffolding per S.F. of building front goes up as the height increases above the first tier. The first tier cost is relatively high due to leveling and alignment.

The minimum efficient crew for erecting and dismantling is three workers. They can set up and remove 18 frame sections per day up to 5 stories high. For 6 to 12 stories high, a crew of four is most efficient. Use two or more on top and two on the bottom for handing up or hoisting. They can also set up and remove 18 frame sections per day. At 7' horizontal spacing, this will run about 800 S.F. per day of erecting and dismantling. Time for placing and removing planks must be added to the above. A crew of three can place and remove 72 planks per day up to 5 stories. For over 5 stories, a crew of four can place and remove 80 planks per day.

The table below shows the number of pieces required to erect tubular steel scaffolding for 1000 S.F. of building frontage. This area is made up of a scaffolding system that is 12 frames (11 bays) long by 2 frames high.

For jobs under twenty-five frames, add 50% to the rental cost. Rental rates will be lower for jobs over three months duration. Large quantities for long periods can reduce rental rates by 20%.

Description of Component	Number of Pieces for 1000 S.F. of Building Front	Unit
5′ Wide Standard Frame, 6′-4″ High	24	Ea.
Leveling Jack & Plate	24	↓
Cross Brace	44	↓
Side Arm Bracket, 21″	12	↓
Guardrail Post	12	↓
Guardrail, 7′ section	22	↓
Stairway Section	2	↓
Stairway Starter Bar	1	↓
Stairway Inside Handrail	2	↓
Stairway Outside Handrail	2	↓
Walk-Through Frame Guardrail	2	↓

Scaffolding is often used as falsework over 15′ high during construction of cast-in-place concrete beams and slabs. Two foot wide scaffolding is generally used for heavy beam construction. The span between frames depends upon the load to be carried with a maximum span of 5′.

Heavy duty shoring frames with a capacity of 10,000#/leg can be spaced up to 10′ O.C. depending upon form support design and loading.

Scaffolding used as horizontal shoring requires less than half the material required with conventional shoring.

On new construction, erection is done by carpenters.

Rolling towers supporting horizontal shores can reduce labor and speed the job. For maintenance work, catwalks with spans up to 70′ can be supported by the rolling towers.

R015433-10 Contractor Equipment

Rental Rates shown elsewhere in the data set pertain to late model high quality machines in excellent working condition, rented from equipment dealers. Rental rates from contractors may be substantially lower than the rental rates from equipment dealers depending upon economic conditions; for older, less productive machines, reduce rates by a maximum of 15%. Any overtime must be added to the base rates. For shift work, rates are lower. Usual rule of thumb is 150% of one shift rate for two shifts; 200% for three shifts.

For periods of less than one week, operated equipment is usually more economical to rent than renting bare equipment and hiring an operator.

Costs to move equipment to a job site (mobilization) or from a job site (demobilization) are not included in rental rates, nor in any Equipment costs on any Unit Price line items or crew listings. These costs can be found elsewhere. If a piece of equipment is already at a job site, it is not appropriate to utilize mob/demob costs in an estimate again.

Rental rates vary throughout the country with larger cities generally having lower rates. Lease plans for new equipment are available for periods in excess of six months with a percentage of payments applying toward purchase.

Rental rates can also be treated as reimbursement costs for contractor-owned equipment. Owned equipment costs include depreciation, loan payments, interest, taxes, insurance, storage, and major repairs.

Monthly rental rates vary from 2% to 5% of the cost of the equipment depending on the anticipated life of the equipment and its wearing parts. Weekly rates are about 1/3 the monthly rates and daily rental rates are about 1/3 the weekly rates.

The hourly operating costs for each piece of equipment include costs to the user such as fuel, oil, lubrication, normal expendables for the equipment, and a percentage of the mechanic's wages chargeable to maintenance. The hourly operating costs listed do not include the operator's wages.

The daily cost for equipment used in the standard crews is figured by dividing the weekly rate by five, then adding eight times the hourly operating cost to give the total daily equipment cost, not including the operator. This figure is in the right hand column of the Equipment listings under Equipment Cost/Day.

Pile Driving rates shown for the pile hammer and extractor do not include leads, cranes, boilers or compressors. Vibratory pile driving requires an added field specialist during set-up and pile driving operation for the electric model. The hydraulic model requires a field specialist for set-up only. Up to 125 reuses of sheet piling are possible using vibratory drivers. For normal conditions, crane capacity for hammer type and size is as follows.

Crane Capacity	Hammer Type and Size		
	Air or Steam	Diesel	Vibratory
25 ton	to 8,750 ft.-lb.		70 H.P.
40 ton	15,000 ft.-lb.	to 32,000 ft.-lb.	170 H.P.
60 ton	25,000 ft.-lb.		300 H.P.
100 ton		112,000 ft.-lb.	

Cranes should be specified for the job by size, building and site characteristics, availability, performance characteristics, and duration of time required.

Backhoes & Shovels rent for about the same as equivalent size cranes but maintenance and operating expenses are higher. The crane operator's rate must be adjusted for high boom heights. Average adjustments: for 150′ boom add 2% per hour; over 185′, add 4% per hour; over 210′, add 6% per hour; over 250′, add 8% per hour and over 295′, add 12% per hour.

Tower Cranes of the climbing or static type have jibs from 50′ to 200′ and capacities at maximum reach range from 4,000 to 14,000 pounds. Lifting capacities increase up to maximum load as the hook radius decreases.

Typical rental rates, based on purchase price, are about 2% to 3% per month.

Erection and dismantling run between 500 and 2000 labor hours. Climbing operation takes 10 labor hours per 20′ climb. Crane dead time is about 5 hours per 40′ climb. If crane is bolted to side of the building add cost of ties and extra mast sections. Climbing cranes have from 80′ to 180′ of mast while static cranes have 80′ to 800′ of mast.

Truck Cranes can be converted to tower cranes by using tower attachments. Mast heights over 400′ have been used.

A single 100′ high material **Hoist and Tower** can be erected and dismantled in about 400 labor hours; a double 100′ high hoist and tower in about 600 labor hours. Erection times for additional heights are 3 and 4 labor hours per vertical foot respectively up to 150′, and 4 to 5 labor hours per vertical foot over 150′ high. A 40′ high portable Buck hoist takes about 160 labor hours to erect and dismantle. Additional heights take 2 labor hours per vertical foot to 80′ and 3 labor hours per vertical foot for the next 100′. Most material hoists do not meet local code requirements for carrying personnel.

A 150′ high **Personnel Hoist** requires about 500 to 800 labor hours to erect and dismantle. Budget erection time at 5 labor hours per vertical foot for all trades. Local code requirements or labor scarcity requiring overtime can add up to 50% to any of the above erection costs.

Earthmoving Equipment: The selection of earthmoving equipment depends upon the type and quantity of material, moisture content, haul distance, haul road, time available, and equipment available. Short haul cut and fill operations may require dozers only, while another operation may require excavators, a fleet of trucks, and spreading and compaction equipment. Stockpiled material and granular material are easily excavated with front end loaders. Scrapers are most economically used with hauls between 300′ and 1-1/2 miles if adequate haul roads can be maintained. Shovels are often used for blasted rock and any material where a vertical face of 8′ or more can be excavated. Special conditions may dictate the use of draglines, clamshells, or backhoes. Spreading and compaction equipment must be matched to the soil characteristics, the compaction required and the rate the fill is being supplied.

R015433-15 Heavy Lifting

Hydraulic Climbing Jacks

The use of hydraulic heavy lift systems is an alternative to conventional type crane equipment. The lifting, lowering, pushing, or pulling mechanism is a hydraulic climbing jack moving on a square steel jackrod from 1-5/8″ to 4″ square, or a steel cable. The jackrod or cable can be vertical or horizontal, stationary or movable, depending on the individual application. When the jackrod is stationary, the climbing jack will climb the rod and push or pull the load along with itself. When the climbing jack is stationary, the jackrod is movable with the load attached to the end and the climbing jack will lift or lower the jackrod with the attached load. The heavy lift system is normally operated by a single control lever located at the hydraulic pump.

The system is flexible in that one or more climbing jacks can be applied wherever a load support point is required, and the rate of lift synchronized.

Economic benefits have been demonstrated on projects such as: erection of ground assembled roofs and floors, complete bridge spans, girders and trusses, towers, chimney liners and steel vessels, storage tanks, and heavy machinery. Other uses are raising and lowering offshore work platforms, caissons, tunnel sections and pipelines.

R015436-50 Mobilization

Costs to move rented construction equipment to a job site from an equipment dealer's or contractor's yard (mobilization) or off the job site (demobilization) are not included in the rental or operating rates, nor in the equipment cost on a unit price line or in a crew listing. These costs can be found consolidated in the Mobilization section of the data and elsewhere in particular site work sections. If a piece of equipment is already on the job site, it is not appropriate to include mob/demob costs in a new estimate that requires use of that equipment. The following table identifies approximate sizes of rented construction equipment that would be hauled on a towed trailer. Because this listing is not all-encompassing, the user can infer as to what size trailer might be required for a piece of equipment not listed.

3-ton Trailer	20-ton Trailer	40-ton Trailer	50-ton Trailer
20 H.P. Excavator	110 H.P. Excavator	200 H.P. Excavator	270 H.P. Excavator
50 H.P. Skid Steer	165 H.P. Dozer	300 H.P. Dozer	Small Crawler Crane
35 H.P. Roller	150 H.P. Roller	400 H.P. Scraper	500 H.P. Scraper
40 H.P. Trencher	Backhoe	450 H.P. Art. Dump Truck	500 H.P. Art. Dump Truck

R024119-10 Demolition Defined

Whole Building Demolition - Demolition of the whole building with no concern for any particular building element, component, or material type being demolished. This type of demolition is accomplished with large pieces of construction equipment that break up the structure, load it into trucks and haul it to a disposal site, but disposal or dump fees are not included. Demolition of below-grade foundation elements, such as footings, foundation walls, grade beams, slabs on grade, etc., is not included. Certain mechanical equipment containing flammable liquids or ozone-depleting refrigerants, electric lighting elements, communication equipment components, and other building elements may contain hazardous waste, and must be removed, either selectively or carefully, as hazardous waste before the building can be demolished.

Foundation Demolition - Demolition of below-grade foundation footings, foundation walls, grade beams, and slabs on grade. This type of demolition is accomplished by hand or pneumatic hand tools, and does not include saw cutting, or handling, loading, hauling, or disposal of the debris.

Gutting - Removal of building interior finishes and electrical/mechanical systems down to the load-bearing and sub-floor elements of the rough building frame, with no concern for any particular building element, component, or material type being demolished. This type of demolition is accomplished by hand or pneumatic hand tools, and includes loading into trucks, but not hauling, disposal or dump fees, scaffolding, or shoring. Certain mechanical equipment containing flammable liquids or ozone-depleting refrigerants, electric lighting elements, communication equipment components, and other building elements may contain hazardous waste, and must be removed, either selectively or carefully, as hazardous waste, before the building is gutted.

Selective Demolition - Demolition of a selected building element, component, or finish, with some concern for surrounding or adjacent elements, components, or finishes (see the first Subdivision (s) at the beginning of appropriate Divisions). This type of demolition is accomplished by hand or pneumatic hand tools, and does not include handling, loading, storing, hauling, or disposal of the debris, scaffolding, or shoring. "Gutting" methods may be used in order to save time, but damage that is caused to surrounding or adjacent elements, components, or finishes may have to be repaired at a later time.

Careful Removal - Removal of a piece of service equipment, building element or component, or material type, with great concern for both the removed item and surrounding or adjacent elements, components or finishes. The purpose of careful removal may be to protect the removed item for later re-use, preserve a higher salvage value of the removed item, or replace an item while taking care to protect surrounding or adjacent elements, components, connections, or finishes from cosmetic and/or structural damage. An approximation of the time required to perform this type of removal is 1/3 to 1/2 the time it would take to install a new item of like kind (see Reference Number R260105-30). This type of removal is accomplished by hand or pneumatic hand tools, and does not include loading, hauling, or storing the removed item, scaffolding, shoring, or lifting equipment.

Cutout Demolition - Demolition of a small quantity of floor, wall, roof, or other assembly, with concern for the appearance and structural integrity of the surrounding materials. This type of demolition is accomplished by hand or pneumatic hand tools, and does not include saw cutting, handling, loading, hauling, or disposal of debris, scaffolding, or shoring.

Rubbish Handling - Work activities that involve handling, loading or hauling of debris. Generally, the cost of rubbish handling must be added to the cost of all types of demolition, with the exception of whole building demolition.

Minor Site Demolition - Demolition of site elements outside the footprint of a building. This type of demolition is accomplished by hand or pneumatic hand tools, or with larger pieces of construction equipment, and may include loading a removed item onto a truck (check the Crew for equipment used). It does not include saw cutting, hauling or disposal of debris, and, sometimes, handling or loading.

R024119-20 Dumpsters

Dumpster rental costs on construction sites are presented in two ways.

The cost per week rental includes the delivery of the dumpster; its pulling or emptying once per week, and its final removal. The assumption is made that the dumpster contractor could choose to empty a dumpster by simply bringing in an empty unit and removing the full one. These costs also include the disposal of the materials in the dumpster.

The Alternate Pricing can be used when actual planned conditions are not approximated by the weekly numbers. For example, these lines can be used when a dumpster is needed for 4 weeks and will need to be emptied 2 or 3 times per week. Conversely the Alternate Pricing lines can be used when a dumpster will be rented for several weeks or months but needs to be emptied only a few times over this period.

R053100-10 Decking Descriptions

General - All Deck Products

A steel deck is made by cold forming structural grade sheet steel into a repeating pattern of parallel ribs. The strength and stiffness of the panels are the result of the ribs and the material properties of the steel. Deck lengths can be varied to suit job conditions, but because of shipping considerations, are usually less than 40 feet. Standard deck width varies with the product used but full sheets are usually 12″, 18″, 24″, 30″, or 36″. The deck is typically furnished in a standard width with the ends cut square. Any cutting for width, such as at openings or for angular fit, is done at the job site.

The deck is typically attached to the building frame with arc puddle welds, self-drilling screws, or powder or pneumatically driven pins. Sheet to sheet fastening is done with screws, button punching (crimping), or welds.

Composite Floor Deck

After installation and adequate fastening, a floor deck serves several purposes. It (a) acts as a working platform, (b) stabilizes the frame, (c) serves as a concrete form for the slab, and (d) reinforces the slab to carry the design loads applied during the life of the building. Composite decks are distinguished by the presence of shear connector devices as part of the deck. These devices are designed to mechanically lock the concrete and deck together so that the concrete and the deck work together to carry subsequent floor loads. These shear connector devices can be rolled-in embossments, lugs, holes, or wires welded to the panels. The deck profile can also be used to interlock concrete and steel.

Composite deck finishes are either galvanized (zinc coated) or phosphatized/painted. Galvanized deck has a zinc coating on both the top and bottom surfaces. The phosphatized/painted deck has a bare (phosphatized) top surface that will come into contact with the concrete. This bare top surface can be expected to develop rust before the concrete is placed. The bottom side of the deck has a primer coat of paint.

A composite floor deck is normally installed so the panel ends do not overlap on the supporting beams. Shear lugs or panel profile shapes often prevent a tight metal to metal fit if the panel ends overlap; the air gap caused by overlapping will prevent proper fusion with the structural steel supports when the panel end laps are shear stud welded.

Adequate end bearing of the deck must be obtained as shown on the drawings. If bearing is actually less in the field than shown on the drawings, further investigation is required.

Roof Deck

A roof deck is not designed to act compositely with other materials. A roof deck acts alone in transferring horizontal and vertical loads into the building frame. Roof deck rib openings are usually narrower than floor deck rib openings. This provides adequate support of the rigid thermal insulation board.

A roof deck is typically installed to endlap approximately 2″ over supports. However, it can be butted (or lapped more than 2″) to solve field fit problems. Since designers frequently use the installed deck system as part of the horizontal bracing system (the deck as a diaphragm), any fastening substitution or change should be approved by the designer. Continuous perimeter support of the deck is necessary to limit edge deflection in the finished roof and may be required for diaphragm shear transfer.

Standard roof deck finishes are galvanized or primer painted. The standard factory applied paint for roof decks is a primer paint and is not intended to weather for extended periods of time. Field painting or touching up of abrasions and deterioration of the primer coat or other protective finishes is the responsibility of the contractor.

Cellular Deck

A cellular deck is made by attaching a bottom steel sheet to a roof deck or composite floor deck panel. A cellular deck can be used in the same manner as a floor deck. Electrical, telephone, and data wires are easily run through the chase created between the deck panel and the bottom sheet.

When used as part of the electrical distribution system, the cellular deck must be installed so that the ribs line up and create a smooth cell transition at abutting ends. The joint that occurs at butting cell ends must be taped or otherwise sealed to prevent wet concrete from seeping into the cell. Cell interiors must be free of welding burrs, or other sharp intrusions, to prevent damage to wires.

When used as a roof deck, the bottom flat plate is usually left exposed to view. Care must be maintained during erection to keep good alignment and prevent damage.

A cellular deck is sometimes used with the flat plate on the top side to provide a flat working surface. Installation of the deck for this purpose requires special methods for attachment to the frame because the flat plate, now on the top, can prevent direct access to the deck material that is bearing on the structural steel. It may be advisable to treat the flat top surface to prevent slipping.

A cellular deck is always furnished galvanized or painted over galvanized.

Form Deck

A form deck can be any floor or roof deck product used as a concrete form. Connections to the frame are by the same methods used to anchor floor and roof decks. Welding washers are recommended when welding a deck that is less than 20 gauge thickness.

A form deck is furnished galvanized, prime painted, or uncoated. A galvanized deck must be used for those roof deck systems where a form deck is used to carry a lightweight insulating concrete fill.

R078413-30 Firestopping

Firestopping is the sealing of structural, mechanical, electrical and other penetrations through fire-rated assemblies. The basic components of firestop systems are safing insulation and firestop sealant on both sides of wall penetrations and the top side of floor penetrations.

Pipe penetrations are assumed to be through concrete, grout, or joint compound and can be sleeved or unsleeved. Costs for the penetrations and sleeves are not included. An annular space of 1″ is assumed. Escutcheons are not included.

A metallic pipe is assumed to be copper, aluminum, cast iron or similar metallic material. An insulated metallic pipe is assumed to be covered with a thermal insulating jacket of varying thickness and materials.

A non-metallic pipe is assumed to be PVC, CPVC, FR Polypropylene or similar plastic piping material. Intumescent firestop sealant or wrap strips are included. Collars on both sides of wall penetrations and a sheet metal plate on the underside of floor penetrations are included.

Ductwork is assumed to be sheet metal, stainless steel or similar metallic material. Duct penetrations are assumed to be through concrete, grout or joint compound. Costs for penetrations and sleeves are not included. An annular space of 1/2″ is assumed.

Multi-trade openings include costs for sheet metal forms, firestop mortar, wrap strips, collars and sealants as necessary.

Structural penetrations joints are assumed to be 1/2″ or less. CMU walls are assumed to be within 1-1/2″ of the metal deck. Drywall walls are assumed to be tight to the underside of metal decking.

Metal panel, glass or curtain wall systems include a spandrel area of 5′ filled with mineral wool foil-faced insulation. Fasteners and stiffeners are included.

R224000-10 Water Consumption Rates

Fixture Type	Water Supply Fixture Unit Value		
	Hot Water	Cold Water	Combined
Bathtub	1.0	1.0	1.4
Clothes Washer	1.0	1.0	1.4
Dishwasher	1.4	0.0	1.4
Kitchen Sink	1.0	1.0	1.4
Laundry Tub	1.0	1.0	1.4
Lavatory	0.5	0.5	0.7
Shower Stall	1.0	1.0	1.4
Water Closet (tank type)	0.0	2.2	2.2
Full Bath Group w/bathtub or shower stall	1.5	2.7	3.6
Half Bath Group w/W.C. and Lavatory	0.5	2.5	2.6
Kitchen Group w/Dishwasher and Sink	1.9	1.0	2.5
Laundry Group w/Clothes Washer and Laundry Tub	1.8	1.8	2.5
Hose bibb (sillcock)	0.0	2.5	2.5

Notes:
Typically, WSFU = 1GPM

Supply loads in the building water-distribution system shall be determined by total load on the pipe being sized, in terms of water supply fixture units (WSFU) and gallons per minute (GPM) flow rates. For fixtures not listed, choose a WSFU value of a fixture with similar flow characteristics. Water Fixture Supply Units determined the required water supply to fixtures and their service systems. Fixture units are equal to one (1) cubic foot of water drained in a 1-1/4″ pipe per minute. It is not a flow rate unit but a design factor.

R224000-20 Fixture Demands in Gallons per Fixture per Hour

The table below is based on a 140°F final temperature except for dishwashers in public places where 180°F water is mandatory.

Supply Systems for Flush Tanks			Supply Systems for Flushometer Valves		
Load	Demand		Load	Demand	
WSFU	GPM	CU. FT.	WSFU	GPM	CU. FT.
1.0	3.0	0.041040	-	-	-
2.0	5.0	0.068400	-	-	-
3.0	6.5	0.868920	-	-	-
4.0	8.0	1.069440	-	-	-
5.0	9.4	1.256592	5.0	15	2.0052
6.0	10.7	1.430376	6.0	17.4	2.326032
7.0	11.8	1.577424	7.0	19.8	2.646364
8.0	12.8	1.711104	8.0	22.2	2.967696
9.0	13.7	1.831416	9.0	24.6	3.288528
10.0	14.6	1.951728	10.0	27	3.60936
11.0	15.4	2.058672	11.0	27.8	3.716304
12.0	16.0	2.138880	12.0	28.6	3.823248
13.0	16.5	2.205720	13.0	29.4	3.930192
14.0	17.0	2.272560	14.0	30.2	4.037136
15.0	17.5	2.339400	15.0	31	4.14408
16.0	18.0	2.906240	16.0	31.8	4.241024
17.0	18.4	2.459712	17.0	32.6	4.357968
18.0	18.8	2.513184	18.0	33.4	4.464912
19.0	19.2	2.566656	19.0	34.2	4.571856
20.0	19.6	2.620218	20.0	35.0	4.678800
25.0	21.5	2.874120	25.0	38.0	5.079840
30.0	23.3	3.114744	30.0	42.0	5.611356
35.0	24.9	3.328632	35.0	44.0	5.881920
40.0	26.3	3.515784	40.0	46.0	6.149280
45.0	27.7	3.702936	45.0	48.0	6.416640
50.0	29.1	3.890088	50.0	50.0	6.684000

Notes:
When designing a plumbing system that utilizes fixtures other than, or in addition to, water closets, use the data provided in the Supply Systems for Flush Tanks section of the above table.

To obtain the probable maximum demand, multiply the total demands for the fixtures (gal./fixture/hour) by the demand factor. The heater should have a heating capacity in gallons per hour equal to this maximum. The storage tank should have a capacity in gallons equal to the probable maximum demand multiplied by the storage capacity factor.

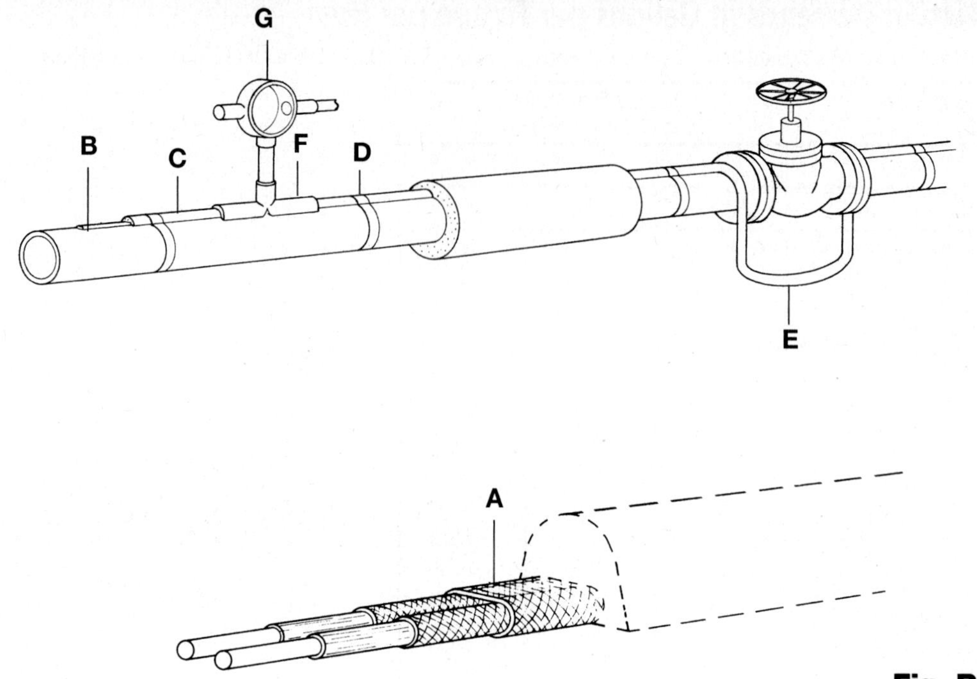

Fig. R238313-11

R238313-10 Heat Trace Systems

Before you can determine the cost of a HEAT TRACE installation, the method of attachment must be established. There are four (4) common methods:

1. Cable is simply attached to the pipe with polyester tape every 12′.
2. Cable is attached with a continuous cover of 2″ wide aluminum tape.
3. Cable is attached with factory extruded heat transfer cement and covered with metallic raceway with clips every 10′.
4. Cable is attached between layers of pipe insulation using either clips or polyester tape.

Example: Components for method 3 must include:

A. Heat trace cable by voltage and watts per linear foot.
B. Heat transfer cement, 1 gallon per 60 linear feet of cover.
C. Metallic raceway by size and type.
D. Raceway clips by size of pipe.

When taking off linear foot lengths of cable add the following for each valve in the system. (E)

In all of the above methods each component of the system must be priced individually.

SCREWED OR WELDED VALVE:

1/2″	=	6″
3/4″	=	9″
1″	=	1′ -0″
1-1/2″	=	1′ -6″
2″	=	2′
2-1/2″	=	2′ -6″
3″	=	2′ -6″
4″	=	4′ -0″
6″	=	7′ -0″
8″	=	9′ -6″
10″	=	12′ -6″
12″	=	15′ -0″
14″	=	18′ -0″
16″	=	21′ -6″
18″	=	25′ -6″
20″	=	28′ -6″
24″	=	34′ -0″
30″	=	40′ -0″

FLANGED VALVE:

1/2″	=	1′ -0″
3/4″	=	1′ -6″
1″	=	2′ -0″
1-1/2″	=	2′ -6″
2″	=	2′ -6″
2-1/2″	=	3′ -0″
3″	=	3′ -6″
4″	=	4′ -0″
6″	=	8′ -0″
8″	=	11′ -0″
10″	=	14′ -0″
12″	=	16′ -6″
14″	=	19′ -6″
16″	=	23′ -0″
18″	=	27′ -0″
20″	=	30′ -0″
24″	=	36′ -0″
30″	=	42′ -0″

BUTTERFLY VALVES:

1/2″	=	0′
3/4″	=	0′
1″	=	1′ -0″
1-1/2″	=	1′ -6″
2″	=	2′ -0″
2-1/2″	=	2′ -6″
3″	=	2′ -6″
4″	=	3′ -0″
6″	=	3′ -6″
8″	=	4′ -0″
10″	=	4′ -0″
12″	=	5′ -0″
14″	=	5′ -6″
16″	=	6′ -0″
18″	=	6′ -6″
20″	=	7′ -0″
24″	=	8′ -0″
30″	=	10′ -0″

R238313-10 Heat Trace Systems (cont.)

Add the following quantities of heat transfer cement to linear foot totals for each valve:

Nominal Valve Size	Gallons of Cement per Valve
1/2″	0.14
3/4″	0.21
1″	0.29
1-1/2″	0.36
2″	0.43
2-1/2″	0.70
3″	0.71
4″	1.00
6″	1.43
8″	1.48
10″	1.50
12″	1.60
14″	1.75
16″	2.00
18″	2.25
20″	2.50
24″	3.00
30″	3.75

The following must be added to the list of components to accurately price HEAT TRACE systems:

1. Expediter fitting and clamp fasteners (F)
2. Junction box and nipple connected to expediter fitting (G)
3. Field installed terminal blocks within junction box
4. Ground lugs
5. Piping from power source to expediter fitting
6. Controls
7. Thermostats
8. Branch wiring
9. Cable splices
10. End of cable terminations
11. Branch piping fittings and boxes

Deduct the following percentages from labor if cable lengths in the same area exceed:

150′ to 250′	10%	351′ to 500′	20%
251′ to 350′	15%	Over 500′	25%

Add the following percentages to labor for elevated installations:

15′ to 20′ high	10%	31′ to 35′ high	40%
21′ to 25′ high	20%	36′ to 40′ high	50%
26′ to 30′ high	30%	Over 40′ high	60%

R238313-20 Spiral-Wrapped Heat Trace Cable (Pitch Table)

In order to increase the amount of heat, occasionally heat trace cable is wrapped in a spiral fashion around a pipe, increasing the number of feet of heater cable per linear foot of pipe.

Engineers first determine the heat loss per foot of pipe (based on the insulating material, its thickness, and the temperature differential across it). A ratio is then calculated by the formula:

$$\text{Feet of Heat Trace per Foot of Pipe} = \frac{\text{Watts/Foot of Heat Loss}}{\text{Watts/Foot of the Cable}}$$

The linear distance between wraps (pitch) is then taken from a chart or table. Generally, the pitch is listed on a drawing leaving the estimator to calculate the total length of heat tape required. An approximation may be taken from this table.

Feet of Heat Trace Per Foot of Pipe																
	Nominal Pipe Size in Inches															
Pitch In Inches	1	1¼	1½	2	2½	3	4	6	8	10	12	14	16	18	20	24
3.5	1.80															
4	1.65															
5	1.46	1.60	1.80													
6	1.34	1.45	1.55	1.75												
7	1.25	1.35	1.43	1.57	1.75											
8	1.20	1.28	1.34	1.45	1.60	1.80										
9	1.16	1.23	1.28	1.37	1.51	1.68										
10	1.13	1.19	1.24	1.32	1.44	1.57	1.82									
15	1.06	1.08	1.10	1.15	1.21	1.29	1.42	1.78								
20	1.04	1.05	1.06	1.08	1.13	1.17	1.25	1.49	1.73							
25		1.04	1.04	1.06	1.08	1.11	1.17	1.33	1.51	1.72						
30				1.04	1.05	1.07	1.12	1.24	1.37	1.54	1.70	1.80				
35					1.06	1.06	1.09	1.17	1.28	1.42	1.54	1.64	1.78			
40						1.05	1.07	1.14	1.22	1.33	1.44	1.52	1.64	1.75		
50							1.05	1.09	1.15	1.22	1.29	1.35	1.44	1.53	1.64	1.83
60								1.06	1.11	1.16	1.21	1.25	1.31	1.39	1.46	1.62
70								1.05	1.08	1.12	1.17	1.19	1.24	1.30	1.35	1.47
80									1.06	1.09	1.13	1.15	1.19	1.24	1.28	1.38
90									1.04	1.06	1.10	1.13	1.16	1.19	1.23	1.32
100										1.05	1.08	1.10	1.13	1.15	1.19	1.23

Note: Common practice would normally limit the lower end of the table to 5% of additional heat. Above 80% an engineer would likely opt for two (2) parallel cables.

R260102-20 Labor Adjustment Factors

Labor Adjustment Factors are provided for Divisions 26, 27, and 28 to assist the mechanical estimator account for the various complexities and special conditions of any particular project. While a single percentage has been entered on each line of Division 26 01 02.20, it should be understood that these are just suggested midpoints of ranges of values commonly used by mechanical estimators. They may be increased or decreased depending on the severity of the special conditions.

The group for "existing occupied buildings" has been the subject of requests for explanation. Actually there are two stages to this group: buildings that are existing and "finished" but unoccupied, and those that also are occupied. Buildings that are "finished" may result in higher labor costs due to the workers having to be more careful not to damage finished walls, ceilings, floors, etc. and may necessitate special protective coverings and barriers. Also corridor bends and doorways may not accommodate long pieces of pipe or larger pieces of equipment. Work above an already hung ceiling can be very time consuming. The addition of occupants may force the work to be done on premium time (nights and/or weekends), eliminate the possible use of some preferred tools such as pneumatic drivers, powder charged drivers, etc. The estimator should evaluate the access to the work area and just how the work is going to be accomplished to arrive at an increase in labor costs over "normal" new construction productivity.

R260105-30 Electrical Demolition (Removal for Replacement)

The purpose of this reference number is to provide a guide to users for electrical "removal for replacement" by applying the rule of thumb: 1/3 of new installation time (typical range from 20% to 50%) for removal. Remember to use reasonable judgment when applying the suggested percentage factor. For example:

Contractors have been requested to remove an existing fluorescent lighting fixture and replace with a new fixture utilizing energy saver lamps and electronic ballast:

In order to fully understand the extent of the project, contractors should visit the job site and estimate the time to perform the renovation work in accordance with applicable national, state and local regulation and codes.

The contractor may need to add extra labor hours to his estimate if he discovers unknown concealed conditions such as: contaminated asbestos ceiling, broken acoustical ceiling tile and need to repair, patch and touch-up paint all the damaged or disturbed areas, tasks normally assigned to general contractors. In addition, the owner could request that the contractors salvage the materials removed and turn over the materials to the owner or dispose of the materials to a reclamation station. The normal removal item is 0.5 labor-hour for a lighting fixture and 1.5 labor-hours for new installation time. Revise the estimate times from 2 labor-hours work up to a minimum 4 labor-hours work for just a fluorescent lighting fixture.

For removal of large concentrations of lighting fixtures in the same area, apply an "economy of scale" to reduce estimating labor hours.

Figure R260110-10 Typical Overhead Service Entrance

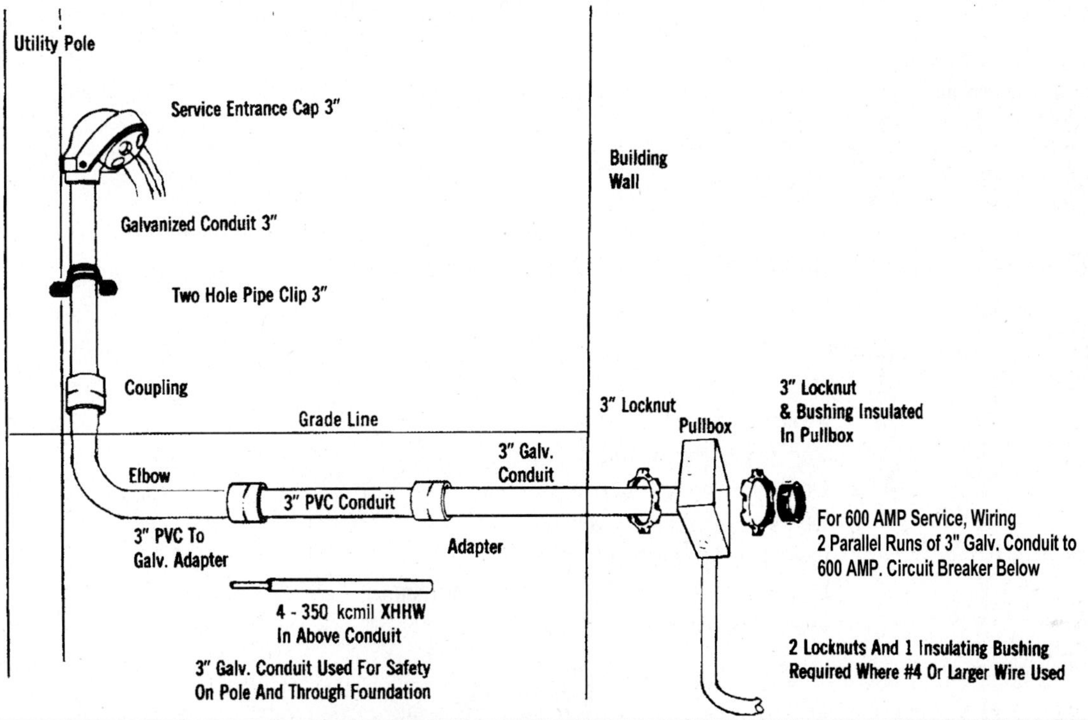

Figure R260110-11 Typical Commercial Electric System

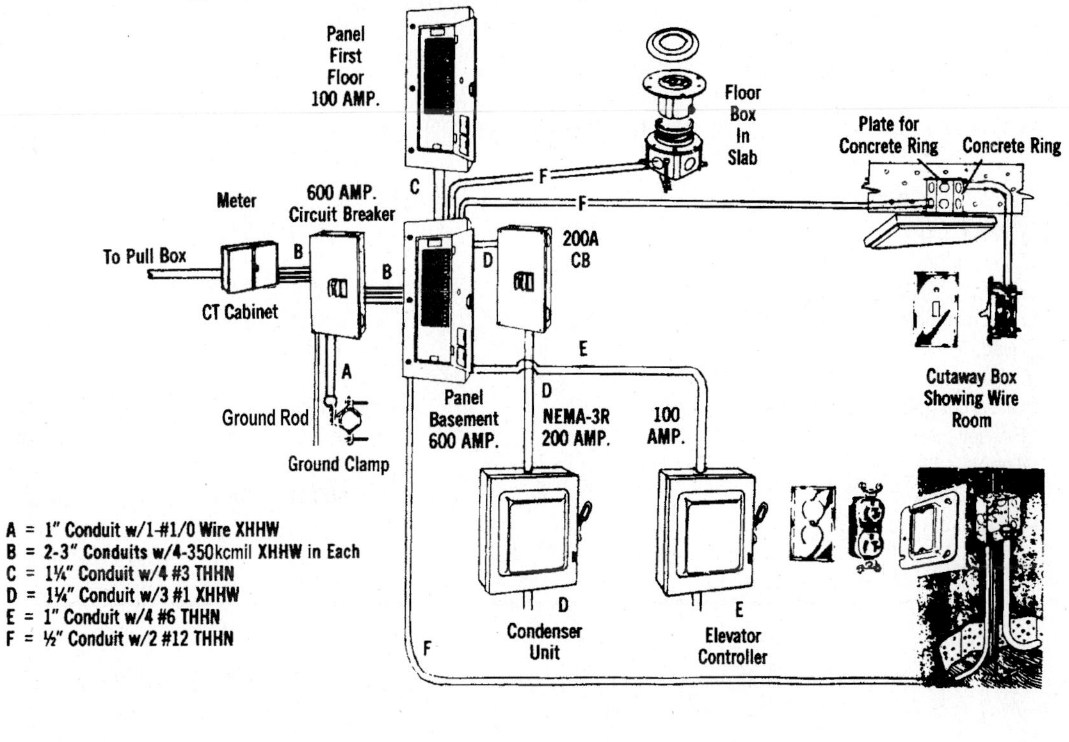

Figure R260110-12 Preliminary Procedure

1. Determine building size and use.
2. Develop total load in watts.
   a. Lighting
   b. Receptacle
   c. Air Conditioning
   d. Elevator
   e. Other power requirements
3. Determine best voltage available from utility company.
4. Determine cost from tables for loads (a) through (e) above.
5. Determine size of service from formulas (R260110-17).
6. Determine costs for service, panels, and feeders from tables.

Figure R260110-13 Office Building 90′ x 210′, 3 story, w/garage

Garage Area = 18,900 S.F.
Office Area = 56,700 S.F.
Elevator = 2 @ 125 FPM

Tables	Power Required		Watts	
D5010-1151	Garage Lighting .5 Watt/S.F.		9,450	
	Office Lighting 3 Watts/S.F.		170,100	
D5010-1151	Office Receptacles 2 Watts/S.F.		113,400	
D5010-1151, R262213-27	Low Rise Office A.C. 4.3 Watts/S.F.		243,810	
D5010-1152, 1153	Elevators - 2 @ 20 HP = 2 @ 17,404 Watts/Ea.		34,808	
D5010-1151	Misc. Motors + Power 1.2 Watts/S.F.		68,040	
		Total	639,608	Watts

Voltage Available

277/480V, 3 Phase, 4 Wire

Formula

D5010-116

$$\text{Amperes} = \frac{\text{Watts}}{\text{Volts x Power Factor x 1.73}} = \frac{639{,}608}{480\text{V x .8 x 1.73}} = 963 \text{ Amps}$$

Use 1200 Amp Service

System	Description	Unit Cost	Unit	Total
D5020 210 0200	Garage Lighting (Interpolated)	$3.68	S.F.	$ 69,552
D5020 210 0540	Office Lighting (Using 32 W lamps)	12.45	S.F.	705,915
D5020 115 0880	Receptacle-Undercarpet	4.47	S.F.	253,449
D5020 140 0280	Air Conditioning	0.82	S.F.	46,494
D5020 135 0320	Misc. Pwr.	0.45	S.F.	25,515
D5020 145 2120	Elevators - 2 @ 20HP	3,425.00	Ea.	6,850
D5010 130 1250	Underground Electric Service-1200 Amp	105,400.00	Ea.	105,400
D5010 230 0480	Feeder - Assume 200 feet	504.00	L.F.	100,800
D5010 240 0580	Panels - 277/480V, 1200 Amp	37,450.00	Ea.	37,450
D5030 910 0400	Fire Detection	45,400.00	Ea.	45,400
		Total		$1,396,825
		or		$1,396,800

Table D5010-1151 Nominal Watts Per S.F. for Electric Systems for Various Building Types

Type Construction	1. Lighting	2. Devices	3. HVAC	4. Misc.	5. Elevator	Total Watts
Apartment, luxury high rise	2	2.2	3	1		
Apartment, low rise	2	2	3	1		
Auditorium	2.5	1	3.3	.8		
Bank, branch office	3	2.1	5.7	1.4		
Bank, main office	2.5	1.5	5.7	1.4		
Church	1.8	.8	3.3	.8		
College, science building	3	3	5.3	1.3		
College, library	2.5	.8	5.7	1.4		
College, physical education center	2	1	4.5	1.1		
Department store	2.5	.9	4	1		
Dormitory, college	1.5	1.2	4	1		
Drive-in doughnut shop	3	4	6.8	1.7		
Garage, commercial	.5	.5	0	.5		
Hospital, general	2	4.5	5	1.3		
Hospital, pediatric	3	3.8	5	1.3		
Hotel, airport	2	1	5	1.3		
Housing for the elderly	2	1.2	4	1		
Manufacturing, food processing	3	1	4.5	1.1		
Manufacturing, apparel	2	1	4.5	1.1		
Manufacturing, tools	4	1	4.5	1.1		
Medical clinic	2.5	1.5	3.2	1		
Nursing home	2	1.6	4	1		
Office building, high rise	3	2	4.7	1.2		
Office building, low rise	3	2	4.3	1.2		
Radio-TV studio	3.8	2.2	7.6	1.9		
Restaurant	2.5	2	6.8	1.7		
Retail store	2.5	.9	5.5	1.4		
School, elementary	3	1.9	5.3	1.3		
School, junior high	3	1.5	5.3	1.3		
School, senior high	2.3	1.7	5.3	1.3		
Supermarket	3	1	4	1		
Telephone exchange	1	.6	4.5	1.1		
Theater	2.5	1	3.3	.8		
Town Hall	2	1.9	5.3	1.3		
U.S. Post Office	3	2	5	1.3		
Warehouse, grocery	1	.6	0	.5		

Rule of Thumb: 1 KVA = 1 HP (Single Phase)

Three Phase:

Watts = 1.73 x Volts x Current x Power Factor x Efficiency

$$\text{Horsepower} = \frac{\text{Volts x Current x 1.73 x Power Factor}}{\text{746 Watts}}$$

Table D5010-1152 Horsepower Requirements for Elevators with 3 Phase Motors

Type	Maximum Travel Height in Ft.	Travel Speeds in FPM	Capacity of Cars in Lbs.		
			1200	1500	1800
Hydraulic	70	70	10	15	15
		85	15	15	15
		100	15	15	20
		110	20	20	20
		125	20	20	20
		150	25	25	25
		175	25	30	30
		200	30	30	40
Geared Traction	300	200			
		350			
			2000	2500	3000
Hydraulic	70	70	15	20	20
		85	20	20	25
		100	20	25	30
		110	20	25	30
		125	25	30	40
		150	30	40	50
		175	40	50	50
		200	40	50	60
Geared Traction	300	200	10	10	15
		350	15	15	23
			3500	4000	4500
Hydraulic	70	70	20	25	30
		85	25	30	30
		100	30	40	40
		110	40	40	50
		125	40	50	50
		150	50	50	60
		175	60		
		200	60		
Geared Traction	300	200	15		23
		350	23		35

The power factor of electric motors varies from 80% to 90% in larger size motors. The efficiency likewise varies from 80% on a small motor to 90% on a large motor.

Table D5010-1153 Watts per Motor

90% Power Factor & Efficiency @ 200 or 460V			
HP	Watts	HP	Watts
10	9024	30	25784
15	13537	40	33519
20	17404	50	41899
25	21916	60	49634

Table R260110-17 Electrical Formulas

Ohm's Law

Ohm's Law is a method of explaining the relation between voltage, current, and resistance in an electrical circuit. It is practically the basis of all electrical calculations. The term "electromotive force" is often used to designate pressure in volts. This formula can be expressed in various forms.

To find the current in amperes:

$$\text{Current} = \frac{\text{Voltage}}{\text{Resistance}} \quad \text{or} \quad \text{Amperes} = \frac{\text{Volts}}{\text{Ohms}} \quad \text{or} \quad I = \frac{E}{R}$$

The flow of current in amperes through any circuit is equal to the voltage or electromotive force divided by the resistance of that circuit.

To find the pressure or voltage:

Voltage = Current x Resistance or Volts = Amperes x Ohms or E = I x R

The voltage required to force a current through a circuit is equal to the resistance of the circuit multiplied by the current.

To find the resistance:

$$\text{Resistance} = \frac{\text{Voltage}}{\text{Current}} \quad \text{or} \quad \text{Ohms} = \frac{\text{Volts}}{\text{Amperes}} \quad \text{or} \quad R = \frac{E}{I}$$

The resistance of a circuit is equal to the voltage divided by the current flowing through that circuit.

Power Formulas

One horsepower = 746 watts One kilowatt = 1000 watts

The power factor of electric motors varies from 80% to 90% in the larger size motors.

Single-Phase Alternating Current Circuits

Power in Watts = Volts x Amperes x Power Factor

To find current in amperes:

$$\text{Current} = \frac{\text{Watts}}{\text{Volts x Power Factor}} \quad \text{or}$$

$$\text{Amperes} = \frac{\text{Watts}}{\text{Volts x Power Factor}} \quad \text{or} \quad I = \frac{W}{E \text{ x } PF}$$

To find current of a motor, single phase:

$$\text{Current} = \frac{\text{Horsepower x 746}}{\text{Volts x Power Factor x Efficiency}} \quad \text{or}$$

$$I = \frac{HP \text{ x } 746}{E \text{ x } PF \text{ x Eff.}}$$

To find horsepower of a motor, single phase:

$$\text{Horsepower} = \frac{\text{Volts x Current x Power Factor x Efficiency}}{\text{746 Watts}}$$

$$HP = \frac{E \text{ x } I \text{ x } PF \text{ x Eff.}}{746}$$

To find power in watts of a motor, single phase:

Watts = Volts x Current x Power Factor x Efficiency or

Watts = E x I x PF x Eff.

To find single phase kVA:

$$\text{1 Phase kVA} = \frac{\text{Volts x Amps}}{1000}$$

Three-Phase Alternating Current Circuits

Power in Watts = Volts x Amperes x Power Factor x 1.73

To find current in amperes in each wire:

$$\text{Current} = \frac{\text{Watts}}{\text{Voltage x Power Factor x 1.73}} \quad \text{or}$$

$$\text{Amperes} = \frac{\text{Watts}}{\text{Volts x Power Factor x 1.73}} \quad \text{or} \quad I = \frac{W}{E \text{ x } PF \text{ x } 1.73}$$

To find current of a motor, 3 phase:

$$\text{Current} = \frac{\text{Horsepower x 746}}{\text{Volts x Power Factor x Efficiency x 1.73}} \quad \text{or}$$

$$I = \frac{HP \text{ x } 746}{E \text{ x } PF \text{ x Eff. x } 1.73}$$

To find horsepower of a motor, 3 phase:

$$\text{Horsepower} = \frac{\text{Volts x Current x 1.73 x Power Factor}}{\text{746 Watts}}$$

$$HP = \frac{E \text{ x } I \text{ x } 1.73 \text{ x } PF}{746}$$

To find power in watts of a motor, 3 phase:

Watts = Volts x Current x 1.73 x Power Factor x Efficiency or

Watts = E x I x 1.73 x PF x Eff.

To find 3 phase kVA:

$$\text{3 phase kVA} = \frac{\text{Volts x Amps x 1.73}}{1000} \quad \text{or}$$

$$\text{kVA} = \frac{V \text{ x } A \text{ x } 1.73}{1000}$$

Power Factor (PF) is the percentage ratio of the measured watts (effective power) to the volt-amperes (apparent watts)

$$\text{Power Factor} = \frac{\text{Watts}}{\text{Volts x Amperes}} \text{ x } 100\%$$

A Conceptual Estimate of the costs for a building when final drawings are not available can be quickly figured by using **Table R260110-18 Cost Per S.F. for Electrical Systems for Various Building Types.** The following definitions apply to this table.

1. **Service and Distribution:** This system includes the incoming primary feeder from the power company, main building transformer, metering arrangement, switchboards, distribution panel boards, stepdown transformers, and power and lighting panels. Items marked (*) include the cost of the primary feeder and transformer. In all other projects the cost of the primary feeder and transformer is paid for by the local power company.
2. **Lighting:** Includes all interior fixtures for decor, illumination, exit, and emergency lighting. Fixtures for exterior building lighting are included, but parking area lighting is not included unless mentioned. See also Section D5020 for a detailed analysis of lighting requirements and costs.
3. **Devices:** Includes all outlet boxes, receptacles, switches for lighting control, dimmers, and cover plates.
4. **Equipment Connections:** Includes all materials and equipment for making connections for heating, ventilating, and air conditioning, as well as food service and other motorized items requiring connections.
5. **Basic Materials:** This category includes all disconnect power switches not part of service equipment, raceways for wires, pull boxes, junction boxes, supports, fittings, grounding materials, wireways, busways, and wire and cable systems.
6. **Special Systems:** Includes installed equipment only for the particular system such as fire detection and alarm, sound, emergency generator, and others as listed in the table.

Table R260110-18 Cost per S.F. for Electric Systems for Various Building Types

System	1. Service & Distribution	2. Lighting	3. Devices	4. Equipment Connections	5. Basic Materials	6a. Fire Alarm & Detection	6b. Telephone	6c. Television Distribution
Auto Sales with Repair	$7.02	$5.46	$1.17	$1.17	$12.87	$4.29	$1.95	$0.00
Banking Institutions	11.20	8.00	0.80	2.40	17.60	9.60	6.40	0.00
Detention Centers	14.76	12.30	1.64	1.64	20.50	8.20	1.64	0.00
Fire Stations	9.78	6.90	1.73	1.15	16.68	5.75	1.73	1.15
Hospitals	15.21	8.45	2.54	2.54	23.66	6.76	3.38	0.85
Industrial Buildings	19.20	14.40	2.88	2.88	27.84	3.84	1.92	1.92
Medical Clinics & Offices	8.16	6.12	1.53	1.02	11.73	4.08	3.06	1.02
Mixed Use	15.23	8.70	2.90	2.18	14.50	4.35	2.90	2.90
Multi-Family Housing	4.96	4.96	1.24	1.24	8.68	1.86	1.86	0.93
Nursing Home & Assisted Living	5.36	4.02	1.01	1.34	6.70	2.68	2.01	1.68
Office Buildings	7.20	6.72	1.44	1.92	12.96	4.80	3.84	0.96
Parking Garage	1.40	1.23	0.18	0.35	1.75	1.84	0.44	0.00
Parking Garage/Mixed Use	5.67	4.41	0.63	0.63	7.25	2.52	1.26	0.63
Police Stations	9.84	7.38	1.85	2.46	15.38	6.77	1.85	1.23
Public Assembly Buildings	7.84	8.96	1.68	2.80	14.00	4.48	1.68	1.12
Recreational	8.72	7.63	1.64	2.18	14.72	4.36	1.64	2.18
Restaurants	11.88	9.24	1.98	2.64	19.80	7.92	1.32	3.30
Retail	6.88	7.74	0.43	1.72	14.62	3.87	1.29	0.00
Schools	7.12	6.23	1.34	1.78	9.79	3.56	1.34	1.34
University, College & Private School Classroom & Admin Buildings	9.10	8.03	1.61	2.14	13.38	4.28	1.07	1.61
University, College & Private School Dormitories	6.64	6.64	1.25	1.66	10.38	3.32	0.83	1.25
University, College & Private School Science, Eng. & Lab Buildings	9.54	8.48	1.59	2.12	14.84	4.24	1.59	1.06
Warehouses	7.28	6.37	1.37	2.28	10.92	5.46	1.82	0.91

COST ASSUMPTIONS:

Each of the projects analyzed in Table R260110-18 was bid within the last 10 years in the northeastern part of the United States. Bid prices have been adjusted to Jan. 1 levels. The list of projects is by no means all-inclusive, yet by carefully examining the various systems for a particular building type, certain cost relationships will emerge. The use of Square Foot/Cubic Costs, in the Reference Section, along with the Project Size Modifier, should produce a budget S.F. cost for the electrical portion of a job that is consistent with the amount of design information normally available at the conceptual estimate stage.

Table R260110-18 Cost per S.F. for Electric Systems for Various Building Types (cont.)

System	6d. Intercom	6e. Sound System	6f. Video Monitoring	6g. Internet	6h. Emergency Generator	6i. Access Control	6j. Master Clock System
Auto Sales with Repair	$0.00	$0.39	$1.56	$1.95	$0.78	$0.39	$0.00
Banking Institutions	0.00	0.00	8.00	7.20	1.60	7.20	0.00
Detention Centers	2.46	2.46	3.28	0.00	4.92	8.20	0.00
Fire Stations	1.73	1.73	1.73	1.73	2.30	2.30	1.15
Hospitals	2.54	1.69	1.69	1.69	10.14	2.54	0.85
Industrial Buildings	1.92	1.92	1.92	5.76	3.84	2.88	2.88
Medical Clinics & Offices	1.53	1.02	2.55	4.59	2.04	2.55	0.00
Mixed Use	2.18	1.45	3.63	4.35	4.35	2.90	0.00
Multi-Family Housing	0.62	0.00	0.62	3.10	0.00	0.93	0.00
Nursing Home & Assisted Living	1.34	0.67	1.68	3.02	1.34	0.67	0.00
Office Buildings	0.96	0.96	1.44	1.92	1.44	1.44	0.00
Parking Garage	0.00	0.00	0.70	0.18	0.26	0.44	0.00
Parking Garage/Mixed Use	0.63	0.63	2.52	1.89	1.26	1.58	0.00
Police Stations	1.85	1.85	2.46	2.46	3.69	2.46	0.00
Public Assembly Buildings	0.00	6.72	1.68	1.68	1.68	1.68	0.00
Recreational	0.00	2.18	1.64	2.73	2.73	1.64	0.55
Restaurants	0.00	3.30	1.32	1.32	1.98	0.00	0.00
Retail	0.86	0.43	2.15	0.43	1.29	1.29	0.00
Schools	1.34	2.23	2.23	1.78	1.78	1.78	0.89
University, College & Private School Classroom & Admin Buildings	1.61	1.61	1.07	2.68	1.61	2.68	1.07
University, College & Private School Dormitories	1.66	0.83	1.25	2.08	1.66	1.25	0.83
University, College & Private School Science, Eng. & Lab Buildings	1.59	0.53	1.06	2.12	1.59	1.59	1.06
Warehouses	0.91	0.46	2.28	1.37	1.82	2.28	0.00

Table R260120-10 ASHRAE Climate Zone Map

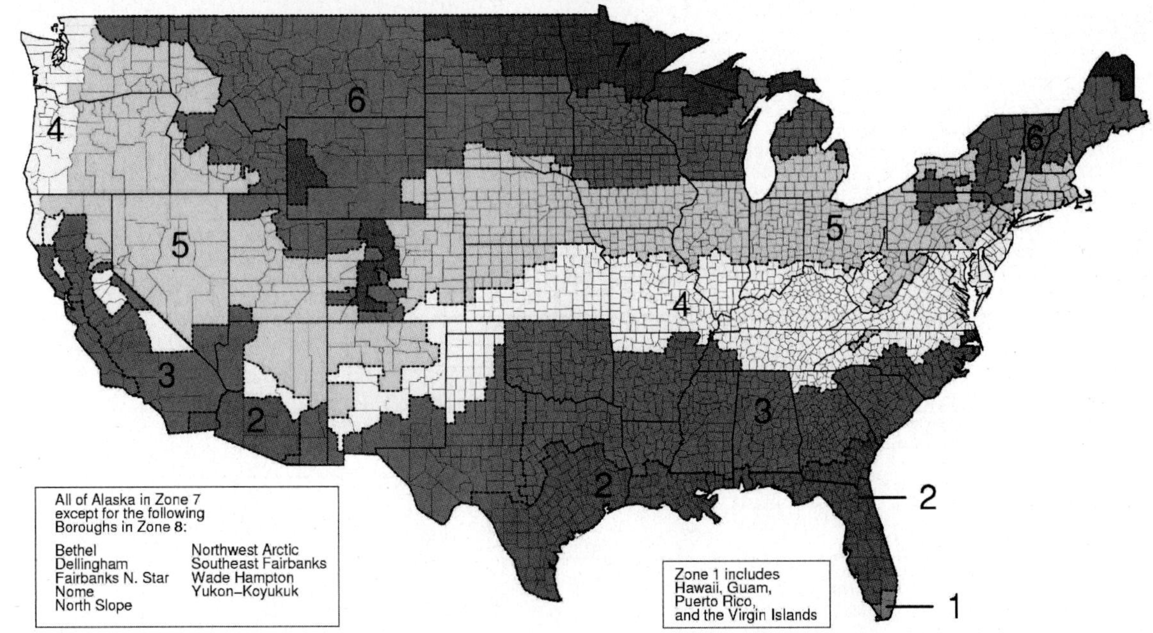

Table R260120-20 Watts per Square Foot for Lighting and Misc. Power by Building Type & Space

Building / Space	Percent	Lighting	Misc
Apartment, Low: Area = 20,000 SF; Floors = 2; Heating = DX Coils; Cooling = DX Coils			
Room	85%	0.50	0.10
Storage	8%	1.19	0.00
Laundry	7%	1.28	0.15
Weighted Average		**0.61**	**0.10**
Apartment, Mid: Area = 40,000 SF; Floors = 5; Heating = DX Coils; Cooling = DX Coils			
Room	71%	0.50	0.30
Corridor	16%	0.57	0.00
Storage	7%	1.19	0.00
Laundry	6%	1.28	0.15
Average		**0.61**	**0.22**
Apartment, High: Area = 72,000 SF; Floors = 8; Heating = DX Coils; Cooling = DX Coils			
Room	71%	0.50	0.30
Corridor	16%	0.57	0.00
Storage	7%	1.19	0.00
Laundry	6%	1.28	0.15
Weighted Average		**0.61**	**0.22**
Assisted Living: Area = 10,000 SF; Floors = 1; Heating = Furnace; Cooling = DX Coils			
Room	70%	1.46	0.25
Dining	15%	1.85	0.10
Food Prep	10%	1.19	1.00
Care	5%	1.34	1.00
Weighted Average		**1.49**	**0.34**

Building / Space	Percent	Lighting	Misc
Auditorium: Area = 70,000 SF; Floors = 1; Heating = Hot Water Coils; Cooling = Chilled Water Coils			
Theater	70%	0.90	
Lobby	15%	1.50	
Office	5%	1.30	
Corridor	5%	0.60	
MEP	5%	0.70	
Weighted Average		**0.99**	
Bank: Area = 25,000 SF; Floors = 2; Heating = Furnace; Cooling = DX Coils			
Bank	60%	2.33	0.45
Corridor	10%	0.57	0.00
Office	10%	1.49	0.75
Lobby	5%	1.52	0.25
Restrooms	5%	0.77	0.10
Conference	4%	0.92	0.10
MEP	4%	0.81	0.10
Production	2%	1.64	0.70
Weighted Average		**1.82**	**0.38**
Community Center: Area = 35,000 SF; Floors = 1; Heating = Furnace; Cooling = DX Coils			
Convention	50%	1.27	
Dining	15%	1.85	
Food Prep	15%	1.19	
Storage	10%	1.19	
Corridor	5%	0.57	
Restrooms	5%	0.77	
Weighted Average		**1.28**	
Convention Center: Area = 150,000 SF; Floors = 2; Heating = Hot Water Coils; Cooling = Chilled Water Coils			
Convention	65%	1.27	0.25
Conference	20%	0.92	0.10
Dining	5%	1.85	0.10
Corridor	4%	0.57	0.00
Food Prep	3%	1.19	1.00
Restrooms	3%	0.77	0.10
Weighted Average		**1.18**	**0.22**

Building / Space	Percent	Lighting	Misc
Day Care: Area = 2,500 SF; Floors = 1; Heating = Furnace; Cooling = DX Coils			
Classroom	45%	1.45	
Corridor	15%	0.57	
Library	15%	1.67	
Food Prep	10%	1.19	
Restrooms	7%	0.77	
Office	5%	1.49	
Storage	3%	1.19	
Weighted Average		**1.27**	
Fitness Center: Area = 20,000 SF; Floors = 1; Heating = Furnace; Cooling = DX Coils			
Exercise	80%	1.13	0.10
Corridor	5%	0.57	0.00
MEP	5%	0.81	0.10
Office	5%	1.24	0.75
Restrooms	7%	0.77	0.10
Weighted Average		**1.07**	**0.13**
Hospital: Area = 250,000 SF; Floors = 4; Heating = Hot Water Coils; Cooling = Chilled Water Coils			
Medical	60%	1.34	1.00
Laboratory	15%	3.19	1.00
Corridor	10%	0.57	0.00
Laundry	5%	1.28	0.15
MEP	5%	0.81	0.10
Restrooms	5%	0.77	0.10
Weighted Average		**1.48**	**0.77**
Hotel: Area = 180,000 SF; Floors = 10; Heating = Furnace; Cooling = DX Coils			
Room	75%	1.46	
Meeting Center	15%	1.27	
Corridor	8%	0.57	
MEP	2%	0.81	
Weighted Average		**1.35**	

Steps:

1. Determine climate zone using R260120-10
2. Use R260120-20 to determine lighting and miscellaneous power for appropriate building type
3. Use corresponding building type and climate zone in R260120-30 to determine other systems

*Values for R260120-20 & -30 were derived by performing an energy analysis using the eQUEST® software from James J. Hirsch & Associates. eQUEST is a trademark of James J. Hirsch

**Additional systems may be necessary

Table R260120-20 Watts per Square Foot for Lighting and Misc. Power by Building Type & Space (cont)

Building / Space	Percent	Lighting	Misc
Manufacturing, General: Area = 100,000 SF; Floors = 10; Heating = Furnace; Cooling = DX Coils			
Work	60%	2.66	1.00
Storage	25%	1.19	0.00
Office	10%	1.24	0.75
Restrooms	3%	0.77	0.10
MEP	2%	0.81	0.10
Weighted Average		**2.06**	**0.68**
Manufacturing, High Tech: Area = 200,000 SF; Floors = 1; Heating = Furnace; Cooling = DX Coils			
Work	45%	3.19	1.00
Office	27%	1.24	0.75
Corridor	18%	0.57	0.00
Dining	3%	1.85	0.10
Conference	2%	0.92	0.10
Server	2%	1.24	5.00
MEP	2%	0.81	0.10
Food Prep	1%	1.19	1.00
Weighted Average		**2.00**	**0.77**
Medical Clinic: Area = 20,000 SF; Floors = 1; Heating = Furnace; Cooling = DX Coils			
Clinic	50%	1.40	
General Office	15%	1.30	
Private Office	10%	1.30	
Laboratory	10%	1.30	
Storage	5%	0.60	
Restrooms	5%	0.60	
MEP	5%	0.70	
Weighted Average		**1.25**	
Motel: Area = 10,000 SF; Floors = 1; Heating = DX Coils; Cooling = DX Coils			
Room	95%	1.46	0.25
Office	3%	1.24	0.75
MEP	2%	0.81	0.10
Weighted Average		**1.44**	**0.26**
Museum: Area = 20,000 SF; Floors = 1; Heating = Hot Water Coils; Cooling = Chilled Water Coils			
Exhibit Area	65%	1.03	0.25
Theater	15%	1.02	0.25
Lobby	5%	1.77	0.25
MEP	5%	0.81	0.10
Office	5%	1.49	0.75
Restrooms	5%	0.77	0.10
Weighted Average		**1.06**	**0.26**
Office, Low: Area = 25,000 SF; Floors = 2; Heating = Furnace; Cooling = DX Coils			
Office	70%	1.30	0.75
Corridor	10%	0.60	0.00
Lobby	5%	1.10	0.25
Restrooms	5%	0.60	0.10
Conference	4%	1.60	0.10
MEP	4%	0.70	0.10
Production	2%	1.50	0.70
Weighted Average		**1.18**	**0.56**
Office, Mid: Area = 125,000 SF; Floors = 4; Heating = Hot Water Coils; Cooling = Chilled Water Coils			
Office Open	40%	1.24	0.75
Office Private	30%	1.49	0.75
Corridor	10%	0.57	0.00
Lobby	5%	1.52	0.25
Restrooms	5%	0.77	0.10
Conference	4%	0.92	0.10
MEP	4%	0.81	0.10
Production	2%	1.64	0.70
Weighted Average		**1.22**	**0.56**
Office, High: Area = 250,000 SF; Floors = 8; Heating = Hot Water Coils; Cooling = Chilled Water Coils			
Office Open	45%	1.24	0.75
Office Private	25%	1.49	0.75
Corridor	10%	0.57	0.00
Lobby	5%	1.52	0.25
Conference	4%	0.92	0.10
Production	2%	1.64	0.70
Restrooms	5%	0.77	0.10
MEP	4%	0.81	0.10
Weighted Average		**1.20**	**0.56**
Restaurant, Bar/Lounge: Area = 4,000 SF; Floors = 1; Heating = Furnace; Cooling = DX Coils			
Lounge	35%	1.85	0.10
Dining	30%	1.85	0.10
Food Prep	25%	1.19	1.00
MEP	5%	0.81	0.10
Restrooms	5%	0.77	0.10
Weighted Average		**1.58**	**0.33**
Restaurant, Full: Area = 5,000 SF; Floors = 1; Heating = Furnace; Cooling = DX Coils			
Dining	60%	1.85	0.10
Food Prep	30%	1.19	1.00
Restrooms	5%	0.77	0.10
MEP	5%	0.81	0.10
Weighted Average		**1.55**	**0.37**
Restaurant, Quick: Area = 2,500 SF; Floors = 1; Heating = Furnace; Cooling = DX Coils			
Dining	50%	1.85	0.10
Food Prep	35%	1.19	1.00
Restrooms	10%	0.77	0.10
MEP	5%	0.81	0.10
Weighted Average		**1.46**	**0.42**
Store, Convenience: Area = 3,000 SF; Floors = 1; Heating = Furnace; Cooling = DX Coils			
Retail	80%	2.38	0.25
Office	10%	1.49	0.75
Restrooms	10%	0.77	0.10
Weighted Average		**2.13**	**0.29**
Store, Department: Area = 120,000 SF; Floors = 2; Heating = Hot Water Coils; Cooling = Chilled Water Coils			
Retail	55%	2.38	0.25
Exhibit Area	15%	1.03	0.25
Storage	16%	1.19	0.00
Office	5%	1.24	0.75
Smoking Lounge	2%	1.85	0.10
Restrooms	2%	0.77	0.10
MEP	5%	0.81	0.10
Weighted Average		**1.81**	**0.22**
Store, Large: Area = 70,000 SF; Floors = 1; Heating = Furnace; Cooling = DX Coils			
Retail	65%	2.38	0.25
Storage	20%	1.19	0.00
Office	5%	1.24	0.75
Dining	3%	1.85	0.10
Food Prep	1%	1.19	1.00
Lounge	2%	1.85	0.10
Restrooms	2%	0.77	0.10
MEP	2%	0.81	0.10
Weighted Average		**1.98**	**0.22**
Store, Small: Area = 5,000 SF; Floors = 1; Heating = Furnace; Cooling = DX Coils			
Retail	58%	2.38	0.25
Exhibit Area	15%	1.03	0.25
Storage	15%	1.19	0.00
Office	5%	1.24	0.75
Restrooms	5%	0.77	0.10
MEP	2%	0.81	0.10
Weighted Average		**1.83**	**0.23**
Store, Strip Mall: Area = 15,000 SF; Floors = 1; Heating = Furnace; Cooling = DX Coils			
Retail	38%	2.38	0.25
Atrium	20%	1.55	0.13
Exhibit Area	15%	1.03	0.25
Storage	15%	1.19	0.00
Office	5%	1.24	0.75
Restrooms	5%	0.77	0.10
MEP	2%	0.81	0.10
Weighted Average		**1.66**	**0.20**
Store, Warehouse: Area = 150,000 SF; Floors = 1; Heating = Furnace; Cooling = DX Coils			
Retail	75%	2.38	0.25
Storage	20%	1.19	0.00
Office	4%	1.24	0.75
Restrooms	1%	0.77	0.10
Weighted Average		**2.08**	**0.22**
School, Elementary: Area = 35,000 SF; Floors = 1; Heating = Furnace; Cooling = DX Coils			
Classroom	50%	1.45	0.50
Corridor	15%	0.57	0.00
Gym	10%	1.13	0.10
Dining	5%	1.85	0.10
Food Prep	5%	1.19	1.00
Library	5%	1.78	0.25
Auditorium	5%	1.62	0.25
Restrooms	5%	0.77	0.10
Weighted Average		**1.28**	**0.35**
School, Middle: Area = 75,000 SF; Floors = 1; Heating = Furnace; Cooling = DX Coils			
Classroom	50%	1.45	0.50
Corridor	14%	0.57	0.00
Gym	9%	1.13	0.10
Auditorium	7%	1.62	0.25
Dining	6%	1.85	0.10
Food Prep	5%	1.19	1.00
Library	5%	1.78	0.25
Restrooms	4%	0.77	0.10
Weighted Average		**1.31**	**0.35**
School, High: Area = 150,000 SF; Floors = 2; Heating = Furnace; Cooling = DX Coils			
Classroom	45%	1.45	0.50
Corridor	10%	0.57	0.00
Gym	10%	1.13	0.10
Dining	10%	1.85	0.10
Food Prep	5%	1.19	1.00
Library	5%	1.78	0.25
Auditorium	10%	1.62	0.25
Restrooms	5%	0.77	0.10
Weighted Average		**1.36**	**0.34**
School, College: Area = 250,000 SF; Floors = 4; Heating = Furnace; Cooling = DX Coils			
Classroom	50%	1.45	0.50
Office	15%	1.49	0.75
Corridor	12%	0.57	0.00
Gym	10%	1.13	0.10
Library	5%	1.78	0.25
Dining	3%	1.85	0.10
Restrooms	3%	0.77	0.10
Food Prep	2%	1.19	1.00
Weighted Average		**1.32**	**0.41**
Service Station: Area = 2,000 SF; Floors = 1; Heating = Furnace; Cooling = DX Coils			
Workshop	70%	1.31	0.50
Office	10%	1.49	0.75
Restrooms	10%	0.77	0.10
Retail	10%	2.38	0.25
Weighted Average		**1.38**	**0.46**
Storage, High Bay: Area = 200,000 SF; Floors = 1; Heating = Furnace; Cooling = DX Coils			
Storage	85%	1.19	0.00
Office	10%	1.24	0.75
Restrooms	3%	0.77	0.10
MEP	2%	0.81	0.10
Weighted Average		**1.17**	**0.08**
Storage, Low Bay: Area = 70,000 SF; Floors = 1; Heating = Furnace; Cooling = DX Coils			
Storage	85%	1.19	0.00
Office	10%	1.24	0.75
Restrooms	3%	0.77	0.10
MEP	2%	0.81	0.10
Weighted Average		**1.17**	**0.08**

Table R260120-30 Watts per S.F. for Various Systems by Building Type & Climate Zone

Building / Zone	Heating	Cooling	Heat rejection	Auxiliary (pumps)	Vent fan	Supp heat pump
Apartment, Low						
Zone 1	0.42	3.65	0.00	0.00	0.12	1.47
Zone 2	0.63	3.53	0.00	0.00	0.12	4.01
Zone 3	0.64	3.45	0.00	0.00	0.13	4.63
Zone 4	0.65	3.09	0.00	0.00	0.13	7.41
Zone 5	0.67	2.88	0.00	0.00	0.12	10.30
Zone 6	0.69	2.66	0.00	0.00	0.13	10.68
Zone 7	0.85	2.11	0.00	0.00	0.12	11.76
Average	**0.65**	**3.05**	**0.00**	**0.00**	**0.13**	**7.18**
Apartment, Mid						
Zone 1	0.00	1.90	0.00	0.00	0.11	0.00
Zone 2	0.43	1.82	0.00	0.00	0.11	2.12
Zone 3	0.48	1.69	0.00	0.00	0.11	2.32
Zone 4	0.67	1.67	0.00	0.00	0.12	4.25
Zone 5	0.70	1.54	0.00	0.00	0.12	4.79
Zone 6	0.72	1.45	0.00	0.00	0.12	5.07
Zone 7	0.93	1.39	0.00	0.00	0.12	5.11
Average	**0.56**	**1.63**	**0.00**	**0.00**	**0.12**	**3.38**
Apartment, High						
Zone 1	0.00	2.11	0.00	0.00	0.14	0.00
Zone 2	0.00	2.03	0.00	0.00	0.13	0.00
Zone 3	0.48	1.88	0.00	0.00	0.14	1.75
Zone 4	0.57	1.77	0.00	0.00	0.14	4.22
Zone 5	0.66	1.64	0.00	0.00	0.14	5.40
Zone 6	0.71	1.63	0.00	0.00	0.15	5.64
Zone 7	0.91	1.18	0.00	0.00	0.14	5.75
Average	**0.48**	**1.75**	**0.00**	**0.00**	**0.14**	**3.25**
Assisted Living						
Zone 1	0.00	2.65	0.00	0.04	0.31	0.00
Zone 2	0.00	2.63	0.00	0.04	0.31	0.00
Zone 3	0.00	2.57	0.00	0.04	0.31	0.00
Zone 4	0.00	2.50	0.00	0.04	0.31	0.00
Zone 5	0.00	2.42	0.00	0.04	0.30	0.00
Zone 6	0.00	1.99	0.00	0.04	0.32	0.00
Zone 7	0.00	1.90	0.00	0.04	0.30	0.00
Average	**0.00**	**2.38**	**0.00**	**0.04**	**0.31**	**0.00**
Auditorium						
Zone 1	0.00	2.32	0.34	0.37	1.03	0.00
Zone 2	0.00	2.32	0.34	0.38	1.03	0.00
Zone 3	0.00	2.29	0.33	0.38	1.04	0.00
Zone 4	0.00	2.26	0.29	0.35	1.05	0.00
Zone 5	0.00	2.20	0.34	0.39	1.04	0.00
Zone 6	0.00	1.71	0.14	0.34	1.05	0.00
Zone 7	0.00	1.38	0.23	0.36	1.04	0.00
Average	**0.00**	**2.07**	**0.29**	**0.37**	**1.04**	**0.00**
Bank						
Zone 1	0.00	3.32	0.00	0.00	0.60	0.00
Zone 2	0.00	3.28	0.00	0.00	0.61	0.00
Zone 3	0.00	3.28	0.00	0.00	0.61	0.00
Zone 4	0.00	3.21	0.00	0.00	0.60	0.00
Zone 5	0.00	3.06	0.00	0.00	0.59	0.00
Zone 6	0.00	2.82	0.00	0.00	0.61	0.00
Zone 7	0.00	2.66	0.00	0.00	0.60	0.00
Average	**0.00**	**3.09**	**0.00**	**0.00**	**0.60**	**0.00**

Building / Zone	Heating	Cooling	Heat rejection	Auxiliary (pumps)	Vent fan	Supp heat pump
Community Center						
Zone 1	0.00	2.70	0.00	0.00	0.44	0.00
Zone 2	0.00	2.66	0.00	0.00	0.44	0.00
Zone 3	0.00	2.66	0.00	0.00	0.45	0.00
Zone 4	0.00	2.44	0.00	0.00	0.45	0.00
Zone 5	0.00	2.42	0.00	0.00	0.44	0.00
Zone 6	0.00	2.16	0.00	0.00	0.44	0.00
Zone 7	0.00	1.91	0.00	0.00	0.44	0.00
Average	**0.00**	**2.42**	**0.00**	**0.00**	**0.45**	**0.00**
Convention Center						
Zone 1	0.00	1.46	0.25	0.27	0.31	0.00
Zone 2	0.00	1.44	0.25	0.27	0.29	0.00
Zone 3	0.00	1.43	0.24	0.26	0.30	0.00
Zone 4	0.00	1.42	0.23	0.26	0.28	0.00
Zone 5	0.00	1.30	0.29	0.31	0.22	0.00
Zone 6	0.00	1.17	0.12	0.29	0.16	0.00
Zone 7	0.00	0.90	0.20	0.31	0.16	0.00
Average	**0.00**	**1.30**	**0.22**	**0.28**	**0.25**	**0.00**
Day Care						
Zone 1	0.00	3.47	0.00	0.02	0.29	0.00
Zone 2	0.00	3.42	0.00	0.02	0.28	0.00
Zone 3	0.00	3.40	0.00	0.02	0.29	0.00
Zone 4	0.00	3.29	0.00	0.02	0.29	0.00
Zone 5	0.00	3.08	0.00	0.02	0.29	0.00
Zone 6	0.00	2.29	0.00	0.02	0.29	0.00
Zone 7	0.00	2.12	0.00	0.02	0.24	0.00
Average	**0.05**	**3.01**	**0.05**	**0.07**	**0.29**	**0.05**
Fitness Center						
Zone 1	0.00	4.97	0.00	0.00	0.59	0.00
Zone 2	0.00	4.94	0.00	0.00	0.59	0.00
Zone 3	0.00	4.80	0.00	0.00	0.60	0.00
Zone 4	0.00	4.76	0.00	0.00	0.60	0.00
Zone 5	0.00	4.75	0.00	0.00	0.59	0.00
Zone 6	0.00	4.13	0.00	0.00	0.60	0.00
Zone 7	0.00	3.27	0.00	0.00	0.60	0.00
Average	**0.00**	**4.52**	**0.00**	**0.00**	**0.59**	**0.00**
Hospital						
Zone 1	0.00	1.54	0.23	0.26	0.80	0.00
Zone 2	0.00	1.47	0.22	0.25	0.80	0.00
Zone 3	0.00	1.44	0.22	0.25	0.81	0.00
Zone 4	0.00	1.42	0.22	0.25	0.81	0.00
Zone 5	0.00	1.37	0.23	0.27	0.81	0.00
Zone 6	0.00	1.26	0.15	0.25	0.82	0.00
Zone 7	0.00	1.07	0.19	0.26	0.82	0.00
Average	**0.00**	**1.36**	**0.21**	**0.26**	**0.81**	**0.00**
Hotel						
Zone 1	0.00	1.77	0.00	0.01	0.26	0.00
Zone 2	0.00	1.64	0.00	0.01	0.26	0.00
Zone 3	0.00	1.62	0.00	0.01	0.27	0.00
Zone 4	0.00	1.62	0.00	0.01	0.27	0.00
Zone 5	0.00	1.51	0.00	0.01	0.27	0.00
Zone 6	0.00	1.25	0.00	0.01	0.28	0.00
Zone 7	0.00	1.23	0.00	0.01	0.28	0.00
Average	**0.00**	**1.52**	**0.00**	**0.01**	**0.27**	**0.00**

Table R260120-30 Watts per S.F. for Various Systems by Building Type & Climate Zone (cont.)

Building / Zone	Heating	Cooling	Heat rejection	Auxiliary (pumps)	Vent fan	Supp heat pump
Manufacturing, General						
Zone 1	0.00	1.46	0.00	0.00	0.13	0.00
Zone 2	0.00	1.45	0.00	0.00	0.13	0.00
Zone 3	0.00	1.43	0.00	0.00	0.13	0.00
Zone 4	0.00	1.39	0.00	0.00	0.13	0.00
Zone 5	0.00	1.39	0.00	0.00	0.13	0.00
Zone 6	0.00	1.21	0.00	0.00	0.13	0.00
Zone 7	0.00	1.00	0.00	0.00	0.13	0.00
Average	**0.00**	**1.33**	**0.00**	**0.00**	**0.13**	**0.00**
Manufacturing, High Tech						
Zone 1	0.00	2.15	0.00	0.00	0.17	0.00
Zone 2	0.00	2.12	0.00	0.00	0.17	0.00
Zone 3	0.00	2.04	0.00	0.00	0.17	0.00
Zone 4	0.00	2.01	0.00	0.00	0.17	0.00
Zone 5	0.00	1.88	0.00	0.00	0.17	0.00
Zone 6	0.00	1.63	0.00	0.00	0.17	0.00
Zone 7	0.00	1.50	0.00	0.00	0.17	0.00
Average	**0.00**	**1.90**	**0.00**	**0.00**	**0.17**	**0.00**
Medical Clinic						
Zone 1	0.00	3.15	0.00	0.00	0.54	0.00
Zone 2	0.00	3.09	0.00	0.00	0.53	0.00
Zone 3	0.00	3.07	0.00	0.00	0.54	0.00
Zone 4	0.00	3.02	0.00	0.00	0.54	0.00
Zone 5	0.00	2.99	0.00	0.00	0.54	0.00
Zone 6	0.00	2.58	0.00	0.00	0.55	0.00
Zone 7	0.00	2.45	0.00	0.00	0.52	0.00
Average	**0.00**	**2.91**	**0.00**	**0.00**	**0.54**	**0.00**
Motel						
Zone 1	0.97	2.68	0.00	0.00	0.19	2.15
Zone 2	1.19	2.52	0.00	0.00	0.18	4.43
Zone 3	1.19	2.52	0.00	0.00	0.19	4.81
Zone 4	1.19	2.42	0.00	0.00	0.21	7.39
Zone 5	1.28	2.26	0.00	0.00	0.21	7.82
Zone 6	1.29	2.07	0.00	0.00	0.23	8.89
Zone 7	1.39	1.97	0.00	0.00	0.23	9.51
Average	**1.21**	**2.35**	**0.00**	**0.00**	**0.21**	**6.43**
Museum						
Zone 1	0.00	3.77	0.00	0.11	0.67	0.00
Zone 2	0.00	3.71	0.00	0.12	0.77	0.00
Zone 3	0.00	3.59	0.00	0.12	0.72	0.00
Zone 4	0.00	3.47	0.00	0.14	0.74	0.00
Zone 5	0.00	3.42	0.00	0.16	0.51	0.00
Zone 6	0.00	2.39	0.00	0.15	0.23	0.00
Zone 7	0.00	1.69	0.00	0.17	0.24	0.00
Average	**0.00**	**3.15**	**0.00**	**0.14**	**0.55**	**0.00**
Office, Low						
Zone 1	0.00	2.90	0.00	0.02	0.29	0.00
Zone 2	0.00	2.90	0.00	0.02	0.30	0.00
Zone 3	0.00	2.81	0.00	0.02	0.30	0.00
Zone 4	0.00	2.70	0.00	0.02	0.29	0.00
Zone 5	0.00	2.66	0.00	0.02	0.29	0.00
Zone 6	0.00	2.04	0.00	0.02	0.30	0.00
Zone 7	0.00	1.82	0.00	0.02	0.29	0.00
Average	**0.00**	**2.55**	**0.00**	**0.02**	**0.29**	**0.00**

Building / Zone	Heating	Cooling	Heat rejection	Auxiliary (pumps)	Vent fan	Supp heat pump
Office, Mid						
Zone 1	0.00	1.61	0.31	0.33	0.45	0.00
Zone 2	0.00	1.60	0.29	0.32	0.46	0.00
Zone 3	0.00	1.59	0.28	0.34	0.42	0.00
Zone 4	0.00	1.56	0.27	0.33	0.43	0.00
Zone 5	0.00	1.55	0.34	0.36	0.37	0.00
Zone 6	0.00	1.29	0.16	0.34	0.31	0.00
Zone 7	0.00	1.10	0.22	0.35	0.32	0.00
Average	**0.00**	**1.47**	**0.27**	**0.34**	**0.40**	**0.00**
Office, High						
Zone 1	0.00	1.70	0.30	0.33	0.44	0.00
Zone 2	0.00	1.59	0.29	0.32	0.41	0.00
Zone 3	0.00	1.59	0.32	0.34	0.42	0.00
Zone 4	0.00	1.58	0.28	0.35	0.42	0.00
Zone 5	0.00	1.58	0.32	0.36	0.41	0.00
Zone 6	0.00	1.11	0.16	0.29	0.33	0.00
Zone 7	0.00	0.86	0.23	0.31	0.37	0.00
Average	**0.00**	**1.43**	**0.27**	**0.33**	**0.40**	**0.00**
Restaurant, Bar/Lounge						
Zone 1	0.00	3.07	0.00	0.06	0.24	0.00
Zone 2	0.00	2.87	0.00	0.06	0.25	0.00
Zone 3	0.00	2.85	0.00	0.06	0.24	0.00
Zone 4	0.00	2.83	0.00	0.06	0.24	0.00
Zone 5	0.00	2.80	0.00	0.06	0.24	0.00
Zone 6	0.00	1.88	0.00	0.06	0.24	0.00
Zone 7	0.00	1.87	0.00	0.06	0.23	0.00
Average	**0.00**	**2.59**	**0.00**	**0.06**	**0.24**	**0.00**
Restaurant, Full						
Zone 1	0.00	3.37	0.00	0.05	0.38	0.00
Zone 2	0.00	3.30	0.00	0.05	0.39	0.00
Zone 3	0.00	3.25	0.00	0.05	0.39	0.00
Zone 4	0.00	3.20	0.00	0.05	0.39	0.00
Zone 5	0.00	3.03	0.00	0.05	0.38	0.00
Zone 6	0.00	2.35	0.00	0.05	0.39	0.00
Zone 7	0.00	2.33	0.00	0.05	0.38	0.00
Average	**0.00**	**2.98**	**0.00**	**0.05**	**0.38**	**0.00**
Restaurant, Quick						
Zone 1	0.00	3.78	0.00	0.08	0.48	0.00
Zone 2	0.00	3.72	0.00	0.08	0.50	0.00
Zone 3	0.00	3.64	0.00	0.08	0.50	0.00
Zone 4	0.00	3.60	0.00	0.08	0.50	0.00
Zone 5	0.00	3.42	0.00	0.08	0.49	0.00
Zone 6	0.00	2.74	0.00	0.08	0.51	0.00
Zone 7	0.00	2.69	0.00	0.08	0.49	0.00
Average	**0.00**	**3.37**	**0.00**	**0.08**	**0.50**	**0.00**
Store, Convenience						
Zone 1	0.00	4.08	0.00	0.02	0.29	0.00
Zone 2	0.00	3.66	0.00	0.02	0.30	0.00
Zone 3	0.00	3.60	0.00	0.02	0.30	0.00
Zone 4	0.00	3.46	0.00	0.02	0.29	0.00
Zone 5	0.00	3.28	0.00	0.02	0.29	0.00
Zone 6	0.00	2.66	0.00	0.02	0.27	0.00
Zone 7	0.00	2.50	0.00	0.02	0.24	0.00
Average	**0.00**	**3.32**	**0.00**	**0.02**	**0.28**	**0.00**

Table R260120-30 Watts per S.F. for Various Systems by Building Type & Climate Zone (cont.)

Building / Zone	Heating	Cooling	Heat rejection	Auxiliary (pumps)	Vent fan	Supp heat pump
Store, Department						
Zone 1	0.00	1.65	0.20	0.23	0.63	0.00
Zone 2	0.00	1.61	0.20	0.23	0.63	0.00
Zone 3	0.00	1.59	0.19	0.22	0.64	0.00
Zone 4	0.00	1.52	0.19	0.23	0.64	0.00
Zone 5	0.00	1.51	0.21	0.24	0.63	0.00
Zone 6	0.00	1.32	0.13	0.21	0.63	0.00
Zone 7	0.00	0.98	0.17	0.23	0.63	0.00
Average	**0.00**	**1.45**	**0.18**	**0.23**	**0.63**	**0.00**
Store, Large						
Zone 1	0.00	2.68	0.00	0.00	0.16	0.00
Zone 2	0.00	2.61	0.00	0.00	0.17	0.00
Zone 3	0.00	2.61	0.00	0.00	0.17	0.00
Zone 4	0.00	2.56	0.00	0.00	0.16	0.00
Zone 5	0.00	2.53	0.00	0.00	0.16	0.00
Zone 6	0.00	1.84	0.00	0.00	0.16	0.00
Zone 7	0.00	1.50	0.00	0.00	0.16	0.00
Average	**0.00**	**2.33**	**0.00**	**0.00**	**0.16**	**0.00**
Store, Small						
Zone 1	0.00	3.60	0.00	0.01	0.25	0.00
Zone 2	0.00	3.51	0.00	0.01	0.26	0.00
Zone 3	0.00	3.38	0.00	0.01	0.25	0.00
Zone 4	0.00	3.32	0.00	0.01	0.25	0.00
Zone 5	0.00	3.23	0.00	0.01	0.24	0.00
Zone 6	0.00	2.49	0.00	0.01	0.23	0.00
Zone 7	0.00	2.17	0.00	0.01	0.21	0.00
Average	**0.00**	**3.10**	**0.00**	**0.01**	**0.24**	**0.00**
Store, Strip Mall						
Zone 1	0.00	3.36	0.00	0.02	0.25	0.00
Zone 2	0.00	3.30	0.00	0.02	0.25	0.00
Zone 3	0.00	3.14	0.00	0.02	0.25	0.00
Zone 4	0.00	3.14	0.00	0.02	0.25	0.00
Zone 5	0.00	2.24	0.00	0.02	0.24	0.00
Zone 6	0.00	1.96	0.00	0.02	0.25	0.00
Zone 7	0.00	1.64	0.00	0.02	0.24	0.00
Average	**0.00**	**2.52**	**0.00**	**0.02**	**0.25**	**0.00**
Store, Warehouse						
Zone 1	0.00	2.99	0.00	0.00	0.21	0.00
Zone 2	0.00	2.97	0.00	0.00	0.21	0.00
Zone 3	0.00	2.94	0.00	0.00	0.21	0.00
Zone 4	0.00	2.83	0.00	0.00	0.21	0.00
Zone 5	0.00	2.70	0.00	0.00	0.21	0.00
Zone 6	0.00	2.10	0.00	0.00	0.21	0.00
Zone 7	0.00	1.78	0.00	0.00	0.21	0.00
Average	**0.00**	**2.61**	**0.00**	**0.00**	**0.21**	**0.00**
School, Elementary						
Zone 1	0.00	2.73	0.00	0.01	0.21	0.00
Zone 2	0.00	2.69	0.00	0.01	0.21	0.00
Zone 3	0.00	2.63	0.00	0.01	0.21	0.00
Zone 4	0.00	2.61	0.00	0.01	0.20	0.00
Zone 5	0.00	2.51	0.00	0.01	0.20	0.00
Zone 6	0.00	1.71	0.00	0.01	0.20	0.00
Zone 7	0.00	1.64	0.00	0.01	0.20	0.00
Average	**0.00**	**2.36**	**0.00**	**0.01**	**0.20**	**0.00**

Building / Zone	Heating	Cooling	Heat rejection	Auxiliary (pumps)	Vent fan	Supp heat pump
School, Middle						
Zone 1	0.00	2.48	0.00	0.00	0.17	0.00
Zone 2	0.00	2.45	0.00	0.00	0.17	0.00
Zone 3	0.00	2.41	0.00	0.00	0.18	0.00
Zone 4	0.00	2.35	0.00	0.00	0.17	0.00
Zone 5	0.00	2.26	0.00	0.00	0.17	0.00
Zone 6	0.00	1.61	0.00	0.00	0.17	0.00
Zone 7	0.00	1.49	0.00	0.00	0.17	0.00
Average	**0.00**	**2.15**	**0.00**	**0.00**	**0.17**	**0.00**
School, High						
Zone 1	0.00	3.24	0.00	0.01	0.22	0.00
Zone 2	0.00	3.08	0.00	0.01	0.22	0.00
Zone 3	0.00	3.05	0.00	0.01	0.23	0.00
Zone 4	0.00	3.00	0.00	0.01	0.23	0.00
Zone 5	0.00	2.94	0.00	0.01	0.23	0.00
Zone 6	0.00	1.98	0.00	0.01	0.23	0.00
Zone 7	0.00	1.81	0.00	0.01	0.23	0.00
Average	**0.00**	**2.73**	**0.00**	**0.01**	**0.23**	**0.00**
School, College						
Zone 1	0.00	2.92	0.00	0.00	0.20	0.00
Zone 2	0.00	2.91	0.00	0.00	0.20	0.00
Zone 3	0.00	2.78	0.00	0.00	0.20	0.00
Zone 4	0.00	2.72	0.00	0.00	0.20	0.00
Zone 5	0.00	2.43	0.00	0.00	0.20	0.00
Zone 6	0.00	1.77	0.00	0.00	0.20	0.00
Zone 7	0.00	1.51	0.00	0.00	0.19	0.00
Average	**0.00**	**2.43**	**0.00**	**0.00**	**0.20**	**0.00**
Service Station						
Zone 1	0.00	10.42	0.00	0.03	0.47	0.00
Zone 2	0.00	9.01	0.00	0.03	0.46	0.00
Zone 3	0.00	7.82	0.00	0.03	0.49	0.00
Zone 4	0.00	7.02	0.00	0.03	0.47	0.00
Zone 5	0.00	6.13	0.00	0.03	0.46	0.00
Zone 6	0.00	4.32	0.00	0.03	0.45	0.00
Zone 7	0.00	4.18	0.00	0.03	0.40	0.00
Average	**0.00**	**6.99**	**0.00**	**0.03**	**0.46**	**0.00**
Storage, High Bay						
Zone 1	0.00	1.98	0.00	0.00	0.17	0.00
Zone 2	0.00	1.97	0.00	0.00	0.18	0.00
Zone 3	0.00	1.90	0.00	0.00	0.18	0.00
Zone 4	0.00	1.89	0.00	0.00	0.18	0.00
Zone 5	0.00	1.85	0.00	0.00	0.17	0.00
Zone 6	0.00	1.29	0.00	0.00	0.17	0.00
Zone 7	0.00	1.10	0.00	0.00	0.17	0.00
Average	**0.00**	**1.71**	**0.00**	**0.00**	**0.17**	**0.00**
Storage, Low Bay						
Zone 1	0.00	1.87	0.00	0.00	0.16	0.00
Zone 2	0.00	1.85	0.00	0.00	0.16	0.00
Zone 3	0.00	1.82	0.00	0.00	0.16	0.00
Zone 4	0.00	1.77	0.00	0.00	0.16	0.00
Zone 5	0.00	1.76	0.00	0.00	0.16	0.00
Zone 6	0.00	1.20	0.00	0.00	0.16	0.00
Zone 7	0.00	1.00	0.00	0.00	0.16	0.00
Average	**0.00**	**1.61**	**0.00**	**0.00**	**0.16**	**0.00**

R260519-20 Armored Cable

Armored Cable – Quantities are taken off in the same manner as wire.

Bx Type Cable – Productivities are based on an average run of 50′ before terminating at a box fixture, etc. Each 50′ section includes field preparation of (2) ends with hacksaw, identification and tagging of wire. Set up is open coil type without reels attaching cable to snake and pulling across a suspended ceiling or open face wood or steel studding, price does not include drilling of studs.

Cable in Tray – Productivities are based on an average run of 100 L.F. with set up of pulling equipment for (2) 90° bends, attaching cable to pull-in means, identification and tagging of wires, set up of reels. Wire termination to breakers equipment, etc., are not included.

Job Conditions – Productivities are based on new construction to a height of 10′ in an unobstructed area. Material staging is assumed to be within 100′ of work being performed.

R260519-80 Undercarpet Systems

Takeoff Procedure for Power Systems: List components for each fitting type, tap, splice, and bend on your quantity takeoff sheet. Each component must be priced separately. Start at the power supply transition fittings and survey each circuit for the components needed. List the quantities of each component under a specific circuit number. Use the floor plan layout scale to get cable footage.

Reading across the list, combine the totals of each component in each circuit and list the total quantity in the last column. Calculate approximately 5% for scrap for items such as cable, top shield, tape, and spray adhesive. Also provide for final variations that may occur on-site.

Suggested guidelines are:

1. Equal amounts of cable and top shield should be priced.
2. For each roll of cable, price a set of cable splices.
3. For every 1 ft. of cable, price 2-1/2 ft. of hold-down tape.
4. For every 3 rolls of hold-down tape, price 1 can of spray adhesive.

Adjust final figures wherever possible to accommodate standard packaging of the product. This information is available from the distributor.

Each transition fitting requires:

1. 1 base
2. 1 cover
3. 1 transition block

Each floor fitting requires:

1. 1 frame/base kit
2. 1 transition block
3. 2 covers (duplex/blank)

Each tap requires:

1. 1 tap connector for each conductor
2. 1 pair insulating patches
3. 2 top shield connectors

Each splice requires:

1. 1 splice connector for each conductor
2. 1 pair insulating patches
3. 3 top shield connectors

Each cable bend requires:

1. 2 top shield connectors

Each cable dead end (outside of transition block) requires:

1. 1 pair insulating patches

Labor does not include:

1. Patching or leveling uneven floors.
2. Filling in holes or removing projections from concrete slabs.
3. Sealing porous floors.
4. Sweeping and vacuuming floors.
5. Removal of existing carpeting.
6. Carpet square cut-outs.
7. Installation of carpet squares.

Takeoff Procedures for Telephone Systems: After reviewing floor plans identify each transition. Number or letter each cable run from that fitting.

Start at the transition fitting and survey each circuit for the components needed. List the cable type, terminations, cable length, and floor fitting type under the specific circuit number. Use the floor plan layout scale to get the cable footage. Add some extra length (next higher increment of 5 feet) to preconnectorized cable.

Transition fittings require:

1. 1 base plate
2. 1 cover
3. 1 transition block

Floor fittings require:

1. 1 frame/base kit
2. 2 covers
3. Modular jacks

Reading across the list, combine the list of components in each circuit and list the total quantity in the last column. Calculate the necessary scrap factors for such items as tape, bottom shield and spray adhesive. Also provide for final variations that may occur on-site.

Adjust final figures whenever possible to accommodate standard packaging. Check that items such as transition fittings, floor boxes, and floor fittings that are to utilize both power and telephone have been priced as combination fittings, so as to avoid duplication.

Make sure to include marking of floors and drilling of fasteners if fittings specified are not the adhesive type.

Labor does not include:

1. Conduit or raceways before transition of floor boxes
2. Telephone cable before transition boxes
3. Terminations before transition boxes
4. Floor preparation as described in power section

Be sure to include all cable folds when pricing labor.

Takeoff Procedure for Data Systems: Start at the transition fittings and take off quantities in the same manner as the telephone system, keeping in mind that data cable does not require top or bottom shields.

The data cable is simply cross-taped on the cable run to the floor fitting.

Data cable can be purchased in either bulk form in which case coaxial connector material and labor must be priced, or in preconnectorized cut lengths.

Data cable cannot be folded and must be notched at 1 inch intervals. A count of all turns must be added to the labor portion of the estimate. (Note: Some manufacturers have prenotched cable.)

Notching required:

1. 90 degree turn requires 8 notches per side.
2. 180 degree turn requires 16 notches per side.

Floor boxes, transition boxes, and fittings are the same as described in the power and telephone procedures.

Since undercarpet systems require special hand tools, be sure to include this cost in proportion to number of crews involved in the installation.

Job Conditions: Productivity is based on new construction in an unobstructed area. Staging area is assumed to be within 200′ of work being performed.

R260519-90 Wire

Wire quantities are taken off by either measuring each cable run or by extending the conduit and raceway quantities times the number of conductors in the raceway. Ten percent should be added for waste and tie-ins. Keep in mind that the unit of measure of wire is C.L.F. not L.F. as in raceways so the formula would read:

$$\frac{\text{(L.F. Raceway x No. of Conductors) x 1.10}}{100} = \text{C.L.F.}$$

Price per C.L.F. of wire includes:

1. Setting up wire coils or spools on racks
2. Attaching wire to pull in means
3. Measuring and cutting wire
4. Pulling wire into a raceway
5. Identifying and tagging

Price does not include:

1. Connections to breakers, panelboards, or equipment
2. Splices

Job Conditions: Productivity is based on new construction to a height of 10′ in an unobstructed area. Material staging is assumed to be within 100′ of work being performed.

Economy of Scale: If more than three wires at a time are being pulled, deduct the following percentages from the labor of that grouping:

4-5 wires	25%
6-10 wires	30%
11-15 wires	35%
over 15	40%

If a wire pull is less than 100′ in length and is interrupted several times by boxes, lighting outlets, etc., it may be necessary to add the following lengths to each wire being pulled:

Junction box to junction box	2 L.F.
Lighting panel to junction box	6 L.F.
Distribution panel to sub panel	8 L.F.
Switchboard to distribution panel	12 L.F.
Switchboard to motor control center	20 L.F.
Switchboard to cable tray	40 L.F.

Measure of Drops and Riser: It is important when taking off wire quantities to include the wire for drops to electrical equipment. If heights of electrical equipment are not clearly stated, use the following guide:

	Bottom A.F.F.	Top A.F.F.	Inside Cabinet
Safety switch to 100A	5′	6′	2′
Safety switch 400 to 600A	4′	6′	3′
100A panel 12 to 30 circuit	4′	6′	3′
42 circuit panel	3′	6′	4′
Switch box	3′	3′6″	1′
Switchgear	0′	8′	8′
Motor control centers	0′	8′	8′
Transformers - wall mount	4′	8′	2′
Transformers - floor mount	0′	12′	4′

R260519-92 Minimum Copper and Aluminum Wire Size Allowed for Various Types of Insulation

Minimum Wire Sizes									
	Copper		Aluminum			Copper		Aluminum	
Amperes	THW THWN or XHHW	THHN XHHW *	THW XHHW	THHN XHHW *	Amperes	THW THWN or XHHW	THHN XHHW *	THW XHHW	THHN XHHW *
15A	#14	#14	#12	#12	195	3/0	2/0	250kcmil	4/0
20	#12	#12	#10	#10	200	3/0	3/0	250kcmil	4/0
25	#10	#10	#10	#10	205	4/0	3/0	250kcmil	4/0
30	#10	#10	# 8	# 8	225	4/0	3/0	300kcmil	250kcmil
40	# 8	# 8	# 8	# 8	230	4/0	4/0	300kcmil	250kcmil
45	# 8	# 8	# 6	# 8	250	250kcmil	4/0	350kcmil	300kcmil
50	# 8	# 8	# 6	# 6	255	250kcmil	4/0	400kcmil	300kcmil
55	# 6	# 8	# 4	# 6	260	300kcmil	4/0	400kcmil	350kcmil
60	# 6	# 6	# 4	# 6	270	300kcmil	250kcmil	400kcmil	350kcmil
65	# 6	# 6	# 4	# 4	280	300kcmil	250kcmil	500kcmil	350kcmil
75	# 4	# 6	# 3	# 4	285	300kcmil	250kcmil	500kcmil	400kcmil
85	# 4	# 4	# 2	# 3	290	350kcmil	250kcmil	500kcmil	400kcmil
90	# 3	# 4	# 2	# 2	305	350kcmil	300kcmil	500kcmil	400kcmil
95	# 3	# 4	# 1	# 2	310	350kcmil	300kcmil	500kcmil	500kcmil
100	# 3	# 3	# 1	# 2	320	400kcmil	300kcmil	600kcmil	500kcmil
110	# 2	# 3	1/0	# 1	335	400kcmil	350kcmil	600kcmil	500kcmil
115	# 2	# 2	1/0	# 1	340	500kcmil	350kcmil	600kcmil	500kcmil
120	# 1	# 2	1/0	1/0	350	500kcmil	350kcmil	700kcmil	500kcmil
130	# 1	# 2	2/0	1/0	375	500kcmil	400kcmil	700kcmil	600kcmil
135	1/0	# 1	2/0	1/0	380	500kcmil	400kcmil	750kcmil	600kcmil
150	1/0	# 1	3/0	2/0	385	600kcmil	500kcmil	750kcmil	600kcmil
155	2/0	1/0	3/0	3/0	420	600kcmil	500kcmil		700kcmil
170	2/0	1/0	4/0	3/0	430		500kcmil		750kcmil
175	2/0	2/0	4/0	3/0	435		600kcmil		750kcmil
180	3/0	2/0	4/0	4/0	475		600kcmil		

*Dry Locations Only

Notes:

1. Size #14 to 4/0 is in AWG units (American Wire Gauge).
2. Size 250 to 750 is in kcmil units (Thousand Circular Mils).
3. Use next higher ampere value if exact value is not listed in table.
4. For loads that operate continuously increase ampere value by 25% to obtain proper wire size.
5. Table R260519-92 has been written for estimating only. It is based on an ambient temperature of 30°C (86° F). For an ambient temperature other than 30°C (86° F), ampacity correction factors will be applied.

R260519-93 Metric Equivalent, Wire

U.S. vs. European Wire – Approximate Equivalents			
United States		European	
Size AWG or kcmil	Area Cir. Mils. (cmil) mm^2	Size mm^2	Area Cir. Mils.
18	1620/.82	.75	1480
16	2580/1.30	1.0	1974
14	4110/2.08	1.5	2961
12	6530/3.30	2.5	4935
10	10,380/5.25	4	7896
8	16,510/8.36	6	11,844
6	26,240/13.29	10	19,740
4	41,740/21.14	16	31,584
3	52,620/26.65	25	49,350
2	66,360/33.61	–	–
1	83,690/42.39	35	69,090
1/0	105,600/53.49	50	98,700
2/0	133,100/67.42	–	–
3/0	167,800/85.00	70	138,180
4/0	211,600/107.19	95	187,530
250	250,000/126.64	120	236,880
300	300,000/151.97	150	296,100
350	350,000/177.30	–	–
400	400,000/202.63	185	365,190
500	500,000/253.29	240	473,760
600	600,000/303.95	300	592,200
700	700,000/354.60	–	–
750	750,000/379.93	–	–

R260519-94 Size Required and Weight (Lbs./1000 L.F.) of Aluminum and Copper THW Wire by Ampere Load

Amperes	Copper Size	Aluminum Size	Copper Weight	Aluminum Weight
15	14	12	24	11
20	12	10	33	17
30	10	8	48	39
45	8	6	77	52
65	6	4	112	72
85	4	2	167	101
100	3	1	205	136
115	2	1/0	252	162
130	1	2/0	324	194
150	1/0	3/0	397	233
175	2/0	4/0	491	282
200	3/0	250	608	347
230	4/0	300	753	403
255	250	400	899	512
285	300	500	1068	620
310	350	500	1233	620
335	400	600	1396	772
380	500	750	1732	951

R260526-80 Grounding

Grounding When taking off grounding systems, identify separately the type and size of wire.

Example:

Bare copper & size

Bare aluminum & size

Insulated copper & size

Insulated aluminum & size

Count the number of ground rods and their size.

Example:

1. 8′ grounding rod – 5/8″ dia. 20 Ea.
2. 10′ grounding rod – 5/8″ dia. 12 Ea.
3. 15′ grounding rod – 3/4″ dia. 4 Ea.

Count the number of connections; the size of the largest wire will determine the productivity.

Example:

Braze a #2 wire to a #4/0 cable
The 4/0 cable will determine the L.H. and cost to be used.

Include individual connections to:

1. Ground rods
2. Building steel
3. Equipment
4. Raceways

Price does not include:

1. Excavation
2. Backfill
3. Sleeves or raceways used to protect grounding wires
4. Wall penetrations
5. Floor cutting
6. Core drilling

Job Conditions: Productivity is based on a ground floor area, using cable reels in an unobstructed area. The material staging area is assumed to be within 100′ of work being performed.

R260533-20 Conduit To 10′ High

List conduit by quantity, size, and type. Do not deduct for lengths occupied by fittings, since this will be allowance for scrap. Example:

A. Aluminum — size
B. Rigid galvanized — size
C. Steel intermediate (IMC) — size
D. Rigid steel, plastic-coated 20 Mil. — size
E. Rigid steel, plastic-coated 40 Mil. — size
F. Electric metallic tubing (EMT) — size
G. PVC Schedule 40 — size

Types (A) through (E) listed above contain the following per 100 L.F.:

1. (11) Threaded couplings
2. (11) Beam-type hangers
3. (2) Factory sweeps
4. (2) Fiber bushings
5. (4) Locknuts
6. (2) Field threaded pipe terminations
7. (2) Removal of concentric knockouts

Type (F) contains per 100 L.F.:

1. (11) Set screw couplings
2. (11) Beam clamps
3. (2) Field bends on 1/2″ and 3/4″ diameter
4. (2) Factory sweeps for 1″ and above
5. (2) Set screw steel connectors
6. (2) Removal of concentric knockouts

Type (G) contains per 100 L.F.:

1. (11) Field cemented couplings
2. (34) Beam clamps
3. (2) Factory sweeps
4. (2) Adapters
5. (2) Locknuts
6. (2) Removal of concentric knockouts

Labor-hours for all conduit to 10′ include:

1. Unloading by hand
2. Hauling by hand to an area up to 200′ from loading dock
3. Installation of conduit and fittings as described in Conduit models (A) through (G)

Not included in the material and labor are:

1. Staging rental or purchase
2. Structural modifications
3. Wire
4. Junction boxes
5. Fittings in excess of those described in conduit models (A) through (G)
6. Painting of conduit

Fittings

Only those fittings listed above are included in the linear foot totals, although they should be listed separately from conduit lengths, without prices, to ensure proper quantities for material procurement.

If the fittings required exceed the quantities included in the model conduit runs, then material and labor costs must be added to the difference. If actual needs per 100 L.F. of conduit are: (2) sweeps, (4) LBs and (1) field bend, then, (4) LBs and (1) field bend must be priced additionally.

R260533-21 Hangers

It is sometimes desirable to substitute an alternate style of hanger if the support being used is not the type described in the conduit models.

One approach is the substitution method:

1. Find the cost of the type hanger described in the conduit model.
2. Calculate the cost of the desired type hanger (it may be necessary to calculate individual components such as drilling, expansion shields, etc.).
3. Calculate the cost difference (delta) between the two types of hangers.
4. Multiply the cost delta by the number of hangers in the model.
5. Divide the total delta cost for hangers in the model by the length of the model to find the delta cost per L.F. for that model.
6. Modify the given unit costs per L.F. for the model by the delta cost per L.F.

Another approach to hanger configurations would be to start with the conduit only and add all the supports and any other items as separate lines. This procedure is most useful if the project involves racking many runs of conduit on a single hanger; for instance, a trapeze type hanger.

Example: Five (5) 2″ RGS conduits, 50 L.F. each, are to be run on trapeze hangers from one pull box to another. The run includes one 90° bend.

1. List the hangers' components to create an assembly cost for each 2′-wide trapeze.
2. List the components for the 50′ conduit run, noting that 6 trapeze supports will be required.

Job Conditions: Productivities are based on new construction to 10′ high, using scaffolding, scissor lift, bucket lift in an unobstructed area. Material storage is assumed to be within 100′ of work being performed.

Add to labor for elevated installations:

10′ to 14.5′ High–10%	30′ to 35′ High–40%
15′ to 20′ High–20%	35′ to 40′ High–50%
20′ to 25′ High–25%	Over 40′ High–55%
25′ to 30′ High–35%	

Add these percentages to the L.F. labor cost, but not to fittings. Add these percentages only to quantities exceeding the different height levels, rather than the total conduit quantities.

Linear foot price for labor does not include penetrations in walls or floors and must be added to the estimate.

R260533-22 Conductors in Conduit

The table below lists the maximum number of conductors for various sized conduit using THW, TW or THWN insulations.

Copper Wire Size	Conduit Size																										
	½″			¾″			1″			1-¼″			1-½″			2″			2-½″			3″		3-½″		4″	
	TW	THW	THWN	TW	THW	THWN	TW	THW	THWN	TW	THW	THWN	TW	THW	THWN	TW	THW	THWN	TW	THW	THWN	THW	THWN	THW	THWN	THW	THWN
#14	9	6	13	15	10	24	25	16	39	44	29	69	60	40	94	99	65	154	142	93		143		192			
#12	7	4	10	12	8	18	19	13	29	35	24	51	47	32	70	78	53	114	111	76	164	117		157			
#10	5	4	6	9	6	11	15	11	18	26	19	32	36	26	44	60	43	73	85	61	104	95	160	127		163	
#8	2	1	3	4	3	5	7	5	9	12	10	16	17	13	22	28	22	36	40	32	51	49	79	66	106	85	136
#6		1	1		2	4		4	6		7	11		10	15		16	26		23	37	36	57	48	76	62	98
#4		1	1		1	2		3	4		5	7		7	9		12	16		17	22	27	35	36	47	47	60
#3		1	1		1	1		2	3		4	6		6	8		10	13		15	19	23	29	31	39	40	51
#2		1	1		1	1		2	3		4	5		5	7		9	11		13	16	20	25	27	33	34	43
#1					1	1		1	1		3	3		4	5		6	8		9	12	14	18	19	25	25	32
1/0					1	1		1	1		2	3		3	4		5	7		8	10	12	15	16	21	21	27
2/0					1	1		1	1		1	2		3	3		5	6		7	8	10	13	14	17	18	22
3/0					1	1		1	1		1	1		2	3		4	5		6	7	9	11	12	14	15	18
4/0						1		1	1		1	1		1	2		3	4		5	6	7	9	10	12	13	15
250 kcmil								1	1		1	1		1	1		2	3		4	4	6	7	8	10	10	12
300								1	1		1	1		1	1		2	3		3	4	5	6	7	8	9	11
350									1		1	1		1	1		1	2		3	3	4	5	6	7	8	9
400											1	1		1	1		1	1		2	3	4	5	5	6	7	8
500											1	1		1	1		1	1		1	2	3	4	4	5	6	7
600												1		1	1		1	1		1	1	3	3	4	4	5	5
700														1	1		1	1		1	1	2	3	3	4	4	5
750 ▼														1	1		1	1		1	1	2	2	3	3	4	4

R260533-25 Conduit Weight Comparisons (Lbs. per 100 ft.) with Maximum Cable Fill*

Type	1/2″	3/4″	1″	1-1/4″	1-1/2″	2″	2-1/2″	3″	3-1/2″	4″	5″	6″
Rigid Galvanized Steel (RGS)	104	140	235	358	455	721	1022	1451	1749	2148	3083	4343
Intermediate Steel (IMC)	84	113	186	293	379	611	883	1263	1501	1830		
Electrical Metallic Tubing (EMT)	54	116	183	296	368	445	641	930	1215	1540		

*Conduit & Heaviest Conductor Combination

R260533-30 Labor for Couplings and Fittings

The labor included in the unit price lines for couplings is for their installation separate from a fitting. However, the labor included in the unit price lines for fittings covers their complete installation, which may include the labor installation of the coupling(s). If coupling(s) are required to complete a fitting installation, only the material for the required number of couplings needs to be added to the appropriate unit price lines.

R260533-60 Wireway

When "taking off" Wireway, list by size and type.

Example:
1. Screw cover, unflanged + size
2. Screw cover, flanged + size
3. Hinged cover, flanged + size
4. Hinged cover, unflanged + size

Each 10′ length on Wireway contains:
1. 10′ of cover either screw or hinged type
2. (1) Coupling or flange gasket
3. (1) Wall type mount

All fittings must be priced separately.

Substitution of hanger types is done the same as described in R260533-21, "HANGERS," keeping in mind that the wireway model is based on 10′ sections instead of a 100′ conduit run.

Labor-hours for wireway include:
1. Unloading by hand
2. Hauling by hand up to 100′ from loading dock
3. Measuring and marking
4. Mounting wall bracket using two (2) anchor type lead fasteners
5. Installing wireway on brackets, to 10′ high (for higher elevations use factors in R260533-20)

Job Conditions: Productivity is based on new construction, to a height of 10′ in an unobstructed area.

Material staging area is assumed to be within 100′ of work being performed.

R260533-65 Outlet Boxes

Outlet boxes should be included on the same takeoff sheet as branch piping or devices to better explain what is included in each circuit.

Each unit price in this section is a stand alone item and contains no other component unless specified. For example, to estimate a duplex outlet, components that must be added are:
1. 4″ square box
2. 4″ plaster ring
3. Duplex receptacle
4. Device cover

The method of mounting outlet boxes is two (2) plastic shield fasteners.

Outlet boxes plastic, labor-hours include:
1. Marking box location on wood studding
2. Mounting box

Economy of Scale – For large concentrations of plastic boxes in the same area deduct the following percentages from labor-hour totals:

1	to	10	0%
11	to	25	20%
26	to	50	25%
51	to	100	30%
	over	100	35%

Note: It is important to understand that these percentages are not used on the total job quantities, but only areas where concentrations exceed the levels specified.

R260533-70 Pull Boxes and Cabinets

List cabinets and pull boxes by NEMA type and size.

Example:	**TYPE**	**SIZE**
	NEMA 1	6″W x 6″H x 4″D
	NEMA 3R	6″W x 6″H x 4″D

Labor-hours for wall mount (indoor or outdoor) installations include:
1. Unloading and uncrating
2. Handling of enclosures up to 200′ from loading dock using a dolly or pipe rollers
3. Measuring and marking
4. Drilling four (4) anchor type lead fasteners using a hammer drill
5. Mounting and leveling boxes

Note: A plywood backboard is not included.

Labor-hours for ceiling mounting include:
1. Unloading and uncrating
2. Handling boxes up to 100′ from loading dock
3. Measuring and marking
4. Drilling four (4) anchor type lead fasteners using a hammer drill
5. Installing and leveling boxes to a height of 10′ using rolling staging

Labor-hours for free standing cabinets include:
1. Unloading and uncrating
2. Handling of cabinets up to 200′ from loading dock using a dolly or pipe rollers
3. Marking of floor
4. Drilling four (4) anchor type lead fasteners using a hammer drill
5. Leveling and shimming

Labor-hours for telephone cabinets include:
1. Unloading and uncrating
2. Handling cabinets up to 200′ using a dolly or pipe rollers
3. Measuring and marking
4. Mounting and leveling, using four (4) lead anchor type fasteners

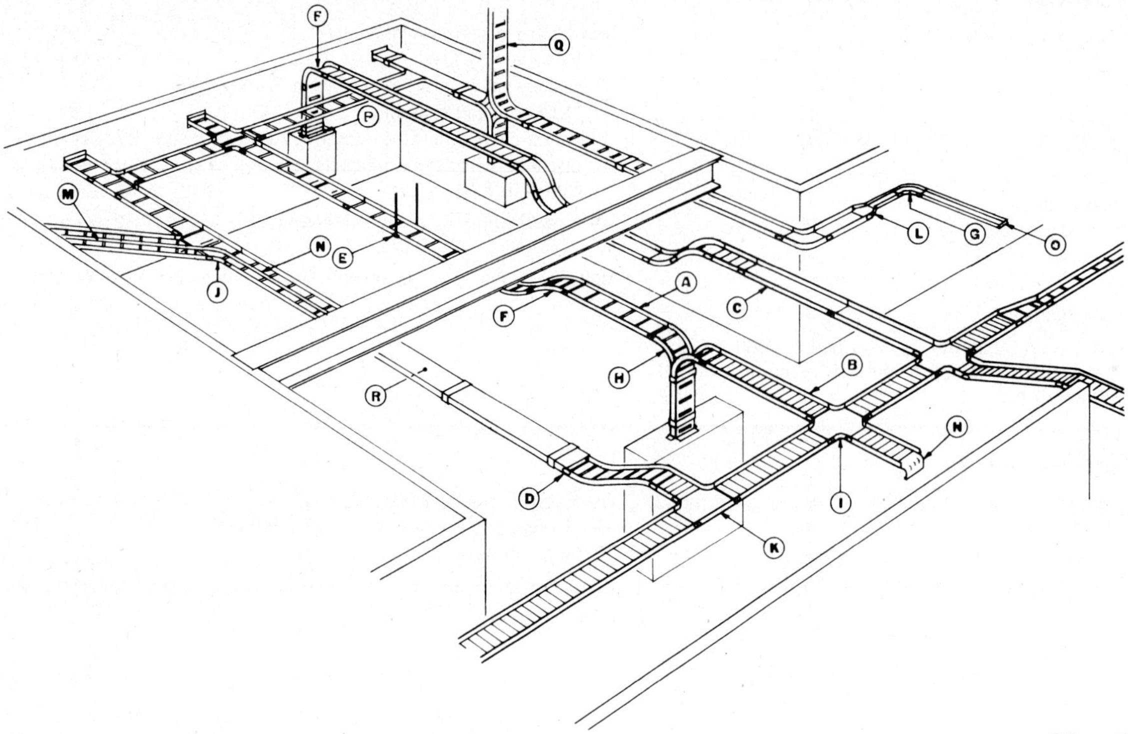

Fig. R260536-11

R260536-10 Cable Tray

Cable Tray - When taking off cable tray it is important to identify separately the different types and sizes involved in the system being estimated. (Fig. R260536-11)

A. – Ladder Type, galvanized or aluminum
B. – Trough Type, galvanized or aluminum
C. – Solid Bottom, galvanized or aluminum

The unit of measure is calculated in linear feet. Do not deduct from this footage any length occupied by fittings. This will be the only allowance for scrap. Be sure to include all vertical drops to panels, switch gear, etc.

Hangers – Included in the linear footage of cable tray is

D. – 1 – Pair of connector plates per 12 L.F.
E. – 1 – Pair clamp type hangers and 4′ of 3/8″ threaded rod per 12 L.F.

Not included are structural supports, which must be priced in addition to the hangers.

Fittings – Identify separately the different types of fittings

A. – Ladder Type, galvanized or aluminum
B. – Trough Type, galvanized or aluminum
C. – Solid Bottom Type, galvanized or aluminum

The configuration, radius and rung spacing must also be listed. The unit of measure is "Ea."

D. – Elbow, vertical Ea.
E. – Elbow, horizontal Ea.
F. – Tee, vertical Ea.
G. – Cross, horizontal Ea.
H. – Wye, horizontal Ea.
I. – Tee, horizontal Ea.
J. – Reducing fitting Ea.

Depending on the use of the system other examples of units which must be included are:

K. – Divider strip L.F.
L. – Drop-outs Ea.
M. – End caps Ea.
N. – Panel connectors Ea.

Wire and cable are not included and should be taken off separately. See Unit Price sections.

Job Conditions – Unit prices are based on a new installation to a work plane of 10′ in an unobstructed area.

Add to labor for elevated installations:

10′ to 14.5′ High	10%
15′ to 20′ High	20%
20′ to 25′ High	25%
25′ to 30′ High	35%
30′ to 35′ High	40%
35′ to 40′ High	50%
Over 40′ High	55%

Add these percentages for L.F. totals but not to fittings. Add percentages to only those quantities that fall in the different elevations. In other words, if the total quantity of cable tray is 200′ but only 75′ is above 15′ then the 10% is added to the 75′ only.

Linear foot costs do not include penetrations through walls and floors which must be added to the estimate.

Cable Tray Covers

Covers – Cable tray covers are taken off in the same manner as the tray itself, making distinctions as to the type of cover. (Fig. R260536-11)

O. – Vented, galvanized or aluminum
P. – Solid, galvanized or aluminum

Cover configurations are taken off separately noting type, specific radius and widths.

Note: Care should be taken to identify from plans and specifications exactly what is being covered. In many systems only vertical fittings are covered to retain wire and cable.

R260539-30 Conduit In Concrete Slab

List conduit by quantity, size and type.

Example:

A. Rigid galvanized steel + size
B. P.V.C. + size

Rigid galvanized steel (A) contains per 100 L.F.:

1. (20) Ties to slab reinforcing
2. (11) Threaded steel couplings
3. (2) Factory sweeps
4. (2) Field threaded conduit terminations
5. (2) Fiber bushings + locknuts
6. (2) Removal of concentric knockouts

P.V.C. (B) contains per 100 L.F.:

1. (20) Ties to slab reinforcing
2. (11) Field cemented couplings
3. (2) Factory sweeps
4. (2) Adapters
5. (2) Removal of concentric knockouts

R260539-40 Conduit In Trench

Conduit in trench is galvanized steel and contains per 100 L.F.:

1. (11) Threaded couplings
2. (2) Factory sweeps
3. (2) Fiber bushings + (4) locknuts
4. (2) Field threaded conduit terminations
5. (2) Removal of concentric knockouts

Note:

Conduit in Unit Price sections do not include:

1. Floor cutting
2. Excavation or backfill
3. Grouting or patching

Conduit fittings in excess of those listed in the above Conduit model must be added. (Refer to R260533-20 for Procedure example.)

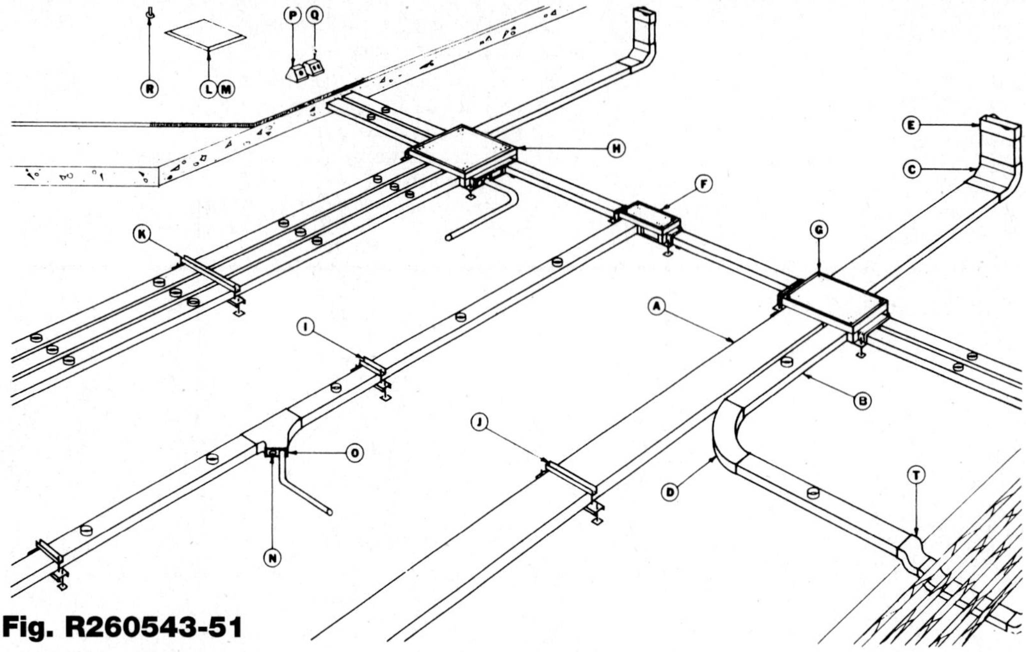

Fig. R260543-51

R260543-50 Underfloor Duct

When pricing Underfloor Duct it is important to identify and list each component, since costs vary significantly from one type of fitting to another. Do not deduct boxes or fittings from linear foot totals; this will be your allowance for scrap.

The first step is to identify the system as either:

FIG. R260543-51 Single Level

FIG. R260543-52 Dual Level

Single Level System

Include on your "takeoff sheet" the following unit price items, making sure to distinquish between Standard and Super duct:

A. Feeder duct (blank) in L.F.
B. Distribution duct (Inserts 2′ on center) in L.F.
C. Elbows (Vertical) Ea.
D. Elbows (Horizontal) Ea.
E. Cabinet connector Ea.
F. Single duct junction box Ea.
G. Double duct junction box Ea.
H. Triple duct junction box Ea.
I. Support, single cell Ea.
J. Support, double cell Ea.
K. Support, triple cell Ea.
L. Carpet pan Ea.
M. Terrazzo pan Ea.
N. Insert to conduit adapter Ea.
O. Conduit adapter Ea.
P. Low tension outlet Ea.
Q. High tension outlet Ea.
R. Galvanized nipple Ea.
S. Wire per C.L.F.
T. Offset (Duct type) Ea.

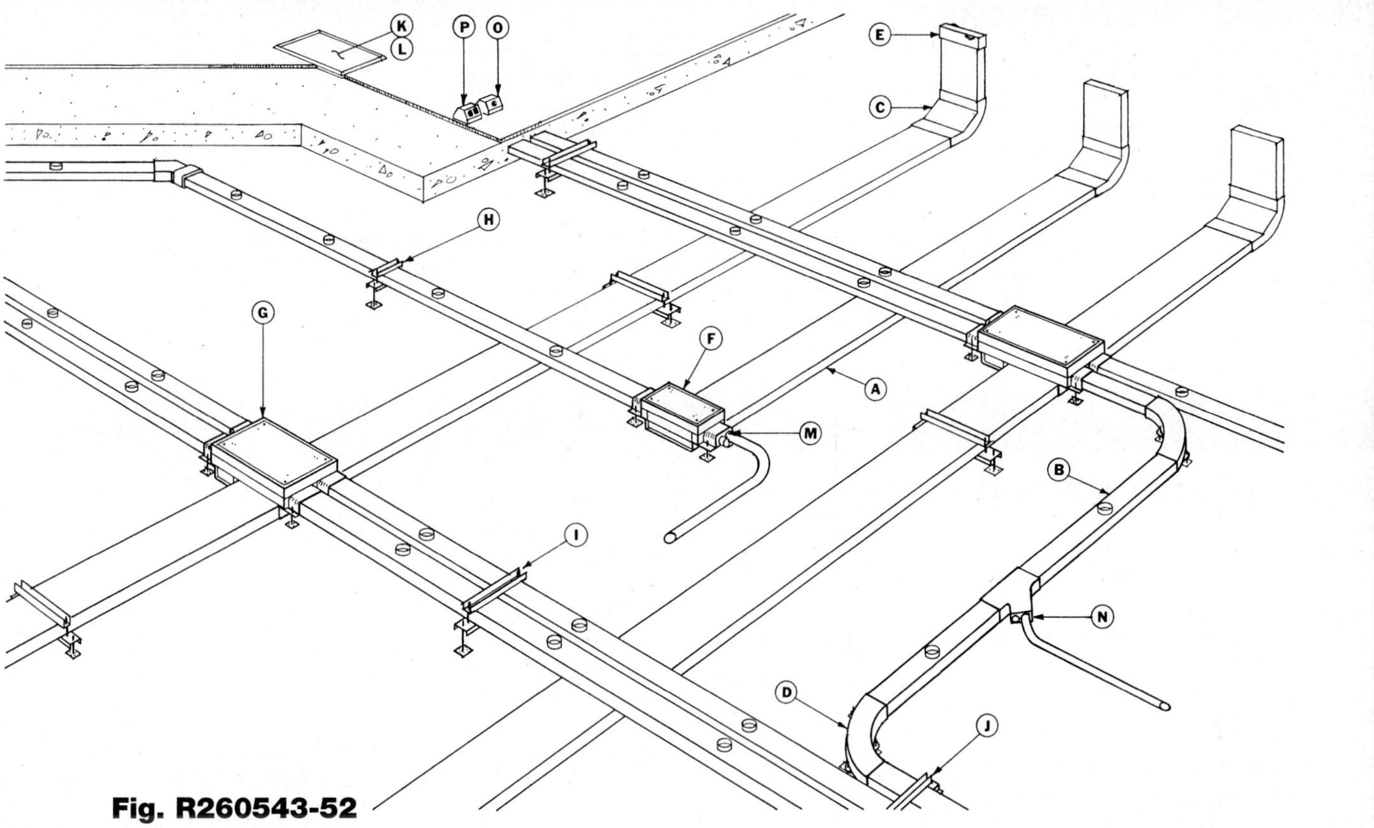

Fig. R260543-52

R260543-50 Underfloor Duct (cont.)

Dual Level System + Labor

Dual Level

Include the following when "taking off" Dual Level systems:

Distinguish between Standard and Super duct.

A. Feeder duct (blank) in L.F.
B. Distribution duct (Inserts 2′ on center) in L.F.
C. Elbows (Vertical), Ea.
D. Elbows (Horizontal), Ea.
E. Cabinet connector, Ea.
F. Single duct, 2 level, junction box, Ea.
G. Double duct, 2 level, junction box, Ea.
H. Support, single cell, Ea.
I. Support, double cell, Ea.
J. Support, triple cell, Ea.
K. Carpet pan, Ea.
L. Terrazzo pan, Ea.
M. Insert to conduit adapter, Ea.
N. Conduit adapter, Ea.
O. Low tension outlet, Ea.
P. High tension outlet, Ea.
Q. Wire per C.L.F.

Note: Make sure to include risers in linear foot totals. High tension outlets include box, receptacle, covers and related mounting hardware.

Labor-hours for both Single and Dual Level systems include:

1. Unloading and uncrating
2. Hauling up to 200′ from loading dock
3. Measuring and marking
4. Setting raceway and fittings in slab or on grade
5. Leveling raceway and fittings

Labor-hours do not include:

1. Floor cutting
2. Excavation or backfill
3. Concrete pour
4. Grouting or patching
5. Wire or wire pulls
6. Additional outlets after concrete is poured
7. Piping to or from Underfloor Duct

Note: Installation is based on installing up to 150′ of duct. If quantities exceed this, deduct the following percentages:

1. 150′ to 250′ - 10%
2. 250′ to 350′ - 15%
3. 350′ to 500′ - 20%
4. over 500′ - 25%

Deduct these percentages from labor only.

Deduct these percentages from straight sections only.

Do not deduct from fittings or junction boxes.

Job Conditions: Productivity is based on new construction.

Underfloor duct to be installed on first three floors.

The material staging area is within 100′ of work being performed.

The area unobstructed and duct are not subject to physical damage.

Electrical — R2605 Common Work Results for Electrical

R260580-75 Motor Connections

Motor connections should be listed by size and type of motor. Included in the material and labor cost are:

1. (2) Flex connectors
2. 18″ of flexible metallic wireway
3. Wire identification and termination
4. Test for rotation
5. (2) or (3) Conductors

Price does not include:

1. Mounting of motor
2. Disconnect switch
3. Motor starter
4. Controls
5. Conduit or wire ahead of flex

Note: When "taking off" motor connections, it is advisable to list connections on the same quantity sheet as motors, motor starters and controls.

Electrical — R2609 Instrumen. & Cont. of Elect. Systems

R260913-80 Switchboard Instruments

Switchboard instruments are added to the price of switchboards according to job specifications. This equipment is usually included when ordering "gear" from the manufacturer and will arrive factory installed.

Included in the labor cost are:

1. Internal wiring connections
2. Wire identification
3. Wire tagging

Transition sections include:

1. Uncrating
2. Hauling sections up to 100′ from loading dock
3. Positioning sections
4. Leveling sections
5. Bolting enclosures
6. Bolting vertical bus bars

Price does not include:

1. Equipment pads
2. Steel channels embedded or grouted in concrete
3. Special knockouts
4. Rigging

Job Conditions: Productivity is based on new construction and equipment to be installed on the first floor within 200′ of the loading dock.

R262213-10 Electric Circuit Voltages

General: The following method provides the user with a simple non-technical means of obtaining comparative costs of wiring circuits. The circuits considered serve the electrical loads of motors, electric heating, lighting and transformers, for example, that require low voltage 60 Hertz alternating current.

The method used here is suitable only for obtaining estimated costs. It is **not** intended to be used as a substitute for electrical engineering design applications.

Conduit and wire circuits can represent from twenty to thirty percent of the total building electrical cost. By following the described steps and using the tables the user can translate the various types of electric circuits into estimated costs.

Wire Size: Wire size is a function of the electric load which is usually listed in one of the following units:

1. Amperes (A)
2. Watts (W)
3. Kilowatts (kW)
4. Volt amperes (VA)
5. Kilovolt amperes (kVA)
6. Horsepower (HP)

These units of electric load must be converted to amperes in order to obtain the size of wire necessary to carry the load. To convert electric load units to amperes one must have an understanding of the voltage classification of the power source and the voltage characteristics of the electrical equipment or load to be energized. The seven A.C. circuits commonly used are illustrated in Figures R262213-11 through R262213-17 showing the tranformer load voltage and the point of use voltage at the point on the circuit where the load is connected. The difference between the source and point of use voltage is attributed to the circuit voltage drop and is considered to be approximately 4%.

Motor Voltages: Motor voltages are listed by their point of use voltage and not the power source voltage.

For example: 460 volts instead of 480 volts
200 instead of 208 volts
115 volts instead of 120 volts

Lighting and Heating Voltages: Lighting and heating equipment voltages are listed by the power source voltage and not the point of wire voltage.

For example: 480, 277, 120 volt lighting
480 volt heating or air conditioning unit
208 volt heating unit

Transformer Voltages: Transformer primary (input) and secondary (output) voltages are listed by the power source voltage.

For example: Single phase 10 kVA
Primary 240/480 volts
Secondary 120/240 volts

In this case, the primary voltage may be 240 volts with a 120 volts secondary or may be 480 volts with either a 120V or a 240V secondary.

For example: Three phase 10 kVA
Primary 480 volts
Secondary 208Y/120 volts

In this case the transformer is suitable for connection to a circuit with a 3 phase, 3 wire or a 3 phase, 4 wire circuit with a 480 voltage. This application will provide a secondary circuit of 3 phase, 4 wire with 208 volts between phase wires and 120 volts between any phase wire and the neutral (white) wire.

R262213-11

3 Wire, 1 Phase, 120/240 Volt System

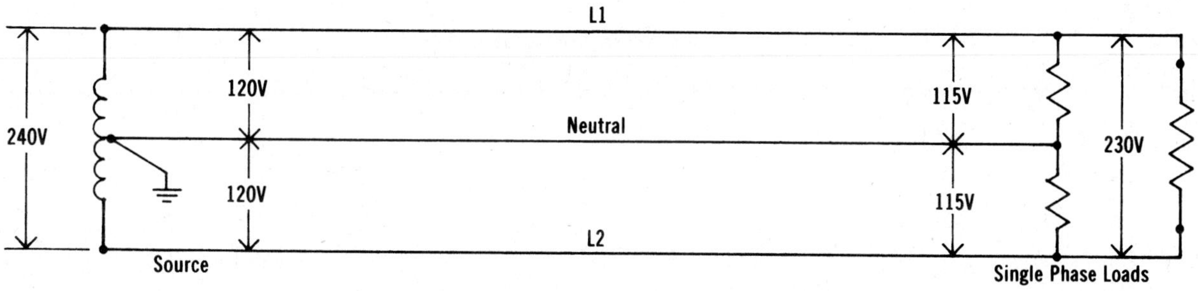

R262213-12

4 Wire, 3 Phase, 208Y/120 Volt System

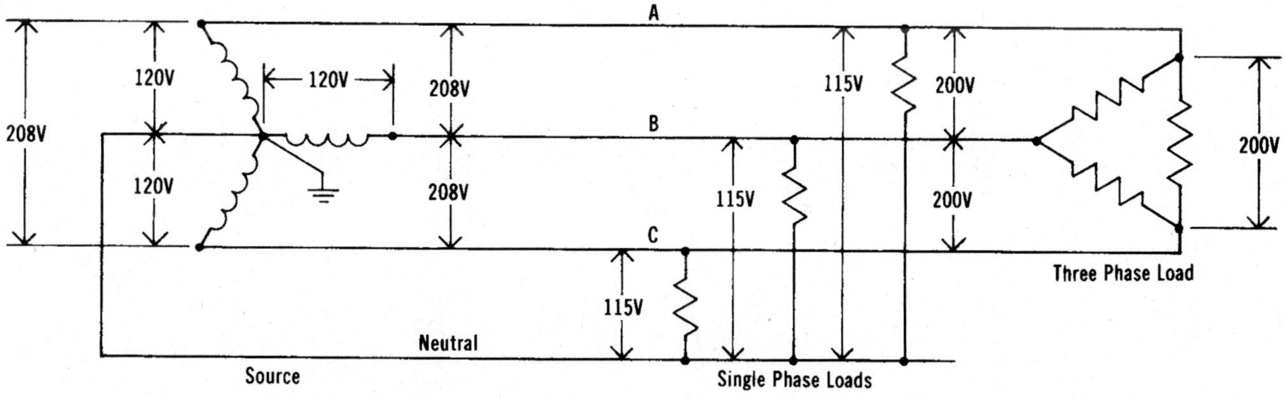

R262213-13 Electric Circuit Voltages (cont.)

3 Wire, 3 Phase 240 Volt System

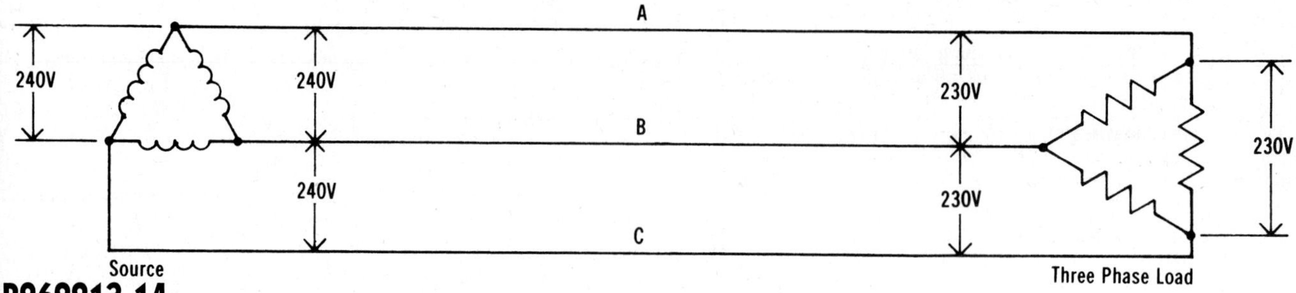

R262213-14

4 Wire, 3 Phase, 240/120 Volt System

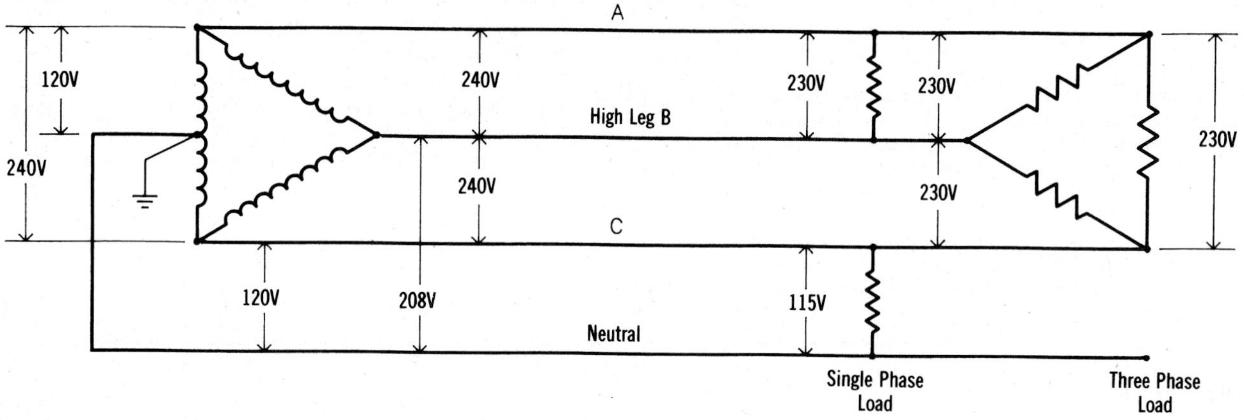

R262213-15

3 Wire, 3 Phase 480 Volt System

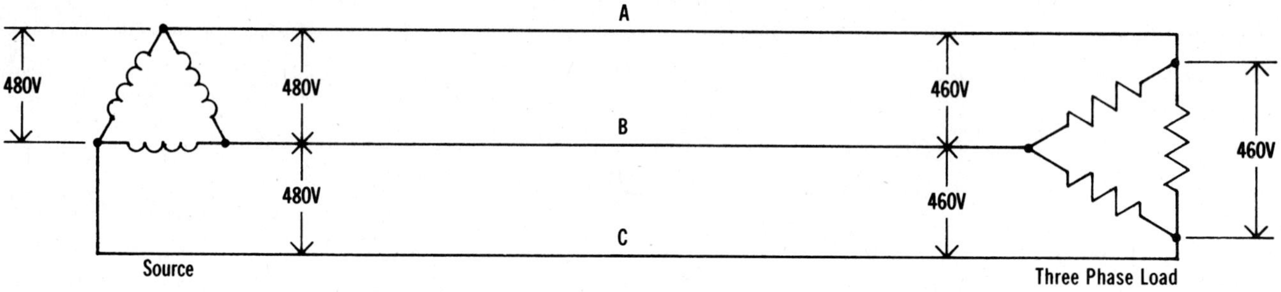

R262213-16

4 Wire, 3 Phase, 480Y/277 Volt System

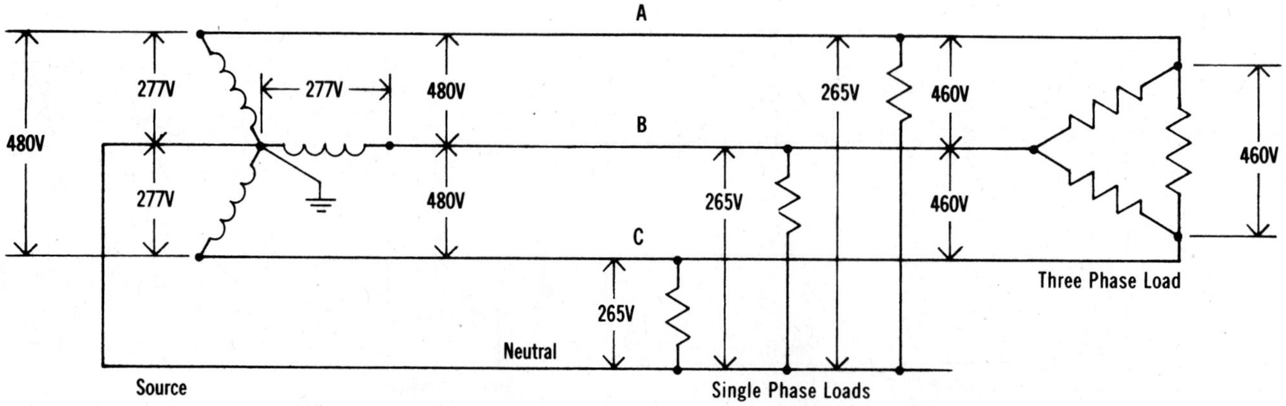

R262213-17 Electric Circuit Voltages (cont.)

3 Wire, 3 Phase, 600 Volt System

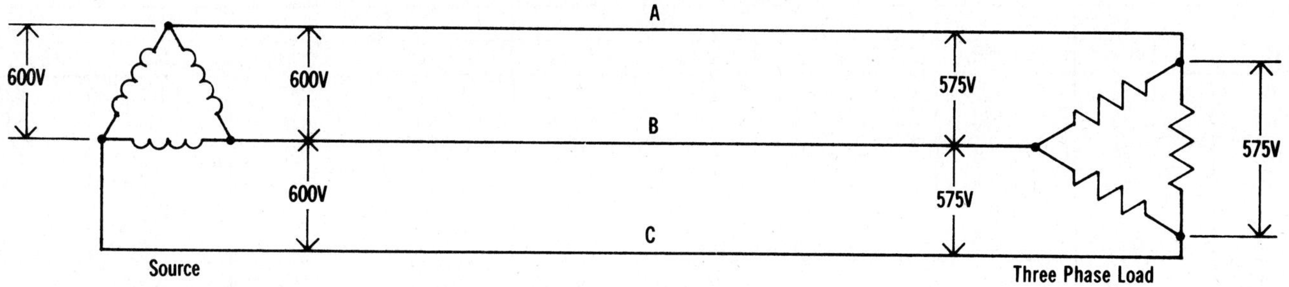

R262213-20 kW Value/Cost Determination

General: Lighting and electric heating loads are expressed in watts and kilowatts.

Cost Determination:

The proper ampere values can be obtained as follows:

1. Convert watts to kilowatts (watts 1000 ÷ kilowatts)
2. Determine voltage rating of equipment.
3. Determine whether equipment is single phase or three phase.
4. Refer to Table R262213-21 to find ampere value from kW, Ton and BTU/hr. values.
5. Determine type of wire insulation – TW, THW, THWN.
6. Determine if wire is copper or aluminum.
7. Refer to Table R260519-92 to obtain copper or aluminum wire size from ampere values.
8. Next refer to Table R260533-22 for the proper conduit size to accommodate the number and size of wires in each particular case.
9. Next refer to unit cost data for the per linear foot cost of the conduit.
10. Next refer to unit cost data for the per linear foot cost of the wire. Multiply cost of wire per L.F. x number of wires in the circuits to obtain total wire cost per L.F.
11. Add values obtained in Step 9 and 10 for total cost per linear foot for conduit and wire x length of circuit = Total Cost.

Notes:

1. 1 Phase refers to single phase, 2 wire circuits.
2. 3 Phase refers to three phase, 3 wire circuits.
3. For circuits which operate continuously for 3 hours or more, multiply the ampere values by 1.25 for a given kW requirement.
4. For kW ratings not listed, add ampere values.

   For example: Find the ampere value of 9 kW at 208 volt, single phase.

   4 kW = 19.2A
   5 kW = 24.0A
   9 kW = 43.2A
5. "Length of Circuit" refers to the one way distance of the run, not to the total sum of wire lengths.

R262213-21 Ampere Values as Determined by kW Requirements, BTU/HR or Ton, Voltage and Phase Values

			Ampere Values						
			120V	208V		240V		277V	480V
kW	Ton	BTU/HR	1 Phase	1 Phase	3 Phase	1 Phase	3 Phase	1 Phase	3 Phase
0.5	.1422	1,707	4.2A	2.4A	1.4A	2.1A	1.2A	1.8A	0.6A
0.75	.2133	2,560	6.2	3.6	2.1	3.1	1.9	2.7	.9
1.0	.2844	3,413	8.3	4.9	2.8	4.2	2.4	3.6	1.2
1.25	.3555	4,266	10.4	6.0	3.5	5.2	3.0	4.5	1.5
1.5	.4266	5,120	12.5	7.2	4.2	6.3	3.1	5.4	1.8
2.0	.5688	6,826	16.6	9.7	5.6	8.3	4.8	7.2	2.4
2.5	.7110	8,533	20.8	12.0	7.0	10.4	6.1	9.1	3.1
3.0	.8532	10,239	25.0	14.4	8.4	12.5	7.2	10.8	3.6
4.0	1.1376	13,652	33.4	19.2	11.1	16.7	9.6	14.4	4.8
5.0	1.4220	17,065	41.6	24.0	13.9	20.8	12.1	18.1	6.1
7.5	2.1331	25,598	62.4	36.0	20.8	31.2	18.8	27.0	9.0
10.0	2.8441	34,130	83.2	48.0	27.7	41.6	24.0	36.5	12.0
12.5	3.5552	42,663	104.2	60.1	35.0	52.1	30.0	45.1	15.0
15.0	4.2662	51,195	124.8	72.0	41.6	62.4	37.6	54.0	18.0
20.0	5.6883	68,260	166.4	96.0	55.4	83.2	48.0	73.0	24.0
25.0	7.1104	85,325	208.4	120.2	70.0	104.2	60.0	90.2	30.0
30.0	8.5325	102,390		144.0	83.2	124.8	75.2	108.0	36.0
35.0	9.9545	119,455		168.0	97.1	145.6	87.3	126.0	42.1
40.0	11.3766	136,520		192.0	110.8	166.4	96.0	146.0	48.0
45.0	12.7987	153,585			124.8	187.5	112.8	162.0	54.0
50.0	14.2208	170,650			140.0	208.4	120.0	180.4	60.0
60.0	17.0650	204,780			166.4		150.4	216.0	72.0
70.0	19.9091	238,910			194.2		174.6		84.2
80.0	22.7533	273,040			221.6		192.0		96.0
90.0	25.5975	307,170					225.6		108.0
100.0	28.4416	341,300							120.0

R262213-25 kVA Value/Cost Determination

General: Control transformers are listed in VA. Step-down and power transformers are listed in kVA.

Cost Determination:

1. Convert VA to kVA. Volt amperes (VA) ÷ 1000 = Kilovolt amperes (kVA).
2. Determine voltage rating of equipment.
3. Determine whether equipment is single phase or three phase.
4. Refer to Table R262213-26 to find ampere value from kVA value.
5. Determine type of wire insulation – TW, THW, THWN.
6. Determine if wire is copper or aluminum.
7. Refer to Table R260519-92 to obtain copper or aluminum wire size from ampere values.
8. Next refer to Table R260533-22 for the proper conduit size to accommodate the number and size of wires in each particular case.
9. Next refer to unit price data for the per linear foot cost of the conduit.
10. Next refer to unit price data for the per linear foot cost of the wire. Multiply cost of wire per L.F. x number of wires in the circuits to obtain total wire cost.
11. Add values obtained in Step 9 and 10 for total cost per linear foot for conduit and wire x length of circuit = Total Cost.

Example: A transformer rated 10 kVA 480 volts primary, 240 volts secondary, 3 phase has the capacity to furnish the following:

1. Primary amperes = 10 kVA x 1.20 = 12 amperes (from Table R262213-26)
2. Secondary amperes = 10 kVA x 2.40 = 24 amperes (from Table R262213-26)

Note: Transformers can deliver generally 125% of their rated kVA. For instance, a 10 kVA rated transformer can safely deliver 12.5 kVA.

R262213-26 Multiplier Values for kVA to Amperes Determined by Voltage and Phase Values

	Multiplier for Circuits	
Volts	2 Wire, 1 Phase	3 Wire, 3 Phase
115	8.70	
120	8.30	
230	4.30	2.51
240	4.16	2.40
200	5.00	2.89
208	4.80	2.77
265	3.77	2.18
277	3.60	2.08
460	2.17	1.26
480	2.08	1.20
575	1.74	1.00
600	1.66	0.96

R262213-60 Oil Filled Transformers

Transformers in this section include:
1. Rigging (as required)
2. Rental of crane and operator
3. Setting of oil filled transformer
4. (4) Anchor bolts, nuts and washers in concrete pad

Price does not include:
1. Primary and secondary terminations
2. Transformer pad
3. Equipment grounding
4. Cable
5. Conduit locknuts or bushings

Transformers in Unit Price sections for dry type, back-boost and isolating transformers include:
1. Unloading and uncrating
2. Hauling transformer to within 200′ of loading dock
3. Setting in place
4. Wall mounting hardware
5. Testing

Price does not include:
1. Structural supports
2. Suspension systems
3. Welding or fabrication
4. Primary & secondary terminations

Add the following percentages to the labor for ceiling mounted transformers:

10' to 15′	= + 15%
15′ to 25′	= + 30%
Over 25′	= + 35%

Job Conditions: Productivities are based on new construction. Installation is assumed to be on the first floor, in an obstructed area to a height of 10′. Material staging area is within 100′ of final transformer location.

R262416-50 Load Centers and Panelboards

When pricing load centers list panels by size and type. List breakers in a separate column of the "quantity sheet," and define by phase and ampere rating.

Material and labor prices include breakers; for example: a 100A, 3-Wire, 102/240V, 18 circuit panel w/ main breaker, as described in the unit cost section, contains 18 single pole 20A breakers.

If you do not choose to include a full panel of single pole breakers, use the following method to adjust material and labor costs.

Example: In an 18 circuit panel only 16 single pole breakers are desired, requiring that the cost of 2 breakers be subtracted from the panel cost.

1. Go to the appropriate unit cost section of the data set to find the unit prices of the given circuit breaker type.
2. Modify those costs as follows:
   Bare material price x 0.50
   Bare labor cost x 0.60.
3. Multiply those modified bare costs by 2 (breakers in this example).
4. Subtract the modified costs for the 2 breakers from the given cost of the panel.

Labor-hours for load center installation includes:

1. Unloading, uncrating, and handling enclosures 200′ from unloading area
2. Measuring and marking
3. Drilling (4) lead anchor type fasteners using a hammer drill
4. Mounting and leveling panel to a height of 6′
5. Preparation and termination of feeder cable to lugs or main breaker
6. Branch circuit identification
7. Lacing using tie wraps
8. Testing and load balancing
9. Marking panel directory

Not included in the material and labor are:

1. Modifications to enclosure
2. Structural supports
3. Additional lugs
4. Plywood backboards
5. Painting or lettering

Note: Knockouts are included in the price of terminating pipe runs and need not be added to the load center costs.

Job Conditions: Productivity is based on new construction to a height of 6′, in an unobstructed area. Material staging area is assumed to be within 100′ of work being performed.

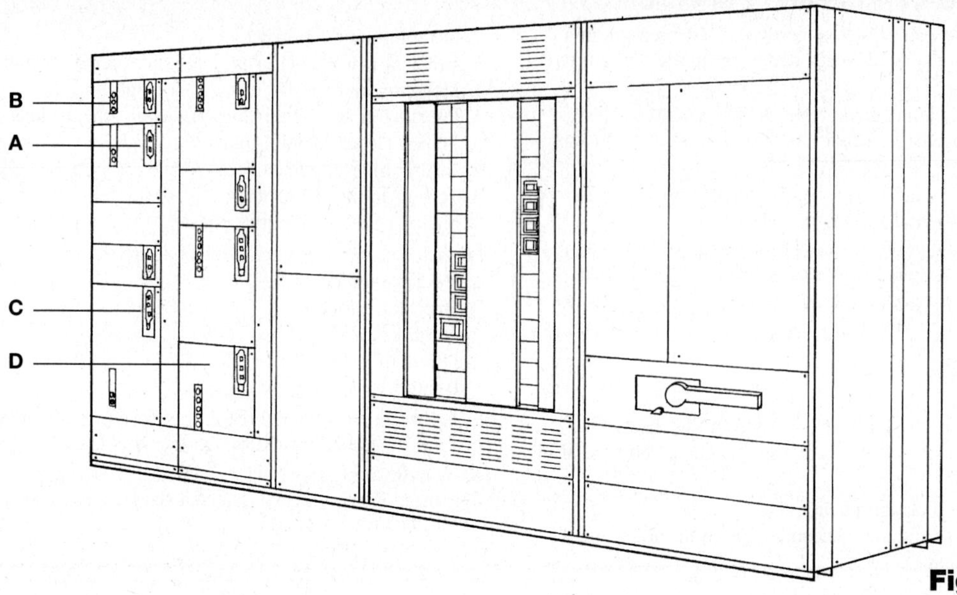

Fig. R262419-61

R262419-60 Motor Control Centers

When taking off motor control centers, list the size, type and height of structures.

Example:
1. 600A, 22,000 RMS, 72″ high
2. 600A, back to back, 72″ high

Next take off individual starters; the number of structures can also be determined by adding the height in inches of starters divided by the height of the structure, and list on the same quantity sheet as the structures. Identify starters by type, horsepower rating, size and height in inches.

Example:

A. Class I, Type B, FVNR starter, 25 H.P., 18″ high.
Add to the list with starters, factory installed controls.

Example:

B. Pilot lights

C. Push buttons

D. Auxiliary contacts

Identify starters and structures as either copper or aluminum and by the NEMA type of enclosure.

When pricing starters and structures, be sure to add or deduct adjustments, using lines in the unit price section.

Included in the cost of motor control structures are:
1. Uncrating
2. Hauling to location within 100′ of loading dock
3. Setting structures
4. Leveling
5. Aligning
6. Bolting together structure frames
7. Bolting horizontal bus bars

Labor-hours do not include:
1. Equipment pad
2. Steel channels embedded or grouted in concrete
3. Pull boxes
4. Special knockouts
5. Main switchboard section
6. Transition section
7. Instrumentation
8. External control wiring
9. Conduit or wire

Material for starters include:
1. Circuit breaker or fused disconnect
2. Magnetic motor starter
3. Control transformer
4. Control fuse and fuse block

Labor-hours for starters include:
1. Handling
2. Installing starter within structure
3. Internal wiring connections
4. Lacing within enclosure
5. Testing
6. Phasing

Job Conditions: Productivity is based on new construction. The motor control location is assumed to be on first floor in an unobstructed area. The material staging area is within 100′ of the final location.

Note: Additional labor-hours must be added if M.C.C. is to be installed on floors other than the first, or if rigging is required.

R262419-65 Motor Starters and Controls

Motor starters should be listed on the same "quantity sheet" as motors and motor connections. Identify each starter by:

1. Size
2. Voltage
3. Type

Example:

A. FVNR, 480V, 2HP, size 00
B. FVNR, 480V, 5HP, size 0, combination type
C. FVR, 480V, size 2

The NEMA type of enclosure should also be identified.

Included in the labor-hours are:

1. Unloading, uncrating and handling of starters up to 200′ from loading area
2. Measuring and marking
3. Drilling (4) anchor type lead fasteners using a hammer drill
4. Mounting and leveling starter
5. Connecting wire or cable to line and load sides of starter (when already lugged)
6. Installation of (3) thermal type heaters
7. Testing

The following are not included unless specified in the unit price description.

1. Control transformer
2. Controls, either factory or field installed
3. Conduit and wire to or from starter
4. Plywood backboard
5. Cable terminations

The following material and labor were included for combination type starters:

1. Unloading, uncrating and handling of starter up to 200′ of loading dock
2. Measuring and marking
3. Drilling (4) anchor type lead fasteners using a hammer drill
4. Mounting and leveling
5. Connecting prepared cable conductors
6. Installation of (3) dual element cartridge type fuses
7. Installation of (3) thermal type heaters
8. Test for rotation

MOTOR CONTROLS

When pricing motor controls make sure you consider the type of control system being utilized. If the controls are factory installed and located in the enclosure itself, then you would add to your starter price the items 5200 through 5800 in the Unit Price section. If control voltage is different from line voltage, add the material and labor cost of a control transformer.

For external control of starters include the following items:

1. Raceways
2. Wire & terminations
3. Control enclosures
4. Fittings
5. Push button stations
6. Indicators

Job Conditions: Productivity is based on new construction to a height of 10′.

Material staging area is assumed to be within 100′ of work being performed.

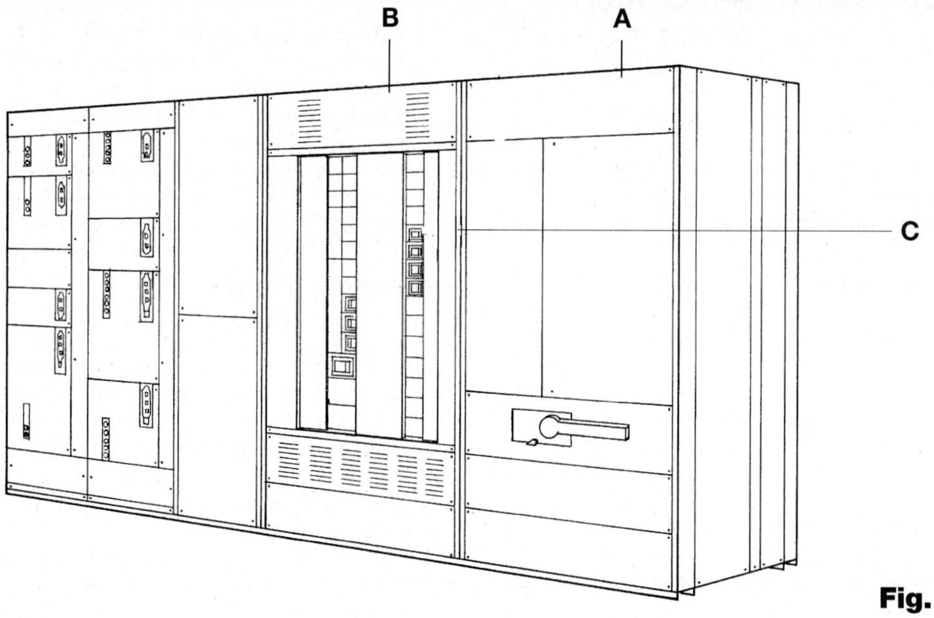

Fig. R262419-81

R262419-80 Distribution Section

After "taking off" the switchboard section, include on the same "quantity sheet" the distribution section; identify by:

1. Voltage
2. Ampere rating
3. Type

Example:

(Fig. R262419-81) (B) Distribution Section

Included in the labor costs of the distribution section are:

1. Uncrating
2. Hauling to 200′ of loading dock
3. Setting of distribution panel
4. Leveling & shimming
5. Anchoring of equipment to pad or floor
6. Bolting of horizontal bus bars between
7. Testing of equipment

Not included in the Distribution section are:

1. Breakers (C)
2. Equipment pads
3. Steel channels embedded or grouted in concrete
4. Pull boxes
5. Special knockouts
6. Transition section
7. Conduit or wire

R262419-82 Feeder Section

List quantities on the same sheet as the distribution section. Identify breakers by: (Fig. R262419-81)

1. Frame type
2. Number of poles
3. Ampere rating

Installation includes:

1. Handling
2. Placing breakers in distribution panel
3. Preparing wire or cable
4. Lacing wire
5. Marking each phase with colored tape
6. Marking panel legend
7. Testing
8. Balancing

R262419-84 Switchgear

It is recommended that "switchgear" or those items contained in the following sections be quoted from equipment manufacturers as a package price.

Switchboard instruments

Switchboard distribution sections

Switchboard feeder sections

Switchboard Service Disc.

Switchboard In-plant Dist.

Included in these sections are the most common types and sizes of factory assembled equipment.

The recommended procedure for low voltage switchgear would be to price (Fig. R262419-81) (A) Main Switchboard

Identify by:

1. Voltage
2. Amperage
3. Type

Example:

1. 120/208V, 4-wire, 600A, nonfused
2. 277/480V, 4-wire, 600A, nonfused
3. 120/208V, 4-wire, 400A w/fused switch & CT compartment
4. 277/480V, 4-wire, 400A, w/fused switch & CT compartment
5. 120/208V, 4-wire, 800A, w/pressure switch & CT compartment
6. 277/480V, 4-wire, 800A, w/molded CB & CT compartment

Included in the labor costs for switchboards are:

1. Uncrating
2. Hauling to 200′ of loading dock
3. Setting equipment
4. Leveling and shimming
5. Anchoring
6. Cable identification
7. Testing of equipment

Not included in the switchboard price are:

1. Rigging
2. Equipment pads
3. Steel channels embedded or grouted in concrete
4. Special knockouts
5. Transition or Auxiliary sections
6. Instrumentation
7. External control
8. Conduit and wire
9. Conductor terminations

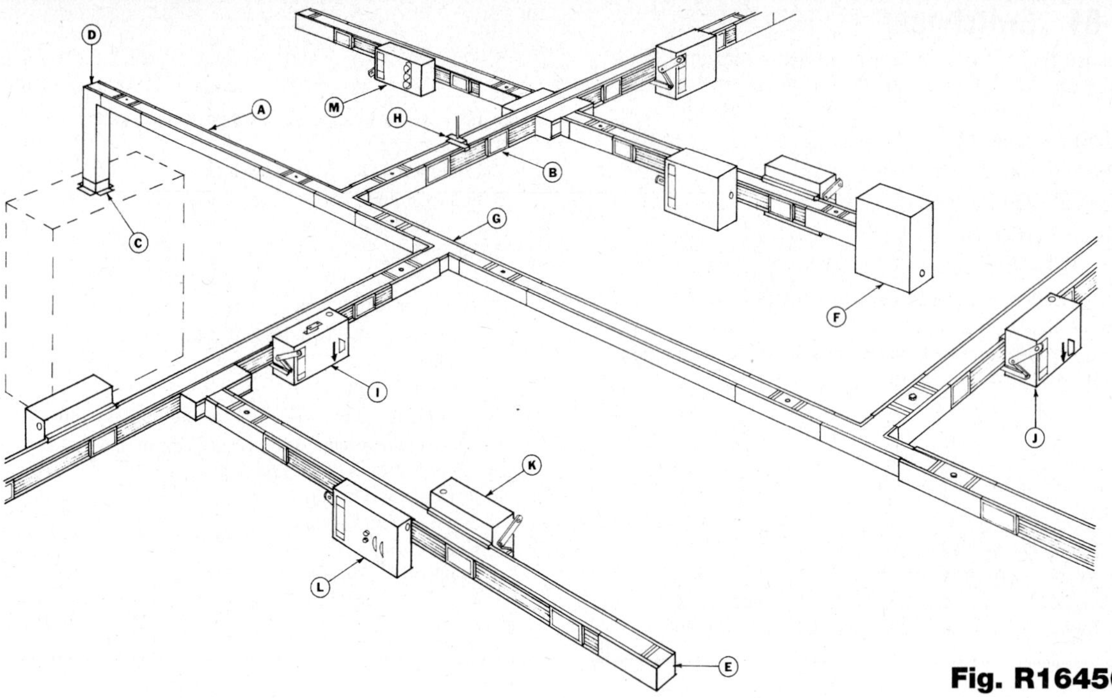

Fig. R16450-101

R262513-10 Aluminum Bus Duct

When taking off bus duct identify the system as either:
1. Aluminum
2. Copper

List straight lengths by type and size
- A. Feeder — 800 A
- B. Plug in — 800 A

Do not measure through fittings as you would on conduit, since there is no allowance for scrap in bus duct systems.

If upon taking off linear foot quantities of bus duct you find your quantities are not divisible evenly by 10 ft., then the remainder must be priced as a special item and quoted from the manufacturer. Do not use the bare material cost per L.F. for these special items. You can, however, safely use the bare labor cost per L.F. for the entire length.

Identify fittings by type and ampere rating.

Example:

C. Switchboard stub, 800 A

D. Elbows, 800 A

E. End box, 800 A

F. Cable tap box, 800 A

G. Tee Fittings, 800 A

H. Hangers

Plug-in Units – List separately plug-in units and identify by type and ampere rating

I. Plug-in switches 600 Volt 3 phase 60 A

J. Plug-in molded case C.B. 60 A

K. Combination starter FVNR NEMA 1

L. Combination contactor & fused switch NEMA 1

M. Combination fusible switch & lighting control 60 A

Labor-hours for feeder and plug-in sections include:
1. Unloading and uncrating
2. Hauling up to 200 ft. from loading dock
3. Measuring and marking
4. Installing hangers
5. Hanging and bolting sections
6. Aligning and leveling
7. Testing

Labor-hours do not include:
1. Modifications to existing structure for hanger supports
2. Threaded rod in excess of 2 ft.
3. Welding
4. Penetrations through walls
5. Staging rental

Deduct the following percentages from labor only:

150 ft. to 250 ft. — 10%
251 ft. to 350 ft. — 15%
351 ft. to 500 ft. — 20%
Over 500 ft. — 25%

Deduct percentage only if runs are contained in the same area.

Example: If the job entails running 100 ft. in 5 different locations do not deduct 20%, but if the duct is being run in 1 area and the quantity is 500 ft. then you would deduct 20%.

Deduct only from straight lengths, not fittings or plug-in units.

R262513-10 Aluminum Bus Duct (cont.)

Add to labor for elevated installations:

10 ft. to 14.5 ft. high	10%
15 ft. to 20 ft. high	20%
21 ft. to 25 ft. high	25%
26 ft. to 30 ft. high	35%
31 ft. to 35 ft. high	40%
36 ft. to 40 ft. high	50%
Over 40 ft. high	55%

Bus Duct Fittings:

Labor-hours for fittings include:

1. Unloading and uncrating
2. Hauling up to 200 ft. from loading dock
3. Installing, fitting, and bolting all ends to in-place sections

Plug-in units include:

1. Unloading and uncrating
2. Hauling up to 200 ft. from loading dock
3. Installing plug-in into in-place duct
4. Connecting load wire to lugs
5. Marking wire
6. Checking phase rotation

Labor-hours for plug-ins do not include:

1. Conduit runs from plug-in
2. Wire from plug-in
3. Conduit termination

Economy of Scale – For large concentrations of plug-in units in the same area deduct the following percentages:

11	to	25	15%
26	to	50	20%
51	to	75	25%
76	to	100	30%
100	and	over	35%

Job Conditions: Productivities are based on new construction in an unobstructed first floor area to a height of 10′ in an unobstructed area.

Material staging area is within 100 ft. of work being performed.

Add to the duct fittings and hangers:

- Plug-in switches (fused)
- Plug-in breakers
- Combination starters
- Combination contactors
- Combination fusible switch and lighting control

Labor-hours for duct and fittings include:

1. Unloading and uncrating
2. Hauling up to 200 ft. from loading dock
3. Measuring and marking
4. Installing duct runs
5. Leveling
6. Sound testing

Labor-hours for plug-ins include:

1. Unloading and uncrating
2. Hauling up to 200 ft. from loading dock
3. Installing plug-ins
4. Preparing wire
5. Wire connections and marking

R262716-40 Standard Electrical Enclosure Types

NEMA Enclosures

Electrical enclosures serve two basic purposes: they protect people from accidental contact with enclosed electrical devices and connections, and they protect the enclosed devices and connections from specified external conditions. The National Electrical Manufacturers Association (NEMA) has established the following standards. Because these descriptions are not intended to be complete representations of NEMA listings, consultation of NEMA literature is advised for detailed information.

The following definitions and descriptions pertain to NONHAZARDOUS locations.

NEMA Type 1: General purpose enclosures intended for use indoors, primarily to prevent accidental contact of personnel with the enclosed equipment in areas that do not involve unusual conditions.

NEMA Type 2: Dripproof indoor enclosures intended to protect the enclosed equipment against dripping noncorrosive liquids and falling dirt.

NEMA Type 3: Dustproof, raintight and sleet-resistant (ice-resistant) enclosures intended for use outdoors to protect the enclosed equipment against wind-blown dust, rain, sleet, and external ice formation.

NEMA Type 3R: Rainproof and sleet-resistant (ice-resistant) enclosures intended for use outdoors to protect the enclosed equipment against rain. These enclosures are constructed so that the accumulation and melting of sleet (ice) will not damage the enclosure and its internal mechanisms.

NEMA Type 3S: Enclosures intended for outdoor use to provide limited protection against wind-blown dust, rain, and sleet (ice) and to allow operation of external mechanisms when ice-laden.

NEMA Type 4: Watertight and dust-tight enclosures intended for use indoors and out – to protect the enclosed equipment against splashing water, seepage of water, falling or hose-directed water, and severe external condensation.

NEMA Type 4X: Watertight, dust-tight, and corrosion-resistant indoor and outdoor enclosures featuring the same provisions as Type 4 enclosures, plus corrosion resistance.

NEMA Type 5: Indoor enclosures intended primarily to provide limited protection against dust and falling dirt.

NEMA Type 6: Enclosures intended for indoor and outdoor use – primarily to provide limited protection against the entry of water during occasional temporary submersion at a limited depth.

NEMA Type 6R: Enclosures intended for indoor and outdoor use – primarily to provide limited protection against the entry of water during prolonged submersion at a limited depth.

NEMA Type 11: Enclosures intended for indoor use – primarily to provide, by means of oil immersion, limited protection to enclosed equipment against the corrosive effects of liquids and gases.

NEMA Type 12: Dust-tight and driptight indoor enclosures intended for use indoors in industrial locations to protect the enclosed equipment against fibers, flyings, lint, dust, and dirt, as well as light splashing, seepage, dripping, and external condensation of noncorrosive liquids.

NEMA Type 13: Oil-tight and dust-tight indoor enclosures intended primarily to house pilot devices, such as limit switches, foot switches, push buttons, selector switches, and pilot lights, and to protect these devices against lint and dust, seepage, external condensation, and sprayed water, oil, and noncorrosive coolant.

The following definitions and descriptions pertain to HAZARDOUS, or CLASSIFIED, locations:

NEMA Type 7: Enclosures intended to use in indoor locations classified as Class 1, Groups A, B, C, or D, as defined in the National Electrical Code.

NEMA Type 9: Enclosures intended for use in indoor locations classified as Class 2, Groups E, F, or G, as defined in the National Electrical Code.

R262726-90 Wiring Devices

Wiring devices should be priced on a separate takeoff form which includes boxes, covers, conduit and wire.

Labor-hours for devices include:

1. Stripping of wire
2. Attaching wire to device using terminators on the device itself, lugs, set screws etc.
3. Mounting of device in box

Labor-hours do not include:

1. Conduit
2. Wire
3. Boxes
4. Plates

Economy of Scale – for large concentrations of devices in the same area deduct the following percentages from labor-hours:

1	to	10	0%
11	to	25	20%
26	to	50	25%
51	to	100	30%
	over	100	35%

R262726-90 Wiring Devices (cont.)

NEMA No.	15 R	20 R	30 R	50 R	60 R
1 125V 2 Pole, 2 Wire	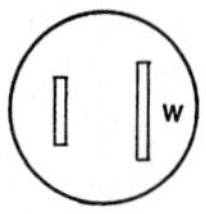				
2 250V 2 Pole, 2 Wire		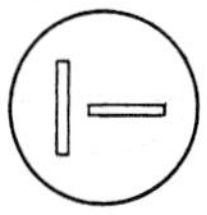			
5 125V 2 Pole, 3 Wire	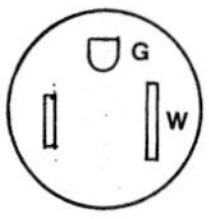	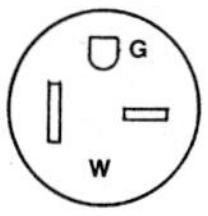		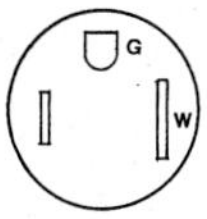	
6 250V 2 Pole, 3 Wire			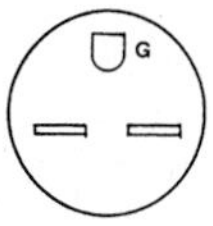	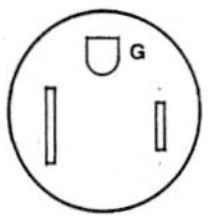	
7 277V, AC 2 Pole, 3 Wire	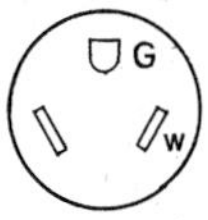	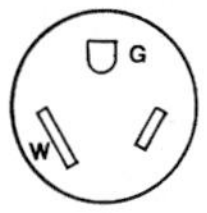		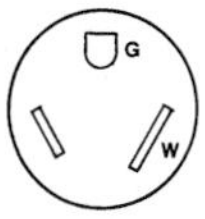	
10 125/250V 3 Pole, 3 Wire		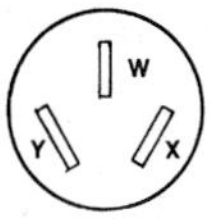	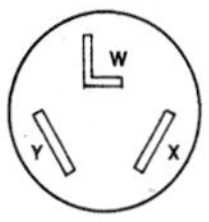	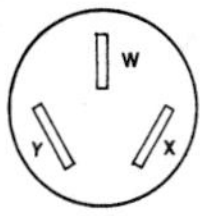	
11 3 Phase 250V 3 Pole, 3 Wire	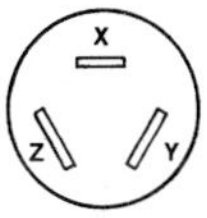	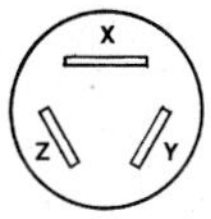	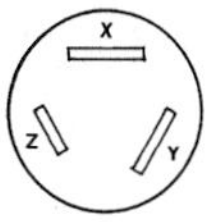	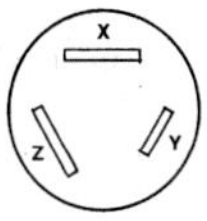	
14 125/250V 3 Pole, 4 Wire	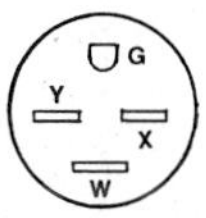	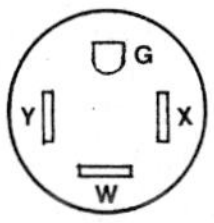	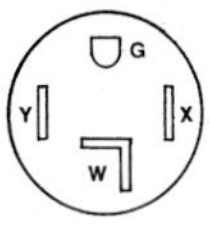	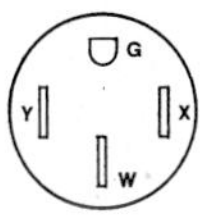	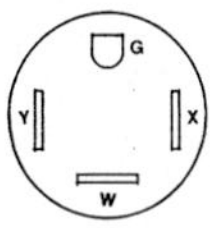
15 3 Phase 250V 3 Pole, 4 Wire	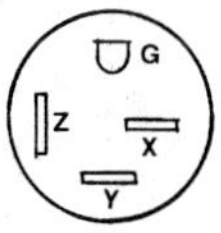	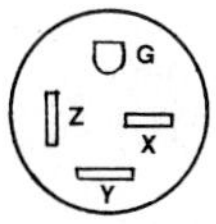	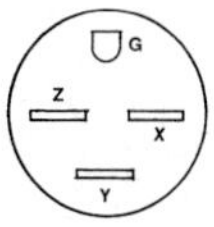	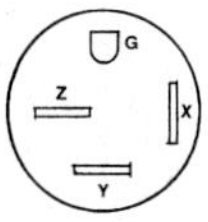	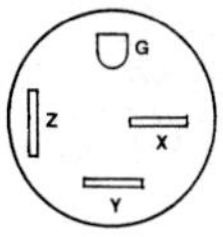
18 3 Phase 208Y/120V 4 Pole, 4 Wire	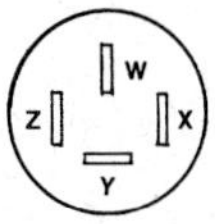	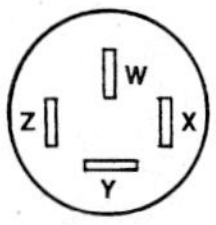	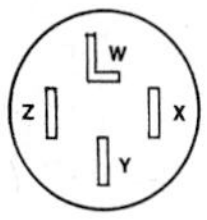	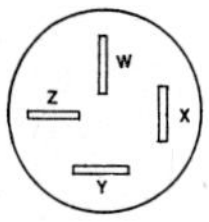	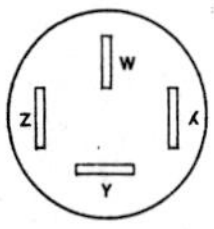

R262726-90 Wiring Devices (cont.)

NEMA No.	15 R	20 R	30 R
L 1 125V 2 Pole, 2 Wire			
L 2 250V 2 Pole, 2 Wire		15A	
L 5 125 V 2 Pole, 3 Wire			
L 6 250 V 2 Pole, 3 Wire			
L 7 227 V, AC 2 Pole, 3 Wire			
L 8 480 V 2 Pole, 3 Wire			
L 9 600 V 2 Pole, 3 Wire			
L 10 125/250V 3 Pole, 3 Wire			
L 11 3 Phase 250 V 3 Pole, 3 Wire			
L 12 3 Phase 480 V 3 Pole, 3 Wire			
L 13 3 Phase 600V 3 Pole, 3 Wire			
L 14 125/250V 3 Pole, 4 Wire			
L 15 3 Phase 250 V 3 Pole, 4 Wire			
L 16 3 Phase 480V 3 Pole, 4 Wire			
L 17 3 Phase 600 V 3 Pole, 4 Wire			
L 18 3 Phase 208Y/120V 4 Pole, 4 Wire			
L 19 3 Phase 480Y/277V 4 Pole, 4 Wire			
L 20 3 Phase 600Y/347V 4 Pole, 4 Wire			
L 21 3 Phase 208Y/120V 4 Pole, 5 Wire			
L 22 3 Phase 480Y/277V 4 Pole, 5 Wire			
L 23 3 Phase 600Y/347V 4 Pole, 5 Wire			

R262816-80 Safety Switches

List each safety switch by type, ampere rating, voltage, single or three phase, fused or nonfused.

Example:

A. General duty, 240V, 3-pole, fused
B. Heavy Duty, 600V, 3-pole, nonfused
C. Heavy Duty, 240V, 2-pole, fused
D. Heavy Duty, 600V, 3-pole, fused

Also include NEMA enclosure type and identify as:

1. Indoor
2. Weatherproof
3. Explosionproof

Installation of safety switches includes:

1. Unloading and uncrating
2. Handling disconnects up to 200′ from loading dock
3. Measuring and marking location
4. Drilling (4) anchor type lead fasteners using a hammer drill
5. Mounting and leveling safety switch
6. Installing (3) fuses
7. Phasing and tagging line and load wires

Price does not include:

1. Modifications to enclosure
2. Plywood backboard
3. Conduit or wire
4. Fuses
5. Termination of wires

Job Conditions: Productivities are based on new construction to an installed height of 6′ above finished floor.

Material staging area is assumed to be within 100′ of work in progress.

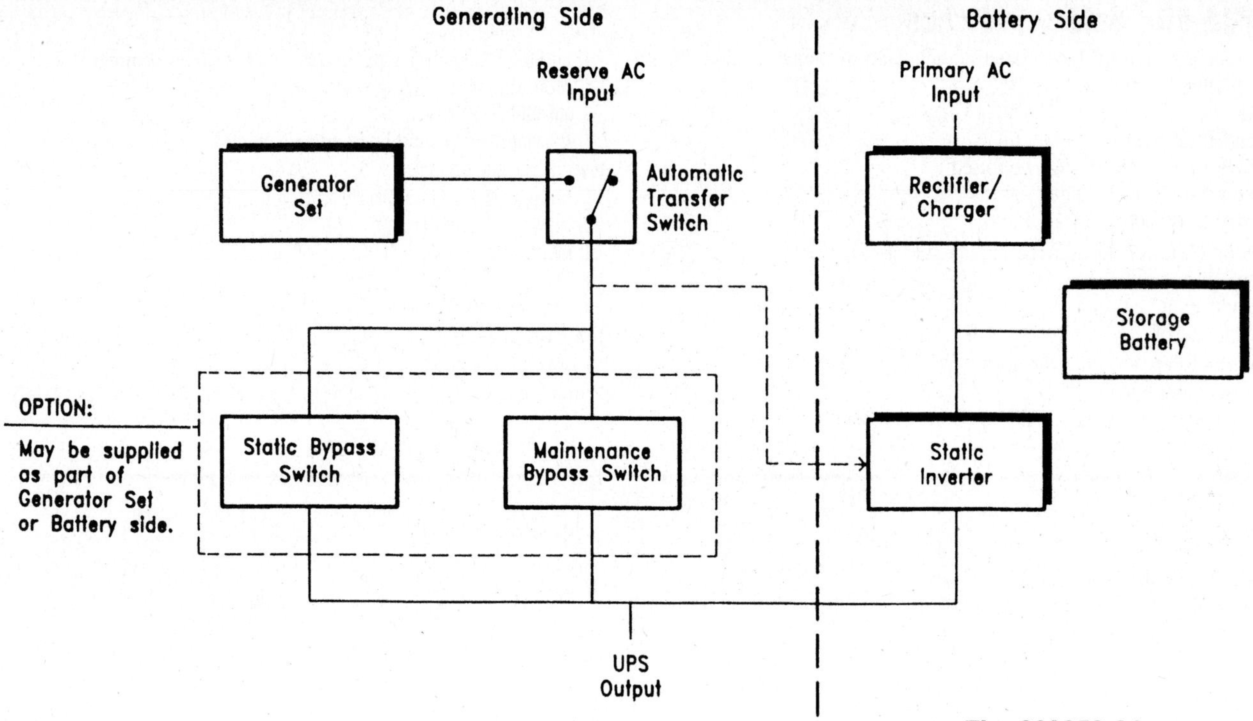

Fig. 263353-81

R263353-80 Uninterruptible Power Supply Systems

General: Uninterruptible Power Supply (UPS) Systems are used to provide power for legally required standby systems. They are also designed to protect computers and provide optional additional coverage for any or all loads in a facility. Figure R263353-81 shows a typical configuration for a UPS System with a generator set.

Cost Determination:

It is recommended that UPS System material costs be obtained from equipment manufacturers as a package. Installation costs should be obtained from a vendor or contractor.

The recommended procedure for pricing UPS Systems would be to identify:

1. Frequency – by Hertz (Hz.)
   For example: 50, 60, and 400/415 Hz.
2. Apparent power and real power
   For example: 200 kVA/170 kW
3. Input/Output voltage
   For example: 120V, 208V or 240V
4. Phase – either single or three-phase
5. Options and accessories – For extended run time more batteries would be required. Other accessories include battery cabinets, battery racks, remote control panel, power distribution unit (PDU), and warranty enhancement plans.

Note:

1. Larger systems can be configured by paralleling two or more standard small size single modules.
   For example: two 15 kVA modules combined together and configured to 30 kVA.
2. Maximum input current during battery recharge is typically 15% higher than normal current.
3. UPS Systems weights vary depending on options purchased and power rating in kVA.

R263413-30 HP Value/Cost Determination

General: Motors can be powered by any of the seven systems shown in Figure R262213-11 through Figure R262213-17 provided the motor voltage characteristics are compatible with the power system characteristics.

Cost Determination:

Motor Amperes for the various size H.P. and voltage are listed in Table R263413-31. To find the amperes, locate the required H.P. rating and locate the amperes under the appropriate circuit characteristics.

For example:

A. 100 H.P., 3 phase, 460 volt motor = 124 amperes (Table R263413-31)

B. 10 H.P., 3 phase, 200 volt motor = 32.2 amperes (Table R263413-31)

Motor Wire Size: After the amperes are found in Table R263413-31 the amperes must be increased 25% to compensate for power losses. Next refer to Table R260519-92. Find the appropriate insulation column for copper or aluminum wire to determine the proper wire size.

For example:

A. 100 H.P., 3 phase, 460 volt motor has an ampere value of 124 amperes from Table R263413-31

B. 124A x 1.25 = 155 amperes

C. Refer to Table R260519-92 for THW or THWN wire insulations to find the proper wire size. For a 155 ampere load using copper wire a size 2/0 wire is needed.

D. For the 3 phase motor three wires of 2/0 size are required.

Conduit Size: To obtain the proper conduit size for the wires and type of insulation used, refer to Table R260533-22.

For example: For the 100 H.P., 460V, 3 phase motor, it was determined that three 2/0 wires are required. Assuming THWN insulated copper wire, use Table R260533-22 to determine that three 2/0 wires require 1-1/2″ conduit.

Material Cost of the conduit and wire system depends on:
1. Wire size required
2. Copper or aluminum wire
3. Wire insulation type selected
4. Steel or plastic conduit
5. Type of conduit raceway selected.

Labor Cost of the conduit and wire system depends on:
1. Type and size of conduit
2. Type and size of wires installed
3. Location and height of installation in building or depth of trench
4. Support system for conduit.

Magnetic starters, switches, and motor connection:

To complete the cost picture from H.P. to Costs additional items must be added to the cost of the conduit and wire system to arrive at a total cost.
1. Assembly Table D5020-160 Magnetic Starters Installed Cost lists the various size starters for single phase and three phase motors.
2. Assembly Table D5020-165 Heavy Duty Safety Switches Installed Cost lists safety switches required at the beginning of a motor circuit and also one required in the vicinity of the motor location.
3. Assembly Table D5020-170 Motor Connection lists the various costs for single and three phase motors.

Worksheet to obtain total motor wiring costs:

It is assumed that the motors or motor driven equipment are furnished and installed under other sections for this estimate and the following work is done under this section:
1. Conduit
2. Wire (add 10% for additional wire beyond conduit ends for connections to switches, boxes, starters, etc.)
3. Starters
4. Safety switches
5. Motor connections

R263413-31 Ampere Values Determined by Horsepower, Voltage and Phase Values

H.P.	Amperes							
	Single Phase			Three Phase				
	115V	208V	230V	200V	208V	230V	460V	575V
1/6	4.4A	2.4A	2.2A					
1/4	5.8	3.2	2.9					
1/3	7.2	4.0	3.6					
1/2	9.8	5.4	4.9	2.5A	2.4A	2.2A	1.1A	0.9A
3/4	13.8	7.6	6.9	3.7	3.5	3.2	1.6	1.3
1	16	8.8	8	4.8	4.6	4.2	2.1	1.7
1-1/2	20	11	10	6.9	6.6	6.0	3.0	2.4
2	24	13.2	12	7.8	7.5	6.8	3.4	2.7
3	34	18.7	17	11.0	10.6	9.6	4.8	3.9
5	56	30.8	28	17.5	16.7	15.2	7.6	6.1
7-1/2	80	44	40	25.3	24.2	22	11	9
10	100	55	50	32.2	30.8	28	14	11
15				48.3	46.2	42	21	17
20				62.1	59.4	54	27	22
25				78.2	74.8	68	34	27
30				92	88	80	40	32
40				120	114	104	52	41
50				150	143	130	65	52
60				177	169	154	77	62
75				221	211	192	96	77
100				285	273	248	124	99
125				359	343	312	156	125
150				414	396	360	180	144
200				552	528	480	240	192
250							302	242
300							361	289
350							414	336
400							477	382

Figure R263413-32

Worksheet for Motor Circuits					
				Cost	
Item	Type	Size	Quantity	Unit	Total
Wire					
Conduit					
Switch					
Starter					
Switch					
Motor Connection					
Other					
Total Cost					

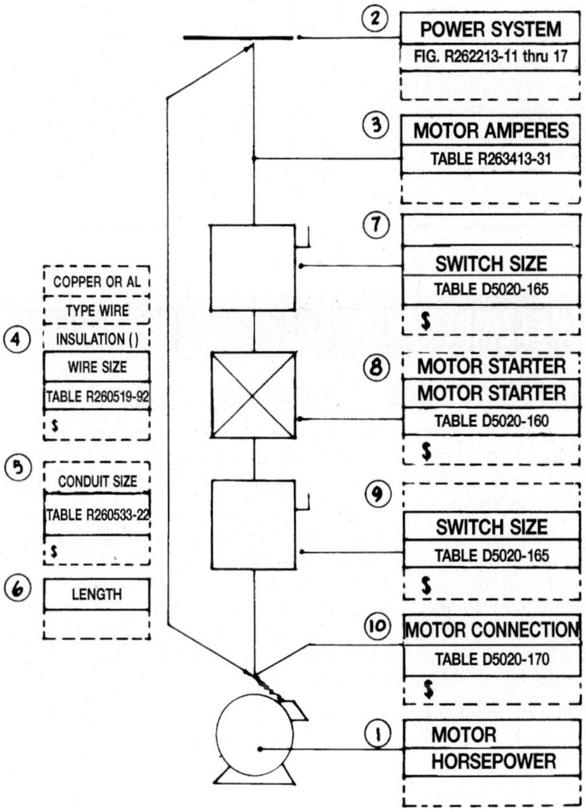

R263413-33 Maximum Horsepower for Starter Size by Voltage

Starter	Maximum HP (3ϕ)			
Size	208V	240V	480V	600V
00	1½	1½	2	2
0	3	3	5	5
1	7½	7½	10	10
2	10	15	25	25
3	25	30	50	50
4	40	50	100	100
5		100	200	200
6		200	300	300
7		300	600	600
8		450	900	900
8L		700	1500	1500

Electrical — R2636 Transfer Switches

R263623-60 Automatic Transfer Switches

When taking off automatic transfer switches identify by voltage, amperage and number of poles.

Example: Automatic transfer switch, 480V, 3 phase, 30A, NEMA 1 enclosure

Labor-hours for transfer switches include:

1. Unloading, uncrating and handling switches up to 200′ from loading dock
2. Measuring and marking
3. Drilling (4) lead type anchors using a hammer drill
4. Mounting and leveling
5. Circuit identification
6. Testing and load balancing

Labor-hours do not include:

1. Modifications in enclosure
2. Structural supports
3. Additional lugs
4. Plywood backboard
5. Painting or lettering
6. Conduit runs to or from transfer switch
7. Wire
8. Termination of wires

Electrical — R2651 Interior Lighting

R265113-40 Interior Lighting Fixtures

When taking off interior lighting fixtures, it is advisable to set up your quantity worksheet to conform to the lighting schedule as it appears on the print. Include the alpha-numeric code plus the symbol on your worksheet.

Take off a particular section or floor of the building and count each type of fixture before going on to another type. It would also be advantageous to include on the same worksheet the pipe, wire, fittings and circuit number associated with each type of lighting fixture. This will help you identify the costs associated with any particular lighting system and in turn make material purchases more specific as to when and how much to order under the classification of lighting.

By taking off lighting first you can get a complete "walk through" of the job. This will become helpful when doing other phases of the project.

Materials for a recessed fixture include:

1. Fixture
2. Lamps
3. 6′ of jack chain
4. (2) S hooks
5. (2) Wire nuts

Labor for interior recessed fixtures include:

1. Unloading by hand
2. Hauling by hand to an area up to 200′ from loading dock
3. Uncrating
4. Layout
5. Installing fixture
6. Attaching jack chain & S hooks
7. Connecting circuit power
8. Reassembling fixture
9. Installing lamps
10. Testing

Material for surface mounted fixtures include:

1. Fixture
2. Lamps
3. Either (4) lead type anchors, (4) toggle bolts, or (4) ceiling grid clips
4. (2) Wire nuts

Material for pendent mounted fixtures include:

1. Fixture
2. Lamps
3. (2) Wire nuts
4. Rigid pendents as required by type of fixtures
5. Canopies as required by type of fixture

Labor hours include the following for both surface and pendent fixtures:

1. Unloading by hand
2. Hauling by hand to an area up to 200′ from loading dock
3. Uncrating
4. Layout and marking
5. Drilling (4) holes for either lead anchors or toggle bolts using a hammer drill
6. Installing fixture
7. Leveling fixture
8. Connecting circuit power
9. Installing lamps
10. Testing

Labor for surface or pendent fixtures does not include:

1. Conduit
2. Boxes or covers
3. Connectors
4. Fixture whips
5. Special support
6. Switching
7. Wire

Economy of Scale: For large concentrations of lighting fixtures in the same area deduct the following percentages from labor:

25	to	50	fixtures	15%
51	to	75	fixtures	20%
76	to	100	fixtures	25%
101 and over				30%

Job Conditions: Productivity is based on new construction in an unobstructed first floor location, to 10′ high.

Material staging is assumed to be within 100′ of work being performed.

Add the following percentages to labor for elevated installations:

10′	to	14.5′	high	10%
15′	to	20′	high	20%
21′	to	25′	high	25%
26′	to	30′	high	35%
31′	to	35′	high	40%
36′	to	40′	high	50%
41′ and over				55%

R265723-10 For Other than Regular Cool White (CW) Lamps

Multiply Material Costs as Follows:					
Regular Lamps	Cool white deluxe (CWX) Warm white deluxe (WWX) Warm white (WW) Natural (N)	x 1.35 x 1.35 x 1.30 x 2.05	Energy Saving Lamps	Cool white (CW/ES) Cool white deluxe (CWX/ES) Warm white (WW/ES) Warm white deluxe (WWX/ES)	x 1.35 x 1.65 x 1.55 x 1.65

Communications — R2713 Communications Backbone Cabling

R271323-40 Fiber Optics

Fiber optic systems use optical fiber such as plastic, glass, or fused silica, a transparent material, to transmit radiant power (i.e., light) for control, communication, and signaling applications. The types of fiber optic cables can be nonconductive, conductive, or composite. The composite cables contain fiber optics and current-carrying electrical conductors. The configuration for one of the fiber optic systems is as follows:

The transceiver module acts as transmitting and receiving equipment in a common house, which converts electrical energy to light energy or vice versa.

Pricing the fiber optic system is not an easy task. The performance of the whole system will affect the cost significantly. New specialized tools and techniques decrease the installing cost tremendously. In the fiber optic section of Means Electrical Cost Data, a benchmark for labor-hours and material costs is set up so that users can adjust their costs according to unique project conditions.

Units for Measure: Fiber optic cable is measured in hundred linear feet (C.L.F.) or industry units of measure - meter (m) or kilometer (km). The connectors are counted as units (EA.)

Material Units: Generally, the material costs include only the cable. All the accessories shall be priced separately.

Labor Units: The following procedures are generally included for the installation of fiber optic cables:

- Receiving
- Material handling
- Setting up pulling equipment
- Measuring and cutting cable
- Pulling cable

These additional items are listed and extended: Terminations

Takeoff Procedure: Cable should be taken off by type, size, number of fibers, and number of terminations required. List the lengths of each type of cable on the takeoff sheets. Total and add 10% for waste. Transfer the figures to a cost analysis sheet and extend.

Communications — R2715 Communications Horizontal Cabling

R271513-75 High Performance Cable

There are several categories used to describe high performance cable. The following information includes a description of categories CAT 3, 5, 5e, 6, and 7, and details classifications of frequency and specific standards. The category standards have evolved under the sponsorship of organizations such as the Telecommunication Industry Association (TIA), the Electronic Industries Alliance (EIA), the American National Standards Institute (ANSI), the International Organization for Standardization (ISO), and the International Electrotechnical Commission (IEC), all of which have catered to the increasing complexities of modern network technology. For network cabling, users must comply with national or international standards. A breakdown of these categories is as follows:

Category 3: Designed to handle frequencies up to 16 MHz.

Category 5: (TIA/EIA 568A) Designed to handle frequencies up to 100 MHz.

Category 5e: Additional transmission performance to exceed Category 5.

Category 6: Development by TIA and other international groups to handle frequencies of 250 MHz.

Category 7: Development to handle a frequency range up to 600 MHz.

R312316-45 Excavating Equipment

The table below lists theoretical hourly production in C.Y./hr. bank measure for some typical excavation equipment. Figures assume 50 minute hours, 83% job efficiency, 100% operator efficiency, 90° swing and properly sized hauling units, which must be modified for adverse digging and loading conditions. Actual production costs in the front of the data set average about 50% of the theoretical values listed here.

Equipment	Soil Type	B.C.Y. Weight	% Swell	1 C.Y.	1-1/2 C.Y.	2 C.Y.	2-1/2 C.Y.	3 C.Y.	3-1/2 C.Y.	4 C.Y.
Hydraulic Excavator "Backhoe" 15′ Deep Cut	Moist loam, sandy clay	3400 lb.	40%	165	195	200	275	330	385	440
	Sand and gravel	3100	18	140	170	225	240	285	330	380
	Common earth	2800	30	150	180	230	250	300	350	400
	Clay, hard, dense	3000	33	120	140	190	200	240	260	320
Power Shovel Optimum Cut (Ft.)	Moist loam, sandy clay	3400	40	170	245	295	335	385	435	475
				(6.0)	(7.0)	(7.8)	(8.4)	(8.8)	(9.1)	(9.4)
	Sand and gravel	3100	18	165	225	275	325	375	420	460
				(6.0)	(7.0)	(7.8)	(8.4)	(8.8)	(9.1)	(9.4)
	Common earth	2800	30	145	200	250	295	335	375	425
				(7.8)	(9.2)	(10.2)	(11.2)	(12.1)	(13.0)	(13.8)
	Clay, hard, dense	3000	33	120	175	220	255	300	335	375
				(9.0)	(10.7)	(12.2)	(13.3)	(14.2)	(15.1)	(16.0)
Drag Line Optimum Cut (Ft.)	Moist loam, sandy clay	3400	40	130	180	220	250	290	325	385
				(6.6)	(7.4)	(8.0)	(8.5)	(9.0)	(9.5)	(10.0)
	Sand and gravel	3100	18	130	175	210	245	280	315	375
				(6.6)	(7.4)	(8.0)	(8.5)	(9.0)	(9.5)	(10.0)
	Common earth	2800	30	110	160	190	220	250	280	310
				(8.0)	(9.0)	(9.9)	(10.5)	(11.0)	(11.5)	(12.0)
	Clay, hard, dense	3000	33	90	130	160	190	225	250	280
				(9.3)	(10.7)	(11.8)	(12.3)	(12.8)	(13.3)	(12.0)
				Wheel Loaders				Track Loaders		
				3 C.Y.	4 C.Y.	6 C.Y.	8 C.Y.	2-1/4 C.Y.	3 C.Y.	4 C.Y.
Loading Tractors	Moist loam, sandy clay	3400	40	260	340	510	690	135	180	250
	Sand and gravel	3100	18	245	320	480	650	130	170	235
	Common earth	2800	30	230	300	460	620	120	155	220
	Clay, hard, dense	3000	33	200	270	415	560	110	145	200
	Rock, well-blasted	4000	50	180	245	380	520	100	130	180

R337116-60 Average Transmission Line Material Requirements (Per Mile)

Terrain:		Flat				Rolling				Mountain			
Item		69kV	161kV	161kV	500kV	69kV	161kV	161kV	500kV	69kV	161kV	161kV	500kV
Pole Type	Unit	Wood	Wood	Steel	Steel	Wood	Wood	Steel	Steel	Wood	Wood	Steel	Steel
Conductor: 397,500 - Cir. Mil., 26/7-ACSR													
Structures	Ea.	12[1]				9[2]				7[2]			
Poles	Ea.	12				18				14			
Crossarms	Ea.	24[3]				9[4]				7[4]			
Conductor	Ft.	15,990				15,990				15,990			
Insulators[5]	Ea.	180				135				105			
Ground Wire	Ft.	5,330				10,660				10,660			
Conductor: 636,000 - Cir. Mil., 26/7-ACSR													
Structures	Ea.	13[1]	11[6]			10[2]	9[2]	6[9]		8[2]	8[2]	6[9]	
Excavation	C.Y.	–	–			–	–	120		–	–	120	
Concrete	C.Y.	–	–			–	–	10		–	–	10	
Steel Towers	Tons	–	–			–	–	32		–	–	32	
Poles	Ea.	13	11			20	18	–		16	16	–	
Crossarms	Ea.	26[3]	33[7]			10[4]	9[8]	–		8[4]	8[8]	–	
Conductor	Ft.	15,990	15,990			15,990	15,990	15,990		15,990	15,990	15,990	
Insulators[5]	Ea.	195	165			150	297	297		120	264	297	
Ground Wire	Ft.	5330	5330			10,660	10,660	10,660		10,660	10,660	10,660	
Conductor: 954,000 - Cir. Mil., 45/7-ACSR													
Structures	Ea.	14[1]	12[6]		4[11]	10[2]	9[2]	6[9]	4[11]	8[2]	8[2]	6[9]	4[13]
Excavation	C.Y.	–	–		200	–	–	125	214	–	–	125	233
Concrete	C.Y.	–	–		20	–	–	10	21	–	–	10	21
Steel Towers	Tons	–	–		57	–	–	33	57	–	–	33	63
Poles	Ea.	14	12		–	20	18	–	–	16	16	–	–
Crossarms	Ea.	28[10]	36[7]		–	10[4]	9[8]	–	–	8[4]	8[8]	–	–
Conductor	Ft.	15,990	15,990		47,970[12]	15,990	15,990	15,990	47,970[12]	15,990	15,990	15,990	47,970[12]
Insulators[5]	Ea.	210	180		288	150	297	297	288	120	264	297	576
Ground Wire	Ft.	5330	5330		10,660	10,660	10,660	10,660	10,660	10,660	10,660	10,660	10,660
Conductor: 1,351,500 - Cir. Mil., 45/7-ACSR													
Structures	Ea.			8[14]				8[14]					
Excavation	C.Y.			220				220					
Concrete	C.Y.			28				28					
Steel Towers	Ton			46				46					
Conductor	Ft.			31,680[15]				31,680[15]					
Insulators	Ea.			528				528					
Ground Wire	Ft.			10,660				10,660					

1. Single pole two-arm suspension type construction
2. Two-pole wood H-frame construction
3. 4¾″ x 5¾″ x 8′ and 4¾″ x 5¾″ x 10′ wood crossarms
4. 6″ x 8″ x 26′-0″ wood crossarm
5. 5¾″ x 10″ disc insulator
6. Single pole construction with 3 fiberglass crossarms (5 fog-type insulators per phase)
7. 7′-0″ fiberglass crossarms
8. 6″ x 10″ x 35′-0″ wood crossarm
9. Laced steel tower, single circuit construction
10. 5″ x 7″ x 8′ and 5″ x 7″ x 10′ wood crossarms
11. Laced steel tower, single circuit 500-kV construction
12. Bundled conductor (3 sub-conductors per phase)
13. Laced steel tower, single circuit restrained phases (500-kV)
14. Laced steel tower, double circuit construction
15. Both sides of double circuit strung

Note: To allow for sagging, a mile (5280 Ft.) of transmission line uses 5330 Ft. of conductor per wire (called a wire mile).

R337119-30 Concrete for Conduit Encasement

The table below lists C.Y. of concrete for 100 L.F. of trench. Conduits separation center to center should meet 7.5″ (N.E.C.).

Number of Conduits	1	2	3	4	6	8	9	Number of Conduits
Trench Dimension	11.5″ x 11.5″	11.5″ x 19″	11.5″ x 27″	19″ x 19″	19″ x 27″	19″ x 38″	27″ x 27″	Trench Dimension
Conduit Diameter 2.0″	3.29	5.39	7.64	8.83	12.51	17.66	17.72	Conduit Diameter 2.0″
2.5″	3.23	5.29	7.49	8.62	12.19	17.23	17.25	2.5″
3.0″	3.15	5.13	7.24	8.29	11.71	16.59	16.52	3.0″
3.5″	3.08	4.97	7.02	7.99	11.26	15.98	15.84	3.5″
4.0″	2.99	4.80	6.76	7.65	10.74	15.30	15.07	4.0″
5.0″	2.78	4.37	6.11	6.78	9.44	13.57	13.12	5.0″
6.0″	2.52	3.84	5.33	5.74	7.87	11.48	10.77	6.0″

Change Orders

Change Order Considerations

A change order is a written document usually prepared by the design professional and signed by the owner, the architect/engineer, and the contractor. A change order states the agreement of the parties to: an addition, deletion, or revision in the work; an adjustment in the contract sum, if any; or an adjustment in the contract time, if any. Change orders, or "extras", in the construction process occur after execution of the construction contract and impact architects/engineers, contractors, and owners.

Change orders that are properly recognized and managed can ensure orderly, professional, and profitable progress for everyone involved in the project. There are many causes for change orders and change order requests. In all cases, change orders or change order requests should be addressed promptly and in a precise and prescribed manner. The following paragraphs include information regarding change order pricing and procedures.

The Causes of Change Orders

Reasons for issuing change orders include:

- Unforeseen field conditions that require a change in the work
- Correction of design discrepancies, errors, or omissions in the contract documents
- Owner-requested changes, either by design criteria, scope of work, or project objectives
- Completion date changes for reasons unrelated to the construction process
- Changes in building code interpretations, or other public authority requirements that require a change in the work
- Changes in availability of existing or new materials and products

Procedures

Properly written contract documents must include the correct change order procedures for all parties—owners, design professionals, and contractors—to follow in order to avoid costly delays and litigation.

Being "in the right" is not always a sufficient or acceptable defense. The contract provisions requiring notification and documentation must be adhered to within a defined or reasonable time frame.

The appropriate method of handling change orders is by a written proposal and acceptance by all parties involved. Prior to starting work on a project, all parties should identify their authorized agents who may sign and accept change orders, as well as any limits placed on their authority.

Time may be a critical factor when the need for a change arises. For such cases, the contractor might be directed to proceed on a "time and materials" basis, rather than wait for all paperwork to be processed—a delay that could impede progress. In this situation, the contractor must still follow the prescribed change order procedures including, but not limited to, notification and documentation.

Lack of documentation can be very costly, especially if legal judgments are to be made, and if certain field personnel are no longer available. For time and material change orders, the contractor should keep accurate daily records of all labor and material allocated to the change.

Owners or awarding authorities who do considerable and continual building construction (such as the federal government) realize the inevitability of change orders for numerous reasons, both predictable and unpredictable. As a result, the federal government, the American Institute of Architects (AIA), the Engineers Joint Contract Documents Committee (EJCDC), and other contractor, legal, and technical organizations have developed standards and procedures to be followed by all parties to achieve contract continuance and timely completion, while being financially fair to all concerned.

Pricing Change Orders

When pricing change orders, regardless of their cause, the most significant factor is when the change occurs. The need for a change may be perceived in the field or requested by the architect/engineer *before* any of the actual installation has begun, or may evolve or appear *during* construction when the item of work in question is partially installed. In the latter cases, the original sequence of construction is disrupted, along with all contiguous and supporting systems. Change orders cause the greatest impact when they occur *after* the installation has been completed and must be uncovered, or even replaced. Post-completion changes may be caused by necessary design changes, product failure, or changes in the owner's requirements that are not discovered until the building or the systems begin to function.

Specified procedures of notification and record keeping must be adhered to and enforced regardless of the stage of construction: *before, during,* or *after* installation. Some bidding documents anticipate change orders by requiring that unit prices including overhead and profit percentages—for additional as well as deductible changes—be listed. Generally these unit prices do not fully take into account the ripple effect, or impact on other trades, and should be used for general guidance only.

When pricing change orders, it is important to classify the time frame in which the change occurs. There are two basic time frames for change orders: *pre-installation change orders,* which occur before the start of construction, and *post-installation change orders,* which involve reworking after the original installation. Change orders that occur between these stages may be priced according to the extent of work completed using a combination of techniques developed for pricing *pre-* and *post-installation* changes.

Factors To Consider When Pricing Change Orders

As an estimator begins to prepare a change order, the following questions should be reviewed to determine their impact on the final price.

General

- *Is the change order work* pre-installation *or* post-installation?

  Change order work costs vary according to how much of the installation has been completed. Once workers have the project scoped in their minds, even though they have not started, it can be difficult to refocus. Consequently they may spend more than the normal amount of time understanding the change. Also, modifications to work in place, such as trimming or refitting, usually take more time than was initially estimated. The greater the amount of work in place, the more reluctant workers are to change it. Psychologically they may resent the change and as a result the rework takes longer than normal. Post-installation change order estimates must include demolition of existing work as required to accomplish the change. If the work is performed at a later time, additional obstacles, such as building finishes, may be present which must be protected. Regardless of whether the change occurs pre-installation or post-installation, attempt to isolate the identifiable factors and price them separately. For example, add shipping costs that may be required pre-installation or any demolition required post-installation. Then analyze the potential impact on productivity of psychological and/or learning curve factors and adjust the output rates accordingly. One approach is to break down the typical workday into segments and quantify the impact on each segment.

Change Order Installation Efficiency

The labor-hours expressed (for new construction) are based on average installation time, using an efficiency level. For change order situations, adjustments to this efficiency level should reflect the daily labor-hour allocation for that particular occurrence.

- *Will the change substantially delay the original completion date?*

  A significant change in the project may cause the original completion date to be extended. The extended schedule may subject the contractor to new wage rates dictated by relevant labor contracts. Project supervision and other project overhead must also be extended beyond the original completion date. The schedule extension may also put installation into a new weather season. For example, underground piping scheduled for October installation was delayed until January. As a result, frost penetrated the trench area, thereby changing the degree of difficulty of the task. Changes and delays may have a ripple effect throughout the project. This effect must be analyzed and negotiated with the owner.

- *What is the net effect of a deduct change order?*

  In most cases, change orders resulting in a deduction or credit reflect only bare costs. The contractor may retain the overhead and profit based on the original bid.

Materials

- *Will you have to pay more or less for the new material, required by the change order, than you paid for the original purchase?*

  The same material prices or discounts will usually apply to materials purchased for change orders as new construction. In some instances, however, the contractor may forfeit the advantages of competitive pricing for change orders. Consider the following example:

  A contractor purchased over $20,000 worth of fan coil units for an installation and obtained the maximum discount. Some time later it was determined the project required an additional matching unit. The contractor has to purchase this unit from the original supplier to ensure a match. The supplier at this time may not discount the unit because of the small quantity, and he is no longer in a competitive situation. The impact of quantity on purchase can add between 0% and 25% to material prices and/or subcontractor quotes.

- *If materials have been ordered or delivered to the job site, will they be subject to a cancellation charge or restocking fee?*

  Check with the supplier to determine if ordered materials are subject to a cancellation charge. Delivered materials not used as a result of a change order may be subject to a restocking fee if returned to the supplier. Common restocking charges run between 20% and 40%. Also, delivery charges to return the goods to the supplier must be added.

Labor

- *How efficient is the existing crew at the actual installation?*

  Is the same crew that performed the initial work going to do the change order? Possibly the change consists of the installation of a unit identical to one already installed; therefore, the change should take less time. Be sure to consider this potential productivity increase and modify the productivity rates accordingly.

- *If the crew size is increased, what impact will that have on supervision requirements?*

  Under most bargaining agreements or management practices, there is a point at which a working foreperson is replaced by a nonworking foreperson. This replacement increases project overhead by adding a nonproductive worker. If additional workers are added to accelerate the project or to perform changes while maintaining the schedule, be sure to add additional supervision time if warranted. Calculate the hours involved and the additional cost directly if possible.

- *What are the other impacts of increased crew size?*

  The larger the crew, the greater the potential for productivity to decrease. Some of the factors that cause this productivity loss are: overcrowding (producing restrictive conditions in the working space) and possibly a shortage of any special tools and equipment required. Such factors affect not only the crew working on the elements directly involved in the change order, but other crews whose movements may also be hampered. As the crew increases, check its basic composition for changes by the addition or deletion of apprentices or nonworking foreperson, and quantify the potential effects of equipment shortages or other logistical factors.

- *As new crews, unfamiliar with the project, are brought onto the site, how long will it take them to become oriented to the project requirements?*

  The orientation time for a new crew to become 100% effective varies with the site and type of project. Orientation is easiest at a new construction site and most difficult at existing, very restrictive renovation sites. The type of work also affects orientation time. When all elements of the work are exposed, such as concrete or masonry work, orientation is decreased. When the work is concealed or less visible, such as existing electrical systems, orientation takes longer. Usually orientation can be accomplished in one day or less. Costs for added orientation should be itemized and added to the total estimated cost.

- *How much actual production can be gained by working overtime?*

  Short term overtime can be used effectively to accomplish more work in a day. However, as overtime is scheduled to run beyond several weeks, studies have shown marked decreases in output. The following chart shows the effect of long term overtime on worker efficiency. If the anticipated change requires extended overtime to keep the job on schedule, these factors can be used as a guide to predict the impact on time and cost. Add project overhead, particularly supervision, that may also be incurred.

Days per Week	Hours per Day	Production Efficiency					Payroll Cost Factors	
		1st Week	2nd Week	3rd Week	4th Week	Average 4 Weeks	@ 1-1/2 Times	@ 2 Times
5	8	100%	100%	100%	100%	100%	100%	100%
	9	100	100	95	90	96	1.056	1.111
	10	100	95	90	85	93	1.100	1.200
	11	95	90	75	65	81	1.136	1.273
	12	90	85	70	60	76	1.167	1.333
6	8	100	100	95	90	96	1.083	1.167
	9	100	95	90	85	93	1.130	1.259
	10	95	90	85	80	88	1.167	1.333
	11	95	85	70	65	79	1.197	1.394
	12	90	80	65	60	74	1.222	1.444
7	8	100	95	85	75	89	1.143	1.286
	9	95	90	80	70	84	1.183	1.365
	10	90	85	75	65	79	1.214	1.429
	11	85	80	65	60	73	1.240	1.481
	12	85	75	60	55	69	1.262	1.524

Effects of Overtime

Caution: Under many labor agreements, Sundays and holidays are paid at a higher premium than the normal overtime rate.

The use of long-term overtime is counterproductive on almost any construction job; that is, the longer the period of overtime, the lower the actual production rate. Numerous studies have been conducted, and while they have resulted in slightly different numbers, all reach the same conclusion. The figure above tabulates the effects of overtime work on efficiency.

As illustrated, there can be a difference between the *actual* payroll cost per hour and the *effective* cost per hour for overtime work. This is due to the reduced production efficiency with the increase in weekly hours beyond 40. This difference between actual and effective cost results from overtime work over a prolonged period. Short-term overtime work does not result in as great a reduction in efficiency and, in such cases, effective cost may not vary significantly from the actual payroll cost. As the total hours per week are increased on a regular basis, more time is lost due to fatigue, lowered morale, and an increased accident rate.

As an example, assume a project where workers are working 6 days a week, 10 hours per day. From the figure above (based on productivity studies), the average effective productive hours over a 4-week period are:

$$0.875 \times 60 = 52.5$$

Depending upon the locale and day of week, overtime hours may be paid at time and a half or double time. For time and a half, the overall (average) *actual* payroll cost (including regular and overtime hours) is determined as follows:

$$\frac{40 \text{ reg. hrs.} + (20 \text{ overtime hrs.} \times 1.5)}{60 \text{ hrs.}} = 1.167$$

Based on 60 hours, the payroll cost per hour will be 116.7% of the normal rate at 40 hours per week. However, because the effective production (efficiency) for 60 hours is reduced to the equivalent of 52.5 hours, the effective cost of overtime is calculated as follows:

For time and a half:

$$\frac{40 \text{ reg. hrs.} + (20 \text{ overtime hrs.} \times 1.5)}{52.5 \text{ hrs.}} = 1.33$$

The installed cost will be 133% of the normal rate (for labor).

Thus, when figuring overtime, the actual cost per unit of work will be higher than the apparent overtime payroll dollar increase, due to the reduced productivity of the longer work week. These efficiency calculations are true only for those cost factors determined by hours worked. Costs that are applied weekly or monthly, such as equipment rentals, will not be similarly affected.

Equipment

- *What equipment is required to complete the change order?*

  Change orders may require extending the rental period of equipment already on the job site, or the addition of special equipment brought in to accomplish the change work. In either case, the additional rental charges and operator labor charges must be added.

Summary

The preceding considerations and others you deem appropriate should be analyzed and applied to a change order estimate. The impact of each should be quantified and listed on the estimate to form an audit trail.

Change orders that are properly identified, documented, and managed help to ensure the orderly, professional, and profitable progress of the work. They also minimize potential claims or disputes at the end of the project.

Back by customer demand!

You asked and we listened. For customer convenience and estimating ease, we have made the 2023 Project Costs available for download at **RSMeans.com/2023books**. You will also find sample estimates, an RSMeans data overview video, and a book registration form to receive quarterly data updates throughout 2023.

Estimating Tips

- The cost figures available in the download were derived from hundreds of projects contained in the RSMeans database of completed construction projects. They include the contractor's overhead and profit. The figures have been adjusted to January of the current year.
- These projects were located throughout the U.S. and reflect a tremendous variation in square foot (S.F.) costs. This is due to differences, not only in labor and material costs, but also in individual owners' requirements. For instance, a bank in a large city would have different features than one in a rural area. This is true of all the different types of buildings analyzed. Therefore, caution should be exercised when using these Project Costs. For example, for courthouses, costs in the database are local courthouse costs and will not apply to the larger, more elaborate federal courthouses.
- None of the figures "go with" any others. All individual cost items were computed and tabulated separately. Thus, the sum of the median figures for plumbing, HVAC, and electrical will not normally total up to the total mechanical and electrical costs arrived at by separate analysis and tabulation of the projects.
- Each building was analyzed as to total and component costs and percentages. The figures were arranged in ascending order with the results tabulated as shown. The 1/4 column shows that 25% of the projects had lower costs and 75% had higher. The 3/4 column shows that 75% of the projects had lower costs and 25% had higher. The median column shows that 50% of the projects had lower costs and 50% had higher.
- Project Costs are useful in the conceptual stage when no details are available. As soon as details become available in the project design, the square foot approach should be discontinued and the project should be priced as to its particular components. When more precision is required, or for estimating the replacement cost of specific buildings, the current edition of *Square Foot Costs with RSMeans data* should be used.
- In using the figures in this section, it is recommended that the median column be used for preliminary figures if no additional information is available. The median figures, when multiplied by the total city construction cost index figures (see City Cost Indexes) and then multiplied by the project size modifier at the end of this section, should present a fairly accurate base figure, which would then have to be adjusted in view of the estimator's experience, local economic conditions, code requirements, and the owner's particular requirements. There is no need to factor in the percentage figures, as these should remain constant from city to city.
- The editors of this data would greatly appreciate receiving cost figures on one or more of your recent projects, which would then be included in the averages for next year. All cost figures received will be kept confidential, except that they will be averaged with other similar projects to arrive at square foot cost figures for next year.

See the website above for details and the discount available for submitting one or more of your projects.

		50 17 00 | Project Costs	UNIT	UNIT COSTS			% OF TOTAL			
				1/4	MEDIAN	3/4	1/4	MEDIAN	3/4	
01	0000	**Auto Sales with Repair**	S.F.							01
	0100	Architectural		146	163	176	58%	64%	67%	
	0200	Plumbing		12.20	12.75	17.05	4.84%	5.20%	6.80%	
	0300	Mechanical		16.30	22	24	6.40%	8.70%	10.15%	
	0400	Electrical		25	31	39	9.05%	11.70%	15.90%	
	0500	Total Project Costs		244	255	262				
02	0000	**Banking Institutions**	S.F.							02
	0100	Architectural		220	270	330	59%	65%	69%	
	0200	Plumbing		8.85	12.35	17.15	2.12%	3.39%	4.19%	
	0300	Mechanical		17.60	24.50	28.50	4.41%	5.10%	10.75%	
	0400	Electrical		43	52	80	10.45%	13.05%	15.90%	
	0500	Total Project Costs		365	410	505				
03	0000	**Courthouse**	S.F.							03
	0100	Architectural		116	228	320	54.50%	58.50%	61%	
	0200	Plumbing		4.38	16.30	16.30	2.07%	3.13%	3.13%	
	0300	Mechanical		27.50	32.50	32.50	6.25%	12.95%	12.95%	
	0400	Electrical		35	40	40	7.65%	16.60%	16.60%	
	0500	Total Project Costs		211	390	520				
04	0000	**Data Centers**	S.F.							04
	0100	Architectural		262	262	262	68%	68%	68%	
	0200	Plumbing		14.35	14.35	14.35	3.71%	3.71%	3.71%	
	0300	Mechanical		36.50	36.50	36.50	9.45%	9.45%	9.45%	
	0400	Electrical		34.50	34.50	34.50	9%	9%	9%	
	0500	Total Project Costs		385	385	385				
05	0000	**Detention Centers**	S.F.							05
	0100	Architectural		243	256	272	52%	53%	60.50%	
	0200	Plumbing		25.50	31	37.50	5.15%	7.10%	7.25%	
	0300	Mechanical		32.50	46.50	55.50	7.55%	9.50%	13.80%	
	0400	Electrical		53.50	63	82	10.90%	14.85%	17.95%	
	0500	Total Project Costs		410	435	510				
06	0000	**Fire Stations**	S.F.							06
	0100	Architectural		141	180	284	46%	54.50%	61.50%	
	0200	Plumbing		14.75	19.70	25.50	4.67%	5.60%	6.35%	
	0300	Mechanical		22	31	42	6.10%	8.25%	10.20%	
	0400	Electrical		33.50	41	57.50	10.75%	12.55%	14.95%	
	0500	Total Project Costs		292	350	465				
07	0000	**Gymnasium**	S.F.							07
	0100	Architectural		121	160	160	57%	64.50%	64.50%	
	0200	Plumbing		2.97	9.75	9.75	1.58%	3.48%	3.48%	
	0300	Mechanical		4.56	41	41	2.42%	14.65%	14.65%	
	0400	Electrical		14.95	29	29	7.95%	10.35%	10.35%	
	0500	Total Project Costs		189	280	280				
08	0000	**Hospitals**	S.F.							08
	0100	Architectural		147	242	263	41.50%	47.50%	48%	
	0200	Plumbing		10.80	44.50	53	6%	7.65%	10.35%	
	0300	Mechanical		65	80.50	105	12.55%	17.95%	23.50%	
	0400	Electrical		32.50	73.50	84.50	10.95%	14.10%	16.85%	
	0500	Total Project Costs		345	520	555				
09	0000	**Industrial Buildings**	S.F.							09
	0100	Architectural		80.50	158	320	52%	56%	82%	
	0200	Plumbing		2.32	6.30	18.20	1.57%	2.11%	6.30%	
	0300	Mechanical		6.60	12.55	60	4.77%	5.55%	14.80%	
	0400	Electrical		10.10	11.50	96	7.85%	13.55%	16.20%	
	0500	Total Project Costs		119	181	595				
10	0000	**Medical Clinics & Offices**	S.F.							10
	0100	Architectural		134	166	218	48.50%	54%	62%	
	0200	Plumbing		12.30	18.55	30.50	4.50%	6.65%	8.75%	
	0300	Mechanical		19.90	30.50	54.50	7.80%	10.85%	15.75%	
	0400	Electrical		27	33.50	51	8.90%	11.20%	13.85%	
	0500	Total Project Costs		231	305	400				

		50 17 00 | Project Costs	UNIT	UNIT COSTS 1/4	UNIT COSTS MEDIAN	UNIT COSTS 3/4	% OF TOTAL 1/4	% OF TOTAL MEDIAN	% OF TOTAL 3/4	
11	0000	**Mixed Use**	S.F.							11
	0100	Architectural		151	209	285	45.50%	52.50%	61.50%	
	0200	Plumbing		8.55	15.55	16.55	3.31%	3.47%	4.18%	
	0300	Mechanical		22.50	49	65	6.10%	13.60%	17.05%	
	0400	Electrical		30	50.50	72.50	8.60%	11.65%	15.65%	
	0500	Total Project Costs		264	460	470				
12	0000	**Multi-Family Housing**	S.F.							12
	0100	Architectural		105	143	233	54.50%	62%	69%	
	0200	Plumbing		9.40	15.15	20.50	5.25%	6.65%	8%	
	0300	Mechanical		9.65	13	37	4.41%	6.05%	10.25%	
	0400	Electrical		12.70	21.50	31	5.65%	7.90%	10.25%	
	0500	Total Project Costs		174	286	370				
13	0000	**Nursing Home & Assisted Living**	S.F.							13
	0100	Architectural		99	143	162	51.50%	55.50%	63.50%	
	0200	Plumbing		10.60	15.95	19	6.25%	7.40%	9.20%	
	0300	Mechanical		8.70	12.85	25	4.04%	6.70%	9.55%	
	0400	Electrical		14.60	25.50	33.50	7.25%	11%	13.10%	
	0500	Total Project Costs		174	224	296				
14	0000	**Office Buildings**	S.F.							14
	0100	Architectural		130	177	244	54.50%	61%	69%	
	0200	Plumbing		7	11	20.50	2.70%	3.78%	5.20%	
	0300	Mechanical		13.70	23.50	36	5.55%	8.15%	11.10%	
	0400	Electrical		18.35	30	48	7.80%	10.10%	12.90%	
	0500	Total Project Costs		221	292	400				
15	0000	**Parking Garage**	S.F.							15
	0100	Architectural		43.50	53	55.50	70%	79%	88%	
	0200	Plumbing		1.43	1.50	2.80	2.05%	2.70%	2.83%	
	0300	Mechanical		1.11	1.71	6.50	2.11%	3.62%	3.81%	
	0400	Electrical		3.81	4.19	8.75	5.30%	6.35%	7.95%	
	0500	Total Project Costs		53	64.50	70				
16	0000	**Parking Garage/Mixed Use**	S.F.							16
	0100	Architectural		141	154	157	61%	62%	65.50%	
	0200	Plumbing		4.52	5.95	9.10	2.47%	2.72%	3.66%	
	0300	Mechanical		19.35	22	31.50	7.80%	13.10%	13.60%	
	0400	Electrical		20.50	29	30	8.20%	12.65%	18.15%	
	0500	Total Project Costs		230	240	248				
17	0000	**Police Stations**	S.F.							17
	0100	Architectural		159	225	277	49%	61%	61.50%	
	0200	Plumbing		21	25.50	25.50	5.05%	5.55%	7.70%	
	0300	Mechanical		47.50	66.50	69	12.35%	14.55%	16.55%	
	0400	Electrical		36	41.50	61.50	9.15%	12.10%	14%	
	0500	Total Project Costs		298	415	455				
18	0000	**Police/Fire**	S.F.							18
	0100	Architectural		155	155	475	55.50%	66%	68%	
	0200	Plumbing		12.40	12.85	47.50	5.45%	5.50%	5.55%	
	0300	Mechanical		19	30	109	8.35%	12.70%	12.80%	
	0400	Electrical		21.50	27.50	124	9.50%	11.75%	14.55%	
	0500	Total Project Costs		228	235	855				
19	0000	**Public Assembly Buildings**	S.F.							19
	0100	Architectural		158	206	320	56.50%	61%	64%	
	0200	Plumbing		8.35	12.25	18.10	2.63%	3.36%	4.39%	
	0300	Mechanical		17.60	30.50	48.50	6.45%	8.75%	12.45%	
	0400	Electrical		26	35	56	8.60%	10.70%	12.80%	
	0500	Total Project Costs		254	340	505				
20	0000	**Recreational**	S.F.							20
	0100	Architectural		152	230	325	49.50%	59%	64.50%	
	0200	Plumbing		11.35	18.30	30	3.08%	4.67%	7.40%	
	0300	Mechanical		18.10	27.50	41	5.15%	6.65%	11.35%	
	0400	Electrical		22	37.50	54.50	7.10%	8.95%	10.80%	
	0500	Total Project Costs		270	390	610				

		50 17 00 | Project Costs	UNIT	UNIT COSTS 1/4	UNIT COSTS MEDIAN	UNIT COSTS 3/4	% OF TOTAL 1/4	% OF TOTAL MEDIAN	% OF TOTAL 3/4	
21	0000	**Restaurants**	S.F.							21
	0100	Architectural		172	270	340	57.50%	60%	63.50%	
	0200	Plumbing		18.95	38	50	7.35%	7.70%	8.75%	
	0300	Mechanical		20.50	27	51	6.50%	8.15%	11.15%	
	0400	Electrical		20.50	33	66	6.75%	10.30%	11.60%	
	0500	Total Project Costs	↓	285	470	570				
22	0000	**Retail**	S.F.							22
	0100	Architectural		77	120	248	54.50%	60%	64.50%	
	0200	Plumbing		9.60	13.40	16.65	4.18%	5.45%	8.45%	
	0300	Mechanical		9	12.75	23.50	4.98%	6.15%	7.05%	
	0400	Electrical		14.30	29	43	7.90%	11.25%	12.45%	
	0500	Total Project Costs	↓	117	208	400				
23	0000	**Schools**	S.F.							23
	0100	Architectural		133	169	226	50.50%	55.50%	60.50%	
	0200	Plumbing		10.60	14.55	21	3.66%	4.57%	6.95%	
	0300	Mechanical		25	36	52.50	8.90%	11.95%	14.55%	
	0400	Electrical		25	34.50	44.50	9.45%	11.25%	13.30%	
	0500	Total Project Costs	↓	242	310	415				
24	0000	**University, College & Private School Classroom & Admin Buildings**	S.F.							24
	0100	Architectural		172	224	272	50%	53.50%	58.50%	
	0200	Plumbing		11.75	16.10	29.50	3.04%	4.30%	6.35%	
	0300	Mechanical		34	51.50	66	9.20%	11.40%	14.40%	
	0400	Electrical		28.50	41	53.50	7.70%	9.95%	12.55%	
	0500	Total Project Costs	↓	297	415	540				
25	0000	**University, College & Private School Dormitories**	S.F.							25
	0100	Architectural		111	195	207	53%	61.50%	68%	
	0200	Plumbing		14.65	21	24	6.35%	6.65%	8.95%	
	0300	Mechanical		6.60	28	44.50	4.13%	9%	11.80%	
	0400	Electrical		7.80	27	41.50	4.75%	7.35%	10.60%	
	0500	Total Project Costs	↓	164	310	370				
26	0000	**University, College & Private School Science, Eng. & Lab Buildings**	S.F.							26
	0100	Architectural		191	226	335	48%	54.50%	58%	
	0200	Plumbing		13.15	19.90	33.50	3.29%	3.77%	5%	
	0300	Mechanical		50.50	94	96.50	11.70%	19.40%	23.50%	
	0400	Electrical		39.50	51.50	53	9%	12.05%	13.15%	
	0500	Total Project Costs	↓	400	430	585				
27	0000	**University, College & Private School Student Union Buildings**	S.F.							27
	0100	Architectural		151	395	395	54.50%	54.50%	59.50%	
	0200	Plumbing		23	23	34	3.13%	4.27%	11.45%	
	0300	Mechanical		43.50	70	70	9.60%	9.60%	14.55%	
	0400	Electrical		38	66	66	9.05%	12.80%	13.15%	
	0500	Total Project Costs	↓	297	730	730				
28	0000	**Warehouses**	S.F.							28
	0100	Architectural		65	98.50	180	60.50%	67%	71.50%	
	0200	Plumbing		3.37	7.20	13.90	2.82%	3.72%	5%	
	0300	Mechanical		3.99	22.50	35.50	4.56%	8.15%	10.70%	
	0400	Electrical		8.40	27	45.50	7.75%	10.10%	18.30%	
	0500	Total Project Costs	↓	96.50	154	310				

Square Foot Project Size Modifier

One factor that affects the S.F. cost of a particular building is the size. In general, for buildings built to the same specifications in the same locality, the larger building will have the lower S.F. cost. This is due mainly to the decreasing contribution of the exterior walls plus the economy of scale usually achievable in larger buildings. The Area Conversion Scale shown below will give a factor to convert costs for the typical size building to an adjusted cost for the particular project.

The Square Foot Base Size lists the median costs, most typical project size in our accumulated data, and the range in size of the projects.

The Size Factor for your project is determined by dividing your project area in S.F. by the typical project size for the particular Building Type. With this factor, enter the Area Conversion Scale at the appropriate Size Factor and determine the appropriate Cost Multiplier for your building size.

Example: Determine the cost per S.F. for a 107,200 S.F. Multi-family housing.

$$\frac{\text{Proposed building area} = 107{,}200 \text{ S.F.}}{\text{Typical size from below} = 53{,}600 \text{ S.F.}} = 2.00$$

Enter Area Conversion Scale at 2.0, intersect curve, read horizontally the appropriate cost multiplier of .94. Size adjusted cost becomes .94 x $286.00 = $268.84 based on national average costs.

Note: For Size Factors less than .50, the Cost Multiplier is 1.1
For Size Factors greater than 3.5, the Cost Multiplier is .90

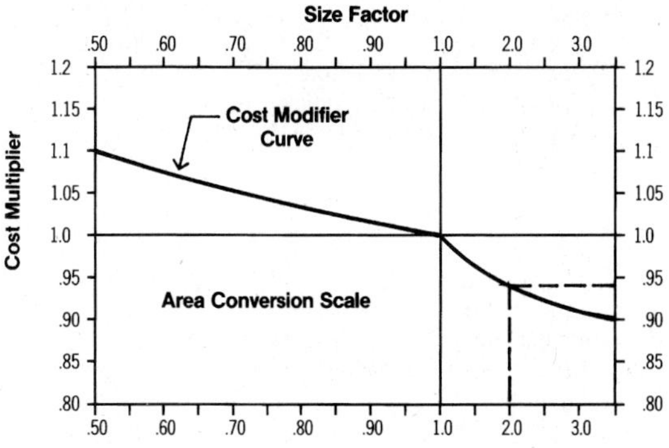

System	Median Cost (Total Project Costs)	Typical Size Gross S.F. (Median of Projects)	Typical Range (Low – High) (Projects)
Auto Sales with Repair	$255.00	24,900	4,700 – 29,300
Banking Institutions	410.00	9,300	3,300 – 38,100
Courthouse	390.00	56,000	24,700 – 70,500
Data Centers	385.00	14,400	14,400 – 14,400
Detention Centers	435.00	37,800	12,300 – 183,330
Fire Stations	350.00	12,400	6,300 – 49,600
Gymnasium	280.00	52,400	22,800 – 82,000
Hospitals	520.00	73,300	12,700 – 410,300
Industrial Buildings	181.00	21,100	5,100 – 200,600
Medical Clinics & Offices	305.00	24,200	2,300 – 327,000
Mixed Use	460.00	31,800	7,200 – 188,900
Multi-Family Housing	286.00	53,600	2,500 – 1,161,500
Nursing Home & Assisted Living	224.00	38,700	1,500 – 242,600
Office Buildings	292.00	21,000	1,100 – 930,000
Parking Garage	64.50	151,800	99,900 – 287,000
Parking Garage/Mixed Use	240.00	254,200	5,300 – 318,000
Police Stations	415.00	25,200	12,700 – 88,600
Police/Fire	235.00	44,300	8,600 – 50,300
Public Assembly Buildings	340.00	20,800	2,200 – 235,300
Recreational	390.00	27,700	1,000 – 223,800
Restaurants	470.00	5,900	2,100 – 42,000
Retail	208.00	26,000	4,000 – 84,300
Schools	310.00	69,400	1,300 – 410,800
University, College & Private School Classroom & Admin Buildings	415.00	48,300	2,400 – 196,200
University, College & Private School Dormitories	310.00	39,200	1,500 – 126,900
University, College & Private School Science, Eng. & Lab Buildings	430.00	60,000	5,300 – 117,600
University, College & Private School Student Union Buildings	730.00	48,700	42,100 – 50,000
Warehouses	154.00	10,900	600 – 303,800

Abbreviations

A	Area Square Feet; Ampere
AAFES	Army and Air Force Exchange Service
ABS	Acrylonitrile Butadiene Stryrene; Asbestos Bonded Steel
A.C., AC	Alternating Current; Air-Conditioning; Asbestos Cement; Plywood Grade A & C
ACI	American Concrete Institute
ACR	Air Conditioning Refrigeration
ADA	Americans with Disabilities Act
AD	Plywood, Grade A & D
Addit.	Additional
Adh.	Adhesive
Adj.	Adjustable
af	Audio-frequency
AFFF	Aqueous Film Forming Foam
AFUE	Annual Fuel Utilization Efficiency
AGA	American Gas Association
Agg.	Aggregate
A.H., Ah	Ampere Hours
A hr.	Ampere-hour
A.H.U., AHU	Air Handling Unit
A.I.A.	American Institute of Architects
AIC	Ampere Interrupting Capacity
Allow.	Allowance
alt., alt	Alternate
Alum.	Aluminum
a.m.	Ante Meridiem
Amp.	Ampere
Anod.	Anodized
ANSI	American National Standards Institute
APA	American Plywood Association
Approx.	Approximate
Apt.	Apartment
Asb.	Asbestos
A.S.B.C.	American Standard Building Code
Asbe.	Asbestos Worker
ASCE	American Society of Civil Engineers
A.S.H.R.A.E.	American Society of Heating, Refrig. & AC Engineers
ASME	American Society of Mechanical Engineers
ASTM	American Society for Testing and Materials
Attchmt.	Attachment
Avg., Ave.	Average
AWG	American Wire Gauge
AWWA	American Water Works Assoc.
Bbl.	Barrel
B&B, BB	Grade B and Better; Balled & Burlapped
B&S	Bell and Spigot
B.&W.	Black and White
b.c.c.	Body-centered Cubic
B.C.Y.	Bank Cubic Yards
BE	Bevel End
B.F.	Board Feet
Bg. cem.	Bag of Cement
BHP	Boiler Horsepower; Brake Horsepower
B.I.	Black Iron
bidir.	bidirectional
Bit., Bitum.	Bituminous
Bit., Conc.	Bituminous Concrete
Bk.	Backed
Bkrs.	Breakers
Bldg., bldg	Building
Blk.	Block
Bm.	Beam
Boil.	Boilermaker
bpm	Blows per Minute
BR	Bedroom
Brg., brng.	Bearing
Brhe.	Bricklayer Helper
Bric.	Bricklayer
Brk., brk	Brick
brkt	Bracket
Brs.	Brass
Brz.	Bronze
Bsn.	Basin
Btr.	Better
BTU	British Thermal Unit
BTUH	BTU per Hour
Bu.	Bushels
BUR	Built-up Roofing
BX	Interlocked Armored Cable
°C	Degree Centigrade
c	Conductivity, Copper Sweat
C	Hundred; Centigrade
C/C	Center to Center, Cedar on Cedar
C-C	Center to Center
Cab	Cabinet
Cair.	Air Tool Laborer
Cal.	Caliper
Calc	Calculated
Cap.	Capacity
Carp.	Carpenter
C.B.	Circuit Breaker
C.C.A.	Chromate Copper Arsenate
C.C.F.	Hundred Cubic Feet
cd	Candela
cd/sf	Candela per Square Foot
CD	Grade of Plywood Face & Back
CDX	Plywood, Grade C & D, exterior glue
Cefi.	Cement Finisher
Cem.	Cement
CF	Hundred Feet
C.F.	Cubic Feet
CFM	Cubic Feet per Minute
CFRP	Carbon Fiber Reinforced Plastic
c.g.	Center of Gravity
CHW	Chilled Water; Commercial Hot Water
C.I., CI	Cast Iron
C.I.P., CIP	Cast in Place
Circ.	Circuit
C.L.	Carload Lot
CL	Chain Link
Clab.	Common Laborer
Clam	Common Maintenance Laborer
C.L.F.	Hundred Linear Feet
CLF	Current Limiting Fuse
CLP	Cross Linked Polyethylene
cm	Centimeter
CMP	Corr. Metal Pipe
CMU	Concrete Masonry Unit
CN	Change Notice
Col.	Column
CO_2	Carbon Dioxide
Comb.	Combination
comm.	Commercial, Communication
Compr.	Compressor
Conc.	Concrete
Cont., cont	Continuous; Continued, Container
Corkbd.	Cork Board
Corr.	Corrugated
Cos	Cosine
Cot	Cotangent
Cov.	Cover
C/P	Cedar on Paneling
CPA	Control Point Adjustment
Cplg.	Coupling
CPM	Critical Path Method
CPVC	Chlorinated Polyvinyl Chloride
C.Pr.	Hundred Pair
CRC	Cold Rolled Channel
Creos.	Creosote
Crpt.	Carpet & Linoleum Layer
CRT	Cathode-ray Tube
CS	Carbon Steel, Constant Shear Bar Joist
Csc	Cosecant
C.S.F.	Hundred Square Feet
CSI	Construction Specifications Institute
CT	Current Transformer
CTS	Copper Tube Size
Cu	Copper, Cubic
Cu. Ft.	Cubic Foot
cw	Continuous Wave
C.W.	Cool White; Cold Water
Cwt.	100 Pounds
C.W.X.	Cool White Deluxe
C.Y.	Cubic Yard (27 cubic feet)
C.Y./Hr.	Cubic Yard per Hour
Cyl.	Cylinder
d	Penny (nail size)
D	Deep; Depth; Discharge
Dis., Disch.	Discharge
Db	Decibel
Dbl.	Double
DC	Direct Current
DDC	Direct Digital Control
Demob.	Demobilization
d.f.t.	Dry Film Thickness
d.f.u.	Drainage Fixture Units
D.H.	Double Hung
DHW	Domestic Hot Water
DI	Ductile Iron
Diag.	Diagonal
Diam., Dia	Diameter
Distrib.	Distribution
Div.	Division
Dk.	Deck
D.L.	Dead Load; Diesel
DLH	Deep Long Span Bar Joist
dlx	Deluxe
Do.	Ditto
DOP	Dioctyl Phthalate Penetration Test (Air Filters)
Dp., dp	Depth
D.P.S.T.	Double Pole, Single Throw
Dr.	Drive
DR	Dimension Ratio
Drink.	Drinking
D.S.	Double Strength
D.S.A.	Double Strength A Grade
D.S.B.	Double Strength B Grade
Dty.	Duty
DWV	Drain Waste Vent
DX	Deluxe White, Direct Expansion
dyn	Dyne
e	Eccentricity
E	Equipment Only; East; Emissivity
Ea.	Each
EB	Encased Burial
Econ.	Economy
E.C.Y	Embankment Cubic Yards
EDP	Electronic Data Processing
EIFS	Exterior Insulation Finish System
E.D.R.	Equiv. Direct Radiation
Eq.	Equation
EL	Elevation
Elec.	Electrician; Electrical
Elev.	Elevator; Elevating
EMT	Electrical Metallic Conduit; Thin Wall Conduit
Eng.	Engine, Engineered
EPDM	Ethylene Propylene Diene Monomer
EPS	Expanded Polystyrene
Eqhv.	Equip. Oper., Heavy
Eqlt.	Equip. Oper., Light
Eqmd.	Equip. Oper., Medium
Eqmm.	Equip. Oper., Master Mechanic
Eqol.	Equip. Oper., Oilers
Equip.	Equipment
ERW	Electric Resistance Welded

Abbreviations

E.S.	Energy Saver
Est.	Estimated
esu	Electrostatic Units
E.W.	Each Way
EWT	Entering Water Temperature
Excav.	Excavation
excl	Excluding
Exp., exp	Expansion, Exposure
Ext., ext	Exterior; Extension
Extru.	Extrusion
f.	Fiber Stress
F	Fahrenheit; Female; Fill
Fab., fab	Fabricated; Fabric
FBGS	Fiberglass
F.C.	Footcandles
f.c.c.	Face-centered Cubic
f'c.	Compressive Stress in Concrete; Extreme Compressive Stress
F.E.	Front End
FEP	Fluorinated Ethylene Propylene (Teflon)
F.G.	Flat Grain
F.H.A.	Federal Housing Administration
Fig.	Figure
Fin.	Finished
FIPS	Female Iron Pipe Size
Fixt.	Fixture
FJP	Finger jointed and primed
Fl. Oz.	Fluid Ounces
Flr.	Floor
Flrs.	Floors
FM	Frequency Modulation; Factory Mutual
Fmg.	Framing
FM/UL	Factory Mutual/Underwriters Labs
Fdn.	Foundation
FNPT	Female National Pipe Thread
Fori.	Foreman, Inside
Foro.	Foreman, Outside
Fount.	Fountain
fpm	Feet per Minute
FPT	Female Pipe Thread
Fr	Frame
F.R.	Fire Rating
FRK	Foil Reinforced Kraft
FSK	Foil/Scrim/Kraft
FRP	Fiberglass Reinforced Plastic
FS	Forged Steel
FSC	Cast Body; Cast Switch Box
Ft., ft	Foot; Feet
Ftng.	Fitting
Ftg.	Footing
Ft lb.	Foot Pound
Furn.	Furniture
FVNR	Full Voltage Non-Reversing
FVR	Full Voltage Reversing
FXM	Female by Male
Fy.	Minimum Yield Stress of Steel
g	Gram
G	Gauss
Ga.	Gauge
Gal., gal.	Gallon
Galv., galv	Galvanized
GC/MS	Gas Chromatograph/Mass Spectrometer
Gen.	General
GFI	Ground Fault Interrupter
GFRC	Glass Fiber Reinforced Concrete
Glaz.	Glazier
GPD	Gallons per Day
gpf	Gallon per Flush
GPH	Gallons per Hour
gpm, GPM	Gallons per Minute
GR	Grade
Gran.	Granular
Grnd.	Ground
GVW	Gross Vehicle Weight
GWB	Gypsum Wall Board
H	High Henry
HC	High Capacity
H.D., HD	Heavy Duty; High Density
H.D.O.	High Density Overlaid
HDPE	High Density Polyethylene Plastic
Hdr.	Header
Hdwe.	Hardware
H.I.D., HID	High Intensity Discharge
Help.	Helper Average
HEPA	High Efficiency Particulate Air Filter
Hg	Mercury
HIC	High Interrupting Capacity
HM	Hollow Metal
HMWPE	High Molecular Weight Polyethylene
HO	High Output
Horiz.	Horizontal
H.P., HP	Horsepower; High Pressure
H.P.F.	High Power Factor
Hr.	Hour
Hrs./Day	Hours per Day
HSC	High Short Circuit
Ht.	Height
Htg.	Heating
Htrs.	Heaters
HVAC	Heating, Ventilation & Air-Conditioning
Hvy.	Heavy
HW	Hot Water
Hyd.; Hydr.	Hydraulic
Hz	Hertz (cycles)
I.	Moment of Inertia
IBC	International Building Code
I.C.	Interrupting Capacity
ID	Inside Diameter
I.D.	Inside Dimension; Identification
I.F.	Inside Frosted
I.M.C.	Intermediate Metal Conduit
In.	Inch
Incan.	Incandescent
Incl.	Included; Including
Int.	Interior
Inst.	Installation
Insul., insul	Insulation/Insulated
I.P.	Iron Pipe
I.P.S., IPS	Iron Pipe Size
IPT	Iron Pipe Threaded
I.W.	Indirect Waste
J	Joule
J.I.C.	Joint Industrial Council
K	Thousand; Thousand Pounds; Heavy Wall Copper Tubing, Kelvin
K.A.H.	Thousand Amp. Hours
kcmil	Thousand Circular Mils
KD	Knock Down
K.D.A.T.	Kiln Dried After Treatment
kg	Kilogram
kG	Kilogauss
kgf	Kilogram Force
kHz	Kilohertz
Kip	1000 Pounds
KJ	Kilojoule
K.L.	Effective Length Factor
K.L.F.	Kips per Linear Foot
Km	Kilometer
KO	Knock Out
K.S.F.	Kips per Square Foot
K.S.I.	Kips per Square Inch
kV	Kilovolt
kVA	Kilovolt Ampere
kVAR	Kilovar (Reactance)
KW	Kilowatt
KWh	Kilowatt-hour
L	Labor Only; Length; Long; Medium Wall Copper Tubing
Lab.	Labor
lat	Latitude
Lath.	Lather
Lav.	Lavatory
lb.; #	Pound
L.B., LB	Load Bearing; L Conduit Body
L. & E.	Labor & Equipment
lb./hr.	Pounds per Hour
lb./L.F.	Pounds per Linear Foot
lbf/sq.in.	Pound-force per Square Inch
L.C.L.	Less than Carload Lot
L.C.Y.	Loose Cubic Yard
Ld.	Load
LE	Lead Equivalent
LED	Light Emitting Diode
L.F.	Linear Foot
L.F. Hdr	Linear Feet of Header
L.F. Nose	Linear Foot of Stair Nosing
L.F. Rsr	Linear Foot of Stair Riser
Lg.	Long; Length; Large
L & H	Light and Heat
LH	Long Span Bar Joist
L.H.	Labor Hours
L.L., LL	Live Load
L.L.D.	Lamp Lumen Depreciation
lm	Lumen
lm/sf	Lumen per Square Foot
lm/W	Lumen per Watt
LOA	Length Over All
log	Logarithm
L-O-L	Lateralolet
long.	Longitude
L.P., LP	Liquefied Petroleum; Low Pressure
L.P.F.	Low Power Factor
LR	Long Radius
L.S.	Lump Sum
Lt.	Light
Lt. Ga.	Light Gauge
L.T.L.	Less than Truckload Lot
Lt. Wt.	Lightweight
L.V.	Low Voltage
M	Thousand; Material; Male; Light Wall Copper Tubing
M^2CA	Meters Squared Contact Area
m/hr.; M.H.	Man-hour
mA	Milliampere
Mach.	Machine
Mag. Str.	Magnetic Starter
Maint.	Maintenance
Marb.	Marble Setter
Mat; Mat'l.	Material
Max.	Maximum
MBF	Thousand Board Feet
MBH	Thousand BTU's per hr.
MC	Metal Clad Cable
MCC	Motor Control Center
M.C.F.	Thousand Cubic Feet
MCFM	Thousand Cubic Feet per Minute
M.C.M.	Thousand Circular Mils
MCP	Motor Circuit Protector
MD	Medium Duty
MDF	Medium-density fibreboard
M.D.O.	Medium Density Overlaid
Med.	Medium
MF	Thousand Feet
M.F.B.M.	Thousand Feet Board Measure
Mfg.	Manufacturing
Mfrs.	Manufacturers
mg	Milligram
MGD	Million Gallons per Day
MGPH	Million Gallons per Hour
MH, M.H.	Manhole; Metal Halide; Man-Hour
MHz	Megahertz
Mi.	Mile
MI	Malleable Iron; Mineral Insulated
MIPS	Male Iron Pipe Size
mj	Mechanical Joint
m	Meter
mm	Millimeter
Mill.	Millwright
Min., min.	Minimum, Minute

Abbreviations

Misc.	Miscellaneous
ml	Milliliter, Mainline
M.L.F.	Thousand Linear Feet
Mo.	Month
Mobil.	Mobilization
Mog.	Mogul Base
MPH	Miles per Hour
MPT	Male Pipe Thread
MRGWB	Moisture Resistant Gypsum Wallboard
MRT	Mile Round Trip
ms	Millisecond
M.S.F.	Thousand Square Feet
Mstz.	Mosaic & Terrazzo Worker
M.S.Y.	Thousand Square Yards
Mtd., mtd., mtd	Mounted
Mthe.	Mosaic & Terrazzo Helper
Mtng.	Mounting
Mult.	Multi; Multiply
MUTCD	Manual on Uniform Traffic Control Devices
M.V.A.	Million Volt Amperes
M.V.A.R.	Million Volt Amperes Reactance
MV	Megavolt
MW	Megawatt
MXM	Male by Male
MYD	Thousand Yards
N	Natural; North
nA	Nanoampere
NA	Not Available; Not Applicable
N.B.C.	National Building Code
NC	Normally Closed
NEMA	National Electrical Manufacturers Assoc.
NEHB	Bolted Circuit Breaker to 600V.
NFPA	National Fire Protection Association
NLB	Non-Load-Bearing
NM	Non-Metallic Cable
nm	Nanometer
No.	Number
NO	Normally Open
N.O.C.	Not Otherwise Classified
Nose.	Nosing
NPT	National Pipe Thread
NQOD	Combination Plug-on/Bolt on Circuit Breaker to 240V.
N.R.C., NRC	Noise Reduction Coefficient/ Nuclear Regulator Commission
N.R.S.	Non Rising Stem
ns	Nanosecond
NTP	Notice to Proceed
nW	Nanowatt
OB	Opposing Blade
OC	On Center
OD	Outside Diameter
O.D.	Outside Dimension
ODS	Overhead Distribution System
O.G.	Ogee
O.H.	Overhead
O&P	Overhead and Profit
Oper.	Operator
Opng.	Opening
Orna.	Ornamental
OSB	Oriented Strand Board
OS&Y	Outside Screw and Yoke
OSHA	Occupational Safety and Health Act
Ovhd.	Overhead
OWG	Oil, Water or Gas
Oz.	Ounce
P.	Pole; Applied Load; Projection
p.	Page
Pape.	Paperhanger
P.A.P.R.	Powered Air Purifying Respirator
PAR	Parabolic Reflector
P.B., PB	Push Button
Pc., Pcs.	Piece, Pieces
P.C.	Portland Cement; Power Connector
P.C.F.	Pounds per Cubic Foot
PCM	Phase Contrast Microscopy
PDCA	Painting and Decorating Contractors of America
P.E., PE	Professional Engineer; Porcelain Enamel; Polyethylene; Plain End
P.E.C.I.	Porcelain Enamel on Cast Iron
Perf.	Perforated
PEX	Cross Linked Polyethylene
Ph.	Phase
P.I.	Pressure Injected
Pile.	Pile Driver
Pkg.	Package
Pl.	Plate
Plah.	Plasterer Helper
Plas.	Plasterer
plf	Pounds Per Linear Foot
Pluh.	Plumber Helper
Plum.	Plumber
Ply.	Plywood
p.m.	Post Meridiem
Pntd.	Painted
Pord.	Painter, Ordinary
pp	Pages
PP, PPL	Polypropylene
P.P.M.	Parts per Million
Pr.	Pair
P.E.S.B.	Pre-engineered Steel Building
Prefab.	Prefabricated
Prefin.	Prefinished
Prop.	Propelled
PSF, psf	Pounds per Square Foot
PSI, psi	Pounds per Square Inch
PSIG	Pounds per Square Inch Gauge
PSP	Plastic Sewer Pipe
Pspr.	Painter, Spray
Psst.	Painter, Structural Steel
P.T.	Potential Transformer
P. & T.	Pressure & Temperature
Ptd.	Painted
Ptns.	Partitions
Pu	Ultimate Load
PVC	Polyvinyl Chloride
Pvmt.	Pavement
PRV	Pressure Relief Valve
Pwr.	Power
Q	Quantity Heat Flow
Qt.	Quart
Quan., Qty.	Quantity
Q.C.	Quick Coupling
r	Radius of Gyration
R	Resistance
R.C.P.	Reinforced Concrete Pipe
Rect.	Rectangle
recpt.	Receptacle
Reg.	Regular
Reinf.	Reinforced
Req'd.	Required
Res.	Resistant
Resi.	Residential
RF	Radio Frequency
RFID	Radio-frequency Identification
Rgh.	Rough
RGS	Rigid Galvanized Steel
RHW	Rubber, Heat & Water Resistant; Residential Hot Water
rms	Root Mean Square
Rnd.	Round
Rodm.	Rodman
Rofc.	Roofer, Composition
Rofp.	Roofer, Precast
Rohe.	Roofer Helpers (Composition)
Rots.	Roofer, Tile & Slate
R.O.W.	Right of Way
RPM	Revolutions per Minute
R.S.	Rapid Start
Rsr	Riser
RT	Round Trip
S.	Suction; Single Entrance; South
SBS	Styrene Butadiere Styrene
SC	Screw Cover
SCFM	Standard Cubic Feet per Minute
Scaf.	Scaffold
Sch., Sched.	Schedule
S.C.R.	Modular Brick
S.D.	Sound Deadening
SDR	Standard Dimension Ratio
S.E.	Surfaced Edge
Sel.	Select
SER, SEU	Service Entrance Cable
S.F.	Square Foot
S.F.C.A.	Square Foot Contact Area
S.F. Flr.	Square Foot of Floor
S.F.G.	Square Foot of Ground
S.F. Hor.	Square Foot Horizontal
SFR	Square Feet of Radiation
S.F. Shlf.	Square Foot of Shelf
S4S	Surface 4 Sides
Shee.	Sheet Metal Worker
Sin.	Sine
Skwk.	Skilled Worker
SL	Saran Lined
S.L.	Slimline
Sldr.	Solder
SLH	Super Long Span Bar Joist
S.N.	Solid Neutral
SO	Stranded with oil resistant inside insulation
S-O-L	Socketolet
sp	Standpipe
S.P.	Static Pressure; Single Pole; Self-Propelled
Spri.	Sprinkler Installer
spwg	Static Pressure Water Gauge
S.P.D.T.	Single Pole, Double Throw
SPF	Spruce Pine Fir; Sprayed Polyurethane Foam
S.P.S.T.	Single Pole, Single Throw
SPT	Standard Pipe Thread
Sq.	Square; 100 Square Feet
Sq. Hd.	Square Head
Sq. In.	Square Inch
S.S.	Single Strength; Stainless Steel
S.S.B.	Single Strength B Grade
sst, ss	Stainless Steel
Sswk.	Structural Steel Worker
Sswl.	Structural Steel Welder
St.; Stl.	Steel
STC	Sound Transmission Coefficient
Std.	Standard
Stg.	Staging
STK	Select Tight Knot
STP	Standard Temperature & Pressure
Stpi.	Steamfitter, Pipefitter
Str.	Strength; Starter; Straight
Strd.	Stranded
Struct.	Structural
Sty.	Story
Subj.	Subject
Subs.	Subcontractors
Surf.	Surface
Sw.	Switch
Swbd.	Switchboard
S.Y.	Square Yard
Syn.	Synthetic
S.Y.P.	Southern Yellow Pine
Sys.	System
t.	Thickness
T	Temperature; Ton
Tan	Tangent
T.C.	Terra Cotta
T & C	Threaded and Coupled
T.D.	Temperature Difference
TDD	Telecommunications Device for the Deaf
T.E.M.	Transmission Electron Microscopy
temp	Temperature, Tempered, Temporary
TFFN	Nylon Jacketed Wire

Abbreviations

TFE	Tetrafluoroethylene (Teflon)
T. & G.	Tongue & Groove; Tar & Gravel
Th., Thk.	Thick
Thn.	Thin
Thrded	Threaded
Tilf.	Tile Layer, Floor
Tilh.	Tile Layer, Helper
THHN	Nylon Jacketed Wire
THW.	Insulated Strand Wire
THWN	Nylon Jacketed Wire
T.L., TL	Truckload
T.M.	Track Mounted
Tot.	Total
T-O-L	Threadolet
tmpd	Tempered
TPO	Thermoplastic Polyolefin
T.S.	Trigger Start
Tr.	Trade
Transf.	Transformer
Trhv.	Truck Driver, Heavy
Trlr	Trailer
Trlt.	Truck Driver, Light
TTY	Teletypewriter
TV	Television
T.W.	Thermoplastic Water Resistant Wire
UCI	Uniform Construction Index
UF	Underground Feeder
UGND	Underground Feeder
UHF	Ultra High Frequency
U.I.	United Inch
U.L., UL	Underwriters Laboratory
Uld.	Unloading
Unfin.	Unfinished
UPS	Uninterruptible Power Supply
URD	Underground Residential Distribution
US	United States
USGBC	U.S. Green Building Council
USP	United States Primed
UTMCD	Uniform Traffic Manual For Control Devices
UTP	Unshielded Twisted Pair
V	Volt
VA	Volt Amperes
VAT	Vinyl Asbestos Tile
V.C.T.	Vinyl Composition Tile
VAV	Variable Air Volume
VC	Veneer Core
VDC	Volts Direct Current
Vent.	Ventilation
Vert.	Vertical
V.F.	Vinyl Faced
V.G.	Vertical Grain
VHF	Very High Frequency
VHO	Very High Output
Vib.	Vibrating
VLF	Vertical Linear Foot
VOC	Volatile Organic Compound
Vol.	Volume
VRP	Vinyl Reinforced Polyester
W	Wire; Watt; Wide; West
w/	With
W.C., WC	Water Column; Water Closet
W.F.	Wide Flange
W.G.	Water Gauge
Wldg.	Welding
W. Mile	Wire Mile
W-O-L	Weldolet
W.R.	Water Resistant
Wrck.	Wrecker
WSFU	Water Supply Fixture Unit
W.S.P.	Water, Steam, Petroleum
WT., Wt.	Weight
WWF	Welded Wire Fabric
XFER	Transfer
XFMR	Transformer
XHD	Extra Heavy Duty
XHHW	Cross-Linked Polyethylene Wire Insulation
XLPE	
XLP	Cross-linked Polyethylene
Xport	Transport
Y	Wye
yd	Yard
yr	Year
Δ	Delta
%	Percent
~	Approximately
Ø	Phase; diameter
@	At
#	Pound; Number
<	Less Than
>	Greater Than
Z	Zone

Index

D

E

M

Q

R

S

T

U

V

Notes

Notes

Notes

Notes

Division Notes

		CREW	DAILY OUTPUT	LABOR-HOURS	UNIT	BARE COSTS MAT.	BARE COSTS LABOR	BARE COSTS EQUIP.	BARE COSTS TOTAL	TOTAL INCL O&P

Division Notes

		CREW	DAILY OUTPUT	LABOR-HOURS	UNIT	BARE COSTS MAT.	LABOR	EQUIP.	TOTAL	TOTAL INCL O&P

Division Notes

		CREW	DAILY OUTPUT	LABOR-HOURS	UNIT	BARE COSTS MAT.	LABOR	EQUIP.	TOTAL	TOTAL INCL O&P

Division Notes

I	CREW	DAILY OUTPUT	LABOR-HOURS	UNIT	BARE COSTS				TOTAL INCL O&P
					MAT.	LABOR	EQUIP.	TOTAL	

2023 Training Class Options

A tradition of excellence in construction cost information and services since 1942

Virtual classes offered monthly. Call for the schedule. 877.620.6245

Gordian offers training classes in a variety of formats—eLearning training modules, instructor-led classes, on-site training, and virtual training classes, as well as custom solutions. Please visit our website at rsmeans.com/products/training/seminars for our current schedule of class offerings.

Training classes that are offered in one or more of our formats are: Building Systems and the Construction Process; Construction Cost Estimating: Concepts & Practice; Introduction to Estimating; Scope of Work for Facilities Estimating; Facilities Construction Estimating; Fundamentals to Construction Cost Estimating; Maintenance & Repair Estimating for Facilities; Mechanical & Electrical Estimating; RSMeans CostWorks CD; and RSMeans Data Online Training.

Registration Information

How to register

By Phone

Register by phone at 877.620.6245

Online

Register online at rsmeans.com/products/services/training

Note: Purchase orders or credits cards are required to register.

Instructor-led Government Pricing

All federal government employees save off the regular seminar price. Other promotional discounts cannot be combined with the government discount. Call 781.422.5115 for government pricing.

If you have any questions or you would like to register for any class or purchase a training module, call us at 877.620.6245.

Construction Cost Estimating: Concepts and Practice

This one- or two-day introductory course to improve estimating skills and effectiveness starts with the details of interpreting bid documents and ends with the summary of the estimate and bid submission.

Topics include:

- Using plans and specifications to create estimates
- The takeoff process – deriving all tasks with correct quantities
- Summarizing the estimate to arrive at the final number
- Formulas for area and cubic measure, adding waste and adjusting productivity to specific projects
- Evaluating subcontractors' proposals and prices
- Adding insurance and bonds
- Understanding how labor costs are calculated
- Submitting bids and proposals

Who should attend: project managers, architects, engineers, owners' representatives, contractors, and anyone responsible for budgeting or estimating construction projects.

Fundamentals to Construction Cost Estimating

This self-paced course focuses on unit price estimating for facilities renovation, repair, and remodeling. Combining hands-on skill building with a discussion of best estimating practices and real-life problems, this informative online course will boost your estimating skills, bring you up to date with key concepts, and provide tips and guidelines that can save you time and help you avoid costly estimating oversights and errors.

Topics include:

- The three phases of estimating
- Bid document review
- How to perform quantity takeoffs
- How to price the work

Who should attend: facilities professionals and anyone involved in facilities planning, design, and construction.

For novice estimators, this course can serve as a primer to Facilities Construction Estimating Self-Paced Training or the following live training courses: Facilities Construction Estimating, Mechanical & Electrical Estimating, Assessing Scope of Work for Facilities Estimating, or Maintenance & Repair Estimating.

Mechanical & Electrical Estimating

This two-day course teaches attendees how to prepare more accurate and complete mechanical/electrical estimates, avoid the pitfalls of omission and double-counting, and understand the composition and rationale within the RSMeans data mechanical/electrical database.

Topics include:
- The unique way mechanical and electrical systems are interrelated
- M&E estimates – conceptual, planning, budgeting, and bidding stages
- Order of magnitude, square foot, assemblies, and unit price estimating
- Comparative cost analysis of equipment and design alternatives

Who should attend: architects, engineers, facilities managers, mechanical and electrical contractors, and others who need a highly reliable method for developing, understanding, and evaluating mechanical and electrical contracts.

Facilities Construction Estimating

In this two-day course, professionals working in facilities management can get help with their daily challenges to establish budgets for all phases of a project.

Topics include:
- Determining the full scope of a project
- Understanding of RSMeans data and what is included in prices
- Identifying appropriate factors to be included in your estimate
- Creative solutions to estimating issues
- Organizing estimates for presentation and discussion
- Special estimating techniques for repair/remodel and maintenance projects
- Appropriate use of contingency, city cost indexes, and reference notes
- Techniques to get to the correct estimate quickly

Who should attend: facility managers, engineers, contractors, facility tradespeople, planners, and project managers.

Assessing Scope of Work for Facilities Construction Estimating

This two-day practical training program addresses the vital importance of understanding the scope of projects in order to produce accurate cost estimates for facilities repair and remodeling.

Topics include:
- Discussions of site visits, plans/specs, record drawings of facilities, and site-specific lists
- Review of CSI divisions, including means, methods, materials, and the challenges of scoping each topic
- Exercises in scope identification and scope writing for accurate estimating of projects
- Hands-on exercises that require scope, takeoff, and pricing

Who should attend: corporate and government estimators, planners, facility managers, and others who need to produce accurate project estimates.

CostWorks CD Self-Paced Training Course

This self-paced course helps users become more familiar with the functionality of the CD. Each menu, icon, screen, and function found in the program is explained in depth. Time is devoted to hands-on estimating exercises.

Topics include:
- Searching the database using all navigation methods
- Exporting RSMeans data to your preferred spreadsheet format
- Viewing crews, assembly components, and much more
- Automatically regionalizing the database

This training session requires users to bring a laptop computer to class and to follow along using a purchased copy of RSMeans data CostWorks CD.

When you register for this course you will receive an outline for your laptop requirements.

Maintenance & Repair Estimating for Facilities

This two-day course teaches attendees how to plan, budget, and estimate the cost of ongoing and preventive maintenance and repair for existing buildings and grounds.

Topics include:
- The most financially favorable maintenance, repair, and replacement scheduling and estimating
- Preventive planning and facilities upgrading
- Determining both in-house and contract-out service costs
- Annual, asset-protecting M&R plan

Who should attend: facility managers, maintenance supervisors, buildings and grounds superintendents, plant managers, planners, estimators, and others involved in facilities planning and budgeting.

RSMeans Data Online Training

Construction estimating is vital to the decision-making process at each state of every project. Our online solution works the way you do. It's systematic, flexible, and intuitive. In this self-paced course you will see how you can estimate any phase of any project faster and better.

Topics include:
- Customizing our online estimating solution
- Making the most of RSMeans data "Circle Reference" numbers
- How to integrate your cost data
- Generating reports, exporting estimates to MS Excel, sharing, collaborating, and more

Also offered as a self-paced or on-site training program!

RSMeans data Training Cancellation Policy

Virtual Training (Individual)

If you are unable to attend a training class, a colleague may substitute at any time before the session starts by notifying the training registrar at 781.422.5115 or your sales representative. Gordian is not responsible for sending duplicate materials to the substitute colleague.

If you are unable to find a substitute and cancel fewer than ten (10) business days prior to the training class, you will either forfeit the registration fee or be allowed to apply your registration fee to the same class only once within the same calendar year. No-shows will forfeit their registration fees and no rescheduling is permitted. In the unfortunate circumstance that Gordian must cancel your event, Gordian will work with you to reschedule your attendance in the same training class at a later date or will fully refund your registration fee.

Any on-demand (self-paced) training modules are not eligible for cancellation, substitution, transfer, return, or refund.

Virtual Training (Private Group)

If you provide notice more than ten (10) business days prior to the training class, Gordian will work to reschedule your event. If you cancel your event fewer than ten (10) business days prior to the training class, you are responsible for paying for the trainer's time for the cancelled training, as well as the full cost of materials and shipping. In the unfortunate circumstance that Gordian must cancel your event, Gordian will work with you to reschedule your attendance in the same training class at a later date or will fully refund your registration fee.

Public Training Events (Individual)

If you are unable to attend a training conference, a colleague may substitute no fewer than ten (10) business days before the session starts by notifying the training registrar at 781.422.5115 or your sales representative. Gordian is not responsible for sending duplicate materials to the substitute colleague.

If you are unable to find a substitute and cancel fewer than ten (10) business days prior to the conference, you will forfeit the registration fee. No-shows will forfeit their registration fees and no rescheduling is permitted. In the unfortunate circumstance that Gordian must cancel your event, Gordian will fully refund your registration fee.

On-Site Training (Private Group)

If you provide notice more than ten (10) business days prior to the training class, Gordian will work with you to reschedule your event, but you are responsible for rescheduling fees associated with the trainer's time, airfare, and lodging. If you cancel fewer than ten (10) business days before your event, you are responsible for the full cost of the event. In the unfortunate event that Gordian must cancel your event, Gordian will work with you to reschedule your attendance at a later date or will fully refund your registration fee.

AACE Approved Courses

The AACE recognizes .1 CEUs per hour of training attended for all of Gordian's virtual training courses.

AIA Continuing Education

We are registered with the AIA Continuing Education System (AIA/CES) and are committed to developing quality learning activities in accordance with the CES criteria. Many seminars meet the AIA/CES criteria for Quality Level 2. AIA members may receive 14 learning units (LUs) for each two-day course.

Daily Course Schedule

The first day of each seminar session begins at 8:30 a.m. and ends at 4:30 p.m. The second day begins at 8:00 a.m. and ends at 4:00 p.m. Participants are urged to bring a hand-held calculator since many actual problems will be worked out in each session.

Continental Breakfast

Your registration includes the cost of a continental breakfast and a morning and afternoon refreshment break. These informal segments allow you to discuss topics of mutual interest with other seminar attendees. You are free to make your own lunch and dinner arrangements.

Hotel/Transportation Arrangements

We arrange to hold a block of rooms at most host hotels. To take advantage of special group rates when making your reservation, be sure to mention that you are attending the Gordian RSMeans data seminar. You are, of course, free to stay at the lodging place of your choice. Hotel reservations and transportation arrangements should be made directly by seminar attendees.

Important

Class sizes are limited, so please register as soon as possible.